a LANGE medical book

Basic & Clinical
Endocrinology

fourth edition

a LANGE medical book

Basic & Clinical
Endocrinology

fourth edition

Edited by

Francis S. Greenspan, MD
Clinical Professor of Medicine and Radiology
Department of Medicine, and Chief, Thyroid Clinic
University of California, San Francisco

John D. Baxter, MD
Professor of Medicine, Director of the Metabolic
Research Unit, and Chief, Division of Endocrinology,
Moffitt Hospital, University of California, San Francisco

APPLETON & LANGE
Norwalk, Connecticut

95 96 97 98 / 10 9 8 7 6 5 4 3

Prentice Hall International (UK) Limited, *London*
Prentice Hall of Australia Pty. Limited, *Sydney*
Prentice Hall Canada, Inc., *Toronto*
Prentice Hall Hispanoamericana, S.A., *Mexico*
Prentice Hall of India Private Limited, *New Delhi*
Prentice Hall of Japan, Inc., *Tokyo*
Simon & Schuster Asia Pte. Ltd., *Singapore*
Editora Prentice Hall do Brasil Ltda., *Rio de Janeiro*
Prentice Hall, *Englewood Cliffs, New Jersey*

ISSN:0891-2068

Acquisitions Editor: Shelley Reinhardt
Production Editor: Christine Langan
Designer: Kathy Hornyak

ISBN 0-8385-0560-0
90000

9 780838 505601

PRINTED IN THE UNITED STATES OF AMERICA

Table of Contents

3. Growth 128

Dennis M. Styne, MD

4. The Thyroid Gland 160

Francis S. Greenspan, MD

The Authors

Claude S. Arnaud, MD
Professor of Medicine and Physiology, University of California, San Francisco.

David C. Aron, MD
Professor of Medicine, Division of Clinical and Molecular Endocrinology, Case Western Reserve University School of Medicine, Cleveland, Ohio; Associate Chief Medical Service, Veterans Affairs Medical Center, Cleveland, Ohio.

John D. Baxter, MD
Professor of Medicine, Director of the Metabolic Research Unit, and Chief of the Division of Endocrinology, Moffitt Hospital, University of California, San Francisco.

Christopher C. Benz, MD
Associate Professor of Medicine, University of California, San Francisco.

Edward G. Biglieri, MD
Professor of Medicine, Emeritus, Clinical Study Center, San Francisco General Hospital, San Francisco.

Glenn Braunstein, MD
Professor of Medicine, School of Medicine, University of California, Los Angeles; Chairman, Department of Medicine, Cedars-Sinai Medical Center.

George E. Bray, MD
Professor, Pennington Biomedical Research Center, Louisiana State University, Baton Rouge, Louisiana.

Bayard D. Catherwood, MD
Professor of Medicine, Emory University, Atlanta, Georgia; Chief, Endocrinology and Metabolism Section, Veterans Affairs Medical Center, Atlanta, Georgia.

Felix A. Conte, MD
Professor of Pediatrics, University of California, San Francisco.

Haile T. Debas, MD
Professor and Chairman, Department of Surgery, University of California, San Francisco.

Leonard J. Deftos, MD
Professor of Medicine, University of California, San Diego; San Diego VA Medical Center, La Jolla, California.

James W. Findling, MD
Clinical Professor of Medicine, University of Wisconsin and Medical College of Wisconsin, Milwaukee

Peter H. Forsham, MD
Professor Emeritus Medicine and Pediatrics, University of California, San Francisco.

Alan Goldfien, MD
Professor Emeritus, Department of Medicine, Obstetrics & Gynecology & Reproductive Sciences and the Cardiovascular Research Institute, University of California, San Francisco.

Francis S. Greenspan, MD
Clinical Professor of Medicine and Radiology, University of California, San Francisco; Chief, Thyroid Clinic, Division of Endocrinology and Department of Medicine, University of California, San Francisco.

Susan L. Greenspan, MD
Assistant Professor of Medicine, Harvard Medical School, Boston, Massachusetts; Director, Osteoporosis and Metabolic Bone Disease Clinic, Beth Israel Hospital, Boston, Massachusetts.

Melvin Grumach, MD
Professor of Pediatrics, University of California, San Francisco.

John P. Kane, MD, PhD
Professor of Medicine, Biochemistry and Biophysics, University of California, San Francisco.

John H. Karam, MD
Professor of Medicine, Chief, Clinical Endocrinology, University of California, San Francisco.

Claudio E. Kater, MD
Associate Professor of Medicine and Director, Adrenal and Hypertension Unit, Division of Endocrinology, Escola Paulista de Medicina, Brazil.

John L. Kitzmiller, MD
Professor of Obstetrics & Gynecology, University of California, San Francisco, and Chairman, Department of Obstetrics & Gynecology, Good Samaritan Hospital, San Jose, California.

Brian J. Lewis, MD
Clinical Professor of Medicine, University of California, San Francisco; Staff Physician, The Permanente Medical Group, San Francisco, California.

Mary J. Malloy, MD
Clinical Professor of Pediatrics and Medicine, and Director, Pediatric Lipid Clinic, University of California, San Francisco.

Mary C. Martin, MD
Associate Professor, Department of Obstetrics, Gynecology & Reproductive Sciences, University of California, San Francisco.

Scott E. Monroe, MD
Adjunct Associate Professor of Obstetrics, Gynecology & Reproductive Sciences, University of California, San Francisco.

Sean J. Mulvihill, MD
Associate Professor in Residence, Department of Surgery, University of California, San Francisco.

David J. Ramsay, MD
Professor of Physiology, University of California, San Francisco.

Neil Resnick, MD
Assistant Professor of Medicine, Harvard Medical School, Boston, Massachusetts; Chief of Geriatrics, Brigham and Womens Hospital, Boston, Massachusetts.

Gordon J. Strewler, MD
Professor of Medicine, Chief, Endocrine Unit, VA Medical Center, San Francisco, California.

Dennis M. Styne, MD
Professor and Chair, Department of Pediatrics, University of California, Davis, Sacramento, California.

Robert N. Taylor, MD, PhD
Associate Professor of Obstetrics & Gynecology, Department of Obstetrics, Gynecology & Reproductive Sciences, University of California, San Francisco.

J. Blake Tyrrell, MD
Clinical Professor of Medicine, Chief, Clinical Endocrinology and Metabolism, Metabolic Research Unit, University of California, San Francisco.

Clinton W. Young, MD
Assistant Clinical Professor of Medicine, University of California, San Francisco.

Preface

Endocrinology has passed through many phases, from the first concept of a "chemical messenger," to the isolation and identification of a myriad of hormones and analysis of their actions and control systems. However, in recent years, with the introduction of the techniques of molecular biology, endocrinology has enjoyed unparalleled growth and vitality. These techniques have expanded the field in exciting new ways such as understanding the complex mechanisms of hormone synthesis, hormonal actions and interactions, the introduction of new and precise diagnostic methods, the production of purified hormones and analogues, and the clinical implications of these phenomena. Molecular biology is pushing the boundaries of endocrinology and in so doing is creating opportunities not only in the laboratory but also at the bedside.

The fourth edition of *Basic & Clinical Endocrinology* introduces the reader to this new era. The first chapter, General Concepts of Endocrinology, reviews the broad scope of the science of Endocrinology, the applications of molecular biology to this discipline, and the overall approach to the diagnosis and treatment of endocrine diseases. Succeeding chapters address individual systems. These chapters have all been updated to emphasize recent advances, but they are strongly clinically oriented. They will allow the reader to understand not only the pathophysiology of endocrine disease but will also provide an excellent guide to the clinical diagnosis and management of endocrine syndromes.

This book will be an ideal text for medical students taking their first course in Endocrinology; for students, residents and fellows working with endocrine patients in the clinics; for practicing physicians including internists, pediatricians, gynecologists, and surgeons who want to update their knowledge of Endocrinology in order to better manage their patients; and for subspecialists who want to review a complex area of Endocrinology in order to understand the latest developments. The physiologic approach and the practical clinical applications presented throughout the book will make it a valuable addition to every medical library.

San Francisco
August, 1993

Francis S. Greenspan, MD
John D. Baxter, MD

a LANGE medical book

Basic & Clinical
Endocrinology

fourth edition

General Concepts of Endocrinology

1

John D. Baxter, MD

ACRONYMS USED IN THIS CHAPTER

ACTH	Adrenocorticotropic hormone; corticotropin		**InsP$_3$**	Inositol 1,4,5-triphosphate
ADH	Antidiuretic hormone; vasopressin		**ITP**	Inosine triphosphate
ADP	Adenosine diphosphate		**LDL**	Low-density lipoprotein
ANP	Atrial natriuretic peptide		**LH**	Luteinizing hormone
API1	Transcription factor API1		**MEN**	Multiple endocrine neoplasia
ATP	Adenosine triphosphate		**MRI**	Magnetic resonance imaging
cAMP	Cyclic adenosine monophosphate		**NMR**	Nuclear Magnetic Resonance
CAT	Chloramphenicol acetyltransferase		**mRNA**	Messenger RNA
CBG	Corticosteroid-binding globulin; transcortin		**NFIL-6**	Transcription factor NFIL-6
CCK	Cholecystokinin		**NO**	Nitric oxide
cDNA	Complementary DNA		**PCR**	Polymerase chain reaction
CG	Chorionic gonadotropin		**PGDF**	Platelet-derived growth factor
cGMP	Guanosine 3',5'-cyclic monophosphate		**PI3K**	Phosphatidylinositol 3'-kinase
CGRH	Calcitonin gene-related hormone		**PIP$_2$**	Phosphatidylinositol 4,5-biphosphonate
COMT	Catechol-O-methyltransferase		**Pit-1**	Pituitary transcription factor
CREB	cAMP response element-binding protein		**PLC**	Phospholipase C
CRH	Corticotropin-releasing hormone		**PNMT**	Phenylethanolamine-O-methyltransferase
CT	Computed tomography		**POMC**	Proopiomelanocortin
DAG	Diacylglycerol		**PRL**	Prolactin
DNA	Deoxyribonucleic acid		**PTH**	Parathyroid hormone
DOPA	Dihydroxyphenylalanine		**RFLP**	Restriction fragment length polymorphism
EDRF	Endothelium-derived relaxing factor		**RNA**	Ribonucleic acid
EGF	Epidermal growth factor		**rRNA**	Ribosomal RNA
ELISA	Enzyme-linked immunosorbent assay		**RYRs**	Ryanodine receptors
FGF	Fibroblast growth factor		**SHBG**	Sex hormone-binding globulin
FSH	Follicle-stimulating hormone		**snRNPs**	Small nuclear ribonuclear protein particles
GABA	γ-Aminobutyric acid		**T$_3$**	3',3,5-L-Triiodothyronine; triiodothyronine
GAP	GTPase-activating protein		**T$_4$**	3,3',5,5'-L-Tetraiodothyronine; thyroxine
GDP	Guanosine diphosphate		**TBG**	Thyroid hormone-binding globulin
GH	Growth hormone		**TBPA**	Thyroid hormone-binding prealbumin;
GnRH	Gonadotropin-releasing hormone			transthyretin
GRH	Growth hormone-releasing hormone		**TGFα, TGFβ**	Transforming growth factors α and β
GTP	Guanosine triphosphate		**TRH**	Thyrotropin-releasing hormone
HRE	Hormone regulatory element		**tRNA**	Transfer RNA
hsp90	Heat shock protein 90		**TSH**	Thyroid-stimulating hormone, thyrotropin
IGF-1	Insulin-like growth factor-1		**VIP**	Vasoactive intestinal polypeptide
IGF-2	Insulin-like growth factor-2		**VMA**	Vanillylmandelic acid

THE ENDOCRINE SYSTEM

The endocrine system and the nervous system are the major means by which the body communicates information between different cells and tissues (Figure 1–1). This transmitted information results in regulation of numerous body functions. The term "endocrine" refers to the internal secretion of biologically active substances; this contrasts with "exocrine" secretion, which is secretion outside the body, eg, through the sweat glands or ducts leading

Part of the material in this chapter is based on material written by the author for a chapter entitled "Gene Expression and Recombinant DNA in Endocrinology and Metabolism" in: *Endocrinology and Metabolism,* 2nd ed. Felig P et al (editors). McGraw-Hill, 1987.

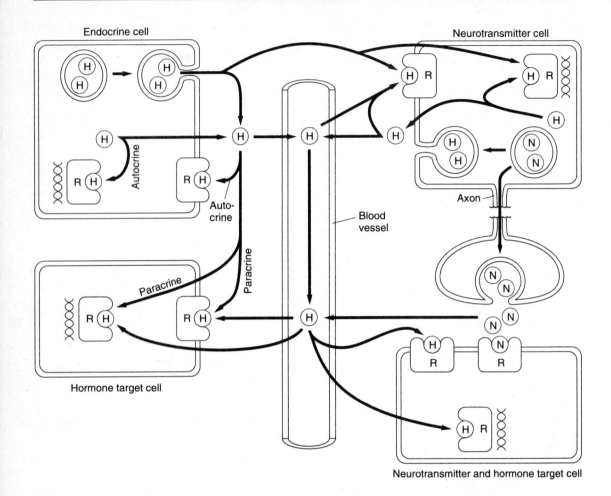

Figure 1–1. Actions of hormones and neurotransmitters and their interrelationships. Both endocrine and neurotransmitter cells release hormones that they synthesize either from secretory vesicles or by diffusion. These hormones may act on the same cell in which they are produced (autocrine) without leaving the cell or after their release and subsequent binding to receptors in or on the cell. They may act on other target cells in their vicinity, including neurotransmitter cells, without entering the circulation (paracrine). They may go to the target cell through the circulation (hormonal). Neurotransmitter cells produce neurotransmitters that are released at nerve terminals. These same neurotransmitters can be released to act as hormones through the synaptic junctions or directly by the cell. (H, hormone; R, receptor; N, neurotransmitter.)

into the gastrointestinal tract. The endocrine system uses hormones to convey its information. Thus, a **hormone** is typically defined as a substance released by an endocrine gland and transported through the bloodstream to another tissue where it acts to regulate the functions of the target tissue. These actions are mediated by the binding of the hormone to **receptor molecules,** which are the loci to which the hormones are bound in mediating their responses. The receptors must (1) distinguish the hormone from all of the millions of other molecules to which they are exposed and (2) transmit the binding information into postreceptor events. The hormones are allosteric effectors that alter the conformations of the allosteric receptor proteins to which they bind.

The system is diverse and complex, with varied and sophisticated mechanisms that actuate and control the synthesis and release of hormones, their transport in the circulation, and their metabolism and delivery to the surface or the interior of the cells upon which they act. Other mechanisms regulate the sensitivity of cells to hormones in the target tissues and the specific responses the hormones can elicit.

In addition to the traditional views of the system outlined above, an expanded view must also be described. Hormones commonly act without ever entering the circulation (Figure 1–1). Complex interrelations exist between the nervous, immune, and other systems. Molecules that are usually not considered hormones may *act* as hormones, and tissues ordinarily not considered to be endocrine glands may *produce and release* hormones. The interrelationships between then endocrine and nervous systems are briefly described below and in Chapter 2. The relationships between the endocrine and immunologic systems are described in some detail below. Also described are the class of molecules termed "eicosanoids," which have numerous relationships with the endocrine system.

This chapter attempts to provide an overview of endocrinology from a conceptual framework, including basic science and clinical principles, and to provide background information on those principles of endocrinology that are important for diagnosing and managing patients with endocrine disease.

PARACRINE & AUTOCRINE ACTIONS

As mentioned above, hormones not only reach target tissues through the circulation but can also act locally in the vicinity in which they are released (Figure 1–1). When they act locally on cells other than those that produce them, the action is called **paracrine**—illustrated by the actions of sex steroids in the ovary, angiotensin II in the kidney, and platelet-derived growth factor released by platelets. As a variant of this action, the hormone in the membrane of one cell can interact directly with a receptor on a juxtaposed cell. This is seen, for example, with some hematopoietic growth factors and is termed **juxtacrine** regulation. The hormone can also act on the cell in which it is produced, a phenomenon referred to as **autocrine;** the hormone may be released by the cell and then act on it, or it may act inside the cell without ever being released. For example, insulin released by the pancreatic islet B cells can inhibit insulin release by the same cells, and somatostatin can inhibit its release from pancreatic D cells (Chapter 14). Autocrine actions appear to be especially important with cancer cells that synthesize various oncogene products which act in the same cell to stimulate cell division and promote the overall growth of the cancer.

TYPES OF HORMONES

Hormones are derived from the major classes of compounds used by the body for general functional purposes (Figure 1–2). Thus, they are either proteins (including glycoproteins) or derived from them, amino acid analogues, or lipids. The polypeptide hormones are the direct translation products of specific mRNAs, cleavage products of larger precursor proteins, or modified peptides. The catecholamines and thyroid hormones are derivatives of amino acids. The steroid hormones and vitamin D are derived from cholesterol. The eicosanoids such as prostaglandins, prostacyclins, and leukotrienes, which are related to hormones (see below), are derived from fatty acids. Whereas hormones are referred to as such when their structures are known, they have been called **factors** when their activities have been isolated, but their structures are not known.

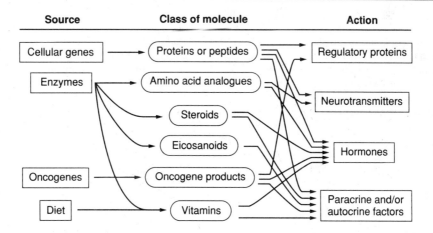

Figure 1–2. Relations between the source, class of molecules, and actions of various species of molecules involved in the endocrine system. These molecules are or become hormones, eicosanoids, oncogene products, and vitamins. Normal genes encode proteins that are regulatory proteins, neurotransmitters, hormones, and paracrine or autocrine factors (or polypeptides from which these are derived). Normal genes also encode enzymes that participate in generating amino acid analogues that can be neurotransmitters, hormones and autocrine or paracrine factors, steroids that can be hormones or autocrine or paracrine factors, or eicosanoids that can be autocrine or paracrine factors. Oncogenes encode proteins that can be regulatory proteins, hormones, or autocrine or paracrine factors. Vitamins can be obtained from the diet or in some cases synthesized by the body, and the latter can act as hormones or as autocrine or paracrine factors.

VITAMINS & HORMONES

Classically, vitamins (Figure 1–2) are defined as essential substances that are required in small quantities from the diet. They are not utilized by the body as fuels, like foods, but mostly serve as mediators of enzymatic reactions and control processes in the body. However, vitamin D can be produced by the body in individuals who have sufficient exposure to sunlight and is a required vitamin only in individuals who do not have adequate exposure. Other vitamins, such as the retinoids, are also metabolized by the body from precursor forms to active products. Some vitamins act by mechanisms similar to the mechanisms of hormone actions. 1,25-(OH)$_2$ cholecalciferol (1,25-(OH)$_2$D$_3$) and the retinoids (retinoic acid, 9-*cis*-retinoic acid, and probably others) act through receptors of the same family as the steroid and thyroid hormones (discussed below).

HORMONES & ONCOGENES

Oncogenes are cancer-promoting genes (Chapter 19; Figure 1–2). They are commonly either altered (eg, by mutation) or overexpressed versions of normal cellular genes. They were originally described in cancer-promoting viruses that appear to have derived their oncogenes from their host's cellular genes. In many cases, oncogenes are analogues either of hormones, hormone receptors, or molecules involved in transmitting hormone actions. Oncogenes from viruses are designated "v-," and the normal cellular counterparts are designated "c-." The v-*erb* A oncogene from the chicken erythroleukemia virus is similar to the thyroid hormone receptor (thus designated as c-*erb* A), and the v-*erb* B oncogene is similar to the epidermal growth factor (EGF) receptor (c-*erb* B). It is usual for the oncogene to have a function different from its normal cellular counterpart. Thus, for example, unlike the thyroid hormone receptor, the v-*erb* A oncogene product (v-erb A) does not bind thyroid hormone and in general is a transcriptional repressor. Other examples of oncogenes and the types of products they encode are H-*ras* and K-*ras*, G proteins involved in intracellular signaling; *abl*, tyrosine kinase; *jun,* a subunit of the AP1 transcription factor; and *sis,* the platelet-derived growth factor (PDGF) B chain.

HORMONES & THE IMMUNE SYSTEM

There are complex interrelationships between the endocrine and immune systems. The immune system responds to foreign substances and learns to ignore the body's chemicals by complex receptor mechanisms that utilize "second messengers" in ways similar to the endocrine system. Whereas cell-cell interactions participate in many steps, a process more unique to the immune system, major regulation also occurs through release of chemical signals by immunologic cells that act either systemically or locally. Thus, immunologically competent cells release cytokines that can stimulate growth, regulate specific processes, destroy target cells through cytotoxic lymphokines, and mediate suppressor cell effects to block B cells from producing antibodies. For example, activated T lymphocytes release lymphokines that attract macrophages and neutrophils to an area of infection. Various complement proteins act in a paracrine fashion by attracting and activating macrophages. Interleukins, interferons, tumor necrosis factor, plasminogen activator, and other peptides are representative of these factors. In some cases, peptides traditionally considered as hormones (eg, ACTH, PRL) are produced by cells of the immune system. Their roles are currently being deciphered.

There is also extensive regulation of the immune system by hormones (discussed in a later section on actions of hormones), and substances released by cells of the immune system can affect the function of the endocrine system and the release of hormones.

EICOSANOIDS: PROSTAGLANDINS, THROMBOXANES, LEUKOTRIENES, & RELATED COMPOUNDS

Eicosanoids are compounds (including prostaglandins) that are derived from polyunsaturated fatty acids with 18-, 20-, or 22-carbon skeletons (Figure 1–2). Among these, **arachidonic acid** (all-*cis*-5,8,11,14-eicosatetraenoic acid) is the most important and abundant precursor for the various eicosanoids in humans. The derivatives of these substances include the prostaglandins, prostacyclins, leukotrienes, and thromboxanes. These fatty acid derivatives are ubiquitous in mammalian cells. They are produced by most cells, and are released with little storage. They are cleared rapidly from the circulation and are thought to act predominantly in a paracrine or autocrine fashion. They have mechanisms of action that are similar to the hormones that act on the

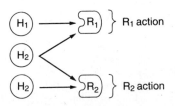

Figure 1–3. Classes of hormone action (see text). Hormone action should be classified according to the receptor irrespective of which hormone interacts with it.

cell surface (discussed below). Eicosanoid synthesis is frequently stimulated in response to hormones; thus, these molecules serve as mediators of hormone action. For example, changes in prostaglandin synthesis are a common feature of hormones acting on the kidney. Eicosanoids can also regulate hormone release and actions. For example, prostaglandin E (PGE) compounds inhibit the release of growth hormone (GH) and prolactin (PRL) from the pituitary and of norepinephrine from sympathetic presynaptic nerve endings. Eicosanoids affect essentially every type of cell in some way, including effects on hemostasis, smooth muscle contraction, calcium ion mobilization, renal and reproductive function, and injury, inflammatory, immunologic, vascular, airway, and gut responses.

CLASSES OF HORMONE ACTION

Traditionally, hormones were classified according to the types of actions they mediate. For example, glucocorticoids were named for their carbohydrate-regulating activities, mineralocorticoids for their salt-regulating activities, and pituitary tropic hormones for the types of tropism they exerted. Other hormones were named for the gland from which they were released (thyroid hormone, parathyroid hormone). This type of nomenclature is imprecise and should be abandoned. The major problem relates to the cross-reactivity of the hormones. Thus, glucocorticoids can regulate mineral metabolism, insulin can act in ways similar to insulin-like growth factors-1 and 2 (IGF-1 and IGF-2; somatomedins), and chorionic gonadotropin can act like thyroid-stimulating hormone. The reason for these cross-reactivities is that a given hormone can act through receptors normally attributed to other hormones. Thus, glucocorticoids can act through binding to mineralocorticoid receptors; insulin can act through binding to IGF receptors; and chorionic gonadotropin (CG) can act through binding to the thyrotropin-stimulating hormone (TSH) receptor. A further problem is that classifying hormones according to a given type of action does not acknowledge other types of actions—even through the same receptor. The actions of glucocorticoids, for instance, are diverse, and those on carbohydrate metabolism comprise only a selected feature of their actions. Classification according to the gland is also confusing given that more than one hormone can be produced by the gland.

Whereas the author does not propose changing the names of hormones—these names reflect their history—he does believe that a more rigorous and user-friendly system can be recommended (Figure 1–3). This system, used by pharmacologists for many years, avoids the problems described above. The receptors through which the hormone acts classify the

action. Catecholamine actions through α and β receptors and subclasses of this overall designation are most familiar to clinicians and scientists. With respect to other hormones, most of the actions of glucocorticoids, for example, are mediated through a class of receptors termed "glucocorticoid" receptors; such actions should be characterized as "glucocorticoid." When a glucocorticoid acts through another class of receptors, its actions should be named according to that class of receptors. Thus, when cortisol acts through the mineralocorticoid receptor in a manner analogous to aldosterone, that action should be termed a "mineralocorticoid" action of cortisol. This convention of describing classes of hormone action will be observed in this chapter.

ENDOCRINE & NERVOUS SYSTEM RELATIONSHIPS: NEUROENDOCRINOLOGY

NEUROTRANSMITTERS & HORMONES

Traditionally, the endocrine system has been distinguished from the nervous system—the major other mechanism by which the body communicates information between cells—by the fact that the nervous system is connected to its target tissues through neurons that carry and transmit the chemical signals (Figure 1–1). Thus, the **neurotransmitter,** which mediates the synaptic transmission between two neurons, is synthesized in the cell body of the neuron and travels down the axon, where it is stored in synaptic vesicles and released upon depolarization. Neuron-to-neuron interaction occurs at the synapse, where the neurotransmitter is released and binds to specific receptors on the postsynaptic neuron. Examples of neurotransmitter receptors are the α_1, α_2, β_1, and β_2 adrenergic, muscarinic cholinergic, and nicotinic cholinergic receptors and the serotonergic, dopaminergic, and γ-aminobutyric acid (GABA) receptors. These vary in their relative levels in various parts of the brain. Thus, the neurotransmitter acts in the vicinity of the target, does not travel through the circulation, and in this sense acts in a paracrine fashion. By this means, the nervous system can release high concentrations of the transmitter to the target and avoid releasing the transmitter at other loci. The concentration of the neurotransmitter at the synapse is also rapidly decreased through degradation or re-uptake by the surrounding tissues. A given neuron may have multiple inputs through both multiple synapses and several different neurotransmitters. These inputs can be synergistic or antagonistic. A

neuromodulator is a substance that is released in the vicinity of the synapse and augments or blocks the release of the neurotransmitter. A given neuron may also release more than one neurotransmitter. A common pattern in this respect is the concomitant release of a bioamine and a neuropeptide. Thus, parasympathetic nerves contain both acetylcholine and vasoactive intestinal polypeptide (VIP), and sympathetic nerves can contain both norepinephrine and neuropeptide Y.

By contrast, when a hormone circulates, it is in general distributed to all tissues, and reliance is placed on the receptor to generate responses in specific cells and to discriminate the hormone from all of the other myriad molecules to which it is exposed (Figure 1–1).

However, there are many similarities between the two systems that blur the distinctions. **Neuroendocrinology** is the discipline that takes as its subject matter the nervous and endocrine system interactions. The same molecule can be a neurotransmitter and a hormone (Figure 1–1). Catecholamines released by the adrenal medulla are hormones, and when released by the nerve terminals they are neurotransmitters. A number of hormones and hormone receptors are produced in the central nervous system. For example, there is more thyrotropin-releasing hormone (TRH) outside the hypothalamus, which is ordinarily considered to be the major site of its production, than inside. The neurotransmitter actions of TRH include increased motor activity, arousal, tremor, and enhanced peripheral sympathetic activity. Dopamine, corticotropin-releasing hormone (CRH), calcitonin gene-related hormone (CGRH), somatostatin, gonadotropin-releasing hormone (GNRH), vasoactive intestinal peptide (VIP), gastrin, secretin, cholecystokinin, and other hormones and their receptors are found in various parts of the brain, and all are both hormones and neurotransmitters. **Neurosteroids** are produced by the brain to act locally. Interestingly, some hypothalamic hormones—growth hormone-releasing hormone (GRH) for example— are not found in the brain outside the hy- pothalamus even though GRH is found in many tissues outside the central nervous system and pituitary (pancreas, thyroid gland, lung, gastrointestinal tract, and kidney). Both hormones and neurotransmitters are also present in various tissues generally considered to be neither endocrine nor neural. The mechanisms of action of the hormones and neurotransmitters are similar. For example, the receptors for adrenergic receptors are similar in the central nervous system and the peripheral tissues, and the neurotransmitters utilize the same signaling pathways through cyclic AMP (cAMP), Ca^{2+}, protein kinase C, and phosphoinositide turnover. Neurons may have hormone receptors in regions distinct from the region of the synapse. Thus, these two systems, neural and endocrine, have much in common.

HYPOTHALAMIC-PITUITARY RELATIONSHIPS

The primary neuroendocrine interface is at the hypothalamus and pituitary. Chapter 2 describes the anatomic relations between the hypothalamus and the pituitary and the regulation of the relevant hormones. The hypothalamus contains several nuclei of neuronal cells; within these nuclei are groups of specialized cells that release a particular hormone or hormones. The hypothalamus also regulates other brain functions, including temperature, appetite, thirst, sexual behavior, defensive reactions such as rage and fear, and body rhythms; it has extensive communications with other brain regions.

The hypothalamus contains two types of neurosecretory cells that propagate action potentials, release hormones, and are regulated by both hormonal and central nervous system input. **Neurohypophysial neurons** traverse the hypothalamic-pituitary stalk and release vasopressin and oxytocin from nerve endings in the posterior pituitary; **hypophysiotropic neurons** release hormones into the median eminence and therefore into the hypothalamic-pituitary vessels.

Hypothalamic Neurotransmitters

The hypothalamic neurotransmitters, like those elsewhere in the central nervous system, are simple amino acids, bioamines, or peptides. The amino acids include glutamate and glycine; little is known about their influences on the endocrine system. The bioamines include dopamine, norepinephrine, epinephrine, serotonin, acetylcholine, GABA, and histamine. Dopamine is a major regulator of prolactin release and has complex influences on somatostatin release (see Chapter 2 and below). The noradrenergic neurons release norepinephrine and couple neuroendocrine with autonomic systems; they do not directly affect pituitary function. Serotonin may be made in the pituitary and may be involved in generating circadian rhythms. GABA is present in more cells of the hypothalamus than any other transmitter, in the median eminence and posterior pituitary, and is probably an inhibitory neurotransmitter. The roles of epinephrine, acetylcholine, and histamine are less well defined, though epinephrine may stimulate pituitary hormone release. The neuropeptides include VIP, substance P, neurotensin, components of the renin-angiotensin system, cholecystokinin (CCK), opioid peptides, atrial natriuretic peptides (ANPs) and related peptides, galanin, endothelin, and neuropeptide Y. VIP, also found in the pituitary, stimulates the release of several pituitary hormones, including prolactin, growth hormone and corticotropin (ACTH), and has vasodilator and excitatory actions in the central nervous system. Substance P stimulates prolactin and inhibits CRH-stimulated ACTH release and is a pain neurotransmitter in peripheral nerves. Neurotensin is a systemic vasodilator, can cause hypothermia when injected centrally, and can affect glucagon, somatostatin, growth hormone, and prolactin release. The roles of the components of the renin-angiotensin system are not well defined. Cholecystokinin may affect satiety and prolactin release. The opioid peptides such as β-endorphin, met- and leu-enkephalins, and dynorphin are produced in the pituitary and in the periphery, have receptors distributed throughout the central nervous system, mediate analgesic and behavioral responses, and can affect ACTH, growth hormone, and prolactin release, but overall they do not appear to have a major role in neuroendocrine regulation. The roles of the other neuropeptides are less well understood.

Hypothalamic-Anterior Pituitary Relations

Vessels of a hypophysial-pituitary portal system deliver blood from the median eminence of the hypothalamus to the anterior pituitary (there may be some flow in the opposite direction). This system delivers hormones released from hypothalamic neuronal axons in the median eminence to the anterior pituitary (adenohypophysis); this gland has little nervous innervation and is dominantly dependent on vascular delivery of hormones for regulation of its functions. Hypophysiotropic hormones regulate hormone release from the anterior pituitary. Stimulating hormones (releasing hormones) include TRH, gonadotropin-releasing hormone (GnRH), CRH, GRH, prolactin-releasing factor, and vasopressin. Inhibitory hormones include somatostatin and dopamine (prolactin-inhibiting factor). Some releasing hormones can regulate the level of more than one hormone, and more than one releasing hormone can affect a pituitary hormone. Thus, TRH stimulates both TSH and prolactin release, and ACTH release is stimulated by both CRH and vasopressin. The anterior pituitary also produces several other endocrine proteins such as renin, chorionic gonadotropin, chromogranin A, and neuromedin and in some cases hypothalamic peptides such as VIP and TRH.

The release of anterior pituitary hormones is regulated by three different means (Figure 1–4). First, **spontaneous rhythms** originating in the brain promote basal hormone release. This release is dominantly pulsatile, as illustrated by the patterns of luteinizing hormone (LH) and follicle-stimulating hormone (FSH) release, though the pattern can vary. The amplitude and frequency of the pulses are governed by several factors, including intrinsic properties of the cells and rhythms established by the central nervous system. These rhythms can be **ultradian** (shorter than a day), **circadian** (approximately 24 hour periodicity), or **infradian** (periodicity > 24 hours). The suprachiasmatic nucleus appears to play a major role in the rhythms and has extensive interconnections with the hypothalamus. The pituitary hormones have mainly circadian rhythms, which are

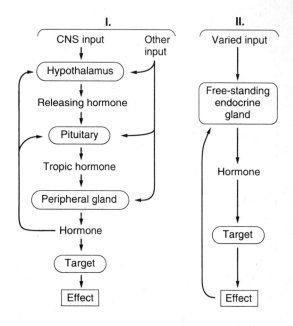

Figure 1–4. The two major types of control of endocrine gland function. *I:* The hypothalamic-pituitary-target gland systems involve the release of a series of hormones beginning with central nervous system regulation of releasing hormones from the hypothalamus that stimulate the pituitary to release tropic hormones which act on peripheral glands to release hormones. These hormones can be regulated by other factors. The hormones from the peripheral glands exert feedback control on the hypothalamus and pituitary. *II:* Free-standing endocrine glands (eg, parathyroid and islet cells) release hormones that stimulate a target tissue to produce an effect (eg, a rise in calcium or fall in blood sugar) which in turn modifies the function of the gland.

influenced by a number of factors and especially the sleep-wake cycle. Second, hormones from the peripheral glands and perhaps the pituitary regulate pituitary hormone release through **feedback loops.** Thus, cortisol, thyroid hormone, and estrogens inhibit the release of their tropic hormones: ACTH, TSH, and LH, respectively. Third, **intervening influences** such as stress, nutritional influences, illnesses, and other hormones can influence hormone release. Thus, stress increases the release of ACTH, growth hormone, and prolactin, and systemic illness can suppress the hypothalamic-pituitary-thyroid axis and the release of gonadotropins. Immunomodulatory substances such as interleukin-1 and interleukin-2 and epinephrine can increase CRH and ACTH release; and angiotensin II, interleukin-2, cholecystokinin, and oxytocin can stimulate ACTH release. The thymic hormone thymosin β_4, whose secretion may be decreased with estrogens, can increase GnRH release.

PRL and GH are both regulated by releasing hormones (prolactin-releasing factor and GRH, respectively) and by inhibitory hormones (dopamine and somatostatin, respectively). The inhibitory hormone is more dominant with PRL, whereas the stimulatory hormone is more dominant for GH; hypothalamic lesions that disrupt delivery of hormones to the anterior pituitary result in elevated prolactin and depressed growth hormone levels (Chapter 2). GH and PRL do not act like other endocrine glands that feedback-regulate their release, but insulin-like growth factor-1 (IGF-1), produced in response to GH, feeds back to inhibit GH release. The feedback influences can be directed at the pituitary, the hypothalamus, or, typically, at both.

The tropic anterior pituitary hormones (ACTH, FSH, LH, TSH) stimulate in their cognate target glands (adrenals, gonads, and thyroid gland) both the release of other hormones and other functions. In these cases, the hormones from the target glands regulate, mostly through negative feedback—but sometimes positive feedback, as with estradiol—release of both the hypothalamic and the pituitary hormone. The gonads also produce other hormones—inhibin, follistatin, and activin—that also regulate tropic hormone release. These regulatory networks tend to regulate hormone levels within a narrow range (see the sections on the various glands or systems). The level of hormone maintained by the regulatory influence is referred to as the set point.

Hypothalamic-Posterior Pituitary Relations

The posterior pituitary (Chapter 2), or neurohypophysis, is an extension of the hypothalamus and is composed mostly of neural tissue. Nerve terminals from axons that originated in the hypothalamus are located in the gland. These release hormones, vasopressin and oxytocin, into the circulation.

THE PINEAL GLAND

The pineal gland, discussed in Chapter 2, provides an interface free of the blood-brain barrier between the brain, the cerebral circulation, and the cerebrospinal fluid. The gland indirectly receives photosensory information that influences its production of melatonin, derived from serotonin. In animals, melatonin can have antireproductive functions, block GnRH-induced LH release, and have other effects on hormone release, but its role in humans is not well defined.

GENE EXPRESSION & RECOMBINANT DNA IN ENDOCRINOLOGY & METABOLISM

The proliferation of information about genes and their functions—and the applications and anticipated applications of recombinant DNA technology to practical medical problems over the past few decades—has had a major impact on endocrinology and has provided information about the pathogenesis, diagnosis, and treatment of endocrine disorders. Studies of hormones and their genes have played a major role in the overall applications of recombinant DNA technology.

GENES & THEIR EXPRESSION

The landmark discovery of the structure of DNA by Watson and Crick in 1953 launched the modern era of molecular biology. This discovery revealed immediately how, with replication, "like could reproduce like," and it suggested how information contained in the genome might be transmitted to direct processes in the cell. Following this development, a number of subsequent discoveries elucidated how genes are replicated, how DNA is transcribed into RNAs, and how messenger RNA (mRNA) is translated into protein.

DNA Structure

The structure of DNA is shown in Figure 1–5. The backbone of DNA is composed of deoxyribose molecules linked by phosphate groups. These linkages occur through the 3′-hydroxyl moiety of the first sugar and the 5′-phosphate moiety of the next sugar. Since the 5′ phosphate of the first sugar and the 3′ phosphate of the last sugar are free, the direction of the molecule is said to be from 5′ to 3′. These designations are used for orientation. Genes are described as being transcribed into RNA from 5′ to 3′, since the first sugar of the RNA product contains a 5′-triphosphate group. The 5′ end of a gene ordinarily refers to its transcriptional start site, or its "upstream" portion; the 3′ end designates the "downstream" portion of the gene, where transcription is terminated.

Connected to each sugar of the DNA backbone is one of four **bases:** adenine (A), guanine (G), cytosine (C), and thymine (T). Adenine and guanine are **purines;** cytosine and thymine are **pyrimidines.** A base to which only a sugar is attached is called a **nucleoside;** a base to which both a sugar and a phosphate group are attached is called a **nucleotide.** For example, adenine (base) bound to ribose is termed adenosine (nucleoside); adenosine coupled to a phosphate group is designated adenylic acid (nucleotide). When nucleotides are linked together in a polymer, they generate a **nucleic acid.**

DNA contains two nucleic acid strands that are antiparallel to each other (ie, running in opposite directions) such that the A moieties of one strand are hydrogen-bonded to the T moieties of the complementary strand and the C and G moieties are similarly bonded to each other. This **complementary base pairing** means that the order of the bases along

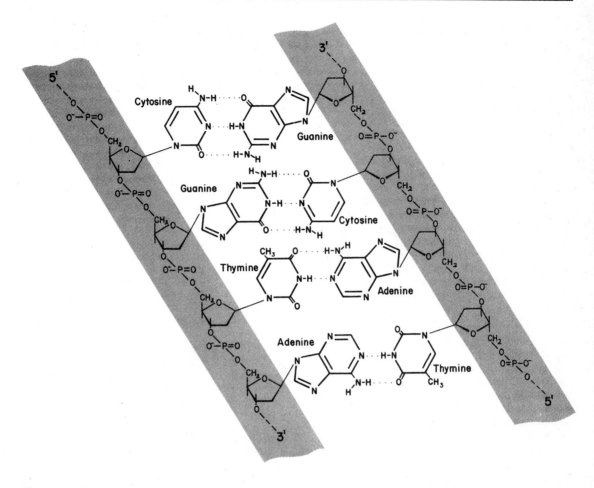

Figure 1–5. Structural features of a short segment of double-stranded DNA. Shaded areas show the sugar-phosphate backbones running antiparallel to one another (one running from the 5' and 3' and the other from 3' to 5'). The unshaded area shows the pyrimidines cytosine (C) and thymine (T), the purines guanine (G) and adenine (A), and the hydrogen bonding of C to G and A to T.

one strand of DNA dictates the order along the other strand. This feature is critical in DNA replication and transcription and in translation for determining the structures of the progeny DNA and RNA gene products. The two strands are wound around each other in a **double helix.**

Chromatin Structure

In mammalian cells, the DNA when extended would be much longer than the cell. It is packaged and folded in chromatin by proteins in the cell nucleus. The major chromatin proteins are the highly basic **histones.** The DNA is wrapped around octamers of histones; higher-order structures are formed by packaging of clusters of histones. Histone H1, high mobility group proteins, transcription factors (discussed below), and other proteins perform other functions in maintaining overall chromatin structure and regulating DNA transcription and replication.

DNA Replication

DNA replicates (Figure 1–6) through separation of the individual strands and the alignment of nucleoside triphosphates along the strands by complementary base pairing. The sugar moieties are connected enzymatically, resulting in **complementary** DNA strands that are base-paired to yield two identical double helices. The many steps in this process are complex. Since one strand in each newly formed helix is from the parent and the other is newly synthesized, the process is called **semiconservative replication.**

RNA Structure & Function

The first step in gene expression is transcription of DNA into RNA (Figure 1–7). RNA is similar to DNA except that (1) the sugar moiety is ribose instead of deoxyribose, and (2) the base uracil (U) replaces T, and U base-pairs with A. RNA is ordinarily not double-stranded, though it may fold onto itself

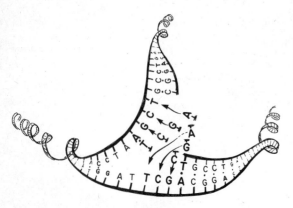

Figure 1–6. Highly simplified depiction of the essential features of DNA replication. The double helix unwinds, and two daughter strands of DNA are synthesized. Each of the resulting DNA molecules contains one strand of the original (parent) DNA molecule (semiconservative replication). Complementary base pairing directs the sequence of addition of nucleotide triphosphates by DNA polymerase (not shown). Each daughter strand of DNA is synthesized in the direction of 5′ to 3′, requiring one strand to be synthesized in a discontinuous fashion.

when there is complementarity, and some RNA viruses are double-stranded.

The three major RNA classes are messenger RNA **(mRNA)**, transfer RNA **(tRNA)**, and ribosomal RNA **(rRNA)**. There are also several minor classes.

mRNA is translated into protein (see below). tRNA is involved in transferring amino acids into protein. rRNA is contained in ribosomes (along with proteins) that are involved in protein synthesis. As shown in Figure 1–8, mRNA binds to the ribosome along with tRNAs with their covalently bound amino acids to facilitate the insertion of amino acids into growing protein chains. Each type of tRNA in the series of tRNA molecules is specific for an amino acid that can bind to the tRNA covalently. Such "charged" tRNA molecules participate in the incorporation of amino acid into protein through the formation of peptide bonds. Of the other RNA species, small RNAs participate in RNA processing and can have catalytic activities. They may also serve as part of the signal recognition particle for protein insertion into the endoplasmic reticulum.

Gene Structure & Expression

In addition to the DNA segments that are copied into RNA, other segments receive signals that regulate gene transcription (**control sequences**, or **regulatory sequences;** see Figure 1–7); determine where the enzymes involved in transcription (ie, the RNA polymerases) start; and set the basal level of the gene's expression. These latter regions are called **promoters.** RNA polymerase II is involved in transcription of genes that encode mRNA. Promoters for this enzyme are mostly located just upstream from the starting point of transcription. In contrast, the promoters for tRNA and rRNA genes may be located

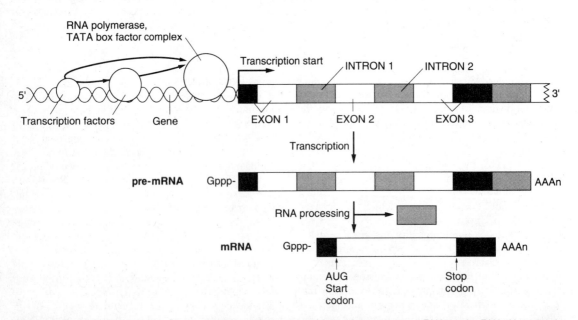

Figure 1–7. Gene transcription. Shown are schematic representations of a gene, pre-mRNA, and mRNA. Note the depicted interactions of transcription factors with each other and proximal TATA box factors. Exons are shown as open or dark boxes, introns as gray boxes.

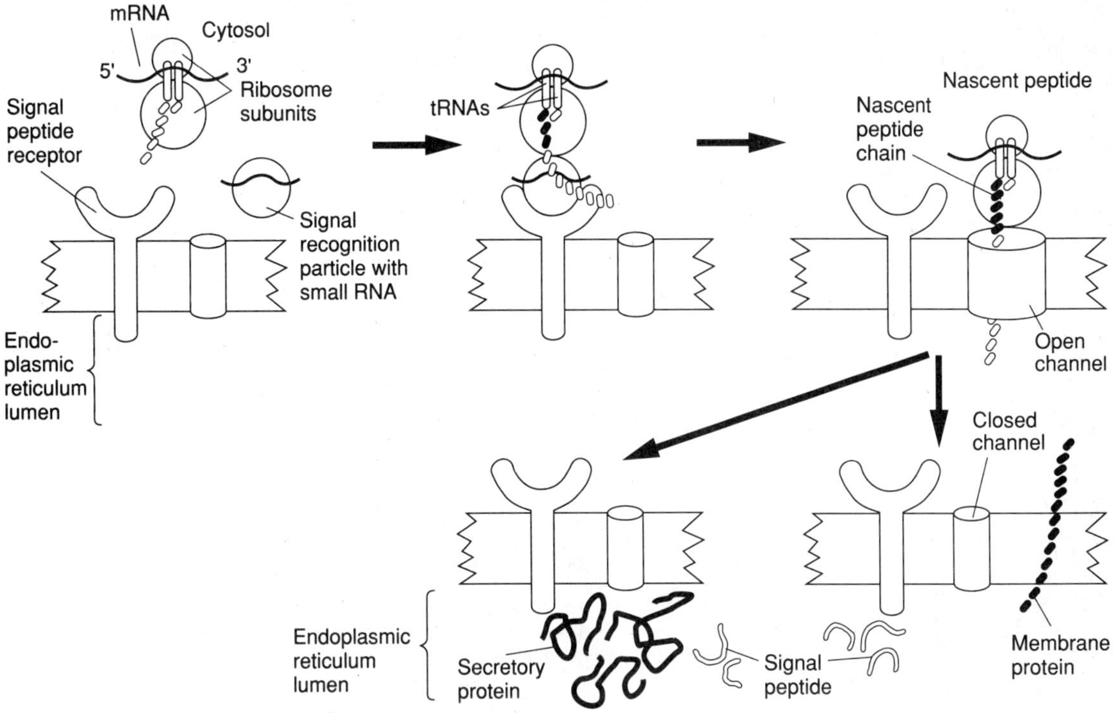

Figure 1–8. Schematic representation of the steps in the synthesis of proteins that are secreted or inserted into the membrane. The first step involves formation of a complex on the endoplasmic reticulum between the nascent polypeptide chain (on the ribosome-tRNA-mRNA complex), the signal recognition particle (containing a small RNA), and a signal peptide receptor. This complex then facilitates insertion of the nascent peptide chain into a channel through which it passes. A signal peptidase located in the interior of the endoplasmic reticulum removes the signal peptide sequence. The secretory protein is then present in the endoplasmic reticulum. For integral membrane proteins, stop transfer sequences that probably bind to receptors in the membrane hold a portion of the protein in the membrane.

in part downstream from the transcription initiation site. The two strands of DNA are separated during transcription, and RNA polymerase facilitates base pairing along one of the strands and subsequent polymerization from individual ribonucleoside triphosphates that serve as building blocks. At the end of the gene, poorly defined signals terminate transcription, apparently over a limited region rather than at a discrete site, and at a considerable distance downstream from the 3′-terminus of the mature RNA.

The structure of a mammalian gene encoding an mRNA is shown schematically in Figure 1–7. The initial DNA transcript is a precursor mRNA (**pre-mRNA**) that contains **exons** (sequences that occur in mature mRNA), **introns** (sequences that interrupt the exons and are removed in the processing of pre-mRNA to mature mRNA), and 3′-flanking sequences (see below). Small nuclear ribonuclear protein particles (snRNPs) associate with the newly synthesized RNA to participate in formation of a **spliceosome** that excises the introns and religates the exon sequences. Consensus splicing sequences in the pre-mRNA at the intron-exon borders dictate the location of excision and religation. Most but not all human

genes have introns; the number of introns can vary from 0 to over 50; the existence of introns has probably facilitated evolution. RNA processing leads to the formation of mature mRNA with impressive accuracy. However, the same pre-mRNA can sometimes be alternatively processed to yield different mRNAs from the same transcript. For example, pre-mRNA from the calcitonin gene is processed in brain and certain other tissues to an mRNA that encodes calcitonin gene-related peptide (CGRP; Figure 1–9). By contrast, calcitonin mRNA is made primarily in the perifollicular cells of the thyroid gland (Figure 1–9). These two mRNAs have in common the sequences at the 5′ end that encode the amino-terminal portion of the precursor protein molecules. They differ in the 3′ sequences that encode the carboxyl-terminal portions of the molecules. Thus, this mechanism allows one gene to serve as two genes. As another example, variant forms of the thyroid hormone receptors are generated by differences in RNA processing.

In most mRNA molecules, two other modifications occur (Figure 1–7). The 3′ end is cleaved, and a chain of A (adenosine) residues—the poly(A) tail—

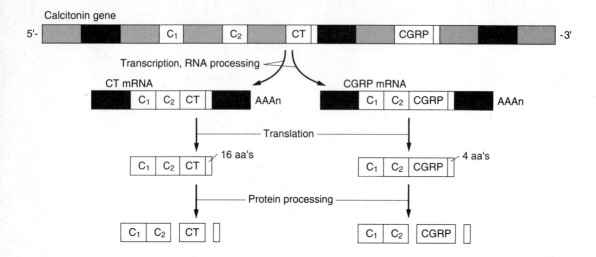

Figure 1–9. Variations in RNA processing as illustrated by the processing of calcitonin pre-mRNA. Shown is a schematic representation of the calcitonin gene with the two pathways of pre-mRNA processing that yield calcitonin or CGRP. Introns and flanking DNA are shown as gray boxes, sequences that form nontranslated portions of the mRNA as dark boxes, and protein sequences as open boxes. C_1 and C_2 refer to sequences that are common for both proteins but removed during protein processing. CT refers to sequences comprising calcitonin and CGRP to sequences comprising CGRP. In both cases, a few amino acids are removed from the carboxyl-terminus of the protein, and these are shown as open boxes.

is added to the newly generated 3′ end of the mRNA. This tailing occurs at the point of cleavage of the RNA; the site of cleavage is ordinarily dictated by the sequence AAUAAA located upstream from the site of polyadenylation. Second, a **cap,** consisting of a methylated guanosine inserted in the reverse orientation, is added to the 5′ end of the mRNA. The DNA upstream from the start of transcription is called the **5′-flanking DNA,** and that downstream from the completion of transcription is called the **3′-flanking DNA,** although the latter usually refers to the DNA following the poly(A) addition site. Mature mRNA contains untranslated nucleotides (**5′-untranslated sequences**) between the 5′ cap site and the first AUG methionine codon and between the translational stop codon (see below) and the 3′ end of the mRNA (**3′-untranslated sequences**).

Protein Synthesis

After its formation in the nucleus, the mRNA is transported to the cytoplasm, where it is translated into a protein whose amino acid sequence is determined by the codons of the mRNA according to the genetic code. Each **codon** consists of three nucleotides. The first mRNA codon is almost always AUG, which codes for methionine; codons for other amino acids then follow. The RNA structure surrounding the first AUG codon also facilitates the initiation of translation, which occurs with remarkable fidelity. Individual amino acids are each covalently linked to a specific tRNA. These tRNA molecules bind to the mRNA through an **anticodon loop** con-

taining three nucleotides that are complementary to those of a specific codon with the mRNA. For example, 3′-UAC-5′ on the anticodon loop pairs with 5′-AUG-3′ on the mRNA. Thus, successive codons within the RNA determine which tRNAs will enter the ribosome and when. Since each tRNA can only be "loaded" by a specific amino acid (by an aminoacyl synthetase), translation specificity is a result of both this feature and the linear array of nucleotides in the mRNA.

Whereas each codon is unambiguous in terms of its amino acid specificity, the code is redundant in that more than one codon specifies a given amino acid (except for tryptophan and methionine). Thus, if the nucleic acid sequence of an mRNA is known, the amino acid sequence of its protein translation product will be known with certainty. Conversely, if the amino acid sequence of a protein is known, the nucleic acid sequence of the mRNA and the gene from which it is transcribed can only be partially known. At the end of each coding segment is a "stop" codon, which is UAA, UAG, or UGA; these do not recognize tRNA, and when the ribosome reaches them as it moves along the mRNA in the process of protein synthesis, translation ceases and the ribosome dissociates from the mRNA.

Translation occurs on the ribosome that moves along the mRNA as translation proceeds (Figure 1–8). This particle is made of ribosomal RNAs and proteins and consists of two subunits. The small subunit anchors the amino acid carrying tRNAs to the ribosome and binds the mRNA, and the large subunit also binds the tRNA and catalyzes the formation of peptide bonds in the growing peptide chain. Translation proceeds from the 5′- to the 3′-direction along the mRNA, and amino acids are added to the carboxyl-terminus of the growing peptide chain. Therefore, the 5′ codon of the mRNA corresponds to the amino-terminus of the protein.

REGULATION OF GENE EXPRESSION

The activities of various genes show wide variations in different cells. Thus, growth hormone and insulin are produced exclusively in the pituitary gland and pancreatic B cells, respectively. Other genes are expressed more widely. For example, the renin gene is expressed in the kidney and several extrarenal tissues. The gene for ANP is expressed in the heart and extracardiac tissues.

These differences are due mainly to the regulation of gene expression, since in general the structure of DNA is the same in various cells of the body. One exception is that in many cases DNA can be methylated at cytosine residues; this can block the ability of the gene to be transcribed and is inherited when the gene is replicated. Methylation of one of the two X chromosomes causes it to be transcriptionally inactivated and the methylation pattern to be passed on to progeny cells. Another exception occurs with the immune system, where mutations and gene rearrangements—with division of the various cells—result in production of millions of different immunoglobulin genes in the differentiated somatic cells from a relatively small number of genes in the germ line progenitor cells.

There are examples of regulation of gene expression at essentially every step in gene expression, including the initiation and termination of transcription, processing of pre-mRNA, mRNA degradation, and translation. However, the principal control of gene expression occurs at the level of initiation of transcription.

Transcription is initiated at proximal promoter elements that comprise the first 30 or so nucleotides upstream from the transcription start site (Figure 1–7). This region usually contains a so-called **TATA box** with the sequence TATA or similar sequences. This structure binds a complex of proteins known as **TATA box factors;** these include a TATA box binding protein (TBP, or TFIID). Other factors, such as TFIIA, TFIIB, TFIIE, TFIIF, TEIIG, TFIIH, TFIII, and RNA polymerase, are then recruited to the promoter. Some of these factors also bind RNA polymerase. Some promoters do not contain TATA boxes and initiate transcription through the participation of the same factors plus another sequence-specific binding factor called the initiator, TFIII. Collectively, these factors are called the general or basal transcrip-

tion machinery, since they are common to all promoters transcribed by RNA polymerase II.

Other proteins can bind to the basal factors to enhance or depress their ability to act in conjunction with the polymerase to regulate transcription initiation (Figure 1–7). The interaction of these other **transcription factors** is facilitated by the existence of DNA sequences located usually further upstream from the TATA box that bind the factors. These factors usually bind to the DNA in the first 200 nucleotides upstream from the TATA box, but they also bind to DNA sites located several thousand nucleotides upstream—or downstream in introns, coding sequences, or the 3′-flanking DNA. Some transcription factors do not bind to the DNA but make protein-protein contacts with the TATA box or other DNA-bound transcription factors. Bending of the DNA may facilitate such interactions. The ability of a gene to be expressed and regulated is also influenced by the overall chromatin structure, and in some cases transcription factors influence local positioning of the histones and other proteins to achieve transcriptional regulation.

A well-characterized transcription factor is **Pit-1,** present in pituitary cells (somatotrophs, thyrotrophs, and lactotrophs). This factor, when deficient, can lead to dwarfism, with growth hormone, prolactin, and TSH deficiencies. It regulates both the pituitary differentiation of these cells and the expression of the hormone genes. It binds to the growth hormone and prolactin promoters upstream from the TATA box and is critical for high-level expression of this gene. Pit-1 is a member of a larger group of transcription factors termed **homeobox proteins** that are extensively involved in regulating differentiation and development. These factors in general have discrete and modular domains that are involved in the various functions (DNA binding, activation, etc) of the protein; such modular features are described in a subsequent section for the steroid and thyroid hormone receptors. Transcription factors may also inhibit transcription through analogous mechanisms.

The receptors for thyroid and steroid hormones, vitamin D, and retinoic acid and its analogues are members of a superfamily of DNA-binding transcription factors whose function is described below. Hormones that act on the cell surface can regulate the activity of transcription factors and thereby regulate gene expression at the level of transcription (see below). For example, the transcriptional activity of Pit-1 can be regulated by phosphorylation in response to both A and C kinases (see below). Pit-1 actions can be synergistic with those of the thyroid or glucocorticoid hormone or retinoic acid receptors. The growth hormone promoter contains sites that can bind the thyroid hormone and retinoic acid receptors.

Typically, a number of different transcription factors contribute to the activity of a promoter. For example, the growth hormone promoter also utilizes the transcription factors Sp1 and GHF-3. Thus, the concerted efforts of these transcription factors that associate with DNA sequences placed as cassettes—and with the non-DNA-bound proteins through protein-protein interactions—determine the overall activities of genes. This programming provides for many different combinatorial influences that can lead to wide swings in gene expression.

Regulation of gene expression at other levels occurs less commonly than transcriptional control. Tissue-specific regulation of splicing of pre-mRNA from the calcitonin gene was mentioned above. Hormones and other factors can regulate mRNA levels (and, consequently, protein levels) by affecting mRNA stability; in many cases, this occurs through transcriptional regulation of expression of proteins that either degrade the mRNA or affect its stability in some other way. The rates of degradation of particular mRNAs can be dictated in some way by nucleotide sequences in either the 5′-untranslated, translated, or 3′-untranslated portions of the mRNA. Regulation of the efficiency of mRNA translation is occasionally observed. An unusual mechanism is seen with the apolipoprotein B gene; the mRNA transcript in the liver results in a large protein (apo-B-100), whereas in the intestine, a single base in the mRNA is altered posttranscriptionally (RNA editing) to produce a translational stop codon that results in a protein of MW 48,000 (apo-B-48).

MECHANISMS OF GENETIC DISEASE

The mechanisms for genetic diseases, including those of the endocrine system, are increasingly being deciphered. These can involve a number of types of mutations of DNA that include the following: (1) point mutations, with effects on the translated protein, RNA processing or stability, or gene expression; (2) deletions, which result in loss of the ability to produce the protein or in the production of a truncated protein; and (3) rearrangements, which affect gene expression or protein structure. With most genetic diseases (sickle cell anemia is an exception), several different mutations cause the disease. Thus, with familial hypercholesterolemia, over 25 different types of mutations have been described that affect the function of the LDL receptor and lead to hypercholesterolemia.

The effects of these mutations are varied. Mutations in the steroid receptors can lead to defective function, as is seen with point mutations in the androgen receptor (an X-linked gene), causing testicular feminization; in the vitamin D receptor, resulting in vitamin D-resistant rickets; in growth hormone receptors or Pit-1, resulting in growth deficiency; in insulin receptors, resulting in diabetes mellitus; etc. Other mutations result in altered activity of the gene product with deleterious consequences. For example,

in the syndrome of generalized resistance to thyroid hormone, the mutant thyroid hormone receptor can interact with the remaining normal thyroid hormone receptors to block their function (**dominant negative mutant**). A dominant negative Pit-1 can block the function of the normal Pit-1 to promote growth hormone deficiency. A mutant form of the low-density lipoprotein (LDL) receptor is defective in internalization. An unusual rearrangement occurs in a syndrome of dexamethasone-treatable hypertension. In this syndrome, the promoter for a gene ordinarily expressed in the adrenal zona fasciculata has been rearranged to link it to the coding sequences of a gene ordinarily expressed in the zona glomerulosa whose product converts corticosterone to aldosterone. This results in excessive aldosterone production in the zona fasciculata and in ACTH-dependent hypertension (see Chapter 7).

Whereas most genetic diseases decrease the likelihood of survival and thus tend to disappear, in some cases such diseases appear to have been selected for in evolution. This is the case with sickle and thalassemia as protection against malaria. Many endocrine diseases also appear to be too common for random occurrence. 21-Hydroxylase deficiency and familial hypercholesterolemia are examples.

RECOMBINANT DNA TECHNOLOGY

Recombinant DNA technology was launched by the discovery that DNA could be cut and spliced together with other DNAs to form **recombinant DNA** outside the cell and that these hybrids could be replicated in bacteria (Figures 1–10 and 1–11). Recombinant DNAs can also be inserted back into eukaryotic (nucleated) cells such as those from yeasts or mammals for their analysis. This technology allows many DNA molecules to be obtained from a single starting molecule; has facilitated examination of cellular processes; and has provided practical approaches to diagnosis and treatment, such as the production of hormones that cannot be synthesized in adequate quantity or purity by other means.

Critical for using this new technology are the **restriction enzymes** or **restriction endonucleases** that bind DNA at specific sequences and cleave it at these loci in a characteristic fashion. These enzymes are used by bacteria to destroy foreign DNA while they protect their own genetic information by appropriate modifications. The cleavage commonly yields short single-stranded ends that are complementary to each other ("sticky ends"). Thus, sticky ends from two DNA fragments from different sources generated by the same enzyme will base-pair to form hybrid DNA molecules that can be ligated together enzymatically to form a recombinant DNA molecule (Figure 1–10). Cleavage with some restriction enzymes yields blunt-ended fragments that can be ligated less efficiently to

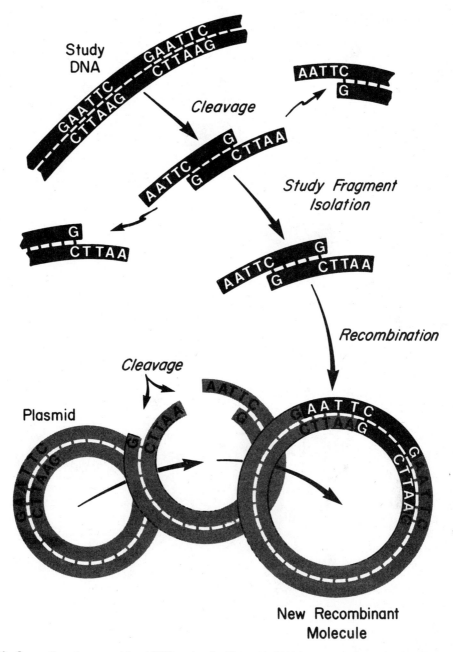

Figure 1–10. Generation of a recombinant DNA molecule. The study DNA is cleaved with a restriction enzyme (in this case *Eco*RI), and the released fragment is purified (eg, separated from the parent DNA on the basis of size by agarose gel electrophoresis). A suitable plasmid containing a unique site for the same enzyme is prepared by cleavage with the enzyme and is then mixed with the purified fragment. The complementary overhanging ends anneal to one another and are then ligated together enzymatically (DNA ligase) to yield a new recombinant DNA molecule.

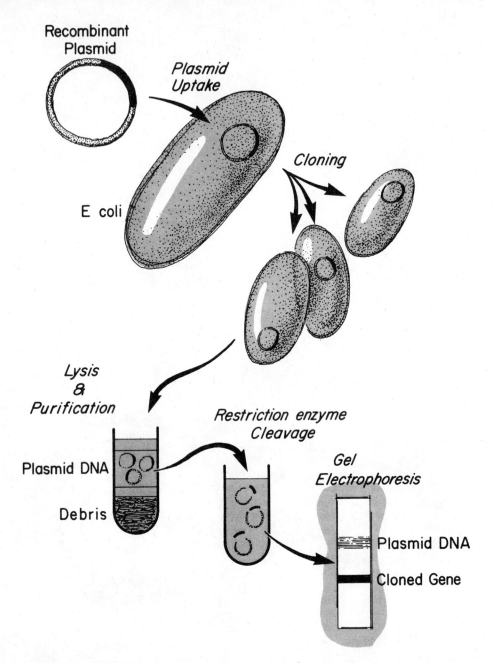

Figure 1–11. Cloning of DNA. Bacteria are treated to facilitate the uptake of recombinant plasmids containing the DNA insert of interest. Culturing in the presence of an antibiotic selects for those bacteria harboring a plasmid containing an appropriate antibiotic resistance gene (resident on the same plasmid as the insert). Those bacteria that have failed to take up the plasmid will succumb to the antibiotic. Single colonies (a clone) of the now-resistant bacteria are selected for mass culture and are then lysed and the cloned plasmid DNA purified. Cleavage with the appropriate restriction enzyme will release the DNA insert, yielding quantities of homogeneous DNA suitable for further experimentation (eg, for sequencing or preparation of specific radiolabeled DNA probes).

other blunt-ended fragments, although at a lower efficiency.

Plasmids (Figure 1–11), frequently the starting material for such reconstructions, are one type of **vector** for propagating recombinant DNA molecules. Plasmids are circular double-stranded DNA molecules that replicate in bacterial hosts as episomes, ie, extrachromosomally. They frequently contain one or more genes that confer antibiotic resistance. A recombinant plasmid as depicted in Figure 1–10 can be taken up into a bacterium, usually *E coli,* by rendering the bacterium permeable (Figure 1–11) and can subsequently replicate within the bacterial cell. If a plasmid containing an antibiotic resistance gene is used, bacteria harboring the plasmid can be enriched by culturing them with the antibiotic. The population of cells derived from a single parent cell harboring a unique piece of foreign DNA is referred to as a **clone of cells,** and the DNA contained within them is said to be cloned (Figure 1–11). Once a clone is obtained, the bacteria can be grown in large quantities, the plasmid DNA isolated, and the inserted DNA cleaved from the plasmid with the restriction enzyme. This DNA can then be electrophoretically separated from the plasmid DNA and characterized.

Bacteriophages are viruses that infect bacteria. Variants of bacteriophage λ are used extensively as vectors for molecular cloning. The foreign DNA is inserted into the middle of the single chromosome in these variants, and the recombinant DNA is then incubated with bacteriophage proteins ("packaged") to produce viable bacteriophages. These bacteriophages are then used to infect "lawns" of bacteria. During infection, a single phage particle attacks a bacterium and replicates within it. These bacteriophages mature and eventually lyse the bacterium. The released bacteriophages then infect neighboring bacteria and repeat the process. Each starting virus finally produces a clear "plaque" of lysed bacteria containing a clone of that bacteriophage. Individual clones of bacteriophages can be propagated by letting them infect other bacterial cultures. Bacteriophages are particularly efficient for producing a large number of clones from a mixture of starting DNAs because the viral DNA is inserted into cells more efficiently than plasmid DNA. Furthermore, larger DNA pieces can be inserted into bacteriophages than plasmids. Some bacteriophage λ and plasmid variants contain a promoter and other structures that allow inserted DNA to be expressed. Cosmids are bacteriophage λ variants that accommodate very large pieces of DNA; these are especially useful for analyzing chromosomal gene fragments, eg, in the human genome project.

HYBRIDIZATION

Recombinant DNA technology makes extensive use of the propensity of single-stranded DNA or RNA to anneal through base pairing (hybridize) to a complementary strand of DNA or RNA. This precise process, based on the binding of A to T or of U or C to G, permits a single-stranded nucleic acid to find its complement among millions of noncomplementary molecules. For example, a radiolabeled homogeneous piece of DNA can be used as a **probe** to (1) identify a complementary piece of DNA or RNA that has been size-fractionated on a gel; (2) to localize a single colony of bacteria (from among hundreds of thousands) that harbors a plasmid containing complementary sequences; or (3) to quantify levels of a specific mRNA. The latter process consists of allowing the probe to hybridize to a mixture of mRNA molecules, either in solution or after the RNA has been transferred to filter paper; eliminating the nonhybridized probe; and then measuring the radioactivity in the hybrids, which reflects the amount of specific mRNA present.

DNA SEQUENCING

Once a cloned gene has been isolated and its expression characterized by hybridization, the DNA is often sequenced to determine the structure of the protein it encodes and of gene segments that control its expression. Two methods currently available allow the rapid sequencing of homogeneous DNA populations. The **chemical degradation technique** uses DNA fragments radiolabeled at one end. In each reaction, each DNA molecule is cleaved only once and at only one of the four nucleotides (A residues, for instance). This results in a series of DNA fragments extending from the radiolabeled end to each location of the given nucleotide (ie, at each A) in the original DNA fragment. The sizes of these DNAs, visualized after their size fractionation and radioautography, correspond to the positions of the base (eg, A residues) in the starting DNA. The **chain termination technique** uses single-stranded DNAs as templates for complementary DNA synthesis. DNA synthesis is initiated at a particular site with a small "primer" oligonucleotide that hybridizes to it. Each reaction contains radiolabeled nucleoside triphosphate precursors and a modified nucleotide analogue at low concentration that is incorporated at low frequency, but when this happens, further elongation is blocked. This results in radiolabeled fragments that end at each of the positions of the nucleotide (dideoxy ATP, for example). By determining the size of the bands on a sizing gel, the positions of the complementary base in the original template DNA can be determined. Four different reactions are run, each including a separate modified nucleotide to determine the locations of the four nucleotides.

These methods allow the sequencing even of genes several thousand nucleotides in length in a reasonable period of time. The methods have been refined, automated, and adapted for computer analysis, such that the sequencing of the entire human genome is now realistic. One modification that simplifies the dideoxy method is the incorporation of specific dyes onto specific chain terminators such that all chain termination reactions can be done in the same tube, loaded onto the same slot on a gel, and distinguished visually because of their different colors.

POLYMERASE CHAIN REACTION

The **polymerase chain reaction (PCR)** method is widely used to amplify DNA. This involves incubating two DNA "primer" molecules and DNA polymerase with a given DNA or DNA mixture. The first primer hybridizes to one end of the DNA to be amplified and primes initiation of DNA replication at that site. The second primer is complementary to the opposite DNA strand at the other end of the DNA to be amplified. The polymerase first synthesizes DNA strands initiated from the primers. The polymerase is heat-stable, and after each round of replication the DNA strands are heated—to separate them and to provide templates for the next round of replication— and the mixture is then returned to the reaction temperature and replication is resumed. DNA synthesized after the first two rounds of replication will be primed mainly from newly synthesized copies that have termini corresponding to the primer sites. Progressive cycles greatly amplify the DNA sequences spanning the region between the two primers. Thus, only a minute fraction (even one copy) of the DNA to be amplified is required. This PCR-amplified DNA can then be used for DNA sequencing, hybridization, or molecular cloning. Variations of the priming schemes, including priming on mRNA, are allowing PCR to be used increasingly for isolation of gene sequences for cloning. PCR methodology is also particularly suitable for analyzing genetic diseases and detecting foreign DNA such as viral or bacterial DNA in biologic specimens.

SOURCES OF DNA FOR MOLECULAR CLONING

Three different sources of DNA are ordinarily used for molecular cloning: DNA produced by chemical synthesis, cellular mRNA transcribed into DNA by reverse transcription, and chromosomal DNA.

DNA Synthesis

DNA molecules composed of as many as 100 nucleotides can now be synthesized rapidly by mechanical synthesizers. An entire gene can be constructed by combining several oligonucleotides synthesized in this fashion. This approach was used for the first recombinant DNA synthesis of human insulin. More commonly, smaller DNA fragments are produced for

recombinant DNA research, particularly since the advent of PCR, which allows DNA sequences between two primers up to 1000 base pairs apart to be readily synthesized enzymatically. These fragments may contain restriction enzyme sites for constructing recombinant DNA molecules; may be used as probes for hybridization reactions; or may be used to prepare hybrid or mutated genes for protein production or research.

Reverse Transcription of mRNA

DNA strands complementary to mRNA (cDNA) isolated from cells can be produced from the mRNA template using deoxyribonucleoside triphosphates and reverse transcriptase. This enzyme is isolated from RNA retroviruses that copy their RNA into DNA (reverse transcription). The single-stranded cDNA is then copied into a double-stranded molecule by DNA polymerase.

Since any given cell contains thousands of different mRNA molecules, reverse transcription of total cellular mRNA will yield thousands of different cDNA molecules. To obtain a particular cDNA from this mixture, the investigator usually generates a large number of clones from the cDNA (a so-called cDNA library), each harboring the same parent plasmid but a different cDNA insert. These are then screened to find the clone of bacteria containing plasmids or bacteriophages with the cDNA insert of interest. Screening of a cDNA library may be performed in several ways, two of which will be discussed.

First, if even a portion of the amino acid sequence of the protein encoded by the mRNA is known, a partial DNA sequence for the cDNA can be predicted through knowledge of the genetic code. Small DNA probes with the nucleotide sequence complementary to the cDNA are then synthesized, radiolabeled, and hybridized to the DNA of the clones comprising the cDNA library to identify the cDNA of interest.

A second approach for screening is to inset the cDNA into a site in the vector that is in the middle of a bacterial gene, so that the cDNA codons will be expressed as part of a "fusion protein" containing bacterial and cDNA-encoded amino acid sequences. Screening this cDNA expression library with an antibody to the protein product of interest will permit identification of the clone producing the appropriate fusion protein.

Chromosomal Genes

Using techniques analogous to those employed for cDNA cloning, the portions of a chromosome that contain the gene of interest can be cloned. Chromosomal DNA isolated from cell nuclei is sheared randomly by sonication, restriction site linkers are added, and the fragments are cloned in the appropriate bacteriophage. A radiolabeled cDNA or chemically synthesized oligonucleotide may then be used to screen for the clone with the chromosomal insert of interest as described above.

TRANSFER OF CLONED GENES INTO MAMMALIAN CELLS

DNA can be transferred, or "transfected," into mammalian cells in several ways to study gene function or produce proteins for scientific or commercial uses. For example, DNA can be microinjected into the cell nucleus, phagocytosed by the cells in calcium phosphate precipitates, directly electroporated into recipients, or inserted when incorporated into viral vectors (eg, from retroviruses or bovine papillomavirus) used to infect the cells.

Most of the transfected DNA will not become integrated into the host chromosome and be stably expressed. However, some of this DNA may be transiently expressed, and its function can be studied for a short time (hours to days; transient expression assays). Those few cells in which the transfected DNA has become integrated and replicated along with the host DNA can, when needed, be isolated—eg, by "co-transfecting" the DNA of interest with DNA containing a "selectable" gene such as the gene encoding resistance to neomycin. Culturing the cells with a neomycin analogue will ordinarily kill those cells that do not express the antibiotic resistance gene, and only the cells that express the neomycin resistance gene will propagate. These cells will usually have integrated the study gene as well. This procedure depends on the fact that the co-transfected gene and a selectable marker commonly fuse together and insert into the same DNA site.

Mammalian cells can amplify certain DNA sequences, including transfected DNA. Cells that harbor such amplified DNA can be selected for by applying pressure like that described above with neomycin resistance. This method can be used for production of recombinant proteins in mammalian cells for pharmaceutical or other purposes by maximizing the number of gene copies and hence expression of the gene of interest.

Gene transfer into mammalian cells has been enormously useful for studying the mechanisms of gene expression and its regulation and the functions, actions, synthesis, and metabolism of hormones, hormone receptors, and other molecules involved in endocrinology and endocrine disease. For example, a gene that expresses a hormone receptor can be transfected into cells, and its binding to hormones, second messenger signaling, and other functions can be studied. Mutations of the gene can be prepared to examine the importance to its function of individual domains of the gene product. A convenient way to study the control of gene expression is to link the promoter to be studied with the coding sequences of a "reporter" gene such as that which encodes for chloramphenicol acetyltransferease (CAT) or luciferase, whose function is easily measured. For example, information about hormone response elements is derived chiefly from such studies. If the promoter of a gene, assessed by changes in CAT expression, responds to a hormone-receptor complex, it is likely that sequences on the transfected promoter mediate the response. These sequences can be identified by further mutation of the promoter segment followed by transfer to another (initially hormone receptor-unresponsive) promoter to see if they convey responsiveness.

PRODUCTION OF MEDICALLY IMPORTANT PROTEINS BY RECOMBINANT DNA TECHNIQUES

A major use of recombinant DNA technology is to produce medically useful proteins. Recombinant DNA techniques are the only means available for producing proteins of moderate to large size in quantity. Methods for chemically synthesizing peptides, though considerably improved, are not efficient for producing large proteins (eg, > 50 amino acids). Whereas some proteins, such as insulin, can be obtained from animals, this approach (even for insulin) has limitations and is impractical for obtaining large quantities of scarce proteins such as GH and erythropoietin.

Mammalian DNA sequences can be expressed in bacteria, yeasts, or mammalian cells. For production in bacteria, for example, the protein coding sequences can be inserted downstream from bacterial regulatory sequences that include a promoter, a ribosomal binding site, and an AUG methionine-initiating codon. Yeasts have plasmids similar to those of bacteria and are sometimes advantageous because they cam be made to secrete the protein. A disadvantage of mammalian cells is that it is more expensive to propagate them than bacteria or yeasts, but they can have advantages—eg, mammalian cells can add carbohydrate groups to the proteins when necessary. Plasminogen activators now in clinical use and more complex proteins such as factor VIII are being produced by mammalian cells.

The major products produced by recombinant DNA methods now used to treat endocrine disorders are insulin and growth hormone. Other recombinant DNA products may be considered as hormones. Those now in use include erythropoietin, granulocyte colony-stimulating factor, interleukin-2, and interferons. Currently in clinical trials are a number of growth factors (epidermal, fibroblast, platelet-derived, insulin-like, etc) that may be useful in facilitating wound repair or for treating other growth problems. It is likely that other products will be forthcoming. Even products such as vaccines may have an impact on endocrine diseases, since infections may cause autoimmune diseases that affect the endocrine system.

In addition to the direct uses of recombinant DNA-produced proteins for therapy, recombinant DNA techniques are being used increasingly for drug design. Sophisticated means are being improved to determine the three-dimensional structures of proteins, mostly by x-ray diffraction and magnetic resonance (MR) spectroscopy. The applications of computer technology to analysis of drug-target interactions and to screening of libraries of compounds for their potential to bind to drug targets are also accelerating at a rapid pace. The capability to produce drug targets such as receptors for hormones and enzymes involved in important functions now allows their structures to be determined and application of these methods along with organic chemical synthesis and drug testing to produce novel pharmaceuticals. The reporter systems described above can be used to screen for agonist or antagonist molecules that interact with receptors. Recombinant methods can be used to produce mutated proteins for structure-activity analyses that facilitate drug design. Mutations in bacteriophage can be engineered to produce large libraries of peptides for screening.

DIAGNOSIS OF GENETIC DISEASE USING DNA

The DNA of cells obtained from blood, amniotic fluid, or biopsy material can be analyzed utilizing recombinant DNA technology. DNA based tests are available for diagnosis of such classic genetic diseases as thalassemia, sickle cell anemia, and phenylketonuria, and these tests have recently been applied to such endocrinologic conditions as familial hypercholesterolemia, congenital adrenal hyperplasia, and multiple endocrine neoplasia (MEN) type I. Genetic differences also contribute to many more common diseases in which the specific genetic defect has not yet been defined (eg, hypertension and type II diabetes mellitus), and the ability to analyze genes in detail may permit the detection and analysis of DNA segments responsible for these diseases.

Although a gene can be isolated from an individual and its primary structure determined, this procedure is currently cumbersome and not adaptable for general clinical use. However, when the locus of the proposed defect is strongly suspected, the PCR methodology, discussed in an earlier section, can be successfully employed.

Currently, the most prevalent technique for diagnosing genetic diseases is **restriction fragment length polymorphism** (RFLP) methodology (Figure 1–12). This approach generally involves isolating DNA from a patient and his or her relatives, cleaving it with restriction enzymes, running it on gels, transferring it to nitrocellulose filters, and hybridizing it

with particular DNA probes. This method utilizes **genetic polymorphisms,** ie, differences in the primary structures of genes, such as between the two alleles of a given gene in the same or different individuals that are reflected in a difference in the site of a given restriction fragment. Such differences occur both in transcribed and in flanking DNA sequences and are mutations generated at low frequency in the process of DNA replication. Most are "silent" and have no effect on the function of the gene or its products. Nevertheless, these mutations are inherited and can be used as **genetic markers.** The polymorphisms that have been most useful are those where the mutations result in differences in a restriction endonuclease cleavage site or in a length of inserted DNA.

To understand the use of polymorphisms, first assume that a mutation in one base results in a genetic trait, eg, susceptibility to developing a disease such as diabetes mellitus. Somewhere in or around the affected gene, the individual is likely to have additional silent polymorphic differences in comparison to other people (Figure 1–12). Cleavage of the affected individual's DNA with a battery of restriction enzymes will result in DNA fragments that differ in size from those of other people and reveal the differences. Subjecting the fragments to size fractionation on a gel and performing hybridization to a radiolabeled probe from the gene as described above will allow identification of the aberrant fragment. This type of analysis requires only an established linkage between a disease and a restriction fragment length polymorphism (RFLP) and an appropriate DNA probe; it is not necessary to know anything about the gene product. Indeed, the associated mutation may be millions of bases distant from the site of the RFLP.

In practice, the RFLP pattern is compared in afflicted and nonafflicted family members to establish the diagnosis; multiple mutations of independent origin commonly account for a given genetic disease, so a different RFLP pattern will exist for unrelated afflicted patients. For diseases such as sickle cell anemia, however, in which a single mutation accounts for all known cases, a change in a restriction enzyme site at the locus of the mutation can be used for general diagnosis. Figure 1–12 illustrates the approach with a hypothetical defect in a family. It can be seen that in all cases, the disease cosegregates with the "B" allele.

TRANSGENIC ANIMALS

Transgenic animals contain foreign DNA in their genomes. The availability of transgenic mice is greatly changing the study of gene function; this technology is also likely to change animal husbandry techniques. Transgenic mice are prepared by microinjecting DNA into a fertilized mouse egg and then placing the egg into a pseudopregnant mouse.

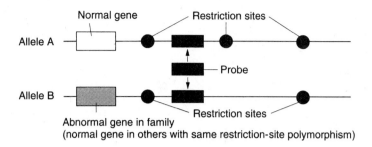

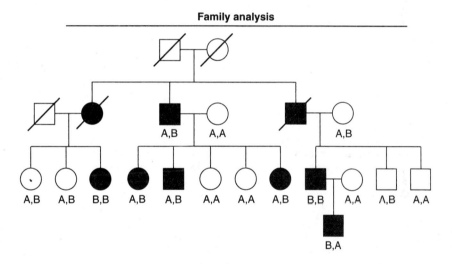

Figure 1–12. Diagnosis of genetic diseases. Shown in the top portion are two representative alleles with differences in a restriction site (nothing to do with the disease). In this example, the loss of the site in allele B is linked to a mutation that results in disease. Note that the allele B associated with the defective gene may be present with the missing restriction site in other unaffected individuals. Shown in the middle portion are representations of gel analysis results that distinguish the two alleles (in this case RFLPs). Shown at the bottom is an analysis of a family with the disease. Boxes represent males, circles females. Dark boxes or circles depict people who are or were afflicted. A diagonal line through the box or square indicates that the individual is deceased. Note that the disease always segregates with the B allele but that in the family depicted in the far right, a B allele contributed by the unafflicted persons does not contain the defective gene.

The recipient mouse then produces offspring containing the transfected DNA. Because the transfected DNA was placed in the egg, many of the cells of the resulting offspring will contain the transfected DNA. The progeny from such animals can then be used to produce more offspring containing the foreign DNA and to obtain animals in which all of the cells contain the transgene.

Transgenic animals have a number of uses. Transcription control in the animal can be studied by linking putative transcriptional control regions to reporter sequences (described earlier). The consequences of overexpression of proteins systemically or in specific tissues can be examined by utilizing the relevant promoters linked to the coding sequences of the gene. For example, recent overexpression of the renin gene in a number of rat tissues resulted in severe hypertension without elevations of plasma renin—implying the potential for extrarenal and local activity of the renin-angiotensin system. A particularly important recent application has been the ability to perform "gene knockout" experiments. In these experiments, means have been developed to selectively delete a gene in tissue culture cells. These cells are then incorporated into the developing embryo and become part of the transgenic animal. For example, this approach demonstrated important developmental actions of the parathyroid hormone (PTH)-related gene that encodes a PTH-related hormone which produces hypercalcemia with certain malignancies. Tumor-producing genes such as that contained within the simian virus 40 (SV40) T antigen can be expressed using the relevant promoter to cause tumors in the transgenic animals from which relevant cells can be cultured. For example, these methods resulted in the first cells in continuous culture that produced LH and GnRH.

POTENTIAL FOR GENE THERAPY

The ability to transfer genes into mammalian cells has heralded the era of gene therapy. In principle, such approaches could work for a variety of endocrine problems such as states of deficiency of insulin, GH, and PTH. It could also be used to treat excess states such as hypertension and hypercholesterolemia. For example, cholesterol levels were markedly reduced in mice that overexpressed an LDL receptor transgene. In many cases, a number of problems will have to be overcome, such as the targeting of the transgene in the appropriate tissue (insulin gene expression in the pancreas, for example), the correct or needed level of expression of the gene (as with the insulin gene), and potential mutations of the transgene in recipient cells. However, it is already clear that many of these potential problems can be bypassed. To date, this methodology is being applied on a relatively narrow scale, but the power of this technology will provide many other approaches.

EVOLUTION OF THE ENDOCRINE SYSTEM

CELLULAR CONTROL NETWORKS

The endocrine system probably had its origins with intracellular communication in lower forms. For example, cAMP and protein phosphorylation reactions that mediate hormone actions in humans exert regulatory roles in bacteria. These mechanisms have been extended in higher species and establish response systems for hormones. **Simple control systems** are used mostly for regulation within the bacterium, but they also set the stage for responses to external stimuli. Indeed, bacteria also respond to chemotactic and other external stimuli that are analogous to endocrine control. Therefore, the evolution of the endocrine system can be discussed in terms of the evolution of both response networks and of signals that communicate between the cells (hormones).

In both cases, the regulatory control elements appear to be modifications of essential substances. Tomkins noted years ago that most intracellular communication mediators were derivatives of simple molecules. Thus, cAMP is derived from ATP. He noted that it would be difficult for ATP to be a regulatory molecule, since marked variations in ATP that might be required for regulation might impair cellular function. He speculated that substances such as cAMP were originally generated as by-products of ATP and might be produced preferentially when ATP hydrolysis to ADP was not occurring. This type of process was a simple form of **complex regulation,** and in this example, cAMP formation might be signaled by idling of ATP hydrolysis. Therefore, a regulatory system might be established if the cell learned to regulate processes that overcame the reason for the idling. In this complex regulation, cAMP production can be regulated independently of ATP production or hydrolysis, thereby giving the organism much greater flexibility for control. Indeed, cAMP is produced when bacteria are starved for glucose and is a symbol of glucose deprivation. The cAMP in turn induces enzymes that metabolize alternative substrates such as lactose to overcome the deficiency of glucose. The cAMP became the symbol, the precursor to hormone, for the signal, glucose deprivation. The response limb for cAMP in bacteria is a transcription factor whose activity is affected by cAMP binding. This could have arisen, for example, by combining a derivative of a primitive nucleotide binding site with that for a DNA binding protein or in analogous ways.

THE ORIGINS OF HORMONES

Hormones are also derived from more essential elements: peptides from proteins, steroids from cholesterol, and catecholamines and thyroid hormones from amino acids. These compounds may have been originally produced by analogous processes. For example, originally, steroid production might have been controlled by processes that affected cholesterol synthesis or utilization, eg, by signals that affected cell growth. Thyroid or catecholamine production could be regulated by processes that affected amino acid or protein metabolism. Once the original hormones, the precursors to today's hormones, were generated, modifications of them gave the additional needed properties in terms of being secreted, receptor binding, bioavailability (including binding to transport proteins), and ability to be degraded or cleared.

INTRACELLULAR COMMUNICATION

Once hormones interact with receptors in or on the target cells, intracellular communication events are initiated. These can involve modification reactions such as phosphorylation and may have effects on gene expression or ion levels. These events only required that the regulatory substances be released. In bacteria, these could have been simple mechanisms; however, in higher organisms, more sophisticated means have been developed not only to release hormones, sometimes in a specific direction, but to regulate their release. The common thread is that the same intracellular control networks could be used in the target cells.

EVOLUTION OF GENES INVOLVED IN THE ENDOCRINE SYSTEM

Genes evolved to encode all aspects of the endocrine system: enzymes involved in hormone synthesis, processing, release, transport and metabolism; hormone receptors; proteins involved in signaling hormone-receptor actions; and other proteins. Genes evolve through duplications of ancestral genes, rearrangements of genes, movements of parts of genes to the same or other genes, and specific mutations. For example, it appears that polypeptide hormone genes are composed of parts of primitive genes and that duplications of these genes, insertions from other genes, and subsequent mutations were used to generate the final product. In addition, families of genes evolved by duplications and additional modifications. Examples of families of genes include the growth hormone, prolactin, and placental lactogen (chorionic somatomammotropin) family and the glycoprotein hormones that share the same α-subunit and have homologous β-subunits. Genes involved in the synthesis of other classes of hormones and encoding hormone receptors probably evolved in a similar way. For example, there are similarities in some genes involved in steroid hormone biosynthesis. Genes encoding the receptors for the steroid hormones, thyroid hormones, retinoids, and vitamin D belong to a "superfamily" that also encode other proteins involved in regulation of transcription. Genes encoding the receptors for GH and PRL belong to a large family that includes the receptors for many hematopoietic factors.

The organization of genes with introns and exons has probably facilitated the movement of DNA segments into and out of genes during evolution. The inserted segment could contain structures that either code for amino acids or contain regulatory sequences. Introns facilitate such rearrangements by allowing genetic events to be somewhat imprecise. For example, insertion of a segment with an exon flanked by two introns into an intron of an existing gene would result in an altered mRNA product that would be translated into a protein containing the new amino acids encoded by the added exon. For this event, breaks in the DNA need to occur somewhere in the middle of the intron in segments that do not contain critical control structures such as those which affect RNA processing. Without introns, such insertions would be much more difficult to achieve without compromising the original gene. By modifying existing genes and either deleting or adding other segments that have special functions, such evolutionary events have resulted in tremendous diversity and specialization of all of the functions of the human endocrine system.

INTEGRATIVE NETWORKS

Evolution has resulted in the development of integrative networks. For example, coordinated responses regulate cardiovascular functions, metabolism, and other processes. These processes involve integrated actions of a given hormone within the same cell and in different tissues and complementary or counterbalancing multihormonal influences, sometimes overlapping and not always in the same direction. Integrative networks probably developed in several ways. For example, once a hormone learned to regulate a given response—eg, glucose metabolism—it might have been easy for it to evolve to regulate other processes for which the influence on glucose was advantageous. For example, glucocorticoids "learned" to regulate glucose metabolism. These hormones may have been an "anxiety" stimulus for preparation for starvation, and one response would be to increase glucose production and glycogen storage. It might then have been easy for the hormones to incorporate other actions, such as those on lipid and amino acid metabolism, that were complementary in this setting. Such networks, once established, would probably be relatively stable evolutionarily. However, they could be modified and expanded, and gene duplications could allow complementary and even antagonistic hormones and response networks to diverge from these networks that would better serve the host. Hormones with counterbalancing actions could then develop in an analogous fashion. Thus, the hormones gradually established the complex patterns that are seen today.

EVOLUTION OF THE ENDOCRINE GLANDS

In primitive systems, cell-cell communication occurred through the release of substances into the media to act on adjacent cells—paracrine control. Many also developed primitive nervous systems that ultimately evolved into today's more complicated ones. The nervous system remains the dominant means for intercellular communication; however, the nervous system alone was insufficient or at least not optimal for all of the types of regulation that were possible, and it would be advantageous to have additional control mechanisms. This probably happened in two ways. First, since cells were already releasing signals that were acting in paracrine or autocrine fashions, it would be simple to allow them to travel through the circulation to act as hormones. Secondly, nerve cells could become endocrine cells either by secreting hormones themselves, as now occurs with the central nervous system (see above), or allowing neurotransmitters to move farther than the synapse and act as hormones or in a paracrine fashion. Examples of the latter are the posterior pituitary and the adrenal medulla, where nerve terminals release vasopressin and oxytocin and epinephrine, respectively. Whereas in most cases the endocrine glands release hormones for systemic availability, in limited circumstances anatomic structures have formed which allow more local delivery. This is observed in the portal system of the hypothalamus and pituitary and with insulin and glucagon delivery first to the liver. An additional specialization in this regard was the development of a large component of the endocrine system, the pituitary, in proximity to the central nervous system, where it could be centrally controlled.

HORMONE SYNTHESIS & RELEASE

PEPTIDES

Peptide hormones are proteins of various sizes that are synthesized as discussed in the earlier section on gene expression. The synthesized proteins are inserted into vesicles for secretion, folded, and may be processed through proteolysis or other modifications. Folding is determined both by the protein's primary sequence and by auxiliary proteins.

For secretion (Figure 1–8), the protein is inserted into the **endoplasmic reticulum,** where it ultimately reaches secretory vesicles. This process is facilitated by a **signal sequence** or protein "pre-" portion consisting of 15–25 largely hydrophobic amino-terminal amino acids on the newly synthesized protein. This sequence binds to a signal recognition particle consisting of six proteins and a small RNA, and the binding temporarily slows further elongation, allowing time for the nascent chain to reach the endoplasmic reticulum. This complex then binds to a signal recognition particle receptor in the membrane of the endoplasmic reticulum, resulting in the vectoral transit of the growing peptide chain through an aqueous channel into the endoplasmic space. Following translation, the signal sequence is removed, and the protein **(preprohormone)** is released into the space, leaving either the mature hormone or a **prohormone** that will undergo further modifications. Some proteins, such as fibroblast growth factor, have receptors on the outer surface of the cell but do not have a signal peptide sequence. The mechanisms by which these proteins get outside the cell are not known. Possibilities include their release upon cell death or transport by peptide transporters.

Following transit of the protein into the endoplasmic reticulum, the protein then moves through a series of specialized compartments where it may also be further modified before it is released (Figure 1–13). Vesicles bud from the endoplasmic reticulum and move to and fuse with the **Golgi apparatus,** where their contents are delivered. The vesicles are covered by a protein coat that enables them to bind to the Golgi apparatus membranes (Figure 1–13). The Golgi complex contains several compartments, including a *cis*-Golgi network that acts as a "filter" to remove proteins that inappropriately escape from the endoplasmic reticulum; a Golgi stack, consisting of several distinct compartments, where certain processing events occur; and a *trans*-Golgi network from which proteins with differing destinations (lysosomes, secretory storage vesicles, plasma membrane domains) diverge. Transport vesicles bud from each of these compartments in a process that requires small GTP-binding proteins. These coated vesicles then fuse with the membranes of the next compartment in a process that requires ATP hydrolysis and other proteins, including GTP binding proteins (and GTP hydrolysis) and the release and recycling of the coat proteins. Finally, secretory vesicles bud out from the *trans*-Golgi network and are transported to the cell surface, where they fuse with the membrane to deliver their contents to the outside of the cell. Movement of vesicles through the cell to the surface commonly occurs along microtubule tracks.

Hormones are released from the cell both constitutively **(constitutive pathway)** and in response to stimuli **(regulated secretory pathway;** Figure 1–13). Most endocrine cells (eg, pituitary, parathyroids, pancreas) utilize the regulated secretory pathway; thus, they store the peptide hormones in secretory granules, and release them in response to stimuli. By storing these products, a secretory cell is able to release them over a short period at a rate that greatly exceeds the cell's synthesizing capacity. This is the case in the pancreatic islets, parathyroid gland, and pituitary gland. However, the liver, which releases angiotensinogen, and the placenta, which releases CG and placental lactogen (chorionic somatomammotropin), utilize only the constitutive

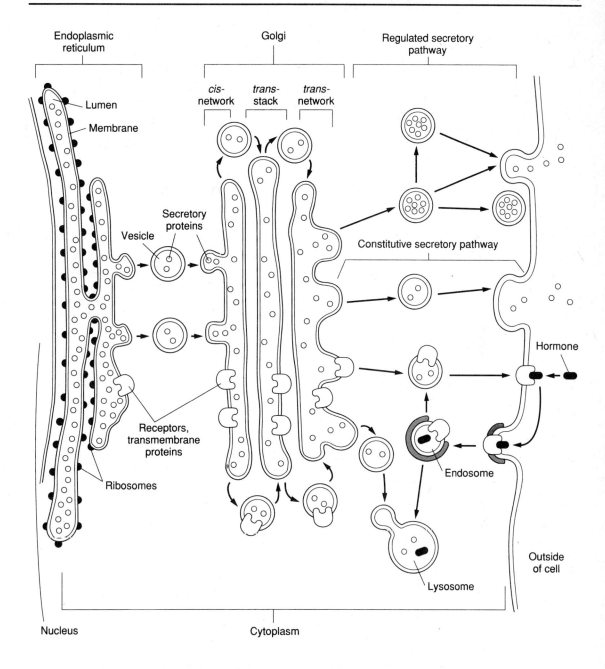

Figure 1–13. Routes through the cell for membrane and secreted proteins. Shown is a schematic representation, not to scale, of the various cellular compartments and constituents, and arrows designating the various trafficking. The pathways are described in the text. Not shown are the different membrane-associated proteins that participate in the structural organization and function of the various cellular compartments. Note the reuptake of membrane receptors and the routing of the endosome to either the lysosome or back to the surface.

pathway. Features of the structures of proteins target them to the various pathways. The regulated pathway is dominant in that fusion proteins of constitutively released and regulated secretory proteins are released by the regulated pathway. The vesicles of the two pathways differ; those of the regulated pathway are packed with secretory proteins to a very high concentration, which gives them a very high density in electron micrographs. These granules accumulate in the cell in the absence of a secretory stimulus until the latter results in the release of their contents by fusion with the plasma membrane. Secretion is directed with respect to the orientation of the cell such that hormones are released into the circulation.

In some cases, hormones are also secreted along with other proteins. Neurophysins, released from the precursors to vasopressin and oxytocin, bind these hormones and accompany them from their sites of synthesis in the hypothalamus to their storage sites in the posterior pituitary. Chromogranin A is commonly found in secretory vesicles of endocrine cells such as the parathyroid gland; this protein may facilitate aggregation of stored proteins or may be a hormone precursor.

Some peptide hormones undergo little further modifications, as is the case with GH and PRL. In other cases, cleavage of the "prohormones" inside the cell generates the final hormone. For example, proinsulin is converted to insulin by removal of the C peptide sequences, leaving the A and B chains that are attached through disulfide bonds. In this case, the C peptide serves originally to align the molecule so that these bonds could form and mature insulin could be properly folded (Chapter 15). ACTH, a 39-amino-acid protein, and several other peptides (N-terminal fragment, betalipotropin) are released proteolytically from the much larger protein **proopiomelanocortin (POMC)** in the anterior pituitary (Chapter 2). In some cases, there may be differential processing in various cells. For example in the intermediate pituitary of the rat, POMC may be alternatively processed to yield β-endorphin and corticotropin-like intermediate lobe protein. Dibasic amino acids commonly serve as cleavage sites for these proteases.

The various hormones also may be processed in different sites. Most proteins are processed in the dense secretory granules of the regulated secreted pathway. The cleavage of proinsulin to insulin, prorenin to renin, and POMC to its peptides are examples. However, ANP appears to be cleaved in association with release of its precursor, perhaps on the outside of the cell. In the central nervous system, some peptides (eg, TRH) are processed in the neuronal perikarya, whereas others are processed in the axons and terminals (GnRH precursor). In the circulation, the decapeptide angiotensin I is generated from angiotensinogen by the actions of renin, and the octapeptide angiotensin II is generated from angiotensin I through the actions of converting enzyme.

In some cases, sugars or other modifications are added during or after translation. Sugar groups are usually added via nitrogen linkage to asparagine residues (This occurs rarely if ever for cytoplasmic proteins), but they may be added to serine, threonine, or hydroxylysine residues. The N-linked oligosaccharides are initially added in the endoplasmic reticulum and usually consist of N-acetylglucosamine and mannose residues; further modifications occur in the Golgi complex with addition to the mannose core of variable numbers of glucosamine-galactose-sialic acid residues. Both the α- and β-subunits of the glycoprotein hormones (FSH, LH, TSH, and CG) are glycosylated; this modification facilitates association of these two subunits and is necessary for optimal activities of the hormones. Glycosylation may also affect the stability of the hormones in the circulation. Proteins may be sulfated on their oligosaccharides as is seen with the glycoprotein hormones. The glycoprotein hormones also illustrate the less common situation whereby the mature hormone is actually the product of two different genes. Hormones may be phosphorylated as is seen with PTH, and the carboxyl-terminus may be amidated; in many cases, the modifications are of unknown significance.

When the contents of secretory granules are released in response to a stimulus, the granule membranes fuse with those of the cell membrane, and the contents of the granule are then released by exocytosis. Ca^{2+} is important for these processes. Agents that stimulate the release of polypeptide and catecholamine hormones stimulate Ca^{2+} influx into the cytoplasm through specific Ca^{2+} channels. This triggers fusion of the secretory vesicles with the membrane and the release of their stored hormones. The mechanisms for stimulating Ca^{2+} release are discussed in the subsequent section on mechanisms of hormone action. Thus, the activators of Ca^{2+} channels and of phospholipase C are candidates to promote secretion. In the pancreatic B cells, high glucose levels increase intracellular ATP levels (or ATP/ADP levels) that in turn inhibit K^+ efflux through specific membrane channels, resulting in depolarization of the membrane and opening of Ca^{2+} channels. The rise in Ca^{2+} then opens K^+ channels, resulting in repolarization of the membrane and thus terminating the secretion stimulus. cAMP can also stimulate hormone secretion through a kinase-stimulated phosphorylation and activation of Ca^{2+} channels and through amplification of other signals that promote increases in intracellular Ca^{2+}.

THYROID HORMONES

Thyroid hormones are synthesized solely in the thyroid gland, though about 70% of the major active thyroid hormone, $3',3,5$-L-triiodothyronine (T_3), is produced in the peripheral tissues through deiodination of 3′,5′,3,5-L-tetraiodothyronine (thyroxine; T_4). The mechanisms of thyroid hormone synthesis are discussed in detail in Chapter 4 and are discussed here briefly for perspective. The thyroid gland cells concentrate iodine for thyroid hormone synthesis by active transport. The thyroid gland cells are arranged in follicles that surround colloidal material, and they produce a large multisubunit glycoprotein, thyroglobulin. The iodine is rapidly oxidized and coupled to tyrosine aromatic rings on the thyroglobulin (organification). Tyrosine residues are then coupled together to yield thyronines. Both organification and coupling are catalyzed by thyroid peroxidase on the apical surface of the cell in microvilli that extend into the colloid space. Thyroglobulin is released—along with its attached thyronines—into the follicle, where it serves as a storage for the hormones. Thyroid hormones are formed by reuptake of the thyroglobulin by endocytosis and its proteolytic digestion by lysosomal hydrolyases and perhaps thyroid peroxidase, yielding the various thyronines. Under normal conditions, the gland releases T_4 and T_3 in about a 10:1 ratio, probably through an active transport mechanism.

STEROIDS

The steroid hormones are produced in the adrenals, ovaries, testes, placenta, and to some extent in peripheral tissues (Figure 1–14). The overall pathways in these glands are similar, though differences in the specific enzymes present in the various cell types generate differences in the actual pathways taken to achieve the final product and thus result in differences in the steroids that are produced.

Steroids are derived from cholesterol produced either by de novo synthesis or by uptake of LDL through LDL receptors. There is some storage of cholesterol in cholesterol esters in lipid droplets that are abundant in steroidogenic cells. When the steroid-producing glands are stimulated, this cholesterol is liberated through stimulation of cholesterol esterase, and some additional cholesterol is produced through stimulation of cholesterol synthesis by the gland. Nevertheless, with time, enhanced cholesterol uptake is the prevalent mechanism for increasing steroidogenesis. These glands have particularly high concentrations of LDL receptors that are increased further by steroidogenic stimuli such as tropic hormones. This is due mostly to depletion of intracellular cholesterol by the stimulus with consequent removal of the usual feedback inhibition of LDL receptor production (Chapter 6). This decrease also increases cholesterol synthesis, which further facilitates steroidogenesis. Steroid production after such stimulation can be ten times basal production.

The rate-limiting step in steroid hormone production is the cleavage of cholesterol to form pregnenolone through the actions of a cytochrome P450-cholesterol side cleavage enzyme (P450scc) located on the inner mitochondrial membrane. This enzyme (and other P450 enzymes catalyzing steroid hormone biosynthesis) utilizes (1) a flavoprotein, which is adrenodoxin reductase for the mitochondrial cytochromes P450scc, P450c11β, P450c11AS (also called P), and P450c1α and cytochrome P450 reductase for the microsomal enzymes P450c17 (17-hydroxylase), P450c21 (21-hydroxylase, and P450c25 (vitamin D 25-hydroxylase); (2) an iron sulfur protein (adrenodoxin with mitochondrial but not microsomal PA50s); (3) NADPH; and (4) oxygen. Cholesterol is hydroxylated at C_{22} and then C_{20}, and the product is cleaved to yield pregnenolone plus isocapraldehyde. The activity of this step is regulated by the major tropic stimuli (ACTH, FSH, LH, CG) in all of the steroidogenic tissues. The details of how this is done are not known, but it appears that the stimuli increase the availability of free unesterified cholesterol for the step, probably by stimulating the transfer of cholesterol from the inner to the outer mitochondrial membrane through cAMP stimulation of an activator protein and polyphosphoinositides.

Pregnenolone then moves out of the mitochondria to the endoplasmic reticulum, where it undergoes a series of modifications. Such movement of these precursors between the mitochondria and the endoplasmic reticulum may be facilitated by sterol carrier proteins or movement on a membrane surface.

In the adrenocortical zona fasciculata and zona reticularis (Chapter 6), pregnenolone is sequentially converted to 17α-OH-pregnenolone (by cytochrome P450c17), 17α-OH-progesterone (by the 3β-hydroxysteroid dehydrogenase-$\Delta^{4,5}$-isomerase enzyme complex, which converts the 5,6 to the -4,5- double bond), and 11-deoxycortisol (by cytochrome P450c21). The production of 17α-OH-pregnenolone from pregnenolone is referred to as the Δ^5 pathway because the -5,6 double bond is preserved. 11-Deoxycortisol then flows back into the mitochondria where cortisol, the final active product, is formed through 11-β hydroxylation through the actions of cytochrome P450c11. This enzyme is lacking in the gonads, which do not produce cortisol or aldosterone.

The adrenal glomerulosa (Chapter 7) produces progesterone from pregnenolone through the actions of 3β-hydroxysteroid dehydrogenase-$\Delta^{4,5}$-isomerase (see above). This is called the Δ^4 pathway. The glomerulosa lacks cytochrome P450c17 and uniquely contains a mitochondrial P450c11AS (corticosterone methyl oxidase I). Progesterone is hydroxylated at C_{21} by P450c21 to produce 11-deoxycorticosterone (DOC) and by P450c11AS at C_{11} to produce corticosterone, which is converted to aldosterone through the addition of an aldehyde group at position 18 through the activity of P45011AS.

For androgen (Chapter 9) and estrogen (Chapter 10) production, the side chains at position 17 of 17α-

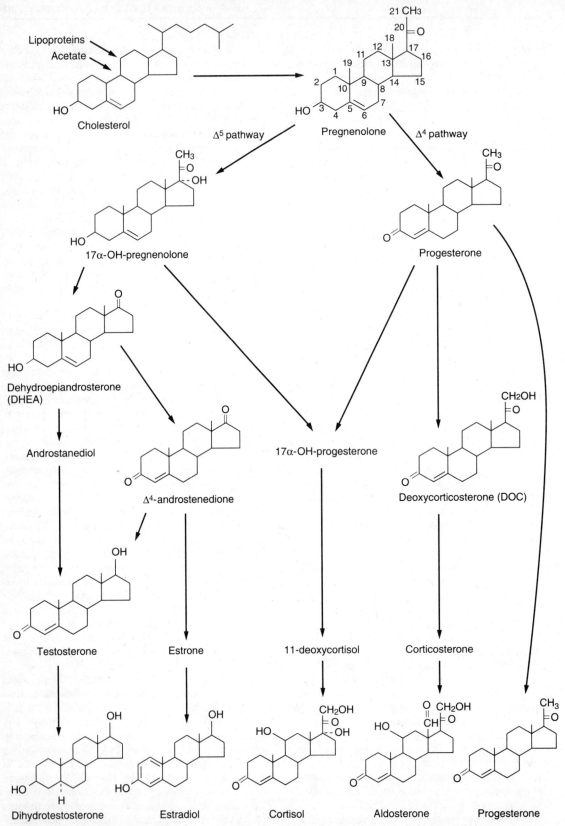

Figure 1–14. Pathways of synthesis of the major classes of steroid hormones. Cholesterol is derived from acetate by synthesis or from lipoprotein particles. The numbering of the steroid molecule is shown for pregnenolone. The major pathways thought to be used are shown. (See also Figures 6–4, 7–1, 9–2, 10–4, and 11–13.)

OH-pregnenolone or 17α-OH-progesterone are removed by C17,20-lyase activity (contained in cytochrome P450c17) to yield dehydroepiandrosterone (DHEA) and androstenedione, respectively. DHEA production is a major pathway in both the adrenals and the gonads and greatly exceeds that of androstenedione. Subsequent steps, which lead to the production of the major estrogen estradiol and the androgen testosterone, take place in the gonads but to only a minute extent in the adrenals.

The major pathway for testosterone production in the testis (Chapter 9) is in the Leydig cells through the Δ^5 pathway from pregnenolone to DHEA and androstanediol, before the steroids are converted to the Δ^4 derivatives, androstenedione to testosterone, and DHEA to androstenediol and then testosterone through the actions of 17β-hydroxysteroid dehydrogenase. Many androgen actions are mediated by dihydrotestosterone; this steroid is produced mostly in the target tissues through the activity of 5α-reductase, and very little is made in the testis.

In the ovary (Chapter 10), granulosa cells lack cytochromes P450c11, P450c17, and P450c21 and therefore produce mostly progesterone. This progesterone then is taken up by the nearby theca cells, which convert it into androstenedione, which then returns to the granulosa cells, where it is converted to estrone by the actions of aromatase. This enzyme also converts testosterone to estradiol; the concentrations of aromatase in the granulosa cells are such that almost all of the testosterone is converted to estradiol and little testosterone is released. Estrone and estradiol can also be produced from DHEA and androstenedione in peripheral tissues such as adipose tissue because of the presence of aromatase.

Once synthesized, the newly synthesized steroids are released rapidly. As is not the case with other classes of hormones, there is little storage of the steroids by the glands, and increased steroid release always reflects increased synthesis.

VITAMIN D

The active form of vitamin D, 1,25-$(OH)_2$-cholecalciferol (1,25-$[OH]D_2$), is derived from vitamin D_3 (cholecalciferol; Chapter 5). Cholecalciferol is obtained either from the diet or from the conversion of 7-dehydrocholesterol (present in the skin) in response to ultraviolet irradiation via a 6,7-*cis* isomer intermediate (previtamin D). Vitamin D_2 (ergocalciferol), which is present in plants and differs from vitamin D_3 in having a double bond at C_{22} and C_{23}, a methyl group at C_{24}, and several features of the A ring of the molecule, also serves as a precursor of active vitamin D products. The ultimate vitamin D products are a mixture of compounds derived from these two compounds and can vary depending on the

dietary intake (Chapter 5). Thus, in the absence of adequate dietary vitamin D, there is a need for adequate sunlight, with higher amounts being required for dark-skinned races. Vitamins D_2 and D_3 are transported to the liver bound to a vitamin D transport protein where the actions of a microsomal cytochrome P450c25 convert them to 25-OH derivatives, 25-OH-cholecalciferol (25-OHD$_3$) for vitamin D_3. 25-OHD$_3$ then circulates bound to an α-globulin transport protein; in the proximal tubular cells of the kidney, 25-OHD$_3$ is converted to 1,25-$(OH)_2D_3$ by the actions of a mitochondrial cytochrome P450c1α. This latter step is rate-limiting for overall 1,25-$(OH)_2D_3$ production and is regulated chiefly by PTH and phosphate ions. States of vitamin D deficiency are best assessed by measuring 25-OHD$_3$ levels in serum. Vitamin D may also be hydroxylated at C_{24} and C_{26}. The significance of the products resulting from these steps is unknown.

CATECHOLAMINES

The catecholamines are synthesized in nervous tissues from which the adrenal medulla is derived. This gland is the major source for circulating epinephrine, whose synthesis is described in detail in Chapter 8 and summarized only briefly here.

Catecholamines are synthesized from tyrosine and then stored in granules analogous to those that secrete polypeptide hormones. Tyrosine is converted to dihydroxyphenylalanine (DOPA) by tyrosine hydroxylase, and DOPA is converted to dopamine in the cytoplasm by aromatic L-amino acid decarboxylase. Dopamine is then taken up by a catecholamine transporter into the granule membrane, where it is converted to norepinephrine (by dopamine β-hydroxylase), the final product released by most catecholamine-producing cells of the body. However, in the adrenal medulla and only a few other locations, phenylethanolamine-O-methyltransferase (PNMT) is present; in these cases, the norepinephrine leaves the vesicle to return to the cytoplasm, where PNMT converts norepinephrine to epinephrine, which is taken up by the granules for secretion. The catecholamines are stored in these granules with chromogranin A and ATP and are released with these constituents.

EICOSANOIDS

Arachidonic acid is the most important and abundant precursor of the various eicosanoids in humans and is rate-limiting for eicosanoid synthesis (Figure 1–15). Arachidonic acid is formed from linoleic acid (18:2n-6; an essential fatty acid) in most cases through desaturation and elongation to homo-γ linoleic acid (20:5n-3) and subsequent desaturation. Whereas eicosanoids are not stored by cells, arachi-

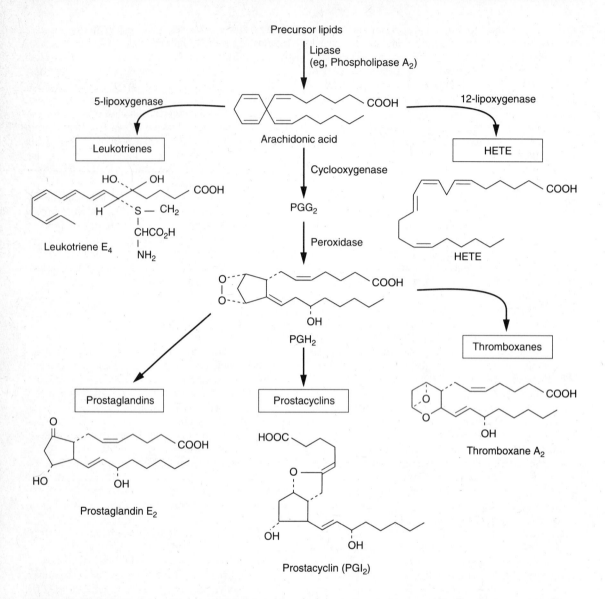

Figure 1–15. Major pathways for synthesis of the major classes of eicosanoids: prostaglandins, prostacyclins, thromboxanes, and leukotrienes. All steps in the pathways are not shown. Below each pathway, enclosed by boxes, is a representative compound of the class. (HETE, hydroxyeicosatetraenoic acid; PGG$_2$, prostaglandin G$_2$; PGH$_2$, prostaglandin H$_2$.)

donic acid precursor stores are present in membrane lipids from which it is released in response to various stimuli through actions of phospholipases. Phospholipase A$_2$—or both phospholipase C and diglyceride lipase—catalyze the cleavage of esterified arachidonic acid from the 2 position of glycerophospholipids in the lipid bilayer of the cell (Figure 1–15). The lipid content of the various cells differs, and this results in different patterns of eicosanoid production from different cell types. Phospholipase A$_2$ activity in vitro can be strongly inhibited by glucocorticoids through the induction of proteins called **lipocortins;**

this may contribute to glucocorticoid suppression of certain inflammatory reactions, but the importance of this block in humans is not established.

Arachidonic acid can be converted to the endoperoxide prostaglandin H$_2$, which is the precursor to the **prostaglandins, prostacyclins,** and **thromboxanes,** or it can be acted on by other lipoxygenases to form the leukotrienes and other eicosanoids such as HETE. For prostaglandin synthesis, **cyclooxygenase** (also called endoperoxide synthetase) converts arachidonic acid to the unstable endoperoxide, PGG$_2$, which is rapidly reduced to PGH$_2$. Cyclooxygenase is widely distributed throughout the body (except for erythrocytes and lymphocytes) and is inhibited by aspirin, indomethacin, and other nonsteroidal anti-inflammatory agents. Depending on the tissue, PGH_2 can be converted to: other prostaglandins (eg, PGD_2, PGE_2, PGF_2 [via PGE_2]) in reactions involving prostaglandin synthetases; prostacyclins (eg, PGI_2) in reactions involving prostacyclin synthetase, which is prevalent in endothelial and smooth muscle cells, fibroblasts, and macrophages; and thromboxanes (eg, thromboxane A_2 [TXA_2]), which is prevalent in platelets and macrophages, by a series of reactions in which thromboxane synthetase is involved. Arachidonic acid metabolism by 5-lipoxygenase results in leukotriene production, and metabolism by 12-lipoxygenase results in 12-HPETE (hydroxyperoxy-eicosatetraenoic acid) that is converted to HETE. Arachidonic acid can also be oxygenated by cytochrome P450 monoxygenases to various omega oxidation products and epoxides and derivatives that may have biologic activities.

HORMONE TRANSPORT

Hormones circulate both free and bound to plasma proteins. There are major differences between the various hormones in the extent of their association with the plasma proteins. In general, the binding of hormones to plasma is through noncovalent interactions, although cholesterol is considered to be bound through ester bonds to phosphatidylcholine. However, even in this case, the esterified cholesterol is bound through hydrophobic interactions to the lipoprotein particles.

STEROID HORMONES & VITAMIN D

All of the steroid hormones are bound to plasma proteins to some extent—high-affinity binding to specific globulins and relatively low-affinity and nonspecific binding to proteins such as albumin. The major binding proteins are corticosteroid-binding globulin (CBG; transcortin), which binds both cortisol and progesterone, and sex hormone-binding globulin (SHBG), which binds testosterone and estradiol (testosterone more tightly than estradiol). These proteins are present in sufficient concentrations that over 90% of the total cortisol and about 98% of the testosterone and estradiol are bound. The levels of their binding capacities in some cases exceed only slightly the normal concentrations of the steroid, so that with higher levels a much higher proportion of the hormone can be free. With cortisol, for example, the

CBG capacity for cortisol is about 25 µg/dL (690 ng/dL). Aldosterone does not bind to a specific protein, with the result that only about 50% of the plasma aldosterone is bound.

Vitamin D circulates mostly bound to vitamin D-binding protein. This protein binds 25-OHD_3 more tightly than $1,25\text{-(OH)}_2\text{D}_3$ or previtamin D_3.

THYROID HORMONES

Thyroid hormones circulate bound to plasma proteins such that 0.04% of the T_4 and 0.4% of the T_3 are free. About 68% of the T_4 and 80% of the T_3 are bound by the glycoprotein thyroid hormone-binding globulin (TBG). About 11% of the T_4 and 9% of the T_3 are bound to transthyretin (thyroid hormone-binding prealbumin; TBPA). The remainder is bound to albumin.

POLYPEPTIDE HORMONES

Most polypeptide hormones circulate at low concentrations unbound to other proteins, although there are exceptions. Exceptions include several different IGF-1-binding proteins that bind IGF-1. Vasopressin and oxytocin are bound to neurophysins. Growth hormone binds to a protein that is identical to the hormone-binding portion of the growth hormone receptor.

REGULATION OF THE PLASMA BINDING PROTEINS

The levels of the plasma binding proteins can vary with both disease states and drug therapy. For example, CBG, SHBG, and TBG levels are increased by estrogens. SHBG levels are increased by thyroid hormones, and SHBG and TBG levels are decreased by androgens.

ROLE OF PLASMA BINDING

An understanding of the roles of plasma binding of hormones is just emerging. In general, the hormones are sufficiently soluble to circulate unassociated at levels at which they are highly active. Cholesterol may be an exception if it is considered a hormone. With the steroid and thyroid hormones, deficiency states characterized by genetic defects with very low levels of transport proteins are not associated with clinical abnormalities. Recently, the transthyretin gene, which encodes the protein responsible for most of the thyroid hormone binding in the plasma of mice, was deleted in this species, and the animals were phenotypically normal. Thus, there is no evidence that these proteins are essential.

In most cases, (1) it is the free hormone that is active; (2) the free levels of the hormone are responsible for the feedback and related regulatory influences that control hormone release (see below); (3) the free levels of hormones are related to the rates of their clearance; and (4) clinical states correlate best with the free levels of hormones. The latter is a critical consideration in many cases, as with states of adrenal or thyroid hormone excess and deficiency. With these hormones, factors that affect the levels of plasma binding proteins can spuriously elevate or depress the total hormone levels in otherwise normal individuals, or the changes could mask pathologic hormone excess or deficiency states. These considerations are discussed later.

It appears that transport proteins may greatly facilitate an even delivery of hormones to the target tissues. In a tissue such as the liver, for example, a hormone that is totally free would be completely sequestered as the blood flows through the proximal portions of the tissue, whereas if it were mostly bound, the free hormone would be sequestered in proximal portions and additional hormone would be available for more distal portions through the dissociation of plasma-bound hormone to facilitate more even delivery. With polypeptide hormones, plasma binding can increase the half-life of the hormone in the circulation; it may also facilitate its delivery into the target tissues.

METABOLISM & ELIMINATION OF HORMONES

PEPTIDE HORMONES

In general, peptide hormones have short half-lives (a few minutes) in the circulation, as occurs with ACTH, insulin, glucagon, PTH, and the releasing hormones. As has been said, the glycosylated glycoprotein hormones are more stable, and CG has a half-life of several hours. Although there may be some degradation of the hormone by proteases in the circulation, the major mechanism for hormone degradation is binding by cell surface receptors for the hormone or through non-receptor cell surface hormone-binding sites, with subsequent uptake into the cell (**internalization;** see below) and degradation by enzymes in the cell membrane or inside the cell. A number of specific enzymes mediate these processes, which differ for the various hormones. In addition, several steps may be involved. The first of these may inactivate the hormone, and this can be due—eg, in the case of insulin—to reduction of disulfide bonds in the protein. An important overall source for these enzymes is the lysosome, which may fuse with endocytosed vesicles to expose its enzymes contents and its acid environment to the internalized hormone-receptor complex. An advantage of the short circulating half-lives of some classes of hormones is that the duration of the response can be relatively short. In addition, the persistent presence of significant levels of many classes of hormones that act on the cell surface results in down-regulation of the responsiveness to the hormone that may not be desirable.

STEROID HORMONES & VITAMIN D

The hydrophobic steroid hormones and the D vitamins are filtered by the kidney and generally reabsorbed. For example, about 1% of the cortisol produced daily ends up in the urine. These compounds are ordinarily handled by metabolizing them to inactive species and to more water-soluble forms that are more effectively eliminated. The free steroid fraction is assessable to metabolic inactivation. The inactivations are accomplished by converting hydroxyl groups to keto groups, reducing double bonds, and conjugating the steroids with glucuronide and sulfate groups. Over 50 different steroid metabolites have been described.

The production of active hormones by metabolism in peripheral tissues, as is seen with androgens, estrogens, and vitamin D, is discussed above in the section on hormone synthesis. In addition, metabolism in peripheral tissues can direct the type of steroid that binds to the receptor. Aldosterone is ordinarily the major mineralocorticoid hormone responsible for the salt-retaining actions of the steroid hormones. This steroid binds to the mineralocorticoid receptor only about ten times more tightly than cortisol, whose total and free concentrations in the circulation are about 1000 times and 100 times (respectively) those of aldosterone, such that cortisol should ordinarily be the main occupant of the mineralocorticoid receptors. This in fact occurs in tissues such as the brain and pituitary, but in the kidney, cortisol is avidly converted to the essentially inactive cortisone and possibly other species; some types of licorice or congenital defects can block the conversion and results in a mineralocorticoid excess state that is due to cortisol (Chapter 7).

THYROID HORMONES

The metabolism of thyroid hormones is discussed in Chapter 4. The circulating half-lives of T_4 (7 days) and T_3 (about 1 day) are longer than for most hormones. These differences are due to the higher affinity of T_4 than T_3 for TBG. The hormones are degraded to inactive forms by microsomal deiodinases.

The type I 5'-deiodinase is prevalent in most peripheral tissues, including liver and kidney, and is responsible for most of the production of T_3. A type II 5'-deiodinase present in the pituitary and central nervous system is involved in generating T_3 for feedback inhibition of TSH release. The 5'-deiodinases also convert reverse T_3 (3,3',5'-L-triiodothyronine) to 3,3'-T_2 (3,3'-diiodothyronine). 5-Deiodinases act on T_4 to generate reverse T_3 and on T_3 to generate 3,3'-T_2. Deaminations and decarboxylations of the alanine side chains as well as conjugations with glucuronic acid and sulfate groups are also involved in degrading thyroid hormones.

CATECHOLAMINES

The metabolism of the catecholamines is discussed in Chapter 8. These compounds are cleared rapidly. with half-lives of 1–2 minutes. Clearance is primarily by cellular uptake and metabolism, and only about 2–3% of the norepinephrine that enters the circulation is excreted in the urine. Furthermore, a significant amount of the catecholamine metabolites in the circulation reflect catecholamines whose degradation occurred within adrenergic neuron terminals, a point of importance for interpreting clinical data. The catecholamines are degraded by two principal routes, catechol-O-methyltransferase (COMT) and monoamine oxidase (MAO). The measurement of some of the metabolites—normetanephrine, metanephrine, and vanillylmandelic acid (VMA)—can be useful in evaluating cases of possible catecholamine overproduction.

EICOSANOID METABOLISM

Prostaglandins are rapidly metabolized—within seconds—by enzymes that are widely distributed. Prominent in the metabolism is oxidation of the 15-hydroxyl group of the prostaglandin that renders the molecule to be inactive. Subsequent other reactions involve both oxidations and reductions.

REGULATION OF THE ENDOCRINE SYSTEM

The effective concentration of a hormone is determined by the rates of its production, delivery to the target tissue, and degradation. All of these processes are finely regulated to achieve the physiologic level of the hormone. However, the importance of the steps may differ in some cases. By far the most highly regulated process is hormone production. With many classes of hormones, the short half-lives of the hormones provide means of terminating the responses and thus preventing excessive responses. The latter are also blunted by negative regulation of both hormone responsiveness (discussed below) and release, as well as by other factors. For example, in stress, glucocorticoids produced in excess probably blunt the actions of a number of hormones that would otherwise be harmful (see Chapter 6). Thus, when the actions and half-lives of the hormones are short, the hormone response can be terminated by simply stopping release of the hormone. An exception is thyroid hormone, with its long half-life. Details of the controls of the individual systems are provided in subsequent chapters on the various glands and systems.

There are a number of different patterns of regulation of hormone release. Many hormones are linked to the hypothalamic-pituitary axis (discussed in detail in the section on neuroendocrinology; Figure 1–4). These involve both classic feedback loops by hormones that are released by peripheral glands (cortisol, thyroid hormone, etc) and more subtle control, as is seen with GH and PRL.

However, many other systems are more free-standing. This is illustrated by the parathyroid glands (Chapter 5) (see Figure 1–4) and by the pancreatic islets (Chapter 15). With the parathyroid glands, the Ca^{2+} concentration that is increased in the plasma by the hormone exerts a dominant feedback inhibition on the release of PTH. With insulin, depression of the glucose levels in response to insulin action results in cessation of the stimulus to release more insulin. In addition, in both cases, the release of the hormone and the overall state of the gland is influenced by numerous other factors.

The stimuli to regulate hormone production include essentially all of the types of regulatory molecules, including hormones such as the tropic hormones and counterregulatory hormones (discussed above), traditional growth factors, eicosanoids, and ions. For example, potassium ion is an important regulator of the adrenal zona glomerulosa. The production of the various eicosanoids is regulated by local factors acting on the cells in which these products are released. For example, tropic stimulation of most endocrine glands results in enhancement of eicosanoid production.

The production of hormones is regulated at multiple levels. First, synthesis of the hormone can be regulated at the level of transcription, as is commonly seen with the polypeptide hormones or the enzymes involved in the synthesis of other hormones such as the steroids. It can also be affected by posttranscriptional mechanisms. Second, release of the hormone stored in secretory granules from tissues that contain the regulated secretory pathway is regulated by secretagogues, as was discussed in the section on hormone synthesis. The secretory cells can store the peptide hormones in sufficient quantity so that the amount released over a short time period can exceed the rate of synthesis of the hormone. And third, stimulation of endocrine glands by tropic hormones and other factors such as growth factors can increase the number and size of cells that are actively producing the hormone.

MECHANISMS OF HORMONE ACTION

HORMONE RECEPTORS

Hormones act through their binding to specific receptors (defined above). The binding of hormones to these receptors in general triggers a conformational change in the receptor such that it conveys information to other specific elements of the cell. These receptors are located either on the cell surface or intracellularly. The surface receptor-hormone interactions generally signal the formation of "second messengers" that set off cascades of events which lead to the hormone responses. The intracellular receptor-hormone interactions generally result in influences on gene expression. Only a few years ago, the documentation that putative receptors are receptors was based on correlative types of information. However, with the cloning of the receptor genes and the ability to mutate them and transfer the native and mutated genes back into mammalian cells where their function can be studied, the demonstration of receptor function has become a reality.

The distribution of hormone receptors shows enormous variability. Receptors for a few hormones, such as insulin and glucocorticoids, are widely distributed, whereas those for most hormones have a more limited distribution. The presence of the receptors is the first determinant of whether the tissue will respond to the hormone. However, molecules that participate in postreceptor events are also critical; these determine not only whether the tissue will respond to the hormone but also the specifics of the response. The latter allow the same hormone to have different responses in different tissues. In addition, different hormones can utilize similar downstream mechanisms such that two different hormones can have the same effect on the same tissue (Figure 1–16).

Hormone-Receptor Interactions

Hormones find the surface of the cell through their solubility and their dissociation from plasma binding proteins when present. Hormones that bind to cell surface receptors are then available for binding to the receptors. The steroid hormones appear to penetrate the cell's plasma membrane freely and bind to cytoplasmic receptors. In some cases (eg, estrogens), the hormone also needs to penetrate the cell nucleus (perhaps through pores in the nuclear membrane) to bind to the nuclear-localized receptors. The case with thyroid hormone is not clear. Evidence supports the notion that these hormones enter cells through transport mechanisms; it is not clear how they penetrate the nuclear membrane.

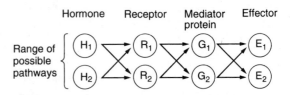

Figure 1–16. Possible pathways of transmission of hormonal signals. Each hormone can work through one or more receptors; each hormone-receptor complex can work through one or more mediator proteins (either G proteins or other signaling mechanism), and each mediating protein or enzyme activated by hormone-receptor complexes can affect one or more effector functions.

The hormones in general bind reversibly and noncovalently to their receptors. The binding is due to three types of forces. First, there are hydrophobic influences whereby hydrophobic surfaces on the hormone and receptor interact with each other in preference to water. Second, complementary charged groups on the hormone and the receptor facilitate the interactions. These influences are important for fitting the hormone into the receptor. And third, van der Waals forces, which are extremely distance-dependent, can contribute to attractive effects on the binding.

This binding most commonly conforms to a bimolecular reaction as follows: Hormone (H) + Receptor (R) = Hormone-Receptor (HR) complex. The rate of HR formation is proportionate to the concentration of H and R and can be defined by an association rate constant, k_1. Thus,

$$\text{Rate of association} = k_1[H][R]$$

where the brackets indicate concentrations. Similarly, the rate of dissociation of the hormone from the receptor is proportionate to the concentration of HR and can also be defined by a dissociation rate constant, k_2, such that the

$$\text{Rate of dissociation} = k_2[HR]$$

At equilibrium, the rates of association and dissociation are equal, that

$$k_1[H][R] = k_2[HR]$$

On rearrangement,

$$\frac{[H][R]}{[HR]} = \frac{k_2}{k_1} = K_d$$

K_d is also a constant that is termed the **equilibrium dissociation constant.**

The equation can also be expressed as $[HR]/[H][R] = k_1/k_2 = K_a$, the equilibrium association constant. This equation is commonly rearranged for analysis in the form of the **Scatchard equation,** in which R_T is substituted for the total number of receptors, $[B]$ = hormone bound to receptor, and $[F]$ = free hormone. Thus, $[R] = [R_T] - [B]$. The Scatchard equation is therefore

$$\frac{[B]}{[F]} = \left(\frac{-1}{K_d}\right)[B] + \frac{R_T}{K_d}$$

Examination shows this to be the equation for a straight line. Thus, if the results of a binding reaction are plotted as $[B]/[F]$ versus $[B]$ and a straight line is obtained, it is likely that the hormone-receptor interaction corresponds to a bimolecular reaction. In this case, the slope of the line indicates the K_d, and the intercept on the abscissa the total number of receptor sites. This reaction is the one most commonly used by endocrinologists to analyze the thermodynamics of hormone-receptor interactions. Shown in Figure 1–17 are the results of performing a hypothetical binding reaction that is bimolecular. The plot is shown as bound versus free and in the Scatchard form, which reveals a linear relation.

From analysis of the binding reaction, other information can be obtained. At low concentrations of hormone, the binding reaction is nearly linear with respect to increasing hormone, and when the receptors become more than half saturated, the additional binding decreases progressively until a plateau is reached as the receptor becomes saturated with the hormone (Figure 1–17). By rearranging the Scatchard equation, it can be seen also that if the receptors are half-saturated with the hormone, then $[B] = 1/2[R_T]$, $1/2[R_T]/[F] = (-1/K_d)(1/2)[R_T] + [R_T]/K_d$, and $K_d = [F]$. Thus, the hormone concentration that half-saturates the receptors is the K_d (Figure 1–17). From this analysis, it is also apparent that for most hormone-responsive systems, the influence of increasing hormones is greatest when the receptors are relatively undersaturated. Most hormones circulate at levels near to or below the K_d for the hormone-receptor interaction, ie, at concentrations where changes in their levels can have significant influences on the hormone response. These K_d's are usually in the 0.01–100 nanomolar range, and the number of receptor sites per cell usually varies from a few hundred to over 100,000.

In some cases, the hormone-receptor interactions

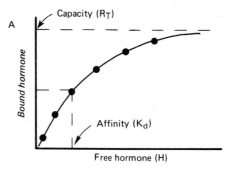

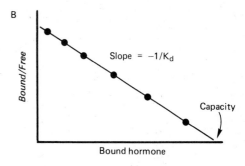

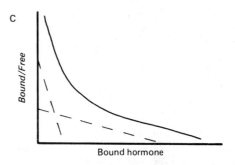

Figure 1–17. Schematic representation of *A,* the relation between hormone concentration and receptor binding; *B,* a Scatchard plot of the binding data; and *C,* a convex Scatchard plot that could reflect either negative cooperativity or two classes of sites. Note in *A* that the hormone concentration at which 50% saturation of the receptors occurs is equal to the K_d and in *B* that the data of A are linearized by the Scatchard plot. The dashed lines in *C* are the contributions of two separate reactions that together result in the curved Scatchard plot.

are more complex. These mostly occur when the hormone is interacting with a receptor complex with multiple subunits and where binding of the hormone to the first subunit alters the affinity of other subunits for the hormone. This can increase (positive cooperativity) or decrease (negative cooperativity) the affinity of the hormone for the receptor. Positive cooperativity results in a convex and negative cooperativity in a concave (Figure 1–17, bottom) Scatchard plot. Experimental artifacts and the existence of two independent classes of sites can also result in nonlinear

Scatchard plots. Surprisingly, cooperative binding is rarely observed with hormone-receptor interactions; insulin-receptor interactions in some circumstances may be an exception.

Hormone Agonists, Antagonists, & Partial Agonists

Substances that interact with the hormone-binding site of the receptor can have **agonist, antagonist,** or **partial agonist** (also called **partial antagonist**) activities. Substances that do not interact with the receptor or interact with it but do not affect the binding of hormones are termed **inactive.** An agonist fully induces the receptors to trigger postreceptor events. An antagonist is able to bind to the receptor and to block the binding of an agonist, but it does not trigger postreceptor responses. In this way, it does not elicit a response but it does block the response to the agonist, providing that it is present in a concentration sufficient to block agonist binding. In general, antagonists bind to the same site on the receptor as agonists and prevent agonist binding through direct physical occupancy; however, in some circumstances, antagonists can bind to the receptor at a different site and block agonist binding through allosteric changes in the receptor. A partial agonist (partial antagonist) is intermediate; it binds to the receptors but elicits only a partial change in them such that even when the receptors are fully occupied by the partial agonist, the hormone response will be intermediate. Generally, the activities of agonists, antagonists, and partial agonists are explained by the fact that agonists induce allosteric changes in the receptors that are not elicited by antagonists. These are explained by two types of models. In the induced fit model, the binding induces a change in the molecule, whereas in the allosteric equilibrium model, the agonist binds preferentially to the active form of the molecule that is in equilibrium with the inactive form and stabilizes it. Partial agonists are bound to both forms with the degree of partial agonism or antagonism being related in general to the extent of preferential binding to the inactive versus active forms of the receptors.

Non-Receptor Hormone Binding

Receptors are not the only proteins that bind hormones—numerous other proteins bind them as well. These include the plasma binding proteins (discussed above) and other transport-like molecules that are commonly found in peripheral tissues, enzymes involved in the metabolism or synthesis of steroids, and other as yet unidentified proteins. These proteins can bind the hormone as tightly as or more tightly than the receptors; however, they differ from receptors in that they do not transmit the information from binding into postreceptor events.

One special class of molecules binds the hormones or hormone complexes on the surface of cells and participates in the internalization of them. The most extensively studied are the low-density lipoprotein (LDL) "receptors" that bind the cholesterol-carrying LDL particles and internalize them (Chapter 17). These receptors are important for cholesterol uptake, eg, in cells of the adrenal for steroid biosynthesis and in the liver to clear the plasma of cholesterol. Genetic defects of these receptors result in hypercholesterolemia. The internalized LDL particles can provide cholesterol for steroid synthesis or insertion into the cell membrane. In addition, the cholesterol released from the particles' feedback inhibits cholesterol synthesis. Thus, the LDL receptors are, strictly speaking, not receptors but LDL uptake proteins. Unfortunately, the term "receptor" has been used so extensively that it is unlikely that it will be changed. Some of the "receptors" for ANP and insulin-like growth factor-2 (IGF-2) do not have a clearly defined function and may have chiefly uptake roles. In these cases, they should not be called receptors.

Receptors and nonreceptor hormone binding molecules are ordinarily distinguished by both their binding properties and their abilities to mediate postreceptor responses. Thus, with receptors the relative abilities of a series of hormone agonists and antagonists to bind to the receptors will parallel their abilities, respectively, to elicit hormone responses or block agonist responses. Receptors will be capable of transferring hormone responsiveness with gene transfer experiments.

Relations Between Hormone-Receptor Binding & Responses

Understanding the relations between hormone-receptor binding and the subsequent response elicited by the hormone is helpful sometimes in considering hormone therapy and clinical states. Such considerations will allow the clinician to better appreciate the significance of hormone measurements and of pharmacologic administration of hormones.

The nuclear receptors are present in small quantities—several thousand per cell—and are ordinarily limiting for the magnitude of the hormone response. This means that if there were more receptors, the hormone response at concentrations of the hormone that saturate the receptors would be greater. In these cases, the relative saturation of the receptors parallels the hormone response (Figure 1–18). By contrast, the cell surface receptors frequently are not limiting, so that saturation of only a fraction of the receptors results in a maximal hormone response.

This situation has been referred to as **spare receptors,** and the dose-response curve is shifted to the left of the hormone-receptor occupancy curve (Figure 1–18). However, the receptors are not really spare; at hormone concentrations below those which are maximally effective, the hormone response is proportionate to [H][R]. Thus, in this situation, the response to a given hormone concentration will be greater with

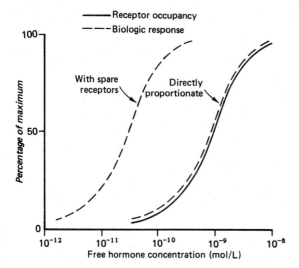

Figure 1–18. Schematic representation of the relationship between the extent of receptor occupancy and the hormone concentration for the case where the receptors are limiting for the magnitude of the response (directly proportionate) and spare receptors.

more receptors. With cell surface receptors, the generation of second messengers and the ability of each receptor to interact with more than one effector molecule (discussed below) provides an amplification of the response. For example, each hormone-receptor complex can activate several G protein molecules that regulate adenylyl cyclase, and each molecule of the enzyme can generate several molecules of cAMP that are produced in excess, such that the next step in the hormone response, cAMP-dependent protein kinase A, can become limiting.

Structures of Hormone Receptors

A. Polypeptide Hormone, Catecholamine, and Eicosanoid Cell Surface Receptors: The polypeptide hormone, catecholamine, and eicosanoid receptors are localized on the cell surface. Receptors for neurotransmitters and other substances such as adenosine are also located on the cell surface. These receptors are inserted into the cell membrane initially through the signal peptide mechanism described above in the section on peptide hormone synthesis. However, with these proteins and other integral membrane proteins such as adenylyl cyclases, **stop transfer sequences** in the protein halt the transit of the protein through the membrane and leave it there (Figure 1–8). These sequences probably bind to a receptor in the membrane that differs from the signal peptide receptor to facilitate the stop. Variations in this theme result in the assembly of proteins with multiple domains that span the membranes as occurs with a number of cell surface hormone receptors. These mechanisms also result in the presence of receptors in the endoplasmic reticulum, Golgi appara-

tus, and other intracellular membranes. The functional role of these intracellular receptors—except as a source for outside surface receptors and in receptor turnover through internalization (discussed below)—has not been clarified. In some cases, receptors can be modified in other ways such as through the addition of myristate to N-terminal glycine residues or palmitate groups to cysteine residues.

Schematic representations of the structures of several different cell surface receptors are shown in Figure 1–19. These receptors may have from one to several different subunits, and each subunit may have from one up to seven membrane-spanning domains. These structures can be roughly subdivided into extracellular, transmembrane, and intracellular portions.

The extracellular portion of the receptor that binds the hormone may be either entirely separated from the cell membrane or embedded into it. The hormones may bind to receptor monomer units, or binding may occur as dimers, in which case there can be cooperativity to the binding. For the domains for the growth hormone and one form of the ANP receptor, for example, the hormone-binding domain can be cleaved from the membrane intact and shown to retain hormone-binding properties similar to those of the intact receptor. The structure of GH bound to its receptor has been elucidated by x-ray crystallography. This is the only case where the structure of the hormone-binding site for a classic hormone receptor has been elucidated. Each GH molecule binds to two identical receptor subunits. The surprising finding was that different structures on GH interact with each subunit even though the contact area of the binding site on the receptor in each case is identical. With the catecholamine receptors, the ligands bind to portions of the receptors embedded in the membrane.

Hormone binding to the receptors induces changes in their conformation that are transmitted through the transmembrane domain of the protein into the intracellular domains of the receptors. The change in the intracellular domains of the receptor induces signaling for postreceptor events. In a number of cases, as typified by growth factor receptors, hormone-receptor interactions induce dimerization or a clustering of the hormone-receptor complexes that may participate in activation of postreceptor events. The transmembrane portions of the receptors are highly hydrophobic to accommodate their association with the plasma membrane.

The internal portions of the receptors contain the effector functions that transmit the internal information. The receptors can be grouped into two general categories based on whether the internal domains have catalytic activity or primarily interact with G proteins (discussed below). The first category is represented by the receptors for insulin, IGF-1 and EGF, which have a large external hormone binding domain, a short membrane spanning domain, and a

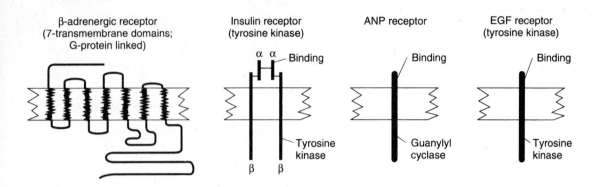

Figure 1–19. Representation of various types of membrane receptors with examples of each type.

moderate-sized internal domain that possesses hormone-regulated tyrosine kinase activity. These receptors can have one subunit (EGF receptor) or more, as illustrated by the insulin receptor with four subunits linked by disulfide bonds (Figure 1–19). In this case, two α-subunits are entirely external and contain the ligand-binding domains, and the two β-subunits are linked to the α-subunits on the outside of the cell, extend through the membrane, and possesses the tyrosine kinase activity. The receptors for ANP that have guanylyl cyclase activity also belong to this class. The LDL receptors and IGF-2 receptors (which are also the mannose-6-phosphate receptors) are structurally similar to these receptors but lack tyrosine kinase activity. The second family of receptors, which interacts with the G proteins, generally contains the seven transmembrane domains, two short and one moderate-sized cytoplasmic loops, and one cytoplasmic carboxyl-terminal tail. The α-adrenergic, β-adrenergic, muscarinic cholinergic, rhodopsin, glucagon, ANP (one type), TRH, and other receptors are members of this family.

B. Steroid and Thyroid Hormone Nuclear Receptors: Steroid and thyroid hormone receptors are encoded by genes that form a large superfamily of transcription factors which include not only the receptors for these hormones, but also those for vitamin D, retinoids such as retinoic acid and 9-*cis*-retinoic acid, putative receptors whose ligands have not yet been identified (so called orphan receptors), and other transcription factors that may not be activated by specific ligand binding (Figure 1–20). Each receptor is composed of a single polypeptide chain. There can be one (steroid receptors) or more than one (thyroid hormone receptors) gene for each receptor class, and variations in expression such as RNA processing can generate alternative receptor forms. They are transported to the nucleus either following their synthesis (eg, thyroid hormone receptors) or following their binding to the hormone. This transport occurs through pores and requires nuclear localization sequences on the receptors that bind to pore receptors

to facilitate the transfer—an ATP-dependent process.

The receptors can be roughly divided into three domains (Figure 1–20) that can be subdivided further into (1) an amino-terminal (N-terminal) domain, (2) a centrally located DNA binding domain, and (3) a carboxyl-terminal ligand-binding domain. The various receptor domains function in an essentially modular fashion.

The amino-terminal domain displays the greatest variations between the various members of the family in terms both of size and of amino acid sequence. It is smaller for the thyroid hormone receptor and much larger for the glucocorticoid receptor. Whereas in some cases, this domain is essential for particular receptor actions, in other cases, this domain is not essential for receptor function but enhances the activities of the other domains. For example, when the larger domain of the glucocorticoid receptor is used to replace the equivalent domain of the thyroid hormone receptor, the activity of the thyroid hormone receptor is increased. This domain is highly phosphorylated in most cases, though the importance of the phosphorylations has not been established.

The centrally placed DNA binding domain has the major function of binding to DNA. This domain contains two **zinc fingers** in which four cysteine residues of each finger form coordination complexes with zinc ions. Between the two zinc fingers is an α-helix that fits into the major groove of the DNA when the receptor binds to DNA. (The winding of DNA in the double helix results in a broader major groove and a narrower minor groove.) The zinc fingers also aid in the specificity of DNA binding. The DNA binding domain also contains regions that may participate in receptor dimerization. The DNA binding domains of the various receptors of the family display greater homology than do the other domains.

The carboxyl-terminal ligand-binding domain contains a ligand (usually hormone) binding site that binds the cognate hormone with high affinity and specificity. The structures of the ligands that bind show considerable variations, and there are also

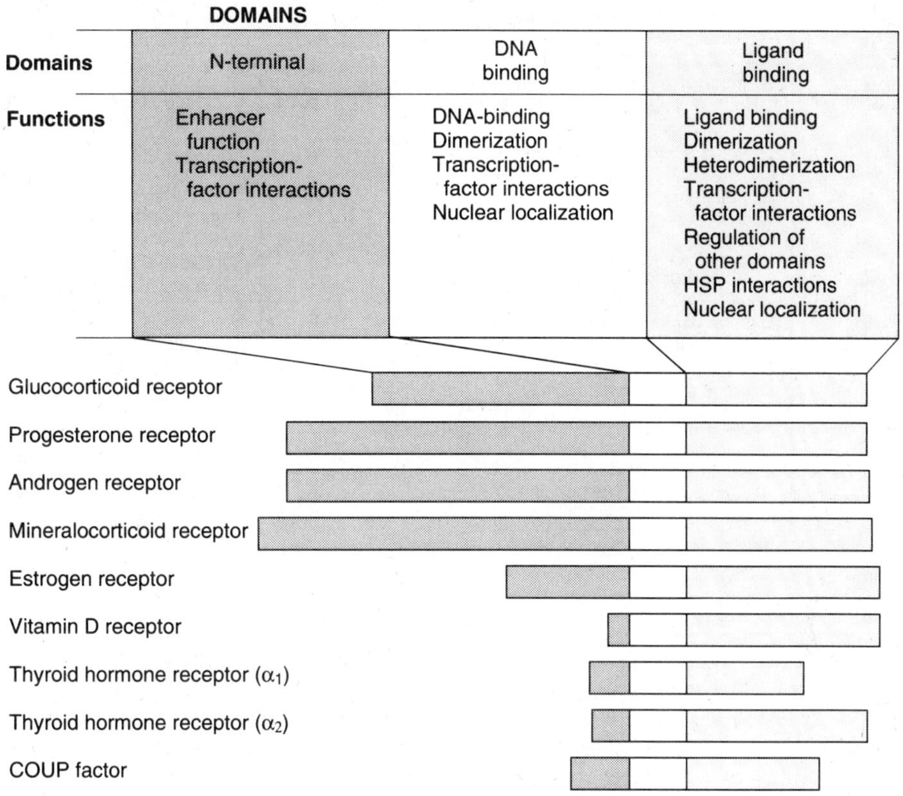

Domains	N-terminal	DNA binding	Ligand binding
Functions	Enhancer function Transcription-factor interactions	DNA-binding Dimerization Transcription-factor interactions Nuclear localization	Ligand binding Dimerization Heterodimerization Transcription-factor interactions Regulation of other domains HSP interactions Nuclear localization

Glucocorticoid receptor

Progesterone receptor

Androgen receptor

Mineralocorticoid receptor

Estrogen receptor

Vitamin D receptor

Thyroid hormone receptor (α_1)

Thyroid hormone receptor (α_2)

COUP factor

Figure 1–20. Structures of receptors of the steroid-thyroid hormone superfamily. Shown at the top are the classification of the domains and followed by some of the functions of the individual domains. Shown at the bottom are examples of the various receptors with the various domains drawn to scale. The last two structures, the thyroid hormone α_2 receptor and the COUP (chicken ovalbumin upstream promoter) transcription factor, are shown for comparison and represent members of the group thought not to bind a hormone. The ligand-binding domain can inhibit the function of the DNA binding domain, but it also may cooperate with other transcription factors.

structural variations in this domain between the various members of the family. The carboxyl-terminal ligand-binding domain also participates in receptor dimerization and heterodimerization, nuclear localization, and interactions with other transcription factors, including proximal promoter proteins. Hormone binding to this site results in conformational changes in the receptors that influence their association with other proteins, the other domains of the receptors, and the receptors' transcriptional regulatory properties.

SECOND MESSENGERS & HORMONE ACTION

The hormones whose receptors are located on the cell surface transmit their information through second messengers. The second messengers utilized by a number of hormones are listed in Table 1–1. In general, these mechanisms involve activation of adenylyl cyclase, guanylyl cyclase, phospholipase C, phospholipase A_2, tyrosine kinases, Ca^{2+} channels, and others. Multiple hormones can activate the same second messenger system (Figure 1–16). Conversely, a given hormone-receptor complex can activate more than one second messenger system (Figure 1–16). The circumstances where these various combinations occur vary according to the specific receptors involved; the degree of hormone-receptor complex occupancy, which is an index of the density of active hormone-receptor complexes; tissue-specific influences; and changing intracellular conditions.

The mechanisms for transmission of hormone-receptor binding into cellular events remain poorly understood for several classes of receptors. This is particularly true for the growth hormone-prolactin-placental lactogen (chorionic somatomammotropin) hormone family. These hormones not only share homology in their sequences; their receptors share a great deal of structural homology and are now known to form part of a larger superfamily of receptors, including those for hematopoietic growth factors (erythropoietin, colony-stimulating factors), interleukins, and, more distantly, interferons.

Table 1–1. Examples of major second messengers for hormones.

Adenylyl cyclase-cAMP system	**Stimulatory:** β-adrenergic, GRH, CRH, VIP; prostaglandins (E, D, and I); glucagon, vasopressin, LH, FSH, TSH, CG, ACTH, PTH **Inhibitory:** α_2-adrenergic, opioids, somatostatin, angiotensin II, acetylcholine (muscarinic), dopamine
Phospholipase C, InsP$_3$-Ca^{2+}-protein kinase C	α_1-adrenergic, GnRH, TRH, dopamine, PGF$_{2\alpha}$, TXA$_2$, endoperoxides, leukotrienes, vasopressin, bradykinin, acetylcholine, substance P, neuropeptide Y, endothelin, PTH, angiotensin II
Tyrosine kinase	Insulin, macrophage-colony stimulating factor (M-CSF), platelet-derived growth factor (PDGF)
Guanylyl cyclase	Endothelium-derived releasing factor (EDRF), atrial natriuretic factor, acetylcholine, histamine, bradykinin

Table 1–2. G protein subunits and their actions.[1]

Subunit	Actions
α_s	Stimulate adenylyl cyclase Stimulate Ca^{2+} channel
α_q	Stimulate phospholipase C
α_i	Inhibit adenylyl cyclase Stimulate phospholipase C Inhibit Ca^{2+} channel Stimulate phosphodiesterase Stimulate K$^+$ channel
β	Stimulate adenylyl cyclase Stimulate Ca^{2+} channel Stimulate phospholipase C
γ	Inhibit adenylyl cyclase Stimulate phosphodiesterase Stimulate K$^+$ channel

[1] The table lists the various classes of subunits. In each case, the classification refers to a gene family; and each member of a subclass may have activities different from those indicated.

The late Earl Sutherland and his colleagues discovered the first second messenger system. These workers found that a number of hormones activate adenylyl cyclase. This second messenger system works through the hormone-receptor complex interactions with a protein complex that binds guanylyl nucleotides and is part of a larger family of proteins that binds these nucleotides (Table 1–2).

Guanylyl Nucleotide Binding Proteins

Guanylyl nucleotide binding proteins mediate a large number of different types of hormone-receptor interactions and other regulatory processes. Of these, the largest and most extensively used class for regulation are the heterotrimeric **G proteins.** These proteins are composed of αβγ subunits that are encoded by at least 16 different α and several different β and γ genes. The other major group are smaller monomeric proteins of which the ras proteins, discussed below, are extensively involved in regulation. With the heterodimeric proteins, the α-subunit binds and is activated by GTP (Figure 1–21). This simultaneously promotes dissociation of the βγ dimer and release of the active α-subunit-GTP complex. The GTP-activated α-subunits—and, in some cases, the other subunits—then regulate a number of different processes (Table 1–2), including stimulation effects on adenylyl cyclase, Ca^{2+} and K$^+$ channels, phospholipase C, and cGMP phosphodiesterase; and inhibitory effects on adenylyl cyclase or Ca^{2+} channels. The circumstances where the various influences are more prominent vary in different conditions and in relation to the total magnitude of hormone-receptor occupancy. The intrinsic GTPase activity of the G protein hydrolyses

GTP to form GDP. This conversion results in reassociation of the α-subunit with the βγ subunit complex, thereby inactivating the G protein complex and terminating the stimulation. Other details of the function of these G proteins are provided in the following sections.

Regulation of Adenylyl Cyclase

Adenylyl cyclases comprise a number of different enzymes (at least eight). Whereas all are stimulated by α_s, the differences in the various cyclases allows for diversity in their responsiveness to other activators and inhibitors (eg, Ca^{2+}-calmodulin; see below). A number of hormones and other factors regulate adenylyl cyclase activity. Hormonal regulators are listed in Table 1–1. Nonhormonal regulators include neurotransmitters, light in the retina, adenosine, eicosanoids, nonhydrolyzable GTP analogues, the terpene forskolin, cholera, and pertussis toxins, and others. These compounds have been extremely useful experimentally. Adenylyl cyclase activity can be inhibited by higher concentrations of Ca^{2+} and thus by hormones and other effectors that increase intracellular Ca^{2+} activity. However, Ca^{2+} can also bind to calmodulin, and this complex can activate adenylyl cyclase.

A. Activation of Adenylyl Cyclase: The binding of the hormone to the receptor promotes the receptor's interactions with the stimulatory G$_s$ protein complex (Figure 1–21). In the basal state, the complex may be associated with adenylyl cyclase. The hormone-receptor complex association stimulates the α-subunit (α_s) to bind GTP and to dissociate from the βγ subunit complex. The β- and γ-subunits anchor the complex to the plasma membrane and also participate in regulatory roles, including the regulation of

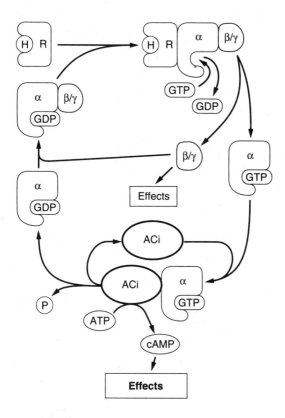

Figure 1–21. Activation of adenylyl cyclase by hormone-receptor complexes. The hormone-receptor complex interacts with the heterodimeric G protein, with stimulation of GTP binding of the α-subunit of the complex, dissociation of the β/γ subunit complex, activation of adenylyl cyclase, and stimulation of the α-subunit GTPase activity. The cAMP generated by the cyclase activates protein kinase A with subsequent phosphorylation of substrates with diverse responses. The β/γ subunit complex may also have independent effects. (ACa, active adenylyl cyclase; ACi, inactive adenylyl cyclase.)

adenylyl cyclase activity. The GTP binding stimulates the G protein to activate adenylyl cyclase. The hormone-receptor complex also rapidly dissociates from the G protein complex and can then activate other G protein complexes. However, this dissociation can also result in a decreased affinity of the hormone for the receptor, thus promoting dissociation of the hormone from the receptor and providing one mechanism for terminating the hormone response. Nonhydrolyzable analogues of GTP can bind to the G protein complex and activate it in an essentially irreversible fashion. The α-subunit can also be ADP-ribosylated in response to cholera toxin, that activates it.

B. Inhibition of Adenylyl Cyclase: A number of hormone-receptor interactions inhibit adenylyl cyclase. This inhibition usually occurs through a subunit complex similar to that which stimulates adenylyl cyclase except that the α-subunit, α_i, mediates the

inhibition (Table 1–2). However, in some cases, such inhibition may also occur through βγ. Pertussis toxin blocks the inactivation of adenylyl cyclase through its ADP-ribosyltransferase activity on the α_i subunit.

cAMP

cAMP is generated from ATP by the actions of adenylyl cyclase, activated as described in the preceding section (Figure 1–21). Adenylyl cyclase is a glycoprotein with a molecular weight of about 150,000. The cAMP generation also requires magnesium ion, which forms a complex with ATP to serve as the substrate for the reaction.

cAMP exists at a concentration of around 0.01–1 μmol/L in cells, as compared to mmol/L levels of ATP. Thus, ATP availability is ordinarily not the rate-limiting factor for activation. cAMP ordinarily has a relatively short half-life and is rapidly degraded by phosphodiesterases. There are circumstances in which the activity of phosphodiesterase is regulated (eg, by calmodulin; see below); however, in general, cAMP levels are controlled by regulating cAMP production rather than degradation. Phosphodiesterase activity is blocked by methylxanthines such as caffeine and theophylline, an action that probably forms part of the mechanisms of action of these drugs.

Activation of Protein Kinase A

Most of the known actions of cAMP in mammalian cells are mediated through activation by the nucleotide of specific serine and threonine protein kinases, termed protein kinase A. In bacteria, cAMP can bind to specific receptors and stimulate activation of transcription. The mechanisms of activation of protein kinase A are shown in Figures 1–21 and 1–22. cAMP binds to the regulatory subunits of a complex containing two regulatory subunits and two catalytic subunits. Binding by the regulatory subunits to the catalytic subunit inactivates the latter. The binding of two cAMP molecules to each regulatory subunit promotes the dissociation of the regulatory subunits from the catalytic subunit. Freed of their inhibition, the catalytic subunits then phosphorylate proteins using ATP as the phosphate-donating chemical. In addition to the serine and threonine requirements of the substrate, the amino acid sequence around the serine and threonine moieties is important.

Multiple proteins are thus phosphorylated by kinase A. Some examples of the kinase A-regulated processes and proteins are shown in Table 1–3. Phosphorylation can affect the conformations of these proteins and therefore their activities. The changes can be stimulatory or inhibitory. For example, kinase A-induced phosphorylation activates glycogen phosphorylase and inhibits glycogen synthetase (Figure 1–23). Given the broad substrate specificity of the kinase, it is likely that many if not most of the kinase A-induced phosphorylations do not have any biologic influence.

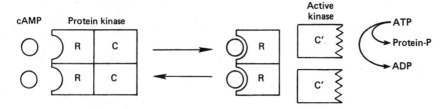

Figure 1–22. Activation of protein kinase A by cAMP. In the absence of cAMP there is a complex of two regulatory and two catalytic subunits. The regulatory subunits inhibit the activity of the catalytic subunits. cAMP binding promotes dissociation of the regulatory subunits from the catalytic subunits, thereby activating them. The catalytic subunits then phosphorylate diverse substrates.

Activation of Tyrosine Kinase

Several protein hormone receptors have intrinsic hormone-sensitive tyrosine kinase activities (Figures 1–19 and 1–24; Table 1–1), including receptors for insulin, EGF, and PDGF. The hormone-receptor interaction-induced conformational changes in these receptors activate tyrosine kinase activity. In many cases, the receptor autophosphorylates itself, and this amplifies the tyrosine kinase activity. Once activated, the enzyme can also activate other substrates. A general mechanism for this is through SH2 domains that bind to the phosphotyrosine on the receptor and are present on a number of proteins involved in cytoplasmic signaling. These proteins include phospholipase C (PLC), p21*ras* GTPase-activating protein (GAP), phosphatidylinositol (PI) 3'-kinase (PI3K), and intracellular Src and Src-like tyrosine kinases. The activities of these proteins are regulated by binding by mechanisms that are being deciphered, which may include binding-induced allosteric changes, or tyrosine phosphorylations, or concentration of the binding protein in the vicinity of the plasma membrane. The consequences of activation of phospholipase C and GAP are discussed below. The Src and Src-like tyrosine kinases are involved in growth control, and enhancement of their activities by tyrosine kinase receptors may participate (along with effects on ras, see below) in control of growth by this class of mediators. The activation of PI3K results in phosphorylation of the inositol ring of PI at the D-3 position. Tyrosine kinases have also been postulated to activate other enzymes, in some cases through binding domains other than SH2, though the significance of these binding domains has not been clarified. Enzymes that are probably activated by tyrosine kinase include glycogen synthetase phosphatase, which activates glycogen synthetase by removing an inhibitory phosphate group; pyruvate dehydrogenase; pyruvate kinase; and hormone-sensitive lipase.

Tyrosine phosphatases remove the tyrosine phosphate groups and terminate the actions of the phosphorylated proteins. These can be soluble and transmembrane; interestingly, the soluble enzymes contain the SH2 domains, through which they probably bind to the phosphorylated substrates. The membrane forms resemble hormone receptors, and one of these, the leukocyte common antigen (CD45), has been linked to T cell receptor action; in this case, tyrosine dephosphorylation appears to activate a tyrosine kinase (p56-lck). Thus, these enzymes serve more functions than simply to counteract the actions of the kinases. In contrast to serine-threonine phosphorylation, tyrosine phosphorylation appears to be transient even when normal responses are elicited, and the actions of the phosphatases are important for these events.

Activation of Phospholipase C & Phosphoinositide Hydrolysis

This pathway is utilized by several different classes of receptors, including those with seven transmembrane domains and tyrosine kinase activity. Like adenylyl cyclases, phospholipase C activity is present in a number of enzymes. The activation of phospholipase C (PLC) by receptors that have tyrosine kinase activity is discussed in the preceding section. The hormone receptors with seven transmembrane domains (eg, vasopressin) appear to activate the enzyme through a G protein, G_q (Table 1–2). The inactivated PLC is present mostly in the cytosol. Binding of the hormone-bound and autophosphorylated tyrosine kinase to PLC results in both activation of the enzyme and its recruitment to the cell membrane, where its phospholipid substrate is located (Figure 1–25). The activated phospholipase C cleaves the phospholipid phosphatidylinositol 4,5-bisphosphate (PIP_2) to diacylglycerol (DAG) and in-

Table 1–3. Examples of protein kinase A-regulated processes and proteins.[1]

- Adenylyl cyclase desensitization (adenylyl cyclase)
- Glycogen synthesis (phosphorylase kinase and glycogen synthetase)
- Lipolysis (hormone-sensitive lipase)
- Steroidogenesis
- Transcription (CREB and AP1 factors)
- Voltage-dependent Ca²⁺ channels, eg, increased cardiac force of contraction and relaxation rate

[1] Processes are shown followed in some cases in parentheses by the kinase A-modified proteins involved.

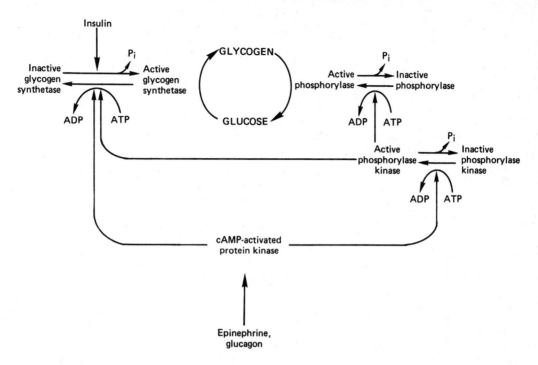

Figure 1–23. Simplified scheme of glycogen synthesis and breakdown. Note the effects of activation of protein kinase A by cAMP and of tyrosine kinase by insulin.

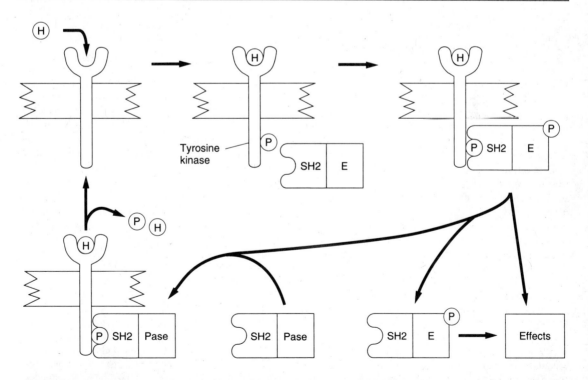

Figure 1–24. Activation of tyrosine kinase activity by hormone-receptor complexes. In this example, the tyrosine kinase activity of the receptor is activated by the changes in the hormone-receptor complex induced by hormone binding to the receptor. The phosphorylated receptor then interacts with an inactive enzyme containing an SH2 domain that the phosphorylated receptor. The enzyme is phosphorylated which activates it to elicit other effects. The receptor is later dephosphorylated by tyrosine phosphatases (Pase).

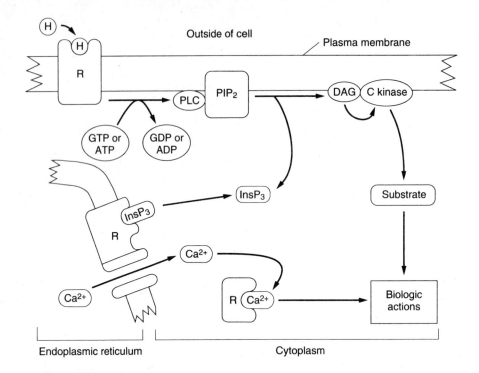

Figure 1–25. Activation of phospholipase C by hormone-receptor complexes, with regulation of intracellular Ca^{2+} and activation of protein kinase C. As described in the text, the activation can be through several different types of influences, including G protein mechanisms (using GTP) or tyrosine phosphorylation (using ATP). Shown here are $InsP_3$ receptors on the endoplasmic reticulum membranes, though in some cases these receptors are also located on the plasma membrane. ($InsP_3$, inositol 1,4,5-trisphosphate; PLC, phospholipase C; PIP_2, phospholipid phosphatidylinositol 4,5-bisphosphonate; DAG, diacylglycerol.)

ositol 1,4,5-trisphosphate ($InsP_3$; Figure 1–25). DAG activates C kinase, and $InsP_3$ promotes an increase in intracellular Ca^{2+}.

Calcium Ion

Calcium ion is involved extensively in the mediation of a number of hormone-independent processes such as neurotransmission, muscular contraction, secretion, other contractile processes, and activation of enzymes. It is also used extensively as a mediator of hormone action. As discussed above in the section on peptide hormone synthesis, this ion is present at lower concentrations in the cytosol (0.01–0.1 μmol/L) and higher concentrations (about 1 mmol/L) in extracellular fluids and intracellular organelles. Several Ca^{2+}-dependent ATPases actively extrude Ca^{2+} out of the cytosol and into the extracellular space or organelles. Hormones and other effector substances stimulate the release into the cytosol of calcium ions from these sources. The Ca^{2+} moves into the cytosol through specific calcium ion channels that are regulated by the effectors (Figure 1–25).

Ca^{2+} release into the cytosol from the outside of the cell is triggered by membrane depolarization in muscle and neuronal cells, and the increase in Ca^{2+}

triggers a further increase in intracellular Ca^{2+} by promoting its release from intracellular organelles such as the sarcoplasmic reticulum. Ryanodine receptors (RYRs) can be present on these organelles and respond both to the calcium fluxes and to surface receptors. However, the principal way hormones promote the increase in intracellular Ca^{2+} is through stimulation of the production of $InsP_3$ produced by phospholipase C-mediated breakdown of PIP_2 (discussed above; Figure 1–25). $InsP_3$ binds to specific receptors on internal organelles such as the endoplasmic reticulum, whose subunits also comprise a calcium channel, to promote Ca^{2+} entry into the cytosol (Figure 1–25). These effects may be facilitated by other products of $InsP_3$ breakdown. In some cases there may also be $InsP_3$ receptors on the plasma membrane. Changes in Ca^{2+} appear to occur in waves across the cell, and in endocrine cells this appears to be facilitated by the $InsP_3$-induced changes in Ca^{2+}.

Ca^{2+} binds to various proteins to affect their properties (Figures 1–25 and 1–26). The mechanism of control by Ca^{2+} is most clear in the case of skeletal muscle, in which Ca^{2+} binds to troponin C, which induces a conformational change in the troponin complex and thus triggers muscular contraction. The

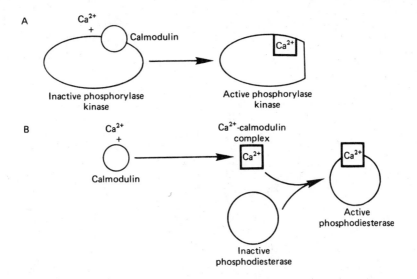

Figure 1–26. Activation of phosphorylase kinase *(A)* and of phosphodiesterase *(B)* by Ca^{2+}-calmodulin complexes.

most extensively studied Ca^{2+} receptor in terms of hormone action is **calmodulin,** MW about 16,700, which binds four calcium ions (Figures 1–25 and 1–26). This binding alters the property of calmodulin to activate cellular processes. In smooth muscle, the Ca^{2+}-calmodulin complex activates myosin light chain kinase, which induces contraction by phosphorylation of myosin light chain. Ca^{2+}-calmodulin complexes also bind to and activate Ca^{2+}-calmodulin-dependent protein kinase, which has an extensive role in neuronal signal transduction, including neurotransmitter synthesis and release. The activation induces autophosphorylation of the kinase, which converts the enzyme to a Ca^{2+}-independent form and traps the calmodulin. Ca^{2+}-calmodulin complexes are also involved in regulating cell growth and division, inhibiting or stimulating adenylyl cyclase, stimulating cAMP phosphodiesterase (Figure 1–26), activating phospholipase A_2, and regulating nuclear transcriptional responses through poorly understood mechanisms. Ca^{2+}-calmodulin complexes activate a specific serine-threonine protein phosphatase, **calcineurin,** which is involved in mediating the actions of the T cell receptor in T lymphocytes and the IgE receptor in mast cells. The immunosuppressants cyclosporine and FK 506 block the activity of this phosphatase. Calmodulin may also be a component of an enzyme complex, as is the case with phosphorylase kinase (Figure 1–26).

Protein Kinase C

Protein kinase C is activated in response to DAG, generated as described above (Figure 1–25). However, DAG can also be generated by hydrolysis of other phospholipids, particularly phosphatidylcholine, and these sources may be important, especially later in the generation of cellular responses. Phospholipases D and A_2 may be important in this generation, and these enzymes may be activated directly or indirectly by hormone-receptor complexes. There are several different species of protein kinase C, ie, serine and threonine kinases whose substrate specificities differ from that of kinase A. These kinases phosphorylate a diverse set of substrates to affect their abilities to regulate a spectrum of intracellular events. A frequent pattern is that these proteins act synergistically with Ca^{2+} responses. In addition, Ca^{2+} can enhance protein kinase activation, and protein kinase C appears to be involved in generating regular oscillations of intracellular Ca^{2+} by exerting negative feedback control over induced inositol phospholipid hydrolysis.

Activation of Guanylyl Cyclase

Guanylyl cyclase generates guanosine 3′,5′-cyclic monophosphate (cGMP) from GTP. cGMP binds to and activates a specific protein kinase (G kinase) that is analogous to kinase A in that it is a serine and threonine kinase except that it is activated by cGMP and the subunit structure differs. Guanylyl cyclase is activated by ANP, Ca^{2+}, and some nonhormonal mechanisms. One form of the enzyme is membrane-bound, but unlike adenylyl cyclase, there is a soluble form of the enzyme. The soluble form can be activated by nitric oxide (NO) alone or perhaps as part of another compound; NO is also endothelium-derived relaxing factor (EDRF) and mediates the actions of certain vasodilators such as bradykinin and acetylcholine. Its formation is also Ca^{2+}-dependent (see above). A membrane form of the enzyme is part of the ANP receptor and is activated by it (Figure 1–19). This receptor generally resembles those with tyrosine kinase activity. The precise substrates for G kinase are not known, but their function is presumably activated by the phosphorylation analogous to the substrates of A kinase.

Ras

Ras is a G protein activated by GTP binding and inactivated when the GTPase activity of the protein converts the GTP to GDP. Ras was originally described as an oncogene, and mutated or overexpressed ras molecules are extensively involved in human cancers. The normal cellular ras is also involved in regulating a number of processes, including cell growth. All ras proteins are prenylated, and some are palmitoylated, which apparently facilitates their interactions with cell membranes. Activated ras molecules in turn activate several different ras-dependent protein kinases, and DAG and InsP$_3$ through phospholipase C are known second messengers. Cellular effects of oncogenic ras can sometimes be blocked by inhibitors of protein kinase C, though this does not completely block the effects of normal ras. All of the mechanisms by which ras can be activated are not known. However, hormones that activate tyrosine kinase activity can regulate ras through the binding of an SH2 site containing protein (Grb2, others) to the receptor and the association of this protein with another protein (mSos1) that is thereby brought to the cell membrane. This protein activates the ras protein by promoting exchange of GTP for GDP. These actions may link the growth factor and other receptors with tyrosine kinase activity to regulation of cell growth. Another protein, RasGRF, activates ras by another as yet undefined mechanism. The activation of ras—ordinarily GDP-bound ras—enhances GDP dissociation and GTP binding of the protein. A GTPase activity of ras converts the GTP back to GDP and thus terminates its activity. Another protein, GAP protein, binds to ras, enhances its GTPase activity, and keeps it in an inactivated state; this protein also binds to tyrosine kinase receptors and may participate in regulation of ras, but it may not be the target for mitogenic stimulation through ras.

INTERNALIZATION OF CELL SURFACE RECEPTORS

Cell surface receptors are internalized (Figure 1–13), ie, brought into the cell. In most cases, this process occurs in structures termed **coated pits** in which the protein **clathrin** has accumulated along the inside of the plasma membrane. Receptors or hormone-receptor complexes located at these coated pits are internalized by invagination of the membrane. The membrane then forms a vesicle inside the cell, with loss of the clathrin coat. Internalization is in some cases (eg, insulin receptor) stimulated by binding of the ligand to the receptor, but in other cases

(LDL receptor) it is not stimulated, and even the unliganded receptor is internalized. The insulin-induced internalization of its receptor requires the autophosphorylation of the receptor. The internalized receptor-containing vesicle is termed an endosome or receptosome and is acidic, analogous to the lysosome. Inside these vesicles, the hormone, when present, usually dissociates from the receptors. Depending on the specific case, the endosome may fuse with the lysosome, in which case the hormone and receptor are usually degraded by the enzymes and the highly acidic environment of the lysosome. This mechanism contributes to negative regulation of the receptors by the hormone. However, the endosomes may also return to the cell surface and fuse with it, returning the hormone or hormone-receptor complex to the cell surface.

There is controversy about whether the internalized surface-active hormones also act inside the cell. The potential for this action is suggested by the fact that receptors and hormone-receptor complexes can enter the cells. However, in most cases, direct evidence that these hormones act inside the cell is lacking, and more studies are needed to resolve the issue. The receptors therefore are in a constant state of flux, with new receptor synthesis delivering them to the cell surface and the internalization process—with degradation—removing them from the cell's surface.

TRANSCRIPTIONAL REGULATION BY HORMONE RECEPTORS

Most classes of hormones regulate transcription. The members of the steroid-thyroid hormone superfamily of receptors regulate transcription more directly through their binding to specific DNA sequences and the interactions of receptor domains with other transcription factors. The hormones that bind to cell surface receptors act on transcription through their second messengers, which affect transcription factors directly or indirectly through modification reactions.

Regulation of Transcription by Members of the Steroid-Thyroid Hormone Superfamily of Receptors

Regulation of transcription by members of the steroid-thyroid hormone receptor superfamily can be classified initially in terms of whether the unliganded, hormone-free receptors are or are not associated with DNA. The hormone-free steroid hormone receptors are associated with heat shock proteins that stabilize the receptors, prevent their binding to DNA, and may facilitate binding of the steroid (Figure 1–27). These unliganded receptors are mostly located in the cell cytoplasm, though some are in the nucleus (Figure 1–27); most of the unliganded estrogen receptors are present in the nucleus. Several different

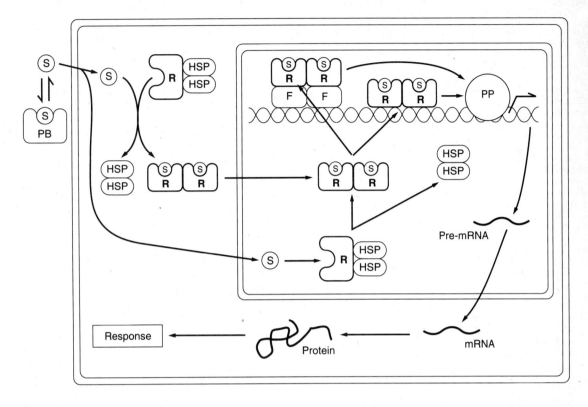

Figure 1–27. Regulation of transcription by steroid hormones. (S, steroid hormone; PB, plasma binding protein; HSP, heat shock proteins [only two are shown; as described in the text, more proteins can be part of this complex]; R, receptors; F, transcription factor; PP, proteins that bind at the proximal promoter.) Note that steroid-receptor complexes can work through receptor-DNA interactions or receptor interactions with other proteins.

heat shock proteins have been reported in association with the steroid hormone receptors, and two molecules of heat shock protein 90 (hsp90) appear to be the most important and most prevalent examples. Other factors have been proposed to participate in the receptor-heat shock protein interaction. Hormone binding to the receptors induces conformational changes that promote dissociation of the heat shock proteins and expose on the receptors a DNA binding site, a nuclear localization signal (in most cases), and dimerization and heterodimerization functions. The receptors then bind to specific hormone regulatory element (HRE) sequences on the DNA (Figure 1–27). These receptors ordinarily bind to the DNA as pre-formed homodimers, though the strength of dimerization in the absence of DNA varies considerably between the various members of the set. Since the unliganded receptors are mostly not bound to DNA in the absence of the ligand, they are mostly inactive transcriptionally in this setting.

Other members of the family, including the thyroid hormone, vitamin D, and retinoic acid receptors, are probably not associated with the heat shock proteins and migrate to the nucleus and bind to specific DNA sequences in the absence of the hormone (Figure 1–28). These unliganded DNA-bound receptors may have no effect or may repress or activate transcription.

The HRE elements are specific for each receptor, though there are overlapping activities and some redundancy to the structures. A glucocorticoid receptor response element would be called a GRE and a thyroid hormone receptor response element a TRE. These sites have consensus core half-sites of six nucleotides.

For the steroid hormone receptors, the overall site is usually composed of two half-sites arranged as a palindrome with a variable number (usually < 7) of nucleotides between them (spacer). The term "palindrome" refers to the orientation of the half-site sequences, which read identically running in opposite directions on opposite strands of the DNA. These palindromic sites bind the receptor dimers, with the alpha-helix between each zinc finger of the DNA binding domain of the receptor fitting into the major groove of the DNA along the sequence of the consensus. When the spacing is correct, each monomeric unit of the receptor dimer binds specifically to the half-site; however, when the spacing is not optimal or when one half-site does not fit the consensus, the

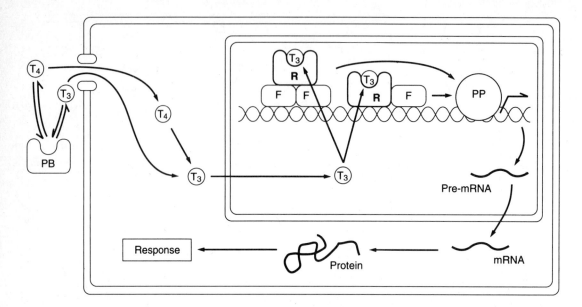

Figure 1–28. Regulation of transcription by thyroid hormones. T_3 and T_4 are triiodothyronine and thyroxine, respectively; other abbreviations are the same as in Figure 1–27. Note that the hormone probably enters through an active transport mechanism.

dimer can still bind, albeit with a lower affinity and although the contact points with one half-site are nonspecific.

With thyroid hormone, vitamin D, and retinoic acid receptor response elements, the DNA sites tend to be more direct repeats, though palindromes exist and can be functional. The emerging pattern with these elements is that the receptors frequently exist as heterodimers with these receptors and with other factors (Figure 1–28). Thus, the thyroid hormone receptors form strong heterodimers with retinoid X receptors (whose ligands may be 9-*cis*-retinoic acid) and act synergistically with these elements. Hormone binding to these receptors alters the receptors' transcriptional activation functions. In general, these actions are positive, enhancing transcription, but in many cases they are also negative. The binding of hormone receptors to DNA can also induce a bending of the DNA that may facilitate the ability of the proteins bound to the DNA to interact with each other.

These classes of receptors may also in some circumstances act by binding to other transcription factors through protein-protein interactions without the need for the receptor to bind to DNA (Figures 1–27 and 1–28). A factor that commonly interacts with these receptors, AP1, is a complex of two factors called jun and fos, named for oncogene products.

The mechanisms by which transcription factors work is discussed in the preceding sections on gene expression. It is presumed that portions of the hormone receptors bound to DNA or to other proteins

interact with other proteins, often associated with the basal transcriptional apparatus, and facilitate their functions. These interactions can be facilitatory, in which case transcription is stimulated; or inhibitory, in which case transcription is inhibited. Receptors may also inhibit transcription by remaining inactive and binding to sites on DNA where other transcription factors can also bind, thus blocking their binding to DNA and subsequently their transcriptional activities.

As alluded to in the discussion on heterodimers, various hormone receptors can act synergistically or antagonistically through interactions with other transcription factors. These activities show enormous variability even for the same two factors, and the specific functions can depend on the nature of the DNA site to which the factors bind and on other aspects of the promoter context. For example, jun and fos can act synergistically with or antagonistically to the thyroid or glucocorticoid hormone receptors. The thyroid hormone receptors act synergistically with the Pit-1 factor described earlier.

Regulation of Transcription by Hormones That Work Through Second Messengers

Hormones that work through second messengers have many influences on transcription. These actions ordinarily occur through modifications of the transcription factors or of other proteins that secondarily modify transcription factors (Figure 1–29). These modifications are similar to those described above resulting from kinase activities, Ca^{2+}-induced modifica-

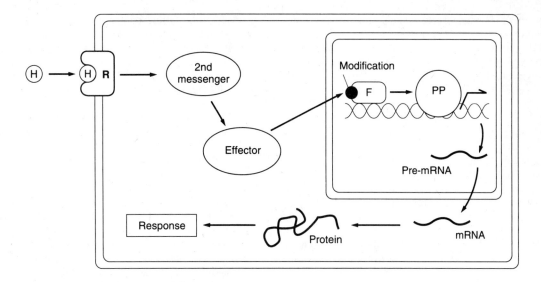

Figure 1–29. Regulation of transcription by hormones that act on the cell surface. (H, hormone; 2nd, second messenger. Other abbreviations are the same as in Figure 1–27.)

tions of enzyme activities, etc. cAMP regulates the rate of transcription of a number of genes, including those for hormones such as somatostatin and the glycoprotein hormones. These actions are mediated by a cAMP response element-binding protein (CREB) transcription factor. This protein is phosphorylated in response to cAMP. The phosphorylation activates the transcriptional regulatory properties of CREB. CREB binds to specific DNA sequences and is a common transcription factor. The AP1 protein complex discussed above is also regulated by cAMP and is phosphorylated in response to kinase A to enhance the transcriptional regulatory properties of AP1. cAMP-induced phosphorylation of the transcription factor NFIL-6 increases its binding in the nucleus. Phorbol esters that activate kinase C and calcium ions are extensively involved in the regulation of transcription. Kinase C modifies the activities of various transcription factors such as the AP1 complex. The precise mechanisms by which Ca^{2+} acts have not been elucidated. The CREB protein, however, appears to be one of the Ca^{2+}-responsive factors. Modifications of these proteins and their multiple interactions with different transcription factors provide opportunities for diverse and complex patterns of effects on transcription control that are needed for higher organisms.

REGULATION OF RESPONSIVENESS TO HORMONES

The responsiveness to hormones is extensively regulated, and this is an important consideration in both hormone therapy and evaluation of certain dis-

eases. The most common example may be type II diabetes mellitus, in which plasma insulin levels are commonly elevated in the face of frank hyperglycemia; these abnormalities are due to the fact that the disease is characterized by resistance to the actions of insulin. Regulation of responsiveness by the homologous hormone (the hormone's regulation of its own responsiveness) is the most frequently observed influence, though there is extensive regulation of responsiveness by other hormones, ions, eicosanoids, neurotransmitters, metabolic events, and other influences.

Sometimes the body adjusts to the potential for regulation of responsiveness by the homologous hormone by releasing hormones in a pulsatile manner, as is seen with FSH, LH, ACTH, and growth hormone. This can be an important consideration in hormone therapy. For example, administration of LHRH analogues can lead to down-regulation of LHRH responsiveness such that continued administration of the hormone effectively becomes antagonist therapy, as is utilized clinically, for example in therapy for prostate cancer (Chapter 19).

Homologous Hormone

The usual pattern of regulation by the homologous hormone is negative control of responsiveness. However, the homologous hormone can also enhance the sensitivity to its own actions, as occurs with angiotensin II, which enhances the sensitivity of the adrenal zona glomerulosa to its actions. Regulation by the homologous hormone is most extensive with hormones that act on cell surface receptors, though homologous regulation by steroid and thyroid hormones also is observed. Both glucocorticoid and thyroid hormones negatively regulate the levels of their receptors and their responsiveness.

Homologous regulation occurs through several mechanisms. This can involve a change both in receptor numbers and in receptor-effector coupling. Receptor numbers are regulated in some cases by modifying the rate of transcription of the receptor genes, as is seen with steroid and thyroid hormone and some cell surface receptors. In some cases, as with adrenergic receptors, regulation of mRNA levels occurs through effects on mRNA stability. Hormone-induced internalization can increase receptor degradation. Receptors can be modified to influence their activities. Activating phospholipase C, cAMP-activated protein kinase A, and another kinase, β-adrenergic receptor kinase (BARK), can all contribute to β-adrenergic receptor desensitization. These latter effects are rapid and readily reversible. Inhibiting adenylyl cyclase can decrease receptor phosphorylation and promote enhanced receptor responsiveness. However, many aspects of receptor down-regulation are not well characterized.

Other Factors

The levels of receptors and of hormone responsiveness are also regulated extensively by other hormones. For example, estrogen regulates positively the levels of the progesterone receptor in breast tissue, and estrogen plus FSH up-regulate the levels of the LH receptors in developing ovarian follicles. Glucose can affect the sensitivity to insulin. The mechanisms of these influences are similar to those discussed above in the section on regulation by the homologous hormone.

ACTIONS OF HORMONES

Hormones affect all tissues and organ systems of the body and are important from very early in embryonic development throughout life. The details of these effects are the subject matter of this book. Some general patterns are described below.

DEVELOPMENTAL EFFECTS

Hormones influence the development of the fetus and the child. These actions are extensive, with effects on essentially all systems of the body. The profound developmental abnormalities resulting from severe hypothyroidism and cretinism serve as an example of effects on the central nervous system. The influence of hormones on sexual development are il-lustrated by the failure of male sexual development in the androgen-deficient state. Deficiency of growth hormone results in severe growth deficiency.

CELL GROWTH & CANCER

Hormones are important for the growth of a number of cell types. Prominent examples are the actions of the tropic factors that regulate the growth of endocrine glands, eg, the actions of ACTH, angiotensin II, TSH, LH, and FSH on growth of cells of the adrenal glands, thyroid gland, ovary, and testis. In addition, peptide hormones such as growth hormone and IGF-1 and -2 directly stimulate both linear growth and cellular proliferation in other tissues. Other peptides such as fibroblast growth factor (FGF), platelet-derived growth factor, and transforming growth factors α and β are growth factors both in multiple tissues and in endocrine glands. Thyroid hormones can stimulate the growth of several tissues. Steroid hormones can both inhibit or stimulate cell growth. For example, glucocorticoids inhibit the growth of several cell types and even kill some lymphocyte cell types, whereas estradiol—and testosterone and dihydrotestosterone—can stimulate the growth of breast and prostatic tissues, respectively. Compounds that inhibit estrogen and androgen action are used to treat breast and prostate cancers.

Hormones have extensive interrelationships with cancer, as described in Chapter 19. Prostatic, breast, endometrial, and other cancers can be dependent on the steroid hormones. Thyroid cancers can be dependent on and influenced by TSH. Many oncogenes are analogues of growth factors or growth factor receptors, as described above and in Chapter 19.

CENTRAL NERVOUS SYSTEM EFFECTS

Many interrelationships between the endocrine and nervous systems are described above. Hormones act as neurotransmitters, and neurotransmitters are extensively involved in regulating endocrine functions. Hormones also regulate a number of other functions in the central nervous system such as mood, appetite, memory, and cognitive function. Hormones can also have secondary influences on the central nervous system through their effects on general metabolism. The profound mental abnormalities seen with severe hypothyroidism, with slowed mentation that can progress to frank coma; the psychosis that can occur with glucocorticoid excess; the enhanced sense of smell observed in the addisonian patient; the mental abnormalities that can be seen with both hypoglycemia or hyperglycemia—all serve to underscore the potentials for hormones to influence the nervous system.

EFFECTS ON METABOLISM

Hormones regulate the metabolism of all major classes of chemicals. Carbohydrate, fat, protein, and amino acid and nucleic acid metabolism are tightly regulated by insulin, glucagon, and other pancreatic peptides, somatostatin, growth hormone, catecholamines (epinephrine, norepinephrine), thyroid hormones, glucocorticoids, and other hormones. These interactions are coordinated in a complex way to provide for finely tuned regulation and responsiveness to circumstances such as stress or starvation. Insulin is dominant in lowering the blood glucose and in stimulating the metabolism of glucose and the synthesis of fat, proteins, and nucleic acids. By contrast, cortisol, glucagon, catecholamines, and growth hormone tend to elevate the blood sugar by diverse mechanisms. However, these hormones differ in their effects on protein, fat, and nucleic acid metabolism.

A number of different enzymes and specific processes are affected by hormones. These include regulation of the uptake of glucose, amino acids, nucleosides, and other small molecules. For example, insulin increases glucose uptake by promoting redistribution of glucose transporters to the plasma membrane. Enzymes regulated include, among others, those involved in gluconeogenesis, lipolysis, glycogen synthesis, amino acid metabolism and synthesis, and lipid synthesis.

EFFECTS ON CARDIOVASCULAR & RENAL FUNCTION

Hormones are extensively involved in the regulation of cardiovascular and renal function. The renin-angiotensin system, atrial natriuretic peptide, endothelins, catecholamines, steroid hormones, thyroid hormone, prostaglandins, kinins, modulators of immunologic and inflammatory reactions, substance P, calcitonin gene-related peptide, and other substances all can profoundly affect this system. These can affect heart rate and contractility. Effects of hormones on blood pressure are complex, with varied influences on arteries and veins having both constrictor and dilator functions. The growth factor properties of hormones can influence cardiovascular development, muscular hypertrophy, and muscular hyperplasia and are involved in pathologic processes leading to hypertensive vascular changes, atherosclerosis, heart failure, and cardiac hypertrophy. Hormones influence renal function by regulating renal blood flow, glomerular filtration rate, and the transport of ions, water, and other chemicals. Hormones activate both active and passive transport processes through activation of channels, stimulating the synthesis of new channels, providing greater energy for active transport, or promoting the redistribution of channels.

Drugs that block many of these systems, such as converting enzyme inhibitors, beta-blockers, and mineralocorticoid hormone antagonists, are used extensively in therapy.

EFFECTS ON MINERAL & WATER METABOLISM

Hormones are intimately involved in both mineral and water metabolism. The regulation of calcium and phosphate ion concentrations is discussed in the following section. A major regulator of serum osmolality and water excretion is vasopressin. The mineralocorticoid aldosterone has emerged as a dominant regulator of serum sodium and potassium and to some extent the chloride and bicarbonate ion concentrations and of the overall balance of these ions. Ionic balance is also regulated by other hormones, including ANP, insulin, glucagon, catecholamines, angiotensin II, and PTH.

EFFECTS ON SKELETAL FUNCTIONS

Bone is in a continuing state of remodeling under complex control by hormones and other factors. These actions control both the growth of bone, through the actions of IGF-1, and bone mineralization, through influences on both the matrix and the mineral phase. Examples of such influences include the effects of parathyroid hormone on bone remodeling, the actions of vitamin D overall on calcium metabolism, the effects of estrogens to prevent osteoporosis, and the osteoporosis that can develop with glucocorticoid excess.

EFFECTS ON REPRODUCTIVE FUNCTION

The role of the gonadotropins in regulating ovarian and testicular function and the secretion of hormones from these organs is discussed above. The male sex steroids, testosterone and dihydrotestosterone, regulate development of male sexual characteristics such as penile and prostate growth, voice, and muscular development and affect libido and sexual behavior. The female sex steroids regulate the functions of female reproductive organs, including the menstrual cycle and ovulation.

Pregnancy is regulated extensively by hormones. Hormones are critical for egg and sperm development, preparation of the uterus for conception and implantation, and development of the fetus. The placenta itself produces a number of hormones, some of which are mostly unique (CG, chorionic somato-mammotropin) and others that are also produced abundantly by other glands (progesterone and other steroid hormones),

RELEASE OF OTHER HORMONES

Hormones are extensively involved in regulating the production and release of the homologous hormone and of other hormones. These aspects are described in the sections on neuroendocrinology, synthesis of hormones, regulation of the endocrine system, and the mechanisms of hormone action.

EFFECTS ON IMMUNOLOGIC FUNCTIONS

There is extensive regulation of the immune system by hormones. The glucocorticoids and sex steroids are the hormones whose immunologic effects are best understood. Thyroid hormone, GH, catecholamines, PRL, and other hormones have all been reported to influence immunologic or inflammatory functions, but the roles of these and of other hormones are still being defined.

The major hormone class known to affect lymphokines is the glucocorticoids, which can blunt immunologic and inflammatory responses at high doses. This action forms the basis for the extensive use of glucocorticoids to suppress inflammatory and immunologic responses. The roles of normal levels of glucocorticoids are still being unraveled.

The sex steroids affect the immune response generally in a suppressive way. Castration in animals can result in enlargement of lymph nodes and spleen, increased graft versus host disease, decreased skin graft rejection, and stimulation of in vitro T lymphocyte mitogen responsiveness. These effects are mainly on cellular immune responses; influences on humoral responses are less clear. Estrogens may stimulate antibody production, and females tend to have higher levels of the major immunoglobulin classes under both basal and stimulated conditions than males. Females tend to have a higher incidence of autoimmune diseases and more active cellular and humoral immune responses than males. These differences (sometimes referred to as **sexual dimorphisms**) are not observed before puberty.

Pregnancy, with its associated changes in a number of hormones, commonly results in amelioration of autoimmune diseases. The mechanisms for these changes are not known. It is noteworthy that the peptide hormone whose concentrations are the highest reported to date for any hormone is placental chorionic somatomammotropin, which has weak GH and PRL activities. Could this hormone have some im-

munoregulatory roles? Pregnancy tends to suppress the cellular but not humoral immune responses, and this may contribute to prevention of maternal rejection of fetal tissues. Their susceptibility to a number of viral and fungal diseases is increased. This immunosuppression is most pronounced in the second and third trimesters of pregnancy. By about 3–6 months postpartum, there is a rebound, with a reduction in sex steroid levels and an increase in the incidence of autoimmune diseases.

DISORDERS OF THE ENDOCRINE SYSTEM

Disorders of the endocrine system result principally in states of excess or deficiencies of hormones due to hyperfunctioning or hypofunctioning of the glands. However, the endocrinologist is also confronted with specific tumors and other problems with endocrine glands that may not be associated with excesses or deficiencies, primary or secondary abnormalities in sensitivity to hormones, and iatrogenic syndromes. The types of abnormalities that in principle can occur are illustrated in Figure 1–30.

HYPOFUNCTION (Figure 1–30)

Destruction of the Gland

A common mechanism for glandular hypofunction is destruction of the gland. The most common cause of destruction of endocrine glands is autoimmune disease. This is seen in most cases of insulin-dependent diabetes mellitus, hypothyroidism, adrenal insufficiency, and gonadal failure. In fact, a polyglandular failure syndrome (Schmidt's syndrome) can result in destruction of several different endocrine glands (and in other abnormalities such as pernicious anemia and vitiligo) in the same patient due to autoimmune mechanisms. With the pituitary gland, an insult such as a tumor or hypotension due to shock or hemorrhage is more typically responsible. Any of the endocrine glands may be damaged, with consequent hypofunction, by neoplasms, infection, or hemorrhage.

Extraglandular Disorders

Endocrine hypofunction can be due to defects outside traditional glands. In some cases, these are simply due to damage to tissues not considered traditional endocrine glands in which the hormones involved are produced or are converted to active forms; it could be argued that these disorders simply represent damage to endocrine glands that happen to

Hypofunction   **Hyperfunction**

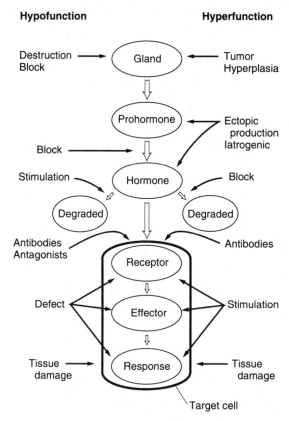

Figure 1–30. Causes of hypofunction and hyperfunction of the endocrine system. (Reprinted from Baxter JD in: *Cecil's Textbook of Medicine.* Wyngaarden JB, Smith LH Jr (editors). Saunders, 1985.)

be organs with other major functions. Thus, renal disease can result in defective conversion of 25-$(OH)D_3$ to $1,25\text{-}(OH)_2D_3$, with consequent metabolic abnormalities, damage to the renin-producing juxtaglomerular cells causing hyporeninemic hypoaldosteronism, and damage to erythropoietin-producing cells causing anemia. In congenital 5α-reductase deficiency, there is impaired dihydrotestosterone production from testosterone in androgen target tissues, resulting in partial androgen deficiency. Alternatively, this disorder could be classified as a defect of hormone biosynthesis (see below).

In some cases, factors that influence hormone degradation or sensitivity can precipitate or aggravate hormone deficiency when there is preexisting insufficient reserve in the endocrine gland. For example, glucocorticoid therapy increases the need for insulin and can precipitate latent diabetes mellitus or aggravate existing diabetes. Thyroid hormones increase the metabolism of cortisol, and treatment of hypothyroidism with thyroid hormone can unmask latent adrenal deficiency. Treatment with the anticonvulsant phenytoin can accelerate the degradation of

glucocorticoids and increase the need for these hormones.

Specific Defects in Hormone Biosynthesis

Endocrine hypofunction can be due to congenital defects in hormone synthesis. The types of mutations that can produce these defects are described in the preceding section on genetic diseases. These can be due to defects in the genes that either encode the hormones, regulate hormone production, encode hormone-producing enzymes, or are involved in hormone metabolism. With the adrenal gland, 21-hydroxylase syndrome is one of the most common of all genetic diseases. Other congenital adrenal gland defects include the 11- and 18-hydroxylase syndromes. Congenital defects also occur with the thyroid gland. Dietary iodine deficiency results in deficient thyroid hormone biosynthesis. Mutations in genes encoding polypeptide hormones can lead to hormone deficiency by underproducing or not producing the hormone or by producing a defective hormone. Forms of growth deficiency can result from mutations or deletions in the GH gene, defective production of GRH, or mutations in the gene for the transcription factor Pit-1, which regulates GH synthesis. A rare form of diabetes mellitus results from a mutation in the insulin gene with consequent defective insulin.

HYPERFUNCTION
(Figure 1–30)

Hyperfunction of most endocrine glands results usually from tumors. Tumors can occur in many endocrine glands, producing excess hormone, have been reported. Thus, tumors of the pituitary can lead to overproduction of most of the hormones (ACTH, GH, PRL, TSH, LH, FSH, etc); in some cases, this leads to stimulation of other glands, resulting in hyperplasia, as is seen with pituitary ACTH- or TSH-producing tumors.

Tumors of the parathyroid glands can overproduce PTH; of the parafollicular cells of the thyroid, calcitonin; of the follicular cells, thyroid hormone; of the pancreatic islets, insulin or glucagon; of the adrenals, cortisol, aldosterone, deoxycorticosterone, androgens, and other steroids; of the stomach, gastrin; of the kidney, renin or erythropoietin; etc. There are also syndromes of multiple endocrine neoplasia, in which there is a predisposition to develop tumors of several glands. Most tumors of the thyroid gland do not overproduce thyroid hormone. Similarly, it is rare for ovarian or testicular tumors to overproduce steroids or for posterior pituitary tumors to overproduce oxytocin or vasopressin.

Also quite common is the phenomenon of ectopic

hormone production (Chapter 20). Thus, tumors of many types can overproduce various hormones. In general, these are polypeptide hormones and include ACTH, PTH, ADH, FSH, LH, calcitonin, various releasing hormones, GH, and PRL. Some hormones, on the other hand, are rarely if ever expressed ectopically, as is the case with insulin.

Some glands develop idiopathic hyperplasia. This can rarely be seen with ACTH hypersecretion by the pituitary, for example. It can also be seen with the parathyroids, resulting in hyperparathyroidism. Hyperplasia of the adrenal zona fasciculata and zona reticularis can result in cortisol hypersecretion, and hyperplasia of the zona glomerulosa can result in primary aldosteronism. In these cases, there presumably is some specific stimulus producing the hyperplasia, but these have not yet been identified. However, a specific genetic defect associated with parathyroid hyperplasia has been identified.

Autoimmune stimulation resulting in hyperfunction is seen commonly with hyperthyroidism. Hyperinsulinism can be seen early in the course of development of insulin-dependent diabetes mellitus, but in other cases autoimmune stimulation leading to hyperfunction is rare.

DEFECTS IN SENSITIVITY TO HORMONES

Genetic and acquired defects in sensitivity to hormones play a part in many endocrine diseases and are dominant for some conditions. Most of these result in resistance to the hormone.

Primary resistance to a number of hormones has been established; it may be due to a number of different types of defects either in the hormone receptor or to functions distal to the receptor. Genetic defects in receptors resulting in syndromes of resistance have been reported for glucocorticoids, thyroid hormones, androgens, vitamin D, PTH, ADH, GH, insulin, and TSH. Postreceptor defects are known to occur in some cases of pseudohypoparathyroidism and also with non-insulin-dependent diabetes mellitus. In fact, non-insulin-dependent diabetes mellitus may reflect the most commonly encountered known problem of hormone resistance, though it remains to be established whether there is a primary defect in responsiveness to insulin.

Acquired resistance to hormones occurs in a number of situations. It can occur when there is frank disease that damages the target tissue and interferes with its ability to respond to the hormone, as is seen with renal disease and insensitivity to vasopressin and liver disease and insensitivity to glucagon. In diabetes mellitus, hyperglycemia, insulin excess, stress responses, and increased levels of other hormones (such as GH, cortisol, and glucagon), all lead to insulin resistance that can be difficult to counteract with therapy. Acquired resistance to hormones may

occur in the course of therapy with these hormones. This is particularly true with GnRH analogues and calcitonin and sometimes occurs with glucocorticoids. In fact, the acquired resistance with GnRH analogues forms the basis for their use in prostate cancer. In this setting, the GnRH-induced down regulation of GnRH responsiveness shuts down FSH and LH release with a consequent reduction in testosterone production. Immunologic mechanisms can lead to acquired resistance, as can occur with antibodies produced to hormones (eg, with insulin or GH therapy), or receptors (eg, to insulin receptors).

The clinical presentations of these syndromes show considerable variations. The hallmarks of hormone resistance are an elevated hormone level with clinical manifestations of its deficiency and failure of hormonal replacement to correct the disorder. However, resistance can be partial, with some response to higher hormone doses and a more subtle clinical presentation. Thus, in some cases, the syndromes simply resemble hormone deficiency states, as is the case with testicular feminization syndrome (androgen insensitivity), rickets (vitamin D insensitivity), and nephrogenic diabetes insipidus (ADH insensitivity). In other cases, the clinical presentation is more complex. For example, in the syndrome of generalized resistance to thyroid hormone, the clinical presentation may have features of euthyroidism, hyperthyroidism (tachycardia, poor attention), and hypothyroidism (poor growth). This is because there is a mutated β form of the thyroid hormone receptor that interferes with but does not completely block the function of the remaining α and β receptors in many tissues. Thus, the thyroid hormone excess results in variable responses depending on the receptor status in the different tissues. Clinical manifestations due to compensatory adaptation occur in other states as well. The block that occurs in 11β-hydroxylase syndrome results in defective cortisol production, but this is compensated for by elevated ACTH production and enough cortisol production to overcome the block. However, the excess stimulation results in excess deoxycorticosterone, which produces a mineralocorticoid excess state.

Primary hyperresponsiveness to hormones has rarely been encountered. This may occur in low-renin hypertension in humans and in primary aldosteronism with hyperplasia that may be a variant of primary aldosteronism. Acquired hypersensitivity can be observed, as with catecholamine hypersensitivity in hyperthyroidism and increased sensitivity to insulin with cortisol deficiency.

SYNDROMES OF HORMONE EXCESS DUE TO ADMINISTRATION OF EXOGENOUS HORMONE OR MEDICATION

Patients with syndromes of hormone excess resulting from administration of exogenous hormones fall into two groups. The first consists of those who self-administer excess quantities of a hormone or hormonal analogue. Examples are athletes who wish to improve their performances with androgens or growth hormone, individuals who wish to lose weight or be more stimulated and take thyroid hormone, or those who achieve a sense of well-being or relief of symptoms without improvement in their condition and take glucocorticoids. With the second subgroup, the administration is inadvertent. For example, the author has observed Cushing's syndrome in a patient who received glucocorticoids but was not told she had been given a glucocorticoid. Outbreaks of hyperthyroidism have occurred when meat containing thyroid gland tissue was consumed. Some preparations of licorice and some nasal sprays contain substances that produce a mineralocorticoid excess state.

DISORDERS OF THE ENDOCRINE GLANDS NOT ASSOCIATED WITH DISEASE

The endocrine glands can be affected by diseases just like other tissues of the body, and these can cause problems unrelated to the endocrine excess or deficiency state. For example, pituitary tumors can cause increased intracranial pressure or neurologic or ocular problems, or may lead to infections when they extend outside the sella turcica. Thyroid tumors or large goiters can cause local problems in the neck.

APPROACH TO THE PATIENT WITH ENDOCRINE DISEASE

In their extreme forms, most endocrine diseases are relatively easy to identify. However, treatment at late stages in general is neither as easy nor as successful as when the disease is identified earlier. Early manifestations of endocrine diseases can be quite subtle, manifested by less obvious features in the history, the physical examination, and in the laboratory. The body compensates for hormonal deficiencies in such a way that the disease may be in a very late stage by the time it presents itself. In addition, the clinical presentation for a given condition can differ depending on its chronicity, and in some cases even a severe deficiency state may not have had time for obvious manifestations to develop.

For these reasons, it is critical to use all available means to optimize diagnostic accuracy and treatment. The clinician must make decisions about whether treatment should be instituted immediately before time-consuming tests leading to definitive diagnosis have been completed. With chronic disorders, it is sometimes prudent to wait until the disease itself provides information that makes diagnosis easier; in other cases, such a course can be disastrous.

HISTORY & PHYSICAL EXAMINATION

A carefully performed history and physical examination can provide information that cannot be obtained from laboratory testing. Some diagnoses, such as hypertension, are in fact based on the physical examination alone. Even in cases where the history and physical are nonrevealing, they enable the physician to select appropriate laboratory tests and avoid unnecessary testing. Most specialists have a fund of stories about consultations on extensively studied patients where simply elicited symptoms or signs led to a clear diagnosis that could have been made without extensive testing. Thus, a carefully performed history should address those aspects that will lead to the diagnosis, the plan of approach, or both. It should also elicit relevant information from the history and physical examination that aids in overall management—eg, information about how much tissue damage or physical deformity has occurred, how long the disease has been present, the effect the various manifestations have had on the patient, and relevant aspects from the social, family, and personal histories.

Many manifestations of endocrine disease are those that are frequently due to nonendocrine or unknown causes (Table 1–4). These include tiredness, malaise, weakness, headache, anorexia, depression, weight gain or loss, bruising, constipation, and many others. Even with some common endocrine diseases, the major complaints can be due chiefly to nonendocrine causes. For example, hyperthyroidism is a common disease, though only a small fraction of people with weight loss suffer from hyperthyroidism. Adrenal insufficiency is a rare disease and an even rarer cause of nausea. Nevertheless, endocrine diseases are a part of the differential diagnoses for these complaints, and the primary care physician as well as the endocrinologist should be aware of them.

LABORATORY & IMAGING STUDIES

Laboratory evaluations are critical for both making and confirming endocrine diagnoses and for helping to rule out specific diagnoses. The growing sophistication of these tests has led endocrinologists to place increasing reliance on them. However, these tests cannot replace good clinical judgment that utilizes all available information in making clinical decisions.

Laboratory tests in general measure either the level of the hormone in some body fluid, the sequelae of the hormone, or the sequelae of the process that contributed to the hormone abnormality. The tests can be performed under random or basal conditions, pre-

Table 1–4. Examples of manifestations of endocrine disease.
(The manifestations do not occur in all cases, and the severity can vary markedly).

Abdominal pain	Addisonian crisis; diabetic ketoacidosis; hyperparathyroidism.
Amenorrhea or oligomenorrhea	Adrenal insufficiency, adrenogenital syndrome, anorexia nervosa, Cushing's syndrome, hyperprolactinemic states, hypopituitarism, hypothyroidism, menopause, ovarian failure, polycystic ovaries, pseudohermaphroditic syndromes.
Anemia	Adrenal insufficiency, gonadal insufficiency, hypothyroidism, hyperparathyroidism, panhypopituitarism.
Anorexia	Addison's disease, diabetic ketoacidosis, hypercalcemia (eg, hyperparathyroidism), hypothyroidism.
Constipation	Diabetic neuropathy, hypercalcemia, hypothyroidism, pheochromocytoma.
Depression	Adrenal insufficiency, Cushing's syndrome, hypercalcemic states, hypoglycemia, hypothyroidism.
Diarrhea	Hyperthyroidism, metastatic carcinoid tumors, metastatic medullary thyroid carcinoma.
Fever	Adrenal insufficiency, hyperthyroidism (severe: thyroid storm), hypothalamic disease.
Hair changes	Decreased body hair (hypothyroidism, hypopituitarism, Cushing's syndrome, thyrotoxicosis); hirsutism (androgen excess states, Cushing's syndrome, acromegaly).
Headache	Hypertensive episodes with pheochromocytoma, hypoglycemia, pituitary tumors.
Hypothermia	Hypoglycemia, hypothyroidism.
Libido changes	Adrenal insufficiency, Cushing's syndrome, hypercalcemia, hyperprolactinemia, hyperthyroidism, hypokalemia, hypopituitarism, hypothyroidism, poorly controlled diabetes mellitus.
Nervousness	Cushing's syndrome, hyperthyroidism.
Polyuria	Diabetes insipidus, diabetes mellitus, hypercalcemia, hypokalemia.
Skin changes	Acanthosis nigricans (obesity, polycystic ovaries, severe insulin resistance, Cushing's syndrome, acromegaly); acne (androgen excess); hyperpigmentation (adrenal insufficiency, Nelson's syndrome); dry (hypothyroidism); hypopigmentation (panhypopituitarism); striae, plethora, bruising, ecchymoses (Cushing's syndrome); vitiligo (autoimmune thyroid disease, Addison's disease).
Weakness and fatigue	Addison's disease, Cushing's syndrome, diabetes mellitus, hypokalemia (eg, primary aldosteronism, Bartter's syndrome), hypothyroidism, hyperthyroidism, hypercalcemia (eg, hyperparathyroidism, panhypopituitarism, pheochromocytoma).
Weight gain	Central nervous system disease, Cushing's syndrome, hypothyroidism, insulinoma, pituitary tumors.
Weight loss	Adrenal insufficiency, anorexia nervosa, endocrine cancer, hyperthyroidism, insulin-dependent diabetes mellitus, panhypopituitarism, pheochromocytoma.

cisely defined conditions, or in response to some provocative stimulus. In measuring hormone levels, the **sensitivity** of the assay refers to the lowest concentration of the hormone that can be accurately detected, and the **specificity** refers to the extent to which cross-reacting species that are not intended for the measurement are scored inappropriately as the hormone in the assay.

Measurements of Hormone Levels: Basal Levels

Immunologic assays have become the dominant technology utilized to measure levels of hormones in body fluids even though there are other ways to measure them. Most measurements are made on blood or urine samples. The hormone is measured either directly from the samples or following extraction and purification. Most measurements are of the active hormone, though measurement of either a metabolite or precursor of the hormone or a concomitantly released substance sometimes provides the best information. Thus, in general, in assessing vitamin D status, it is more informative to measure the precursor

hormone, $25\text{-}(OH)D_3$ even though the final active hormone is $1,25\text{-}(OH)_2D_3$. In 21-hydroxylase syndrome, the clinical problem is a deficiency of cortisol or aldosterone, whereas the most sensitive measurement is of the plasma 17α-hydroxyprogesterone level, a precursor of the hormone. In looking for a pheochromocytoma, levels of metabolites of epinephrine are sometimes more informative than the active hormone, ie, epinephrine.

Plasma & Urine Assays

Assays of hormones in blood samples—plasma or serum—will provide an indication of the level of hormone at that time. For hormones with long half-lives whose levels do not change rapidly (eg, thyroxine), measurements from samples taken randomly provide an integrated assessment of hormonal status. For hormones with shorter half-lives, such as epinephrine or cortisol, the assay will provide information only for the time of sample collection. Thus, with a pheochromocytoma that episodically releases epinephrine, elevated plasma epinephrine levels would be found only during periods of release and not between them. Spontaneous Cushing's disease can be associated with an increased number of pulses of cortisol release with normal plasma cortisol levels between pulses. In the early stages of development of Addison's disease, the number of pulses of cortisol release can be decreased, but occasional releases can occur following which the plasma cortisol can be in the normal range.

Urine assays measure levels of hormones or metabolites, and the collection period can be a random sample or, more often, a timed collection (usually 24 hours). Interpretations of urinary measurements must account for the fact that the urinary levels reflect renal handling of the hormone. Urine measurements were utilized even more frequently in the past because larger quantities of the hormone could be obtained in many cases. However, with the high sensitivity of today's powerful immunoassays, this advantage of urine is disappearing. Thus, blood measurements are usually preferred. An advantage of urinary assays is that in some cases they can provide an integrated assessment of hormonal status. With cortisol, for example, only about 1–3% of the hormone released by the adrenal gland appears in the urine, but measurement of the urine cortisol in a 24-hour "urine free cortisol" sample provides an excellent assessment of the integrated production of cortisol. This is important, since cortisol is released episodically, and a random plasma cortisol can be in the normal range in the face of mild to moderate Cushing's disease. Urinary assays are frequently used to document aldosterone excess in primary aldosteronism and epinephrine excess in pheochromocytoma.

Free Hormone Levels

As discussed above in the section on plasma binding, many hormones circulate bound to plasma proteins, and in general it is the free hormone fraction that is biologically relevant. Thus, assessment of the free hormone levels is more critical than assessment of total hormone levels. A number of tests measuring free hormone levels are commercially available. These assays can utilize equilibrium dialysis, ultrafiltration, competitive binding, and other means. However, such tests are not commonly used. One commonly used test is the **free thyroxine index,** which is used to measure the free hormone indirectly by assessing the capacity of the plasma to take up T_4; this is inversely proportionate to the saturation of the binding proteins by the endogenous hormones and directly proportionate to the fraction of the total hormone that is free (See Chapter 4). Measurement of free calcium rather than total calcium ion concentration is also coming into increased usage. It is likely that in the next decade there will be greatly increased utilization of measurements of free hormone concentrations. As mentioned above, in some cases—cortisol for example—urinary levels of the hormone can provide an indirect assessment of the plasma free hormone concentration.

Immunoassays

Hormone immunoassays utilize antibodies with high affinity to the hormone, raised in animals. The antibodies can be polyclonal or monoclonal. If the human hormone to which the antibody is to be raised is different enough from that in the animal, the unmodified hormone can be used to raise the antibodies. However, for hormones that have conserved structures and high homology with the animal hormone—and especially with very small hormones such as steroids or releasing factors that are not very immunogenic—the hormone is used as a hapten and linked to a highly immunogenic molecule or in other ways incorporated into a larger molecule for raising antibodies.

Polyclonal antibodies are ordinarily obtained in the animal that produces a number of different antibodies. Rabbits, guinea pigs, sheep, and goats have been popular for this purpose. With polyclonal populations of antibodies, there can be many antibodies with extremely high affinities for the hormone that will therefore provide a high level of sensitivity. However, in the entire polyclonal population in the animal, antibodies to the antigen make up a very low proportion of the total antibody population.

Monoclonal antibodies are obtained by several means; they are commonly obtained by injecting the antigen into a mouse or rat or by incubating it with cells in vitro. The animal spleen or the cells incubated in vitro are then immortalized by fusing them to myeloma cells or transforming them with tumor viruses. This produces a number of clones of antibody-producing cells. The clones are then screened with the hormone antigen until a suitable antibody-producing clone is found. A major disadvantage of monoclonal antibodies is that many of the antibodies have a low affinity for the hormone, and considerable screening is necessary to obtain a high-affinity antibody. In addition, each antibody reacts with only one epitope on the antigen, and these antibodies are not as useful for traditional reagent-limiting assays. However, these antibodies are critical for the "sandwich assays" described below.

In practice, measurement of hormone levels by **radioimmunoassay** involves incubating the plasma or urine sample or an extract with the antibody and then measuring the levels of antigen-antibody complexes by several means. The classic radioimmunoassays utilize very high-affinity antibodies immobilized (at low concentrations to permit maximal sensitivity) on the surface of a test tube, polystyrene bead, or paramagnetic particle. The standard antigen that binds to the antibody is radiolabeled in such a way that the radiolabeling does not block its binding to the antibody. The unknown sample and the antibody are incubated, and the radiolabeled antigen is added either

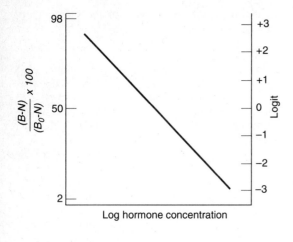

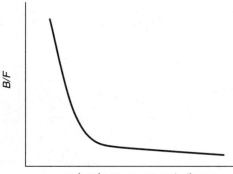

Figure 1–31. Standard curve of hormone radioimmunoassay. (B, counts bound; F, free counts; N, nonspecific count; B_o, maximum number of counts bound when only antibody and labeled hormone are incubated. (Reproduced, with permission, from Vaitukaitis J: In: *Hormone Assays in Endocrinology and Metabolism,* 2nd ed. Felig P et al (editors). McGraw-Hill, 1987.)

at zero time or later. A standard curve is prepared using the antibody and a known concentration of hormone. From this curve, the extent of inhibition by the added hormone of the binding of the labeled hormone is plotted, usually as the amount of bound label as a function of the log of the total antigen concentration, which ordinarily gives a sigmoid curve (Figure 1–31). Alternatively, a log-logit plot can be used to linearize the data (Figure 1–31). The level of hormone in the sample is obtained by relating the value to the standard curve.

Immunoassays traditionally utilized radiolabeled hormones as the antigen. Most commonly, this was radiolabeled iodine that can be obtained with a very high specific activity. However, the disadvantages with radioactivity in terms of shelf life and escalating expense for disposal have led to increasing use of nonisotopic means to perform immunoassays in which the antigen is linked to an enzyme, fluorescent label, chemiluminescent label, or latex particle that can be agglutinated with the antigen, or in some other way so that it can be detected. The enzyme-linked immunosorbent assays (**ELISAs**) that utilize antibody-coated microtiter plates and an enzyme-labeled reporter antibody are sometimes as sensitive as radioimmunoassays.

A recent modification of immunoassays is the **sandwich technique,** which utilizes two different monoclonal antibodies each of which recognizes a separate portion of the hormone. This aspect is a major limitation of the technique, as it is difficult to utilize it for small molecules for which separable reactive domains cannot be obtained. The assay is performed by using the first antibody, attached preferably in excess relative to the amount of hormone in the sample, to a solid support matrix to adsorb the hormone to be assayed. Following removal of the plasma and washing, the second (labeled) antibody is then incubated with the bound hormone, first antibody complex. The amount of binding of the second antibody is then proportionate to the concentration of hormone in the sample. Use of the two antibodies results in a markedly enhanced specificity with a great reduction in background levels, thus improving both the sensitivity and the specificity of the assay.

Nonimmunologic Assays

Nonimmunologic assays include chemical assays, which take advantage of chemically reactive groups in the molecule; bioassays, which assess the activity of the hormone incubated with cells or tissues in vitro or injected into an animal; and receptor-binding and other assays, which exploit the high affinity of the hormone for receptors or other molecules such as plasma-binding proteins. These assays are rarely used. The fact that assays which substitute for or complement immunoassays have not come into general use is an indication of the power of immunoassays. For example, immunoassays are in general superior to receptor assays because antibodies can be obtained that have much higher affinities for hormones than receptors. An example of a receptor assay is one using cultured cells of a thyroid tumor (FRTL-5 cells) that contain TSH receptors, to detect antibodies to these receptors that occur in Graves' disease.

Indirect Measurements of Hormonal Status

Measurement of hormonal status can be even more important than measuring the levels of the hormone and in many situations provides critical complementary information. Even when hormone levels are measured, it is common to obtain at least one index of the effects of the hormone in diagnosing an endocrine disease. The blood glucose level is generally more useful than the plasma insulin level in diagnosing and treating diabetes mellitus. Plasma insulin levels can be high in the face of frank hyperglycemia in non-insulin-dependent diabetes mellitus, and in insulin-dependent diabetes mellitus insulin levels are a much less reliable index of diabetic status than the blood glucose. Measurement of the serum calcium level is critical for evaluating hyperparathyroidism. Measurement of plasma renin levels is critical for evaluating primary aldosteronism. The most common cause of elevated aldosterone levels is dehydration, exercise, diuretic therapy, and other conditions that produce secondary aldosteronism; in these settings, the plasma renin levels tend to be high rather than low.

Provocative Tests

In many cases, the hormone level is best interpreted following some provocative challenge, though increasingly, more sophisticated ways to bypass the need for such tests are being developed. For example, with thyroid disease, provocative tests are rarely needed, whereas with adrenal insufficiency or glucocorticoid excess, heavy reliance is placed on such tests. With thyroid disease, the slow clearance of the hormone results in basal levels of hormone that are highly informative, whereas the pulsatile nature of cortisol release results in fluctuating plasma cortisol levels. This problem is bypassed in the evaluation of adrenal insufficiency by administering an analogue of ACTH that maximally stimulates the adrenal (Chapter 6).

The diagnosis of Cushing's disease reflects another different type of problem. Once cortisol hypersecretion has been documented, the cause must be identified. The clinician takes advantage of the fact that pituitary microadenomas are suppressed by the glucocorticoid dexamethasone to a greater extent than adrenal tumors or ectopic ACTH-producing tumors. Similarly, GnRH analogues (which stimulate FSH and LH release), TRH (which stimulates both prolactin and TSH release), and insulin hypoglycemia (which stimulates the release of ACTH and GH) can be used to evaluate pituitary reserve (Chapter 2). In evaluating primary aldosteronism, provocative stimuli (diuresis, posture, inhibition of converting enzyme) are sometimes used to increase renin release.

Imaging Studies

Imaging studies are gaining increasing usage in the diagnosis and follow-up of endocrine diseases. Magnetic resonance imaging (MRI) and computed tomography (CT) have been especially important in this regard. These procedures allow visualization of endocrine glands at a much greater resolution than in the past. This is true especially for the pituitary and adrenals. The endocrinologist can also resort to other sophisticated procedures that involve selective sampling from particular sites. For example, selective venous catheterization of the petrosal sinuses can be particularly useful in detecting ACTH hypersecretion in Cushing's disease, and selective sampling of the renal veins can be helpful in the diagnosis of renovascular hypertension.

Biopsy Procedures

Occasionally, biopsy is critical in the diagnosis of endocrine diseases. In general, this is used to define or diagnose neoplasia. Thus, the use of fine-needle biopsy of the thyroid gland (Chapter 4) has had a major impact on the evaluation of thyroid nodules.

Clinical Interpretation of Laboratory Tests

Many salient points in interpreting laboratory tests are mentioned in the preceding sections; these and other points can be summarized as follows:

(1) Any result must be interpreted in light of clinical knowledge of the patient using data from the history and physical examination.

(2) Basal levels of hormones or peripheral effects of hormones must be interpreted in light of the way the hormone is released and controlled.

(3) Hormone levels must in many cases be interpreted in conjunction with information from other tests that reflect the patient's status—the serum PTH level in light of the serum calcium; the serum aldosterone level in light of the plasma renin level; the serum gonadotropin levels in light of the estradiol or testosterone levels; etc.

(4) Occasionally, urinary measurements are superior to plasma tests for assaying the integrated release of hormone.

(5) The ranges of normal values can vary from one laboratory to the next. The proper normal value should be used.

(6) Laboratory tests must be interpreted with knowledge of the value of the test. The reported normal ranges for tests cannot be used as absolutes and must be interpreted in light of the clinical situation.

(7) Occasionally, laboratory test results are interfered with by extraneous or contaminating substances. For example, in illness, lipids in the plasma sometimes interfere with measurement of thyroid hormone-binding capacity. Heparin can release free fatty acids into the plasma, leading to displacement of T_3 and T_4 from plasma proteins and spurious readings for the binding capacity. In pregnancy, CG can cross-react in the TSH assay. Antibodies generated when hormones are used in therapy (insulin, GH, etc) can lead to great increases in the total hormone owing to their sequestration of the hormone.

(8) Provocative tests are sometimes necessary.

(9) Imaging studies may help with the diagnosis, especially with respect to the source of hormone hypersecretion.

IN SUMMARY, the diagnosis of endocrine disease requires the integration of a set of data, including that

Table 1–5. Hormones used in endocrinologic management for other than replacement.

Hormone or Analogue	Use	Evaluation
Glucocorticoid	Suppression of inflammatory or immune responses	
Growth hormone	Small stature	Wasting syndromes Osteoporosis
PTH		Osteoporosis
IGF-1		Osteoporosis Wasting syndromes
Octreotide acetate	Inhibition of GH release Diarrhea	Neuroendocrine tumors
Progesterone Estrogens Testosterone	Contraception Prostate cancer Breast cancer	
Prostaglandins	Induce labor, terminate pregnancy, maintain patent ductus arteriosus at surgery	

from the history and physical examination and from the laboratory tests. Given the sophistication of today's tests, diagnoses can usually be made with certainty. However, there are many situations where it is difficult to obtain a clear diagnosis; and the procedures to make a definitive diagnosis have more risk than the disease over a short period of time. In these cases a decision to follow the patient must be made. For example, this sometimes occurs with ACTH-dependent Cushing's syndrome, where the differentiation between an occult carcinoid tumor and a small pituitary adenoma as the source of ACTH hypersecretion would require risky invasive procedures. In today's environment of cost containment, the efficiency of diagnosis must be a priority. Today's tests allow for both efficiency of diagnosis at an unprecedented level and for spending at an unprecedented level as well. The physician can avoid unnecessary expenses through the use of good judgment.

TREATMENT OF ENDOCRINE DISEASES

A number of modalities are available for treating endocrine diseases. In many cases, hormone replacement will correct the problem. This is true, for instance, with hypothyroidism and adrenal insufficiency. In other cases, replacement is not so simple. For example, whereas recombinant GH is available to treat GH deficiency, it still must be injected and is expensive. A useful form of PTH is not available to treat hypoparathyroidism; effective PTH therapy will probably require a long-acting PTH preparation. In this case, the patient is treated in less than ideal fashion with high doses of vitamin D and calcium. In other cases, replacement is not optimally effective. Although insulin therapy will effectively control the hyperglycemia and prevent acidosis in most patients

with diabetes mellitus, the long-term complications of the disease still occur with most regimes utilized today. These result, at least in part, from the fact that we do not replace insulin in an ideal manner. By injecting it into the periphery, it is not delivered first to the liver, and the kinetics of the injected hormone bear only a distant relationship to those that occur with normal individuals.

For hormone excess states, treatment is ordinarily directed at the cause of the excess, usually a tumor or autoimmune condition. Tumors are removed when possible. We cannot yet treat the autoimmune condition that results in hyperthyroidism, so therapy is directed at reducing the secretions of the thyroid gland by pharmacologic blockade, radioiodine therapy, or surgical removal (Chapter 4). Hormone production may also be blocked by pharmacologic means in many other instances. For example, with prolactin hypersecretion, use of the dopamine receptor agonist bromocriptine is commonly preferred to surgical removal of a small prolactinoma. Octreotide acetate, a somatostatin analogue, is sometimes used to block GH hypersecretion. Inhibitors of steroid production such as ketoconazole are used to treat states in which the source of excess steroid production cannot be removed or found.

In many cases, it is necessary to control the sequelae of hormone excess by alternative means. Thus, beta-blockers are useful to control the sequelae of hyperthyroidism, alpha-blockers to control the sequelae of pheochromocytoma, mineralocorticoid antagonists to control blood pressure and hypokalemia in primary aldosteronism, and inhibitors of cholesterol biosynthesis to treat hypercholesterolemia, as with familial hypercholesterolemia. With hypertension, a number of modalities are available to block hormone systems. Examples are ACE inhibitors to block the

Table 1–6. Examples of hormone antagonists used in therapy.

Antagonist to	Use
Progesterone	Contraceptive, abortion
Glucocorticoid	Spontaneous Cushing's syndrome
Mineralocorticoid	Primary and secondary mineralocorticoid excess
Androgen	Prostate cancer
Estrogen	Breast cancer
GnRH	Prostate cancer
β-Adrenergic hormones	Hypertension, hyperthyroidism
Prostaglandin	Acute and chronic inflammatory disease

renin-angiotensin system, calcium channel blocker-sor beta-blockers to inhibit second messenger signaling, or diuretics to lower blood volume.

USES OF HORMONES IN THERAPY OF NONENDOCRINE DISEASE

The diverse actions of hormones have allowed them to be used extensively in therapy. Hormone an-tagonists are also used extensively. Hormone action is blocked in some cases with the use of enzyme inhibitors. Tables 1–5 and 1–6 present some examples of hormone and hormone analogue agonists (including eicosanoids) and antagonists, respectively, that are used in therapy. The most extensively used agonists are probably the glucocorticoids that are given to millions of Americans annually, largely to suppress inflammatory and immunologic responses. That the glucocorticoids would have this application came as a great surprise to the medical world, and Hench, Kendall, and Reichstein received the Nobel Prize for this discovery about 1 year after cortisone was first given to a patient with rheumatoid arthritis. Given this unexpected application, it is likely that uses of hormones for therapy will be greatly expanded over the next 20 years. For example, it is likely that the use of GH will be considerably expanded as information from more clinical trials becomes available. There is preliminary evidence that this hormone could blunt some of the nitrogen wasting that occurs with glucocorticoid therapy, and it might ameliorate the development of osteoporosis. Probably the most extensively used hormone antagonists are the beta-adrenergic blocking agents.

REFERENCES

General
Aaronson SA: Growth factors and cancer. Science 1991;254:1146.
Sporn MB, Roberts AB: Autocrine secretion—10 years later. Ann Intern Med 1992;117:408.
Stryer L: *Biochemistry,* 3rd ed. Freeman, 1988.

Recombinant DNA & Gene Expression
Alberts B et al: *Molecular Biology of the Cell,* 2nd ed. Garland, 1989.
Aritonarakis SE: Diagnosis of genetic disorders at the DNA level. N Engl J Med 1989;320:153.
Ausubel FM: *Current Protocols in Molecular Biology.* Greene Associates and Wiley Interscience, 1992.
Brown MS, Goldstein JL: A receptor-mediated pathway for cholesterol homeostasis. Science 1986;232:34.
Chisaka O, Capecchi MR: Regionally restricted developmental deficits resulting from targeted disruption of the mouse homeobox gene *hox*-1.5. Nature 1991;350:473.
Laybourn PJ, Kadonaga JT: Role of nucleosomal cores and histone H1 in regulation of transcription by RNA polymerase II. Science 1991;254:238.
Loh EY et al: Polymerase chain reaction with single-sided specificity: Analysis of T cell receptor delta chain. Science 1989.:243:217.
Mulligan RC: The basic science of gene therapy. Science 1993;260:926.
Nanes MS, Catherwood BD: The genetics of multiple endocrine neoplasia syndromes. Annu Rev Med 1992;43:253.

Ptashne M, Gann AAA: Activators and targets. Nature 1990;346:329.
Sawadogo M, Sentenac A: RNA polymerase B (II) and general transcription factors. Annu Rev Biochem 1990;59:711.
Sharp PA: TATA-binding protein is a classless factor. Cell 1992;68:819.
Ueno A et al: Netropsin specifically enhances RNA polymerase II termination at terminator sites in vitro. Proc Natl Acad Sci U S A 1992;89:3676.
Wahle E, Keller W: The biochemistry of 3′-end cleavage and polyadenylation of messenger RNA precursors. Annu Rev Biochem 1992;61:419.
Watson JD et al: *Molecular Biology of the Gene,* 4th ed. Benjamin/Cummings, 1987.

Evolution of the Endocrine System
Baxter JD, Rousseau GG: Glucocorticoids and the metabolic code. In: *Glucocorticoid Hormone Action.* Baxter JD, Rousseau GG (editors). Springer-Verlag, 1979.
Howard JC: Molecular evolution: How old is a polymorphism? Nature 1988;332:588.
Rotter JI, Diamond JM: What maintains the frequencies of human genetic diseases? Nature 1987;329:289.
Tomkins GM: The metabolic code. Science 1975;189:760.

Hormone Synthesis, Transport & Metabolism & Regulation of the Endocrine System
Alexander NN: Oxidative cleavage of tryptophanyl peptide bonds during chemical- and peroxidase-catalyzed iodinations. J Biol Chem 1974;249:1946.

Episkopou V et al: Disruption of the transthyretin gene results in mice with depressed levels of plasma retinol and thyroid hormone. Proc Natl Acad Sci U S A 1993;90:2375.

Gill G: Biosynthesis, secretion, and metabolism of hormones. In: *Endocrinology and Metabolism,* 2nd ed. Felig P, et al (editors). McGraw-Hill, 1987.

Hammond GL: Molecular properties of corticosteroid binding globulin and the sex-steroid binding proteins. Endocr Rev 1990;11:65.

Lieberman S, Prasad VVK: Heterodox notions on pathways of steroidogenesis. Endocr Rev 1990;11:469.

Lingappa VR: Intracellular traffic of newly synthesized proteins; current understanding and future prospects. J Clin Invest 1989;83:739.

Mendel CM et al: Uptake of thyroxine by the perfused rat liver: Implications for the free hormone hypothesis. Am J Physiol 1988;255:E110.

Miller WL: Molecular biology of steroid hormone synthesis. Endocr Rev 1988;9:295.

Reaves BJ, Dannies PS: Is a sorting signal necessary to package proteins into secretory granules? Mol Cell Endocrinol 1991;79:C141.

Rothman JE, Ora L: Molecular dissection of the secretory pathway. Nature 1992;355:409.

Stewart PM et al: Localization of renal 11β-dehydrogenase by in situ hybridization: autocrine not paracrine protector of the mineralocorticoid receptor. Endocrinology 1991;128:2129.

Zawalich WS, Rasmussen H: Control of insulin secretion: a model involving Ca^{++}, cAMP and diacylglycerol. Mol Cell Endocrinol 1990;70:119.

Neuroendocrinology

Bloom FE: Neurotransmitters: Past, present, and future directions. FASEB J 1988;2:32.

Martin JB, Reichlin S: *Clinical Neuroendocrinology,* 2nd ed. Davis, 1987.

Veldhuis JD (editor): Neuroendocrinology I. Med Clin North Am 1992;21:767; Neuroendocrinology II. Med Clin North Am 1993;22:1.

Mechanisms of Hormone Action

Archer TK et al: Transcription factor access is mediated by accurately positioned nucleosomes on the mouse mammary tumor virus promoter. Mol Cell Biol 1991; 11:688.

Beato M: Gene regulation by steroid hormones. Cell 1989;56:335.

Berridge MJ: Inositol trisphosphate and calcium signalling. Nature 1993;361:315.

Bodine PV, Litwack G: The glucocorticoid receptor and its endogenous regulators. Receptor 1990–91;1:83.

Bortner DM, Langer SJ, Ostrowski MC: Non-nuclear oncogenes and the regulation of gene expression in transformed cells. Critic Rev Oncogen 1993;4:137.

Birnbaumer L: Receptor-to-effector signaling through G proteins: Roles for βγ dimers as well as α subunits. Cell 1992;71:1069.

Davis TN: What's new with calcium? Cell 1992;71:557.

de Vos AM et al: Human growth hormone and extracellular domain of its receptor: Crystal structure of the complex. Science 1992;255:306.

Drouin J et al: Homodimer formation is rate limiting for high affinity DNA binding by glucocorticoid receptor. Mol Endocrinol 1992;6:1299.

Evans RM: The steroid and thyroid hormone receptor superfamily. Science 1988;240:889.

Fischer EH et al: Protein tyrosine phosphatases: A diverse family of intracellular and transmembrane enzymes. Science 1991;253:401.

Green S, Chambon P: Nuclear receptors enhance our understanding of transcription regulation. Trends Genet 1988;4:309.

Hadcock JR, Malbon CC: Agonist regulation of gene expression of adrenergic receptors and G proteins J Neurochem 1993;60:1.

Haeiwara M et al: Transcriptional attenuation following cAMP induction requires PP-1 mediated dephosphorylation of CREB. Cell 1992;70:105.

Hunter T, Karin M: The regulation of transcription by phosphorylation. Cell 1992;70:375.

Kelly PA et. al.: The prolactin/growth hormone receptor family. Endocr Rev 1991;12:235.

Kerr LD, Inoue J, Verma IM: Signal transduction: the nuclear target. Curr Opin Cell Biol 1992;4:496.

Koch CA et al: SH2 and SH3 domains: Elements that control interactions of cytoplasmic signalling proteins. Science 1991;252:668.

Koesling D et al: Sequence homologies between guanylyl cyclases and structural analogies to other signal-transducing proteins. FEBS Letters 1991;280:301.

Logan MA: Thyroid hormone receptors: Multiple forms, multiple possibilities. Endocr Rev 1993;14:184.

McCormick F: How receptors turn ras on. Nature 1993;363:15.

Metz R, Ziff E: cAMP stimulates the C/EBP-related transcription factor rNFIL-6 to trans-locate to the nucleus and induce c-fos transcription. Genes Develop 1991;5:1754.

Nishizuka Y: Intracellular signaling by hydrolysis of phospholipids and activation of protein kinase C. Science 1992;258:607.

Pincus MR et al: Pathways for activation of the ras-oncogene-encoded P21 protein. Ann Clin Lab Sci 1992;22:323.

Pratt WB et al: Interaction of hsp90 with steroid receptors: organizing some diverse observations and presenting the newest concepts. Mol Cell Endocrinol 1990;74:C69.

Smith D, Toft DO: Steroid receptors and their associated proteins. Mol Endocrinol 1993;7:4.

Taylor SI et al: Mutations in the insulin receptor gene. Endocr Rev 1992;13:566.

Immunoendocrinology

Foxwell BM, Barrett K, Feldman M: Cytokine receptors: structure and signal transduction. Clin Exp Immunol 1992;90:161.

Logan A: Endocrinology and the immune system. Lancet 1992;340:420.

Rees RC: Cytokines as biological response modifier. J Clin Path 1992;45:93.

Hormone Assays

Collins WP (editor): *Complementary Immunoassays.* Wiley, 1988.

Ekins R, Chu F, Biggart E: Fluorescence spectroscopy and its application to a new generation of high sensitivity, multi-microspot, multianalyte immunoassay. Clin Chim Acta 1990;194:91.

Ekins R: Measurement of free hormones in blood. Endocr Rev 1990;11:5.

Gosling JP: A decade of development in immunoassay methodology. Clin Chem 1990;36:1408.

Makin HLJ, Newton R (editors): *High Performance Liquid Chromatography in Endocrinology. Monographs on Endocrinology,* vol 30. Springer-Verlag, 1988.

Moore GP: Genetically engineered antibodies. Clin Chem 1989;35:1849.

Ngo TT (editor): *Nonisotopic Immunoassay.* Plenum, 1988.

Sugii A et al: One-step synthesis of a cortisol derivative for radioiodination and application of the ^{125}I-labeled cortisol to radioimmunoassay. Chem Pharm Bull (Tokyo) 1987;35:5000.

Van Dyke K, Van Dyke R (editors): *Luminescence Immunoassay and Molecular Applications.* CRC Press, 1990.

Vaitukaitis JL: Hormone assays. In: *Endocrinology and Metabolism,* 2nd ed. Felig P et al (editors). McGraw-Hill, 1987.

2

Hypothalamus and Pituitary

J. Blake Tyrrell, MD, James W. Findling, MD & David C. Aron, MD

The hypothalamus and pituitary gland form a unit which exerts control over the function of several endocrine glands—thyroid, adrenals, and gonads—as well as a wide range of physiologic activities. This unit constitutes a paradigm of neuroendocrinology—brain-endocrine interactions. The actions and interactions of the endocrine and nervous systems whereby the nervous system regulates the endocrine system and endocrine activity modulates the activity of the central nervous system constitute the major regulatory mechanisms for virtually all physiologic activities. The immune system also interacts with both endocrine and nervous systems (see Chapter 1). These neuroendocrine interactions are also important in disease pathophysiology. This chapter will review the normal functions of the pituitary gland, the neuroendocrine control mechanisms of the hypothalamus and their disorders.

Nerve cells and endocrine gland cells which are both involved in cell-to-cell communication share certain characteristic features—secretion of chemical messengers (neurotransmitters or hormones) and electrical activity. A single chemical messenger—peptide or amine—can be secreted by neurons as a neurotransmitter or neural hormone and by endocrine gland cells as a classic hormone. Examples of such multifunctional chemical messengers are shown in Table 2–1. The cell-to-cell communication may occur by four mechanisms: (1) neural communication via synaptic junctions; (2) endocrine communication via circulating hormones; (3) paracrine communication via messengers that diffuse in the interstitial fluid to adjacent target cells (without entering the bloodstream); and (4) autocrine communication via messengers that diffuse in the interstitial fluid to where the messengers act on the cells that secreted them (Figure 2–1). The two major mechanisms of neural regulation of endocrine function are direct innervation and neurosecretion (neural secretion of hormones). The adrenal medulla, kidney, parathyroid gland, and pancreatic islets are endocrine tissues which receive direct autonomic innervation (see Chapters 5, 7, 8, and 15). An example of neurosecretory regulation is the hormonal secretion of certain hypothalamic nuclei into the portal hypophysial vessels, which regulate the hormone-secreting cells of the anterior lobe of the pituitary. Another example of

neurosecretory regulation is the posterior lobe of the pituitary gland, which is made up of the endings of neurons whose cell bodies reside in hypothalamic nuclei. These neurons secrete vasopressin and oxytocin into the general circulation.

Anatomy & Embryology

The anatomic relationships between the pituitary and the main nuclei of the hypothalamus are shown in Figure 2–2. The posterior lobe of the pituitary (neurohypophysis) is of neural origin, arising embryologically as an evagination of the ventral hypothalamus and the third ventricle. The neurohypophysis consists of the axons and nerve endings of neurons whose cell bodies reside in the supraoptic and paraventricular nuclei of the hypothalamus and supporting tissues. This hypothalamo-neurohypophysial nerve

---

ACRONYMS USED IN THIS CHAPTER

ACTH	Adrenocorticotropic hormone
ADH	Antidiuretic hormone (vasopressin)
cAMP	Cyclic adenosine monophosphate
CLIP	Corticotropin-like intermediate lobe peptide
DI	Diabetes insipidus
FSH	Folllicle-stimulating hormone
GABA	Gamma-aminobutyric acid
GAP	GnRH-associated peptide
GH	Growth hormone (somatotropin)
GnRH	Gonadotropin-releasing hormone
GRH	Growth hormone-releasing hormone
hGH	Human growth hormone
hMG	Human menopausal gonadotropin
LH	Luteinizing hormone
ß-LPH	ß-Lipotropin
MEN	Multiple endocrine neoplasia
MRI	Magnetic resonance imaging
MSH	Melanocyte-stimulating hormone
PIH	Prolactin-inhibiting hormone
PRH	Prolactin-releasing hormone
PRL	Prolactin
SHBG	Sex hormone-binding globulin
SIADH	Syndrome of inappropriate secretion of antidiuretic hormone
TRH	Thyrotropin-releasing hormone
TSH	Thyroid-stimulating hormone (thyrotropin)
VIP	Vasoactive intestinal polypeptide

Table 2–1. Neuroendocrine messengers: Substances that function as neurotransmitters, neural hormones, and classic hormones.

	Neurotransmitter (Present in Nerve Endings)	Hormone Secreted by Neurons	Hormone Secreted by Endocrine Cells
Dopamine	+	+	+
Norepinephrine	+	+	+
Epinephrine	+		+
Somatostatin	+	+	+
Gonadotropin-releasing hormone (GnRH)	+	+	+
Thyrotropin-releasing hormone (TRH)	+	+	
Oxytocin	+	+	+
Vasopressin	+	+	+
Vasoactive intestinal polypeptide (VIP)	+	+	
Cholecystokinin (CCK)	+		+
Glucagon	+		+
Enkephalins	+		+
Pro-opiomelano-cortin derivatives	+		+
Other anterior pituitary hormones	+		+

tract contains approximately 100,000 nerve fibers. Repeated swellings along the nerve fibers ranging in thickness from 1 to 50 μm constitute the nerve terminals.

The human fetal anterior pituitary anlage is initially recognizable at 4–5 weeks of gestation, and rapid cytologic differentiation leads to a mature hypothalamic-pituitary unit at 20 weeks. The anterior pituitary (adenohypophysis) originates from Rathke's pouch, an ectodermal evagination of the oropharynx, and migrates to join the neurohypophysis. The portion of Rathke's pouch in contact with the neurohypophysis develops less extensively and forms the intermediate lobe. This lobe remains intact in some species, but in humans its cells become interspersed with those of the anterior lobe and develop the capacity to synthesize and secrete pro-opiomelanocortin and adrenocorticotropic hormone (ACTH). Remnants of Rathke's pouch may persist at the boundary of the neurohypophysis, resulting in small colloid cysts. In addition, cells may persist in the lower portion of Rathke's pouch beneath the sphenoid bone, the pharyngeal pituitary. These cells have the potential to secrete hormones and have been reported to undergo adenomatous change.

The pituitary gland itself lies at the base of the skull in a portion of the sphenoid bone called the sella turcica ("Turkish saddle"). The anterior portion, the tuberculum sellae, is flanked by posterior projections of the sphenoid wings, the anterior clinoid processes; the dorsum sellae forms the posterior wall, and its upper corners project into the posterior clinoid processes. The gland is surrounded by dura, and the roof is formed by a reflection of the dura attached to the clinoid processes, the diaphragma sellae. In healthy individuals, the arachnoid membrane and, therefore, cerebrospinal fluid are prevented from entering the sella turcica by the diaphragma sellae. The pituitary stalk and its blood vessels pass through an opening in this diaphragm. The lateral walls of the gland are in direct apposition to the cavernous sinuses and separated from them by dural membranes. The optic chiasm lies 5–10 mm above the diaphragma sellae and anterior to the stalk (Figure 2–3).

The size of the pituitary gland, of which the anterior lobe constitutes two-thirds, varies considerably.

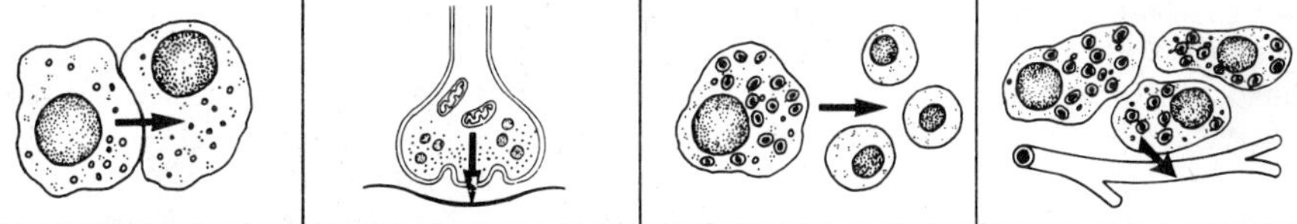

	GAP JUNCTIONS	SYNAPTIC	PARACRINE	ENDOCRINE
Message transmission	Directly from cell to cell	Across synaptic cleft	By diffusion in interstitial fluid	By circulating body fluids
Local or general	Local	Local	Locally diffuse	General
Specificity depends on	Anatomic location	Anatomic location and receptors	Receptors	Receptors

Figure 2–1. Intercellular communication by chemical mediators.

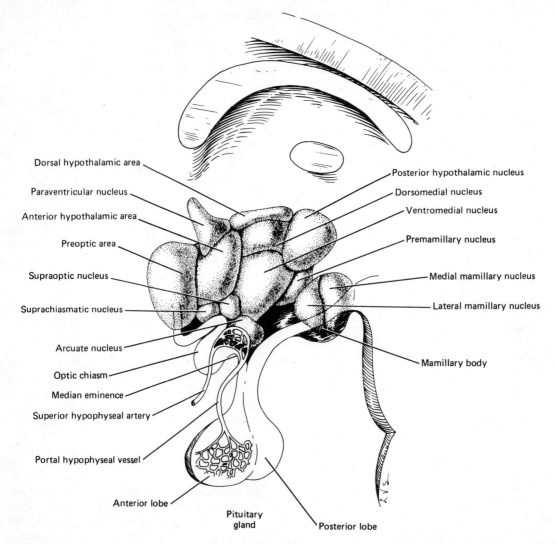

Dorsal hypothalamic area
Paraventricular nucleus
Anterior hypothalamic area
Preoptic area
Supraoptic nucleus
Suprachiasmatic nucleus
Arcuate nucleus
Optic chiasm
Median eminence
Superior hypophyseal artery
Portal hypophyseal vessel
Anterior lobe
Pituitary gland
Posterior lobe
Posterior hypothalamic nucleus
Dorsomedial nucleus
Ventromedial nucleus
Premamillary nucleus
Medial mamillary nucleus
Lateral mamillary nucleus
Mamillary body

Figure 2–2. The human hypothalamus, with a superimposed diagrammatic representation of the portal hypophysial vessels. (Reproduced, with permission, from Ganong WF: *Review of Medical Physiology,* 15th ed. Appleton & Lange, 1993.)

It measures approximately 15 × 10 × 6 mm and weighs 500–900 mg; it may double in size during pregnancy. The sella turcica tends to conform to the shape and size of the gland, and for that reason there is considerable variability in its contour.

Blood Supply

The anterior pituitary is the most richly vascularized of all mammalian tissues, receiving 0.8 mL/g/min from a portal circulation connecting the median eminence of the hypothalamus and the anterior pituitary. Arterial blood is supplied from the internal carotid arteries via the superior, middle, and inferior hypophysial arteries. The superior hypophysial arteries form a capillary network in the median eminence of the hypothalamus that recombines in long portal

veins draining down the pituitary stalk to the anterior lobe, where they break up into another capillary network and re-form into venous channels. The pituitary stalk and the posterior pituitary are supplied directly from branches of the middle and inferior hypophysial arteries (Figures 2–2 and 2–3).

Venous drainage of the pituitary, the route through which anterior pituitary hormones reach the systemic circulation, is variable, but venous channels eventually drain via the cavernous sinus posteriorly into the superior and inferior petrosal sinuses to the jugular bulb and vein (Figure 2–4). The axons of the neurohypophysis terminate on capillaries that drain via the posterior lobe veins and the cavernous sinuses to the general circulation. The hypophysial-portal system of capillaries allows control of anterior pituitary func-

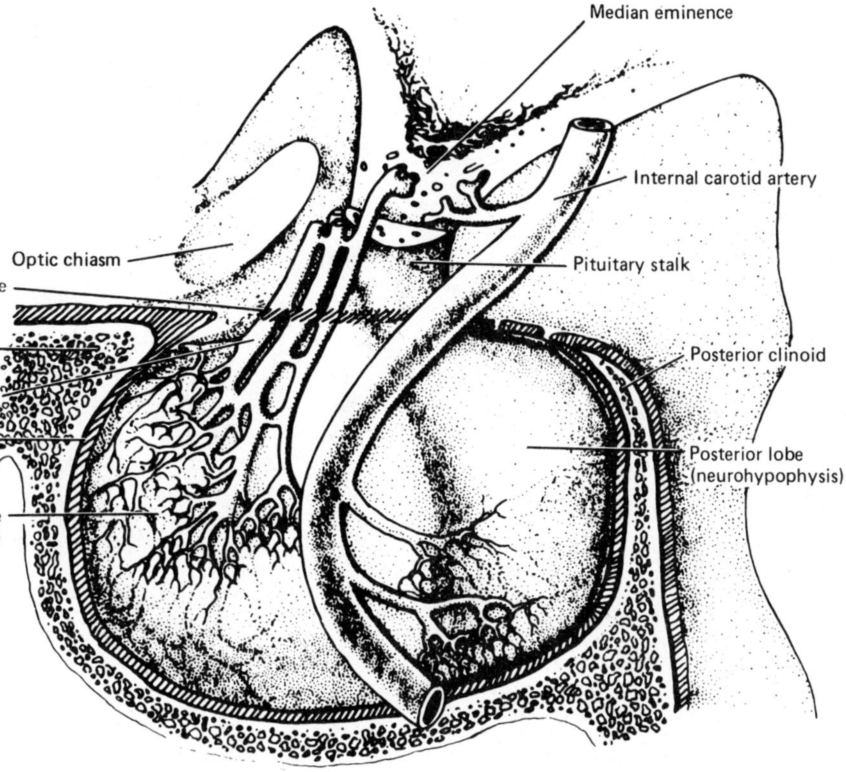

Figure 2–3. Anatomic relationships and blood supply of the pituitary gland. (Reproduced, with permission, from Frohman LA: Diseases of the anterior pituitary. In: *Endocrinology and Metabolism.* Felig P et al [editors]. McGraw-Hill, 1981.)

tion by the hypothalamic hypophyseotropic hormones secreted into the portal hypophysial vessels. This provides a short, direct connection to the anterior pituitary from the ventral hypothalamus and the median eminence (Figure 2–5). There may also be retrograde blood flow between the pituitary and hypothalamus, providing a possible means of direct feedback between pituitary hormones and their neuroendocrine control.

Histology

Anterior pituitary cells were originally classified as acidophils, basophils, and chromophobe cells. Immunocytochemical and electron microscopic techniques now permit classification of cells by their specific secretory products: somatotrophs (growth hormone [GH]-secreting cells), lactotrophs (prolactin [PRL]-secreting cells), thyrotrophs (cells secreting thyroid-stimulating hormone [thyrotropin; TSH]), corticotrophs (cells secreting adrenocorticotropic hormone [corticotropin; ACTH] and related peptides), and gonadotrophs (luteinizing hormone [LH]- and follicle-stimulating hormone [FSH]-secreting cells).

Development of the capacity for expression of hormone secretion depends upon a variety of factors including the transcription factor Pit-1. Abnormalities of this factor have been associated with the development of hypopituitarism.

A. Somatotrophs: The GH-secreting cells are acidophilic in standard hematoxylin and eosin preparations and are usually located in the lateral portions of the anterior lobe. Granule size by electron microscopy is 150–600 nm in diameter. These cells account for about 50% of the adenohypophysial cells.

B. Lactotrophs: The PRL-secreting cell is a second but distinct acidophil-staining cell randomly distributed in the anterior pituitary. These cells account for 10–25% of anterior pituitary cells. Granule size averages approximately 550 nm on electron microscopy. There are two types of lactotrophs: sparsely granulated and densely granulated. These cells proliferate during pregnancy as a result of elevated estrogen levels and account for the twofold increase in gland size.

C. Thyrotrophs: These TSH-secreting cells, because of their glycoprotein product, are basophilic

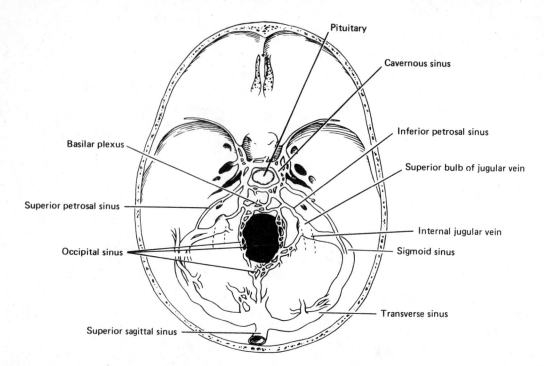

Figure 2–4. Venous drainage of the pituitary gland—the route by which adenohypophysial hormones reach the systemic circulation. (Reproduced, with permission, from Findling JW et al: Selective venous sampling for ACTH in Cushing's syndrome: Differentiation between Cushing's disease and the ectopic ACTH syndrome. Ann Intern Med 1981;94:647.)

and also show a positive reaction with periodic acid-Schiff (PAS) stain. Thyrotrophs are the least common pituitary cell type, making up less than 10% of adenohypophysial cells. The thyrotroph granules are small (50–100 nm); these cells are usually located in the anteromedial and anterolateral portions of the gland. During states of primary thyroid failure, the cells demonstrate marked hypertrophy, increasing overall gland size.

D. Corticotrophs: ACTH and its related peptides (see below) are secreted by basophilic cells that are embryologically of intermediate lobe origin and usually located in the anteromedial portion of the gland. Corticotrophs represent 15–20% of adenohypophysial cells. Electron microscopy shows that these secretory granules are about 360 nm in diameter. In states of glucocorticoid excess, corticotrophs undergo degranulation and a microtubular hyalinization known as Crooke's hyaline degeneration.

E. Gonadotrophs: LH and FSH originate from basophil-staining cells, whose secretory granules are about 200 nm in diameter. These cells constitute 10–15% of anterior pituitary cells, and they are located throughout the entire anterior lobe. They become hypertrophied and cause the gland to enlarge during states of primary gonadal failure such as menopause, Klinefelter's syndrome, and Turner's syndrome.

F. Other Cell Types: Despite immunocytochemical staining with antibodies directed against all of the known anterior pituitary hormones, some cells remain unstained. These are chromophobes by conventional staining methods, but electron microscopy has identified secretory granules in many of them. These cells have been called null cells; they may give rise to nonfunctioning adenomas. It is not certain whether they represent undifferentiated primitive secretory cells or whether they produce as yet unidentified hormones, such as adrenal androgen-stimulating hormone, ovarian growth factor, or aldosterone-stimulating factor. Mammosomatotrophs contain both GH and PRL; these bihormonal cells are most often seen in pituitary tumors. Human chorionic gonadotropin is also secreted by the anterior pituitary gland, but its cell of origin and physiologic significance are uncertain.

HYPOTHALAMIC HORMONES

The hypothalamic hormones can be divided into those secreted into hypophysial portal blood vessels and those secreted by the neurohypophysis directly into the general circulation. The eight known hypothalamic hormones are listed with their structures

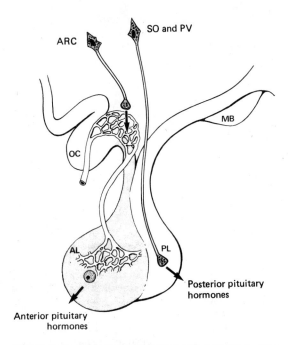

Figure 2–5. Secretion of hypothalamic hormones. The hormones of the posterior lobe (PL) are released into the general circulation from the endings of supraoptic and paraventricular neurons, whereas hypophyseotropic hormones are secreted into the portal hypophysial circulation from the endings of arcuate and other hypothalamic neurons. (AL, anterior lobe; MB, mamillary bodies; OC, optic chiasm.)

in Table 2–2. Their cellular location in the hypothalamus is illustrated in Figure 2–6.

Hypophyseotropic Hormones

The hypophyseotropic hormones which regulate the secretion of anterior pituitary hormones include growth hormone releasing hormone (GRH), somatostatin, dopamine, thyrotropin releasing hormone (TRH), corticotropin-releasing hormone (CRH), and gonadotropin-releasing hormone (GnRH). Most of the anterior pituitary hormones are controlled by stimulatory hormones, but growth hormone and especially prolactin are also regulated by inhibitory hormones. Some hypophyseotropic hormones are multifunctional. The hormones of the hypothalamus are secreted episodically and not continuously, and in some cases—eg, CRH and TRH—there is an underlying circadian rhythm.

A. GRH: GRH stimulates growth hormone (GH) secretion by somatotrophs. GRH-secreting neurons are located in the arcuate nuclei (Figures 2–2 and 2–6), and axons terminate in the external layer of the median eminence. Two peptides (of 40 and 44 amino acids) with potent GH-releasing activity were isolated from separate pancreatic tumors in patients with clinical manifestations of growth hormone excess (acromegaly) associated with somatotroph hyperplasia (see below). GRH is synthesized from a larger precursor of 107 or 108 amino acids. These precursors differ by the presence or absence of a serine at position 103. The function of other secretory products derived from this precursor is unknown. Full bi-

Table 2–2. Hypothalamic hormones.

Hormone	Structure
Posterior pituitary hormones	
Arginine vasopressin	$\overset{\lceil S \text{———} S \rceil}{\text{Cys-Tyr-Phe-Gln-Asn-Cys-Pro-Arg-Gly-NH}_2}$
Oxytocin	$\overset{\lceil S \text{———} S \rceil}{\text{Cys-Tyr-Ile-Gln-Asn-Cys-Pro-Leu-Gly-NH}_2}$
Hypophyseotropic hormones	
Thyrotropin-releasing hormone (TRH)	(pyro)Glu-His-Pro-NH$_2$
Gonadotropin-releasing hormone (GnRH)	(pyro)Glu-His-Trp-Ser-Tyr-Gly-Leu-Arg-Pro-Gly-NH$_2$
Somatostatin[1]	$\overset{\lceil S \text{————} S \rceil}{\text{Ala-Gly-Cys-Lys-Asn-Phe-Phe-Trp-Lys-Thr-Phe-Thr-Ser-Cys}}$
Growth hormone–releasing hormone (GRH)	Tyr-Ala-Asp-Ala-Ile-Phe-Thr-Asn-Ser-Tyr-Arg-Lys-Val-Leu-Gly-Gln-Leu-Ser-Ala-Arg-Lys-Leu-Leu-Gln-Asp-Ile-Met-Ser-Arg-Gln-Gln-Gly-Glu-Ser-Asn-Gln-Glu-Arg-Gly-Ala-Arg-Ala-Arg-Leu-NH$_2$
Prolactin-inhibiting hormone (PIH, dopamine)	HO—⟨benzene ring⟩—CH$_2$CH$_2$NH$_2$, with HO groups
Corticotropin-releasing hormone (CRH)	Ser-Gln-Glu-Pro-Pro-Ile-Ser-Leu-Asp-Leu-Thr-Phe-His-Leu-Leu-Arg-Glu-Val-Leu-Glu-Met-Thr-Lys-Ala-Asp-Gln-Leu-Ala-Gln-Gln-Ala-His-Ser-Asn-Arg-Lys-Leu-Leu-Asp-Ile-Ala-NH$_2$

[1] In addition to the tetradecapeptide shown here (somatostatin 14), an N-terminal extended molecule (somatostatin 28) and a 12-amino acid form (Somatostatin 28 [1-12]) are found in most tissues.

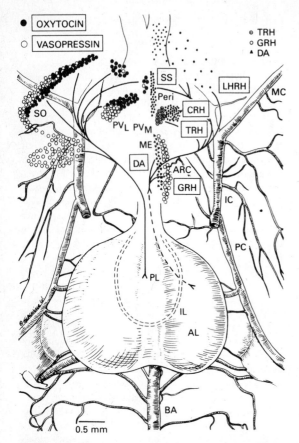

Figure 2–6. Location of cell bodies of hypophyseotropic hormone-secreting neurons projected on a ventral view of the hypothalamus and pituitary of the rat. (AL, anterior lobe; ARC, arcuate nucleus; BA, basilar artery; IC, internal carotid; IL, intermediate lobe; MC, middle cerebral; ME, median eminence; PC, posterior cerebral; peri, periventricular nucleus; PL, posterior lobe; PVL and PVM, lateral and medial portions of paraventricular nucleus; SO, supraoptic nucleus.) The names of the hormones are enclosed in the boxes. (Courtesy of LW Swanson and ET Cunningham Jr.)

ologic activity of these releasing factors appears to reside in the 1–29 amino acid sequence of the N-terminal portion of the molecule. Human GRH is strikingly similar to many gastrointestinal peptides, including secretin, gastrin, vasoactive intestinal polypeptide (VIP), and gastric inhibitory peptide. Like CRH, GRH has a rather long half-life (50 minutes).

B. Somatostatin: Somatostatin inhibits the secretion of GH and TSH. Somatostatin-secreting cells are located in the periventricular region immediately above the optic chiasm (Figures 2–2 and 2–6) with nerve endings found diffusely in the external layer of the median eminence.

Somatostatin, a tetradecapeptide, has been found not only in the hypothalamus but also in the D cells of the pancreatic islets, the gastrointestinal mucosa,

and the C-cells (parafollicular cells) of the thyroid. The somatostatin precursor has 116 amino acids. Processing of the carboxyl terminal region of preprosomatostatin results in the generation of the tetradecapeptide somatostatin 14 and an N-terminal extended form containing 28 amino acid residues (somatostatin 28). Somatostatin 14 is the major species in the hypothalamus, while somatostatin 28 is found in the gut. Processing of somatostatin 28 produces somatostatin 14 and a duodecapeptide from the N-terminal extension (somatostatin 28 [1–12]). The function of this latter peptide is unknown. In addition to its profound inhibitory effect on GH secretion, somatostatin also has important inhibitory influences on many other hormones, including insulin, glucagon, gastrin, secretin, and VIP. This inhibitory hypothalamic peptide plays a role in the physiologic secretion of TSH by augmenting the direct inhibitory effect of thyroid hormone on the thyrotrophs; administration of anti-somatostatin antibodies results in a rise in circulating TSH level.

C. Dopamine: Dopamine, the primary prolactin-inhibitory hormone (PIH), is found in the portal circulation and binds to dopamine receptors in lactotrophs. The hypothalamic control of PRL secretion, unlike that of the other pituitary hormones, is predominantly inhibitory. Thus, disruption of the hypothalamic-pituitary connection by stalk section, hypothalamic lesions, or pituitary autotransplantation increases PRL secretion. Dopamine-secreting neurons (tuberoinfundibular dopaminergic system) are located in the arcuate nuclei and their axons terminate in the external layer of the median eminence, primarily in the same area as the GnRH endings (laterally) and to a lesser extent medially (Figures 2–2 and 2–6). The neurotransmitter gamma-aminobutyric acid (GABA) and cholinergic pathways also appear to inhibit PRL release.

D. Prolactin-Releasing Factors: The best-studied PRL-releasing factor is thyrotropin-releasing hormone (see below). However, there are several discordant responses, suggesting that TRH is not the only PRL-releasing factor. The PRL increase associated with sleep, during stress, and after nipple stimulation or suckling is not accompanied by an increase in TRH or TSH. Another hypothalamic peptide, VIP, stimulates PRL release in humans. Serotonergic pathways may also stimulate PRL secretion, as demonstrated by the increased PRL secretion after the administration of serotonin precursors and by the reduction of secretion following treatment with serotonin antagonists.

E. Thyrotropin-Releasing Hormone (TRH): TRH, a tripeptide, is the major hypothalamic factor in TSH secretion. Human TRH is synthesized from a large precursor of 242 amino acids that contains six copies of TRH. TRH-secreting neurons are located in the medial portions of the paraventricular nuclei (Figures 2–2 and 2–6), and their axons terminate in the medial portion of the external layer of the median eminence. TRH has been found in the hypothalamus as well as the portal blood; perfusion of pituitary stalk vessels with TRH evokes TSH release, and interruption of the hypothalamic-pituitary portal vessels decreases TSH secretion.

F. Corticotropin-Releasing Hormone (CRH): CRH, a 41-amino-acid peptide, stimulates the secretion of adrenocorticotropic hormone (ACTH) and other products of its precursor molecule, pro-opiomelanocortin. The structure of human CRH is identical to that of rat CRH. CRH is synthesized from a precursor of 196 amino acids. CRH has a long plasma half-life (approximately 60 minutes), and both ADH and angiotensin II potentiate CRH-mediated secretion of ACTH. In contrast, oxytocin inhibits CRH-mediated ACTH secretion. CRH-secreting neurons are found in the anterior portion of the paraventricular nuclei just lateral to the TRH-secreting neurons (Figures 2–2 and 2–6); their nerve endings are found in all parts of the external layer of the median eminence. CRH is also secreted from human placenta. The level of this hormone increases significantly during late pregnancy and delivery; however, its function is unknown.

G. Gonadotropin-Releasing Hormone (GnRH): The secretion of Luteinizing Hormone (LH) and follicle-stimulating hormone (FSH) is controlled by a single stimulatory hypothalamic hormone, gonadotropin-releasing hormone (GnRH). GnRH is a linear decapeptide that stimulates only LH and FSH; it has no effect on other pituitary hormones except in some patients with acromegaly and Cushing's disease (see below). The precursor of GnRH—pro-GnRH—contains 92 amino acids. ProGnRH also contains the sequence of a 56-amino-acid polypeptide called GnRH-associated peptide (GAP). This secretory product exhibits prolactin-inhibiting activity, but its physiologic role is unknown. GnRH-secreting neurons are located primarily in the in preoptic area of the anterior hypothalamus and their nerve terminal are found in the lateral portions of the external layer of the median eminence adjacent to the pituitary stalk (Figures 2–2 and 2–6).

Posterior Pituitary Hormones

The hypothalamo-neurohypophysial system secretes two nonapeptides: antidiuretic hormone (ADH) (also known as arginine vasopressin) and oxytocin. They are synthesized in large cell bodies of neurons (magnocellular neurons) in the supraoptic nuclei and the lateral and superior parts of the paraventricular nuclei (Figures 2–2 and 2–6). ADH is an important regulator of water balance; it also is a potent vasoconstrictor and plays a role in regulation of cardiovascular function. Oxytocin causes contraction of smooth muscle, especially of the myoepithelial cells that line the ducts of the mammary gland, thus causing milk ejection.

ADH and oxytocin are basic nonapeptides (MW 1084 and 1007, respectively) characterized by a ring structure with a disulfide linkage (see Table 2–2). They are synthesized by separate cells (ie, there is no co-secretion or synthesis) from prohormones which contain both the peptide and an associated binding peptide or neurophysin specific for the hormone: neurophysin II for ADH and neurophysin I for oxytocin. Since the hormone and neurophysin are synthesized from the same prohormone, defects in gene expression result in deficiency of both products. For example, the Brattleboro rat has a deficiency of ADH and neurophysin II (but not of oxytocin and neurophysin I). Following synthesis and initial processing, secretory granules containing the prohormone migrate by axoplasmic flow (2–3 mm/h) to the nerve endings of the posterior lobe. In the secretory granules, further processing produces the mature nonapeptide and its neurophysin, which are co-secreted in equimolar amounts by exocytosis. Action potentials that reach the nerve endings increase the Ca^{2+} influx and initiate hormone secretion.

Neuroendocrinology: The Hypothalamus as Part of a Larger System

The hypothalamus is involved in many nonendocrine functions such as regulation of body temperature and food intake and is connected with many other parts of the nervous system. The brain itself is influenced by both direct and indirect hormonal effects. Steroid and thyroid hormones cross the blood-brain barrier and produce specific receptor-mediated actions (see Chapters 4 and 6). Peptides in the general circulation which do not cross the blood-brain barrier elicit their effects indirectly, eg, insulin-mediated changes in blood glucose concentration. In addition, communication between the general circulation and the brain may take place via the circumventricular organs, which are located outside the blood-brain barrier (see below). Moreover, hypothalamic hormones in extrahypothalamic brain function as neurotransmitters or neurohormones. They are also found in other tissues where they function as hormones (endocrine, paracrine, or autocrine). For example, somatostatin-containing neurons are widely distributed in the nervous system. Somatostatin is also found in the pancreatic islets (D cells), the gastrointestinal mucosa, and the C cells of the thyroid gland (parafollicular cells). Somatostatin is not only secreted into the general circulation and diffused locally—it is also secreted into the lumen of the gut, where it may affect gut secretion. A hormone with this activity has been called a "lumone." Hormones common to the brain, pituitary, and gastrointestinal tract include not only TRH and somatostatin but also vasoactive intestinal polypeptide (VIP) and peptides derived from pro-opiomelanocortin (see Chapter 14).

Hypothalamic function is regulated both by hormone-mediated signals—eg, negative feedback—and by neural inputs from a wide variety of sources. These nerve signals are mediated by neurotransmitters including acetylcholine, dopamine, norepinephrine, epinephrine, serotonin, gamma-aminobutyric acid, and opioids. The hypothalamus can be considered a final common pathway by which signals from multiple systems reach the anterior pituitary. For example, cytokines that play a role in the response to infection, such as the interleukins, are also involved in regulation of the hypothalamic-pituitary-adrenal axis. This system of immunoneuroendocrine interactions is important in the organism's response to a variety of stresses.

The hypothalamus also sends signals to other parts of the nervous system. For example, while the major nerve tracts of the magnocellular neurons containing vasopressin and oxytocin terminate in the posterior pituitary, nerve fibers from the paraventricular and supraoptic nuclei project to many other parts of the nervous system. In the brain stem, vasopressinergic neurons are involved in the autonomic regulation of blood pressure. Similar neurons project to the gray matter and are implicated in higher cortical functions. Fibers terminating in the median eminence permit release of ADH into the hypophysial-portal system; delivery of ADH in high concentrations to the anterior pituitary may facilitate its involvement in the regulation of ACTH secretion. Magnocellular neurons also project to the choroid plexus where they may release ADH into the cerebrospinal fluid. In addition to magnocellular neurons, the paraventricular nuclei contain cells with smaller cell bodies—parvicellular neurons. Such neurons are also found in other regions of the nervous system and may contain other peptides such as CRH and TRH.

The Pineal Gland & the Circumventricular Organs

The circumventricular organs are secretory midline brain structures that arise from the ependymal cell lining of the ventricular system (Figure 2–7). These organs are located adjacent to the third ventricle—subfornical organ, subcommissural organ, oganum vasculosum of the lamina terminalis, pineal, and part of the median eminence—and at the roof of the fourth ventricle—area postrema (Figure 2–7). The tissues of these organs have relatively large interstitial spaces and have fenestrated capillaries which being highly permeable, permit diffusion of large molecules from the general circulation; elsewhere in the brain tight capillary endothelial junctions prevent such diffusion—the blood-brain barrier. For example, angiotensin II (see Chapter 7) is involved in the regulation of water intake, blood pressure, and secretion of vasopressin. In addition to its peripheral effects, circulating angiotensin II acts on the subfornical organ resulting in increase in water intake.

The pineal gland, considered by the 17th century

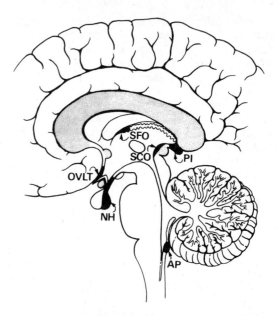

Figure 2–7. Circumventricular organs. The neurohypophysis (NH) and adjacent median eminence, the organum vasculosum of the lamina terminalis (OVLT), the subfornical organ (SFO), and the area postrema (AP) are shown projected on a sagittal section of the human brain. The pineal (PI) and the subcommissural organ (SCO) are also shown but probably do not function as circumventricular organs. (Reproduced, with permission, from Ganong WF: *Review of Medical Physiology,* 15th ed. Appleton & Lange, 1993.)

French philosopher Descartes to be the seat of the soul, is located at the roof of the posterior portion of the third ventricle. The pineal gland in humans and other mammals has no direct neural connections with the brain except for sympathetic innervation via the superior cervical ganglion. The pineal gland secretes melatonin, an indole synthesized from serotonin by 5-methoxylation and N-acetylation (Figure 2–8). The pineal releases melatonin into the general circulation and into the cerebrospinal fluid. Melatonin secretion is regulated by the sympathetic nervous system and is increased in response to hypoglycemia and darkness. The pineal also contains other bioactive peptides and amines including TRH, somatostatin, GnRH, and norepinephrine. The physiologic role of the pineal is not known, although it appears to be involved in regulation of gonadal function and development and in endocrine rhythms.

The pineal gland may be the site of pineal cell tumors (pinealomas) or germ cell tumors (germinomas). Neurologic signs and symptoms are the predominant clinical manifestations, eg, increased intracranial pressure, visual abnormalities, ataxia, and Parinaud's syndrome—upward gaze palsy, absent pupillary light reflex, paralysis of convergence, and wide based gait. Endocrine manifestations result

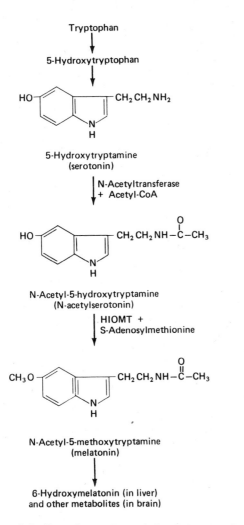

Tryptophan

↓

5-Hydroxytryptophan

↓

5-Hydroxytryptamine
(serotonin)

↓ N-Acetyltransferase
+ Acetyl-CoA

N-Acetyl-5-hydroxytryptamine
(N-acetylserotonin)

↓ HIOMT +
S-Adenosylmethionine

N-Acetyl-5-methoxytryptamine
(melatonin)

↓

6-Hydroxymelatonin (in liver)
and other metabolites (in brain)

Figure 2–8. Formation and metabolism of melatonin. (HIOMT, hydroxyindole-O-methyltransferase.) (Reproduced, with permission, from Ganong WF: *Review of Medical Physiology,* 15th ed. Appleton & Lange, 1993.)

primarily from deficiency of hypothalamic hormones (diabetes insipidus, hypopituitarism, or disorders of gonadal development). Treatment involves surgical removal or decompression, radiation therapy, and hormone replacement (see below).

ANTERIOR PITUITARY HORMONES

The six major anterior pituitary hormones— ACTH, GH, PRL, TSH, LH, and FSH—may be classified into three groups: corticotropin-related peptides (ACTH, β-LPH, melanocyte-stimulating hormone [MSH], and endorphins); the somatomammotropins (GH and PRL), which are also peptides; and the glycoproteins (LH, FSH, and TSH). The

chemical features of these hormones are illustrated in Table 2–3.

ACTH & RELATED PEPTIDES

Biosynthesis

ACTH is a 39-amino-acid peptide hormone (MW 4500) processed from a large precursor molecule, pro-opiomelanocortin (POMC) (MW 28,500). Within the corticotroph, a single mRNA directs the synthesis and processing of POMC into smaller biologically active fragments (Figure 2–9) which include β-LPH, α-MSH, β-MSH, β-endorphin, and the N-terminal fragment of pro-opiomelanocortin. Most of these peptides are glycosylated, which accounts for differences in the reporting of molecular weights. These carbohydrate moieties are responsible for the basophilic staining of corticotrophs.

Two of these fragments are contained within the structure of ACTH: α-MSH is identical to $ACTH_{1-13}$, and corticotropin-like intermediate lobe peptide (CLIP) represents $ACTH_{18-39}$ (Figure 2–9). Although these fragments are found in species with developed intermediate lobes (eg, the rat), they are not secreted as separate hormones in humans. β-Lipotropin, a fragment with 91 amino acids (1–91), is secreted by the corticotroph in equimolar quantities with ACTH. Within the β-LPH molecule exists the amino acid sequence for β-MSH (41–58), γ-LPH (1–58), and β-endorphin (61–91).

The N-terminal fragment (131 amino acids) of pro-opiomelanocortin has been isolated and sequenced. The first 76 amino acids of this N-terminal sequence appear to be the physiologically relevant form of this fragment. Plasma levels of this peptide increase in response to hypoglycemic stress. It may be an adrenal growth factor and may potentiate ACTH action on steroidogenesis.

Function

ACTH stimulates the secretion of glucocorticoids, mineralocorticoids, and androgenic steroids from the adrenal cortex (see Chapters 6 and 7). The amino-terminal end (residues 1–18) is responsible for this biologic activity. ACTH binds to receptors on the adrenal cortex and provokes steroidogenesis through the mediation of cAMP.

The hyperpigmentation observed in states of ACTH hypersecretion (eg, Addison's disease, Nelson's syndrome) appears to be primarily due to ACTH. Because α- and β-MSH do not exist as separate hormones in humans, the exact cause of this increased pigmentation remains unclear.

The physiologic function of β-LPH and its family of peptide hormones, including β-endorphin, is not completely understood. However, both β-LPH and β-endorphin have the same secretory dynamics as

Table 2–3. Characteristics of anterior pituitary hormones.[1]

Pituitary Hormone	Molecular Weight	Amino Acids		Other Features
I. Corticotropin-lipotropin				
ACTH	4,500	39		
β-Lipotropin	11,200	91		All of these hormones are derived from a common precursor.
β-Endorphin	4,000	31		
II. Glycoprotein				
LH	29,000	Alpha subunit:	89	
		Beta subunit:	115	
FSH	29,000	Alpha subunit:	89	All have 2 subunits, with the alpha subunit being identical in each and the beta subunit conferring biologic specificity.
		Beta subunit:	115	
TSH	28,000	Alpha subunit:	89	
		Beta subunit:	112	
III. Somatomammotropin				
GH	21,500	191		Evolved from a common hormone.
PRL	22,000	198		

[1]Adapted from Frohman LA: Diseases of the anterior pituitary. Chap 7, pp 151–231, in: *Endocrinology and Metabolism*. Felig P et al (editors). McGraw-Hill, 1981.

ACTH; they increase in response to stress, hypoglycemia, and metyrapone and are suppressible with glucocorticoids. These hormones, including the N-terminal fragment, also parallel ACTH in disease states—eg, they are elevated in Addison's disease, Cushing's disease, and Nelson's syndrome and suppressed by glucocorticord excess. Furthermore, there is evidence that β-endorphin acts as an "endogenous opiate," suggesting a role in pain appreciation. It may affect the endocrine regulation of other pituitary hormones and perhaps also the neural control of breathing.

Measurement

The development of an immunoradiometric assay using monoclonal antibodies has provided a sensitive and practical clinical ACTH assay for the evaluation of pituitary-adrenal disorders. The basal morning concentration ranges from 10 to 50 pg/mL (2.2–11.1 pmol/L). Its short plasma half-life (7–12 minutes) and episodic secretion cause wide and rapid fluctuations both in its plasma concentration and in that of cortisol.

Although β-LPH has a longer half-life than ACTH and is more stable in plasma, its measurement has not been extensively utilized. Current data suggest that the normal concentration of β-LPH is 10–40 pg/mL (1–4 pmol/L).

Secretion

The physiologic secretion of ACTH is mediated through neural influences by means of a complex of hormones, the most important of which is corticotropin-releasing hormone (CRH) (Figure 2–10).

CRH stimulates ACTH in a pulsatile manner: Diurnal rhythmicity causes a peak before awakening and a decline as the day progresses. The diurnal rhythm is a reflection of neural control and provokes concordant diurnal secretion of cortisol from the adrenal cortex (Figure 2–11). This episodic release of ACTH is independent of circulating cortisol levels—ie, the magnitude of an ACTH impulse is not related to preceding plasma cortisol levels. An example is the persistence of diurnal rhythm in patients with primary adrenal failure (Addison's disease). ACTH secretion also increases in response to feeding in both humans and animals.

Many stresses stimulate ACTH, often superseding the normal diurnal rhythmicity. Physical, emotional, and chemical stresses such as pain, trauma, hypoxia, acute hypoglycemia, cold exposure, surgery, depression, and pyrogen and vasopressin administration have all been shown to stimulate ACTH and cortisol secretion. The increase in ACTH levels during stress is mediated by vasopressin as well as CRH. Although physiologic cortisol levels do not blunt the ACTH response to stress, exogenous corticosteroids in high doses suppress it.

Negative feedback of cortisol and synthetic glucocorticoids on ACTH secretion occurs at both the hypothalamic and pituitary levels via two mechanisms: "Fast feedback" is sensitive to the rate of change in cortisol levels, while "slow feedback" is sensitive to the absolute cortisol level. The first mechanism is probably nonnuclear; ie, this phenomenon occurs too rapidly to be explained by the influence of corticosteroids on nuclear transcription of the specific mRNA responsible for ACTH. "Slow feedback," occurring later, may be explained by a nuclear-mediated mechanism and a subsequent decrease in synthesis of ACTH. This latter form of negative feedback is the type probed by the clinical dexamethasone suppression test. In addition to the negative feedback of corticoids, ACTH also inhibits its own secretion (short loop feedback).

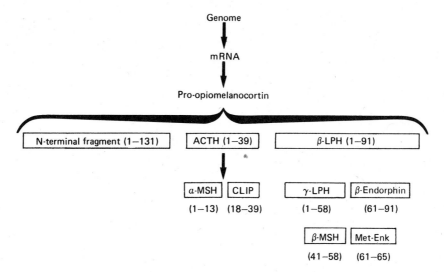

Figure 2–9. The processing of pro-opiomelanocortin (MW 28,500) into its biologically active peptide hormones. Abbreviations are expanded in the text.

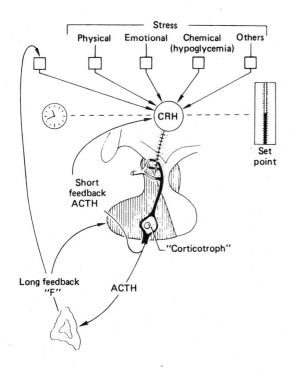

Figure 2–10. The hypothalamic-pituitary-adrenal axis, illustrating negative feedback by cortisol ("F") at the hypothalamic and pituitary levels. A short negative feedback loop of ACTH on the secretion of corticotropin-releasing hormone (CRH) also exists. (Reproduced, with permission, from Gwinup G, Johnson B: Clinical testing of the hypothalamic-pituitary-adrenocortical system in states of hypo- and hypercortisolism. Metabolism 1975; 24:777.)

GROWTH HORMONE

Biosynthesis

Growth hormone (GH; somatotropin) is a 191-amino-acid polypeptide hormone (MW 21,500) synthesized and secreted by the somatotrophs of the anterior pituitary. Its larger precursor peptide, preGH (MW 28,000), is also secreted but has no physiologic significance.

Function

The primary function of growth hormone (somatotropin) is promotion of linear growth. Its basic metabolic effects serve to achieve this result, but most of the growth-promoting effects are mediated by insulin-like growth factor 1 (IGF-1; also known as somatomedin C) (see Chapter 3).

Growth hormone, via IGF-1, increases protein synthesis by enhancing amino acid uptake and directly accelerating the transcription and translation of mRNA. In addition, GH tends to decrease protein catabolism by mobilizing fat as a more efficient fuel source: It directly causes the release of fatty acids from adipose tissue and enhances their conversion to acetyl-CO, from which energy is derived. This protein-sparing effect is an important mechanism by which GH promotes growth and development.

GH also affects carbohydrate metabolism. In excess, it decreases carbohydrate utilization and impairs glucose uptake into cells. This GH-induced insulin resistance appears to be due to a postreceptor impairment in insulin action. These events result in glucose intolerance and secondary hyperinsulinism.

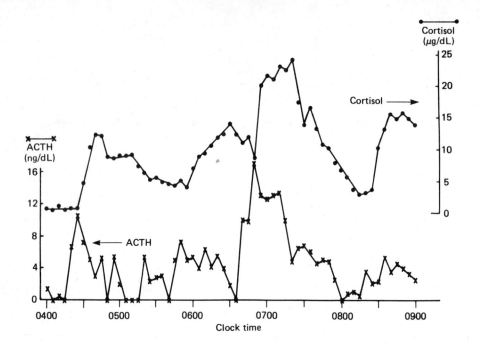

Figure 2–11. The episodic, pulsatile pattern of ACTH secretion and its concordance with cortisol secretion in a healthy human subject during the early morning. (Reproduced, with permission, from Gallagher TF et al: ACTH and cortisol secretory patterns in man. J Clin Endocrinol Metab 1973;36:1058.)

Measurement

GH circulates mainly unbound in plasma and has a half-life of 20–50 minutes. The healthy adult secretes approximately 400 μg/d (18.6 nmol/d); in contrast, young adolescents secrete about 700 μg/d (32.5 nmol/d).

The early morning GH concentration in fasting adults is less than 5 ng/mL (232 pmol/L) and usually less than 2 ng/mL (93 pmol/L). There are no significant sex differences.

Concentrations of IGF-1 are determined by radioreceptor assays or radioimmunoassays. Determining the levels of these mediators of GH action may result in more accurate assessment of the biologic activity of GH (see Chapter 3).

Secretion

The secretion of GH is mediated by two hypothalamic hormones: growth hormone-releasing hormone (GRH) and somatostatin (growth hormone-inhibiting hormone). These hypothalamic influences are tightly regulated by an integrated system of neural, metabolic, and hormonal factors. Because neither GRH nor somatostatin can be measured directly, the net result of any factor on GH secretion must be considered as the sum of its effects on these hypothalamic hormones. Table 2–4 summarizes the many factors that affect GH secretion in physiologic, pharmacologic, and pathologic states.

A. GRH: Both the 40- and the 44-amino-acid forms of GRH are present in the human hypothalamus; however, their physiologic significance is not clear. GRH stimulates cAMP production by somatotrophs and stimulates both GH synthesis and secretion. The effects of GRH are partially blocked by somatostatin. The administration of GRH to normal humans leads to rapid release of GH (within minutes); levels peak at 30 minutes and are sustained for 60–120 minutes.

Other peptide hormones such as ADH, ACTH, and α-MSH may act as GH-releasing factors when present in pharmacologic amounts. Even thyrotropin- and gonadotropin-releasing hormones (TRH and GnRH) often cause GH secretion in patients with acromegaly; however, it is not certain whether any of these effects are mediated by the hypothalamus or represent direct effects on the somatotroph.

B. Somatostatin: Somatostatin, a tetradecapeptide, is a potent inhibitor of GH secretion. It decreases cAMP production in GH-secreting cells and inhibits both basal and stimulated GH secretion. Somatostatin secretion is increased by elevated levels of GH and IGF-1. A long-acting analogue of somatostatin, octreotide acetate, has been used therapeutically in the management of GH excess and in conditions such as pancreatic and carcinoid tumors that cause diarrhea.

C. Neural Control: The neural control of basal

Table 2–4. Factors affecting growth hormone secretion.[1]

Increase	Decrease[2]
Physiologic	
Sleep	Postprandial hyperglycemia
Exercise	Elevated free fatty acids
Stress (physical or psycho-logic)	
Postprandial:	
Hyperaminoacidemia	
Hypoglycemia (relative)	
Pharmacologic	
Hypoglycemia:	Hormones:
Absolute: insulin or 2-deoxyglucose	Somatostatin
	Growth hormone
Relative: postglucagon	Progesterone
Hormones:	Glucocorticoids
GRH	Neurotransmitters, etc:
Peptide (ACTH, α-MSH, vasopressin)	Alpha-adrenergic antago-nists (phentolamine)
Estrogen	Beta-adrenergic agonists (isoproterenol)
Neurotransmitters, etc:	Serotonin antagonists (methysergide)
Alpha-adrenergic agonists (clonidine)	Dopamine antagonists (phenothiazines)
Beta-adrenergic antago-nists (propranolol)	
Serotonin precursors	
Dopamine agonists (levo-dopa, apomorphine, bromocriptine)	
GABA agonists (musci-mol)	
Potassium infusion	
Pyrogens (*Pseudomonas* endotoxin)	
Pathologic	
Protein depletion and star-vation	Obesity
Anorexia nervosa	Acromegaly: dopamine agonists
Ectopic production of GRH	Hypo- and hyperthyroidism
Chronic renal failure	
Acromegaly:	
TRH	
GnRH	

[1] Modified and reproduced, with permission, from Frohman LA: Diseases of the anterior pituitary. Chap 7, pp 151–231, in: *Endocrinology and Metabolism,* Felig P et al (editors). McGraw-Hill, 1981.
[2] Suppressive effects of some factors can be demonstrated only in the presence of a stimulus.

GH secretion results in irregular and intermittent release associated with sleep and varying with age. Peak levels occur 1–4 hours after the onset of sleep (during stages 3 and 4) (Figure 2–12). These nocturnal sleep bursts, which account for nearly 70% of daily GH secretion, are greater in children and tend to decrease with age. Glucose infusion will not suppress this episodic release. Emotional, physical, and chemical stress, including surgery, trauma, exercise, electroshock therapy, and pyrogen administration, provoke GH release; and impairment of secretion, leading to growth failure, has been well documented in children with severe emotional deprivation (see Chapter 3).

D. Metabolic Control: The metabolic factors af-

fecting GH secretion include all fuel substrates: carbohydrate, protein, and fat. Glucose administration, orally or intravenously, lowers GH in healthy subjects and provides a simple physiologic maneuver useful in the diagnosis of acromegaly (see below). In contrast, hypoglycemia stimulates GH release. This effect depends on intracellular glycopenia, since the administration of 2-deoxyglucose (a glucose analogue that causes intracellular glucose deficiency) also increases GH. This response to hypoglycemia depends on both the rate of change in blood glucose and the absolute level attained.

A protein meal or intravenous infusion of amino acids (eg, arginine) causes GH release. Paradoxically, states of protein-calorie malnutrition also increase GH, possibly as a result of decreased IGF-1 production and lack of inhibitory feedback.

Fatty acids suppress GH responses to certain stimuli, including arginine and hypoglycemia. Fasting stimulates GH secretion, possibly as a means of mobilizing fat as an energy source and preventing protein loss.

E. Effects of Other Hormones: Responses to stimuli are blunted in states of cortisol excess and during hypo- and hyperthyroidism. Although estrogen enhances GH secretion in response to stimulation, estradiol has been used to treat acromegaly because it decreases somatomedin production.

F. Effects of Neuropharmacologic Agents: Many neurotransmitters and neuropharmacologic agents affect GH secretion. Biogenic amine agonists and antagonists act at the hypothalamic level and alter GRH or somatostatin release. Dopaminergic, alpha-adrenergic, and serotonergic agents all stimulate GH release.

Dopamine agonists such as levodopa, apomorphine, and bromocriptine increase GH secretion, whereas dopaminergic antagonists such as phenothiazines inhibit GH. The effect of levodopa, a precursor of both norepinephrine and dopamine, may be mediated by its conversion to norepinephrine, since its effect is blocked by the alpha-adrenergic antagonist phentolamine. Moreover, phentolamine suppresses GH release in response to other stimuli such as hypoglycemia, exercise, and arginine, emphasizing the importance of alpha-adrenergic mechanisms in modulating GH secretion.

Beta-adrenergic agonists inhibit GH, and beta-adrenergic antagonists such as propranolol enhance secretion to provocative stimuli.

PROLACTIN

Biosynthesis

Prolactin (PRL) is a 198-amino-acid polypeptide hormone (MW 22,000) synthesized and secreted from the lactotrophs of the anterior pituitary. Despite

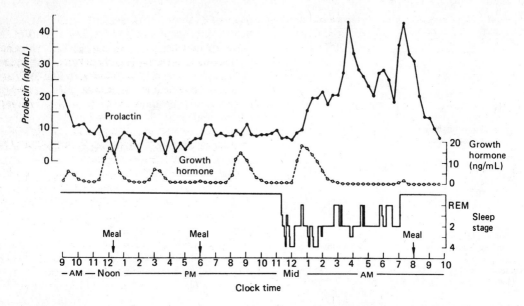

Figure 2–12. Sleep-associated changes in prolactin (PRL) and growth hormone (GH) secretion in humans. Peak levels of GH occur during sleep stages 3 or 4; the increase in PRL is observed 1–2 hours after sleep begins and is not associated with a specific sleep phase. (Reproduced, with permission, from Sassin JF et al: Human prolactin: 24-hour pattern with increased release during sleep. Science 1972;177:1205.)

evolution from an ancestral hormone common to GH and human placental lactogen (hPL), PRL shares only 16% of its residues with the former and 13% with hPL. A precursor molecule (MW 40,000–50,000) is also secreted and may constitute 8–20% of the PRL plasma immunoreactivity in healthy persons and in patients with PRL-secreting pituitary tumors.

Function

PRL stimulates lactation in the postpartum period (see Chapter 13). During pregnancy, PRL secretion increases and, in concert with many other hormones (estrogen, progesterone, hPL, insulin, and cortisol), promotes additional breast development in preparation for milk production. Despite its importance during pregnancy, PRL has not been demonstrated to play a role in the development of normal breast tissue in humans. During pregnancy, estrogen enhances breast development but blunts the effect of PRL on lactation; the decrease in both estrogen and progesterone after parturition allows initiation of lactation. Accordingly, galactorrhea may accompany the discontinuance of oral contraceptives or estrogen therapy. Although basal PRL secretion falls in the postpartum period, lactation is maintained by persistent breast suckling.

PRL levels are very high in the fetus and in newborn infants, declining during the first few months of life.

Although PRL does not appear to play a physiologic role in the regulation of gonadal function, hyperprolactinemia in humans leads to hypogonadism.

In women, initially there is a shortening of the luteal phase; subsequently, anovulation, oligomenorrhea or amenorrhea, and infertility occur. In men, PRL excess leads to decreased testosterone synthesis and spermatogenesis, which clinically present as decreased libido, impotence, and infertility. The exact mechanisms of PRL inhibition of gonadal function are unclear, but the principal one appears to be alteration of hypothalamic-pituitary control of gonadotropin secretion. Basal LH and FSH levels are normal or subnormal; however, their pulsatile secretion is decreased and the midcycle LH surge is suppressed in women. Gonadotropin reserve, as assessed with GnRH, is usually normal or even exaggerated.

Measurement

The PRL secretory rate is approximately 400 μg/d (18.6 nmol/d). The hormone is cleared by the liver (75%) and the kidney (25%), and its half-time of disappearance from plasma is about 50 minutes.

Basal levels of PRL in adults vary considerably, with a mean of 13 ng/mL (0.6 nmol/L) in women and 5 ng/mL (0.23 nmol/L) in men. The upper range of normal in most laboratories is 15–20 ng/mL (0.7–0.9 nmol/L).

Secretion

The hypothalamic control of PRL secretion is predominantly inhibitory, and dopamine is the most important inhibitory factor. The administration of dopamine or its precursor levodopa, either in vitro or in vivo, inhibits PRL release; drugs that block dopamine receptors (eg, phenothiazines, metoclopramide) or cause hypothalamic dopamine depletion (reserpine, methyldopa) stimulate PRL release. The physiologic, pathologic, and pharmacologic factors influencing PRL secretion are listed in Table 2–5.

A. Prolactin-Releasing Factors: TRH is a potent prolactin-releasing factor that evokes release of PRL at a threshold dose similar to that which stimulates release of TSH. An exaggerated response of both TSH and PRL to TRH is observed in primary hypothyroidism, and their responses are blunted in hyperthyroidism. In addition, PRL secretion is also stimulated by VIP and serotonergic pathways.

B. Episodic and Sleep-Related Secretion: PRL secretion is episodic. An increase is observed 60–90 minutes after sleep begins but, in contrast to GH, is not associated with a specific sleep phase. Peak levels are usually attained between 4 and 7 AM (Figure 2–12). This sleep-associated augmentation of PRL release is not part of a circadian rhythm, like that of ACTH; it is related strictly to the sleeping period regardless of when it occurs during the day.

C. Other Stimuli: Stresses, including surgery, exercise, hypoglycemia, and acute myocardial infarction, cause significant elevation of PRL levels. Nip-
ple stimulation in nonpregnant women also increases PRL. This neurogenic reflex may also occur from chest wall injury such as mechanical trauma, burns, surgery, and herpes zoster of thoracic dermatomes. This reflex discharge of PRL is abolished by denervation of the nipple or by spinal cord or brain stem lesions.

D. Effects of Other Hormones: Many hormones influence PRL release. Estrogens augment basal and stimulated PRL secretion after 2–3 days of use (an effect that is of special clinical importance in patients with PRL-secreting pituitary adenomas); glucocorticoids tend to suppress TRH-induced PRL secretion; and thyroid hormone administration may blunt the PRL response to TRH.

E. Effects of Pharmacologic Agents: (Table 2–5.) Many pharmacologic agents alter PRL secretion. Dopamine agonists (eg, bromocriptine) decrease secretion, forming the basis for their use in states of PRL excess. Dopamine antagonists (eg, phenothiazines) augment PRL release. There is good correlation between the antipsychotic potency of these drugs and their hyperprolactinemic response, perhaps related to the extent of dopamine antagonism. Serotonin agonists will enhance PRL secretion; serotonin receptor blockers suppress stress- and nursing-associated PRL release.

Table 2–5. Factors affecting prolactin secretion.

Increase	Decrease
Physiologic	
Pregnancy	
Nursing	
Nipple stimulation	
Exercise	
Stress (hypoglycemia)	
Sleep	
Seizures	
Neonatal	
Pharmacologic	
TRH	Dopamine agonists (levo-
Estrogen	dopa, apomorphine, bro-
VIP	mocriptine, pergolide)
Dopamine antagonists (phe-	GABA
nothiazines, haloperidol,	
metoclopramide, reser-	
pine, methyldopa, amox-	
apine, opiates)	
Opioids	
Monoamine oxidase inhibi-	
tors	
Cimetidine (intravenous)	
Verapamil	
Licorice	
Pathologic	
Pituitary tumors	Pseudohypoparathyroidism
Hypothalamic/pituitary stalk	Pituitary destruction or re-
lesions	moval
Neuraxis irradiation	Lymphocytic hypophysitis
Chest wall lesions	
Spinal cord lesions	
Hypothyroidism	
Chronic renal failure	
Severe liver disease	

THYROTROPIN

Biosynthesis

Thyrotropin (thyroid-stimulating hormone, TSH) is a glycoprotein (MW 28,000) composed of two noncovalently linked alpha and beta subunits. The structure of the alpha subunit of TSH resembles that of the other glycoprotein molecules—FSH, LH, and human chorionic gonadotropin (hCG)—but the beta subunit differs in these glycoproteins and is responsible for their biologic and immunologic specificity. The peptides of these subunits appear to be synthesized separately and united before the carbohydrate groups are attached. The intact molecule is then secreted, as are small amounts of nonlinked subunits.

Function

The beta subunit of TSH attaches to high-affinity receptors in the thyroid, stimulating iodide uptake, hormonogenesis, and release of T_4 and T_3. This occurs through activation of adenylyl cyclase and the generation of cAMP. TSH secretion also causes an increase in gland size and vascularity by promoting mRNA and protein synthesis. (For a more detailed description, see Chapter 4.)

Measurement

TSH circulates unbound in the blood with a half-life of 50–60 minutes. With ultrasensitive immunoradiometric assays for measuring TSH concentration, the normal range is usually 0.5–5.0 μU/mL (0.5–5.0 m U/L). These new assays are helpful in the diagnosis of primary hypothyroidism and hyperthyroidism; however, TSH levels alone cannot be used to evaluate pituitary or hypothalamic hypothyroidism.

The alpha subunit can be detected in about 80% of normals, with a range of 0.5–2 ng/mL. Plasma alpha subunit levels increase after administration of TRH in normal subjects, and basal levels are elevated in primary hypothyroidism and in patients with pure alpha subunit-secreting pituitary adenomas.

Secretion

The secretion of TSH is controlled by both stimulatory (TRH) and inhibitory (somatostatin) influences from the hypothalamus and in addition is modulated by the feedback inhibition of thyroid hormone on the

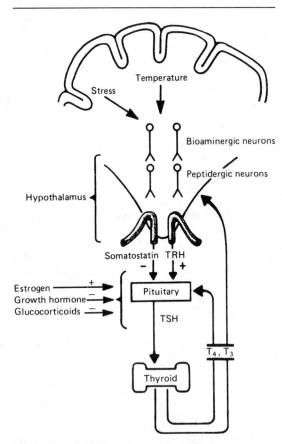

Figure 2–13. Diagram of the hypothalamic-pituitary-thyroid axis, illustrating the negative feedback of thyroid hormones (T_4, T_3) predominantly at the pituitary level. Hypothalamic factors may stimulate (TRH) or suppress (somatostatin) TSH secretion. Estrogen, GH, and glucocorticoids influence the effects of TRH on TSH secretion. (Reproduced, with permission, from Martin JB, Reichlin S, Brown GM: *Clinical Neuroendocrinology*. Davis, 1977.)

hypothalamic-pituitary axis (Figures 2–13 and 4–21).

A. TRH: The response of TSH to TRH is modulated by the circulating concentration of thyroid hormones. Small changes in serum levels (even within the physiologic range) cause substantial alterations in the TSH response to TRH. As shown in Figure 2–14, the administration of T_3 (15 μg) and T_4 (60 μg) to healthy persons for 3–4 weeks suppresses the TSH response to TRH despite only small increases in circulating T_3 and T_4 levels. Thus, the secretion of TSH is inversely proportionate to the concentration of thyroid hormone.

The set point (the level at which TSH secretion is maintained) is determined by TRH. Deviations from this set point result in appropriate changes in TSH release. Administration of TRH increases TSH within 2 minutes, and this response is blocked by previous T_3 administration; however, larger doses of TRH may overcome this blockade—suggesting that both T_3 and TRH act at the pituitary level to influence TSH secretion. In addition, T_3 and T_4 inhibit mRNA for TRH synthesis in the hypothalamus, indicating that a negative feedback mechanism operates at this level also.

B. Somatostatin: This inhibitory hypothalamic peptide augments the direct inhibitory effect of thyroid hormone on the thyrotrophs. Infusion of somatostatin blunts the early morning TSH surge and will suppress high levels of TSH in primary hypothyroidism. Octreotide acetate, a long-acting somatostatin analogue, has been used successfully to inhibit TSH secretion in some patients with TSH-secreting pituitary tumors.

C. Neural Control: In addition to these hypothalamic influences on TSH secretion, neurally mediated factors may be important. Dopamine physiologically inhibits TSH secretion. Intravenous dopamine administration will decrease TSH in both healthy and hypothyroid subjects as well as blunt the TSH response to TRH. Thus, as expected, dopaminergic agonists such as bromocriptine inhibit TSH secretion and dopaminergic antagonists such as metaclopramide increase TSH secretion in euthyroid subjects. Bromocriptine has also been effective in the management of some TSH-secreting pituitary tumors.

D. Temperature and Stress: Because thyroid hormone has such a critical role in the regulation of thermogenesis, the cold-induced increase of TSH in rats is not surprising. Nonetheless, neither acute nor chronic exposure to cold in adult humans has been shown to stimulate TSH release.

The effects of stress could affect TSH at various levels of the hypothalamic-pituitary-thyroid axis or by alteration of peripheral thyroid metabolism; however, except for insulin-induced hypoglycemia, stressful stimuli have not been demonstrated to have a direct influence on the secretion of TSH in humans.

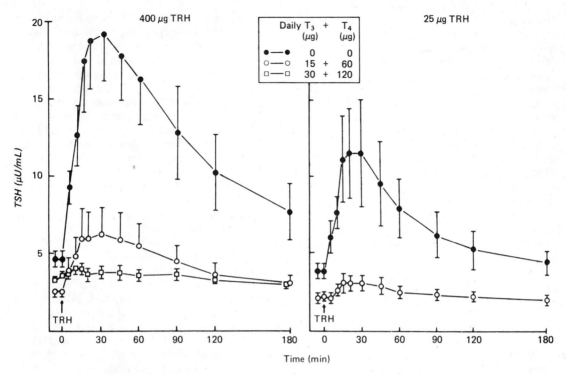

Figure 2–14. Administration of small doses of T_3 (15 μg) and T_4 (60 μg) to healthy subjects inhibits the TSH response to 2 doses (400 μg, left; 25 μg, right) of TRH (protirelin). (Reproduced, with permission, from Snyder PJ, Utiger RD: Inhibition of thyrotropin-releasing hormone by small quantities of thyroid hormones. J Clin Invest 1972;51:2077.)

E. Effects of Cortisol and Estrogens: Glucocorticoid excess has been shown to impair the sensitivity of the pituitary to TRH and to be able to lower serum TSH to undetectable levels. However, estrogens increase the sensitivity of the thyrotroph to TRH; women have a greater TSH response to TRH than men do, and pretreatment of men with estradiol will increase their TRH-induced TSH response. (See also Chapter 4 and Table 4–6.)

GONADOTROPINS: LUTEINIZING HORMONE, FOLLICLE-STIMULATING HORMONE

Biosynthesis

Luteinizing hormone (LH) and follicle-stimulating hormone (FSH) are glycoprotein gonadotropins composed of alpha and beta subunits and secreted by the same cell. The specific beta subunit confers on these hormones their unique biologic activity, as it does with TSH and hCG. The biologic activity of hCG, a placental glycoprotein, closely resembles that of LH. Human menopausal gonadotropin (hMG, menotropins)—an altered mixture of pituitary gonadotropins recovered from the urine of postmenopausal women—is a preparation with FSH-like activity. Menotropins and chorionic gonadotropin are used clinically for induction of spermatogenesis or ovulation (see Chapters 9 and 10).

Function

LH and FSH bind to receptors in the ovary and testis and regulate gonadal function by promoting sex steroid production and gametogenesis.

In men, LH stimulates testosterone production from the interstitial cells of the testes (Leydig cells). Maturation of spermatozoa, however, requires both LH and FSH. FSH stimulates testicular growth and enhances the production of an androgen-binding protein by the Sertoli cells, which are a component of the testicular tubule necessary for sustaining the maturing sperm cell. This androgen-binding protein causes high local concentrations of testosterone near the sperm, an essential factor in the development of normal spermatogenesis (see Chapter 9).

In women, LH stimulates estrogen and progesterone production from the ovary. A surge of LH in the mid menstrual cycle is responsible for ovulation, and continued LH secretion subsequently stimulates the corpus luteum to produce progesterone by enhancing the conversion of cholesterol to pregnenolone. Development of the ovarian follicle is largely under FSH control, and the secretion of estrogen from this follicle is dependent on both FSH and LH.

Measurement

The normal levels of LH and FSH vary with the age of the subject (see Appendix). They are low before puberty and elevated in postmenopausal women. A nocturnal rise of LH in boys and the cyclic secretion of FSH and LH in girls usually herald the onset of puberty before clinical signs are apparent. In women, LH and FSH vary during the menstrual cycle; during the initial phase of the cycle (follicular), LH steadily increases, with a midcycle surge that initiates ovulation. FSH, on the other hand, initially rises and then decreases during the later follicular phase until the midcycle surge, which is concordant with LH. Both LH and FSH levels fall steadily after ovulation (Figure 2–15). (See Chapter 10.)

LH and FSH levels in men are similar to those in women during the follicular phase. The alpha subunit, shared by all the pituitary glycoprotein hormones, can also be measured (see TSH) and will rise following GnRH administration. The normal responses of LH and FSH to GnRH are shown in Table 2–6.

Secretion

The secretion of LH and FSH is controlled by gonadotropin-releasing hormone (GnRH), which maintains basal gonadotropin secretion, generates the phasic release of gonadotropins for ovulation, and determines the onset of puberty.

A. Episodic Secretion: In both males and females, secretion of LH and FSH is episodic, with secretory bursts that occur each hour and are mediated by a concordant episodic release of GnRH. The amplitude of these secretory surges is greater in patients with primary hypogonadism. The pulsatile nature of GnRH release is critical for sustaining gonadotropin secretion. A continuous, prolonged infusion of GnRH in women evokes an initial increase in LH and FSH followed by prolonged suppression of gonadotropin secretion. This phenomenon may be explained by down-regulation of GnRH receptors on the pituitary gonadotrophs. Consequently, long-acting synthetic analogs of GnRH may be used clinically to suppress LH and FSH secretion in conditions such as precocious puberty.

B. Positive Feedback: Circulating sex steroids affect GnRH secretion and thus LH and FSH secretion by both positive and negative (inhibitory) feedback mechanisms. During the menstrual cycle, estrogens provide a positive influence on GnRH effects on LH and FSH secretion, and the rise in estrogen during the follicular phase is the stimulus for the LH and FSH ovulatory surge. This phenomenon suggests that the secretion of estrogen is to some extent influenced by an intrinsic ovarian cycle. Progesterone amplifies the duration of the LH and FSH surge and augments the effect of estrogen. After this midcycle surge, the developed egg leaves the ovary. Ovulation occurs ap-

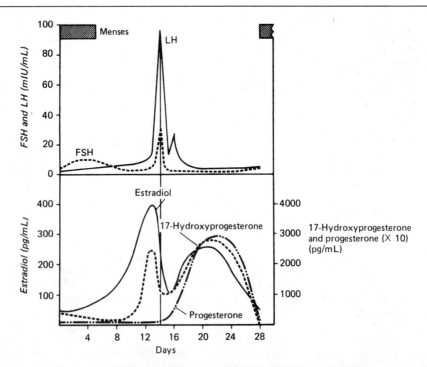

Figure 2–15. The secretory pattern of gonadotropins (LH, FSH) and sex steroids (estradiol, progesterone) during the normal female menstrual cycle. A midcycle surge of LH and FSH, stimulated by the rise in estradiol during the follicular phase, results in ovulation. After ovulation, the luteinized follicle secretes progesterone. (Reproduced, with permission, from Odell WD, Moyer DL: *Physiology of Reproduction.* Mosby, 1971.)

Table 2–6. Normal gonadotropin responses (± SD) to Gn/RH (100 μg).

	Mean Maximum Exchange		Mean Maximum Exchange	
	LH		FSH	
	(μg/L)	(IU/L)	(μg/L)	(IU/L)
Women				
Follicular phase	2.1 ± 0.4	17 ± 3	1.0 ± 0.3	3 ± 1
Around LH peak	20.8 ± 6.2	162 ± 49	2.7 ± 1.0	8 ± 3
Luteal phase	6.3 ± 1.0	49 ± 8	1.0 ± 0.1	3 ± 0.4
Men				
Age 18–40	4.1 ± 0.8	32 ± 6	1.0 ± 0.3	3 ± 1
Age over 65	2.9 ± 0.5	23 ± 4	1.0 ± 0.3	3 ± 1

Conversion factors: For LH (LER 960), 1 ng = 7.8 mIU; for FSH (LER 869), 1 ng = 3 mIU.

proximately 10–12 hours after the LH peak and 24–36 hours after the estradiol peak. The remaining follicular cells in the ovary are converted, under the influence of LH, to a progesterone-secreting structure, the corpus luteum. After about 12 days, the corpus luteum involutes, resulting in decreased estrogen and progesterone levels and then uterine bleeding. (See Chapter 10.)

C. Negative Feedback: Negative feedback effects of sex steroids on gonadotropin secretion also occur. In women, primary gonadal failure or menopause results in elevations of LH and FSH, which can be suppressed with long-term, high-dose estrogen therapy. However, a shorter duration of low-dose estrogen may enhance the LH response to GnRH. In men, primary gonadal failure with low circulating testosterone levels is also associated with elevated gonadotropins. However, testosterone is not the sole inhibitor of gonadotropin secretion in men, since selective destruction of the tubules (eg, by cyclophosphamide therapy) results in azoospermia and elevation of only FSH.

Inhibin, a polypeptide (MW 32,000) secreted by the Sertoli cells of the seminiferous tubules, is the major factor that inhibits FSH secretion by negative feedback. Inhibin, which has been purified and sequenced by analysis of its complementary DNA, consists of separate alpha and beta subunits connected by a disulfide bridge. Androgens stimulate inhibin production; this peptide may help to locally regulate spermatogenesis.

ENDOCRINOLOGIC EVALUATION OF THE HYPOTHALAMIC-PITUITARY AXIS

The precise assessment of the hypothalamic-pituitary axis has been made possible by radioimmunoassays of the major anterior pituitary hormones and their specific target gland hormones. In addition, four synthetic hypothalamic hormones: TRH (protirelin) and GnRH (gonadorelin), which are available commercially; and the more recently synthesized ovine CRH and human GRH (GRH-40 and GRH-44) can be used to assess hypothalamic-pituitary reserve. .

This section describes the principles involved in testing each pituitary hormone as well as special situations (eg, drugs, obesity) that may interfere with pituitary function or pituitary testing. Specific protocols for performing and interpreting diagnostic procedures are outlined at the end of this section. The clinical manifestations of either hypo- or hypersecretion of anterior pituitary hormones are discussed in subsequent sections.

EVALUATION OF ACTH

ACTH deficiency leads to adrenocortical insufficiency, characterized by decreased secretion of cortisol and the adrenal androgens; aldosterone secretion, controlled primarily by the renin-angiotensin axis, is usually maintained.

Plasma ACTH Levels

Basal ACTH measurements are usually unreliable indicators of pituitary secretory reserve, since its short plasma half-life and episodic secretion result in wide fluctuations in plasma levels. Therefore, the interpretation of plasma ACTH levels requires the simultaneous assessment of cortisol secretion by the adrenal cortex. These measurements are of greatest utility in differentiating primary and secondary adrenocortical insufficiency and in establishing the etiology of Cushing's syndrome (see the later section on Cushing's disease and also Chapter 6).

Evaluation of ACTH Deficiency

In evaluating ACTH deficiency, measurement of basal cortisol levels is also unreliable. Although morning cortisol values are usually less than 10 μg/dL (276 nmol/L) in states of diminished pituitary ACTH reserve, such low levels also occur in normal subjects because of the episodic nature of ACTH secretion. In addition, patients with ACTH deficiency following removal of ACTH-secreting pituitary adenomas or withdrawal of synthetic glucocorticoid therapy may have basal cortisol values exceeding 10 μg/dL (276 nmol/L) that fail to increase in response to a stressful stimulus. Consequently, the diagnosis of ACTH hyposecretion (secondary adrenal insufficiency) must be established by provocative testing of the reserve capacity of the hypothalamic-pituitary axis.

Adrenal Stimulation

Since adrenal atrophy develops as a consequence of prolonged ACTH deficiency, the initial and most convenient approach to evaluation of the hypothalamic-pituitary-adrenal axis is assessment of the plasma cortisol response to synthetic ACTH (cosyntropin). In normal individuals, injection of cosyntropin (250 μg) causes a rapid increase (within 30 minutes) of cortisol to at least 20 μg/dL (552 nmol/L), and this response usually correlates with the cortisol response to insulin-induced hypoglycemia. A subnormal cortisol response to ACTH confirms adrenocortical insufficiency. However, a normal response does not directly evaluate the ability of the hypothalamic-pituitary axis to respond to stress (see Chapter 6). Thus, patients withdrawn from long-term glucocorticoid therapy may have an adequate increase in cortisol following exogenous ACTH that precedes complete recovery of the hypothalamic-pituitary-adrenal axis. Therefore, such patients should receive glucocorticoids during periods of stress for at least 1 year after steroids are discontinued, unless the hypothalamic-pituitary axis is shown to be responsive to stress as described below.

Pituitary Stimulation

Direct evaluation of pituitary ACTH reserve can be performed by means of insulin-induced hypoglycemia metyrapone administration or CRH stimulation. These studies are unnecessary if the cortisol response to rapid ACTH stimulation is subnormal.

A. Insulin-Induced Hypoglycemia: The stimulus of neuroglycopenia associated with hypoglycemia (blood glucose < 40 mg/dL) evokes a stress-mediated activation of the hypothalamic-pituitary-adrenal axis. Subjects should experience adrenergic symptoms (diaphoresis, tachycardia, weakness, headache) associated with the fall in blood sugar. In normal persons, plasma cortisol increases to more than 20 μg/dL (552 mmol/L), indicating normal ACTH reserve. Although plasma ACTH also rises, its determination has not proved to be as useful, since pulsatile secretion requires frequent sampling, and the normal response is not well standardized. Although insulin-induced hypoglycemia most reliably predicts ACTH secretory capacity in times of stress, this procedure requires a physician's presence and is contraindicated in elderly patients, patients with cerebrovascu-

lar or cardiovascular disease, and those with seizure disorders. It should be used with caution in patients in whom diminished adrenal reserve is suspected, since severe hypoglycemia may occur; in these patients, the test should always be preceded by the ACTH adrenal stimulation test.

B. Metyrapone Stimulation: Metyrapone administration is an alternative method for assessing ACTH secretory reserve. Metyrapone inhibits P450c11 (11β-hydroxylase), the enzyme that catalyzes the final step in cortisol biosynthesis (see Chapter 6). The inhibition of cortisol secretion interrupts negative feedback on the hypothalamic-pituitary axis, resulting in a compensatory increase in ACTH. The increase in ACTH secretion stimulates increased steroid biosynthesis proximal to P450c11, and the increase can be detected as an increase in the precursor steroid (11-deoxycortisol) in plasma or by increases in urinary 17-hydroxycorticosteroids, which measure the urinary metabolite of 11-deoxycortisol. Two methods are available. The overnight test is preferred because of its simplicity; it is performed by administering 2–3 g of metyrapone orally at midnight. Plasma 11-deoxycortisol is determined the following morning and rises to greater than 7 μg/dL (0.19 μmol/L) in healthy individuals. Again, the test should be used cautiously in patients with suspected adrenal insufficiency and should be preceded by a rapid ACTH stimulation test (see above). Metyrapone may also be given in doses of 750 mg every 4 hours for 24 hours, with collection of urine for 17-hydroxycorticosteroid determination before, during, and for 24 hours after metyrapone. The urinary 17-hydroxycorticosteroid concentration doubles in healthy individuals. The test is cumbersome because of the difficulty in collecting 24-hour urine samples, and there is a danger of provoking symptomatic adrenal insufficiency because of the large metyrapone doses.

C. CRH Stimulation: Ovine CRH administered intravenously is used to assess ACTH secretory dynamics. In healthy subjects, CRH (1 μg/kg) provokes a peak ACTH response within 15 minutes and a peak cortisol response within 30–60 minutes. This dose may be associated with mild flushing, occasional shortness of breath, tachycardia, and hypotension. Patients with primary adrenal insufficiency have elevated basal ACTH levels and exaggerated responses to CRH. Secondary adrenal insufficiency results in an absent ACTH response to CRH in patients with pituitary corticotroph destruction; however, in patients with hypothalamic dysfunction, there is a prolonged and augmented ACTH response to CRH with a delayed peak.

ACTH Hypersecretion

ACTH hypersecretion is manifested by adrenocortical hyperfunction (Cushing's syndrome). The diagnosis and differential diagnosis of ACTH hypersecretion are outlined in a later section on Cushing's disease and also in Chapter 6.

EVALUATION OF GROWTH HORMONE

The evaluation of GH secretory reserve is important in the assessment of children with short stature and in adults with suspected hypopituitarism. Provocative tests are necessary because basal levels of GH are usually low and do not distinguish between normal and GH-deficient conditions.

Insulin-Induced Hypoglycemia

The most reliable stimulus of GH secretion is insulin-induced hypoglycemia. In normal individuals, GH levels will increase to more than 10 ng/mL (465 pmol/L) after adequate hypoglycemia is achieved. Since 10% of normal individuals fail to respond to hypoglycemia, other stimulatory tests may be necessary.

Tests with Levodopa, Arginine & Other Stimuli

GH rises after oral administration of levodopa, a precursor of dopamine and norepinephrine that readily crosses the blood-brain barrier. About 80% of healthy subjects have a GH response greater than 6 ng/mL (279 pmol/L), and the mean maximal response is 28 ng/mL (1302 pmol/L). This test is safer than insulin-induced hypoglycemia in older patients. An Arginine infusion will raise GH in 70% of healthy individuals. Pretreatment with estrogen will enhance this response in many of the nonresponders, most of whom are men. Other stimuli, such as propranolol and glucagon, have also been utilized in assessing GH secretory capacity.

GRH Test

Both forms of human GRH (GRH-40 and GRH-44) have been used to evaluate GH secretory capacity. A dose of GRH (1 μg/kg) promptly stimulates GH; the mean peak is 10–15 ng/mL (465–697 pmol/L) at 30–60 minutes in healthy subjects. There is usually a small increase in IGF-1 levels 24 hours after the administration of GRH.

Exercise Test

An exercise test requiring 15 minutes of rapid stair-climbing is a convenient way to assess GH secretion. Hypogonadal or prepubertal children are usually pretreated for 3 days with estrogen, and an increment of greater than 5 ng/mL (232 pmol/L) constitutes a normal response.

GH Hypersecretion

The evaluation of GH hypersecretion is discussed in the section on acromegaly and is most conveniently assessed by suppression testing with oral glucose.

EVALUATION OF PROLACTIN

PRL secretion by the pituitary is the most resistant to local damage, and decreased PRL secretory reserve indicates severe intrinsic pituitary disease.

Prolactin Reserve

The administration of TRH is the simplest and most reliable means of assessing PRL reserve. Although the response of PRL to TRH varies somewhat according to sex and age (Table 2–7), PRL levels usually increase twofold 15–30 minutes after TRH administration. In addition, insulin-induced hypoglycemia will evoke a stress-related increase in PRL.

PRL Hypersecretion

PRL hypersecretion is a common endocrine problem. Its evaluation is discussed in the section on prolactinomas.

EVALUATION OF TSH

Basal Measurements

The laboratory evaluation of TSH secretory reserve begins with an assessment of target gland secretion; thyroid function tests (Free Thyroxine [FT_4], or Free Thyroxine Index [FT_4I]) should be obtained. Normal thyroid function studies in a clinically euthyroid patient indicate adequate TSH secretion, and no further studies are warranted. Laboratory evidence of hypothyroidism requires measurement of a TSH level. With primary thyroid gland failure, the TSH level will be elevated; low or normal TSH in the presence of hypothyroidism suggests hypothalamic-pituitary dysfunction.

Table 2–7. Normal responses to TSH and prolactin to TRH (500 μg).

	TSH	
	(μU/mL)	(mU/L)
Maximum Δ TSH		
Women and men aged <40	≥ 6	≥ 6
Men aged 40–79	≥ 2	≥ 2
Time of maximum Δ TSH (min)	≤ 45	
	Prolactin	
	(ng/mL)	(pmol/L)
Basal, men and women	< 15	< 681
Maximum Δ prolactin		
Men aged 20–39	25–49	681–1818
Men aged 40–59	19–50	454–2272
Men aged 60–79	5–90	227–4090
Women aged 20–39	30–120	1383–5454
Women aged 40–59	20–120	909–5454
Women aged 60–79	10–100	454–4545

[1] Reproduced, with permission, from Snyder PJ et al: Diagnostic value of thyrotrophin-releasing hormone in pituitary and hypothalamic diseases: Assessment of thyrotrophin and prolactin secretion in 100 patients. Ann Intern Med 1974;61:751.

TRH Test

In healthy subjects, TRH (protirelin) produces an increase of TSH of at least 6 μU/mL (6 mU/L) within 15–30 minutes (Table 2–7). In patients with primary hypothyroidism, an elevated TSH level confirms the diagnosis; thus, the TRH test is not indicated. Patients with secondary hypothyroidism have normal to low basal TSH levels, and an impaired or absent TSH response in these patients implicates hypothalamic-pituitary failure. Patients with hypothalamic disease often show a delayed TSH response (60–120 minutes) to TRH (see Figure 4–25) and, less commonly, an exaggerated TSH increase. Unlike gonadotropic function, prolonged TRH deficiency does not impair TSH responsiveness. Many patients with hypothyroidism due to pituitary disease have normal responses to TRH, or responses that resemble hypothalamic dysfunction. Accordingly, the TRH test is not always a reliable way to differentiate pituitary from hypothalamic disease.

Responsiveness to TRH is often impaired in patients with hypothalamic pituitary disease (eg, acromegaly, Cushing's syndrome) who are euthyroid. Since GH or cortisol excess may decrease the TSH response to TRH, an absent response does not always indicate destruction of thyrotrophs. (See also Chapter 4.)

EVALUATION OF LH & FSH

Testosterone & Estrogen Levels

The evaluation of gonadotropin function also requires assessment of target gland secretory function, and measurement of gonadal steroids (testosterone in men, estradiol in women) is useful in the diagnosis of hypogonadism. In women, the presence of regular menstrual cycles is strong evidence that the hypothalamic-pituitary-gonadal axis is intact. Estradiol levels rarely fall below 50 pg/mL (184 pmol/L), even during the early follicular phase. A level of less than 30 pg/mL (110 pmol/L) in the presence of oligomenorrhea or amenorrhea is indicative of gonadal failure. In men, serum testosterone (normal range, 300–1000 ng/dL (10–35 nmol/L) is a sensitive index of gonadal function.

LH & FSH Levels

In the presence of gonadal insufficiency, high LH and FSH levels are a sign of primary gonadal disease; low or normal LH and FSH suggest hypothalamic-pituitary dysfunction (hypogonadotropic hypogonadism).

GnRH Test

LH and FSH secretory reserves may be assessed with the use of synthetic GnRH (gonadorelin). Administration of GnRH causes a prompt increase in plasma LH and a lesser and slower increase in FSH (for normal responses, see Table 2–6). The LH response to GnRH is lowest during the follicular phase and greatest during the ovulatory surge. Normal subjects may have no FSH response to GnRH. On the other hand, in prepubertal children and in some patients with hyperprolactinemia, the FSH response is greater than that of LH.

A single GnRH test does not distinguish hypothalamic from pituitary disease. Patients with disturbances of the hypothalamus and pituitary may have an absent, normal, or exaggerated gonadotropin response to GnRH. Hypothalamic disease with longstanding GnRH deficiency results in an absent LH response to GnRH, but normal responsiveness may be restored with more prolonged and intermittent stimulation.

Clomiphene Test

Clomiphene citrate, an antiestrogen that blocks estrogen receptors, causes a state of functional estrogen deficiency resulting in GnRH and gonadotropin release. The occurrence of a normal menstrual period approximately 12 days after administration of the drug or evidence of ovulation by basal body temperature constitutes a normal response. Failure of LH levels to increase after 5–10 days of clomiphene in a patient with a normal GnRH test suggests hypothalamic disease. (See Chapter 10.)

PROBLEMS IN EVALUATION OF THE HYPOTHALAMIC-PITUITARY AXIS

This section briefly outlines some of the disorders and conditions that may cause confusion and lead to misinterpretation of pituitary function tests. The effects of drugs are described in the next section.

Obesity

GH dynamics are impaired in many obese patients; all provocative stimuli, including insulin-induced hypoglycemia, arginine, levodopa, and glucagon plus propranolol, often fail to provoke GH secretion. The GH response to GRH is also impaired in obesity and improves with weight loss. Obesity may increase urinary 17-hydroxycorticosteroid levels and the cortisol secretory rate; however, urinary free cortisol excretion is unchanged. Plasma cortisol demonstrates normal diurnal variation and responds to hypoglycemia. The cortisol response to CRH is also blunted in obesity.

Diabetes Mellitus

Although glucose normally suppresses GH secretion, most type I diabetic individuals have normal or elevated GH levels that often do not rise further in response to hypoglycemia or arginine. Levodopa will increase GH in some diabetic patients, and even a dopamine infusion (which produces no GH change in nondiabetic subjects, since it does not cross the blood-brain barrier) will stimulate GH in diabetic patients. Despite the increased GH secretion in patients with inadequately controlled diabetes, the GH response to GRH in insulin-dependent diabetic patients is similar to that of nondiabetic subjects. IGF-1 levels are low in insulin-deficient diabetes despite the elevated GH levels.

Uremia

Basal levels of GH, PRL, LH, FSH, TSH, and free cortisol tend to be elevated, for the most part owing to prolongation of their plasma half-life. GH may paradoxically increase following glucose administration and is often hyperresponsive to a hypoglycemic stimulus. Although the administration of TRH (protirelin) has no effect on GH secretion in healthy subjects, the drug may increase GH in patients with chronic renal failure. The response of PRL to TRH is blunted and prolonged. Gonadotropin response to synthetic GnRH usually remains intact. Dexamethasone suppression of cortisol may be impaired.

Starvation & Anorexia Nervosa

GH secretion increases with fasting and malnutrition, and such conditions may cause a paradoxical increase in GH following glucose administration. Severe starvation, such as occurs in patients with anorexia nervosa, may result in low levels of gonadal steroids. LH and FSH responses to GnRH may be intact despite a state of functional hypogonadotropic hypogonadism. Cortisol levels may be increased and fail to suppress adequately with dexamethasone. PRL and TSH dynamics are usually normal despite a marked decrease in circulating total thyroid hormones (see Chapter 4).

Depression

Depression may alter the ability of dexamethasone to suppress plasma cortisol and may elevate cortisol secretion; the response to insulin-induced hypoglycemia usually remains intact. The ACTH response to CRH is blunted in endogenous depression. Some depressed patients also have abnormal GH dynamics: TRH may increase GH, and hypoglycemia or levodopa may fail to increase GH. These patients may also show blunted TSH responses to TRH.

EFFECTS OF PHARMACOLOGIC AGENTS ON HYPOTHALAMIC-PITUITARY FUNCTION

Glucocorticoid excess impairs the GH response to hypoglycemia, the TSH response to TRH, and the LH response to GnRH. Estrogens tend to augment GH dynamics as well as the PRL and TSH response to TRH. Estrogens increase plasma cortisol secondary to a rise in corticosteroid-binding globulin and may result in inadequate suppression with dexamethasone.

Phenytoin enhances the metabolism of dexamethasone, making studies with this agent difficult to interpret. Phenothiazines may blunt the GH response to hypoglycemia and levodopa and frequently cause

hyperprolactinemia. The many other pharmacologic agents that increase PRL secretion are listed in Table 2–5.

Narcotics, including heroin, morphine, and methadone, may all raise PRL levels and suppress GH and cortisol response to hypoglycemia.

In chronic alcoholics, alcohol excess or withdrawal may increase cortisol levels and cause inadequate dexamethasone suppression and an impaired cortisol increase after hypoglycemia.

ENDOCRINE TESTS OF HYPOTHALAMIC-PITUITARY FUNCTION

Methods for performing endocrine tests and their normal responses are described below. The indications for and the clinical utility of these procedures are described in the preceding section and will be mentioned again in the section on pituitary and hypothalamic disorders.

Rapid ACTH Stimulation Test (Cosyntropin Test)

Method: Administer synthetic $ACTH_{1-24}$ (cosyntropin), 250 µg intravenously or intramuscularly. The test may be performed at any time of the day or night and does not require fasting.

Sample collection: Obtain samples for plasma cortisol at 0 and 30 minutes or at 0 and 60 minutes.

Possible side effects; contraindications: Rare allergic reactions have been reported.

Interpretation: A normal response is a peak plasma cortisol level > 20 µg/dL (552 nmol/L).

Insulin Hypoglycemia Test

Method: Give nothing by mouth after midnight. Start an intravenous infusion with normal saline solution. Regular insulin is given intravenously in a dose sufficient to cause adequate hypoglycemia (blood glucose < 40 mg/dL). The dose is 0.1–0.15 unit/kg (healthy subjects); 0.2–0.3 unit/kg (obese subjects or those with Cushing's syndrome or acromegaly); 0.05 unit/kg (patients with suspected hypopituitarism).

Sample collection: Collect blood for glucose determinations every 15 minutes during the study. Samples of GH and cortisol are obtained at 0, 30, 45, 60, 75, and 90 minutes.

Possible side effects; contraindications: A physician must be in attendance. Symptomatic hypoglycemia (diaphoresis, headache, tachycardia, weakness) is necessary for adequate stimulation and occurs 20–35 minutes after insulin is administered in most patients. If severe central nervous system signs or symptoms occur, intravenous glucose (25–50 mL of 50% glucose) should be given immediately; otherwise, the test can be terminated with a meal or oral glucose. This test is contraindicated in the elderly or in patients with cardiovascular or cerebrovascular disease and seizure disorders.

Interpretation: Symptomatic hypoglycemia and a fall in blood glucose to less than 40 mg/dL (2.2 mmol/L) will increase GH to a maximal level greater than 10 ng/mL (454 pmol/L); some investigators regard an increment of 6 ng/mL (279 pmol/L) as normal. Plasma cortisol should increase to a peak level of at least 20 μg/dL (552 nmol/L).

Metyrapone Tests

Method:

Overnight test: Metyrapone is given orally between 11 and 12 PM with a snack to minimize gastrointestinal discomfort. The dose is 2 g for patients weighing less than 70 kg; 2.5 g for patients weighing 79–90 kg; and 3 g for patients weighing over 90 kg.

Three-day test: Twenty-four-hour urine collections are made for 3 consecutive days, and metyrapone, 750 mg, is given every 4 hours for six doses on the second day.

Sample collection:

Overnight test: Blood for plasma 11-deoxycortisol and cortisol determinations is obtained at 8 AM the morning after metyrapone is given.

Three-day test: The three consecutive 24-hour urine samples are analyzed for 17-hydroxycorticosteroids and creatinine determinations.

Possible side effects; contraindications: Gastrointestinal upset may occur. Adrenal insufficiency may occur. Metyrapone should not be used in sick patients or those in whom primary adrenal insufficiency is suspected.

Interpretation:

Overnight test: Serum 11-deoxycortisol should increase to > 7 μg/dL (0.19 μmol/L). Cortisol should be < 10 μg/dL (0.28 μmol/L) in order to ensure adequate inhibition of 11β-hydroxylation.

Three-day test: Urine 17-hydroxycorticosteroids should double on day 2 or 3.

Levodopa Test

Method: The patient should be fasting and at bed rest after midnight. Levodopa, 500 mg, is given by mouth.

Sample collection: Blood samples for plasma GH determinations are obtained at 0, 30, and 60 minutes.

Possible side effects; contraindications: Nausea and vomiting may occur 45–60 minutes after levodopa is given. This test is safer than the insulin hypoglycemia test in older patients.

Interpretation: A normal response is a maximal level of GH greater than 6 ng/mL (279 pmol/L); however, the peak response is usually more than 20 ng/mL (930 pmol/L).

Arginine Infusion Test

Method: The patient should be fasting after midnight. Give arginine hydrochloride, 0.5 g/kg intravenously, up to a maximum of 30 g over 30 minutes.

Pretreatment with estrogen in postmenopausal women and in men can also be done.

Sample collection: Blood for plasma GH determinations is collected at 0, 30, 60, 90, and 120 minutes. Arginine infusion also stimulates insulin and glucagon.

Possible side effects; contraindications: Nausea and vomiting may occur. This test is contraindicated in patients with severe liver disease, renal disease, or acidosis.

Interpretation: The response is greater in women than in men. The lower limit of normal for the peak GH response is 6 ng/mL (279 pmol/L) in non-estrogen-treated patients and 10 ng/mL (465 pmol/L) in estrogen-treated patients and premenopausal women.

Glucose-Growth Hormone Suppression Test

Method: The patient should be fasting after midnight. Give glucose, 75–100 g orally.

Sample collection: GH and glucose should be determined at 0, 30, and 60 minutes after glucose administration.

Possible side effects; contraindications: Patients may complain of nausea after the large glucose load.

Interpretation: GH levels are suppressed to less than 2 ng/mL (93 pmol/L). in healthy subjects. Failure of adequate suppression or a paradoxical rise may be seen in acromegaly, starvation, protein-calorie malnutrition, and anorexia nervosa.

TRH Test

Method: Fasting is not required, but since nausea may occur, it is preferred. Give protirelin, 500 μg intravenously over 15–30 seconds. The patient should be kept supine, since slight hypertension or hypotension may occur. Protirelin is supplied in vials of 500 μg, although 400 μg will evoke normal responses.

Sample collection: Blood for determination of plasma TSH, PRL, or GH (in the case of suspected acromegaly) is obtained at 0, 30, and 60 minutes; a 90-minute sample for TSH may be necessary in cases of suspected tertiary hypothyroidism. An abbreviated test utilizes samples taken at 0 and 30 minutes only.

Possible side effects; contraindications: No serious complications have been reported. Most patients complain of a sensation of urinary urgency and a metallic taste in the mouth; other symptoms include flushing, palpitations, and nausea. These symptoms occur within 1–2 minutes of the injection and last 5 minutes at most.

Interpretation: Normal TSH and PRL responses to TRH are outlined in Table 2–7. GH should not increase in healthy subjects.

GnRH Test

Method: The patient should be at rest but need not be fasting. Give GnRH (gonadorelin), 100 μg intravenously, over 15 seconds.

Sample collection: Blood samples for LH and FSH determinations are taken at 0, 30, and 60 minutes. Since the FSH response is somewhat delayed, a 90-minute specimen may be necessary.

Possible side effects; contraindications: Side effects are rare, and no contraindications have been found.

Interpretation: This response is dependent on sex and time of the menstrual cycle. Table 2–6 illustrates the mean maximal change in LH and FSH after GnRH administration. An increase of LH of 1.3–2.6 μg/L (11.7–23.4 IU/L) is considered to be normal; FSH usually responds more slowly and less markedly. FSH may not increase even in healthy subjects.

Clomiphene Test

Method: Clomiphene is administered orally. For women, give 100 mg daily for 5 days (being on day 5 of the cycle if the patient is menstruating); for men, give 100 mg daily for 7–10 days.

Sample collection: Blood for LH and FSH determinations is drawn before and after clomiphene is given.

Possible side effects; contraindications: This drug may, of course, stimulate ovulation, and women should be advised accordingly.

Interpretation: In women, LH and FSH levels peak on the fifth day to a level above the normal range. After the fifth day, LH and FSH levels decline. In men, LH should double after 1 week; FSH will also increase, but to a lesser extent.

CRH Test

Method: CRH (1μg/kg) is given intravenously as a bolus injection.

Sample collection: Blood samples for ACTH and cortisol are taken at 0, 15, 30, and 60 minutes.

Possible side effects; contraindications: Flushing often occurs. Transient tachycardia and hypotension have also been reported.

Interpretation: The ACTH response is dependent on the assay utilized and occurs 15 minutes after CRH is administered. The peak cortisol response occurs at 30–60 minutes and is usually greater than 10 μg/dL (276 nmol/L).

GRH Test

Method: GRH (1 μg/kg) is given intravenously as a bolus injection.

Sample collection: Blood samples for GH are drawn at 0, 30, and 60 minutes.

Possible side effects; contraindications: Mild flushing and a metallic taste or smell occur in a few patients.

Interpretation: The range of normal responses is wide. Most patients have a peak GH response of greater than 10 ng/mL (465 pmol/L) at 30–60 minutes.

NEURORADIOLOGIC EVALUTION

Symptoms of pituitary hormone excess or deficiency, headache, or visual disturbance lead the clinician to consider a hypothalamic-pituitary disorder. In this setting, accurate neuroradiologic assessment of the hypothalamus and pituitary is essential in confirming the existence and defining the extent of hypothalamic-pituitary lesions; however, the diagnosis of such lesions should be based on both endocrine and radiologic criteria. This is because variability of pituitary anatomy in the normal population may lead to false-positive interpretations. Furthermore, patients with pituitary microadenomas may have normal neuroradiologic studies. Imaging studies must be interpreted in light of the fact that 10–20% of the general population harbor nonfunctional and asymptomatic pituitary microadenomas.

MRI is the current procedure of choice for imaging the hypothalamus and pituitary. It has superseded the use of CT since it allows better definition of normal structures and has better resolution in defining tumors. Arteriography is rarely utilized at present except in patients with intrasellar or parasellar aneurysms.

Magnetic Resonance Imaging (MRI)

Imaging is performed in sagittal and coronal planes at 1.5–2 mm intervals. This allows clear definition of hypothalamic and pituitary anatomy and can accurately visualize lesions as small as 3–5 mm. The use of the heavy-metal contrast agent gadolinium allows even more precise differentiation of small pituitary adenomas from normal anterior pituitary tissue and other adjacent structures.

A. Normal Anatomy: The normal anterior pituitary is 5–7 mm in height and approximately 10 mm in its lateral dimensions. The superior margin is flat or concave but may be upwardly convex with a height of 10–12 mm in healthy menstruating young women. The floor of the sella turcica is formed by the bony roof of the sphenoid sinus, and its lateral margins are formed by the dural membranes of the cavernous sinuses, which contain the carotid arteries and the third, fourth, and sixth cranial nerves. The posterior pituitary appears on MRI as a high-signal-intensity structure, the "posterior pituitary bright spot," which is absent in patients with diabetes insipidus. The pituitary stalk, which is normally in the midline, is 2–3 mm in diameter and 5–7 mm in length. The pituitary stalk joins the inferior hypothalamus below the third ventricle and posterior to the optic chiasm. All of these normal structures are readily visualized with MRI; the normal pituitary and the pituitary stalk show increased signal intensity with gadolinium.

B. Microadenomas: These lesions, which range from 2 mm to 10 mm in diameter, appear as low-signal-intensity lesions with MRI and do not usually enhance with gadolinium. Adenomas less than 5 mm in diameter may not be visualized and do not usually alter the normal pituitary contour. Lesions greater than 5 mm in diameter create a unilateral convex superior gland margin and usually cause deviation of the pituitary stalk toward the side opposite the adenoma.

MRI scans must be interpreted with caution, since minor abnormalities occur in 10–20% of patients who have had incidental high-resolution scans but no clinical pituitary disease. These abnormalities may of course represent the clinically insignificant pituitary abnormalities seen in 10–20% of the general population, and they may also be due to small intrapituitary cysts, which usually occur in the pars intermedia. Artifacts within the sella turcica associated with the bones of the skull base may also result in misinterpretation of imaging studies. Finally, many patients with pituitary microadenomas have normal high-resolution MRI scans. Therefore, despite increased accuracy of neuroradiologic diagnosis, the presence or absence of a small pituitary tumor and the decision concerning its treatment must be based on the entire clinical picture.

C. Macroadenomas: Pituitary adenomas greater than 10 mm in diameter are readily visualized with MRI scans, and the scan will also define the adjacent structures and degree of extension of the lesion. Thus, larger tumors show compression of the normal pituitary and distortion of the pituitary stalk. Adenomas larger than 1.5 cm frequently have suprasellar extension, and MRI scans show compression and upward displacement of the optic chiasm. Less commonly, there is lateral extension and invasion of the cavernous sinus.

D. Other Uses: High-resolution MRI scanning is also a valuable tool in the diagnosis of empty sella syndrome, hypothalamic tumors, and other parasellar lesions.

PITUITARY & HYPOTHALAMIC DISORDERS

Hypothalamic-pituitary lesions present with a variety of manifestations, including pituitary hormone hypersecretion and hyposecretion, sellar enlargement, and visual loss. The approach to evaluation should be designed to ensure early diagnosis at a stage when the lesions are amenable to therapy.

Etiology & Early Manifestations

In adults, the commonest cause of hypothalamic-pituitary dysfunction is a pituitary adenoma, of which the great majority are hypersecreting. Thus, the earliest symptoms of such tumors are due to endocrinologic abnormalities, and these precede sellar enlargement and local manifestations such as headache and visual loss, which are late manifestations seen only in patients with larger tumors or suprasellar extension.

In children, pituitary adenomas are uncommon; the most frequent structural lesions causing hypothala-

mic-pituitary dysfunction are craniopharyngiomas and other hypothalamic tumors. These also usually manifest as endocrine disturbances (low GH levels, delayed puberty, diabetes insipidus) prior to the development of headache, visual loss, or other central nervous system symptoms.

Common & Later Manifestations

A. Pituitary Hypersecretion: PRL is the hormone most commonly secreted in excess amounts by pituitary adenomas, and it is usually elevated in patients with hypothalamic disorders as well. Thus, PRL measurement is essential in evaluating patients with suspected pituitary disorders and should be performed in patients presenting with galactorrhea, gonadal dysfunction, secondary gonadotropin deficiency, or enlargement of the sella turcica. Hypersecretion of GH or ACTH leads to the more characteristic syndromes of acromegaly and Cushing's disease (see below).

B. Pituitary Insufficiency: Although panhypopituitarism is a classic manifestation of pituitary adenomas, it is present in less than 20% of patients in current large series because of earlier diagnosis of these lesions.

At present, the earliest clinical manifestation of a pituitary adenoma in adults is hypogonadism secondary to elevated levels of PRL, GH, or ACTH and cortisol—or interference with transport of GnRH—rather than to destruction of anterior pituitary tissue. Thus, patients with hypogonadism should first be screened with FSH/LH measurements to exclude primary gonadal failure (elevated FSH/LH) and those with hypogonadotropic hypogonadism should have serum PRL levels measured and be examined for clinical evidence of GH or ACTH and cortisol excess.

In children, short stature is the most frequent clinical presentation of hypothalamic-pituitary dysfunction; in these patients, GH deficiency should be considered.

TSH or ACTH deficiency is relatively unusual in current series of patients and usually indicates panhypopituitarism. Thus, patients with secondary hypothyroidism or hypoadrenalism should undergo a complete assessment of pituitary function and neuroradiologic studies, since panhypopituitarism and large pituitary tumors are common in this setting. PRL measurement is again essential, since prolactinomas are the most frequent pituitary tumors in adults.

C. Enlarged Sella Turcica: Patients may present with enlargement of the sella turcica, which may be noted on radiographs performed for head trauma or on sinus series. These patients usually have either a pituitary adenoma or empty sella syndrome. Evaluation should include clinical assessment of pituitary dysfunction and measurements of PRL and thyroid and adrenal function. Pituitary function is usually normal in the empty sella syndrome; this diagnosis can be confirmed by MRI. Patients with clinical or laboratory evidence of pituitary dysfunction usually have a pituitary adenoma.

D. Visual Field Defects: Patients presenting with bitemporal hemianopsia or unexplained visual field defects or visual loss should be considered to have a pituitary or hypothalamic disorder until proved otherwise. The initial steps in diagnosis should be neuro-ophthalmologic evaluation and neuroradiologic studies with MRI which will reveal the tumor if one is present. These patients should also have PRL measurements and be assessed for anterior pituitary insufficiency, which is especially common with large pituitary adenomas.

In addition to causing visual field defects, large pituitary lesions may occasionally extend laterally into the cavernous sinus, compromising the function of the third, fourth, or sixth cranial nerve, leading to diplopia.

E. Diabetes Insipidus: Diabetes insipidus is a common manifestation of hypothalamic lesions but is rare in primary pituitary lesions. Diagnostic evaluation is described later. In addition, all patients should undergo radiologic evaluation and assessment of anterior pituitary function.

EMPTY SELLA SYNDROME

Etiology & Incidence

The empty sella syndrome occurs when the subarachnoid space extends into the sella turcica, partially filling it with cerebrospinal fluid. This process causes remodeling and enlargement of the sella turcica and flattening of the pituitary gland.

Primary empty sella syndrome resulting from congenital incompetence of the diaphragma sellae (Figure 2–16) is common, with a prevalence in autopsy series ranging from 5% to 23%. It is the most frequent cause of enlarged sella turcica. An empty sella is also commonly seen after pituitary surgery or radiation therapy and may also occur following postpartum pituitary infarction (Sheehan's syndrome). In addition, both PRL-secreting and GH-secreting pituitary adenomas may undergo subclinical hemorrhagic infarction and cause contraction of the overlying suprasellar cistern downward into the sella. Therefore, the presence of an empty sella does not exclude the possibility of a coexisting pituitary tumor.

Pathogenesis

The pathogenesis of primary empty sella syndrome is uncertain. It has been postulated that increased cerebrospinal fluid pressure leads to herniation of arachnoid through the diaphragma sellae. A mesenchymal defect may be present in some patients, resulting in hypoplasia of the sellar diaphragm. A kindred has been described in which both primary empty sella syndrome and Rieger's anomaly of the anterior chamber of the eye (a developmental abnormality of mesenchymal origin involving the iris) occurred in an autosomal dominant fashion.

Clinical Features

A. Symptoms and Signs: Most patients are middle-aged obese women. Many have systemic hypertension; benign intracranial hypertension may also occur. Although 48% of patients complain of headache, this feature may have only initiated the evalua-

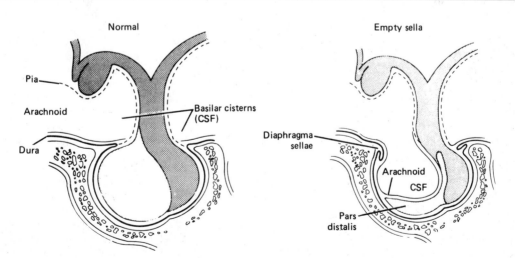

Figure 2–16. Representation of the normal relationship of the meninges to the pituitary gland *(left)* and the findings in the empty sella *(right)* as the arachnoid membrane herniates through the incompetent diaphragma sellae. (Reproduced, with permission, from Jordan RM, Kendall JW, Kerber CW: The primary empty sella syndrome: Analysis of the clinical characteristics, radiographic features, pituitary function, and cerebrospinal fluid adenohypophysial hormone concentrations. Am J Med 1977;62:569.)

tion (ie, skull x-rays), and its relationship with the empty sella is probably coincidental. Serious clinical manifestations are uncommon. Spontaneous cerebrospinal fluid rhinorrhea and visual field impairment may rarely occur.

B. Laboratory Findings: Tests of anterior pituitary function are almost always normal. This observation correlates well with histologic immunocytochemical studies of the pituitary gland in patients with the syndrome. Such studies have demonstrated that the remodeled pituitary gland contains adequate amounts of all six adenohypophysial hormones. TSH, GH, and gonadotropin secretory reserves have rarely been reported to be impaired; however, pituitary hypofunction in such cases may result from subclinical pituitary ischemic damage followed by contraction of glandular tissue and a secondary empty sella.

Endocrine function studies should be performed to exclude pituitary hormone insufficiency or a hypersecretory pituitary adenoma.

Diagnosis

The diagnosis of the empty sella syndrome can be readily confirmed by MRI which demonstrates the presence of cerebrospinal fluid in the sella turcica.

HYPOTHALAMIC DYSFUNCTION

Hypothalamic dysfunction is most often caused by tumors, of which craniopharyngioma is the most common in children, adolescents, and young adults. In older adults, primary central nervous system tumors and those arising from hypothalamic (epidermoid and dermoid tumors) and pineal structures (pinealomas) are more common. Other causes of hypothalamic-pituitary dysfunction are discussed below in the section on hypopituitarism.

Clinical Features

A. Craniopharyngioma: The initial symptoms of craniopharyngioma in children and adolescents are predominantly endocrinologic; however, these manifestations are frequently unrecognized, and at diagnosis over 80% of patients have hypothalamic-pituitary endocrine deficiencies. These endocrine abnormalities may precede presenting symptoms by months or years; GH deficiency is most common, with about 50% of patients having growth retardation and approximately 70% decreased GH responses to stimulation at diagnosis. Gonadotropin deficiency leading to absent or arrested puberty is usual in older children and adolescents; TSH and ACTH deficiency is less common, and diabetes insipidus is present in about 15%.

Symptoms leading to the diagnosis are, unfortunately, frequently neurologic and due to the mass effect of the expanding tumor. Symptoms of increased intracranial pressure such as headache and vomiting

are present in about 42%; decreased visual acuity or visual field defects are the presenting symptoms in another 35%. Plain films of the skull reveal intrasellar or suprasellar calcification in 75% of these children. MRI confirms the tumor in virtually all patients; in 95%, the tumor is suprasellar.

In adults, craniopharyngiomas have similar presentations; ie, the diagnosis is usually reached as a result of investigation of symptoms of increased intracranial pressure, headache, or visual loss. However, endocrine manifestations—especially hypogonadism, diabetes insipidus, or other deficiencies of anterior pituitary hormones—usually precede these late manifestations. Intrasellar or suprasellar calcification is less common in adults (for unknown reasons), but scans again readily demonstrate the tumors, which in adults are almost always both intrasellar and suprasellar.

B. Other Tumors: Other hypothalamic or pineal tumors and primary central nervous system tumors involving the hypothalamus have variable presentations in both children and adults. Thus, presentation is with headache, visual loss, symptoms of increased intracranial pressure, growth failure, various degrees of hypopituitarism, or diabetes insipidus. Endocrine deficiencies usually precede neurologic manifestations. Hypothalamic tumors in childhood may present with precocious puberty.

C. Other Manifestations of Hypothalamic Dysfunction: Lesions in the hypothalamus can cause many other abnormalities, including disorders of consciousness, behavior, thirst, appetite, and temperature regulation. These abnormalities are usually accompanied by hypopituitarism and diabetes insipidus.

Somnolence can occur with hypothalamic lesions, as can a variety of changes in emotional behavior. Decreased or absent thirst may occur and predispose these patients to dehydration. When diminished thirst accompanies diabetes insipidus, fluid balance is difficult to control. Hypothalamic dysfunction may also cause increased thirst, leading to polydipsia and polyuria that may mimic diabetes insipidus. Obesity is common in patients with hypothalamic tumors because of hyperphagia, decreased satiety, and decreased activity. Anorexia and weight loss are unusual manifestations of these tumors.

Temperature regulation can also be disordered in these patients. Sustained or, less commonly, paroxysmal hyperthermia can occur following acute injury due to trauma, hemorrhage, or craniotomy. This problem usually lasts less than 2 weeks. Poikilothermia, the inability to adjust to changes in ambient temperature, can occur in patients with bilateral hypothalamic lesions. These patients most frequently exhibit hypothermia but can also develop hyperthermia during hot weather. A few patients manifest sustained hypothermia due to anterior hypothalamic lesions.

Diagnosis

Patients with suspected hypothalamic tumors should have MRI studies to determine the extent and nature of the tumor. Complete assessment of anterior pituitary function is necessary in these patients, since deficiencies are present in the great majority (see section on hypopituitarism below) and the evaluation will establish the requirements for replacement therapy. PRL levels should also be determined, since most hypothalamic lesions cause hyperprolactinemia either by hypothalamic injury or by damage to the pituitary stalk.

Treatment

Treatment depends upon the type of tumor. Since complete resection of craniopharyngioma is usually not feasible, this tumor is best managed by limited neurosurgical removal of accessible tumor and decompression of cysts, followed by conventional radiotherapy. Patients treated by this method have a recurrence rate of approximately 20%; with surgery alone, the recurrence rate approximates 80%.

Other hypothalamic tumors are usually not completely resectable; however, biopsy is indicated to arrive at a histologic diagnosis.

HYPOPITUITARISM

Hypopituitarism is manifested by diminished or absent secretion of one or more pituitary hormones. The development of signs and symptoms is often slow and insidious, depending on the rate of onset and the magnitude of hypothalamic-pituitary damage—factors that are influenced by the underlying pathogenesis. Hypopituitarism is either a primary event caused by destruction of the anterior pituitary gland or a secondary phenomenon resulting from deficiency of hypothalamic stimulatory (or inhibitory) factors normally acting on the pituitary. Although provocative endocrine testing is useful in evaluating anterior pituitary gland function, it is not always possible (even with the use of hypothalamic releasing hormones) to distinguish between a pituitary and a hypothalamic lesion. Treatment and prognosis depend on the extent of hypofunction, the underlying cause, and the location of the lesion in the hypothalamic-pituitary axis.

Etiology

The etiologic considerations in hypopituitarism are diverse. As shown below and in Table 2–8, a helpful mnemonic device is the phrase "nine I's": Invasive, Infarction, Infiltrative, Injury, Immunologic, Iatrogenic, Infectious, Idiopathic, and Isolated. Most of these lesions may cause pituitary or hypothalamic failure (or both). Establishing the precise cause of hypopituitarism is helpful in determining treatment and prognosis.

A. Invasive: Space-occupying lesions cause hy-

Table 2–8. Hypopituitarism: Etiologic considerations. (The "nine I's.")

Invasive
  Large pituitary tumors
  Craniopharyngioma
  Metastatic tumors
  Primary central nervous system tumors (meningioma, chordoma, optic glioma; epidermoid, dermoid, pineal tumors)
  Carotid aneurysm
  Basal encephalocele
Infarction
  Postpartum necrosis (Sheehan's syndrome)
  Pituitary apoplexy
Infiltrative
  Sarcoidosis
  Hemochromatosis
  Histiocytosis X (Hand-Schüller-Christian disease, eosinophilic granuloma, Letterer-Siwe disease)
Injury
  Head trauma
  Child abuse
Immunologic
  Lymphocytic hypothysitis
Iatrogenic
  Surgery
  Radiation therapy
Infectious
  Mycoses, tuberculosis, syphilis
Idiopathic
  Familial
Isolated
  GH (dwarfism, emotional deprivation)
  LH, FSH (Kallmann's syndrome, weight loss, overtrained athletes, sickle cell anemia)
  TSH (chronic renal failure, pseudohypoparathyroidism)
  ACTH-LPH (lymphocytic hypophysitis, familial)
  PRL (pseudohypoparathyroidism)

popituitarism by destroying the pituitary gland or hypothalamic nuclei or by disrupting the hypothalamic hypophysial portal venous system. Large pituitary adenomas cause hypopituitarism by these mechanisms, and pituitary function may improve after their removal. Small pituitary tumors—microadenomas (< 10 mm in diameter)—characteristically seen in the hypersecretory states (excess PRL, GH, ACTH) do not directly cause pituitary insufficiency. Craniopharyngioma, the most common tumor of the hypothalamic-pituitary region in children, frequently impairs pituitary function by its compressive effects. Primary central nervous system tumors, including meningioma, chordoma, optic glioma, epidermoid tumors, and dermoid tumors, may decrease hypothalamic-pituitary secretion by their mass effects. Metastatic lesions to this area are common (especially breast carcinoma) but rarely result in clinically obvious hypopituitarism. Anatomic malformations such as basal encephalocele and parasellar aneurysms cause hypothalamic-pituitary dysfunction and may enlarge the sella turcica and mimic pituitary tumors.

B. Infarction: Ischemic damage to the pituitary has long been recognized as a cause of hypopituitarism. In 1914, Simmonds reported pituitary necrosis in a woman with severe puerperal sepsis, and in 1937 Sheehan published his classic description of its occurrence following postpartum hemorrhage and vascular collapse. The mechanism for the ischemia in such cases is not certain. Hypotension along with vasospasm of the hypophysial arteries is currently believed to compromise arterial perfusion of the anterior pituitary. During pregnancy, the pituitary gland may be more sensitive to hypoxemia because of its increased metabolic needs or more susceptible to vasoconstrictive influences because of the hyper estrogenic state. Some degree of hypopituitarism has been reported in 32% of women with severe postpartum hemorrhage. Other investigators have noted that the hypopituitarism does not always correlate with the degree of hemorrhage but that there is good correlation between the pituitary lesion and severe disturbances of the clotting mechanism (as in patients with placenta previa). Ischemic pituitary necrosis has also been reported to occur with greater frequency in patients with diabetes mellitus.

The extent of pituitary damage determines the rapidity of onset as well as the magnitude of pituitary hypofunction. The gland has a great secretory reserve, and more than 75% must be destroyed before clinical manifestations are evident. The initial clinical feature in postpartum necrosis may be failure to lactate after parturition; failure to resume normal menstrual periods is another clue to the diagnosis. However, the clinical features of hypopituitarism are often subtle, and years may pass before pituitary insufficiency is recognized following an ischemic insult.

Spontaneous hemorrhagic infarction of a pituitary tumor (pituitary apoplexy) frequently results in partial or total pituitary insufficiency. Pituitary apoplexy is often a fulminant clinical syndrome manifested by severe headache, visual impairment, ophthalmoplegias, meningismus, and an altered level of consciousness. Pituitary apoplexy is usually associated with a pituitary tumor; it may also be related to diabetes mellitus, radiotherapy, or open heart surgery. Acute pituitary failure with hypotension may result, and rapid mental deterioration, coma, and death may ensue. Emergency treatment with corticosteroids (see Chapter 6) and transsphenoidal decompression of the intrasellar contents may be lifesaving and may prevent permanent visual loss. Most patients who have survived pituitary apoplexy have developed multiple adenohypophysial deficits, but infarction of the tumor in some patients may cure the hypersecretory pituitary adenoma and its accompanying endocrinopathy. Pituitary infarction may also be a subclinical event (silent pituitary apoplexy), resulting in improvement of pituitary hormone hypersecretion without impairing the secretion of other anterior pituitary hormones.

C. Infiltrative: Hypopituitarism may be the initial clinical manifestation of infiltrative disease processes such as sarcoidosis, hemochromatosis, and histiocytosis X.

1. Sarcoidosis– The most common intracranial sites of involvement of sarcoidosis are the hypothalamus and pituitary gland. At one time, the most common endocrine abnormality in patients with sarcoidosis was thought to be diabetes insipidus; however, many of these patients actually have centrally mediated disordered control of thirst that results in polydipsia and polyuria, which in some cases explains the abnormal water metabolism. Deficiencies of multiple anterior pituitary hormones have been well documented in sarcoidosis and are usually secondary to hypothalamic insufficiency. Granulomatous involvement of the hypothalamic-pituitary unit is occasionally extensive, resulting in visual impairment, and therefore may simulate the clinical presentation of a pituitary or hypothalamic tumor.

2. Hemochromatosis– Hypopituitarism, particularly hypogonadotropic hypogonadism, is a prominent manifestation of iron storage disease—either idiopathic hemochromatosis or transfusional iron overload. Hypogonadism occurs in most such cases and is often the initial clinical feature of iron excess; complete iron studies should be obtained in any male patient presenting with unexplained hypogonadotropic hypogonadism. If the diagnosis is established early, hypogonadism in hemochromatosis may be reversible with iron depletion. Pituitary deficiencies of TSH, GH, and ACTH may occur later in the course of the disease and are not reversible by iron chelation therapy.

3. Histiocytosis X– Histiocytosis X, the infiltration of multiple organs by well-differentiated histiocytes, is often heralded by the onset of diabetes insipidus and anterior pituitary hormone deficiencies. The disorders in this category include Hand-Schüller-Christian disease, Letterer-Siwe disease, and eosinophilic granuloma of bone (eosinophilic infiltration predominates). Most histologic and biochemical studies have indicated that this infiltrative process involves chiefly the hypothalamus, and hypopituitarism occurs only as a result of hypothalamic damage.

D. Injury: Severe head trauma may cause anterior pituitary insufficiency and diabetes insipidus. Posttraumatic anterior hypopituitarism may be due to injury to the anterior pituitary, the pituitary stalk, or the hypothalamus. Pituitary insufficiency with growth retardation has been described in battered children who suffer closed head trauma with subdural hematoma.

E. Immunologic: Lymphocytic hypophysitis resulting in anterior hypopituitarism is a distinct entity, occurring most often in women during pregnancy or in the postpartum period. It may present as a mass lesion of the sella turcica with visual field disturbances simulating pituitary adenoma. An autoimmune process with extensive infiltration of the gland by lymphocytes and plasma cells destroys the anterior pituitary cells. These morphologic features are similar to those of other autoimmune endocrinopathies, eg, thyroiditis, adrenalitis, and oophoritis. About 50% of patients with lymphocytic hypophysitis have other endocrine autoimmune disease, and circulating pituitary autoantibodies have been found in several cases. It is presently uncertain how this disorder should be diagnosed and treated. It must be considered in the differential diagnosis of women with pituitary gland enlargement and hypopituitarism during pregnancy or the postpartum period.

Lymphocytic hypophysitis may result in isolated hormone deficiencies (especially ACTH or prolactin). Consequently, women with this type of hypopituitarism may continue to menstruate while suffering from secondary hypothyroidism or hypoadrenalism.

F. Iatrogenic: Both surgical and radiation therapy to the pituitary gland may compromise its function. The anterior pituitary is quite resilient during transsphenoidal microsurgery, and despite extensive manipulation during the search for microadenomas, anterior pituitary function is usually preserved. The dose of conventional radiation therapy presently employed to treat pituitary tumors is 4500–5000 cGy and results in a 50–60% incidence of hypothalamic and pituitary insufficiency. Such patients most frequently have modest hyperprolactinemia (PRL 30–100 ng/mL [1.3–4.5 nmol/L]) with GH and gonadotropin failure; TSH and ACTH deficiencies are less common. Heavy particle (proton beam) irradiation for pituitary tumors results in a 20–50% incidence of hypopituitarism. Irradiation of tumors of the head and neck (nasopharyngeal cancer, brain tumors) and prophylactic cranial irradiation in leukemia may also cause hypopituitarism. The clinical onset of pituitary failure in such patients is usually insidious and results from both pituitary and hypothalamic injury.

G. Infectious: Although many infectious diseases, including tuberculosis, syphilis, and mycotic infections, have been implicated as causative agents in pituitary hypofunction, anti-infective drugs have now made them rare causes of hypopituitarism.

H. Idiopathic: In some patients with hypopituitarism, no underlying cause is found. These may be isolated (see below) or multiple deficiencies. Familial forms of hypopituitarism characterized by a small, normal, or enlarged sella turcica have been described. Both autosomal recessive and X-linked recessive inheritance patterns have been reported. The pathogenesis of these familial disorders is uncertain.

I. Isolated: Isolated (monotropic) deficiencies of the anterior pituitary hormones have been described.

1. GH deficiency– In children, congenital monotropic GH deficiency may be sporadic or familial. These children, who may experience fasting hypoglycemia, have a gradual deceleration in growth velocity after 6–12 months of age. Diagnosis must be based on failure of GH responsiveness to provocative stimuli and the demonstration of normal responsiveness of other anterior pituitary hormones. Monotropic GH deficiency and growth retardation have also been observed in children suffering severe emotional deprivation. This disorder is reversed by placing the child in a supportive psychosocial milieu. A more detailed description of GH deficiency and growth failure is provided in Chapter 3.

2. ACTH deficiency– Monotropic ACTH deficiency is rare and is manifested by the signs and symptoms of adrenocortical insufficiency. Lipotropin (LPH) deficiency has also been noted in such patients. The defect in these patients may be due to primary failure of the corticotrophs to release ACTH and its related peptide hormones or may be secondary to impaired secretion of CRH by the hypothalamus. Most acquired cases of monotropic ACTH deficiency are due to lymphocytic hypophysitis.

3. Gonadotropin deficiency– Isolated deficiency of gonadotropins is not uncommon. Kallman's syndrome, an X-linked dominant disorder with incomplete penetrance, is characterized by an isolated defect in GnRH secretion associated with maldevelopment of the olfactory center with hyposmia or anosmia. Sporadic cases occur, and other neurologic defects such as color blindness and nerve deafness have been seen. Since anterior pituitary function is otherwise intact, young men with isolated hypogonadotropic hypogonadism develop a eunuchoid appearance, since testosterone deficiency results in failure of epiphysial closure (see Chapter 9). In women, a state of hypogonadotropic hypogonadism manifested by oligomenorrhea or amenorrhea often accompanies weight loss, emotional or physical stress, and athletic training. Anorexia nervosa and marked obesity both result in hypothalamic dysfunction and impaired gonadotropin secretion. Hypothalamic hypogonadism has also been observed in overtrained male athletes. Sickle cell anemia also causes hypogonadotropic hypogonadism due to hypothalamic dysfunction and results in delayed puberty. Clomiphene treatment has been effective in some cases. Isolated gonadotropin deficiency may also be seen in the polyglandular autoimmune syndrome; this deficiency is related to selective pituitary gonadotrope failure from autoimmune hypophysitis. Other chronic illnesses, eg, poorly controlled diabetes and malnutrition, may result in gonadotropin deficiency. Isolated deficiencies of both LH and FSH without an obvious cause such as those described have been reported but are rare.

4. TSH deficiency– Monotropic TSH deficiency is rare and is caused by a reduction in hypothalamic TRH secretion (tertiary hypothyroidism). Some patients with chronic renal failure appear to have impaired TSH secretion.

5. Prolactin deficiency– PRL deficiency almost always indicates severe intrinsic pituitary damage, and panhypopituitarism is usually present. However, isolated PRL deficiency has been reported after lymphocytic hypophysitis. Deficiencies of TSH and PRL have been noted in patients with pseudohypoparathyroidism.

Clinical Features

The onset of pituitary insufficiency is usually gradual, and the classic course of progressive hypopituitarism is an initial loss of GH and gonadotropin secretion followed by deficiencies of TSH, then ACTH, and finally PRL.

A. Symptoms: Impairment of GH secretion causes decreased growth in children but is, of course, clinically occult in adult patients. Hypogonadism, manifested by amenorrhea in women and decreased libido or impotence in men, may antedate the clinical appearance of a hypothalamic-pituitary lesion.

Hypothyroidism caused by TSH deficiency generally stimulates the clinical changes observed in primary thyroid failure; however, it is usually less severe, and goiter is absent. Cold intolerance, dry skin, mental dullness, bradycardia, constipation, hoarseness, and anemia have all been observed; gross myxedematous changes are uncommon.

ACTH deficiency causes adrenocortical insufficiency, and its clinical features resemble those of primary adrenal failure. Weakness, nausea, vomiting, anorexia, weight loss, fever, and postural hypotension may occur. Since the zona glomerulosa and the renin-angiotensin system are usually intact, the cardiovascular collapse seen in Addison's disease is uncommon. Again, these symptoms are less severe in secondary adrenal insufficiency and, because of their gradual onset, may go undetected for prolonged periods, becoming manifest only during periods of stress. Hypoglycemia aggravated by GH deficiency may occur with fasting and has been the initial presenting feature of some patients with isolated ACTH deficiency. Patients with type I (insulin-dependent) diabetes who develop hypopituitarism often have a reduction in their insulin requirements. In contrast to the hyperpigmentation that occurs during states of ACTH excess (Addison's disease, Nelson's syndrome), depigmentation and diminished tanning have been described as a result of ACTH insufficiency. In addition, lack of ACTH-stimulated adrenal androgen secretion will cause a decrease in body hair if gonadotropin deficiency is also present.

The only symptom of PRL deficiency is failure of postpartum lactation.

B. Signs: Abnormal findings on physical examination may be subtle and require careful observation. Patients with hypopituitarism are not cachectic. A photograph of a cachectic patient with "Simmonds' syndrome" that appeared in some older textbooks of endocrinology caused confusion. That particular patient probably suffered from anorexia nervosa and was found to have a normal pituitary gland at postmortem examination.

Patients with pituitary failure are usually slightly overweight. The skin is fine, pale, and smooth, with fine wrinkling of the face. Body and pubic hair may be deficient or absent, and atrophy of the genitalia may occur. Postural hypotension, bradycardia, decreased muscle strength, and delayed deep tendon reflexes occur in more severe cases. Neuro-ophthalmologic abnormalities depend on the presence of a large intrasellar or parasellar lesion.

C. Laboratory Findings: These may include anemia (related to thyroid and androgen deficiency and chronic disease), hypoglycemia, hyponatremia (related to hypothyroidism and hypoadrenalism, which cause inappropriate water retention, not sodium loss), and low-voltage bradycardia on ECG. Hyperkalemia, which is common in primary adrenal failure, is not present.

Diagnosis

A diagnostic strategy for the evaluation of hypopituitarism is presented in Figure 2–17.

A. Assessment of Target Gland Function: If endocrine hypofunction is suspected, pituitary hormone deficiencies must be distinguished from primary failure of the thyroid, adrenals, or gonads. Basal determinations of each anterior pituitary hormone are useful only if compared to target gland secretion. Baseline laboratory studies should include thyroid function tests (free T_4 or free T_4 index) and determination of serum testosterone levels. Testosterone is a sensitive indicator of hypopituitarism in women as well as in men. In women, a substantial decrease in testosterone is commonly observed in pituitary failure related to hypofunction of the two endocrine glands responsible for its production—the ovary and the adrenal. Adrenocortical reserve should initially be evaluated by a rapid ACTH stimulation test.

B. Evaluation of Prolactin: Since hyperprolactinemia (discussed later), regardless of its cause, leads to gonadal dysfunction, serum PRL should be measured early in the evaluation of hypogonadism.

C. Differentiation of Primary and Secondary Hypofunction: Subnormal thyroid function as shown by appropriate tests, a low serum testosterone level, or an impaired cortisol response to the rapid ACTH stimulation test requires measurement of basal levels of specific pituitary hormones. In primary target gland hypofunction (such as polyglandular failure syndrome), TSH, LH, FSH, or ACTH will be elevated. Low or normal values for these pituitary hormones suggest hypothalamic-pituitary dysfunction.

D. Stimulation Tests: Provocative endocrine testing should then be employed to confirm the diagnosis; to assess the extent of hypofunction; and, when possible, to determine whether the abnormality is at the level of the hypothalamus or pituitary. Evaluation of the secretory reserve of the pituitary

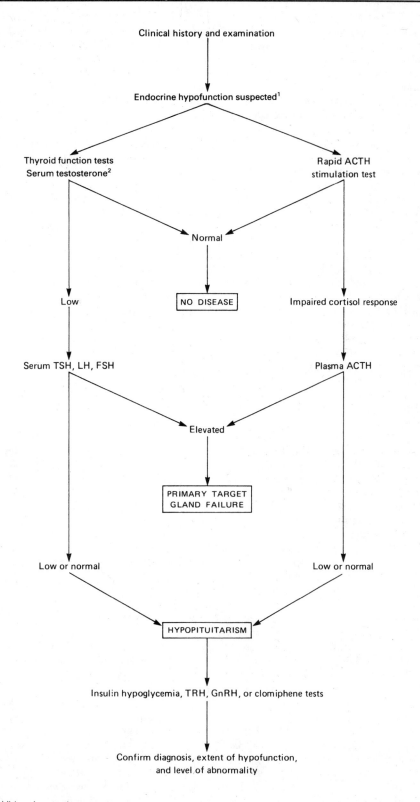

Figure 2–17. Diagnostic evaluation of hypothalamic-pituitary-target gland hypofunction. [1]Evaluate GH in children (see text). [2] Measure prolactin if hypogonadism suspected.

hormones has been discussed earlier. A triple stimulation test combining simultaneous insulin hypoglycemia, TRH, and GnRH can be utilized to test the secretory capacity of all six major anterior pituitary hormones. Alternatively, simultaneous administration of CRH, GRH, TRH, and GnRH simultaneously as a means of assessing complete adenohypophysial function (see above).

Treatment

A. ACTH: Treatment of secondary adrenal insufficiency, like that of primary adrenal failure, must include glucocorticoid support (see Chapter 6). Hydrocortisone (20–30 mg/d orally) or prednisone (5–7.5 mg/d orally) in two or three divided doses provides adequate glucocorticoid replacement for most patients. The minimum effective dosage should be given in order to avoid iatrogenic hypercortisolism. Increased dosage is required during periods of stress such as illness, surgery, or trauma. Patients with only partial ACTH deficiency may need steroid treatment only during stress. A two- to threefold increase in steroid dosage during the stressful situation should be recommended, followed by gradual tapering as the stress resolves. Unlike primary adrenal insufficiency, ACTH deficiency does not usually require mineralocorticoid therapy. Patients with adrenal insufficiency should wear medical alert bracelets so they may receive prompt treatment in case of emergency.

B. TSH: The management of patients with secondary hypothyroidism must be based on clinical grounds and the circulating concentration of serum thyroxine (see Chapter 4). Since some patients with hypothyrotropic hypothyroidism have a normal TSH response to TRH, basal TSH levels and the TRH test should not be used as guidelines for thyroid replacement. The treatment of secondary and tertiary hypothyroidism is identical to that for primary thyroid failure. Levothyroxine sodium, 0.1–0.15 mg/d orally, is usually adequate. Response to therapy is monitored clinically and with measurement of serum free thyroxine.

Caution: Since thyroid hormone replacement in patients with hypopituitarism may aggravate even partial adrenal insufficiency, the adrenal disorder should be treated first.

C. Gonadotropins: The object of treatment of secondary hypogonadism is to replace sex steroids and restore fertility (see Chapters 9 and 10).

1. Estrogens and progesterone– In women, estrogen replacement is essential. Adequate estrogen treatment will maintain secondary sex characteristics (eg, vulvar and vaginal lubrication), prevent osteoporosis, and abolish vasomotor symptoms, with an improvement in sense of well-being. Many estrogen preparations are available, eg, ethinyl estradiol, 0.02–0.05 mg orally daily; conjugated estrogens, 0.3–1.25 mg orally daily; or transdermal estradiol, 0.05–0.1 mg daily. Estrogens should be cycled with a progestin compound (eg, medroxyprogesterone, 5–10 mg orally) to induce withdrawal bleeding and prevent endometrial hyperplasia.

2. Ovulation induction– Ovulation can often be restored in women with hypothalamic-pituitary dysfunction (see Chapter 10). In patients with gonadal failure of hypothalamic origin, clomiphene citrate may cause a surge of gonadotropin secretion resulting in ovulation. Pulsatile subcutaneous injections of GnRH with an infusion pump can also be used to induce ovulation and fertility in women with hypothalamic dysfunction. Combined treatment with FSH (human menopausal gonadotropins; menotropins) and LH (chorionic gonadotropin) can be utilized to provoke ovulation in women with intrinsic pituitary failure. This form of therapy is expensive, and multiple births are a risk.

3. Androgens in women–Because of a deficiency of both ovarian and adrenal androgens, some women with hypopituitarism have diminished libido despite adequate estrogen therapy. Small doses of long-acting androgens (testosterone enanthate, 25–50 mg intramuscularly every 4–8 weeks) may be helpful in restoring sexual activity without causing hirsutism.

4. Androgens in men–In men, testosterone replacement is essential to restore libido and potency, provide adequate beard growth and muscle strength, prevent osteopenia, and improve the sense of well-being. Adequate treatment consists of a long-acting intramuscular preparation such as testosterone enanthate. Three dosage schedules have proved efficacy: 300 mg every 3 weeks, 200 mg every 2 weeks, or 100 mg every week. Side effects, including aggressive sexual behavior, acne, gynecomastia, and fluid retention, are unusual and can be managed by lowering the dosage. Therapy should be withheld in adolescents as long as possible in order to prevent premature epiphysial closure and ensure maximum linear growth. Replacement therapy with oral androgenic preparations should be avoided, since inadequate absorption results in poor androgenization, and serious side effects such as peliosis hepatis (blood-filled cysts within the hepatic parenchyma) may occur. Transdermal testosterone therapy has also been shown to be an effective and acceptable means of administering androgens. Preparations that use this new route of administration may be available soon. (See Chapter 9).

5. Spermatogenesis– Spermatogenesis can be achieved in some patients with the combined use of chorionic gonadotropin and menotropins. If pituitary insufficiency is of recent onset, therapy with chorionic gonadotropin alone may restore both fertility and adequate gonadal steroid production. Pulsatile GnRH infusion pumps have also been used to restore fertility in male patients with secondary hypogonadism.

D. Growth Hormone: (See Chapter 3.) Human growth hormone (hGH) produced by recombinant DNA technology is available for use in children with hypopituitarism. Therapeutic use of human growth hormone in adults with hypopituitarism is under investigation.

PITUITARY ADENOMAS

Advances in endocrinologic and neuroradiologic research in recent years have allowed earlier recognition and more successful therapy of pituitary adenomas. Prolactinomas are the most common type, accounting for about 60% of primary pituitary tumors; GH hypersecretion occurs in approximately 20% and ACTH excess in 10%. Hypersecretion of TSH, the gonadotropins, or alpha subunits is unusual. Nonfunctional tumors currently represent only 10% of all pituitary adenomas, and some of these may in fact be alpha subunit-secreting adenomas.

Early clinical recognition of the endocrine effects of excessive pituitary secretion, especially the observation that PRL excess causes secondary hypogonadism, has led to early diagnosis of pituitary tumors before the appearance of late manifestations such as sellar enlargement, panhypopituitarism, and suprasellar extension with visual impairment.

Pituitary **microadenomas** are defined as intrasellar adenomas less than 1 cm in diameter that present with manifestations of hormonal excess without sellar enlargement or extrasellar extension. Panhypopituitarism does not occur, and such tumors are very successfully treated.

Pituitary **macroadenomas** are those larger than 1 cm in diameter and cause generalized sellar enlargement. Tumors 1–2 cm in diameter confined to the sella turcica can usually be successfully treated; however, larger tumors—and especially those with suprasellar, sphenoid sinus, or lateral extensions—are much more difficult to manage. Panhypopituitarism and visual loss increase in frequency with tumor size and suprasellar extension.

Insights into the pathogenesis and biologic behavior of pituitary tumors have been gained from studies of pituitary tumor clonality and somatic mutations. Analyses of allelic X inactivation of specific genes has shown that most pituitary adenomas are monoclonal, a finding most consistent with a somatic mutation model of tumorigenesis; polyclonanality of tumors would be expected if tonic stimulation by hypothalamic releasing factors were the mechanism underlying neoplastic transformation. In fact, transgenic animals expressing GRH have exhibited pituitary hyperplasia but not pituitary adenomas. Recently, an animal model system for ACTH-secreting pituitary tumors has been developed involving transgenic mice. One somatic mutation has been found in 30–40% of growth hormone-secreting tumors (but not in leukocytes from the same patients): Point mutations in the alpha subunit of the GTP binding portion of the stimulatory regulator of adenylyl cyclase (G_s protein) results in constitutive (autonomous) acti-

vation of pituitary cell growth and function. In studies of anterior pituitary cell ontogeny, Pit-1 is a transcription factor important in pituitary differentiation. The restriction of its expression to somatotrophs, lactotrophs, and thyrotrophs may account for the plurihormonal expression seen in some tumors.

Treatment

Pituitary adenomas are treated with surgery, irradiation, or drugs to suppress hypersecretion by the adenoma or its growth. The aims of therapy are to correct hypersecretion of anterior pituitary hormones, to preserve normal secretion of other anterior pituitary hormones, and to remove or suppress the adenoma itself. These objectives are currently achievable in most patients with pituitary microadenomas; however, in the case of larger tumors, multiple therapies are frequently required and may be less successful.

A. Surgical: Pituitary surgery is the initial therapy of choice at many centers, and the transsphenoidal microsurgical approach to the sella turcica is the procedure of choice; transfrontal craniotomy is required only in the occasional patient with massive suprasellar extension of the adenoma. In the transsphenoidal procedure, the surgeon approaches the pituitary from the nasal cavity through the sphenoid sinus, removes the anterior-inferior sellar floor, and incises the dura. The adenoma is selectively removed; normal pituitary tissue is identified and preserved. Success rates approach 90% in patients with microadenomas. Major complications, including postoperative hemorrhage, cerebrospinal fluid leak, meningitis, and visual impairment, occur in less than 5% and are most frequent in patients with large or massive tumors. Transient diabetes insipidus lasting a few days to 1–2 weeks occurs in approximately 15%; permanent diabetes insipidus is rare. A transient form of the syndrome of inappropriate secretion of antidiuretic hormone (SIADH) with symptomatic hyponatremia occurs in 10% of patients within 5–14 days of transsphenoidal pituitary microsurgery. Surgical hypopituitarism is rare in patients with microadenomas but approaches 5–10% in patients with larger tumors. The perioperative management of such patients should include glucocorticoid administration in stress doses (see Chapter 6) and postoperative assessment of daily weight, fluid balance, and electrolyte status. Mild diabetes insipidus is managed by giving fluids orally; in more severe cases—urine output greater than 5–6 L/24 h—ADH therapy in the form of desmopressin acetate should be administered (see section on diabetes insipidus). SIADH is managed by fluid restriction; however, in more severe cases, hypertonic saline may be required (See section on SIADH.)

B. Radiologic: Pituitary irradiation is usually reserved for patients with larger tumors who have had incomplete resection of large pituitary adenomas.

1. X-ray irradiation– Conventional irradiation using high energy sources, in total doses of 4000–5000 cGy given in daily doses of 180–200 cGy, is most commonly employed. The response to radiation therapy is slow, and 5–10 years may be required to achieve the full effect (see section on acromegaly). Treatment is ultimately successful in about 80% of acromegalics but only about 40% of patients with Cushing's disease. The response rate in prolactinomas is not precisely known, but tumor progression is prevented in most patients. Morbidity during radiotherapy is minimal, though some patients experience malaise and nausea, and serous otitis media may occur. Hypopituitarism is common, and the incidence increases with time following radiotherapy—about 50–60% at 5–10 years. Rare late complications include damage to the optic nerves and chiasm, seizures, and radionecrosis of brain tissue.

2. Heavy particle irradiation– Heavy particle irradiation using alpha particles or protons is also used. Advantages of this technique are the ability to focus the radiation beam precisely; the smaller port allows larger doses (8000–12,000 cGy) to be delivered to the sellar area and limits the radiation exposure of surrounding structures. Disadvantages are the limited availability, and the smaller radiation field which precludes use of this technique in patients with tumors over 1.5 cm in diameter and in those with extrasellar extension. Responses to therapy are more rapid than with conventional irradiation and occur within 2 years in most patients. Successful responses are obtained in a majority of patients with acromegaly or Cushing's disease. Experience with prolactinomas is limited. Neurologic damage and visual impairment are rare complications of heavy particle irradiation, but hypopituitarism occurs in 20–50% and will almost certainly increase with further follow-up.

C. Medical: Medical management of pituitary adenomas became feasible with the availability of bromocriptine, a dopamine agonist. This drug is most successful in the treatment of hyperprolactinemia and is also useful in a few patients with acromegaly or Cushing's disease. Octreotide acetate, a somatostatin analogue, is useful in the therapy of acromegaly and TSH-secreting adenomas. Specifics of the use of these and other medications are discussed below.

Posttreatment Follow-Up

Patients undergoing transsphenoidal microsurgery should be reevaluated 4–6 weeks postoperatively to document that complete removal of the adenoma and correction of endocrine hypersecretion have been achieved. Prolactinomas are assessed by basal PRL measurements, GH-secreting tumors by glucose suppression testing and IGF-1 levels, and ACTH-secreting adenomas by measurement of urine free cortisol and the response to low-dose dexamethasone suppression (see below). Other anterior pituitary hormones—TSH, ACTH, and LH/FSH—should also be assessed as described above in the section on endocrine evaluation. In patients with successful responses, yearly evaluation should be done to watch for late recurrence; late hypopituitarism does not occur after microsurgery. MRI or CT scanning is not necessary in patients with normal postoperative pituitary function but should be utilized in patients with persisting or recurrent disease.

Follow-up of patients treated by pituitary irradiation is also essential, since the response to therapy may be delayed and the incidence of hypopituitarism increases with time. Yearly endocrinologic assessment of both the hypersecreted hormone and the other pituitary hormones is recommended.

1. PROLACTINOMAS

PRL hypersecretion is the most common endocrine abnormality due to hypothalamic-pituitary disorders, and PRL is the hormone most commonly secreted in excess by pituitary adenomas. Most chromophobe adenomas, which were previously classified as "nonfunctional" on the basis of routine histologic studies, have now been shown to be PRL-secreting adenomas.

The understanding that PRL hypersecretion causes not only galactorrhea but also gonadal dysfunction and the use of PRL measurements in screening such patients have permitted recognition of these PRL-secreting tumors before the development of sellar enlargement, hypopituitarism, or visual impairment.

Thus, plasma PRL should be measured in patients with galactorrhea, suspected hypothalamic-pituitary dysfunction, or sellar enlargement and in those with unexplained gonadal dysfunction, including amenorrhea, infertility, decreased libido, or impotence (Table 2–9).

Pathology

PRL-secreting pituitary adenomas arise most commonly from the lateral wings of the anterior pituitary, but with progression they fill the sella turcica and compress the normal anterior and posterior lobes. Tumor size varies greatly from microadenomas to large invasive tumors with extrasellar extension. Most patients have microadenomas, ie, tumors less than 1 cm in diameter at diagnosis. Prolactinomas frequently undergo spontaneous partial necrosis, and thus a partially empty sella turcica accompanies the pituitary adenoma in 30–40% of patients.

Table 2–9. Indications for prolactin measurement.

Galactorrhea
Enlarged sella turcica
Suspected pituitary tumor
Hypogonadotropic hypogonadism
Unexplained amenorrhea
Unexplained male hypogonadism or infertility

Prolactinomas usually appear chromophobic on routine histologic study, reflecting the inadequacy of the techniques used. The cells are small and uniform, with round or oval nuclei and scanty cytoplasm, and secretory granules are usually not visible with routine stains. The stroma contains a diffuse capillary network.

Electron microscopic examination shows that prolactinoma cells characteristically contain secretory granules that usually range from 100 to 500 nm and are spherical. Larger granules (400–500 nm), which are irregular or crescent-shaped, are less commonly seen. The cells show evidence of secretory activity, with a large Golgi area, nucleolar enlargement, and a prominent endoplasmic reticulum. Immunocytochemical studies of these tumors have confirmed that the secretory granules indeed contain PRL.

Clinical Features

The clinical manifestations of PRL excess are the same regardless of the cause (see below). The classic features are galactorrhea and amenorrhea in women and galactorrhea and decreased libido or impotence in men. Although the sex distribution of prolactinomas is approximately equal, microadenomas are much more common in females, presumably because of earlier recognition of the endocrine consequences of PRL excess.

A. Galactorrhea: Galactorrhea occurs in less than half of patients with prolactinomas and is less common in men than in women. It is usually not spontaneous, or may be present only transiently or intermittently; careful breast examination is required in most patients to demonstrate galactorrhea. The absence of galactorrhea despite markedly elevated PRL levels is probably due to concomitant deficiency of the gonadal hormones required to initiate lactation (see Chapter 13).

B. Gonadal Dysfunction:

1. In women– Amenorrhea, oligomenorrhea with anovulation, or infertility is present in approximately 90% of women with prolactinomas. These menstrual disorders usually present concurrently with galactorrhea if it is present but may either precede or follow it. The amenorrhea is usually secondary and may follow pregnancy or oral contraceptive use. Primary amenorrhea occurs in the minority of patients who have onset of hyperprolactinemia during adolescence. The necessity of measuring PRL in patients with unexplained primary or secondary amenorrhea is emphasized by several studies showing that hyperprolactinemia occurs in as many as 20% of patients with neither galactorrhea nor other manifestations of pituitary dysfunction. A number of these patients have been shown to have prolactinomas.

Gonadal dysfunction in these women is due to interference with the hypothalamic-pituitary-gonadal axis by the hyperprolactinemia and except in patients with large or invasive adenomas is not due to destruction of the gonadotropin-secreting cells. This has been documented by the return of menstrual function following reduction of PRL levels to normal by drug treatment or surgical removal of the tumor. Although basal gonadotropin levels are frequently within the normal range despite reduction of sex steroid levels in hyperprolactinemic patients, PRL inhibits both the normal pulsatile secretion of LH and FSH and the midcycle LH surge, resulting in anovulation. The positive feedback effect of estrogen on gonadotropin secretion is also inhibited; in fact, patients with hyperprolactinemia are usually estrogen-deficient.

Estrogen deficiency in women with prolactinomas may be accompanied by decreased vaginal lubrication, other symptoms of estrogen deficiency, and osteopenia as assessed by bone densitometry. Other symptoms may include weight gain, fluid retention, and irritability. Hirsutism may also occur, accompanied by elevated plasma levels of dehydroepiandrosterone (DHEA) sulfate. Patients with hyperprolactinemia may also suffer from anxiety and depression. Treatment with bromocriptine has been shown to improve psychologic distress in such patients.

2. In men– In men, PRL excess may also occasionally cause galactorrhea; however, the usual manifestations are those of hypogonadism. The initial symptom is decreased libido, which may be dismissed by both the patient and physician as due to psychosocial factors; thus, the recognition of prolactinomas in men is frequently delayed, and marked hyperprolactinemia (PRL > 200 ng/mL [9.1 nmol/L]) and sellar enlargement are usual. Unfortunately, prolactinomas in men are often not diagnosed until late manifestations such as headache, visual impairment, or hypopituitarism appear; virtually all such patients have a history of sexual or gonadal dysfunction. Serum testosterone levels are low, and in the presence of normal or subnormal gonadotropin levels, PRL excess should be suspected as well as other causes of hypothalamic-pituitary-gonadal dysfunction (see section on hypopituitarism). Impotence also occurs in hyperprolactinemic males. Its cause is unclear, since testosterone replacement may not reverse it if hyperprolactinemia is not corrected. Male infertility accompanied by reduction in sperm count is a less common initial complaint.

C. Tumor Progression: In general, the growth of prolactinomas is slow, and the natural history of microadenomas has not been well defined.

Differential Diagnosis

The many conditions associated with hyperprolactinemia are listed in Table 2–5. Pregnancy, hypothalamic-pituitary disorders, primary hypothyroidism, and drug ingestion are the most common causes.

Hypothalamic lesions frequently cause PRL hypersecretion by decreasing the secretion of factors that tonically inhibit PRL release (eg, dopamine); the lesions may be accompanied by panhypopituitarism. Similarly, traumatic or surgical section of the pituitary stalk leads to hyperprolactinemia and hypopituitarism. The cause and clinical features of hypothalamic lesions are discussed in previous sections.

Pregnancy leads to a physiologic increase in PRL secretion; the levels increase as pregnancy continues and may reach 200 ng/mL (9.1 nmol/L) during the third trimester. Following delivery, basal PRL levels gradually fall to normal over several weeks but increase in response to breast feeding. Hyperprolactinemia persisting for 6–12 months or longer following delivery is an indication for evaluation. PRL levels are also high in normal neonates.

Several systemic disorders lead to hyperprolactinemia. Primary hypothyroidism is a common cause, and measurement of thyroid function, and especially TSH, should be part of the evaluation. In primary hypothyroidism, there is hyperplasia of both thyrotrophs and lactotrophs, presumably due to TRH hypersecretion. This may result in significant pituitary gland enlargement, which may be mistaken for a PRL-secreting pituitary tumor. The PRL response to TRH is usually exaggerated in these patients. PRL may also be increased in liver disease, particularly in patients with severe cirrhosis, and in patients with chronic renal failure.

PRL excess and galactorrhea may also be caused by breast disease, nipple stimulation, disease or injury to the chest wall, and spinal cord lesions. These disorders increase PRL secretion by stimulation of afferent neural pathways.

The most common cause of hyperprolactinemia is drug ingestion, and a careful history of drug intake must be obtained. Elevated PRL levels, galactorrhea, and amenorrhea may occur following estrogen therapy or oral contraceptive use, but their persistence should suggest prolactinoma. Many other drugs also cause increased PRL secretion and elevated plasma levels (Table 2–5). PRL levels are usually less than 100 ng/mL (4.5 nmol/L), and the evaluation of these patients is primarily by discontinuance of the drug or medication and reevaluation after several weeks. In patients in whom drug withdrawal is not feasible, neuroradiologic studies, if normal, will usually exclude prolactinoma.

Diagnosis

A. General Evaluation: The evaluation of patients with galactorrhea or unexplained gonadal dysfunction with normal or low plasma gonadotropin levels should first include a history regarding menstrual status, pregnancy, fertility, sexual function, and symptoms of hypothyroidism or hypopituitarism. Current or previous use of medication, drugs, or estrogen therapy should be documented. Basal PRL levels, gonadotropins, thyroid function tests, and TSH levels should be established, as well as serum testosterone in men. Liver and kidney function should be assessed. A pregnancy test should be performed in women with recent onset of amenorrhea or galactorrhea.

Patients with galactorrhea but normal menses may not have hyperprolactinemia and usually do not have prolactinomas. If the PRL level is normal, they may be reassured and followed with sequential PRL measurements. Those with elevated levels require further evaluation as described below.

B. Specific Diagnosis: When other causes of hyperprolactinemia have been excluded, the most likely cause of persisting hyperprolactinemia is a prolactinoma, especially if there is associated hypogonadism. Since currently available suppression and stimulation tests do not distinguish PRL-secreting tumors from other causes of hyperprolactinemia, the diagnosis must be established by the assessment of both basal PRL levels and neuroradiologic studies. Patients with large tumors and marked hyperprolactinemia usually present little difficulty. With very rare exceptions, basal PRL levels greater than 200 ng/mL (9.1 nmol/L) are virtually diagnostic of prolactinoma. In addition, since there is a general correlation between the PRL elevation and the size of the pituitary adenoma, these patients usually have sellar enlargement and obvious macroadenomas. Similarly, if the basal PRL level is between 100 and 200 ng/mL (4.5 and 9.1 nmol/L), the cause is usually prolactinoma. These patients may have either micro- or macroadenomas; however, with basal levels of PRL greater than 100 ng/mL (4.5 nmol/L), the PRL-secreting tumor is usually radiologically evident, and again the diagnosis is generally straightforward. Patients with mild to moderate hyperprolactinemia (20–100 ng/mL [0.9–4.5 nmol/L]) present the greatest difficulty in diagnosis, since both PRL-secreting microadenomas and the many other conditions causing hyperprolactinemia (Table 2–5) cause PRL hypersecretion of this degree. In such patients, MRI or CT scanning should be performed and will frequently demonstrate a definite pituitary microadenoma. Scans showing only minor or equivocal abnormalities should be interpreted with caution, because of the high incidence of false-positive scans in the normal population (see neuroradiologic evaluation, above). Since the diagnosis cannot be either established or excluded in patients with normal or equivocal neuroradiologic studies, they require further evaluation or serial assessment (see below).

Treatment

Satisfactory control of PRL hypersecretion, cessation of galactorrhea, and return of normal gonadal function can be achieved in most patients with PRL-secreting microadenomas, although the choice of primary therapy (surgical or medical) remains controversial. In patients with hyperprolactinemia, ovulation should not be induced without careful assessment of pituitary anatomy, since pregnancy may cause further expansion of these tumors as discussed below. All patients with PRL-secreting macroadenomas should be treated, because of the risks of further tumor expansion, hypopituitarism, and visual impairment. Patients with larger prolactinomas—over 2 cm in diameter, or basal PRL levels over 200 ng/mL (9.1 nmol/L)—may require combined therapy with surgery, radiation, and bromocriptine or long-term suppression with bromocriptine alone.

Treatment for all patients with microadenomas is also recommended to prevent early osteoporosis secondary to persisting hypogonadism and to restore fertility. In addition, surgical or medical therapy is more successful in these patients than in those with larger tumors.

Patients with persisting hyperprolactinemia and hypogonadism and normal neuroradiologic studies—ie, those in whom prolactinoma cannot be definitely established—may be managed by observation if hypogonadism is of short duration. However, in patients whose hypogonadism has persisted for more than 6–12 months, bromocriptine should be used to suppress PRL secretion and restore normal gonadal function. In women with suspected or proved prolactinomas, replacement estrogen therapy is contraindicated because of the risk of tumor growth.

A. Surgical:

1. Transsphenoidal microsurgery– This is the surgical procedure of choice in patients with prolactinomas and is the preferred initial method of therapy in some institutions.

a. Microadenomas– In patients with microadenomas, success, as measured by restitution of normal PRL levels, normal menses, and cessation of galactorrhea, is achieved in 85–90% of cases. Success is most likely in patients with basal PRL levels under 200 ng/mL (9.1 nmol/L) and a duration of amenorrhea of less than 5 years. In these patients, the incidence of surgical complications is less than 5%, and hypopituitarism is a rare complication. Thus, in this group of patients with PRL-secreting microadenomas, PRL hypersecretion can be corrected, gonadal function restored, and secretion of TSH and ACTH preserved. Recurrence rates vary considerably in reported series. In our experience, approximately 75% of patients have had long-term remissions, and 25% have had recurrences 5–10 years following surgery.

b. Macroadenomas– Transsphenoidal microsurgery is considerably less successful in restoring normal PRL secretion in patients with macroadenomas; many clinicians would treat these patients with bromocriptine alone. The surgical outcome is directly related to tumor size and the basal PRL level. Thus, in patients with tumors 1–2 cm in diameter without extrasellar extension and with basal PRL levels under 200 ng/mL (9.1 nmol/L), transsphenoidal surgery is successful in about 80% of cases. In patients with higher basal PRL levels and larger tumors, the success rate—defined as complete tumor resection and restoration of normal basal PRL secretion—is about 25–50%. Although surgical results are relatively poor in this latter group of patients, surgery is recommended at many centers as the primary therapy in order to decompress vital structures such as the optic chiasm and to reduce tumor bulk and PRL hypersecretion. Additional therapy with bromocriptine or radiotherapy is required in the subsequent management of these patients (see below).

2. Transfrontal craniotomy– This procedure should be used only in patients with major suprasellar extension of tumor not accessible via the transsphenoidal route in whom decompression of vital structures is required. It must be followed by bromocriptine or radiation therapy, since residual tumor is virtually always present.

B. Medical:

1. Bromocriptine– Bromocriptine (2-bromo-α-ergocryptine mesylate) is a potent dopamine agonist that stimulates dopamine receptors and has effects at both the hypothalamic and pituitary levels. It is effective therapy for a PRL-secreting pituitary adenoma and directly inhibits PRL secretion by the tumor. The dosage is 2.5–10 mg/d orally in divided doses. Side effects consisting of dizziness, postural hypotension, nausea, and occasionall vomiting are common at onset of therapy but usually resolve with continuation of the medication. They can usually be avoided by starting with a low dose and gradually increasing the dose over days to weeks until the PRL level is suppressed to the normal range. An example would be to give 1.25 mg at bedtime for 2 or 3 days and then increase to 2.5 mg; if tolerated, an additional 2.5 mg can be added in the morning. PRL levels should then be assessed. If they remain elevated, the dosage is gradually increased to a total of 7.5–10 mg/d. With these dosages, hyperprolactinemia is controlled in most patients; further increases in dosage are usually not warranted and are usually accompanied by increased side effects. Most patients tolerate doses of 2.5–10 mg without difficulty; however, in 10–15%, persisting postural hypotension and gastrointestinal side effects necessitate discontinuance of therapy.

a. Microadenomas– In patients with microadenomas, bromocriptine successfully reduces PRL levels to normal in over 90% of cases. In addition, correction of hyperprolactinemia allows recovery of normal gonadal function; ovulation and fertility are restored, so that mechanical contraception should be advised if pregnancy is not desired. Bromocriptine induces ovulation in most female patients who wish to become pregnant. In these patients with microadenomas, the risk of major expansion of adenoma during the pregnancy appears to be less than 5%; however, both the patient and the physician must be aware of this potential complication. Current data do not indicate an increased risk of multiple pregnancy, abortion, or fetal malformations in pregnancies induced by bromocriptine; however, the patient should be instructed to discontinue bromocriptine at the first missed menstrual period and obtain a pregnancy test.

At present, there is little evidence that bromocriptine causes permanent resolution of PRL-secreting microadenomas, and virtually all patients have resumption of hyperprolactinemia following discontinuation of therapy even when it has been continued for several years. Although no late toxicity has yet been reported other than the side effects noted above, questions about possible long-term risk and the indicated duration of therapy in such patients with microadenomas are currently unanswered.

b. Macroadenomas– Bromocriptine is effective in controlling hyperprolactinemia in patients with PRL-secreting macroadenomas even when basal PRL levels are markedly elevated. Bromocriptine may be used either as initial therapy or to control residual hyperprolactinemia in patients unsuccessfully treated with surgery or radiotherapy. Bromocriptine should not be used to induce ovulation and pregnancy in women with untreated macroadenomas, since the risk of tumor expansion and visual deficits in the later part of pregnancy is approximately 15–25%. These patients should be treated with surgery prior to induction of ovulation with bromocriptine or by gonadotropin therapy.

Bromocriptine not only reduces PRL secretion in patients with macroadenomas but also reduces tumor size in about 70–80% of patients. Reduction of tumor size with bromocriptine may occur within days to weeks following institution of therapy. The drug has been used to restore vision in patients with major suprasellar extension and chiasmal compression. Tumor reduction in response to bromocriptine is sustained only as long as the medication is continued, and reexpansion of the tumor and recurrence of hyperprolactinemia may occur rapidly following discontinuation of therapy. The question of duration of therapy in patients with macroadenomas remains unanswered.

2. Pergolide– Pergolide mesylate is a long-acting ergot derivative with dopaminergic properties that has been shown to reduce hypersecretion and shrink most PRL-secreting macroadenomas. It is more potent than bromocriptine, requiring doses of 25–300 μg/d to treat hyperprolactinemia. The side effects of pergolide are similar to those of bromocriptine.

C. Radiotherapy: Conventional radiation therapy is reserved for patients with PRL-secreting macroadenomas who have persisting hyperprolactinemia following surgical treatment. In this group of patients, radiotherapy with 4000–5000 cGy prevents further tumor expansion, though PRL levels usually do not fall into the normal range. Impairment of anterior pituitary function occurs in approximately 50–60% of patients.

Experience with heavy particle irradiation in prolactinomas is limited.

Selection of Therapy for Prolactinomas

The selection of therapy for prolactinomas depends on the wishes of the patient, the patient's plans for pregnancy and tolerance of medical therapy, and the availability of a skilled neurosurgeon.

A. Microadenomas: All patients should be treated to prevent tumor progression, osteopenia and the other effects of prolonged hypogonadism. Medical therapy with bromocriptine effectively restores normal gonadal function and fertility, and pregnancy carries only a small risk of tumor expansion. The major disadvantage is the need for chronic therapy. In contrast, transsphenoidal adenectomy, either initially or after a trial of bromocriptine therapy, carries little risk when performed by an experienced neurosurgeon and offers a high probability of long-term remission.

B. Macroadenomas: Primary surgical therapy in these patients frequently does not result in long-term remission, so medical therapy is being used more often, particularly when the patient's prolactin levels are greater than 200 ng/mL (9.1 nmol/L) and the tumor is larger than 2 cm. Although transsphenoidal microsurgery will rapidly decrease tumor size and decompress the pituitary stalk, the optic chiasm, and the cavernous sinuses, there is usually residual tumor and hyperprolactinemia. Thus, these patients will require additional therapy with bromocriptine. Although tumor growth and prolactin secretion can be controlled by medical therapy, therapeutic failure can result from drug intolerance or poor compliance. Radiation therapy is generally reserved for postsurgical patients with residual adenomas who do not tolerate bromocriptine.

2. ACROMEGALY & GIGANTISM

GH-secreting pituitary adenomas are second in frequency to prolactinomas and cause the classic clinical syndromes of acromegaly and gigantism.

The characteristic clinical manifestations are the consequence of chronic GH hypersecretion, which in turn leads to excessive generation of IGF-1 the mediator of most of the effects of GH (see Chapter 3). Although overgrowth of bone is the classic feature, GH excess causes a generalized systemic disorder with deleterious effects and an increased mortality rate, though deaths are rarely due to the space-occupying or destructive effects of pituitary adenoma per se.

Acromegaly and gigantism are virtually always secondary to a pituitary adenoma. Ectopic GRH secretion has been identified as another cause of GH hypersecretion and acromegaly in a few patients with carcinoid or islet cell tumors. Reports of intrapituitary GRH-secreting gangliocytomas in direct contiguity with GH-secreting somatotroph adenomas and a report of a GRH-secreting hypothalamic hamartoma in a patient with acromegaly provide a link between ectopic and eutopic GRH production. Ectopic secretion of GH per se is very rare.

In adults, GH excess leads to acromegaly, the syndrome characterized by local overgrowth of bone, particularly of the skull and mandible. Linear growth does not occur, because of prior fusion of the epiphyses of long bones. In childhood and adolescence, the onset of chronic GH excess leads to gigantism. Many of these patients have associated hypogonadism, which delays epiphysial closure, and the combination of IGF-1 excess and hypogonadism leads to a striking acceleration of linear growth. Most patients with gigantism also have features of acromegaly if GH hypersecretion persists through adolescence and into adulthood.

Pathology

Pituitary adenomas causing acromegaly are usually over 1 cm in diameter when the diagnosis is established. These tumors arise from the lateral wings of the anterior pituitary; less than 20% are diagnosed as microadenomas.

GH-secreting adenomas are of two histologic types: densely and sparsely granulated. However, there appears to be no difference in the degree of GH secretion or clinical manifestations in these patients. About 15% of GH-secreting tumors also contain lactotrophs, and these tumors thus hypersecrete both GH and PRL.

Densely granulated adenomas are acidophilic by light microscopy using routine stains and are usually strongly positive when stained for GH by immunocytochemical techniques. Electron microscopy demonstrates that the cells are similar to normal somatotrophs; ie, they are spherical or oval, with uniform features, round or oval centrally located nuclei, and abundant cytoplasm. The numerous spherical GH-containing granules are electron-dense, ranging in size from 300 to 600 nm, with the majority measuring 350–450 nm.

The sparsely granulated adenomas are chromophobic by light microscopy, a feature that merely reflects the paucity of stainable secretory granules; they are indistinguishable from other chromophobe adenomas except by the demonstration of GH within them by immunocytochemistry. By electron microscopy, the cells do not resemble normal somatotrophs but have variable shape and size; pleomorphic, frequently crescent-shaped nuclei; and globular fibrous bodies within the cytoplasm. The secretory granules measure 100–250 nm, and fewer are present than in normal somatotrophs or densely granulated adenomas.

Etiology & Pathogenesis

Excessive pituitary GH secretion could be secondary to abnormal hypothalamic function, but in most cases it is a primary pituitary disorder. A mutation in the G_s protein leading to excessive cAMP production has been identified in 40% of GH-secreting adenomas. Pituitary adenomas are present in virtually all patients and are usually greater than 1 cm in diameter; hyperplasia alone is rare, and nonadenomatous anterior pituitary tissue does not exhibit somatotroph hyperplasia when examined histologically. In addition, there is a return of normal GH levels and dynamic control of GH secretion following selective removal of the pituitary adenoma.

Indirect evidence that in some patients acromegaly may be a hypothalamic disorder consisting of either increased release of GRH or decreased secretion of somatostatin is based largely on the findings of abnormal GH dynamics in these patients.

Pathophysiology

In acromegaly, GH secretion is increased and its dynamic control is abnormal. Secretion remains episodic; however, the number, duration, and amplitude of secretory episodes are increased, and they occur randomly throughout the 24-hour period. The characteristic nocturnal surge is absent, and there are abnormal responses to suppression and stimulation. Thus, glucose suppressibility is lost (see diagnosis, below), and GH stimulation by hypoglycemia is usually absent. TRH and GnRH may cause GH release, whereas these substances do not normally stimulate GH secretion. Dopamine and dopamine agonists such as bromocriptine and apomorphine, which normally stimulate GH secretion, paradoxically cause GH suppression in about 70–80% of patients with acromegaly.

Most of the deleterious effects of chronic GH hypersecretion are caused by its stimulation of excessive amounts of IGF-1 (see Chapter 3), and plasma levels of this compound are increased in acromegaly. The growth-promoting effects of IGF-1 (DNA, RNA, and protein synthesis) lead to the characteristic proliferation of bone, cartilage, and soft tissues and increase in size of other organs to produce the classic clinical manifestations of acromegaly. The insulin resistance and carbohydrate intolerance seen in acromegaly appear to be direct effects of GH and not due to IGF-1 excess.

Clinical Features

The sex incidence of acromegaly is approximately equal; the mean age at diagnosis is approximately 40 years; and the duration of symptoms is usually 5–10 years before the diagnosis is established.

Acromegaly is a chronic disabling and disfiguring disorder with increased late morbidity and mortality if untreated. Although spontaneous remissions have been described, the course is slowly progressive in the great majority of cases—patients once thought to be "burned out" can almost invariably be shown to have continuing clinical manifestations and GH hypersecretion.

A. Symptoms and Signs: Early manifestations

(Table 2–10) include soft tissue proliferation, with enlargement of the hands and feet and coarsening of the facial features. This is usually accompanied by increased sweating, heat intolerance, oiliness of the skin, fatigue, and weight gain.

At diagnosis, virtually all patients have classic manifestations; acral and soft tissue changes are always present. Bone and cartilage changes affect chiefly the face and skull (Figure 2–18). These changes include thickening of the calvarium; increased size of the frontal sinuses, which leads to prominence of the supraorbital ridges; enlargement of the nose; and downward and forward growth of the mandible, which leads to prognathism and widely spaced teeth. Soft tissue growth also contributes to the facial appearance, with coarsening of the features and facial and infraorbital puffiness. The hands and feet are predominantly affected by soft tissue growth; they are large, thickened, and bulky, with blunt, spade-like fingers (Figure 2–19) and toes. A bulky, sweaty handshake frequently suggests the diagnosis, and there are increases in ring, glove, and shoe sizes. There is generalized thickening of the skin, with increased oiliness and sweating. Acne, sebaceous cysts, and fibromata mollusca (skin tags and papillomas) are common, as is acanthosis nigricans of the axillae and neck and hypertrichosis in women.

These bony and soft tissue changes are accompanied by systemic manifestations, which include hyperhidrosis, heat intolerance, lethargy, fatigue, and increased sleep requirement. Moderate weight gain usually occurs. Paresthesias, usually due to carpal tunnel compression, occur in 70%; sensorimotor neuropathies occur uncommonly. Bone and cartilage overgrowth leads to arthralgias and in long-standing cases to degenerative arthritis of the spine, hips, and knees. Photophobia of unknown cause occurs in about half of cases and is most troublesome in bright sunlight and during night driving.

GH excess leads to generalized visceromegaly, clinically evident as thyromegaly and enlargement of the salivary glands. Enlargement of other organs is usually not clinically detectable.

Hypertension of unknown cause occurs in about 25% of patients and cardiomegaly in about 15%. Cardiac enlargement may be secondary to hypertension, atherosclerotic disease, or, rarely, to "acromegalic cardiomyopathy." Renal calculi occur in 11% secondary to the hypercalciuria induced by GH excess.

Other endocrine and metabolic abnormalities are common and may be due either to GH excess or to mechanical effects of the pituitary adenoma. Glucose intolerance and hyperinsulinism occur in 50% and 70%, respectively, owing to GH-induced insulin resistance. Overt clinical diabetes occurs in a minority, and diabetic ketoacidosis is rare. Hypogonadism occurs in 60% of female and 46% of male patients and is of multifactorial origin; tumor growth and compression may impair pituitary gonadotropin secretion, and associated hyperprolactinemia (see below) or the PRL-like effect of excessive GH secretion may impair gonadotropin and gonadal function. In men, low total plasma testosterone levels may be due to GH suppression of sex hormone-binding globulin (SHBG) levels; in these cases, plasma free testosterone levels may be normal, with normal gonadal function. With earlier diagnosis, hypothyroidism and hypoadrenalism due to destruction of the normal anterior pituitary are unusual and are present in only 13% and 4% of patients, respectively. Galactorrhea occurs in about 15% and is usually caused by hyperprolactinemia from a pituitary adenoma with a mixed cell population of somatotrophs and lactotrophs. Gynecomastia of unknown cause occurs in about 10% of men. Although acromegaly may be a component of multiple endocrine neoplasia (MEN) type I syndrome, it is distinctly unusual, and concomitant parathyroid hyperfunction or pancreatic islet cell tumors are rare.

When GH hypersecretion is present for many years, late complications occur, including progressive cosmetic deformity and disabling degenerative arthritis (which frequently requires operative treatment). In addition, the mortality rate is increased; after age 45, the death rate in acromegaly from cardiovascular and cerebrovascular atherosclerosis and respiratory diseases is twice that of the healthy popu-

Table 2–10. Clinical manifestations of acromegaly in 100 patients.[1]

Manifestations of GH excess	
Acral enlargement	100[2]
Soft tissue overgrowth	100
Hyperhidrosis	88
Lethargy or fatigue	87
Weight gain	73
Paresthesias	70
Joint pain	69
Photophobia	46
Papillomas	45
Hypertrichosis	33
Goiter	32
Acanthosis nigricans	29
Hypertension	24
Cardiomegaly	16
Renal calculi	11
Disturbance of other endocrine functions	
Hyperinsulinemia	70
Glucose intolerance	50
Irregular or absent menses	60
Decreased libido or impotence	46
Hypothyroidism	13
Galactorrhea	13
Gynecomastia	8
Hypoadrenalism	4
Local manifestations	
Enlarged sella	90
Headache	65
Visual deficit	20

[1] Adapted from Tyrrell JB, Wilson CB: Pituitary syndromes. In: Surgical Endocrinology: Clinical Syndromes. Friesen SR (editor). Lippincott, 1978.
[2] Percentage of patients in whom these features were present.

Figure 2–18. Serial photographs of an acromegalic patient at the ages indicated. Note the gradual increase in size of the nose, lips, and skin folds. (Reproduced, with permission, from Reichlin SR: Acromegaly. Med Grand Rounds 1982;1:9.)

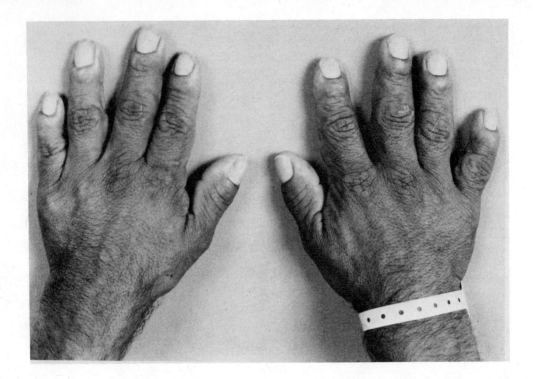

Figure 2–19. Markedly increased soft tissue bulk and blunt fingers in a middle-aged man with acromegaly.

lation. Death rates are highest in patients with hypertension or clinical diabetes mellitus.

Manifestations of the pituitary adenoma are also common in acromegaly; eg, 65% of patients have headache. Although visual impairment was usually present in older series, it now occurs in only 15–20%, since most patients are now diagnosed because of the manifestations of GH excess.

B. Laboratory Findings: Postprandial plasma glucose may be elevated, and serum insulin is increased in 70%. Elevated serum phosphorus (due to increased renal tubular resorption of phosphate) and hypercalciuria appear to be due to direct effects of GH or IGF-1.

C. Imaging Studies: Plain films (Figure 2–20) show sellar enlargement in 90% of cases. Thickening of the calvarium, enlargement of the frontal and maxillary sinuses, and enlargement of the jaw can also be seen. Radiographs of the hand show increased soft tissue bulk, "arrowhead" tufting of the distal phalanges, increased width of intra-articular cartilages, and cystic changes of the carpal bones. Radiographs of the feet show similar changes, and there is increased thickness of the heel pad (normal, < 22 mm).

Diagnosis

Acromegaly is usually clinically obvious and can be readily confirmed by assessment of GH secretion; basal fasting GH levels (normal, 1–5 ng/mL [46.5–232 pmol/L]) are > 10 ng/mL in over 90% of patients and range from 5 ng/mL (232 pmol/L) to

over 500 ng/mL (23,255 pmol/L), with a mean of approximately 50 ng/mL (2325 pmol/L). However, single measurements are not entirely reliable, because GH secretion is episodic in acromegaly and because other conditions may increase GH secretion (see below).

A. Glucose Suppression: Suppression with oral glucose is the simplest and most specific dynamic test for acromegaly. In healthy subjects, oral administration of 100 g of glucose causes a reduction of the GH level to less than 2 ng/mL (93 pmol/L) at 60 minutes. In acromegaly, GH levels may decrease, increase, or show no change; however, they do not decrease to less than 2 ng/mL (93 pmol/L), and this lack of response establishes the diagnosis.

B. IGF-1 Measurement: Measurement of IGF-1 (see Chapter 3) is a useful means of confirming the diagnosis of GH hypersecretion. IGF-1 levels are elevated in virtually all patients with acromegaly (normal ranges vary widely in different laboratories).

C. Other Tests: Additional procedures that help establish or confirm the diagnosis are (1) GH stimulation with TRH; (2) the absence of a nocturnal GH surge; and (3) the paradoxic suppression of GH by levodopa, dopamine, bromocriptine, or apomorphine. These procedures are usually unnecessary except in patients with mild acromegaly who may have normal or only mildly elevated GH levels and equivocal responses to glucose suppression.

D. Tumor Localization: Radiographic localization of the pituitary adenoma causing acromegaly is

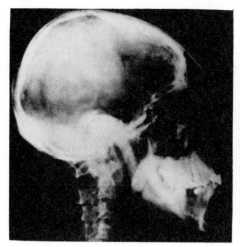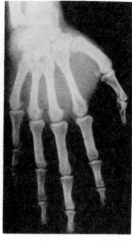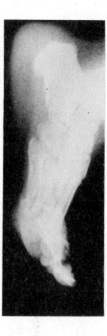

Figure 2–20. Radiologic signs in acromegaly: Left: Skull with enlarged sella turcica and frontal sinuses, thickening of the calvarium, and enlargement of the mandible. Center: Hand with enlarged sesamoid bone and increased soft tissue shadows. Right: Thickened heel pad. (Reproduced, with permission, from Levin SR: Manifestations and treatment of acromegaly. Calif Med [March] 1972;116:57.)

usually straightforward (see Neuroradiologic Evaluation, above). In virtually all patients, tumor location and size can be shown by MRI; 90% have tumors over 1 cm in diameter that are readily visualized. In the rare patient with normal neuroradiologic studies, an extrapituitary ectopic source of GH or GRH should be considered. If the scans suggest diffuse pituitary enlargement or hyperplasia, ectopic GRH should also be suspected.

Differential Diagnosis

A. Other Causes of GH Hypersecretion: The presence of clinical features of GH excess, elevated GH and IGF-1 secretion, and abnormal GH dynamics, together with the demonstration of a pituitary tumor by neuroradiologic studies, are diagnostic of acromegaly. However, other conditions associated with GH hypersecretion must be considered in the differential diagnosis. These include anxiety, exercise, acute illness, chronic renal failure, cirrhosis, starvation, protein-calorie malnutrition, anorexia nervosa, and type I (insulin-dependent) diabetes mellitus. Estrogen therapy may increase GH responsiveness to various stimuli. These conditions may be associated with abnormal GH suppressibility by glucose and by abnormal GH responsiveness to TRH; however, patients with these conditions do not have clinical manifestations of GH excess and are thus readily differentiated from patients with acromegaly. In addition, the conditions listed above do not lead to elevation of IGF-1 concentrations.

B. Ectopic GH or GRH Secretion: These rare patients with acromegaly due to ectopic secretion of GH or GRH have typical clinical manifestations of acromegaly. This may occur in lung carcinoma, carcinoid tumors, and pancreatic islet cell tumors. These syndromes should be suspected in patients with a known extrapituitary tumor who have GH excess or in those with clinical and biochemical features of acromegaly who have radiologic procedures that show normal pituitary glands or that suggest diffuse pituitary enlargement or hyperplasia.

Treatment

All patients with acromegaly should undergo therapy to halt progression of the disorder and to prevent late complications. The objectives of therapy are removal or destruction of the pituitary tumor, reversal of GH hypersecretion, and maintenance of normal anterior and posterior pituitary function. These objectives are currently attainable in most patients, especially those with smaller tumors and only moderate GH hypersecretion. In patients with large tumors who have marked GH hypersecretion, several therapies are usually required to achieve normal GH secretion.

Various criteria exist for what constitutes an adequate response to therapy. Most authors agree that basal GH values under 5 ng/mL (232 pmol/L) and normalization of IGF-1 levels indicate the return of normal GH secretion.

The initial therapy of choice is transsphenoidal microsurgery because of its high success rate, rapid reduction of GH levels, the low incidence of postoperative hypopituitarism, and the low surgical morbidity rate. Conventional radiotherapy (x-ray radiation) is also successful, although a much longer period is required to reduce GH levels to normal, and heavy particle irradiation has limited availability. Medical management with bromocriptine has the disadvantage of requiring chronic therapy to suppress GH secretion, and it is successful in only a minority of patients. It is generally used in patients who have not responded to surgery or irradiation. Octreotide acetate, a long-acting somatostatin analogue, is now available for the treatment of acromegaly.

A. Surgical Treatment: Transsphenoidal selective adenoma removal is the procedure of choice; craniotomy is necessary in the few patients in whom major suprasellar extension precludes the transsphenoidal approach. Successful reduction of GH levels is achieved in approximately 80% of patients. In those with small or moderate-sized tumors (< 2 cm), success is achieved in over 90%, whereas in those with larger tumors and basal GH levels greater than 50 ng/mL (2325 pmol/L)—and particularly in those with major extrasellar extension of the adenoma—successful responses occur in only 60–70%. Recurrence rates in those with a successful initial response are low (about 5% of patients at our institution). Surgical complications (discussed above) occur in less than 5%.

B. Radiotherapy: Conventional supervoltage irradiation in doses of 4500–5000 cGy is successful in 60–80% of patients, though GH levels may not return to normal until years after therapy. Thus, in one series, GH levels were under 10 ng/mL (465 pmol/L) in only 38% of patients at 2 years posttreatment; however, at 5 and 10 years, 73% and 81% had achieved such levels. The incidence of hypopituitarism is appreciable, and in this series hypothyroidism occurred in 19%, hypoadrenalism in 38%, and hypogonadism in approximately 50–60% of patients as a consequence of radiotherapy. Because of the prolonged delay in achieving reduction in GH levels, conventional radiotherapy is generally reserved for patients with persisting GH secretion following pituitary microsurgery.

Heavy particle irradiation is more rapidly effective than conventional irradiation, but because of the limitations of the field size, it can be used only in patients with smaller tumors and those in whom no extrasellar extension is present. About 80% of patients have GH levels under 10 ng/mL (465 pmol/L) at 5 years after irradiation, with most patients having a satisfactory response at 2 years. The incidence of hypopituitarism has been variously reported, but it appears to occur in approximately 40% of patients.

Therapy of acromegaly by radioactive implants within the sella turcica is limited to a few centers. Successful responses are achieved in about 70%; however, there is a significant incidence of hypopituitarism, cerebrospinal fluid rhinorrhea, and meningitis due to local radionecrosis. Because of these complications, the procedure has not gained wide acceptance.

C. Medical: Bromocriptine, a long-acting dopamine agonist, reduces GH levels in 60–80% of patients; however, only a few patients attain levels of 10 ng/mL (465 pmol/L) or less. Thus, bromocriptine is generally used in acromegalics in whom adequate reduction of GH levels has not been achieved with surgery or irradiation.

Octreotide acetate, a long-acting analogue of somatostatin, is effective in the management of acromegaly. It reduces levels of growth hormone and IGF-1 to normal in the majority of patients treated, and in some it has even caused tumor shrinkage. Effective doses appear to be in the range of 100–500 μg given by subcutaneous injection three times daily. The drug is expensive, and the need for subcutaneous injection is a disadvantage, since chronic therapy is required. The long-term effects of this therapy are not yet known.

Response to Treatment

In patients with successful reduction in GH hypersecretion, there is cessation of bone overgrowth. In addition, these patients experience considerable clinical improvement, including reduction in soft tissue bulk of the extremities, decreased facial puffiness, increased energy, and cessation of hyperhydrosis, heat intolerance, and oily skin. Headache, carpal tunnel syndrome, arthralgias, and photophobia are also reversible with successful therapy. Glucose intolerance and hyperinsulinemia as well as hypercalciuria are also reversed in most cases.

Posttreatment Follow-Up

Patients undergoing surgery should be seen 4–6 weeks after the operation for assessment of GH secretion and pituitary function. Those with persisting GH hypersecretion should receive further therapy with radiation, bromocriptine, or octreotide acetate. Patients with postoperative GH levels under 10 ng/mL (465 pmol/L) should have follow-up GH and IGF-1 determinations at 6-month intervals for 2 years and yearly thereafter. Late hypopituitarism after surgery alone does not occur.

Patients treated with radiotherapy should have biannual assessment of GH secretion and annual assessment of anterior pituitary function, since the incidence of late hypopituitarism is appreciable and increases with time following irradiation.

3. ACTH-SECRETING PITUITARY ADENOMAS: CUSHING'S DISEASE

In 1932, Harvey Cushing documented the presence of small basophilic pituitary adenomas in six of eight patients with clinical features of adrenocortical hyperfunction. Years later, ACTH hypersecretion was identified from such tumors and found to be the cause of bilateral adrenal hyperplasia. Pituitary ACTH hypersecretion (Cushing's disease) is now recognized as the most common cause of spontaneous hypercortisolism (Cushing's syndrome) and must be distinguished from the other forms of adrenocorticosteroid excess—ectopic ACTH syndrome and adrenal tumors (see Chapter 6).

Pathology

ACTH-secreting pituitary tumors exist in virtually all patients with Cushing's disease. These tumors are usually benign microadenomas under 10 mm in diameter; 50% are 5 mm or less in diameter, and microadenomas as small as 1 mm have been described. These tumors in Cushing's disease are either basophilic or chromophobe adenomas and may be found anywhere within the anterior pituitary. Rarely, ACTH-secreting tumors are large, with invasive tendencies, and malignant tumors have rarely been reported.

Histologically, the tumors are composed of compact sheets of uniform, well-granulated cells (granule size, 200–700 nm by electron microscopy) with a sinusoidal arrangement and a high content of ACTH and its related peptides (β-LPH, β-endorphin). A zone of perinuclear hyalinization (Crooke's changes) is frequently observed as a result of exposure of the corticotroph cells to prolonged hypercortisolism. A specific ultrastructural finding in these adenomas is the deposition of bundles of perinuclear microfilaments that encircle the nucleus; these are the ultrastructural equivalent of Crooke's hyaline changes seen on light microscopy. In contrast to the adenomas cells, ACTH content in the portion of the anterior pituitary not involved with the tumor is decreased.

Diffuse hyperplasia of anterior pituitary corticotrophs or adenomatous hyperplasia, presumed to result from hypersecretion of corticotropin-releasing hormone (CRH), occurs rarely.

The adrenal glands in Cushing's disease are enlarged, weighing 12–24 g (normal, 8–10 g). Microscopic examination shows a thickened cortex due to hyperplasia of both the zona reticularis and zona fasciculata; the zona glomerulosa is normal. In some cases, ACTH-secreting pituitary adenomas cause bilateral nodular hyperplasia; the adrenals show diffuse bilateral cortical hyperplasia and the presence of one or more nodules that vary from microscopic to several centimeters in diameter, with multiple small nodules being the most common.

Pathogenesis

The weight of current evidence is that Cushing's disease is a primary pituitary disorder and that hypothalamic abnormalities are secondary to hypercortisolism. The endocrine abnormalities in Cushing's disease are as follows: (1) hypersecretion of ACTH, with bilateral adrenocortical hyperplasia and hypercortisolism; (2) absent circadian periodicity of

ACTH and cortisol secretion; (3) absent responsiveness of ACTH and cortisol to stress (hypoglycemia or surgery); (4) abnormal negative feedback of ACTH secretion by glucocorticoids; and (5) subnormal responsiveness of GH, TSH, and gonadotropins to stimulation.

Evidence that Cushing's disease is a primary pituitary disorder is based on the high frequency of pituitary adenomas, the response to their removal, and the interpretation of hypothalamic abnormalities as being secondary to hypercortisolism. These findings suggest that ACTH hypersecretion arises from a spontaneously developing pituitary adenoma and that the resulting hypercortisolism suppresses the normal hypothalamic-pituitary axis and CRH release and thereby abolishes the hypothalamic regulation of circadian variability and stress responsiveness. There is in vitro evidence that the negative feedback effects of glucocorticoids are exerted directly on the pituitary tumor and that other pharmacologic agents such as vasopressin, cyproheptadine, and bromocriptine directly inhibit the ACTH-secreting adenoma. In addition, the abnormalities of GH, TSH, and gonadotropin secretion are also observed in exogenous Cushing's syndrome and are due to the hypercortisolism per se and not to a primary hypothalamic disorder.

Analysis of the response to therapy by pituitary microsurgery sheds some light on the pathogenesis of Cushing's disease. Selective removal of pituitary microadenomas by transsphenoidal microsurgery corrects ACTH hypersecretion and hypercortisolism in most patients. This suggests that the adenoma—not corticotroph hyperplasia—is responsible for the ACTH excess. Postoperatively, these patients experience transient ACTH deficiency with secondary hypoadrenalism. ACTH response to CRH is blunted immediately after complete removal of these tumors. The secretion of the other anterior pituitary hormones is not only preserved but enhanced once the microadenoma is removed. These findings, which suggest that the normal hypothalamic-pituitary axis is suppressed by the hypercortisolism, are supported by the in vitro demonstration of markedly decreased ACTH content in nonadenomatous pituitary tissue removed from patients with active Cushing's disease. After selective removal of the pituitary adenoma, the following return to normal: the circadian rhythmicity of ACTH and cortisol, the responsiveness of the hypothalamic-pituitary axis to hypoglycemic stress, and the dexamethasone suppressibility of cortisol secretion. Thus, in these patients, there is no evidence for a persisting hypothalamic abnormality.

Clinical Features

Cushing's disease presents with the signs and symptoms of hypercortisolism and adrenal androgen excess (see Chapter 6). The onset of these features is usually insidious, developing over months or years. Obesity (with predominantly central fat distribution), hypertension, glucose intolerance, and gonadal dysfunction (amenorrhea or impotence) are common features. Other common manifestations include moon facies, plethora, osteopenia, proximal muscle weakness, easy bruisability, psychologic disturbances, violaceous striae, hirsutism, acne, poor wound healing, and superficial fungal infections. Unlike patients with the classic form of ectopic ACTH syndrome, patients with Cushing's disease rarely have hypokalemia, weight loss, anemia, or hyperpigmentation. Virilization, observed occasionally in patients with adrenal carcinoma, is unusual in Cushing's disease. Clinical symptoms related to the ACTH-secreting primary tumor itself, such as headache or visual impairment, are rare because of the small size of these adenomas.

The usual age range is 20–40 years, but Cushing's disease has been reported in infants and patients over 70. There is a female:male ratio of approximately 8:1. In contrast, the ectopic ACTH syndrome occurs more commonly in men (male:female ratio of 3:1).

Diagnosis

The initial step in the diagnosis of an ACTH-secreting pituitary adenoma is the documentation of endogenous hypercortisolism, which is confirmed by the presence of abnormal cortisol suppressibility to low-dose dexamethasone as well as an increased basal urine free cortisol. A more complete discussion of the diagnosis and differential diagnosis of Cushing's syndrome is presented in Chapter 6.

The differentiation of an ACTH-secreting pituitary tumor from other causes of hypercortisolism must be based on biochemical studies, of which the measurement of basal plasma ACTH levels and the response to high-dose dexamethasone suppression testing are the most reliable.

A. ACTH Levels: Patients with Cushing's disease have normal or modestly elevated ACTH levels ranging from 40 to 200 pg/mL (8.8–44 pmol/L) (normal, 10–50 pg/mL [2.2–11.1 pmol/L]). Low levels (< 20 pg/mL [4.4 pmol/L]) are indicative of an autonomously secreting adrenal tumor, and levels greater than 200 pg/mL (44 pmol/L) suggest an ectopic ACTH-secreting neoplasm. Unfortunately, plasma ACTH levels do not adequately differentiate pituitary from ectopic sources of ACTH hypersecretion. Thus, 30–40% of patients with the ectopic ACTH syndrome have ACTH levels (100–200 pg/mL [22.2–44 pmol/L]) that are in the range seen in Cushing's disease, and some patients actually have "normal" measurements (see Chapter 6).

B. Dexamethasone Suppression Tests: Although all patients with Cushing's syndrome have disordered regulation of glucocorticoid feedback at the hypothalamic-pituitary level (eg, failure of suppression with low-dose dexamethasone), some negative glucocorticoid feedback effect is maintained by ACTH-secreting pituitary tumors. Thus, administration of high-dose dexamethasone will suppress plasma or urine corticosteroids to less than 50% of basal levels (see Chapter 6). Failure of suppression indicates either an ectopic ACTH-secreting tumor or an adrenal neoplasm.

Caution: Caution must be urged in interpreting the results of high-dose dexamethasone suppression tests, since they are not entirely specific. About 15–30% of patients with proved ACTH-secreting tumors fail to suppress steroid levels to less than 50% of baseline, and some patients with the ectopic ACTH syndrome (bronchial or thymic carcinoid) do suppress with high-dose dexamethasone (see Chapter 6).

C. CRH Testing: CRH stimulation testing has been employed as a means of differentiating pituitary from ectopic causes of Cushing's syndrome. In patients with Cushing's disease, CRH administration further increases ACTH and cortisol levels. In contrast, patients with ectopic ACTH syndrome usually have no ACTH or cortisol responses to CRH. However, several exceptions to these typical responses have been observed.

D. Imaging Studies: MRI of the sella turcica localizes pituitary adenomas in less than 50% of cases of ACTH-secreting pituitary adenomas. Both false-positive and false-negative findings occur—emphasizing again the importance of using clinical and biochemical techniques to establish the diagnosis of an ACTH-secreting microadenoma.

Roentgenographic studies of the adrenal glands in Cushing's disease must be interpreted with caution. CT scanning may demonstrate normal, enlarged, or asymmetric adrenal glands; and nodular adrenal hyperplasia secondary to an ACTH-secreting pituitary tumor may appear as a solitary adrenal mass and mimic an adrenal neoplasm.

E. Petrosal Sinus ACTH Sampling: The studies that are employed for the differential diagnosis of ACTH-dependent Cushing's syndrome frequently cannot distinguish pituitary from ectopic ACTH hypersecretion, especially when the neoplasm is small or occult. Therefore, bilateral simultaneous petrosal sinus ACTH sampling with CRH stimulation of ACTH release is now the procedure of choice for patients with occult lesions. This study must be performed by a radiologist skilled in catheterization techniques. (See Chapter 6.)

Problems in Diagnosis

Patients with ectopic ACTH syndrome may be clinically indistinguishable from those with Cushing's disease, and the tumor in each may be radiologically occult. With the advent of specific therapy directed at pituitary microadenomas, establishing the presence or absence of a pituitary source of ACTH hypersecretion is essential. As noted above, selective venous ACTH sampling from the inferior petrosal sinus (pituitary venous effluent) is a useful aid in differential diagnosis.

Problems in diagnosis may also result from intermittent Cushing's disease. In this unusual form of the disorder, ACTH-cortisol hypersecretion fluctuates with periods of normal secretion, during which laboratory studies will be misleading. Proper biochemical confirmation may require repeated studies in these patients.

Treatment

Transsphenoidal microsurgery is the procedure of choice in Cushing's disease. A variety of other therapies—operative, radiologic, pharmacologic—are discussed below.

A. Surgical Treatment: Selective transsphenoidal resection of ACTH-secreting pituitary adenomas is the initial treatment of choice. At operation, meticulous exploration of the intrasellar contents by an experienced neurosurgeon is required. The tumor, which is often found within the anterior lobe tissue, is selectively removed, and normal gland is left intact. If the tumor is too small to locate at surgery, total or hemi-hypophysectomy may be performed in adult patients who are past the age of reproduction and whose biochemical diagnosis has been confirmed with selective venous ACTH sampling.

In about 85% of patients with microadenomas, selective microsurgery is successful in correcting hypercortisolism. Surgical damage to anterior pituitary function is rare, but most patients develop transient secondary adrenocortical insufficiency requiring postoperative glucocorticoid support until the hypothalamic-pituitary-adrenal axis recovers, usually in 6–18 months. Total hypophysectomy is necessary to correct hypercortisolism in another 10% of patients. In the remaining 5% of patients with microadenomas, selective tumor removal is unsuccessful. By contrast, transsphenoidal surgery is successful in only 25% of the 10–15% of patients with Cushing's disease with pituitary macroadenomas or in those with extrasellar extension of tumor.

Transient diabetes insipidus occurs in about 20% of patients, but other surgical complications (eg, hemorrhage, cerebrospinal fluid rhinorrhea, infection, visual impairment, permanent diabetes insipidus) are rare. Hypopituitarism occurs only in patients who undergo total hypophysectomy.

Before the introduction of pituitary microsurgery, bilateral total adrenalectomy was the preferred treatment of Cushing's disease and may still be employed in patients in whom other therapies are unsuccessful. Total adrenalectomy usually corrects hypercortisolism but produces permanent hypoadrenalism, requiring lifelong glucocorticoid and mineralocorticoid therapy. Morbidity is high and relates to poor wound healing, postoperative infection, pancreatic injury, and thromboembolic phenomena. In addition, the ACTH-secreting pituitary adenoma persists and may progress, causing hyperpigmentation and invasive complications (Nelson's syndrome; see below). Persistent hypercortisolism may occasionally follow total adrenalectomy as ACTH hypersection stimulates adrenal remnants or congenital rests. Attempts to transplant adrenal tissue to a readily accessible location, such as the forearm, have been successful in only a few cases and may require several years before the transplant functions satisfactorily; recurrent hyperfunction may result.

B. Radiotherapy: In Cushing's disease, conventional irradiation in doses of 4500–5000 cGy leads to biochemical and clinical improvement in only 40% of adults—although it can lead to improvement in as many as 80% of children. Adjunctive antiadrenal drug therapy has been used with some success, but the ultimate response to radiation therapy is often unsatisfactory, and prolonged drug therapy is required. Because of these low response rates, we do not recommend conventional irradiation as initial therapy.

Heavy particle irradiation, also used as initial therapy in patients with no extrasellar tumor extension, is currently available at only one center in the USA. Alpha particle irradiation is effective in controlling hypercortisolism in 80% of patients, with an incidence of hypopituitarism of approximately one-third. Proton beam therapy is effective in 65% of patients, with a similar incidence of hypopituitarism. Neurologic complications of both forms of therapy include visual loss and oculomotor paralysis. With both of these techniques, there is a lag period of 6–12 months or longer before cortisol secretion returns to normal.

Implantation of radioactive seeds (gold and yttrium) within the sella turcica has also been used in Cushing's disease. Such techniques have achieved a remission rate of 65%, with an additional 16% improved; however, the frequency of operative complications is high, and panhypopituitarism is common.

C. Medical: Drugs that inhibit adrenal cortisol secretion are useful in Cushing's disease, often as adjunctive therapy (see Chapter 6).

Ketoconazole, an imidazole derivative, has been found to strongly inhibit adrenal steroid biosynthesis. It inhibits the cytochrome P450 enzymes P450scc and P450c11. In daily doses of 600–1200 mg, ketoconazole has been effective in the management of Cushing's syndrome. Hepatotoxicity is common, but is usually transient. **Metyrapone,** which inhibits p450c11, and **aminoglutethimide,** which inhibits P450scc, have also been utilized to reduce cortisol hypersecretion.

These drugs are expensive; their use is accompanied by increased ACTH levels that may overcome the enzyme inhibition; and both agents cause gastrointestinal side effects that may limit their effectiveness. More effective control of hypercortisolism with fewer side effects is obtained by combined use of these agents. Adequate data are not available on the long-term use of these drugs as the sole treatment of Cushing's disease. Thus, ketoconazole and aminoglutethimide ordinarily are used while awaiting a response to therapy or in the preparation of patients for surgery.

The adrenolytic drug **mitotane** results in adrenal atrophy predominantly of the zonae fasciculata and reticularis. Remission of hypercortisolism is achieved in approximately 80% of patients with Cushing's disease, but most relapse after therapy is discontinued. Mitotane therapy is limited by the delayed response, which may take weeks or months, and by the frequent side effects, including severe nausea, vomiting, diarrhea, somnolence, and skin rash.

Pharmacologic inhibition of ACTH secretion in Cushing's disease has also been attempted. **Cyproheptadine,** a drug with antiserotonin, antihistamine, and anticholinergic effects, has had the widest use. Although a few well-documented cases of clinical and biochemical remission of Cushing's disease have been reported with its use, cyproheptadine causes unpleasant side effects (sedation, increase appetite, and weight gain) and is usually ineffective in treating ACTH-secreting pituitary adenomas. **Bromocriptine,** a dopamine agonist, has been reported to be effective in rare cases and should probably be reserved for those few patients who have hyperprolactinemia associated with Cushing's disease.

4. ACTH-SECRETING PITUITARY TUMORS FOLLOWING ADRENALECTOMY FOR CUSHING'S DISEASE: NELSON'S SYNDROME

The clinical appearance of an ACTH-secreting pituitary adenoma following bilateral adrenalectomy in patients with Cushing's disease was initially described by Nelson et al in 1958.

Pathogenesis

Based on current evidence, it now seems likely that Nelson's syndrome represents the clinical progression of a preexisting adenoma after the restraint of hypercortisolism on ACTH secretion and tumor growth is removed. That ACTH secretion in Cushing's disease is restrained by the circulating cortisol levels is demonstrated by its stimulation during therapy with ketoconazole or mifepristone (a glucocorticoid antagonist). Furthermore, the tumors in Nelson's syndrome are dexamethasone-suppressible, although larger doses may be required than with untreated Cushing's disease. Thus, following adrenalectomy, the suppressive effect of cortisol is no longer present, ACTH secretion increases, and the pituitary adenoma may progress.

Incidence

The incidence of Nelson's syndrome ranges from 10% to 78%, depending on what criteria are used for diagnosis (see Chapter 6). Pituitary irradiation before or after adrenalectomy does not prevent the development of this syndrome. Approximately 30% of patients adrenalectomized for Cushing's disease develop classic Nelson's syndrome with progressive hyperpigmentation and an obvious ACTH-secreting tumor; another 50% develop evidence of a microadenoma without marked progression; and about 20% never develop a progressive tumor. The reasons for these differences in clinical behavior are uncertain, and they cannot be predicted prior to adrenal surgery. Continued examination, including plasma ACTH levels, visual fields, and sellar radiology, is required following bilateral adrenalectomy in patients with Cushing's disease.

Clinical Features

The pituitary tumors in patients with classic Nelson's syndrome are among the most aggressive and rapidly growing of all pituitary tumors. These patients present with hyperpigmentation and with manifestations of an expanding intrasellar mass lesion. Visual field defects, headache, cavernous sinus invasion with extraocular muscle palsies, and even malignant changes with local or distant metastases may occur. Pituitary apoplexy may also complicate the course of these tumors.

Diagnosis

Plasma ACTH levels are markedly elevated, usually over 1000 pg/mL (222 pmol/L) and often as high as 10,000 pg/mL (2220 pmol/L). The sella turcica is enlarged on routine radiographs; MRI defines the extent of the tumor.

Treatment

Pituitary surgery, either by the transsphenoidal approach or by transfrontal craniotomy, is the initial mode of treatment. Complete resection is usually not possible, because of the large size of these tumors. Conventional radiotherapy is employed postoperatively in patients with residual tumor or extrasellar extension.

5. THYROTROPIN-SECRETING PITUITARY ADENOMAS

Thyrotropin-secreting pituitary adenomas are rare tumors manifested as hyperthyroidism with goiter in the presence of elevated TSH. Patients with TSH-secreting tumors are often resistant to routine ablative thyroid therapy, requiring large, often multiple doses of ^{131}I and several operations for control of thyrotoxicosis. Histologically, the tumors are chromophobe adenomas. They are often very large and cause visual impairment, which alerts the physician to a pituitary abnormality. Patients with these tumors do not have extrathyroidal systemic manifestations of Graves' disease such as ophthalmopathy or dermopathy. Pituitary TSH hypersecretion in the absence of a demonstrable pituitary tumor has also been reported to cause hyperthyroidism in a few patients.

TSH dynamics are variable; TRH (protirelin) administration rarely stimulates TSH secretion from these tumors, nor do dopamine and bromocriptine suppress TSH as they do the TSH hypersecretion of primary hypothyroidism. The diagnosis is based on findings of hyperthyroidism with elevated serum TSH and α-subunit, and neuroradiologic studies consistent with pituitary tumor. Differential diagnosis includes primary hypothyroidism (thyroid failure) in patients who develop major hyperplasia of pituitary thyrotrophs and lactotrophs with sellar enlargement and occasional suprasellar extension.

Treatment should be directed initially at the adenoma, with surgery or radiation therapy. If TSH hypersecretion persists, ablative treatment of the thyroid with either ^{131}I or surgery may be necessary to achieve clinical remission of the thyrotoxic state.

Octreotide acetate, a long-acting somatostatin analogue, has been effective in decreasing TSH secretion from these tumors when given subcutaneously in doses similar to those used for the treatment of acromegaly (see above). Shrinkage of the tumor has also been observed. The long-term effects of this therapy are not yet known, but it appears to be a useful adjunct in patients with residual tumor following surgical resection. (See Chapter 4.)

6. GONADOTROPIN-SECRETING PITUITARY ADENOMAS

Gonadotropin-secreting pituitary adenomas have been well documented in only a few patients. The majority hypersecrete only FSH, but tumors secreting both LH and FSH and a tumor secreting only LH have been described. Enlargement of the sella turcica has been noted in several patients with long-standing primary hypogonadism (eg, Klinefelter's syndrome). In most of these cases, a pituitary tumor was not proved histologically, and such sellar abnormalities probably reflect reactive pituitary enlargement and gonadotropin cell hyperplasia secondary to primary gonadal failure.

Gonadotropin-secreting pituitary adenomas are usually large chromophobe adenomas presenting with visual impairment and are often considered to be functionless before LH and FSH measurements are obtained. Testosterone levels may be low or elevated; in either case, the patients are frequently impotent or infertile. FSH and LH secretory dynamics are abnormal. GnRH may or may not stimulate gonadotropin release from these tumors, and testosterone administration results in subnormal or absent suppression. In addition, LH and FSH secretion in patients is often provoked by TRH, unlike the lack of stimulation observed in healthy individuals. The alpha subunit of the glycoprotein hormones is also secreted in excess from these tumors.

Therapy for gonadotropin-secreting adenomas has been directed at surgical removal. Because of their large size, adequate control of LH/FSH hypersecretion has not been achieved, and radiotherapy is usually required.

7. ALPHA SUBUNIT-SECRETING PITUITARY ADENOMAS

Excessive quantities of the alpha subunit of the glycoprotein pituitary hormones have been observed in association with the hypersecretion of many anterior pituitary hormones (TSH, GH, PRL, LH, FSH). Recently, however, pure alpha subunit hypersecretion has been identified in several patients with large invasive chromophobe adenomas and partial panhypopituitarism. Isolated alpha subunit-secreting tumors may become increasingly recognized, and the determination of the alpha subunit may be a useful marker in patients with presumed "nonfunctioning" pituitary adenomas.

8. NONFUNCTIONAL PITUITARY ADENOMAS

"Nonfunctional" chromophobe adenomas once represented approximately 80% of all primary pituitary tumors; however, with clinical application of radioimmunoassay of anterior pituitary hormones, these tumors currently account for only about 10% of all pituitary adenomas. Thus, the great majority of these chromophobe adenomas have now been documented to be PRL-secreting; a smaller number secrete TSH or the gonadotropins. The incidence of alpha subunit hypersecretion is currently under investigation, and it is likely that the increasing applications of such assays will further decrease the percentage of pituitary adenomas which are truly "nonsecreting."

Nonfunctional tumors are usually large when the diagnosis is established; headache and visual field defects are the usual presenting symptoms. However, endocrine manifestations are usually present for months to years before the diagnosis is made, with gonadotropin deficiency being the most common initial symptom. Hypothyroidism and hypoadrenalism are also common, but the symptoms are subtle and may be missed.

Evaluation should include MRI and visual field testing; endocrine studies should include assessment of pituitary hormones and end-organ function to determine whether the adenoma is hypersecreting or whether hormonal replacement is needed.

Since these tumors are generally large, both surgery and radiation therapy are usually required to prevent tumor progression or recurrence. In the absence of an endocrine index of tumor hypersecretion such as PRL excess, serial scans at yearly intervals are required to assess the response to therapy and to detect possible recurrence.

POSTERIOR PITUITARY

ANTIDIURETIC HORMONE
(ADH; Vasopressin)

ADH acts through two receptors, termed V_1 and V_2, that have different ligand specificities and cellular mechanisms of action (Table 2–11). The V_1 receptors mediate vascular smooth muscle contraction and stimulate prostaglandin synthesis and liver glycogenolysis. Activation of these receptors increases phosphatidylinositol breakdown, thus causing cellular calcium mobilization. The V_2 receptors, which produce the renal actions of vasopressin, activate G proteins and stimulate the generation of cAMP (see Chapter 1).

Renal Actions

The major renal effect of ADH is to increase the water permeability of the luminal membrane of the collecting duct epithelium. In the absence of ADH, permeability of the epithelium is very low and reab-

sorption of water decreases, leading to polyuria. When ADH is present, epithelial permeability increases markedly, and water is reabsorbed. This ADH effect is caused by ADH binding to the V_2 receptor. Subsequent cellular events that are incompletely understood increase water permeability of the luminal membrane by increasing the number of narrow aqueous channels with radii of about 0.2 nm. Thus, diffusion of water through the membrane is enhanced, as is transcellular flow.

As the collecting ducts traverse the renal medulla, the urine passes regions of ever-increasing osmolality up to maximum of 1200 mosm/kg of water at the tip of the papilla. In the presence of ADH, collecting duct fluid equilibrates with this hyperosmotic environment, and urine osmolality approaches that of medullary interstitial fluid. Thus, maximal ADH effect results in low urine flow, and urine osmolality may approximate 1200 mosm/kg; with ADH deficiency, urine flow may be as high as 15–20 mL/min, and urine osmolality is less than 100 mosm/kg.

Cardiovascular Actions

ADH effects on V_1 receptors in peripheral arterioles increase blood pressure. However, ADH blunts this effect by efferent mechanisms such as bradycardia and inhibition of sympathetic nerve activity. These actions may be important during hypovolemia when plasma ADH levels are very high and maintaining tissue perfusion is critical.

OXYTOCIN

Oxytocin primarily affects uterine smooth muscle. It increases both the frequency and the duration of action potentials during uterine contractions. Thus, administration of oxytocin initiates contractions in a quiescent uterus and increases the strength and frequency of muscle contractions in an active uterus. Estrogen enhances the action of oxytocin by reducing the membrane potential of smooth muscle cells, thus lowering the threshold of excitation. Toward the end of pregnancy, as estrogen levels become higher, the membrane potential of uterine smooth muscle cells becomes less negative, rendering the uterus more sensitive to oxytocin. The number of oxytocin receptors in the uterus also increases at this time, and their activation causes cellular calcium to be mobilized through polyphosphatidylinositol hydrolysis.

Female Reproductive System Actions

A. Parturition: As the fetus enters the birth canal, the lower segment of the uterus, the cervix, and then the vagina are dilated, and this causes reflex release of oxytocin. Strong uterine contractions cause further descent of the fetus, further distention, and further release of oxytocin.

B. Lactation: Oxytocin is also involved in lactation. Stimulation of the nipple produces a neurohu-

Table 2–11. Actions of vasopressin.

Target Organ	Type of Receptor	Action
Kidney glomerulus:	V_1	Mesangial cell contraction and ↓ glomerular capillary ultrafiltration coefficient.
Vasa recta	V_1	↓ Medullary blood flow.
Cortical and outer medullary collecting tubules	V_2	↑ Water permeability and NaCl reabsorption.
Inner medullary (papillary) collecting tubules	V_2	↑ Water and urea permeability.
Thick ascending limb of loop of Henle	V_2	↑ Na^{2+}, Cl^-, K^+ reabsorption.
Juxtaglomerular cells	V_1	Suppression of renin release.
Cardiovascular system: Arterioles	V_1	Constriction.
Blood vessel baroreceptors	V_2 ?	Sensitization of baroreflex via area postrema.
	V_1 ?	Desensitization of baroreflex via vasopressin released in brain.
Liver	V_1	↑ Glyconeogenolysis.
Adenohypophysis	V_1	↑ ACTH release.
Brain	?	Enhances passive avoidance behavior.

moral reflex that causes secretion of oxytocin. In turn, oxytocin causes contraction of the myoepithelial cells of the mammary ducts and the ejection of milk.

Other Actions

A number of stimuli that also release ADH such as increased plasma osmolality and hypovolemia cause oxytocin secretion. Since oxytocin is an effective natriuretic agent—particularly at low rates of urine flow—it may be involved in the regulation of sodium balance.

CONTROL OF WATER BALANCE

Water Requirements

Water balance is precisely controlled by an integrated system that balances water intake via thirst mechanism with water output controlled by ADH. The average individual loses 2.5–3 L of water per day (Table 2–12) and must take in that amount in order to maintain balance. Given free access to water, total human body water rarely varies by more than 1–2%. Approximately 1.2 L of water is taken in food or is provided by oxidative metabolism. The remainder is ingested as water or other fluids.

Concentration of Urine

Renal concentrating mechanism are essential to the maintenance of water balance in order for the kidney to excrete osmotically active solutes derived from the diet.

The average human excretes 1.5 L of urine per day at an osmolality of approximately 600 mosm/kg of water, ie, twice the concentration of plasma (Table 2–12). Without the capacity to concentrate urine, 3 L of water at a concentration of 300 mosm/kg would be excreted and the extra water would have to be ingested. During negative water balance, the urine volume may be reduced to 600 mL/d at a maximum urinary concentration of 1200 mosm/kg. This capacity to concentrate the urine four times more than plasma is of extreme importance, since otherwise it would be necessary to take very large quantities of water in the diet.

Urinary concentration mechanisms can reduce but not completely prevent loss of water in the urine. Even if an individual is maximally concentrating urine, obligatory fluid loss is still considerable. This situation is exacerbated in a warm environment, where many liters of fluid may be lost to maintain a constant temperature via sweating. The only way to bring body fluid levels back to normal is by increasing water intake. It is not surprising that many similarities exist between mechanisms involved in the control of thirst and ADH secretion.

Control of Thirst & ADH Secretion

Cellular and extracellular dehydration are the two major mechanisms involved in the control of thirst and ADH secretion.

A. Cellular Dehydration: Cellular dehydration occurs when extracellular fluid osmolality is increased relative to that of intracellular fluids, leading to the efflux of water from cells. When extracellular fluid osmolality increases, all cells, including the hypothalamic osmoreceptors, become dehydrated, thus providing the signal for secretion of ADH. In humans, an increase of only 1% in plasma osmolality stimulates thirst, water intake, and simultaneously ADH (Figures 2–21 and 2–22).

The relationship between plasma ADH concentration and plasma osmolality in humans in presented in Figure 2–21. The exquisite sensitivity of ADH release to changing plasma osmolality is obvious. Figure 2–22 represents the physiologic range of variations in plasma ADH in humans.

B. Extracellular Fluid Dehydration: Extracellu-

Table 2–12. Routes of loss of water in an average adult human.

	mL/24 h
Urine	1500
Skin	600
Lungs	400
Feces	100
	2600

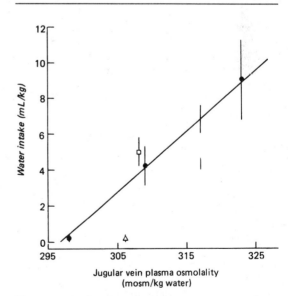

Figure 2–21. Relationship between water intake and jugular vein plasma osmolality. Central osmolality was increased selectively by infusing hypertonic sodium chloride into carotid loops in trained conscious dogs ●. Infusion of hypertonic sucrose was equally effective □, whereas hypertonic urea (△) did not stimulate drinking. (Data from Wood RJ, Rolls BJ, Ramsay DJ: Am J Physiol 1977;323:88.)

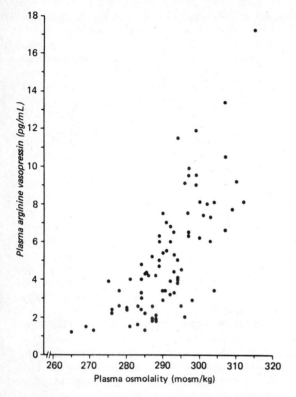

Figure 2–22. Relationship between plasma vasopressin concentration and plasma osmolality in humans during dehydration. (Reproduced, with permission, from Hammer M, Ladefoged J, Olgaard K: Am J Physiol 1980;238: 313.)

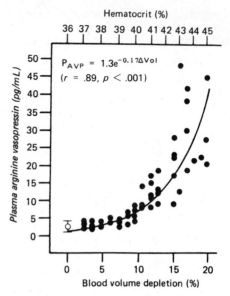

Figure 2–23. Relationship of plasma vasopressin to isosmotic reductions in blood volume in rats. (Reproduced, with permission, from Dunn FL et al: J Clin Invest 1973;52:3212.)

lar fluid dehydration—ie, decreased extracellular fluid volume without a change in osmolality—stimulates thirst and ADH secretion. Thus, hemorrhage reduces extracellular fluid volume and results in both thirst and ADH secretion (Figure 2–23). Small decreases in volume have minimal effects on ADH secretion, but reductions larger than 10% cause a marked stimulation of ADH to values > 100 pg/mL (92.5 pmol/L). These high circulating levels of ADH do not further increase water conservation, since maximum urinary concentration is reached at much lower levels. However, the high levels of ADH may support blood pressure via V_1 receptors.

C. Interaction of Osmolality and Volume: Two major mechanisms are involved in hypovolemic stimulation of thirst and ADH secretion. Moderate reductions in blood volume stimulate low-pressure receptors in the left and right atria and in the pulmonary circulation. With more severe hypovolemia, which reduces blood pressure, the arterial baroreceptors are activated. Responses from these baroreceptor areas in the circulation are then transmitted to magnocellular cells in the hypothalamus (see Figure 2–6). In addition, the renin-angiotensin system may be involved, since hypovolemia stimulates renin se-

cretion and angiotensin formation. Angiotensin II also stimulates thirst and ADH secretion. The relative roles of the direct baroreceptor input and angiotensin mechanisms in the responses to extracellular dehydration have yet to be determined.

The normal day-to-day regulation of water balance therefore involves interaction between osmotic and volume stimuli. In the case of ADH secretion, the fall in extracellular fluid volume sensitizes the release of ADH to a given osmotic stimulus. Thus, for a given increase in plasma osmolality, the increase in plasma ADH will be greater in hypovolemic than in normovolemic states.

In dehydration, increased plasma osmolality results in withdrawal of fluid from cells. Thus, the reduction in total body water is shared equally between intracellular and extracellular fluid compartments. The increase in plasma osmolality and the reduction of extracellular fluid volume act synergistically to stimulate ADH release. In salt depletion, however, plasma ADH concentrations remain constant or even slightly elevated in spite of a fall in plasma osmolality. Hypovolemia in this situation—as a result of osmotic movements of water from the extracellular into the intracellular fluid space—appears to provide the sensitizing influence.

Thirst mechanisms also involve interactions between extracellular fluid volume and osmolality. During periods of dehydration, increased plasma osmolality provides approximately 70% of the increased thirst drive, and the remaining 30% is due to hypovolemia. In salt depletion, the situation is less clear, but the normal or increased drinking that has been observed in experimental animals has been attributed to the associated hypovolemia.

DIABETES INSIPIDUS

Diabetes insipidus is a disorder resulting from deficient ADH action and is characterized by the passage of copious amounts of very dilute urine. This disorder must be distinguished from other polyuric states such as primary polydipsia (see below) and osmotic diuresis. Central (or neurogenic) diabetes insipidus is due to failure of the posterior pituitary to secrete adequate quantities of ADH; nephrogenic diabetes insipidus results when the kidney fails to respond to circulating ADH. The resulting renal concentrating defect leads to the loss of large volumes of dilute urine, ie, free water. This causes cellular and extracellular dehydration, which stimulate thirst and cause polydipsia.

Classification

A. Central (Neurogenic) Diabetes Insipidus: The major causes of central diabetes insipidus are shown in Table 2–13.

Many of the disorders discussed above in the section on pituitary and hypothalamic disorders which cause hypopituitarism may also case diabetes insipidus. Primary pituitary adenomas—even those which are large—rarely cause diabetes insipidus, but hypothalamic tumors such as craniopharyngiomas or other primary central nervous system lesions and infiltrative and invasive lesions cause diabetes insipidus more frequently. These lesions cause diabetes insipidus by damage to the pituitary stalk, which interrupts the hypothalamic-neurohypophysial nerve tracts, or by direct damage to the hypothalamic neurons that synthesize ADH. These disorders cause varying degrees of ADH deficiency.

Diabetes insipidus can also be caused by trauma and is common following surgery for hypothalamic or pituitary tumors. Central diabetes insipidus resulting from head trauma frequently follows a triphasic course. The initial phase is followed by a phase of antidiuresis (as ADH is released from damaged axons) and then by persistent diabetes insipidus. How complete the diabetes insipidus is depends upon the extent of the damage. Resection of hypothalamic tumors via craniotomy frequently results in permanent diabetes insipidus, which may be complicated by disorders of thirst. Transsphenoidal pituitary microsurgery causes postoperative diabetes insipidus in as many as 20% of patients. This does not appear to be due to destruction of the ADH-secreting neural fibers, since the diabetes insipidus frequently lasts only a few days and rarely longer than 2–3 weeks.

Familial central diabetes insipidus, which is inherited as an autosomal dominant, is rare and has its onset in infancy. The number of ADH-containing fibers in the nuclei, nerve tracts, and posterior pituitary is reduced. Idiopathic diabetes insipidus presents in later childhood or adolescence and in adulthood. It is also associated with a decrease in the number of ADH-containing fibers. As many as 30–40% of these patients have antibodies directed against ADH-secreting hypothalamic neurons. The "posterior pituitary bright spot," which is normally visualized by MRI, is absent in patients with familial or idiopathic diabetes insipidus. An autosomal dominant form of central diabetes insipidus occurs in association with diabetes mellitus, optic atrophy, and deafness (DIDMOAD). Diabetes insipidus with enzymatic destruction of circulating ADH by increased plasma levels of vasopressinase may occur during pregnancy.

B. Nephrogenic Diabetes Insipidus: This group of diseases (Table 2–14) is caused by renal unresponsiveness to the physiologic actions of ADH; thus, ADH levels are normal or elevated. Chronic renal diseases, particularly those affecting the medulla and collecting ducts, can cause nephrogenic diabetes insipidus. Thus, if medullary disease (eg, from pyelonephritis, polycystic disease or medullary cystic disease) prevents formation of a medullary concentration gradient, urine passing through the collecting duct system cannot become concentrated.

The electrolyte disorders hypokalemia and hypercalcemia reduce urinary concentrating capacity. Many drugs have been implicated in the development of nephrogenic diabetes insipidus. For example, lithium carbonate reduces the sensitivity of the renal tubule to ADH by its inhibitory effect on ADH-sensitive adenylyl cyclase. The ability of demeclocycline to cause nephrogenic diabetes insipidus has been used to advantage in the management of states of

Table 2–13. Causes of neurogenic diabetes insipidus.

Hypophysectomy, complete or partial.
Surgery to remove suprasellar tumors.
Idiopathic.
Familial.
Tumors and cysts (intra- and suprasellar).
Histiocytosis.
Granulomas.
Infections.
Interruption of blood supply.
Autoimmune.

Table 2–14. Causes of nephrogenic diabetes insipidus.

Chronic renal disease: Any renal disease that interferes with collecting duct or medullary function, eg, chronic pyelonephritis.
Hypokalemia.
Protein starvation.
Hypercalcemia.
Sickle cell anemia.
Sjögren's syndrome.
Drugs, eg, lithium, fluoride, methoxyflurane anesthesia, demeclocycline (Declomycin), colchicine.
Congenital defect.
Familial.

ADH excess (see below). Congenital nephrogenic diabetes insipidus is a rare condition caused by a defect in the response of the renal tubule to ADH, with decreased medullary adenylyl cyclase production. It is most common in males with a family history of transmission through apparently healthy females, suggesting X-linked inheritance, though cases have recently been reported in females. Pregnancy may decrease renal responsiveness to ADH.

Primary Polydipsia

Primary polydipsia (psychogenic polydipsia, compulsive water drinking) is a disorder of thirst that is either due to psychogenic causes or to altered osmotic and nonosmotic regulation of thirst, which involves greatly increased drinking, usually in excess of 5 L of water per day, leading to dilution of the extracellular fluid, inhibition of vasopressin secretion, and water diuresis.

Differential Diagnosis

It is important to distinguish both types of diabetes insipidus and primary polydipsia from other common causes of polyuria. In general, other forms of polyuria involve osmotic or solute diuresis. For example, in diabetes mellitus, increased excretion of glucose and other solutes requires excretion of increased volumes of water. In osmotic diuresis, the osmolality of the urine tends toward that of plasma. In sharp contrast, the osmolality of the urine in diabetes insipidus and psychogenic polydipsia is very low when compared with that of plasma. Thus, a urine specific gravity less than 1.005 (osmolality < 200 mosm/kg of water) will generally rule out polyuria due to osmotic diuresis. After a careful history has been taken, focusing on patterns of drinking and urination behavior and the family history, a series of investigations should be instituted to distinguish between the two types of diabetes insipidus and primary polydipsia. For unknown reasons patients with idiopathic central diabetes insipidus have a predilection for cold beverages. The physiologic principles are set forth in Table 2–15, and the actual procedures are summarized in Table 2–16.

Table 2–16. Differential diagnosis of polyuria.

Procedure	Interpretation
Measure plasma and urine osmolality.	A urine osmolality less than that of plasma is consistent with neurogenic or nephrogenic diabetes insipidus; if both urine and plasma are dilute, that is consistent with psychogenic polydipsia.
Dehydration test: If serum osmolality is less than 295 mosm/kg, allow no fluids for 12–18 hours. Measure body weight, urine flow, urine specific gravity, urine and plasma osmolality every 2 hours. Terminate study if body weight falls more than 3%.	A rise in urine osmolality above that of plasma osmolality indicates psychogenic polydipsia. Urine specific gravity less than 1.005 (or 200 mosm/L) indicates either neurogenic or nephrogenic diabetes insipidus.
Measure serum vasopressin at conclusion of dehydration test.	Normal or high vasopressin level usually indicates nephrogenic diabetes insipidus.
Inject 5 units of aqueous vasopressin or 1 μg DDAVP subcutaneously. Measure urine flow and urine and plasma osmolality	Rise in urine osmolality above that of plasma osmolality indicates neurogenic diabetes insipidus; failure of urine osmolality to rise indicates nephrogenic diabetes insipidus.

A. Plasma and Urine Osmolality: The first test is to take plasma and urine samples simultaneously for estimation of osmolality and sodium. Since in both forms of diabetes insipidus the primary problem is inappropriate water diuresis, the urine will be less concentrated than plasma, whereas the plasma osmolality may be higher than normal depending upon the state of hydration. In primary polydipsia, however, dilute plasma is associated with the production of dilute urine. The poor sensitivity of these levels drawn randomly necessitates dynamic testing. Occasionally, even the tests outlined below do not produce a definitive diagnosis, so that a therapeutic trial of desmopressin may be warranted.

Table 2–15. Results of diagnostic studies in various types of polyuria.

	Neurogenic Diabetes Insipidus	Nephrogenic Diabetes Insipidus	Psychogenic Polydipsia
Random plasma osmolality	↑	↑	↓
Random urine osmolality	↓	↓	↓
Urine osmolality during mild water deprivation	No change	No change	↑
Urine osmolality during nicotine or hypertonic saline	No change	No change	↑
Urine osmolality following vasopressin intravenously	↑	No change	↑
Plasma vasopressin	Low	Normal or high	Low

B. Water Deprivation: The next step is to examine the effect of water deprivation on urine osmolality under supervision. Supervision is necessary both because the patient with primary polydipsia will go to great lengths to obtain water and because the patient with complete diabetes insipidus may become dangerously dehydrated very rapidly. The patient should be weighed and denied access to water and each voided urine sample measured for specific gravity or osmolality (or both). Whereas the healthy individual will soon reduce urine flow to 0.5 mL/min at a concentration greater than that of plasma, the patient with complete diabetes insipidus will maintain a high urine flow at a specific gravity less than 1.005 (200 mosm/kg of water). The test is continued until urinary osmolality plateaus (an hourly increase of < 30 mosm/kg for 3 successive hours). A period of 18 hours is usually ample to confirm the diagnosis. The test should be terminated if the body weight falls by more than 3%, since serious consequences of dehydration may ensue. Patients with primary polydipsia will always increase urine osmolality to values greater than those of plasma. It may be difficult to distinguish these patients from patients with partial central diabetes insipidus.

C. Vasopressin Test: Once the diagnosis of diabetes insipidus is established, the ADH-insensitive (nephrogenic) disease must be distinguished from the ADH-sensitive (central) form. This is done following water deprivation by injection of aqueous vasopressin or desmopressin acetate. Give 5 units of aqueous vasopressin subcutaneously or 1 μg of desmopressin acetate intravenously, intramuscularly, or subcutaneously, and measure urine osmolality after 1 hour; patients with complete central diabetes insipidus will show an increase of > 50% in urine osmolality, while patients with nephrogenic diabetes insipidus show an increase of < 50%. Patients with partial central diabetes insipidus also show increases of < 50%, and patients with primary polydipsia have responses < 9%. In these cases, measurement of ADH levels is particularly helpful.

D. ADH Radioimmunoassays: Sensitive radioimmunoassays for ADH are available that allow plasma ADH to be measured. Random plasma samples are of little value; levels should be measured as part of dynamic testing, either during water deprivation test or with infusions of hyperosmotic saline. Plasma levels should be interpreted based upon nomograms of their relationship to plasma osmolality. Patients with nephrogenic diabetes insipidus have normal or increased levels of ADH following water deprivation, allowing a clear distinction to be made from central forms of diabetes insipidus (Figure 2–24). Patients with partial central diabetes insipidus show a smaller than normal increase in plasma ADH concentration following dehydration or infusion of hypertonic saline.

E. Influence of Endocrine Disease: The diag-

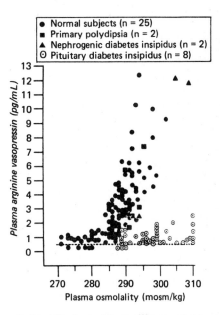

Figure 2–24. Effect of dehydration on plasma vasopressin concentration in normal subjects and patients with polyuria. Note that patients with neurogenic (pituitary) diabetes insipidus cannot increase plasma vasopressin concentration with dehydration, in contrast to patients with psychogenic polydipsia and nephrogenic diabetes insipidus. (Reproduced, with permission, from Robertson GL et al: J Clin Invest 1973;52:2346.)

nosis of central diabetes insipidus is sometimes difficult to make in the presence of anterior pituitary disease. Low or absent levels of glucocorticoids or thyroid hormone reduce the solute load to the kidney and thus reduce urine flow. Patients with normal plasma levels of ADH but hyposecretion of adrenal glucocorticoids will retain a water load. Thus, even if diabetes insipidus is present, coincident thyroid or adrenal insufficiency may mask the polyuria.

Treatment

A. Central Diabetes Insipidus:

1. Treatment of choice– The drug of choice is desmopressin acetate, a synthetic analogue of vasopressin prepared in aqueous solution containing 100 μg/mL. It is administered intranasally as a metered-dose nasal spray that delivers 10 μg (0.1 mL) per spray or via a calibrated plastic catheter in doses of 5–20 μg (0.05–0.2 mL). The frequency of administration varies; patients with mild to moderate diabetes insipidus require one or two doses of 10μg per 24 hours; Patients with severe diabetes insipidus may require 10–20 μg two or three times daily. This agent provides excellent control of polyuria and polydipsia in patients with central diabetes insipidus. Serum osmolality and sodium must be monitored at regular intervals (initially every 1–2 weeks, later every 3 months) to be certain that the dose is appropriate. For patients who cannot tolerate intranasal therapy, desmopressin acetate can be given subcutaneously in single doses of 1–2 μg once or twice daily.

2. Older methods– Lypressin is pure synthetic lysine vasopressin administered by nasal spray. It is effective for only a few hours, so that it must be administered at least every 4–6 hours. Aqueous vasopressin in doses of 5–10 units subcutaneously is also very short-acting (3–6 hours).

B. Nephrogenic Diabetes Insipidus: The underlying disorder should be treated if possible. It is important to recognize familial disease early, since infants are particularly susceptible to neurologic damage due to dehydration. Diuretics are helpful, along with dietary salt restriction if necessary. Prostaglandin synthesis inhibitors may also be useful. The objective is to maintain the patient in a state of mild sodium depletion and reduce the solute load on the kidney, thus enhancing proximal tubular reabsorption. Reduction in distal tubular flow allows some sodium concentration to take place and minimizes loss of water. Patients with partial sensitivity to vasopressin may be treated with large doses of desmopressin acetate (up to 40 μg/4 h intranasally).

SYNDROME OF INAPPROPRIATE SECRETION OF ANTIDIURETIC HORMONE (SIADH)

A variety of disorders are associated with plasma ADH concentrations that are inappropriately high for the plasma osmolality. Thus, water retention accompanies normal water intake, leading to hyponatremia and hypo-osmolality. The urine is usually more concentrated than plasma but in any case is inappropriately concentrated. Overall sodium balance is essentially normal. It is important to rule out renal and endocrine disorders and drug effects that diminish the kidney's capacity to dilute the urine. The syndrome is termed the syndrome of inappropriate secretion of antidiuretic hormone, or SIADH. The clinical picture can be produced experimentally by giving high doses of vasopressin to a healthy subject receiving normal to high fluid intake. Water restriction in patients suspected of having SIADH will result in plasma osmolality and sodium concentration returning to normal.

The diagnostic criteria for SIADH include (1) hyponatremia with corresponding plasma hypo-osmolality (< 280 mosm/kg); (2) urine less than maximally dilute, ie, inappropriately concentrated (> 100 mosm/kg); (3) euvolemia (including absence of congestive heart failure, cirrhosis, and nephrotic syndrome); and (4) absence of renal, adrenal or thyroid insufficiency. Urinary sodium is usually > 20 mmol/d, probably a consequence of increased atrial natriuretic factor. Dynamic testing and plasma ADH levels are usually unnecessary in diagnosis.

Causes of SIADH

The causes of SIADH are outlined in Table 2–17. A number of malignant neoplasms are associated with ectopic production of vasopressin, leading to high plasma vasopressin levels. Bronchogenic carcinomas are particularly apt to be associated with SIADH. Tumors at other sites such as the pancreas and duodenum have also been shown to produce ADH. A number of nonmalignant pulmonary diseases such as tuberculosis and pneumonias are associated with high plasma ADH concentrations. Tuberculous lung tissue has been shown to contain assayable levels of ADH. However, it is not known whether all types of lung disease causing SIADH do so by producing ectopic ADH or by stimulation of pituitary ADH.

Many central nervous system disorders are associated with increased ADH secretion, leading to the clinical picture of SIADH. Temporary causes of SIADH include surgical trauma, anesthesia, pain, opiates and anxiety. A number of drugs implicated in ADH release are listed in Table 2–17. Endocrine disorders such as adrenal insufficiency, myxedema, and anterior pituitary insufficiency may be associated with increased ADH levels and impaired renal excretion of free water. All of these factors—particularly with fluid loading—can lead to hyponatremia and hypo-osmolality. In fact, the majority of hospitalized patients with euvolemic hyponatremia have inappropriately increased ADH levels. The hyponatremia observed in patients with psychosis may reflect a combination of several factors, including inappropriate ADH release and compulsive water drinking.

Types of Osmoregulatory Defects

Serial measurements of serum ADH in patients with SIADH delineate four patterns of osmoregulatory defects in this syndrome. Type A, found in 20% of patients, is characterized by large irregular changes in plasma ADH completely unrelated to serum osmolality. This erratic and irregular secretion of ADH can be associated with both malignant and nonmalignant disease. Type B is found in about 35% of patients and is associated with secretion of ADH

Table 2–17. Conditions associated with SIADH.

Malignant lung disease, particularly bronchogenic carcinoma.
Nonmalignant lung disease, eg, tuberculosis.
Tumors at other sites (especially lymphoma, sarcoma), eg, duodenum, pancreas, brain, prostate, thymus.
Central nervous system trauma and infections.
Drugs that stimulate vasopressin release, eg, clofibrate, chlorpropamide, and other drugs such as thiazides, carbamazepine, phenothiazines, vincristine, cyclophosphamide.
Endocrine diseases: adrenal insufficiency, myxedema, anterior pituitary insufficiency.

serum osmolality. This erratic and irregular secretion of ADH can be associated with both malignant and nonmalignant disease. Type B is found in about 35% of patients and is associated with secretion of ADH that is excessive but proportionate to osmolality. In these patients, the osmotic control of ADH secretion appears to be either set at a low level or abnormally sensitive to changes in serum osmolality. Type C, found in 35% of patients, is characterized by a high basal level of ADH that rises even higher with a rise in serum osmolality. Type D, found in only 10% of patients, represents a different type of problem. ADH is normally suppressed in hypovolemic states and rises normally with increase in osmolality. Thus, SIADH in these patients may be associated with a change in renal sensitivity to serum ADH. Thus far, the pattern of ADH abnormality cannot be correlated with the pathology of the syndrome.

Treatment

The treatment of SIADH depends upon the underlying cause. A patient with drug-induced SIADH is treated by withholding the drug. The treatment of SIADH in a patient with bronchogenic carcinoma is more complicated, however, and the prognosis is poor. Treatment aims to return plasma osmolality to normal without causing further expansion of the extracellular fluid compartment, as would occur following infusion of hyperosmotic solutions.

A. Fluid Restriction: The simplest form of treatment is fluid restriction, although in the long term the excessive thirst associated with this treatment may be difficult to manage.

B. Diuretics: If plasma osmolality is low and rapid correction is required, diuretics such as furosemide in a dose of 1 mg/kg 1 hr can be employed. This prevents the concentration gradient in the medulla from building up and thus decrease the effectiveness of ADH. Because diuresis is accompanied by significant urinary losses of potassium, calcium, and magnesium, these electrolytes should be replaced by intravenous infusion.

C. Other Methods: In an emergency situation with severe hyponatremia, hypertonic saline, ie, 3% sodium chloride is administered either alone or with furosemide. Infusion ratios of 20–40 mL will increase serum sodium by 1–2 meg/L per hr in most patients. However, this must be done with great caution, since fluid overload may precipitate heart failure, central pontine myelinolysis, or circulatory collapse. Drugs (mentioned earlier in this chapter) that reduce the effect of vasopressin on the kidney may be useful. Demeclocycline, 1–2 g/d orally, causes a reversible form of nephrogenic diabetes insipidus, countering the effect of SIADH. However, it is nephrotoxic, and renal function (blood urea nitrogen and serum creatinine) must be monitored carefully. Lithium carbonate has a similar effect, but therapeutic doses are so close to the toxic dose that this drug is rarely useful.

ADH ANTAGONISTS

Improved understanding of structure-activity relationships has made it possible to synthesize agonists and antagonists of neurohypophysial peptides. Two groups of peptides have been synthesized that antagonize the V_1 and V_2 receptors. Further refinement of specific antagonists for specific receptors should lead to the development of powerful therapeutic tools.

REFERENCES

General
Beaulieu E-E, Kelley PA: *Hormones.* Chapman & Hall, 1990.
Frohman LA: Diseases of the anterior pituitary. In: *Endocrinology and Metabolism,* 2nd ed. Felig P et al (editors). McGraw-Hill, 1987.
Imura H (editor): *The Pituitary Gland.* Raven Press, 1985.
Martin JB, Reichlin S: *Clinical Neuroendocrinology,* 2nd ed. Davis, 1987.
Motta M (editor): *Brain Endocrinology,* 2nd ed. Raven Press, 1991.
Thorner MO et al: The anterior pituitary. In: *Williams Textbook of Endocrinology,* 8th ed. Wilson J, Foster DW (editors). Saunders, 1992.

Neuroendocrinology
Blalock JE: A molecular basis for bidirectional communication between the immune and neuroendocrine systems. Physiol Rev 1989;69:1.
Brabant G, Prank K, Schoff C: Pulsatile patterns in hormone secretion. Trends in Endocrinol Metab 1992;3:183.

Casanueva FF: Physiology of growth hormone secretion and action. Endocrinol Metab Clin North Am 1992;21:483.
Chrousos GP: Regulation and dysregulation of the hypothalamic-pituitary-adrenal axis: the corticotropin-releasing hormone perspective. Endocrinol Metab Clin North Am 1991 1992;21:833.
Conn PM, Crowley W Jr: Gonadotropin-releasing hormone and its analogues. N Engl J Med 1991;324:93.
Cross BA, Leng G (editors): The neurohypophysis: Structure, function and control. Prog Brain Res 1983;60:1.
Devesa J, Lima L, Tresguerres JAF: Neuroendocrine control of growth hormone secretion. Trends Endocrinol Metab 1992;3:175.
Frohman LA, Jansson JO: Growth hormone-releasing hormone. Endocr Rev 1986;7:223.
Imura H, Fukata JI, Mori T: Cytokines and endocrine function: An interaction between the immune and neuroendocrine systems. Clin Endocrinol 1991;35:107.
Jacobson L, Sapolsky R: The role of the hippocampus in feedback regulation of the hypothalamic-pituitary-adrenocortical axis. Endocr Rev 1991;12:118.

Loes DJ et al: MR anatomy and pathology of the hypothalamus. Am J Roentgenol 1991;156:579.

Martini L, Ganong WP (editors): *Frontiers in Neuroendocrinology,* Vol 10. Raven Press, 1988.

Orth DN: Corticotropin-releasing hormone in humans. Endocr Rev 1992;13:164.

Preslock JP: The pineal gland: Basic implications and clinical correlation. Endocr Rev 1984;5:282.

Reiter RJ: Pineal melatonin: cell biology of its synthesis and of its physiological interactions. Endocr Rev 1991;12:151.

Richter D: Molecular events in expression of vasopressin and oxytocin and their cognate receptors. Am J Physiol 1988;255:F207.

Schwanzel-Fukuda M et al: Biology of normal luteinizing hormone-releasing hormone neurons during and after their migration from olfactory placode. Endocr Rev 1992;13:623.

ACTH: Cushing's Syndrome

Aron DC et al: Cushing's syndrome: Problems in diagnosis. Medicine 1981;60:25.

Aron DC et al: Cushing's syndrome: Problems in management. Endocr Rev 1982;3:229.

Aron DC, Findling JW, Tyrrell JB: Cushing's disease. Endocrinol Metab Clin North Am 1987;16:705.

Atkinson AB: The treatment of Cushing's syndrome. Clin Endocrinol 1991;34:507.

Crapo L: Cushing's syndrome: A review of diagnostic tests. Metabolism 1979;28:955.

Cunningham SK et al: Normal cortisol response to corticotropin in patients with secondary adrenal failure. Arch Intern Med 1983;143:2276.

Findling JW, Tyrrell JB: Occult ectopic secretion of corticotropin. Arch Intern Med 1986;146:929.

Grossman A: What is the cause of Cushing's disease? Clin Endocrinol 1992;36:451.

Grua JR, Nelson DH: ACTH-producing pituitary tumors. Endocrinol Metab Clin North Am 1991;20:319.

Howlett TA et al: Megavoltage pituitary irradiation in the management of Cushing's disease and Nelson's syndrome: Long-term follow-up. Clin Endocrinol 1989;31:309.

Kaye TB, Crapo L: The Cushing's syndrome: An update on diagnostic tests. Ann Intern Med 1990;112:434.

Leinung MC et al: Diagnosis of corticotropin-producing bronchial carcinoid tumors causing Cushing's syndrome. Mayo Clin Proc 1990;65:1314.

Lindolm J: Endocrine function in patients with Cushing's disease before and after treatment. Clin Endocrinol 1992;36:151.

Mampalam TJ, Tyrrell JB, Wilson CB: Transsphenoidal microsurgery for Cushing's disease: A report of 216 cases. Ann Intern Med 1988;109:487.

Oldfield EH et al: Petrosal sinus sampling with and without corticotropin-releasing hormone for the differential diagnosis of Cushing's syndrome. N Engl J Med 1991;325:897.

Streeten DH et al: Normal and abnormal function of the hypothalamic-pituitary-adrenocortical system in man. Endocr Rev 1984;5:371.

Tindall GT et al: Cushing's disease: Results of transsphenoidal microsurgery with emphasis on surgical failures. J Neurosurg 1990;72:363.

Trainer PJ, Grossman A: The diagnosis and differential diagnosis of Cushing's syndrome. Clin Endocrinol 1993;34:317.

Tyrrell JB et al: Cushing's disease: Selective transsphenoidal resection of pituitary microadenomas. N Engl J Med 1978;298:753.

GH: Acromegaly

Alexander L et al: Epidemiology of acromegaly in the Newcastle region. Clin Endocrinol 1980;12:71.

Barkan AL et al: Acromegaly due to ectopic growth hormone (GH)-releasing hormone (GHRH) production: Dynamic studies of GH and ectopic GHRH secretion. J Clin Endocrinol Metab 1986;63:1057.

Barkan AL: Acromegaly: Diagnosis and therapy. Endocrinol Metab Clin North Am 1989;18:277.

Barzilay J, Heatley GJ, Cushing GW: Benign and malignant tumors in patients with acromegaly. Arch Intern Med 1991;151: 1629.

Bengtsson BA et al: Epidemiology and long-term survival in acromegaly. Acta Med Scand 1988;223:327.

Chang-DeMoranville BM, Jackson MD: Diagnosis and endocrine testing in acromegaly. Endocrinol Metab Clin North Am 1992;21:649.

Ezzat S, Melmed S: Are patients with acromegaly at increased risk for neoplasia? J Clin Endocrinol Metab 1991;72:245.

Ezzat S, Strom C, Melmed S: Colon polyps in acromegaly. Ann Intern Med 1991;114:754.

Faglia G, Arosio M, Bazzoni N: Ectopic acromegaly. Endocrinol Med Clin North Am 1992;21:575.

Lamberts SW: The role of somatostatin in the regulation of anterior pituitary hormone secretion and the use of its analogues in the treatment of human pituitary tumors. Endocr Rev 1989;9:417.

Losa M et al: Evaluation of selective transsphenoidal adenomectomy by endocrinological testing and somatomedin-C measurement in acromegaly. J Neurosurg 1989;70:561.

Melmed S: Acromegaly. N Engl J Med 1990;322:966.

Melmed S (editor): Acromegaly. Endocrinol Metab Clin North Am 1992;21:483.

Melmed S et al: Pituitary tumors secreting growth hormone and prolactin. Ann Intern Med 1986;105:238.

Mims RB, Behune JE: Acromegaly with normal fasting growth hormone concentrations but abnormal growth hormone regulation. Ann Intern Med 1974;81:781.

Mountcastle RB et al: Pituitary adenocarcinoma in an acromegalic patient: Response to bromocriptine and pituitary testing: A review of the literature on 36 cases of pituitary carcinoma. Am J Med Sci 1989;298:109.

Ross DA, Wilson CB: Results of transsphenoidal microsurgery for growth hormone-secreting pituitary adenoma in a series of 214 patients. J Neurosurg 1988;68:854.

Sano T et al: Growth hormone-releasing hormone-producing tumors: Clinical, biochemical, and morphological manifestations. Endocr Rev 1988;9:357.

Vance ML, Harris AG: Long-term treatment of 189 acromegalic patients with the somatostatin analog octreotide: Results of the international multicenter acromegaly study group. Arch Intern Med 1991;151:1573.

PRL: Prolactinoma

Bevan JS et al: Dopamine agonists and pituitary tumor shrinkage. Endocr Rev 1992;13:220.

Biller BMK et al: Progressive trabecular osteopenia in women with hyperprolactinemic amenorrhea. J Clin Endocrinol Metab 1992;75:692.

Carter JN et al: Prolactin-secreting tumors and hypogonadism in 22 men. N Engl J Med 1978;299:847.

Cunnah D, Besser M: Management of prolactinomas. Clin Endocrinol 1991;34:231.

Davis JR, Selby C, Jeffcoate WJ: Oral contraceptive agents do not affect serum prolactin in normal women. Clin Endocrinol 1984;20:427.

Davis JRE, Shepard MC, Heath DA: Giant invasive prolactinoma: A case report and review of nine further cases. Q J Med 1990;74:227.

Faglia G: Should dopamine agonist treatment for prolactinomas be life-long? Clin Endocrinol 1991;34:173.

Greenspan SL et al: Osteoporosis in men with hyperprolactinemic hypogonadism. Ann Intern Med 1986;104:77.

Howlett TA et al: Prolactinomas presenting as primary amenorrhoea and delayed or arrested puberty: Response to medical therapy. Clin Endocrinol 1989;30:131.

Keye WR Jr et al: Amenorrhea, hyperprolactinemia, and pituitary enlargement secondary to primary hypothyroidism: Successful treatment with thyroid replacement. Obstet Gynecol 1976;48:697.

Lamberts SWJ, Quik RFP: A comparison of the efficacy and safety of pergolide and bromocriptine in the treatment of hyperprolactinemia. J Clin Endocrinol Metab 1991;72:635.

Markoff E, Lee DW: On the nature of serum prolactin in two patients with macroprolactinemia. Fertil Steril 1992;58:78.

Mehta AE, Reyes FI, Faiman C: Primary radiotherapy of prolactinomas: Eight- to 15-year follow-up. Am J Med 1987;83:49.

Molitch ME et al: Bromocriptine as primary therapy for prolactin-secreting macroadenomas: Results of a prospective multicenter study. J Clin Endocrinol Metab 1985;60:698.

Molitch ME: Pathologic hyperprolactinemia. Endocrinol Metab Clin North Am 1992;21:877.

Molitch ME: Pregnancy and the hyperprolactinemic woman. N Engl J Med 1985;312:1364.

Popovic EA et al: Malignant prolactinomas. Neurosurgery 1991;29:127.

Randall RV et al: Transsphenoidal microsurgical treatment of prolactin-producing pituitary adenomas: Results in 100 patients. Mayo Clin Proc 1983;58:108.

Schlechte J et al: The natural history of untreated hyperprolactinemia: A prospective analysis. J Clin Endocrinol Metab 1989;68:412.

Schlechte J, Walkner L, Kathol M: A longitudinal analysis of premenopausal bone loss in healthy women and women with hyperprolactinemia. J Clin Endocrinol Metab 1992;75:698.

Serri O et al: Recurrence of hyperprolactinemia after selective transsphenoidal adenomectomy in women with prolactinoma. N Engl J Med 1983;309:280.

Sisam DA, Sheehan JP, Sheeler LR: The natural history of untreated microprolactinomas. Fertil Steril 1987;48:67.

Van't Verlaat JW, Croughs RJM: Withdrawal of bromocriptine after long-term therapy for macroprolactinomas: Effect on plasma prolactin and tumor size. Clin Endocrinol 1991;34:175.

Vance ML et al: Treatment of prolactin-secreting pituitary macroadenomas with the long-acting non-ergot dopamine agonist CV 205-502. Ann Intern Med 1990;112:668.

Webster J et al: Low recurrence rate after partial hypophysectomy for prolactinoma: The predictive value of dynamic prolactin function tests. Clin Endocrinol 1992;33:35.

Gonadotropins (LH/FSH): Gonadotropin-Secreting Pituitary Tumors

Daneshdoost L et al: Inhibition of follicle-stimulating hormone secretion from gonadotroph adenomas by repetitive administration of a gonadotropin-releasing hormone antagonist. J Clin Endocrinol Metab 1990;71:92.

Daneshdoost L et al: Recognition of gonadotroph adenomas in women. N Engl J Med 1991;324:589.

Hurley DM et al: Induction of ovulation and fertility in amenorrheic women by pulsatile low-dose gonadotropin-releasing hormone. N Engl J Med 1984;310:1069.

Jaffe RB, Monroe SE: Hormone interaction and regulation during the menstrual cycle. In: Frontiers in Neuroendocrinology. Martini L, Ganong WF (editors). Raven Press, 1980.

Jameson JL et al: Glycoprotein hormone genes are expressed in clinically nonfunctioning pituitary adenomas. J Clin Invest 1987;80:1472.

Kwekkeboom DJ, deJong FH, Lamberts SW: Gonadotropin release by clinically nonfunctioning and gonadotroph pituitary adenomas in vivo and in vitro: Relation to sex and effects of thyrotropic-releasing hormone, gonadotropin-releasing hormone, and bromocriptine. J Clin Endocrinol Metab 1989;68:1128.

Molitch ME: Gonadotroph cell pituitary adenomas. N Engl J Med 1991;324:626.

Ojeda SR et al. Recent advances in the endocrinology of puberty. Endocr Rev 1980;1:228.

Reyes-Fuentes A, Velduis JD: Neuroendocrine physiology of the normal male gonadal axis. Endocrinol Metab Clin North Am 1993;22:93.

Snyder PJ: Gonadotroph cell adenomas of the pituitary. Endocr Rev 1985;6:552.

South SA, Yankov VI, Evans WS: Normal reproductive endocrinology in the female. Endocrinol Metab Clin North Am 1993;22:1.

TSH: TSH-Secreting Pituitary Tumors

Beck-Peccoz P et al: Treatment of hyperthyroidism due to inappropriate secretion of thyrotropin with somatostatin analogue SMS 201-995. J Clin Endocrinol Metab 1989;68:208.

Comi RJ et al: Response of thyrotropin-secreting pituitary adenomas to a long-acting somatostatin analogue. N Engl J Med 1987;317:12.

Gesundheit N et al: Thyrotropin-secreting pituitary adenomas: Clinical and biochemical heterogeneity. Case reports and follow-up of nine patients. Ann Intern Med 1989;111:827.

Jackson IMD: Thyrotropin-releasing hormone. N Engl J Med 1982;306:145.

Kuzuya N et al: Endocrine and immunohistochemical studies on thyrotropin (TSH)-secreting pituitary adenomas: Responses of TSH, α-subunit, and growth hormone to hypothalamic releasing hormones and their distribution in adenoma cells. J Clin Endocrinol Metab 1990;71:1103.

Larsen PR: Thyroid-pituitary interaction: Feedback regulation of thyrotropin secretion by thyroid hormones. N Engl J Med 1982;306:23.

McCutcheon IE, Weintraub BD, Oldfieid EH: Surgical treatment of thyrotropin-secreting pituitary tumors. J Neurosurg1990;73:674.

Segerson TP et al: Thyroid hormone regulates TRH biosynthesis in the paraventricular nucleus of the rat hypothalamus. Science 1987;238:78.

Pituitary Function Testing & Neuroradiology

Abboud CF: Laboratory diagnosis of hypopituitarism. Mayo Clin Proc 1986;61:35.

Abboud CF, Laws ER Jr: Diagnosis of pituitary tumors. Endocrinol Metab Clin North Am 1988;17:241.

Burrow GN et al: Microadenomas of the pituitary and abnormal sellar tomograms in an unselected autopsy series. N Engl J Med 1981;304:156.

Cohen KL: Metabolic, endocrine, and drug-induced interference with pituitary function tests: A review. Metabolism 1977;26:1165.

Elster AD: Modern imaging of the pituitary. Radiology 1993;187:1.

Feldman HA, Singer I: Endocrinology and metabolism in uremia and dialysis: A clinical review. Medicine 1974;54:345.

Glass AR et al: Endocrine function in human obesity. Metabolism 1981;30:89.

Kucharczyk W et al: Pituitary adenomas: High resolution MR imaging at 1.5 T. Radiology 1986;161:761.

Lufkin EG et al: Combined testing of anterior pituitary gland with insulin, thyrotropin-releasing hormone, and luteinizing hormone-releasing hormone. Am J Med 1983;75:471.

Maroldo TV, Dillon WP, Wilson CB: Advances in diagnostic techniques of pituitary tumors and prolactinomas. Curr Opin Oncol 1992;4:105.

Mosely I: Computed tomography and magnetic resonance imaging of pituitary microadenomas. Clin Endocrinol 1992;36:333.

Sheldon WR Jr et al: Rapid sequential intravenous administration of four hypothalamic releasing hormones as a combined anterior pituitary function test in normal subjects. J Clin Endocrinol Metab 1985;60:623.

Snyder PJ et al: Diagnostic value of thyrotrophin-releasing hormone in pituitary and hypothalamic diseases: Assessment of thyrotrophin and prolactin secretion in 100 patients. Ann Intern Med 1974;81:751.

Webb SM et al: Computerized tomography versus magnetic resonance imaging: A comparative study in hypothalamic-pituitary and parasellar pathology. Clin Endocrinol 1992;36:459.

Pituitary Adenomas: General

Alexander JM et al: Clinically nonfunctioning pituitary tumors are monoclonal in origin. J Clin Invest 1990;86:336.

Arafah BM: Reversible hypopituitarism in patients with large nonfunctioning pituitary adenomas. J Clin Endocrinol Metab 1986;62:1173.

Aron DC, Tyrrell JB, Wilson CW: Pituitary tumors: Current concepts in diagnosis and management. West J Med 1993. [In press.]

Branch CL, Laws ER Jr: Metastatic tumors of the sella turcica masquerading as primary pituitary tumors. J Clin Endocrinol Metab 1987;65:469.

Cusick JF, Hagen TC, Findling JW: Inappropriate secretion of antidiuretic hormone after transsphenoidal surgery for pituitary tumors. N Engl J Med 1984;311:36.

Hammen RE et al: Expression of human growth hormone-releasing factor in transgenic mice results in increased somatic growth. Nature 1985;315:413.

Harris PE et al: Glycoprotein hormone alpha-subunit production in somatotroph adenomas with and without Gs alpha mutations. J Clin Endocrinol Metab 1992;75:918.

Helseth A et al: Transgenic mice that develop pituitary tumors: A model for Cushing's disease. Am J Pathol 1992;140:1071.

Herman V et al: Clonal origin of pituitary adenomas. J Clin Endocrinol Metab 1990;71:1427.

Jameson JL et al: Glycoprotein hormone genes are expressed in clinically nonfunctioning pituitary adenomas. J Clin Invest 1987;80:1482.

Johnson MR et al: The evaluation of patients with a suspected pituitary microadenoma: Computer tomography compared to magnetic resonance imaging. Clin Endocrinol 1992;36:335.

Karga HJ et al: Ras mutations in human pituitary tumors. J Clin Endocrinol Metab 1992;74:914.

Klibanski A et al: Dopaminergic regulation of α-subunit secretion and mRNA levels in alpha subunit-secreting pituitary tumors. J Clin Endocrinol Metab 1988;66:96.

Klibanski A, Zervas NT: Diagnosis and management of hormone-secreting pituitary adenomas. N Engl J Med 1991;324:822.

Kontogeorgos G et al: Multiple adenomas of the human pituitary: A retrospective autopsy study with clinical implications. J Neurosurg 1991;74:243.

Landis CA et al: GTPase inhibiting mutations activate the alpha chain of Gs and stimulate adenylyl cyclase in human pituitary tumours. Nature 1989;340:692.

Molitch ME (editor): Pituitary tumors: Diagnosis and management. Endocrinol Metab Clin North Am 1987;16:475.

Oppenheim DS et al: Prevalence of α-subunit hypersecretion in patients with pituitary tumors: Clinically non-functioning and somatotroph adenomas. J Clin Endocrinol Metab 1990;70:859.

Reincke M et al: The "incidentaloma" of the pituitary gland: Is neurosurgery referred? JAMA 1990;263:2772.

Ridgway EC et al: Pure alpha-secreting pituitary adenomas. N Engl J Med 1981;304:1254.

Russell EJ, Molitch ME: The pituitary "incidentaloma." Ann Intern Med 1990;112:925.

Schulte HM et al: Clonal composition of pituitary adenomas in patients with Cushing's disease: Determination by X-chromosome inactivation analysis. J Clin Endocrinol Metab 1991;73:1302.

Sheithauer BW et al: Pituitary adenomas of the multiple endocrine neoplasia type I syndrome. Semin Diagn Pathol 1987;4:205.

Spada A et al: Clinical, biochemical, and morphological correlates in patients bearing growth hormone-secreting pituitary tumors with or without constitutively active adenylyl cyclase. J Clin Endocrinol Metab 1990;71:1421.

Stenzel-Poore MP et al: Development of Cushing's syndrome in corticotropin-releasing factor transgenic mice. Endocrinology 1992;130:3378.

Wilson CB: Endocrine-inactive pituitary adenomas. Clin Neurosurg 1992;38:10.

Wood DF, Johnston JM, Johnston DG: Dopamine, the dopamine D_2 receptor and pituitary tumours. Clin Endocrinol 1991;35:455.

Yamada S et al: Analysis of hormone secretion by clinically nonfunctioning human pituitary adenomas using the reverse hemolytic plaque assay. J Clin Endocrinol Metab 1989;68:73.

Empty Sella Syndrome

Bergeron C, Kovacs K, Bilbao JM: Primary empty sella: A histologic and immunocytologic study. Arch Intern Med 1979;139:248.

Fleckman AM et al: Empty sella of normal size in Sheehan's syndrome. Am J Med 1983;175:585.

Jordan RM, Kendall JW, Kerber CW: The primary empty sella syndrome: Analysis of the clinical characteristics, radiographic features, pituitary function and cerebrospinal fluid adenohypophysial hormone concentrations. Am J Med 1977;62:569.

Hypopituitarism

Asa SL et al: Lymphocytic hypophysitis of pregnancy resulting in hypopituitarism: A distinct clinicopathologic entity. Ann Intern Med 1981;95:166.

Bell NH: Endocrine complications of sarcoidosis. Endocrinol Metab Clin North Am 1991;20:645.

Edwards DM, Clark JD: Posttraumatic hypopituitarism: Six cases and a review of the literature. Medicine 1986;65:281.

Freda PU et al: Hypothalamic-pituitary sarcoidosis. Trends Endocrinol Metab 1992;3:321.

Males JL, Townsend JL, Schneider RA: Hypogonadotropic hypogonadism with anosmia-Kallmann's syndrome: A disorder of olfactory and hypothalamic function. Arch Intern Med 1973;131:501.

Purnell DC, Randall RV, Rynearson EH: Postpartum pituitary insufficiency (Sheehan's syndrome): Review of 18 cases. Mayo Clin Proc 1964;139:321.

Samaan NA et al: Hypopituitarism after external irradiation: Evidence of both hypothalamic and pituitary origin. Ann Intern Med 1975;83:771.

Schafer AL et al: Clinical consequences of acquired transfusional iron overload in adults. N Engl J Med 1981;304:319.

Schwabe AD (moderator): Anorexia nervosa. Ann Intern Med 1981;94:371.

Snyder PJ et al: Hypopituitarism following radiation therapy of pituitary adenomas. Am J Med 1986; 81:457.

Stosel H, Braunstein GD: Endocrine abnormalities associated with Langerhans cell histiocytosis. Trends Endocrinol Metab 1991;1:393.

Thomsett MJ et al: Endocrine and neurologic outcome in childhood craniopharyngioma: Review of effect of treatment in 42 patients. J Pediatr 1980;97:728.

Veldhuis JD, Hammond, JM: Endocrine function after spontaneous infarction of the human pituitary: Report, review, and reappraisal. Endocr Rev 1980;1:100.

Voss JW, Rosenfeld MG: Anterior pituitary development: Short tales from dwarf mice. Cell 1992;70:527.

Posterior Pituitary

Anderson RJ: Hospital associated hyponatremia. Kidney Int 1986;29:1237.

Bie P: Osmoreceptors, vasopressin, and control of renal water excretion. Physiol Rev 1980;60:961.

Blevins LS Jr, Wand GS: Diabetes insipidus. Crit Care Med 1992;20:69.

Cogan E et al: Natriuresis and atrial natriuretic factor secretion during inappropriate antidiuresis. Am J Med 1988;84:409.

Cowley AW, Liard JF, Ausiello DA: *Vasopressin.* Raven Press, 1988.

Durr JA et al: Diabetes insipidus in pregnancy associated with abnormally high circulating vasopressinase activity. N Engl J Med 1987;316:1070.

Goldman MB, Luchins DJ, Robertson GL: Mechanisms of altered water metabolism in psychotic patients with polydipsia and hyponatremia. N Engl J Med 1988;318:397.

Hill AR et al: Altered water metabolism in tuberculosis: Role of vasopressin. Am J Med 1990;88:357.

Iwasaki Y et al: Aggravation of subclinical diabetes insipidus during pregnancy. N Engl J Med 1991;324:522.

Jenkins JS: Thirst and vasopressin. Clin Endocrinol 1991;35:219.

Kovacs L, Robertson GL: Syndrome of inappropriate antidiuresis. Endocrinol Metab Clin North Am 1992;21:859.

Land H et al: Deduced amino-acid sequence from the bovine oxytocin-neurophysin I precursor cDNA. Nature 1983;302:342.

Land H et al: Nucleotide sequence of cloned cDNA encoding bovine arginine vasopressin-neurophysin II precursor. Nature 1982;295:299.

Moses AM, Scheinman SJ, Oppenheim A: Marked hypotonic polyuria resulting from nephrogenic diabetes insipidus with partial sensitivity to vasopressin. J Clin Endocrinol Metab 1984;59:1044.

Narins RG: Therapy of hyponatremia: Does haste make waste? N Engl J Med 1986;314:1573.

Oelkers W: Hyponatremia and inappropriate secretion of vasopressin (antidiuretic hormone) in patients with hypopituitarism. N Engl J Med 1989;321:492.

Peden NR et al: Wolfram (DIDMOAD) syndrome: A complex long-term problem in management. Q J Med 1986;5R:167.

Robertson GL, Berl T: Pathophysiology of water metabolism. In: *The Kidney.* Brenner BM, Rector FC Jr (editors). Saunders, 1986.

Schrier RW (editor): *Vasopressin.* Raven Press, 1985.

Thompson CJ, Edwards CRW, Baylis PH: Osmotic and non-osmotic regulation of thirst and vasopressin secretion in patients with compulsive water drinking. Clin Endocrinol 1991;35:221.

Verbalis JG, Robinson AG, Moses AM: Postoperative and post-traumatic diabetes insipidus. Front Horm Res 1985;13:247.

Verbalis JG: Hyponatremia, endocrinologic causes and consequences of therapy. Trends Endocrinol Metab 1992;3:1.

Vokes TJ, Robertson GL: Disorders of antidiuretic hormone. Endocrinol Metab Clin North Am 1988; 17:28.

3

Growth

Dennis M. Styne, MD

Assessment of growth in stature is an essential part of the pediatric examination. Growth is an important index of physical and mental health and of the quality of the child's psychosocial environment; chronic problems in any of these areas may be reflected in a decreased growth rate. We will consider influences on normal growth, the normal growth pattern, the measurement of growth, and conditions that lead to disorders of growth.

NORMAL GROWTH

INTRAUTERINE GROWTH

The great changes that take place in the human fetus during intrauterine growth have been summarized by Pierson and Deschamps: From conception to delivery, fetal mass increases 44×10^7 times, compared with a 20-fold increase from birth to adulthood; length increases 3850 times to term, compared with a three- to fourfold increase from birth to adulthood. The determinants of normal prenatal growth are poorly understood, though many factors that lead to abnormal prenatal growth have been identified.

Endocrine Factors

A. Growth Hormone: Although fetal plasma values of growth hormone (GH) are higher than levels reported in most adult acromegalics, GH appears to have little influence on length at birth; infants with GH deficiency have normal birth lengths, and even those with anencephaly (who therefore lack hypothalamic releasing factors) have normal body lengths. Remarkably, although GH concentrations are high at birth, IGF-1 concentrations are exceedingly low in normal neonates. Human chorionic somatomammotropin (hCS), a placental hormone similar in structure to GH and prolactin, may not be essential to fetal growth, since mothers lacking the *hCS* gene have given birth to children with normal birth lengths.

B. Thyroid Hormone: The absence of thyroid

ACRONYMS USED IN THIS CHAPTER	
ACTH	Adrenocorticotropic hormone
cAMP	Cyclic adenosine monophosphate
DNA	Deoxyribonucleic acid
GH	Growth hormone
GnRH	Gonadotropin-releasing hormone
GRH	Growth hormone-releasing hormone
hCG	Human chorionic gonadotropin
hCS	Human chorionic somatomammotropin
hGH	Human growth hormone
IGF	Human insulin-like growth factor (somatomedin)
IGF-1	Human insulin-like growth factor 1
IGF-2	Human insulin-like growth factor 2
IGFBP	Insulin-like growth factor binding protein
IUGR	Intrauterine growth retardation
LH	Luteinizing hormone
LS	Lower segment
NCHS	National Center for Health Statistics
PTH	Parathyroid hormone
RTA	Renal tubular acidosis
RWT	Roche, Wainer, and Thissen method of height prediction
SS	Somatostatin
TBG	Thyroid hormone-binding globulin
TRH	Thyrotropin-releasing hormone
TSH	Thyroid-stimulating hormone (thyrotropin)
US	Upper segment

hormone may have devastating effects on the mental development of a neonate, but hypothyroid newborns have normal length. In fact, perhaps because of the longer duration of pregnancy in hypothyroid fetuses, the hypothyroid newborn may be longer than average.

C. Insulin: Excessive serum insulin concentrations may be associated with increased length in infants of diabetic mothers and in the Beckwith-Wiedemann syndrome, characterized by neonatal hypoglycemia, neonatal gigantism, omphalocele, macroglossia, and hepatomegaly. Inadequate insulin production, found in transient neonatal diabetes mellitus, or insulin resistance, found in the leprechaun syndrome (Donohue syndrome), is associated with short newborn length.

D. Insulin-Like Growth Factors: (IGF-1, formerly somatomedin C [SMC]; and IGF-2, formerly call multiplication stimulating activity [MSA] or somatomedin A [SMA].) In rodents, IGF-2 appears to be of significance in producing normal fetal growth, but its role in human fetuses is not clear. IGF-1 is expressed in various tissues of the fetus and is capable of stimulating differentiation, but the precise role of IGF-1 in fetal growth is not yet established. Serum IGF-1 values do correlate with newborn weight in normal infants. Laron's dwarfism, characterized by an inability to generate IGF-1 (due to a lack of GH receptors), is associated with short birth length.

Maternal & Uterine Factors

Maternal factors, often expressed through the uterine environment, exert more influence on birth size than paternal factors. The height of the mother correlates better with fetal size than the height of the father. First-born infants are on the average 100 g heavier than subsequent infants, maternal age over 38 years leads to decreased birth weight, and male infants are heavier than female infants by an average of 150–200 g. Poor maternal nutrition is the most important condition leading to low birth weight and length on a worldwide basis; it also predisposes the infant to other serious health hazards after birth. Chronic maternal disease and eclampsia can also lead to poor fetal growth. Maternal alcohol ingestion has been shown to have severe adverse effects on fetal length and mental development and to predispose to other physical abnormalities such as microcephaly, mental retardation, midfacial hypoplasia, short palpebral fissures, wide-bridged nose, long philtrum, and narrow vermilion border of the lip. Abuse of other substances and chronic use of some medications (eg, phenytoin) can cause intrauterine growth retardation. Cigarette smoking causes not only retarded intrauterine growth but also decreased postnatal growth for as long as 5 years after parturition. Maternal infection—most commonly rubella, toxoplasmosis, and cytomegalovirus infection—leads to many developmental abnormalities as well as short birth length. Congenital AIDS causes intrauterine growth retardation. In multiple births, the weight of each fetus is usually less than that of the average singleton. Uterine tumors or malformations may decrease fetal growth.

Intrauterine growth retardation (IUGR) is usually defined as a birth weight less than the tenth percentile for gestational age, though it should be clear that 10% of births are not truly abnormal. It is suggested that the third percentile may be more appropriate as a guide to IUGR, while the tenth percentile may characterize the infant small for gestational age (SGA). For term births, 2500 g is the tenth percentile, and this is the lower limit of "normal" in common usage. Proportionate IUGR indicates a small head circumference along with a small body; infants with genetic defects, infections, or toxic exposures fall in this classification and usually do not grow well after birth and reach a shorter ultimate stature in adulthood.

This is in contrast to premature infants with normal weight for gestational age, who recover to the range of normal height and weight for age by age 2 years. To do this, they must have growth rates that are higher than the average for a period of months. Disproportionate IUGR is heralded by relative sparing of the head circumference, which remains in the range of normal percentiles—in contrast to the small body, which is well below average. This condition most often results from fetal malnutrition, and affected infants may experience catch-up growth after birth. Thus, a key point in assessing the patient with short stature is determining gestational age and relating it to birth weight, length, and head circumference.

Chromosomal Abnormalities & Malformation Syndromes

Many chromosomal abnormalities that lead to malformation syndromes also cause poor fetal growth. Other malformation syndromes associated with a normal karyotype are characterized by intrauterine growth retardation. In most cases, endocrine abnormalities have not been noted in either of these situations. For further discussion, the reader is referred to other sources listed in the references at the end of this chapter (especially Smith and Sakati, Nyhan).

POSTNATAL GROWTH

Postnatal growth in stature and weight follows a definite pattern in normal children (Figures 3–1 and 3–2). The highest overall growth rate occurs in the fetus, the highest postnatal growth rate just after birth, and a slower growth rate follows in mid childhood (Figures 3–3 and 3–4). Several investigators report a growth spurt between 6 1/2 and 7 years in both boys and girls. After another plateau, the striking increase in stature known as the pubertal growth spurt follows, causing a second peak of growth velocity. The final decrease then ensues, until the epiphyses of the long bones fuse and growth ceases.

Endocrine Factors

A. Growth Hormone and Insulin-Like Growth Factors: As discussed in Chapter 2, somatotropin, or growth hormone (GH), is suppressed by hypothalamic growth hormone release-inhibiting factor (somatostatin) and stimulated by growth hormone-releasing hormone (GRH). The gene for GH is located on the long arm of chromosome 17 in a cluster of five genes: *GH-N* codes for human GH, *GH2* codes for a variant GH produced in the placenta, *CSH1* and *CSH2* code for prolactin, and *CSH P1* codes for a variant prolactin molecule. Several families are known with deletions of the *GH-N* gene and profound GH deficiency.

Growth hormone's effects are mainly mediated by

Name_____ Date of Birth_____ Record # _____

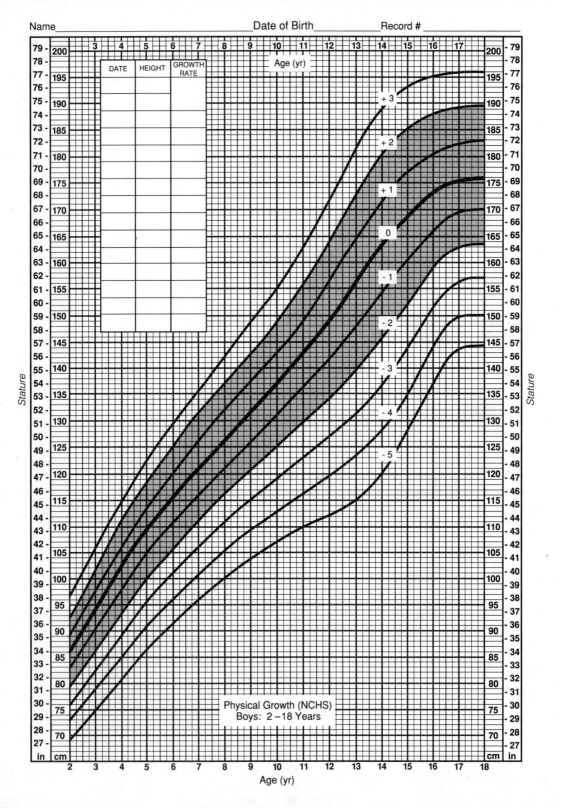

Figure 3–1. Growth chart for boys in the USA. (Redrawn and reprinted with permission of Genentech, Inc. Sources of data: 1976 study of the National Center for Health Statistics [NCHS; Hyattsville, MD]; Hamill PVV et al: Physical growth: National Center for Health Statistics percentiles. Am J Clin Nutr 1979;32:607.)

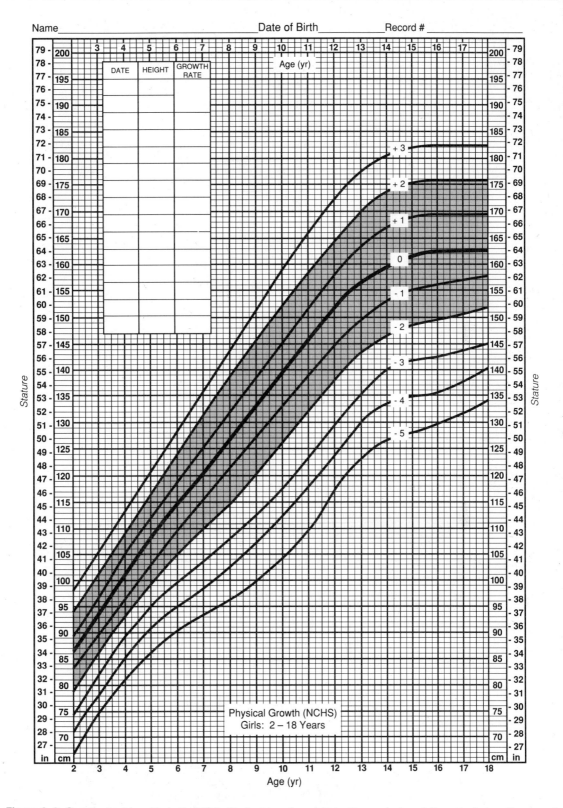

Figure 3–2. Growth chart for girls in the USA. (Redrawn and reprinted with permission of Genentech, Inc. Sources of data: 1976 study of the National Center for Health Statistics [NCHS; Hyattsville, MD]; Hamill PVV et al: Physical growth: National Center for Health Statistics percentiles. Am J Clin Nutr 1979;32:607.)

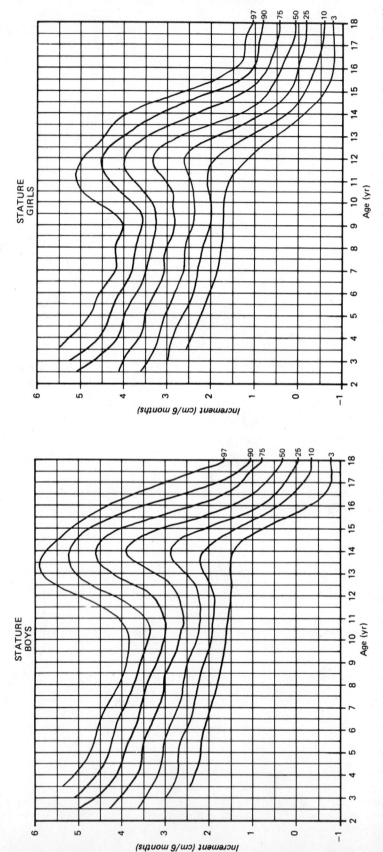

Figures 3–3 and 3–4. Incremental growth charts for boys (Figure 3–3) and girls (Figure 3–4). Height velocity measured over a period of at least 6 months can be compared with the percentiles on the right axis of the charts. (Redrawn and reprinted with permission of Ross Laboratories, Columbus, OH 43216. © 1981 Ross Laboratories. Sources of data: Longitudinal studies of the Fels Research Laboratories [Yellow Springs, OH]; Roche AF, Himes JH: Incremental growth charts. Am J Clin Nutr 1980;33:2041.)

the insulin-like growth factors, but GH also has some direct effects. Growth hormone produces insulin resistance and is a diabetogenic substance, increasing blood sugar. Furthermore, growth hormone is lipolytic.

Growth hormone circulates in plasma bound to a protein with a sequence equivalent to that of the extramembrane domain of the growth hormone receptor. The physiology of GH-binding protein (GHBP) may be of great importance physiologically in growth. For example, obese patients have lower plasma GH concentrations but higher GHBP, while starvation raises GH concentrations and lowers GHBP. This binding protein is regulated differently from the GH membrane receptor and may have other physiologic roles in addition to simply reflecting receptor status.

Because of the difficulty in determining true physiologic GH status (as described below), it appeared that measurement of IGFs would improve diagnostic capabilities in growth failure. However, the control of IGF production and secretion is so complex that this promise has not been fully realized. Thus, measurements of IGF concentrations assist in the diagnosis of GH deficiency but are not diagnostic.

IGF-1 and IGF-2 have structures similar to the proinsulin molecule but differ from insulin in regulation, receptors, and biologic effects. These factors were first recognized when Salmon and Daughaday demonstrated that GH itself could not cause cartilage growth in vitro but that GH administered in vivo to hypopituitary rodents caused the production of polypeptide factors which themselves stimulated cartilage growth. In the ensuing 35 years, the structure of the factors (originally called somatomedins), the genes responsible for their production, and information about their physiology were elucidated.

The single copy gene for prepro-IGF-1 is located on the long arm of chromosome 12. Posttranslational processing produces the 70-amino-acid mature form, and alternative splicing mechanisms produce variants of the molecule in different tissues and developmental stages. The IGF-1 cell membrane receptor (the type I receptor) resembles the insulin receptor in its structure of two α and two β chains. Binding of IGF-1 to type I receptors stimulates tyrosine kinase activity and autophosphorylation of tyrosine molecules, which produce cell differentiation or division (or both). IGF-1 receptors are down-regulated by increased IGF-1 concentrations, while decreased IGF-1 concentrations decrease IGF-1 receptors.

IGF molecules bind to a variety of IGF-binding (IGFBP) proteins; at present, information is available about the molecular weights and other properties of six IGFBPs. The IGFBPs were thought to inhibit IGF action, but there is increasing evidence that in certain conditions IGFBPs may enhance IGF action. IGFBP-1 is a 25-kDa protein: The serum levels of IGFBP-1 are inversely proportionate to insulin levels, but this protein does not appear to be regulated by GH. IGFBP-2 is a 33-kDa protein, and serum concentrations are inversely proportionate to both GH and insulin concentrations. Most IGF-1 circulates bound to IGFBP-3 in a 150-kDa complex. Serum IGFBP-3 is directly proportionate to GH concentrations as well as to nutritional status—thus, in malnutrition, IGFBP-3 and IGF-1 fall while GH rises. IGF-1 directly regulates IGFBP-3 as well.

IGF-1 is produced in most tissues and appears to be exported to neighboring cells to act upon them in a paracrine manner. Thus, blood-borne IGF-1 may not reflect the most significant actions of this growth factor. The liver is a major site of IGF-1 synthesis, and much of the circulating IGF-1 probably originates in the liver. IGF is a progression factor, so that a cell which has been exposed to a competence factor in stage G_0 of the cell cycle and has transited to G_1 can, with IGF-1 exposure in G_1, undergo division in the S phase of the cell cycle. Besides the stimulatory effects of IGF-1 on cartilage growth, IGF-1 has stimulatory effects upon hematopoiesis, ovarian steroidogenesis, myoblast proliferation and differentiation, and differentiation of the lens.

IGF-1 was in short supply until production by recombinant DNA technology became possible. The first clinical studies of IGF-1 administration in human subjects are under way. IGF-1 administration increases nitrogen retention and decreases BUN— and, in GH-resistant patients (Laron dwarfs), IGF-1 stimulates growth without the presence of GH. Thus, IGF-1 may prove useful in treatment of various clinical conditions from pathologic short stature to catabolic states, including the postoperative period.

IGF-2 is a 67-amino-acid peptide. The gene for prepro-IGF-2 is located on the short arm of chromosome 11, close to the gene for prepro insulin. The type II IGF receptor preferentially binds IGF-2 and is identical to the mannose 6-phosphate receptor, a single-chain transmembrane protein. While most of the effects of IGF-2 appear mediated by its interaction with the type I receptor, independent actions of IGF-2 via the type II receptor are described.

Plasma concentrations of the IGFs vary with age and physiologic condition. IGF concentrations are low at term in human beings and remain low until a peak is reached during puberty, with values rising higher than at any other time in life. IGF-1 then decreases to adult levels, values higher than in childhood but lower than in puberty. With advancing age, serum GH and IGF-1 decrease.

GH deficiency leads to lower IGF-1 and IGF-2 concentrations, while GH excess leads to elevated IGF-1 but no change in IGF-2. Because IGF-1 is lower during states of nutritional deficiency, IGF-1 is less useful in the differential diagnosis of conditions of poor growth, which often include impaired nutritional state. IGF-1 suppresses GH secretion, so that patients who lack GH receptors (Laron dwarfs) and are unable to produce IGF-1 have elevated GH concentrations and negligible IGF-1 concentrations.

B. Thyroid Hormone: Although congenital hypothyroid newborns are of normal length, they manifest exceedingly poor growth soon after birth if untreated (permanent mental retardation will result in the absence of therapy for congenital hypothyroidism). Acquired hypothyroidism leads to a markedly decreased growth rate (but no permanent intellectual defects). Bone age advancement is severely delayed in hypothyroidism, usually more so than in GH deficiency. The upper to lower segment ratio (Figure 3–7) is delayed and therefore elevated, owing to poor limb growth.

C. Sex Steroids: Gonadal steroids exert an important influence on the pubertal growth spurt, while absence of these factors is not important in prepubertal growth. Gonadal and adrenal sex steroids in excess can cause a sharp increase in growth rate as well as the premature appearance and progression of secondary sexual features. If unabated, increased sex steroids will cause advancement of skeletal age, premature epiphysial fusion, and short adult stature.

The pubertal rise in gonadal steroids exerts direct and indirect effects upon IGF-1 production. Sex

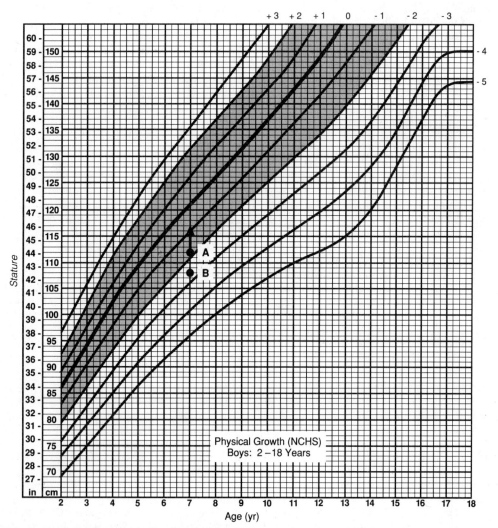

Figure 3–5. Adjustment of height based on midparental stature (Table 3–1). Charts of three boys, each 7 years of age. **A** is 2 SD below the mean, with a height of 112 cm; taking his midparental stature of 158 cm into consideration, his adjusted height of 118 cm *(arrow)* is only 1 SD below the mean, suggesting that he is short because of familial tendency rather than pathology. **B** is almost 3 SD below the mean, with a height of 108 cm; his midparental height of 166 cm causes his adjusted height to rise only 1 cm, suggesting that familial factors may not be the cause of his short stature and he may have a pathologic diagnosis.

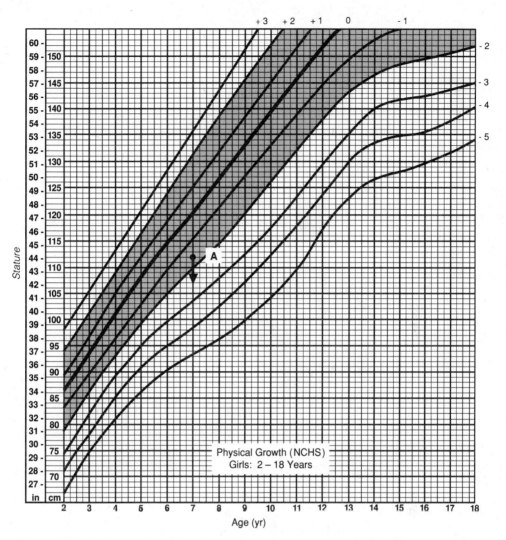

Figure 3–6. Adjustment of height based on midparental stature (Table 3–2). Chart of a girl, 7 years old, with height of 112 cm. She has a midparental stature of 178 cm, causing her adjusted height *(arrow)* to fall 5 cm, suggesting that her short stature is more severe than suspected from the original growth chart and that genetic influences are probably not the cause.

steroids directly stimulate the production of IGF-1 from cartilage as well as increase GH secretion, which also stimulates IGF-1 production directly. Both actions appear important in the pubertal growth spurt.

D. Glucocorticoids: Endogenous or exogenous glucocorticoids in excess will quickly stop growth. The absence of glucocorticoids has little effect on growth if the individual is clinically well in other respects.

Other Factors

A. Genetic Factors: Genetic factors influence final height. Good correlation is found between midparental height and the child's height; appropriate charts and tables have been developed to display this phenomenon (Figures 3–5 and 3–6; Tables 3–1 and 3–2).

B. Socioeconomic Factors: Worldwide, the most common cause of short stature is poverty and its effects. Thus, poor nutrition, poor hygiene, and poor health have effects on growth both before and after birth. In people of the same ethnic group and in the same geographic location, variations in stature are often attributable to these factors. For example, studies have shown that Japanese individuals born and reared in North America were taller than Japanese-born immigrants to North America. Conversely, when socioeconomic factors are equal, the differences in average height between various ethnic groups are mainly genetic.

C. Nutritional Factors: The influence of malnu-

Table 3–1. Parent-specific adjustments (cm) for stature of boys from 3 to 18 years of age.[1]

Age (yr)	Stature (cm)	Mid Parental Stature (cm)																	
		150	152	154	156	158	160	162	164	166	168	170	172	174	176	178	180	182	184
3	86.0– 87.9	7	6	5	5	4	3	2	1	1	0	−1	−2	−3	−3	−4	−5	−6	−7
	88.0– 97.9	8	7	6	5	4	4	3	2	1	0	−1	−1	−2	−3	−4	−5	−5	−6
	98.0–106.9	8	8	7	6	5	4	4	3	2	1	0	0	−1	−2	−3	−4	−4	−5
4	90.0– 93.9	7	6	5	4	4	3	2	1	0	−1	−1	−2	−3	−4	−5	−5	−6	−7
	94.0–103.9	8	7	6	5	4	3	3	2	1	0	−1	−1	−2	−3	−4	−5	−6	−6
	104.0–112.9	8	8	7	6	5	4	3	3	2	1	0	−1	−1	−2	−3	−4	−5	−6
5	96.0–103.9	8	7	6	5	4	3	2	1	0	0	−1	−2	−3	−4	−5	−6	−7	−8
	104.0–113.9	9	8	7	6	5	4	3	2	1	0	0	−1	−2	−3	−4	−5	−6	−7
	114.0–122.9	9	9	8	7	6	5	4	3	2	1	0	0	−1	−2	−3	−4	−5	−6
6	102.0–111.9	8	7	7	6	5	4	3	2	1	0	−1	−2	−3	−4	−5	−6	−7	−8
	112.0–121.9	9	8	7	7	6	5	4	3	2	1	0	−1	−2	−3	−4	−5	−6	−7
	122.0–130.9	10	9	8	7	6	6	5	4	3	2	1	0	−1	−2	−3	−4	−5	−6
7	108.0–117.9	9	8	7	6	5	4	3	2	1	0	−1	−2	−4	−5	−6	−7	−8	−9
	118.0–127.9	10	9	8	7	6	5	4	3	2	1	0	−1	−2	−4	−5	−6	−7	−8
	128.0–136.9	12	10	9	8	7	6	5	4	3	2	1	0	−1	−2	−4	−5	−6	−7
8	114.0–115.9	10	9	8	6	5	4	3	2	1	−1	−2	−3	−4	−5	−6	−8	−9	−10
	116.0–125.9	11	9	8	7	6	5	4	2	1	0	−1	−2	−3	−5	−6	−7	−8	−9
	126.0–135.9	12	10	9	8	7	6	5	3	2	1	0	−1	−2	−4	−5	−6	−7	−8
	136.0–144.9	13	12	10	9	8	7	6	5	3	2	1	0	−1	−2	−4	−5	−6	−7
9	120.0–121.9	11	9	8	7	6	4	3	2	1	0	−2	−3	−4	−5	−7	−8	−9	−10
	122.0–131.9	11	10	9	8	6	5	4	3	1	0	−1	−2	−3	−5	−6	−7	−8	−10
	132.0–141.9	12	11	10	9	7	6	5	4	2	1	0	−1	−2	−4	−5	−6	−7	−9
	142.0–150.9	13	12	11	10	8	7	6	5	4	2	1	0	−1	−3	−4	−5	−6	−7
10	124.0–127.9	11	10	9	7	6	5	3	2	1	−1	−2	−3	−5	−6	−7	−9	−10	−11
	128.0–137.9	12	11	10	8	7	6	4	3	2	0	−1	−2	−4	−5	−6	−8	−9	−10
	138.0–147.9	13	12	11	9	8	7	5	4	3	1	0	−1	−3	−4	−5	−7	−8	−9
	148.0–158.9	14	13	12	11	9	8	7	5	4	3	1	0	−1	−3	−4	−5	−7	−8
11	128.0–133.9	12	10	9	8	6	5	4	2	1	0	−2	−3	−5	−6	−7	−9	−10	−11
	134.0–143.9	12	11	10	8	7	6	4	3	2	0	−1	−2	−4	−5	−6	−8	−9	−10
	144.0–153.9	14	12	11	10	8	7	5	4	3	1	0	−1	−3	−4	−5	−7	−8	−9
	154.0–162.9	15	13	12	11	9	8	7	5	4	3	1	0	−2	−3	−4	−6	−7	−8
12	132.0–141.9	12	10	9	8	6	5	4	2	1	0	−2	−3	−4	−6	−7	−8	−10	−11
	142.0–151.9	13	11	10	9	7	6	5	3	2	1	−1	−2	−3	−5	−6	−7	−9	−10
	152.0–161.9	13	12	11	9	8	7	5	4	3	1	0	−1	−2	−4	−5	−6	−8	−9
	162.0–170.9	14	13	12	10	9	8	6	5	4	2	1	0	−2	−3	−4	−6	−7	−8
13	136.0–139.9	12	10	9	8	6	5	4	2	1	−1	−2	−3	−5	−6	−7	−9	−10	−12
	140.0–149.9	12	11	10	8	7	6	4	3	1	0	−1	−3	−4	−6	−7	−8	−10	−11
	150.0–159.9	13	12	10	9	8	6	5	4	2	1	−1	−2	−3	−5	−6	−7	−9	−10
	160.0–169.9	14	13	11	10	8	7	6	4	3	2	0	−1	−3	−4	−5	−7	−8	−9
	170.0–178.9	15	13	12	11	9	8	6	5	4	2	1	0	−2	−3	−5	−6	−7	−9
14	142.0–145.9	13	11	10	8	7	5	4	2	1	−1	−2	−4	−5	−7	−8	−10	−11	−13
	146.0–155.9	14	12	11	9	8	6	5	3	1	0	−2	−3	−5	−6	−8	−9	−11	−12
	156.0–165.9	15	13	11	10	8	7	5	4	2	1	−1	−2	−4	−5	−7	−8	−10	−11
	166.0–175.9	15	14	12	11	9	8	6	5	3	2	0	−1	−3	−4	−6	−7	−9	−11
	176.0–184.9	16	15	13	12	10	9	7	6	4	3	1	−1	−2	−4	−5	−7	−8	−10
15	148.0–151.9	14	13	11	9	7	6	4	2	0	−1	−3	−5	−7	−8	−10	−12	−14	−15
	152.0–161.9	15	14	12	10	8	7	5	3	1	0	−2	−4	−6	−7	−9	−11	−13	−14
	162.0–171.9	17	15	13	11	10	8	6	4	3	1	−1	−3	−4	−6	−8	−10	−11	−13
	172.0–181.9	18	16	14	13	11	9	7	6	4	2	0	−1	−3	−5	−7	−8	−10	−12
	182.0–190.9	19	17	16	14	12	10	9	7	5	3	2	0	−2	−4	−5	−7	−9	−11
16	156.0–163.9	17	15	13	11	9	7	5	3	1	−1	−3	−5	−7	−9	−11	−13	−16	−18
	164.0–173.9	19	17	15	13	10	8	6	4	2	0	−2	−4	−6	−8	−10	−12	−14	−16
	174.0–183.9	21	19	17	15	12	10	8	6	4	2	0	−2	−4	−6	−8	−10	−12	−14
	184.0–192.9	23	21	19	17	14	12	10	8	6	4	2	0	−2	−4	−6	−8	−10	−12
17	162.0–165.9	17	15	13	11	9	7	4	2	0	−2	−4	−7	−9	−11	−13	−15	−17	−20
	166.0–175.9	20	17	15	13	11	9	6	4	2	0	−2	−4	−7	−9	−11	−13	−15	−18
	176.0–185.9	22	20	18	16	13	11	9	7	5	3	0	−2	−4	−6	−8	−11	−13	−15
	186.0–194.9	25	23	20	18	16	14	12	9	7	5	3	1	−1	−4	−6	−8	−10	−12
18	160.0–165.9	18	16	13	11	9	6	4	2	0	−3	−5	−7	−10	−12	−14	−17	−19	−21
	166.0–175.9	20	18	16	13	11	9	7	4	2	0	−3	−5	−7	−10	−12	−14	−17	−19
	176.0–185.9	23	21	19	16	14	12	9	7	5	3	0	−2	−4	−7	−9	−11	−14	−16
	186.0–194.9	26	24	22	19	17	15	12	10	8	6	3	1	−1	−4	−6	−8	−11	−13

[1] See footnote for Table 3–2.

Table 3–2. Parent-specific adjustments (cm) for stature of girls from 3 to 18 years of age.[1]

Age (yr)	Stature (cm)	Mid Parental Stature (cm)																	
		150	152	154	156	158	160	162	164	166	168	170	172	174	176	178	180	182	184
3	82.0– 83.9	6	5	4	4	3	2	1	1	0	−1	−1	−2	−3	−3	−4	−5	−6	−6
	84.0– 93.9	6	6	5	4	3	3	2	1	1	0	−1	−1	−2	−3	−4	−4	−5	−6
	94.0–102.9	7	7	6	5	4	4	3	2	2	1	0	−1	−1	−2	−3	−3	−4	−5
4	92.0– 93.9	6	6	5	4	3	3	2	1	0	0	−1	−2	−3	−3	−4	−5	−6	−7
	94.0–103.9	7	6	6	5	4	3	2	2	1	0	−1	−1	−2	−3	−4	−4	−5	−6
	104.0–112.9	8	7	7	6	5	4	3	3	2	1	0	0	−1	−2	−3	−3	−4	−5
5	100.0–101.9	8	7	6	5	4	3	2	1	1	0	−1	−2	−3	−4	−5	−5	−6	−7
	102.0–111.9	8	7	6	6	5	4	3	2	1	0	−1	−1	−2	−3	−4	−5	−6	−7
	112.0–120.9	9	8	7	7	6	5	4	3	2	1	1	0	−1	−2	−3	−4	−5	−6
6	106.0–109.9	9	8	7	6	5	4	3	2	1	0	−1	−2	−3	−4	−5	−6	−7	−8
	110.0–119.9	9	9	8	7	6	5	4	3	2	1	0	−1	−2	−3	−4	−5	−6	−7
	120.0–128.9	11	10	9	8	7	6	5	4	3	2	1	0	−1	−2	−3	−4	−5	−6
7	112.0–117.9	9	8	7	6	5	4	3	2	1	0	−1	−2	−3	−4	−5	−6	−7	−8
	118.0–127.9	10	9	8	7	6	5	4	3	2	1	0	−1	−2	−3	−4	−5	−6	−7
	128.0–136.9	11	10	9	8	7	6	5	4	3	2	1	0	−1	−2	−3	−4	−5	−6
8	116.0–123.9	9	8	7	6	5	4	3	2	1	0	−1	−2	−3	−4	−5	−6	−8	−9
	124.0–133.9	10	9	8	7	6	5	4	3	2	1	0	−1	−2	−3	−4	−5	−7	−8
	134.0–142.9	11	10	9	8	7	6	5	4	3	2	1	0	−1	−2	−3	−4	−6	−7
9	122.0–131.9	10	9	8	7	6	5	3	2	1	0	−1	−2	−3	−4	−5	−6	−7	−9
	132.0–141.9	11	10	9	8	7	6	4	3	2	1	0	−1	−2	−3	−4	−5	−7	−8
	142.0–150.9	12	11	10	9	8	6	5	4	3	2	1	0	−1	−2	−3	−5	−6	−7
10	126.0–127.9	10	9	7	6	5	4	3	2	1	0	−1	−2	−3	−5	−6	−7	−8	−9
	128.0–137.9	10	9	8	7	6	5	4	2	1	0	−1	−2	−3	−4	−5	−6	−7	−8
	138.0–147.9	11	10	9	8	6	5	4	3	2	1	0	−1	−2	−3	−4	−5	−7	−8
	148.0–158.9	12	10	9	8	7	6	5	4	3	2	1	0	−1	−3	−4	−5	−6	−7
11	130.0–133.9	10	9	8	6	5	4	3	2	1	0	−1	−2	−3	−4	−6	−7	−8	−9
	134.0–143.9	10	9	8	7	6	5	4	3	1	0	−1	−2	−3	−4	−5	−6	−7	−8
	144.0–153.9	11	10	9	7	6	6	4	3	2	1	0	−1	−2	−3	−5	−6	−7	−8
	154.0–162.9	11	10	9	8	7	6	5	4	3	1	0	−1	−2	−3	−4	−5	−6	−7
12	134.0–139.9	10	9	8	7	6	5	3	2	1	0	−1	−3	−4	−5	−6	−7	−8	−10
	140.0–149.9	11	10	9	7	6	5	4	3	2	0	−1	−2	−3	−4	−6	−7	−8	−9
	150.0–159.9	12	10	9	8	7	6	5	3	2	1	0	−1	−3	−4	−5	−6	−7	−8
	160.0–168.9	12	11	10	9	8	6	5	4	3	2	0	−1	−2	−3	−4	−5	−7	−8
13	140.0–145.9	10	9	8	7	6	4	3	2	1	0	−1	−3	−4	−5	−6	−7	−8	−10
	146.0–155.9	11	10	9	7	6	5	4	3	2	0	−1	−2	−3	−4	−6	−7	−8	−9
	156.0–165.9	12	10	9	8	7	6	5	3	2	1	0	−1	−3	−4	−5	−6	−7	−8
	166.0–174.9	12	11	10	9	8	6	5	4	3	2	1	−1	−2	−3	−4	−5	−7 ·	−8
14	146.0–149.9	10	9	8	6	5	4	3	2	1	0	−1	−3	−4	−5	−6	−7	−8	−9
	150.0–159.9	11	9	8	7	6	5	4	3	1	0	−1	−2	−3	−4	−5	−7	−8	−9
	160.0–169.9	11	10	9	8	7	6	5	3	2	1	0	−1	−2	−3	−5	−6	−7	−8
	170.0–178.9	12	11	10	9	8	6	5	4	3	2	1	0	−2	−3	−4	−5	−6	−7
15	146.0–151.9	10	9	8	7	5	4	3	2	1	−1	−2	−3	−4	−5	−6	−8	−9	−10
	152.0–161.9	11	10	9	7	6	5	4	3	1	0	−1	−2	−3	−4	−6	−7	−8	−9
	162.0–171.9	12	11	10	8	7	6	5	4	2	1	0	−1	−2	−4	−5	−6	−7	−8
	172.0–180.9	13	12	11	9	8	7	6	5	3	2	1	0	−1	−3	−4	−5	−6	−7
16	146.0–151.9	11	10	8	7	6	5	3	2	1	−1	−2	−3	−4	−6	−7	−8	−10	−11
	152.0–161.9	12	10	9	8	7	5	4	3	2	0	−1	−2	−4	−5	−6	−7	−9	−10
	162.0–171.9	13	12	10	9	8	6	5	4	3	1	0	−1	−3	−4	−5	−6	−8	−9
	172.0–180.9	14	13	11	10	9	7	6	5	4	2	1	0	−2	−3	−4	−5	−7	−8
17	148.0–153.9	11	10	9	7	6	5	3	2	1	0	−2	−3	−4	−6	−7	−8	−10	−11
	154.0–163.9	12	11	10	8	7	6	4	3	2	0	−1	−2	−4	−5	−6	−8	−9	−10
	164.0–173.9	13	12	11	9	8	7	5	4	3	1	0	−1	−3	−4	−5	−6	−8	−9
	174.0–182.9	14	13	12	10	9	8	6	5	4	2	1	0	−1	−3	−4	−5	−7	−8
18	148.0–149.9	10	9	8	7	5	4	3	2	1	−1	−2	−3	−4	−6	−7	−8	−9	−10
	150.0–159.9	11	10	8	7	6	5	4	2	1	0	−1	−3	−4	−5	−6	−7	−9	−10
	160.0–169.9	12	11	9	8	7	6	4	3	2	1	0	−2	−3	−4	−5	−6	−8	−9
	170.0–178.9	13	11	10	9	8	7	5	4	3	2	1	−1	−2	−3	−4	−5	−7	−8

[1]These figures can be used to adjust measured stature to account for parental heights. The average of the mother's and father's heights (mid parental stature) is calculated, and the column closest to the figure is selected. The intersection of a row containing the child's age and height range with the column showing the mid parental height is noted, and the adjustment figure is read from the chart. If the figure has no sign, it is added to the child's height (cm). If there is a negative sign, the number is subtracted from the measured height (cm). The adjusted height is read from the chart in Figure 3–1 (boys) or Figure 3–2 (girls) to determine in what percentile the adjusted height falls. If the child is short but the height percentile adjusted for mid parental height is closer to the 50th percentile, the child probably has inherited a familial tendency toward short stature. If the adjusted height percentile remains low, the child's height is probably inappropriate for the genetic potential of the family, and diagnostic studies may be indicated for an organic cause of short stature. (Reprinted with permission of Ross Laboratories, Columbus, OH 43216 © 1983 Ross Laboratories. Source of data: Himes JH, Roche AF, Thissen D: *Parent-Specific Adjustments for Assessment of Recumbent Length and Stature.* Vol 13 of: *Monographs in Paediatrics.* Karger, 1981.)

trition accounts for much of the socioeconomic discrepancy in height noted above, but malnutrition may occur in the midst of plenty and must always be suspected in disorders of growth. Other factors may be blamed for poor growth when nutritional deficiencies are actually responsible. For example, Sherpas were thought to have short stature because of genetic factors or altitude, since they live on the slopes of Mount Everest. Nutritional supplementation increased stature in this group. The developed world places a premium on appearance, so significant numbers of children, chiefly teenagers, voluntarily decrease their caloric intake even if they are not obese; this factor may account for cases of poor growth. Chronic disease, which hampers adequate nutrition, often leads to short stature. For example, bronchopulmonary dysplasia decreases growth to some degree because it increases metabolic demands, shifting nutrient usage from growth; improved nutrition will increase growth in these patients. Feeding problems in infants, resulting from inexperience of parents or poor child-parent interactions (maternal deprivation), may account for poor growth. Deliberate starvation of children by parents is an extreme form of child abuse that may be first discovered because of poor growth.

D. Psychologic Factors: Aberrant intrafamilial dynamics, psychologic stress, or psychiatric disease can inhibit growth either by altering endocrine function or by secondary effects on nutrition (psychosocial dwarfism or maternal deprivation). It is essential to differentiate these situations from bona fide physiologic disease.

E. Chronic Disease: Even aside from the effects of poor nutrition, many chronic systemic diseases interfere with growth. For example, congestive heart failure and asthma, if uncontrolled, are associated with decreased stature; in some cases, final height is in the normal range because growth continues over a longer period of time.

Catch-Up Growth

Correction of growth-retarding disorders may be temporarily followed by an abnormally high growth rate as the child approaches normal height for age. This catch-up growth will occur after initiation of therapy for hypothyroidism and GH deficiency, after correction of glucocorticoid excess, and after appropriate treatment of many chronic diseases. Catch-up growth is usually short-lived and is followed by a more average growth rate.

MEASUREMENT OF GROWTH

Accurate measurement of height is an extremely important aspect of the physical examination of children and adolescents. The onset of a chronic disease may often be determined by an inflection point in the growth chart. In other cases, a detailed growth chart will indicate a normal constant growth rate in a child observed to be short for age. If careful growth records are kept, a diagnosis of constitutional delay in growth and adolescence may be made in such a patient; without previous measurements, the child might be subjected to unnecessary diagnostic testing or months of delay may occur as the child's growth is finally carefully monitored.

Height

The growth charts in most common use indicate the fifth and 95th percentiles as the outer limits of normal. This still leaves ten out of 100 healthy children outside of these boundaries with five out of 100 below the more worrisome "lower limits of normal," and it is both unnecessary and impractical to evaluate 5% of the population. Instead, the examining physician should accurately determine which short children warrant further evaluation and which ones (and their parents) require only reassurance that the child is healthy. When parents see that their child is below the fifth percentile and in a section of the chart colored differently from the "normal area," they assume that there is a serious problem when in most cases the chart simply happens to arbitrarily change color at the fifth percentile rather than the third percentile or lower. Thus, the format of the chart can dictate parental reaction to height, since all parents want their children to be in the "normal range." Figures 3–1 and 3–2 furnish data necessary to evaluate the height of children at various ages using the standard deviation method (SD). Standard deviation determination is more useful in extremely short children below the second or first percentile.

Pathologic short stature is usually more than 2.5 SD below the mean, but a diagnosis of pathologic short stature should not usually be based on a single measurement. Serial measurements are required, because they allow determination of **growth velocity,** which is a more sensitive index of the growth process than a single determination. A very tall child who develops a postnatal growth problem will not fall 2.5 SD below the mean in height for some time but will fall below the mean in growth velocity soon after the onset of the disorder. As Figures 3–3 and 3–4 demonstrate, growth velocity varies at different ages, but as a rough guide, a growth rate of less than 4.5 cm per year between age 4 years and the onset of puberty is abnormal. In children under 4 years of age, normal growth velocity changes more strikingly with age. Healthy term newborns tend to be clustered in length measurements around 21 inches (mostly owing to difficulties in obtaining accurate measurements). In the ensuing months and years, the child's height will enter the channel on the growth chart in which it will continue throughout childhood. Thus, a child with constitutional delay in growth or genetic short stature whose height is at the mean at birth and falls to the tenth percentile at 1 year of age and to the fifth percentile by 2 years of age may in fact be healthy in spite of crossing standard deviation lines in the journey to a growth channel at the fifth percentile. Although the growth rate may decrease during these years, it should not be less than the third percentile for age. A steeper decrease in growth rate is likely be a sign of disease. When a question of abnormal growth arises, previous measurements are always helpful; every physician treating children should record supine length (under 2 years of age) or standing height (after 2 years of age) as well as weight at every office visit. Height and growth velocity should be determined in relation to the standards for the child's age on a graph chart with clear indication of the child's position at measurement (supine or standing).

Relation to Midparental Height

There is a positive correlation between midparental height (the average of the heights of both parents) and the stature of a child. This may be taken into account with charts (Tables 3–1 and 3–2), which indicate the number of centimeters to add or subtract from a child's height to adjust for familial tendencies

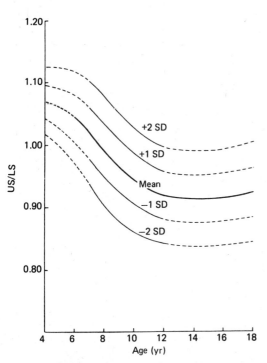

Figure 3–7. Normal upper to lower segment (US:LS) ratios, based on findings in 1015 white children. Values are slightly lower for black children. (Reproduced, with permission, from McKusick V: *Hereditable Disorders of Connective Tissue,* 4th ed. Mosby, 1972.)

when interpreting the child's height for age on a standard growth chart such as Figures 3–1 and 3–2. An abnormal height may be defined as more than 2 SD below the mean for chronologic age when corrected for midparental height by this chart. Figures 3–5 and 3–6 demonstrate adjustment for midparental height.

Technique of Measurement

Length and height must be measured accurately. Hasty measurements derived from marks made at an infant's foot and head while the infant is squirming on the paper on the examining table are useless. Infants must be measured on a firm horizontal surface with a permanently attached rule, a stationary plate perpendicular to the rule for the head, and a movable perpendicular plate for the feet. One person should hold the head stable while another makes sure the knees are straight and the feet are firm against the movable plate. Children over age 2 are measured standing up but cannot be accurately measured on the measuring rod that projects above the common weight scale; the rod is too flexible, and the scale footplate will in fact drop lower when the patient stands on it. Instead, height should be measured with the child standing back to the wall with heels at the wall, ankles together, and knees and spine straight against a vertical metal rule permanently attached to an upright board or wall. Height is measured at the top of the head by a sliding perpendicular plate (or square wooden block). A Harpenden stadiometer is a mechanical measuring device capable of such accurate measurement. Standing height is on the average 1.25 cm less than supine length, and it is essential to record the position of measurement each time; shifting from supine height at 2 years to standing height at 2 1/2 years can falsely suggest an inadequate growth rate over that 6-month period. It is preferable to measure in the metric system, since the smaller gradations make measurements more accurate by eliminating the tendency to round off numbers.

In addition to height or length, other significant measurements include (1) the frontal occipital head circumference; (2) horizontal arm span (between the outspread middle fingertips with the patient standing against a flat backboard); and (3) the upper segment (US) to lower segment (LS) ratio. For the latter, the LS is measured from the top of the symphysis pubis vertically to the floor with the patient standing straight, and the US is determined by subtracting the LS from the height measurement using the standing height measurement techniques noted above. (Normal standard US:LS ratios are shown in Figure 3–7.)

Height & Growth Rate Summary

In summary, we may consider three criteria for pathologically short stature: (1) height more than 2.5 SD below the mean for chronologic age; (2) growth rate below the fifth percentile for chronologic age; and (3) height more than 2 SD below the mean for chronologic age when corrected for midparental height.

Weight

The measured weight should be plotted for age on standard graphs developed by the National Center for Health Statistics (NCHS), which are available from various companies producing baby food or growth hormone. Variation in the weights of children in the USA due to differing diets or activity regimens makes it difficult to compare percentiles of height with percentiles of weight. Weight-for-height charts from the NCHS (often included on the charts that show height and weight) are a better way to determine whether the patient's weight is appropriate. Body mass index (BMI) charts are now available for children and indicate nutritional status.

SKELETAL (BONE) AGE

Skeletal development is a reflection of physiologic maturation. For example, menarche is better correlated with a skeletal age of 13 years than with a given chronologic age. Skeletal age also affords an indication of remaining growth available to a child and can be used to predict adult height. However, skeletal age is not a definitive diagnostic test in any disease; it can assist in diagnosis only when considered along with other factors.

Bone age is determined by comparing the appearance and stage of fusion of epiphyses or shapes of bones on the patient's radiograph with an atlas demonstrating normal skeletal maturation for various ages. The Greulich and Pyle atlas of radiographs of the left hand and wrist is most commonly used in the USA, but other methods of skeletal age determination such as Tanner and Whitehouse maturity scoring are also used. Any skeletal age more than 2 SD above or below the mean for chronologic age is out of the normal range. For newborn infants, knee and foot radiographs are compared with an appropriate skeletal age atlas; for late pubertal children, just before epiphysial fusion, the knee atlas will reveal whether any further growth can be expected or whether the epiphyses are fused.

Height may be predicted by determining skeletal age and height at the time the radiograph was taken and consulting the Bayley-Pinneau tables in the Greulich and Pyle skeletal atlas of the hand. The Roche, Wainer, and Thissen (RWT) method of height prediction uses patient weight and midparental height—in addition to the variables noted above—to calculate predicted height (Table 3–3). Height prediction by any method becomes more accurate as the child approaches the time of epiphysial fusion.

An easier but less precise method of predicting the expected heights of children within a given family is the calculation of target adult height range using parents' heights and correcting for the sex of the child.

For boys, add 5 inches to the mother's height, add the result to the father's height, and divide by 2: this is the target height, and it is expected that sons of these parents will reach a height within 2 SD of this target—or, for simplicity, within 2 inches above and 2 inches below it. For girls, subtract 5 inches from the father's height and add the result to the mother's height and divide by 2, leading to the target height. The range for girls will also be within 2 inches above and below this target.

DISORDERS OF GROWTH

SHORT STATURE DUE TO NONENDOCRINE CAUSES

There are many causes of poor childhood growth and short adult height (Table 3–4). The following discussion covers only the more common conditions, emphasizing those that might be included in an endocrinologic differential diagnosis.

1. CONSTITUTIONAL SHORT STATURE

Constitutional short stature is not a disease but rather a variation from normal for the population and is considered a disorder of the pace of development. There is usually a delay in pubertal development as well as growth (see Constitutional Delay in Adolescence). It is characterized by moderate short stature (usually not far below the fifth percentile), thin habitus, and retardation of skeletal age. The family history often includes similarly affected members (eg, mother with delayed menarche or father who shaved late and grew past his teenage years). The pubertal aspects of this condition are discussed in Chapter 12.

All other causes of decreased growth must be considered and ruled out before the diagnosis can be made with confidence. The patient may be considered physiologically (but not mentally) delayed in development. Characteristic growth patterns include normal birth length and height, with a gradual decrease in percentiles of height for age by 2 years. Onset of puberty is usually delayed for chronologic age but normal for skeletal age. Adult height is in the normal or low normal range. The final height is often less than the predicted height, because growth is less than expected during puberty (see Figure 3–8).

2. GENETIC SHORT STATURE

Short stature may also occur in a familial pattern without retarded bone age or delay in puberty; this is considered "genetic" short stature. Affected children are closer to the mean on the normal population growth charts after correction for midparental height

(Figures 3–5 and 3–6). Adult height depends on the mother's and father's heights. Patients with the combination of constitutional short stature and genetic short stature are quite noticeably short due to both factors and are the patients most likely to seek evaluation.

3. INTRAUTERINE GROWTH RETARDATION

The proportionate IUGR infant will often follow a lifelong pattern of short stature; in comparison, appropriate-for-gestational-age premature infants will usually catch up to the normal range of height and weight by 1–2 years of age. Bone age, age at onset of puberty, and yearly growth rate are normal, and the patients are characteristically thin. Within this grouping are many distinctive genetic or sporadically occurring syndromes. The most common example is Russell-Silver dwarfism, characterized by small size at birth, triangular facies, a variable degree of asymmetry of extremities, and clinodactyly of the fifth finger. Intrauterine infections with cytomegalovirus, rubella virus, *Toxoplasma gondii,* and human immunodeficiency virus are noted to cause IUGR. Furthermore, maternal drug usage, either illicit (eg, cocaine) or legally prescribed (eg, phenytoin) may cause IUGR. Reports of other syndromes in small-for-gestational-age infants can be found in sources listed in the bibliography (Smith and Sakati, Nyhan).

4. SYNDROMES OF SHORT STATURE

Many syndromes have short stature as one of their characteristic features. Some include intrauterine growth retardation and some do not. Common ones are described briefly below. Laurence-Moon (Biedl-Bardet) syndrome, Prader-Willi syndrome, hypothyroidism, glucocorticoid excess, pseudohypoparathyroidism, and GH deficiency combine obesity with short stature. Moderately obese but otherwise normal children without these conditions tend to have slightly advanced bone age and physiologic maturation with increased stature during childhood and early onset of puberty. Thus, short stature in a chubby child must be considered to have an organic cause until proved otherwise.

Turner's Syndrome & Its Variants

While classic Turner's syndrome of 45,XO gonadal dysgenesis (see Chapter 11) is often correctly diagnosed, it is not always appreciated that any phenotypic female with short stature may have a variant of Turner's syndrome. Thus, a karyotype determination should be done for every short girl if no other cause for short stature is found (see Chapters 10, 11, and 12).

Noonan's Syndrome (Pseudo-Turner's Syndrome)

This syndrome shares several phenotypic characteristics of Turner's syndrome, but the karyotype is 46,XX in the female or 46,XY in the male with Noonan's syndrome, and other features clearly differentiate it from Turner's syndrome; pseudo-Turner's syndrome is an autosomal dominant disorder (see Chapters 9 and 12).

Prader-Willi Syndrome

This condition is characterized by infantile hypotonia, acromicria (small hands and feet), mental retardation, almond-shaped eyes, and extreme obesity. Glucose intolerance and delayed puberty are characteristic. This syndrome is associated with abnormalities of chromosome 15 in approximately 50% of affected cases (see Chapter 12).

Laurence-Moon (Biedl-Bardet) Syndrome

This syndrome of retinitis pigmentosa, polydactyly, and obesity is also associated with poor growth and delayed puberty; splitting these patients into the two eponymous syndromes is now recommended depending upon the clinical findings (see Chapter 12). It is inherited as an autosomal recessive disorder.

Autosomal Karyotypic Disorders & Syndromes

Numerous autosomal karyotypic disorders and syndromes of dysmorphic children with or without mental retardation are characterized by short stature. Often the key to diagnosis is the presence of several major or minor physical abnormalities that indicate the need for karyotype determination. Other abnormalities may include unusual body proportions, such as short extremities, leading to aberrant US:LS ratios, and arm spans quite discrepant from stature. Some conditions, such as trisomy 21 (Down's syndrome), are quite common, while others are rare. Details of these syndromes can be found in the references listed at the end of the chapter.

Skeletal Dysplasias

There are more than 100 known types of genetic skeletal dysplasias (osteochondrodysplasias). Often they are noted at birth because of short limbs or trunk, but some are only diagnosed after a period of growth. The most common condition is autosomal dominant achondroplasia. This condition is characterized by short extremities, a relatively large head with a prominent forehead and a depressed nasal bridge, and lumbar lordosis in later life. Adult height is quite short, with a mean of 132 cm for males and 123 cm for females. Limb lengthening operations have been used to improve stature in a few centers. Children with achondroplasia received GH and

Table 3–3. The RWT method for predicting adult stature.[1]

Tables of Multipliers for Boys

Age Yrs	Mos	Recumbent length	Weight	Midparental stature	Skeletal age	Adjustment factor
1	0	0.966	0.199	0.606	-0.673	1.632
1	3	1.032	0.086	0.580	-0.417	-1.841
1	6	1.086	-0.016	0.559	-0.205	-4.892
1	9	1.130	-0.106	0.540	-0.033	-7.528
2	0	1.163	-0.186	0.523	0.104	-9.764
2	3	1.189	-0.256	0.509	0.211	-11.618
2	6	1.207	-0.316	0.496	0.291	-13.114
2	9	1.219	-0.369	0.485	0.349	-14.278
3	0	1.227	-0.413	0.475	0.388	-15.139
3	3	1.230	-0.450	0.466	0.410	-15.729
3	6	1.229	-0.481	0.458	0.419	-16.081
3	9	1.226	-0.505	0.451	0.417	-16.228
4	0	1.221	-0.523	0.444	0.405	-16.201
4	3	1.214	-0.537	0.437	0.387	-16.034
4	6	1.206	-0.546	0.431	0.363	-15.758
4	9	1.197	-0.550	0.424	0.335	-15.400
5	0	1.188	-0.551	0.418	0.303	-14.990
5	3	1.179	-0.548	0.412	0.269	-14.551
5	6	1.169	-0.543	0.406	0.234	-14.106
5	9	1.160	-0.535	0.400	0.198	-13.672
6	0	1.152	-0.524	0.394	0.161	-13.267
6	3	1.143	-0.512	0.389	0.123	-12.901
6	6	1.135	-0.499	0.383	0.085	-12.583
6	9	1.127	-0.484	0.378	0.046	-12.318
7	0	1.120	-0.468	0.373	0.006	-12.107
7	3	1.113	-0.451	0.369	-0.034	-11.948
7	6	1.106	-0.434	0.365	-0.077	-11.834
7	9	1.100	-0.417	0.361	-0.121	-11.756
8	0	1.093	-0.400	0.358	-0.167	-11.701
8	3	1.086	-0.382	0.356	-0.217	-11.652
8	6	1.079	-0.365	0.354	-0.270	-11.592
8	9	1.071	-0.349	0.353	-0.327	-11.498
9	0	1.063	-0.333	0.353	-0.389	-11.349
9	3	1.054	-0.317	0.353	-0.455	-11.118
9	6	1.044	-0.303	0.355	-0.527	-10.779
9	9	1.033	-0.289	0.357	-0.605	-10.306
10	0	1.021	-0.276	0.360	-0.690	-9.671
10	3	1.008	-0.263	0.363	-0.781	-8.848
10	6	0.993	-0.252	0.368	-0.878	-7.812
10	9	0.977	-0.241	0.373	-0.983	-6.540

Tables of Multipliers for Girls

Age Yrs	Mos	Recumbent length	Weight	Midparental stature	Skeletal age	Adjustment factor
1	0	1.087	-0.271	0.386	0.434	21.729
1	3	1.112	-0.369	0.367	0.094	20.684
1	6	1.134	-0.455	0.349	-0.172	19.957
1	9	1.153	-0.530	0.332	-0.374	19.463
2	0	1.170	-0.594	0.316	-0.523	19.131
2	3	1.183	-0.648	0.301	-0.625	18.905
2	6	1.195	-0.693	0.287	-0.690	18.740
2	9	1.204	-0.729	0.274	-0.725	18.604
3	0	1.210	-0.757	0.262	-0.736	18.474
3	3	1.215	-0.777	0.251	-0.729	18.337
3	6	1.217	-0.791	0.241	-0.711	18.187
3	9	1.217	-0.798	0.232	-0.684	18.024
4	0	1.215	-0.800	0.224	-0.655	17.855
4	3	1.212	-0.797	0.217	-0.626	17.691
4	6	1.206	-0.789	0.210	-0.600	17.548
4	9	1.199	-0.777	0.205	-0.582	17.444
5	0	1.190	-0.761	0.200	-0.571	17.398
5	3	1.180	-0.742	0.197	-0.572	17.431
5	6	1.168	-0.721	0.193	-0.584	17.567
5	9	1.155	-0.697	0.191	-0.609	17.826
6	0	1.140	-0.671	0.190	-0.647	18.229
6	3	1.124	-0.644	0.189	-0.700	18.796
6	6	1.107	-0.616	0.188	-0.766	19.544
6	9	1.089	-0.587	0.189	-0.845	20.489
7	0	1.069	-0.557	0.189	-0.938	21.642
7	3	1.049	-0.527	0.191	-1.043	23.011
7	6	1.028	-0.498	0.192	-1.158	24.602
7	9	1.006	-0.468	0.194	-1.284	26.416
8	0	0.938	-0.439	0.196	-1.418	28.448
8	3	0.960	-0.411	0.199	-1.558	30.690
8	6	0.937	-0.384	0.202	-1.704	33.129
8	9	0.914	-0.359	0.204	-1.853	35.747
9	0	0.891	-0.334	0.207	-2.003	38.520
9	3	0.868	-0.311	0.210	-2.154	41.421
9	6	0.845	-0.289	0.212	-2.301	44.415
9	9	0.824	-0.269	0.214	-2.444	47.464
10	0	0.803	-0.250	0.216	-2.581	50.525
10	3	0.783	-0.233	0.217	-2.710	53.548
10	6	0.766	-0.217	0.217	-2.829	56.481
10	9	0.749	-0.203	0.217	-2.936	59.267

Table 3-3 (cont'd).

Age	Months	Recumbent length	Weight	Midparental stature	Skeletal age	Adjustment factor
11	0	0.960	-0.231	0.378	-1.094	-5.010
11	3	0.942	-0.222	0.384	-1.211	-3.206
11	6	0.923	-0.213	0.390	-1.335	-1.113
11	9	0.902	-0.206	0.397	-1.464	1.273
12	0	0.881	-0.198	0.403	-1.597	3.958
12	3	0.859	-0.191	0.409	-1.735	6.931
12	6	0.837	-0.184	0.414	-1.875	10.181
12	9	0.815	-0.177	0.418	-2.015	13.684
13	0	0.794	-0.170	0.421	-2.156	17.405
13	3	0.773	-0.163	0.422	-2.294	21.297
13	6	0.755	-0.155	0.422	-2.427	25.304
13	9	0.738	-0.146	0.418	-2.553	29.349
14	0	0.724	-0.136	0.412	-2.668	33.345
14	3	0.714	-0.125	0.401	-2.771	37.183
14	6	0.709	-0.112	0.387	-2.856	40.738
14	9	0.709	-0.098	0.367	-2.922	43.869
15	0	0.717	-0.081	0.342	-2.962	46.403
15	3	0.732	-0.062	0.310	-2.973	48.154
15	6	0.756	-0.040	0.271	-2.949	48.898
15	9	0.792	-0.015	0.223	-2.885	48.402
16	0	0.839	-0.014	0.167	-2.776	46.391

The RWT method predicts the height of an individual at 18 years of age; after this age the average total increase in stature is 0.6 cm for girls and 0.8 cm for boys.

Age	Months	Recumbent length	Weight	Midparental stature	Skeletal age	Adjustment factor
11	0	0.736	-0.190	0.216	-3.029	61.841
11	3	0.724	-0.179	0.214	-3.108	64.123
11	6	0.716	-0.169	0.211	-3.171	66.093
11	9	0.711	-0.159	0.206	-3.217	67.627
12	0	0.710	-0.151	0.201	-3.245	68.670
12	3	0.713	-0.143	0.193	-3.254	69.140
12	6	0.720	-0.136	0.184	-3.244	68.966
12	9	0.733	-0.129	0.173	-3.214	68.061
13	0	0.752	-0.121	0.160	-3.166	66.339
13	3	0.777	-0.113	0.144	-3.100	63.728
13	6	0.810	-0.105	0.127	-3.015	60.150
13	9	0.850	-0.085	0.106	-2.915	55.522
14	0	0.898	-0.083	0.083	-2.800	49.781

The RWT method predicts the height of an individual at 18 years of age; after this age the average total increase in stature is 0.6 cm for girls and 0.8 cm for boys.

Recumbent length is measured in cm (add 1.25 cm to the standing height, without shoes, if that is available). Weight is measured in kg. The midparental height is calculated by adding the standing height of each parent in cm (without shoes) and dividing by two; if the parents' heights are unknown, in the USA a height of 174.5 cm can be substituted for the father's height or 162 cm for the mother's height. The skeletal age is determined from an x-ray of the left wrist and hand comparing it to the Greulich and Pyle atlas.

A prediction is made by:

1. Recording the child's data as noted below.
2. Finding the multipliers from the charts on these pages, making sure the positive and negative signs are retained for the calculations.
3. Multiplying the data by the multipliers, taking note of the positive or negative sign.
4. Adding the products to the adjustment factor, taking note of the sign of the factor: the result is a prediction of the height at 18 years of age.

DATA	MULTIPLIERS	PRODUCTS
Recumbent length (cm)	× _____	= _____
Weight (kg)	× _____	= _____
Midparental stature (cm)	× _____	= _____
Skeletal age (years)	× _____	= _____
Adjustment factor for age		= +/– _____
Predicted height at age 18 years (cm)		= _____

1Modified and reproduced, with permission, from Roche AF, Wainer H, Thissen D: The RWT method for the prediction of adult stature. *Pediatrics* 1975;**56**:1026, as modified in Styne DM: Growth Disorders. Page 99 in: *Handbook of Clinical Endocrinology.* Fitzgerald PA (editor). Jones Medical Publications, 1986.

Table 3–4. Causes of abnormalities of growth.

I. CAUSES OF SHORT STATURE

Nonendocrine causes
- Constitutional short stature
- Genetic short stature
- Intrauterine growth retardation
- Syndromes of short stature
  - Turner's syndrome and its variants
  - Noonan's syndrome (pseudo-Turner's syndrome)
  - Prader-Willi syndrome
  - Laurence-Moon and Bardet-Biedl syndrome
  - Other autosomal abnormalities and dysmorphic syndromes
- Chronic disease
  - Cardiac disorders
    - Left-to-right shunt
    - Congestive heart failure
  - Pulmonary disorders
    - Cystic fibrosis
    - Asthma
  - Gastrointestinal disorders
    - Malabsorption (eg, celiac disease)
    - Disorders of swallowing
  - Hepatic disorders
  - Hematologic disorders
    - Sickle cell anemia
    - Thalassemia
  - Renal disorders
    - Renal tubular acidosis
    - Chronic uremia
  - Immunologic disorders
    - Connective tissue disease
    - Juvenile rheumatoid arthritis
    - Chronic infection
  - Central nervous system disorders
  - Malnutrition
    - Decreased availability of nutriments
    - Fad diets
    - Voluntary dieting during puberty
    - Anorexia nervosa
    - Anorexia of cancer chemotherapy

Endocrine disorders
- GH deficiency and variants
  - Congenital GH deficiency
    - With midline defects
    - With other pituitary hormone deficiencies
    - Isolated GH deficiency
    - Pituitary agenesis
  - Acquired GH deficiency
    - Hypothalamic-pituitary tumors
    - Histiocytosis X
    - Central nervous system infections
    - Head injuries
    - GH deficiency following cranial irradiation
    - Central nervous system vascular accidents
    - Hydrocephalus
    - Empty sella syndrome
  - Abnormalities of GH action
    - Laron's dwarfism
    - Pygmies
- Psychosocial dwarfism
- Hypothyroidism
- Glucocorticoid excess (Cushing's syndrome)
  - Endogenous
  - Exogenous
- Pseudohypoparathyroidism
- Disorders of vitamin D metabolism
- Diabetes mellitus
- Diabetes insipidus, untreated

II. CAUSES OF TALL STATURE

Nonendocrine causes
- Constitutional tall stature
- Genetic tall stature
- Syndromes of tall stature
  - Cerebral gigantism
  - Marfan's syndrome
  - Homocystinuria
  - Beckwith-Wiedemann syndrome
  - XYY syndrome
  - Klinefelter's syndrome

Endocrine disorders
- Pituitary gigantism
- Sexual precocity
- Thyrotoxicosis
- Infants of diabetic mothers

demonstrated improved growth, but one experienced problems with atlanto-occipital dislocation; GH is not an established therapy for this condition and may have severe side effects.

5. CHRONIC DISEASE

Severe chronic disease involving any organ system can cause poor growth in childhood and adolescence. In many cases, there will be adequate physical findings by the time of consultation to permit diagnosis; in some cases, however—most notably celiac disease and regional enteritis—short stature and decreased growth may precede obvious signs of malnutrition or gastrointestinal disease. In some cases, growth is only delayed. In others, growth can be increased by improved nutrition; patients with gastrointestinal disease, kidney disease, or cancer may benefit from nocturnal parenteral nutritional infusions. Cystic fibrosis combines several causes of growth failure: lung disease impairs oxygenation and predisposes to chronic

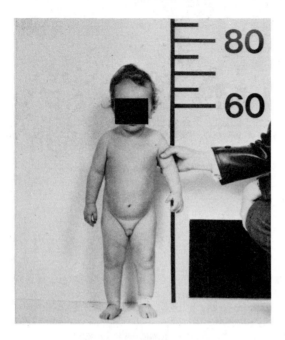

Figure 3–8. A 12-month-old boy with congenital hypopituitarism. He had hypoglycemic seizures at 12 hours of age. At 1 year, he had another hypoglycemic seizure (plasma glucose, 25 mg/dL) associated with an episode of otitis media, and it was noted that his penis was quite small. He was referred for evaluation because of these findings. At 12 months, length was 66.5 cm (–2 SD) and weight was 8.5 kg (–3 SD). The penis was less than 1.5 cm long, and both testes were descended (each 1 cm in diameter). Plasma GH did not rise above 1 ng/mL after arginine and levodopa testing. (No insulin was given because of the history of hypoglycemia.) LH rose only from 8.6 to 11.7 mIU/mL (1 ng of LH [preparation LER 960] = 7.8 mIU) after administration of GnRH (gonadorelin), 100 µg. Serum thyroxine was low (T_4, 6.6 µg/dL; T_4 index, 1.5), and after administration of 200 µg of protirelin (TRH), serum TSH rose with a delayed peak characteristic of tertiary hypothyroidism. Plasma ACTH rose only to 53 pg/mL after metyrapone. Thus, he had GH, ACTH, GnRH, and TRH deficiency. He was given six doses of 2000 units each of chorionic gonadotropin (hCG) intramuscularly over 2 weeks, and plasma testosterone rose to 62 ng/dL. He was then treated with 25 mg of testosterone enanthate every month for 3 months, and his phallus enlarged to 3.5 × 1.2 cm without significant advancement of bone age. With hGH therapy (0.1 unit/kg intramuscularly every other day), he grew at a greater than normal rate for 12 months (catch-up growth), and growth then continued at a normal rate.

infections, gastrointestinal disease decreases nutrient availability, and late-developing abnormalities of the endocrine pancreas cause symptoms of diabetes mellitus. Children with cystic fibrosis experience decreased growth rates after a normal birth size. Children with congestive heart failure due to a variety of congenital heart diseases or acquired myocarditis

grow poorly unless successfully treated with medications or surgery; patients with cyanotic heart disease experience less deficit in growth.

Celiac disease may present initially with growth failure. Early diagnosis can be made by determination of antigliadin antibodies. On a gluten-free diet, patients experience catch-up growth which is strongest in the first year of therapy but continues for several more. Adult height may still be impaired, depending upon the period without treatment.

Patients with chronic hematologic diseases, such as sickle cell anemia or thalassemia, often have poor growth, delayed puberty, and short adult stature. Juvenile rheumatoid arthritis may compromise growth before or after therapy with glucocorticoids.

Chronic renal disease is known to interfere with growth. Hypophosphatemic vitamin D-resistant rickets will usually lead to short adult stature, but treatment with 1α-hydroxyvitamin D_3 (cholecalciferol) and oral phosphate in most cases will lead to normal adult stature. Children with chronic renal failure are reported to have increased growth rate with GH therapy and improved nutrition.

The two forms of renal tubular acidosis, proximal and distal, may both cause short stature. Proximal renal tubular acidosis causes bicarbonate wasting at normal or low plasma bicarbonate concentrations; patients have hypokalemia, alkaline urine pH, severe bicarbonaturia, and, later, acidemia. The condition may be inherited, sporadic, or secondary to many metabolic or medication-induced disorders. Distal renal tubular acidosis is caused by inability to acidify the urine; it may occur in sporadic or familial patterns or be acquired as a result of metabolic disorders or medication therapy. Distal renal tubular acidosis is characterized by hypokalemia, hypercalciuria, and occasional hypocalcemia. The administration of bicarbonate is the primary therapy for either type of renal tubular acidosis, and proper treatment can substantially improve growth rate.

Hypochondroplasia is manifested on a continuum from severe short limb dwarfism to apparent normal development until puberty, when there is an attenuated or absent pubertal growth spurt, leading to short adult stature. Growth hormone is reported to increase growth rate in short-term studies of this condition.

Hemoglobin, white blood cell count, erythrocyte sedimentation rate, serum carotene and folate levels, antigliadin antibodies, plasma bicarbonate levels, and liver and kidney function should be assessed in short but otherwise apparently healthy children before endocrine screening tests are done. Urinalysis should be performed, with attention to specific gravity (to rule out diabetes insipidus) and ability to acidify urine (to evaluate possible renal tubular acidosis). All short girls without a diagnosis should undergo karyotype testing to rule out Turner's syndrome. A list of chronic diseases causing short stature is presented in Table 3–4.

6. MALNUTRITION
(Other Than That Associated With Chronic Disease)

Malnutrition is the most common cause of short stature worldwide. Diagnosis in the developed world is based on historical and physical findings, particularly the dietary history. Food faddism and anorexia nervosa—as well as voluntary dieting due to "fear of obesity"—can cause poor growth. Infection with parasites such as *Ascaris lumbricoides* or *Giardia* can decrease growth. Specific nutritional deficiencies can have particular effects upon growth. For example, severe iron deficiency can cause a thin habitus as well as growth retardation. Zinc deficiency (though probably invoked too often as a cause of growth retardation) can cause anorexia, decreased growth, and delayed puberty, usually in the presence of chronic systemic disease or infection. There are no simple laboratory tests for diagnosis of malnutrition, though IGF-1 concentrations are low in malnutrition, as in GH deficiency.

7. DRUGS

Children with hyperactivity disorders (or those incorrectly diagnosed as such) are frequently managed with chronic dextroamphetamine or methylphenidate administration. In larger doses, these agents can decrease weight gain—possibly because of their effects on appetite—and growth rate. Discontinuing therapy temporarily, usually during vacations from school, allows some catch-up growth in weight and height, but it is controversial whether the height deficit is completely repaired. These drugs must be used in moderation and only in children who definitely need them.

Exogenous glucocorticoids are a potent cause of poor growth (see below).

SHORT STATURE DUE TO ENDOCRINE DISORDERS

1. GROWTH HORMONE DEFICIENCY & ITS VARIANTS
(Table 3–5)

Current concepts of endocrine regulation of growth propose that GH stimulates growth through intermediary substances, the **insulin-like growth factors** (see above).

The incidence of GH deficiency is estimated to approach 1:4000 in the Scottish population and possibly 1:10,000 worldwide, so the disorder should not be considered rare. Most patients with idiopathic GH deficiency apparently lack GRH. Some who have come to autopsy had adequate numbers of pituitary

Table 3–5. Postulated disorders of hGH release and action.

Site of Defect	Clinical Condition
Hypothalamus	Idiopathic GH deficiency due to decreased GRH secretion; hypothalamic tumors.
Pituitary gland	Dysplasia, trauma, surgery, or tumor of the pituitary gland.
Sites of IGF production	Laron's dwarfism with high GH and low IGF concentrations (GH receptor defect). Pygmies with normal GH, low IGF-1, and normal IGF-2 concentrations.
Cartilage	Glucocorticoid-induced growth failure. Resistance to IGF-1.

somatotropes that had considerable GH stores; long-term treatment of these patients with GRH can cause GH release and improve growth. Patients with pituitary tumors or those rare patients with congenital absence of the pituitary gland lack somatotrophs. Several kindreds have been described that lack various regions of the GH gene responsible for producing GH.

Before 1986, the only clinical method of treatment for GH deficiency was replacement therapy with human GH (hGH) from cadaver donors. In 1985 and thereafter, Creutzfeldt-Jakob disease, a degenerative neurologic disease rare in patients so young, was diagnosed in patients who had received natural hGH 10–15 years before. Because of the possibility that prions contaminating donor pituitary glands were transmitted to the GH-deficient patients and caused their death, natural growth hormone from all sources was removed from distribution. Recombinant DNA technology now accounts for the world's current supply of growth hormone.

Commercial growth hormone is currently available in the 191-amino-acid natural-sequence form (somatropin) and the 192-amino-acid methionyl form (somatrem). There is no convincing evidence that either form is clinically superior to the other. GH is now available in virtually unlimited amounts, allowing innovative treatment regimens not previously possible owing to scarce supplies; however, the potential for abuse of GH in athletes or in children of normal size whose parents wish them to be taller than average must now be addressed.

GRH was first isolated from pancreatic GH-releasing tumor, sequenced, and synthesized, but hypothalamic GRH has the same structure as GRH from the pancreatic tumors. GRH has potential in the diagnosis and treatment of GH deficiency; GH-deficient patients have demonstrated lower or absent GH secretion after administration of GRH. Furthermore, episodic doses of GRH have restored GH secretion, insulin-like growth hormone production, and growth in children with idiopathic GH deficiency. The ability of GRH administration to cause pituitary GH secretion further supports the concept that idiopathic GH deficiency is primarily a disease of the hypothalamus, not of the pituitary gland.

IGF-1 (previously called somatomedin C) is now produced by recombinant DNA technology. Although no long-term human treatment program has yet been reported. Initial studies suggest that IGF-1 may be a useful treatment for short stature, particularly in Laron dwarfism (and perhaps African pygmies) where no other treatment is possible. Growth disturbances due to disorders of GH release or action are shown in Table 3–5. Earlier theories suggested the liver as the major source of plasma IGF-1 that affects cartilage, but it is clear that many organs produce IGF-1. In fact, somatomedin is an autocrine or paracrine factor that influences its own cell of origin or neighboring cells rather than solely an endocrine agent that acts at a distance via blood-borne transport. Recombinant DNA technology has increased the supply of IGF-1, and it is used to determine the direct effects of the insulin-like growth factors.

Congenital Growth Hormone Deficiency

Congenital GH deficiency presents with normal birth length but decreased growth rate soon after birth. The disorder is identified by careful measurement in the first year and becomes more obvious by 1–2 years of age. Patients with classic GH deficiency have short stature, obesity with immature facial appearance, immature high-pitched voice, and some delay in skeletal maturation. Less severe forms of partial GH deficiency are described. Males with GH deficiency may have microphallus, especially if the condition is accompanied by gonadotropin-releasing hormone (GnRH) deficiency (Figure 3–8). GH deficiency in the neonate or child can also lead to symptomatic hypoglycemia and seizures; if ACTH deficiency is also present, hypoglycemia is usually more severe. The differential diagnosis of neonatal hypoglycemia in a full-term infant who has not sustained birth trauma must include neonatal hypopituitarism. If microphallus (in a male subject), optic hypoplasia, or some other midline facial or central nervous system defect is noted, the diagnosis of congenital GH deficiency is likely. Congenital GH deficiency is also statistically correlated with breech delivery. Intelligence is normal in GH deficiency unless repeated or severe hypoglycemia has compromised brain development. When thyrotropin-releasing hormone (TRH) deficiency is also present, there may be additional signs of hypothyroidism. Secondary or tertiary hypothyroidism is not generally associated with mental retardation, but a few cases of isolated TRH deficiency and severe mental retardation have been reported.

Congenital GH deficiency may present with midline anatomic defects. Optic hypoplasia with visual defects ranging from nystagmus to blindness is found with variable hypothalamic deficiency, including diabetes insipidus; about half of patients have absence of the septum pellucidum on CT scan or MRI, leading to the diagnosis of septo-optic dysplasia. Cleft palate or other forms of oral dysraphism are associated with GH deficiency in about 7% of cases; thus, such children may need more than nutritional support to improve their growth. Children with a single maxillary incisor and GH deficiency are described.

Congenital absence of the pituitary, which has been found in an autosomal recessive pattern, leads to severe hypopituitarism, including hypoglycemia and hypopituitarism; affected patients have shallow development or absence of the sella turcica. This defect is quite rare.

Hereditary GH deficiency is described in several kindreds. Recent biochemical techniques have defined various genetic defects in affected families. Patients with absent or abnormal *GH* genes do initially respond to exogenous hGH administration, but some soon develop high antibody titers that terminate the effect of therapy; however, one reported kindred continued to grow and did not develop blocking antibodies. Type IA GH deficiency is inherited in an autosomal recessive pattern, and patients have defects in the GH genome; unlike those with classic sporadic GH deficiency, some of these children have been described with short birth lengths. Type IB patients have autosomal recessive GH deficiency but no such gene depletion; type II patients have autosomal dominant GH deficiency; and type III patients have X-linked GH deficiency.

Acquired Growth Hormone Deficiency

Onset of GH deficiency in late childhood or adolescence, particularly if accompanied by other pituitary hormone deficiencies, is ominous and may be due to a hypothalamic-pituitary tumor. The development of posterior pituitary deficiency in addition to anterior pituitary deficiency makes a tumor even more likely. Conditions that cause acquired GH deficiency—craniopharyngiomas, germinomas, gliomas, etc—are described in Chapters 2 and 12. Histiocytosis X was previously considered a common cause of GH deficiency, but recent evidence suggests that this is a rare cause.

The empty sella syndrome is more frequently associated with hypothalamic-pituitary abnormalities in childhood than in adulthood; thus, GH deficiency may be found in affected patients. Some patients—chiefly boys—with constitutional delay in growth and adolescence may have transient GH deficiency by testing before the actual onset of puberty; when testosterone concentrations begin to increase in these patients, GH secretion and growth rate also increase.

Cranial irradiation of the hypothalamic-pituitary region to treat head tumors or acute lymphoblastic leukemia may result in GH deficiency 6–24 months later, owing to radiation-induced hypothalamic (or perhaps pituitary) damage. Such patients must be carefully observed for growth failure after irradiation. If these patients receive spinal irradiation, upper body growth may be impaired, causing a higher US:LS ratio. Abdominal irradiation for Wilms' tumor may lead to decreased growth with an estimated loss of height from megavoltage therapy of 10 cm for treatment at 1 year of age and 7 cm from treatment at 5 years of age. Others receiving gonadal irradiation (or chemotherapy) have impaired gonadal function and lack onset or progression of puberty and the pubertal growth spurt.

Other Types of Growth Hormone Dysfunction or Deficiency

Other disorders of GH production or action are not manifested in the classic manner of GH deficiency.

Laron's dwarfism is characterized by high plasma GH and low plasma IGF-1 concentrations. Growth rate does not increase and IGF-1 values do not rise when exogenous hGH is administered. However, IGF-1 administration raises growth rate and suppresses GH concentrations. The basic defect is an inability to produce IGF-1 in response to growth hormone because of impaired or absent GH receptors. GHBP is absent in the serum. It is inherited as an autosomal recessive disorder.

Very short, poorly growing children with delayed skeletal maturation, normal GH and IGF-1 values, and no signs of organic disease have responded to GH therapy with increased growth rates equal to those of patients with bona fide GH deficiency. These patients may have a variation of constitutional delay in growth or genetic short stature, but a subtle abnormality of GH secretion is possible.

In this era of plentiful GH supplies, there is increasing pressure to treat more children—usually boys—who are not severely short and are not growing extremely slowly and do not have greatly delayed bone ages. While some controlled studies of treatment of such children are under way, little more than anecdotal information and noncontrolled data are at present available about the final height that can be achieved with such treatment.

Pygmies have normal plasma GH, low IGF-1, and normal IGF-2 concentrations. They would not respond to exogenous GH with improved growth rate or a rise in IGF-1. They have a congenital inability to produce IGF-1, which is of greater importance in stimulating growth than is IGF-2. Pygmy children are reported to lack a pubertal growth spurt, suggesting that IGF-1 is essential to attain a normal peak growth velocity. Recent data suggest that Efe pygmies, the shortest of the pygmies, are significantly smaller at birth than neighboring Africans and that growth is slower throughout childhood, leading to statures of progressively more standard deviations

below the mean. Presumably, IGF-1 therapy would increase growth rates in this population during childhood and puberty, but such therapy has not yet been reported.

Diagnosis of Growth Hormone Deficiency

Because basal values of GH are low in normal children and GH-deficient patients alike, the diagnosis of GH deficiency rests upon demonstration of an inadequate rise of serum GH after provocative stimuli. This process is complicated because different radioimmunoassay systems vary widely in their measurements of GH in the same blood sample; a result may be above 10 ng/mL in one assay but only 6 ng/mL in another. The physician must be aware of the standards of the laboratory being used.

The very concept of growth hormone testing provides a further complication. While a patient who does not secrete GH in response to standard challenges is generally considered to be GH-deficient, a normal GH response to these tests may not rule out GH deficiency. Except for sleep studies, testing should occur after an overnight fast; carbohydrate ingestion will suppress GH response. Obesity suppresses GH secretion, and a chubby child may falsely appear to have GH deficiency. Because 10% or more of healthy children will not have an adequate rise in GH with one test of GH reserve, at least two methods of assessing GH reserve are necessary before the diagnosis of classic GH deficiency is assigned. Serum GH values should rise during stage III–IV sleep (usually 90 minutes after onset of sleep) or after 10 minutes of vigorous exercise. After an overnight fast, GH levels should also rise in response to arginine infusion (0.5 g/kg body weight [up to 20 g] over 30 minutes), oral levodopa (125 mg for up to 15 kg body weight, 250 mg for up to 35 kg, or 500 mg for over 35 kg), or clonidine (0.10–0.15 mg/m^2 orally). Side effects of levodopa include nausea; those of clonidine include some drop in blood pressure and drowsiness.

GH levels also rise after acute hypoglycemia due to insulin administration; this test carries a risk of seizure if the blood glucose level drops excessively. An insulin tolerance test may be performed if a 10–25% dextrose infusion is available for emergency administration in the face of hypoglycemic coma or seizure, if the patient can be continuously observed by a physician, and if the patient has no history of hypoglycemic seizures. The patient must have a normal glucose concentration at the beginning of the test. Regular insulin, 0.075–0.1 unit/kg in saline, may be given as an intravenous bolus. In 20–40 minutes, a 50% drop in blood glucose will occur and a rise in serum GH and cortisol should follow. Glucose should be monitored, and an intravenous line must be maintained for emergency dextrose infusion in case the patient becomes unconscious or has a hypoglycemic seizure. If dextrose infusion is necessary, it is imperative that blood glucose not be raised far above the normal range, since hyperosmolality has been reported from overzealous glucose replacement. (See Chapter 2.)

Patients who respond to pharmacologic stimuli (eg, levodopa, clonidine, or insulin) but not to physiologic stimuli such as exercise or sleep were said to have **neurosecretory dysfunction;** these patients may have decreased 24-hour secretion of hGH (or integrated concentrations of hGH) compared with healthy subjects, patterns similar to those observed in GH-deficient patients. The true status of such patients and the role of 24-hour GH monitoring are still controversial; secretagogue testing remains the standard for the diagnosis of GH deficiency, but even pharmacologic testing cannot always determine which patients truly need GH therapy.

IGF-1 values will be low in most GH-deficient subjects, but, as noted above, short patients with normal IGF-1 concentrations have been reported who require GH treatment for improvement of growth rate. In addition, starvation will lower IGF-1 values in healthy children and incorrectly suggest GH deficiency. Children with psychosocial dwarfism—who need family therapy or foster home placement rather than GH therapy—have low GH and IGF-1 concentrations and may falsely appear to have growth hormone deficiency. Likewise, patients with constitutional delay in adolescence will have low IGF-1 values for chronologic age but normal values for skeletal age and may have temporarily decreased GH response to secretagogues. Thus, IGF-1 determinations are not infallible in the diagnosis of GH deficiency. They must be interpreted with regard to nutrition, psychosocial status, and skeletal ages.

Alternative determinations are used to improve the diagnosis of GH deficiency. Low IGF-2 in addition to low IGF-1 levels improve the prediction of GH deficiency. Acid extraction of serum on a Sephadex column to separate IGF from its binding protein yields IGF-1 concentrations more closely related to growth rate and stature than are IGF-1 determinations done by direct radioimmunoassay, as was frequently done in the past. IGFBP-3 is GH-dependent and if low is said to be more indicative than IGF-1 determinations of GH deficiency.

Although pharmacologic tests of GH secretion and plasma IGF-1 values will usually indicate who has classic GH deficiency, the diagnosis will remain in doubt in some cases. This should not lead to the conclusion that all short children should receive GH therapy. Only very short children (height well below the fifth percentile or > 2.5–3.5 SD below the mean) who grow very slowly (growth velocity below the fifth percentile for age) with delayed bone ages meticulously studied in research protocols were shown to benefit from hGH therapy in the absence of classic GH deficiency. Patients with Turner's syndrome and renal failure derived some benefit in careful studies. However, children meeting less stringent criteria have been treated with GH in controlled trials, producing some increase in growth rate, but it is not yet clear whether this increases adult height as the studies are not yet completed. Furthermore, in the absence of classic GH deficiency, no clearly recognized measurement can predict which short child is likely to respond to GH therapy before it is instituted.

Treatment of Growth Hormone Deficiency

A. Hormonal Replacement: GH-deficient children require biosynthetic somatropin (natural-sequence GH) at a dose of 0.18–0.3 mg/kg/wk or somatrem (methionyl GH) at a dose of 0.3 mg/kg/wk administered in one dose per day six or seven times per week during the period of active growth before epiphysial fusion. The increase in growth rate (Figures 3–9, 3–10, and 3–11) is most marked during the first year of therapy. Older children do not respond as well and may require larger doses. GH will not increase growth rate without adequate nutrition and euthyroid status.

Antibodies to GH are present in measurable quantities in the serum of children receiving GH. While antibodies are more frequent in those treated with somatrem than somatropin, a high titer of blocking antibodies with significant binding capacity is rare and only a few patients are reported to have temporarily ceased growing on somatrem therapy.

GH exerts anti-insulin effects. Although clinical diabetes is not a likely result of GH therapy, the long-term effects of a small rise in glucose in an otherwise healthy child are unknown. Another potential risk is the rare tendency to develop slipped capital femoral epiphyses with therapy. Organomegaly and skeletal changes like those found in acromegaly are potential side effects of excessive GH therapy. The discovery of cases of leukemia in young adults previously treated with growth hormone is worrisome, but at present no cause and effect relationship is proved. GH does not increase the recurrence rate of tumors existing before therapy; thus, patients with craniopharyngiomas, for example, may receive GH, if indicated, after the disease is clinically stable, without significant worry that the GH will precipitate a recurrence. Clinicians usually wait 1 year after completion of tumor therapy before starting tumor patients on GH therapy.

B. Psychologic Management and Outcome: Research into the psychologic outcome of patients with short stature is flawed by lack of consistent methods of investigation and lack of controlled studies, but some results are of interest. Children with growth hormone deficiency are the most studied; they have more passive personality traits than do healthy children. Such patients have delayed emotional maturity and suffer from infantilization from

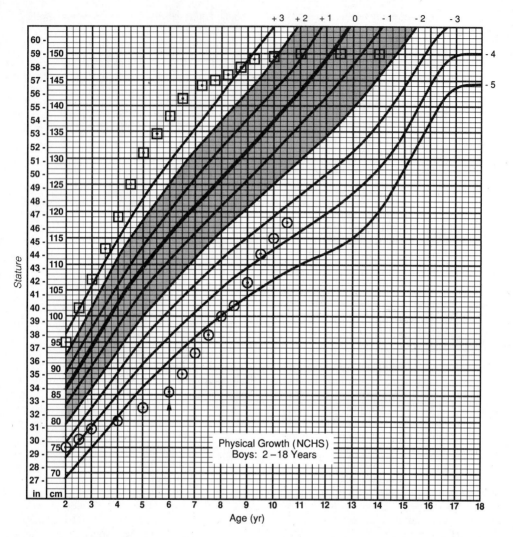

Figure 3–9. Examples of abnormal growth charts. Squares (□) represent the growth pattern of a child (such as patient A in Figure 3–11) with precocious sexual development and early excessive growth leading to premature closure of the epiphyses and cessation of growth. Circles (○) represent growth of a boy (such as patient B in Figure 3–11) with GH deficiency who showed progressively poorer growth until 6 years of age, when he was treated with hGH *(arrow),* after which catch-up growth occurred.

parents, teachers, and peers. Their academic achievement has been generally substandard even if intelligence is normal; this was attributed to delayed emotional maturity or poor body image, both fostered by short stature. However, many of these children have been held back in school because of their size without regard to their academic abilities. Some patients retain a body image of short stature even after normal height has been achieved with treatment. Depression and suicidal behavior can occur in affected adolescents because of the psychologic stress of short stature and delayed development. Thus, the way GH-deficient individuals are perceived by their world appears to be of primary importance in their psychologic outcome; our "heightist" society values physi-

cal stature and equates it with the potential for success, a belief that is not lost on the patients. A supportive environment in which they are not allowed to act younger than their age nor to occupy a "privileged place" in the family is recommended for GH-deficient (or other short) patients. Psychologic help is indicated in severe cases of depression or maladjustment and is helpful in many milder cases.

2. PSYCHOSOCIAL DWARFISM (Figure 3–12)

Children with psychosocial dwarfism present with poor growth, potbellied immature appearance, and

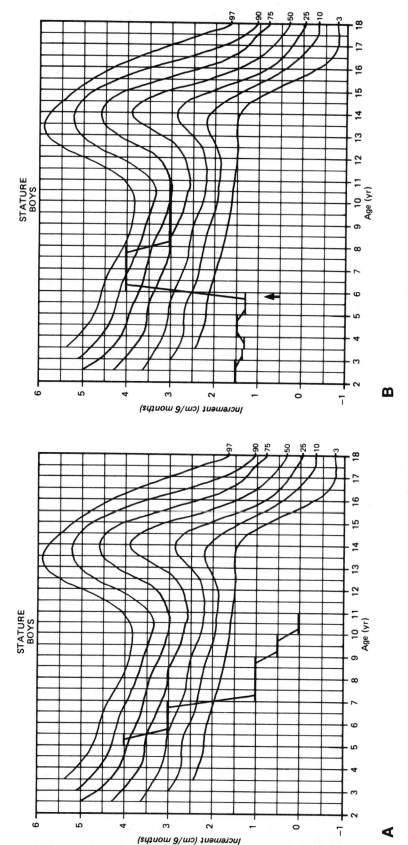

Figure 3–10. Two examples of abnormal growth plotted on a height velocity chart. **A:** The plot is taken from the data recorded as squares in Figure 3–9, describing a patient with precocious puberty, premature epiphysial closure, and cessation of growth. **B:** The plot is taken from the data recorded as circles in Figure 3–9, describing a patient with GH deficiency who was treated with hGH **(arrow)** at age 6. Initial catch-up growth is noted for 2 years, with a lower (but normal) velocity of growth following.

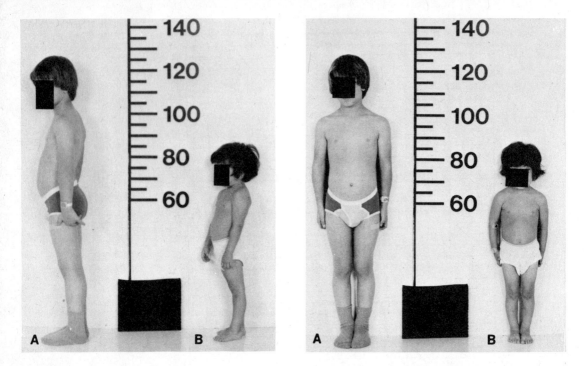

Figure 3–11. Two boys demonstrating extremes of growth. The boy at left in each photograph *(A)* has precocious puberty due to a central nervous system lesion. At 4 4/12 years, he was 125.1 cm tall, which is 5 SD above the mean. (The mean height for a 4-year-old is 101.5 cm.) His testes measured 2 × 3.5 cm each, his penis 9.8 × 2.8 cm. He was muscular and had acne and a deep voice. His bone age was 10 years, the testosterone level was 480 ng/dL, and the LH rose after 100 μg of GnRH (gonadorelin) to 23.4 mIU/mL, which is a pubertal response. His brain CT scan revealed a hamartoma of the tuber cinereum. The boy at right *(B)* at 4 2/12 years was 85 cm tall, which is 4.5 SD below the mean. He had the classic physical and historical characteristics of idiopathic GH deficiency, including early growth failure and a cherubic appearance. His plasma GH values did not rise after provocative testing.

bizarre eating and drinking habits. Parents may report that the affected child begs for food from neighbors, forages in garbage cans, and drinks from toilet bowls. As a rule this tragic condition occurs in only one of several children in a family. Careful questioning and observation reveal a disordered family structure in which the child is either ignored or severely disciplined. Caloric deprivation or physical battering may or may not be a feature of the history. These children have functional hypopituitarism. Testing will often reveal GH deficiency at first, but after the child is removed from the home, GH function quickly returns to normal. Diagnosis rests upon improvement in behavior or catch-up growth in the hospital or in a foster home. Separation from the family is therapeutic, but the prognosis is guarded. Family psychotherapy may be beneficial, but long-term follow-up is lacking.

Growth disorder due to abnormal parent-child interaction in a younger infant is called maternal deprivation. Caloric deprivation due to parental neglect may be of greater significance in this younger age group. Even in the absence of nutritional restriction or full-blown psychosocial dwarfism, constant nega-

tive interactions within a family may inhibit the growth of a child.

3. HYPOTHYROIDISM

Thyroid hormone deficiency decreases growth rate and skeletal development and, if onset is at or before birth, leads to mental retardation. Screening programs for the diagnosis of congenital hypothyroidism have been instituted all over the world, and early treatment following diagnosis in the neonatal period markedly reduces growth failure and mental retardation caused by severe primary congenital hypothyroidism. The more subtle forms of congenital or acquired hypothyroidism in older children (eg, lymphocytic thyroiditis) may lead to growth failure. Characteristics of hypothyroidism are decreased growth rate and short stature, retarded bone age, and an increased US:LS ratio for chronologic age. Patients are apathetic and sluggish and have constipation, bradycardia, coarsening of features and hair, hoarseness, and delayed pubertal development (Figure 4–35). Intelligence is unaffected in late-onset hy-

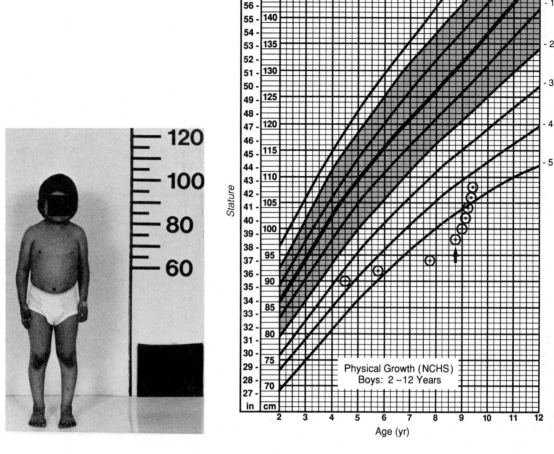

Figure 3–12. Photograph and growth chart of a 9 1/12-year-old boy with psychosocial dwarfism. He had a long history of poor growth (< 3 cm/yr). The social history revealed that he was given less attention and punished more frequently than his 7 sibs. He ate from garbage cans and begged for food, though he was not completely deprived of food at home. When the photograph was taken, he was 99 cm tall (–7 SD) and weighed 14.7 kg (–3 SD). His bone age was 5 years, with growth arrest lines visible. Serum thyroxine was 7.8 µg/dL. Peak serum GH varied from nondetectable to 8 ng/mL on different provocative tests between age 6 years and 8 7/12 years. He was placed in a hospital chronic care facility *(arrow)* for a 6-month period and grew 9 cm, which projects to a yearly growth velocity of 18 cm. On repeat testing, the peak serum GH was 28 ng/mL.

pothyroidism, but the apathy and lethargy may make it seem otherwise.

Hypothyroidism cannot be diagnosed solely on the basis of a low plasma total T_4 value; an indication of a low free T_4 value or low free T_4 index is necessary to rule out the relatively frequent occurrence (1:10,000) of thyroid hormone-binding globulin (TBG) deficiency, which will artifactually lower total T_4 values into the hypothyroid range without affecting the more important free T_4 values or euthyroid status. If a free T_4 determination or if a test of TBG levels (such as a resin T_3 uptake or plasma TBG concentration) is obtained along with the total T_4, this diagnostic trap can be avoided. Since the majority of cases of hypothyroidism are of the primary classifica-

tion, elevated TSH levels will confirm the diagnosis of bona fide hypothyroidism. Positive antimicrosomal or antithyroglobulin antibodies will indicate Hashimoto's (lymphocytic) thyroiditis. Low values of TSH on the newer sensitive assays may suggest secondary (pituitary) or tertiary (hypothalamic) hypothyroidism; such diagnoses must precipitate a search for other hypothalamic-pituitary endocrine deficiencies and central nervous system pathology (see Chapter 4).

4. CUSHING'S SYNDROME

Excess glucocorticoids (either exogenous or endogenous) will lead to decreased growth before obesity and other signs of Cushing's syndrome develop. The underlying disease may be bilateral adrenal hyperplasia due to abnormal ACTH-cortisol regulation in Cushing's disease, autonomous adrenal adenomas, or adrenal carcinoma. The appropriate diagnosis may be missed if urinary cortisol and 17-hydroxycorticosteroid determinations are not interpreted on the basis of the child's body size or if inappropriate doses of dexamethasone are used for testing (appropriate doses are 20 μg/kg/d for the low-dose and 80 μg/kg/d for the high-dose dexamethasone suppression test) (see Chapter 6). Furthermore, daily variations in cortisol production necessitate several urinary or plasma cortisol determinations before Cushing's disease can be appropriately diagnosed or ruled out. Exogenous glucocorticoids that suppress growth may be oral corticosteroids used to treat asthma or even overzealous use of topical corticosteroid ointments or creams. These iatrogenic cases of Cushing's syndrome, if resolved early, may allow catch-up growth and so may not affect final height. Thus, an accurate history of prior medications is important in diagnosis. Treatment of the underlying disorder (eg, transsphenoidal microadenomectomy for Cushing's disease) will restore growth rate to normal (catch-up growth may occur initially) if epiphysial fusion has not occurred, but final height will depend upon the length of the period of growth suppression.

5. PSEUDOHYPOPARATHYROIDISM

Pseudohypoparathyroidism is a rare disorder consisting of a characteristic phenotype and chemical signs of hypoparathyroidism (low serum Ca^{2+} and high serum PO_4^{3-}), though circulating PTH levels are elevated and target tissues fail to respond to exogenous PTH administration. Children with pseudohypoparathyroidism are short and chubby, with characteristic round facies, short fourth and fifth metacarpals, and mental retardation. A defect in the guanyl nucleotide-sensitive regulatory protein that couples PTH-occupied receptors to adenylyl cyclase is the cause. Remarkably, this defect occurs in the same regulatory protein system affected in McCune-Albright syndrome, in which hyperactive endocrine events result (see Chapter 12). Thus, administration of PTH fails to induce a rise in nephrogenous cAMP or an increase in urinary phosphorus. A rarer variant of this disorder (pseudohypoparathyroidism type II), in which administration of PTH produces a rise in nephrogenous cAMP but fails to induce an increase in phosphorus excretion, appears to have a defect distal to the receptor-adenylyl cyclase complex. Treatment with high-dose vitamin D or physiologic replacement with 1,25-dihydroxyvitamin D_3 (calcitriol) and calcium-binding as well as phosphate-binding agents will correct the biochemical defects and control hypocalcemic seizures but will not improve stature or mentation.

Children with the pseudohypoparathyroid phenotype but with normal circulating levels of calcium, phosphate, and PTH have pseudopseudohypoparathyroidism. They require no calcium or vitamin D therapy. (See Chapter 5.)

6. DISORDERS OF VITAMIN D METABOLISM

Short stature and poor growth are features of rickets in its obvious or more subtle forms. The cause may be vitamin D deficiency due to inadequate oral intake, fat malabsorption, inadequate sunlight exposure, anticonvulsant therapy, or renal or hepatic disease. Classic findings include bowing of the legs, chest deformities (rachitic rosary), and characteristic radiographic findings associated with decreased serum calcium and phosphate levels and elevated serum alkaline phosphatase levels. Vitamin D dependency may be diagnosed when vitamin D is required in doses far higher than necessary to resolve vitamin D deficiency. Short stature may be associated with rickets in renal disorders with hypophosphatemia due to a defect in renal reabsorption of phosphate; examples are Fanconi's syndrome (including cystinosis and other inborn errors of metabolism) and renal tubular acidosis.

When treatment is effective in these disorders (eg, vitamin D for vitamin D deficiency or alkali therapy for appropriate types of renal tubular acidosis), growth rate will improve. In the Williams syndrome of infantile hypercalcemia, elfin facies, supravalvular aortic stenosis, and mental retardation, patients have intrauterine growth retardation and greatly reduced height in childhood and as adults. (See Chapter 11.)

7. DIABETES MELLITUS

Growth in insulin-dependent diabetes mellitus depends on the efficacy of therapy; well-controlled diabetes mellitus is compatible with normal growth, while poorly controlled diabetes often causes slow growth. Another factor that may decrease growth rate in children with diabetes mellitus is the increased incidence of Hashimoto's thyroiditis; yearly thyroid function screening is advisable as the peripubertal period approaches. Liver and spleen enlargement in a poorly controlled short diabetic child is Mauriac's syndrome, rarely seen now owing to improved diabetic care. Growth hormone concentrations are higher in children with diabetes, and this factor may play a role in the development of complications of diabetes mellitus. IGF-1 concentrations tend to be normal or low, depending upon glucose control, but judging from the elevated GH, the stimulation of IGF-1 by GH is blocked in these children. (See Chapter 15.)

8. DIABETES INSIPIDUS

Polyuria and polydipsia due to inadequate vasopressin (neurogenic diabetes insipidus) or inability of the kidney to respond to vasopressin (nephrogenic diabetes insipidus) leads to poor caloric intake and decreased growth. With appropriate treatment (see Chapter 2), the growth rate should return to normal. Acquired neurogenic diabetes insipidus may herald a hypothalamic-pituitary tumor, and growth failure may be due to associated GH deficiency.

THE DIAGNOSIS OF SHORT STATURE

As previously stated, an initial decision must be made about whether a child is pathologically short or simply distressed because his or her height is not as close to the 50th percentile as desired by the patient or the parents. Performing unnecessary tests is expensive and may be a source of long-term concern to the parents—a concern that could have been avoided by appropriate reassurance. Alternatively, missing a diagnosis of pathologic poor growth may cause the patient to lose inches of final height.

If a patient's stature, growth rate, or height adjusted for midparental height is sufficiently decreased to warrant evaluation, an orderly approach to diagnosis will eliminate unnecessary laboratory testing. The medical history will provide invaluable information regarding intrauterine course and toxin exposure, birth size and the possibility of birth trauma, mental and physical development, symptoms of systemic diseases (Table 3–4), abnormal diet, and family heights and ages at which pubertal maturation occurred. Evaluation of psychosocial factors affecting the family and the relationship of parents and child can be carried out during the history-taking encounter. Often the diagnosis can be made at this point.

On physical examination, present height—measured without shoes on an accurate measuring device—and weight should be plotted and compared with any previous data available. If no past heights are available, a history of lack of change in clothing and shoe sizes or failure to lengthen skirts or pants may reflect poor growth. Questions about how the child's stature compares with that of his or her peers and whether the child's height has always been in the same relationship to that of classmates are useful. One of the most important features of the evaluation process is to determine height velocity and compare the child's growth rate with the normal growth rate for age. Adjustment for midparental height is calculated and nutritional status determined. Arm span, head circumference, and US:LS ratio are measured. Physical stigmas of syndromes or systemic diseases are evaluated. Neurologic examination is essential.

If no specific diagnosis emerges from the physical examination, a set of laboratory evaluations may prove useful. Complete blood count, urinalysis, and serum chemistry screening with electrolyte measurements may reveal anemia, abnormalities of hepatic or renal disease (including concentration defects), glucose intolerance, acidosis, calcium disorder, or other electrolyte disturbances. Age-adjusted values must be used, since the normal ranges of serum alkaline phosphatase and phosphorus values are higher in children than in adults. A sedimentation rate, serum carotene, or antigliadin or antireticulin antibody determination may indicate connective tissue disease, Crohn's disease, or malabsorption. Determination of total T_4, TSH, and resin T_3 uptake or free T_4 is important. Skeletal age evaluation will not make a diagnosis; however, if the study shows delayed bone age, the possibility of constitutional delay in growth, hypothyroidism, or GH deficiency must be considered. An IGF-1 level, if normal for age, would speak against classic GH deficiency or malnutrition; if low, it must be considered in relation to skeletal age, nutritional status, and general health status. Gonadotropin and sex steroid determinations are performed if puberty is delayed. Serum prolactin may be elevated in cases of hypothalamic disorder. Karyotyping for Turner's syndrome is obtained in any short girl without another diagnosis, especially if puberty is delayed or gonadotropins are elevated. Elevated 24-hour urinary 17-hydroxycorticoids (normal, < 4.5 mg/m^2/24 h [12.4 μmol/m^2/24 h]) and urinary free cortisol (normal, < 60 μg/m^2/24 h [0.166 μmol/m^2]/24 h) signify Cushing's syndrome. If a hypothalamic pituitary disorder is suspected, CT scan or MRI is indicated.

If no diagnosis is apparent after all of the above have been considered and evaluated, more detailed procedures, such as provocative testing for GH deficiency, are indicated. It must be emphasized that a long and expensive evaluation is not necessary until it is likely that psychologic or nutritional factors are not at fault. Likewise, if a healthy-appearing child presents with borderline short stature, normal growth rate, and short familial stature, a period of observation may be more appropriate than laboratory tests.

TALL STATURE DUE TO NONENDOCRINE CAUSES

1. CONSTITUTIONAL TALL STATURE

A subject who has been taller than his or her peers through most of childhood, is growing at a velocity within the normal range with a moderately advanced bone age, and has no signs of the disorders listed below may be considered to be constitutionally advanced. Predicted final height will usually be in the normal adult range for the family.

Exogenous obesity in an otherwise healthy child

will usually lead to moderate advancement of bone age, slightly increased growth rate, and tall stature in childhood. Puberty will be in the early range of normal, and adult stature will conform to genetic influences. As a rule, obesity and short stature should be considered an indication of a potential organic disorder or syndrome.

2. GENETIC TALL STATURE

Children with exceptionally tall parents have a genetic tendency to reach a height above the normal range. The child will be tall for age, will grow at a high normal rate, and the bone age will be close to chronologic age, leading to a tall height prediction. Children with tall stature have been noted to have growth hormone secretory patterns similar to those associated with acromegaly—eg, GH levels increase after TRH administration.

Occasionally, children will be concerned about being too tall as adults. These worries are more common in girls and will sometimes be of greater concern to the parents than to the patient. Final height can be limited by promoting early epiphysial closure with estrogen in girls or testosterone in boys. Such therapy should not be undertaken without careful consideration of the risks involved. Testosterone therapy has been associated with decreasing HDL cholesterol levels as well as causing the onset and progression of acne fulminans, even after therapy has been withdrawn. Estrogen carries the theoretic risk of causing thrombosis, ovarian cysts, and galactorrhea, but few complications have been reported. High-dose estrogen therapy is estimated to decrease predicted final height by as much as 4.5–7 cm. Such therapy will be more effective if started 3–4 years before epiphysial fusion. Some studies suggest that bromocriptine will decrease growth rate in children with tall stature, but other studies have not confirmed this observation. No therapy to limit stature is warranted until a careful assessment of the parents' and the child's expectations and reasons for seeking therapy is performed. Counseling and reassurance are usually more appropriate than endocrine therapy.

3. SYNDROMES OF TALL STATURE

Cerebral Gigantism

The sporadic syndrome of rapid growth in infancy, prominent forehead, high-arched palate, sharp chin, and hypertelorism (Sotos syndrome) is not associated with GH excess. Mentation is usually impaired. The growth rate decreases to normal in later childhood, but stature remains tall.

Marfan's Syndrome

Marfan's syndrome is an autosomal dominant abnormality of connective tissue exhibiting variable penetrance. This condition may be diagnosed by characteristic physical manifestations of tall stature, long thin fingers (arachnodactyly), hyperextension of joints, and superior lens subluxation. Pectus excavatum and scoliosis may be noted. Furthermore, aortic or mitral regurgitation or aortic root dilation may be present, and aortic dissection or rupture may ultimately occur. In patients with this syndrome, arm span exceeds height, and the US:LS ratio is quite low owing to long legs.

Homocystinuria

Patients with homocystinuria have an autosomal recessive deficiency of cystathionine β-synthetase and phenotypes similar to those of patients with Marfan's syndrome. Additional features of homocystinuria include mental retardation, increased incidence of seizures, osteoporosis, inferior lens dislocation, and increased urinary excretion of homocystine with increased plasma homocystine and methionine but low plasma cystine. Thromboembolic phenomena may precipitate a fatal complication. This disease is treated by restricting dietary methionine and, in responsive patients, administering pyridoxine.

Beckwith-Wiedemann Syndrome

This syndrome of the large newborn with omphalocele, macroglossia, hypoglycemia with hyperinsulinism due to pancreatic hyperplasia, fetal adrenocortical cytomegaly, and large kidneys with medullary dysplasia is also associated with increased growth in childhood.

XYY Syndrome

Patients with one (47,XYY) or more (48,XYYY) extra Y chromosomes achieve greater than average adult heights. They have normal birth lengths but higher than normal growth rates. Excess GH secretion has not been documented (see Chapter 11).

Klinefelter's Syndrome

Patients with Klinefelter's syndrome (see Chapter 9) tend toward tall stature, but this is not a constant feature.

TALL STATURE DUE TO ENDOCRINE DISORDERS

1. PITUITARY GIGANTISM

If a GH-secreting pituitary adenoma occurs before epiphysial fusion, the result will be excessive linear growth rather than just the acral overgrowth characteristic of acromegaly. Height velocity will be abnormally rapid, and other somatic signs that occur in acromegaly may be found in addition to increased stature (see Chapter 2). Elevated fasting serum GH and IGF-1 concentrations are diagnostic.

2. SEXUAL PRECOCITY

Early onset of secretion of estrogens or androgens will lead to abnormally increased height velocity. Because bone age is advanced, there will be the paradox of the tall child who, because of early epiphysial closure, is short as an adult. The conditions include complete and incomplete sexual precocity (including virilizing congenital adrenal hyperplasia) (Figures 3–9, 3–10, and 3–11).

3. THYROTOXICOSIS

Excessive thyroid hormone due to endogenous overproduction or overtreatment with exogenous thyroxine will lead to increased growth, advanced bone age, and, if occurring in early life, craniosynostosis. If the condition remains untreated, final height will be reduced.

4. INFANTS OF DIABETIC MOTHERS

Birth weight and size in infants of moderately diabetic mothers will be quite high, although severely diabetic women who have poor control may have babies with intrauterine growth retardation. Severe hypoglycemia and hypocalcemia will be evident in the babies soon after birth. The appearance and size of such babies is so striking that women have been diagnosed as having gestational diabetes as a result of giving birth to affected infants.

REFERENCES

Normal Growth

Hamill PVV et al: Physical growth: National Center for Health Statistics percentiles. Am J Clin Nutr 1979; 32:607.

Himes JH, Roche AF, Thissen D: *Parent-Specific Adjustments for Assessment of Recumbent Length and Stature.* Vol 13 of: *Monographs in Paediatrics.* Karger, 1981.

Pierson M, Deschamps J-P: Growth. In: *Pediatric Endocrinology.* Job J-C, Pierson M (editors). Wiley, 1981.

Preece MA: The insulinlike growth factors. In: *Current Concepts in Pediatric Endocrinology.* Styne DM, Brook GG (editors). Elsevier, 1987.

Roche AF, Himes JH: Incremental growth charts. Am J Clin Nutr 1980;33:2041.

Roche AF, Wainer H, Thissen D: The RWT method for the prediction of adult stature. Pediatrics 1975; 56:1027.

Smith DW: *Growth and Its Disorders.* Vol 15 of: *Major Problems in Clinical Pediatrics.* Schaffer AJ, Markowitz M (editors). Saunders, 1977.

Styne DM: Growth. In: *Pediatric Endocrinology for the House Officer.* Williams & Wilkins, 1988.

Tanner JM, Whitehouse RH: Clinical longitudinal standards for height, weight, height velocity, weight velocity, and stages of puberty. Arch Dis Child 1976;51:170.

US Department of Health, Education, and Welfare, Public Health Service: NCHS Growth Curves for Children: Birth-18 Years, United States. Publication No. (PHS) 78–1650. Series 11, No. 165, 1977.

Short Stature

Appan S et al: Growth and growth hormone therapy in hypochondroplasia. Acta Paediatr Scand 1990;79:796.

Aynsley-Green A, Zachmann M, Prader A: Interrelation of the therapeutic effects of growth hormone and testosterone on growth in hypopituitarism. J Pediatr 1976;89:992.

Bailey RC: The comparative growth of Efe pygmies and African farmers from birth to age 5 years. Ann Hum Biol 1991;18:113.

Balsan S, Tieder M: Linear growth in patients with hypophosphatemic vitamin D-resistant rickets: Influence of treatment regimen and parental height. J Pediatr 1990;116:365.

Bierich JR: Treatment by hGH of constitutional delay of growth and adolescence. Acta Paediatr Scand 1986; 325(Suppl):71.

Borges JLC et al: Stimulation of growth hormone and somatomedin-C in idiopathic GH-deficient subjects by intermittent, pulsatile administration of synthetic human pancreatic tumor growth hormone-releasing factor-40. J Clin Endocrinol Metab 1984;59:1.

Bosio L et al: Growth acceleration and final height after treatment for delayed diagnosis of celiac disease. J Pediatr Gastroenterol Nutr 1990;11:324.

Braga S et al: Familial growth hormone deficiency resulting from a 7.6 kb deletion within the growth hormone gene cluster. Am J Med Genet 1986;25:443.

Brown P: Human growth hormone therapy and Creutzfeldt-Jakob disease: A drama in three acts. Pediatrics 1988;81:85.

Butler GE, McKie M, Ratcliffe SG: The cyclical nature of prepubertal growth. Ann Hum Biol 1990;17:177.

Byard PJ: Early childhood growth in patients with cystic fibrosis. Ann Hum Biol 1990;17:483.

Clarren, SK, Smith DW: The fetal alcohol syndrome. N Engl J Med 1978;298:1063.

Clayton PE et al: Does growth hormone cause relapse of brain tumours? Lancet 1987;1:711.

de Muinck K et al: Dose-response study of biosynthetic human growth hormone (GH) in GH-deficient children: Effects on auxological and biochemical parameters. Dutch Growth Hormone Working Group. J Clin Endocrinol Metab 1992;74:898.

Dean HJ, Bishop A, Winter JS: Growth hormone deficiency in patients with histiocytosis X. J Pediatr 1986;109:615.

Favier AE: Hormonal effects of zinc on growth in children. Biol Trace Elem Res 1992;32:383.

Fine RN et al: Recombinant human growth hormone treatment of children with chronic renal failure: Long-term (1- to 3-year) outcome. Pediatr Nephrol 1991; 5:477.

Friesen HG: A tale of stature. Raben Lecture 1980. Endocrine Rev 1980;1:309.

Groll A et al: Short stature as the primary manifestation of coeliac disease. Lancet 1980;2:1097.

Harris DA et al: Somatomedin-C in normal puberty and in true precocious puberty before and after treatment with a potent luteinizing hormone-releasing hormone agonist. J Clin Endocrinol Metab 1985;61:152.

Harrison HE, Harrison HC: *Disorders of Calcium and Phosphate Metabolism in Childhood and Adolescence.* Vol 19 of: *Major Problems in Clinical Pediatrics.* Schaffer AJ, Markowitz M (editors). Saunders, 1979.

Hintz RL et al: Plasma somatomedin and growth hormone values in children with protein-calorie malnutrition. J Pediatr 1978;92:153.

Jones KL: *Smith's Recognizable Patterns of Human Malformation,* 4th ed. Saunders, 1988.

Kaplan SL et al: Clinical studies with recombinant-DNA-derived methionyl human growth hormone in growth hormone deficient children. Lancet 1986; 1:697.

Kaplan SL, Grumbach MM: Pathophysiology of GH deficiency and other disorders of GH metabolism. In: *Problems in Pediatric Endocrinology.* La Cauza C, Root AW (editors). Academic Press, 1980.

Kaplan SL: Normal growth. In: *Rudolph's Pediatrics,* 19th ed. Appleton & Lange, 1991.

Karlberg J, Wit JM: Linear growth in Sotos syndrome. Acta Paediatr Scand 80:956-957, 1991.

Karlberg J et al: Longitudinal analysis of infantile growth in children with celiac disease. Acta Paediatr Scand 1988;77:516.

Karlberg J, Kjellmer I, Kristiansson B: Linear growth in children with cystic fibrosis. I. Birth to 8 years of age. Acta Paediatr Scand 1991;80:508.

Klein GL, Dungy CI, Galant SP: Growth and the nutritional status of nonsteroid-dependent asthmatic children. Ann Allergy 1991;67:80.

Klein, RG, Mannuzza S: Hyperactive boys almost grown up: III. Methylphenidate effects on ultimate height. Arch Gen Psychiatry 1988;45:1131.

Laron Z: Syndrome of familial dwarfism and high plasma immunoreactive growth hormone. Isr J Med Sci 1974;10:1247.

Laron Z et al: Effects of insulin-like growth factor on linear growth, head circumference, and body fat in patients with Laron-type dwarfism. Lancet 1992;339: 1258.

Levitsky LL: Growth and pubertal pattern in insulin-dependent diabetes mellitus. Semin Adolesc Med 1987; 3:233.

Lovinger RD, Kaplan SL, Grumbach MM: Congenital hypopituitarism associated with neonatal hypoglycemia and microphallus: Four cases secondary to hypothalamic hormone deficiencies. J Pediatr 1975; 87(Part 2):1171.

Miller WL, Kaplan SL, Grumbach MM: Child abuse as a cause of post-traumatic hypopituitarism. N Engl J Med 1980;302:724.

Nyhan WL, Sakati NU: *Genetic and Malformation Syndromes in Clinical Medicine.* Year Book, 1976.

Oberger E, Engstrom I, Karlberg J: Long-term treatment with glucocorticoids/ACTH in asthmatic children: III. Effects on growth and adult height. Acta Paediatr Scand 1990;79:77.

Okabe T et al: Growth-promoting effect of human growth hormone on patients with achondroplasia. Acta Paediatr Jpn 1991;33:357.

Powell GF et al: Emotional deprivation and growth retardation simulating idiopathic hypopituitarism: 2. Endocrinologic evaluation of the syndrome. N Engl J Med 1967;276:1279.

Powell GF, Brasel JA, Blizzard RM: Emotional deprivation and growth retardation simulating idiopathic hypopituitarism. N Engl J Med 1967;276:1271.

Pugliese MI et al: Fear of obesity: A cause of short stature and delayed puberty. N Engl J Med 1983; 309:513.

Reiter EO et al: Variable estimates of serum growth hormone concentrations by different radioassay systems. J Clin Endocrinol Metab 1988;66:68.

Richards GE et al: Delayed onset of hypopituitarism: Sequelae of therapeutic irradiation of central nervous system, eye, and middle ear tumors. J Pediatr 1976; 89:553.

Rosenfeld RG, Northcraft GB, Hintz RL: A prospective, randomized study of testosterone treatment of constitutional delay of growth and development in male adolescents. Pediatrics 1982;69:681.

Safer DJ, Allen RP, Barr E: Growth rebound after termination of stimulant drugs. J Pediatr 1975;86:113.

Sanders JE et al: Growth and development following marrow transplantation for leukemia. Blood 1986; 68:1129.

Schechter J, Kovacs K, Rimoin D: Isolated growth hormone deficiency: Immunocytochemistry. J Clin Endocrinol Metab 1984;59:798.

Shohat M et al: Childhood asthma and growth outcome. Arch Dis Child 1987;62:63.

Silver HK, Finkelstein M: Deprivation dwarfism. J Pediatr 1967;7:317.

Sipponen P et al: Familial syndrome with panhypopituitarism, hypoplasia of the hypophysis, and poorly developed sella turcica. Arch Dis Childhood 1978; 53:664.

Sklar CA et al: Hormonal and metabolic abnormalities associated with central nervous system germinoma in children and adolescents and the effect of therapy: Report of 10 patients. J Clin Endocrinol Metab 1981; 52:9.

Smith PJ et al: Nocturnal pulsatile growth hormone-releasing hormone treatment in growth hormone deficiency. Clin Endocrinol 1986;25:35.

Spiliotis BE et al: Growth hormone neurosecretory dysfunction. JAMA 1984;251:2223.

Styne DM et al: Treatment of Cushing's disease in childhood and adolescence by transsphenoidal microadenomectomy. N Engl J Med 1984;310:889.

Takano K et al: Plasma growth hormone (GH) response to GH-releasing factor in normal children with short stature and patients with pituitary dwarfism. J Clin Endocrinol Metab 1984;58:236.

Tanner JM et al: Relative importance of growth hormone and sex steroids for the growth at puberty of trunk length, limb length, and muscle width in growth hormone-deficient children. J Pediatr 1976;89:1000.

Tanner JM et al: The effect of human growth hormone treatment for 1 to 7 years on the growth of 100 children with growth hormone deficiency, low birth weight, inherited smallness, Turner's syndrome and other complaints. Arch Dis Child 1971;46:745.

Tanner JM, Lejarraga H, Cameron N: The natural history of the Silver-Russell syndrome: A longitudinal study of thirty-nine cases. Pediatr Res 1975;9:611.

Thomsett MJ et al: Endocrine and neurologic outcome in childhood craniopharyngioma: Review of effect of treatment in 42 patients. J Pediatr 1980;97:728.

Thorner MO et al: Acceleration of growth in two children treated with human growth hormone-releasing factor. N Engl J Med 1985;312:2.

Underwood LE, Van Wyk JJ: Normal and aberrant growth. In: *Williams' Textbook of Endocrinology,* 8th ed. Wilson JD, Foster DW (editors). Saunders, 1992.

Van Vliet G et al: Growth hormone can increase growth rate in short normal children: Evaluation of the somatomedin-C generation test in the assessment of children with short stature. N Engl J Med 1983;309:1016.

Zapf J, Walter H, Froesch ER: Radioimmunological determination of insulin-like growth factors I and II in normal subjects and in patients with growth disorders and extrapancreatic tumor hypoglycemia. J Clin Invest 1981;68:1321.

Tall Stature

Conte FA, Grumbach MM: Epidemiological aspects of estrogen use: Estrogen use in children and adolescents: A survey. Pediatrics 1978;62(Suppl):1091.

Costin G, Fefferman RA, Kogut MD: Hypothalamic gigantism. J Pediatr 1973;83:419.

Schwarz HP, Joss EE, Zuppinger KA: Bromocriptine treatment in adolescent boys with familial tall stature: A pair-matched controlled study. J Clin Endocrinol Metab 1987;65:136.

Wettenhall HNB, Cahill C, Roche AF: Tall girls: A survey of 15 years of management and treatment. J Pediatr 1975;86:602.

4

The Thyroid Gland

Francis S. Greenspan, MD

The thyroid gland is the largest organ specialized for endocrine function in the human body. Its function is to secrete a sufficient amount of thyroid hormones, primarily 3,5,3′,5′-*l*-tetraiodothyronine (T_4), and a lesser quantity of 3,5,3′-*l*-triiodothyronine (T_3). Thyroid hormones promote normal growth and development and regulate a number of homeostatic functions, including energy and heat production. In addition, the parafollicular cells of the human thyroid gland secrete calcitonin, which is important in calcium homeostasis (see Chapter 5).

ANATOMY & HISTOLOGY

The thyroid gland originates as an outpouching in the floor of the pharynx, which grows downward anterior to the trachea, bifurcates, and forms a series of cellular cords. These form tiny balls or follicles and develop into the two lateral lobes of the thyroid connected by a thin isthmus. The origin of the gland at the base of the tongue is evident as the foramen cecum. The course of its downward migration is marked by the **thyroglossal duct,** remnants of which may persist in adult life as thyroglossal duct cysts. These are mucus-filled cysts, lined with squamous epithelium, and are usually found in the anterior neck between the thyroid cartilage and the base of the tongue. A remnant of the caudal end of the thyroglossal duct is found in the pyramidal lobe, attached to the isthmus of the gland (Figure 4–1).

The isthmus of the thyroid gland is located just below the cricoid cartilage, midway between the apex of the thyroid cartilage ("Adam's apple") and the suprasternal notch. Each lobe is pear-shaped and measures about 2.5–4 cm in length, 1.5–2 cm in width, and 1–1.5 cm in thickness. The weight of the gland in the normal individual, as determined by ultrasonic examination, varies depending on dietary iodine intake, age, and body weight, but in adults is approximately 10–20 g. Upward growth of the thyroid gland is limited by the attachment of the sternothyroid muscle to the thyroid cartilage; however, posterior and downward growth is unhampered, so that

ACRONYMS USED IN THIS CHAPTER

DIT	Diiodotyrosine
ELISA	Enzyme linked immunoassay
FNAB	Fine-needle aspiration biopsy
FT_4	Free thyroxine
FT_4I	Free thyroxine index
GRTH	Generalized resistance to thyroid hormone
hTg	Human thyroglobulin
hTR	Human thyroid hormone receptor
IP3	Inositol-1,4,5-triphosphate
LATS	Long-acting thyroid stimulator (TSH-R Ab [stim])
MIT	Monoiodotyrosine
PBI	Protein-bound iodine
PIP2	Phosphatidyl inositol-4,5-biphosphate
PRTH	Pituitary resistance to thyroid hormone
RAIU	Radioactive iodide uptake
RER	Rough endoplasmic reticulum
RIA	Radioimmunoassay
rT_3	Reverse T_3; 3,3′,5′-triiodothyronine
T_4	Tetraiodothyronine, levothyroxine
T_3	3,5,3′-Triiodothyronine, liothyronine
T_2	Diiodothyronine
TRE	Thyroid hormone-responsive element
TRH	Thyrotropin-releasing hormone
TBG	Thyroxine-binding globulin
TBP	Thyroxine-binding protein
TBPA	Thyroxine-binding prealbumin; transthyretin
THBR	Thyroid hormone binding ratio
Tg	Thyroglobulin
TPO	Thyroid peroxidase
TSH	Thyroid-stimulating hormone, thyrotropin
TSH-R	TSH receptor
TSH-R Ab [stim]	TSH receptor-stimulating antibody
TSH-R Ab [block]	TSH receptor-blocking antibody

thyroid enlargement, or goiter, will frequently extend posteriorly and inferiorly, or even substernally.

Transverse section of the neck at the level of the thyroid isthmus shows the relationships of the thy-

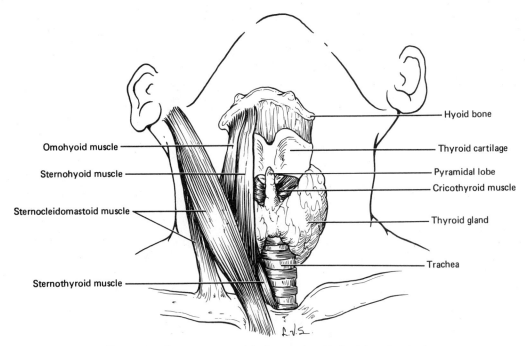

Figure 4–1. Gross anatomy of the human thyroid gland (anterior view).

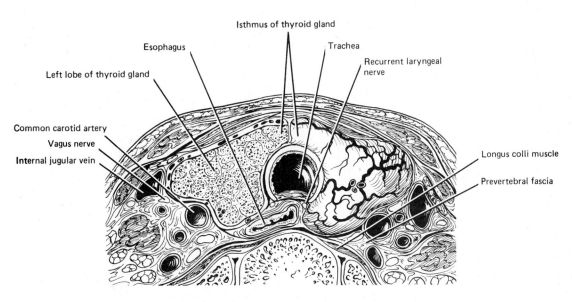

Figure 4–2. Cross section of the neck at the level of T1, showing thyroid relationships. (Reproduced, with permission, from Lindner HH: *Clinical Anatomy.* Appleton & Lange, 1989.)

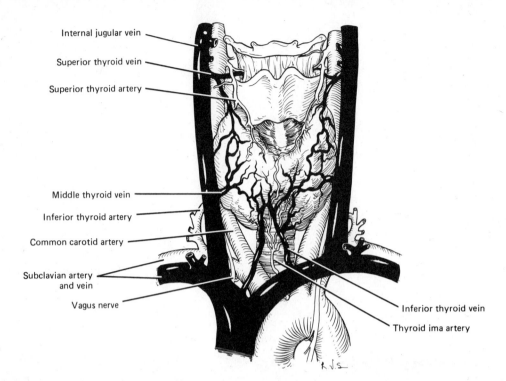

Internal jugular vein
Superior thyroid vein
Superior thyroid artery
Middle thyroid vein
Inferior thyroid artery
Common carotid artery
Subclavian artery and vein
Vagus nerve
Inferior thyroid vein
Thyroid ima artery

Figure 4–3. Arteries and veins related to the thyroid gland. (Reproduced, with permission, from Lindner HH: *Clinical Anatomy.* Appleton & Lange, 1989.)

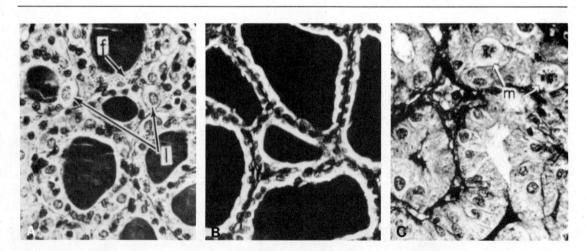

Figure 4–4. A: Normal rat thyroid. A single layer of cuboidal epithelial cells surrounds PAS-positive material in the follicular space (colloid). The larger, lighter-staining cells indicated by the arrows (l) are C cells that produce calcitonin. (F, follicular cells.) **B:** Inactive rat thyroid several weeks after hypophysectomy. The follicular lumens are larger and the follicular cells flatter. **C:** Rat thyroid under intensive TSH stimulation. The animal was fed an iodine-deficient diet and injected with propylthiouracil for several weeks. Little colloid is visible. The follicular cells are tall and columnar. Several mitoses (m) are visible. (Reproduced, with permission, from Halmi NS in: *Histology.* Greep R0, Weiss L [editors]. McGraw-Hill, 1973.)

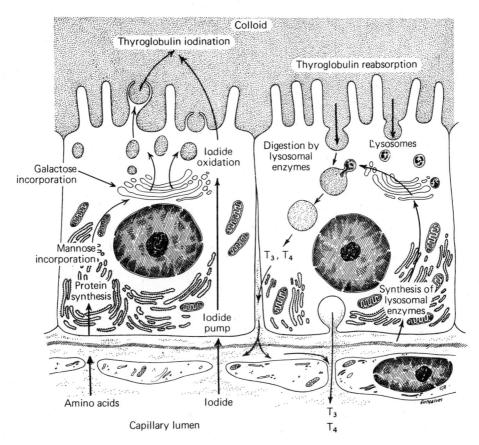

Figure 4–5. Processes of synthesis and iodination of thyroglobulin (left) and its reabsorption and digestion (right). These events occur in the same cell. (Reproduced, with permission, from Junqueira LC, Carneiro J, Kelley R: *Basic Histology,* 7th ed. Appleton & Lange, 1992.)

roid gland to the trachea, esophagus, carotid artery, and jugular vein (Figure 4–2). Ultrasonography, CT scans, or MRI reveal these relationships in vivo.

The thyroid gland has a rich blood supply (Figure 4–3). The superior thyroid artery arises from the common or external carotid artery, the inferior thyroid artery from the thyrocervical trunk of the subclavian artery, and the small thyroid ima artery from the brachiocephalic artery at the aortic arch. Venous drainage is via multiple surface veins coalescing into superior, lateral, and inferior thyroid veins. The blood flow to the thyroid gland is about 5 mL/g/min; in hyperthyroidism, the blood flow to the gland is markedly increased, and a whistling sound, or bruit, may be heard over the lower poles of the gland and may even be felt in the same areas as a vibration, or thrill. Other important anatomic considerations include the two pairs of parathyroid glands that usually lie behind the upper and middle thyroid lobes and the recurrent laryngeal nerves, which course along the trachea behind the thyroid gland.

On microscopic examination, the thyroid gland is found to consist of a series of follicles of varying sizes. The follicles contain a pink-staining material

(with hematoxylin-eosin stain) called "colloid" and are surrounded by a single layer of thyroid epithelium. Tissue culture studies suggest that each follicle may represent an individual clone of cells. These cells become columnar when stimulated by TSH and flattened when resting (Figure 4–4). The follicle cells synthesize thyroglobulin, which is extruded into the lumen of the follicle. The biosynthesis of T_4 and T_3 occurs within thyroglobulin at the cell-colloid interface. Numerous microvilli project from the surface of the follicle into the lumen; these are involved in endocytosis of thyroglobulin, which is then hydrolyzed in the cell to release thyroid hormones (Figure 4–5).

PHYSIOLOGY

STRUCTURE OF THYROID HORMONES

Thyroid hormones are unique in that they contain 59–65% of the trace element iodine. The structures

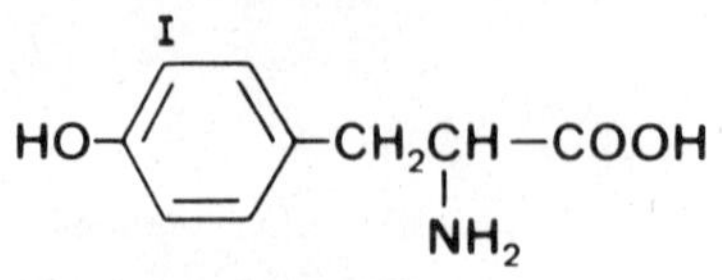

3-Monoiodotyrosine (MIT)

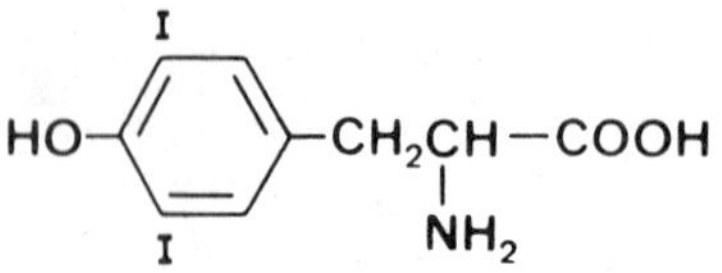

3,5-Diiodotyrosine (DIT)

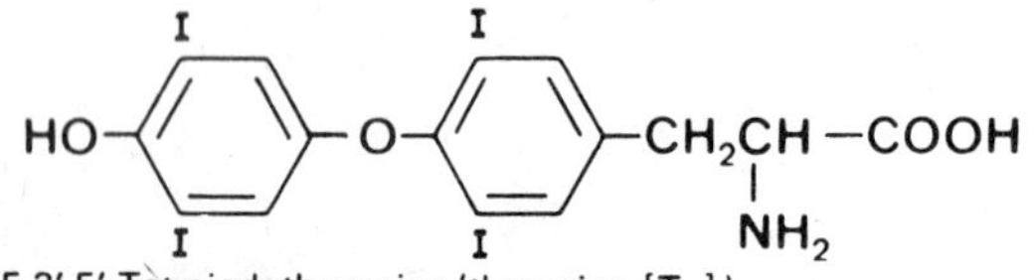

3,5,3',5'-Tetraiodothyronine (thyroxine [T_4])

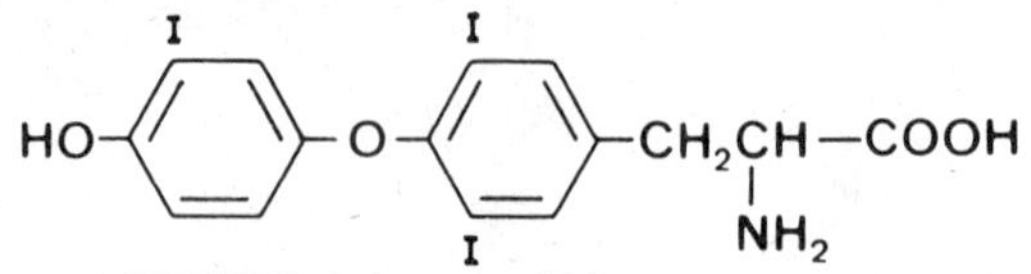

3,5,3'-Triiodothyronine (T_3)

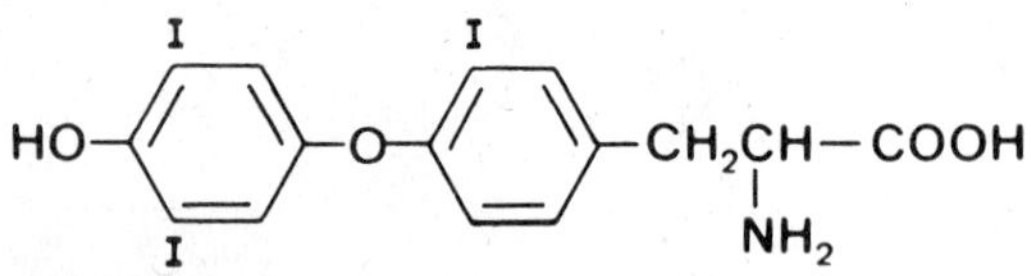

3,3',5'-Triiodothyronine (reverse T_3 [rT_3])

Figure 4–6. Structure of thyroid hormones and related compounds. (Reproduced, with permission, from Murray RK et al: *Harper's Biochemistry,* 22nd ed, Appleton & Lange, 1990.)

of the thyroid hormones, T_4) and T_3, are shown in Figure 4–6. The iodinated thyronines are derived from iodination of the phenolic rings of tyrosine residues in thyroglobulin to form mono- or diiodotyrosine, which are coupled to form T_3 or T_4 (see below).

IODINE METABOLISM

Iodine* enters the body in food or water in the form of iodide or iodate ion, the iodate ion being converted to iodide in the stomach. In the course of millenia, iodine has been leached from the soil and washed down into the oceans, so that in mountainous and inland areas the supply of iodine may be quite limited, whereas the element is plentiful in coastal areas. The thyroid gland concentrates and traps iodide and synthesizes and stores thyroid hormones in thyroglobulin, which compensates for the scarcity of iodine.

*In this chapter, the words "iodine" and "iodide" are used interchangeably.

The recommended intake of iodine is 150 μg/d; if intake is below 50 μg/d, the gland is unable to maintain adequate hormonal secretion, and thyroid hypertrophy (goiter) and hypothyroidism result. In the United States, the average daily intake of iodine increased from a range of 100–200 μg/d in the 1960s to 240–740 μg/d in the 1980s, largely owing to the introduction of iodate as a bread preservative. Other sources of dietary iodine include iodized salt, vitamin preparations, iodine-containing medications, and iodinated contrast media. An approximation of iodine turnover in subjects on this high-iodine diet is depicted in Figure 4–7. Iodide, like chloride, is rapidly absorbed from the gastrointestinal tract and distributed in extracellular fluids as well as in salivary, gastric, and breast secretions. Although the concentration of inorganic iodide in the extracellular fluid pool will vary directly with iodide intake, extracellular fluid I⁻ is usually quite low because of the rapid clearance of iodide from extracellular fluid by thyroidal uptake and renal clearance. In the example shown, the I⁻ concentration in extracellular fluid is 0.6 μg/dL, or a total of 150 μg of I⁻ in an extracellular pool of 25 L. In the thyroid gland, there is active transport of I⁻ from the serum across the basement membrane of the thyroid cell (see below). The thyroid takes up about 115 μg of I⁻ per 24 hours; about 75 μg of I⁻ is utilized for hormone synthesis and stored in thyroglobulin; the remainder leaks back into the extracellular fluid pool. The thyroid pool of organified iodine is very large, averaging 8–10 mg, and represents a store of hormone ånd iodinated tyrosines protecting the organism against a period of iodine lack. From this storage pool, about 75 μg of hormonal iodide is released into the circulation daily. This hormonal iodide is mostly bound to serum thyroxine-binding proteins, forming a circulating pool of about 600 μg of hormonal I⁻ (as T_3 and T_4). From this pool, about 75 μg of I⁻ as T_3 and T_4 is taken up and metabolized by tissues. About 60 μg of I⁻ is returned to the iodide pool and about 15 μg of hormonal I⁻ is conjugated with glucuronide or sulfate in the liver and excreted into the stool. Since most of the dietary iodide is excreted in the urine, 24-hour urinary iodide is an excellent index of dietary intake. The 24-hour radioactive iodine uptake (RAIU) by the thyroid gland is inversely proportionate to the size of the inorganic iodide pool and directly proportionate to thyroidal activity. Typical RAIU curves are shown in Figure 4–8. In the USA, the 24-hour thyroidal radioiodine uptake has decreased from about 40–50% in the 1960s to about 8–30% in the 1990s because of increased dietary iodide intake.

THYROID HORMONE SYNTHESIS & SECRETION

The synthesis of T_4 and T_3 by the thyroid gland involves six major steps: (1) active transport of I⁻

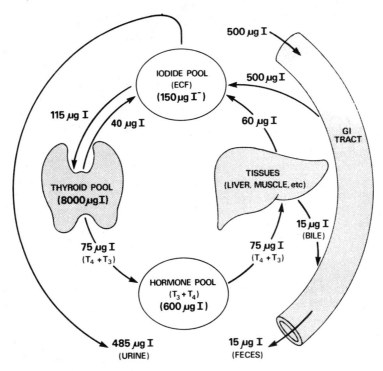

Figure 4–7. Iodine metabolism. The values indicated are representative of those that might be found in a healthy subject ingesting 500 µg of iodine a day. The actual iodine intake varies considerably among different individuals.

across the basement membrane into the thyroid cell (trapping of iodide); (2) oxidation of iodide and iodination of tyrosyl residues in thyroglobulin; (3) coupling of iodotyrosine molecules within thyroglobulin to form T_3 and T_4; (4) proteolysis of thyroglobulin, with release of free iodothyronines and iodotyrosines; (5) deiodination of iodotyrosines within the thyroid cell, with conservation and reuse of the liberated iodide, and (6) under certain circumstances, intrathyroidal 5′-deiodination of T_4 to T_3.

Thyroid hormone synthesis involves a unique glycoprotein, thyroglobulin, and an essential enzyme,

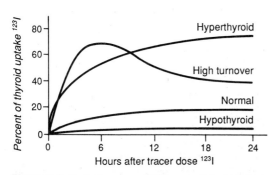

Figure 4–8. Typical curves of 24-hour radioiodine uptake in normal subjects and in patients with thyroid disease.

thyroid peroxidase (TPO). This process is summarized in Figure 4–9.

Thyroglobulin

Thyroglobulin is a large glycoprotein molecule containing 5496 amino acids, with a molecular weight of about 660,000 and a sedimentation coefficient of 19S. It contains about 140 tyrosyl residues and about 10% carbohydrate in the form of mannose, N-acetylglucosamine, galactose, fucose, sialic acid, and chondroitin sulfate. The 19S thyroglobulin compound is a dimer of two identical 12S subunits, but small amounts of the 12S monomer and a 27S tetramer are often present. The iodine content of the molecule can vary from 0.1% to 1% by weight. In thyroglobulin containing 0.5% iodine (26 atoms of iodine per 660-kDa molecule), there would be 5 molecules of monoiodotyrosine (MIT), 4.5 molecules of diiodotyrosine (DIT), 2.5 molecules of thyroxine (T_4), and 0.7 molecules of triiodothyronine (T_3). About 75% of the thyroglobulin monomer consists of repetitive domains with no hormonogenic sites. There are four tyrosyl sites for hormonogenesis on the thyroglobulin molecule: One site is located at the amino-terminal end of the molecule, and the other three are located in a sequence of 600 amino acids at the carboxyl terminal end. There is a surprising homology between this area of the thyroglobulin molecule and the structure of acetylcholinesterase,

IDODIDE TRANSPORT   HORMONE SYNTHESIS   HORMONE SECRETION

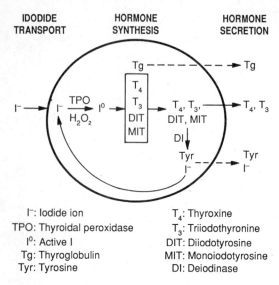

I⁻: Iodide ion
TPO: Thyroidal peroxidase
I⁰: Active I
Tg: Thyroglobulin
Tyr: Tyrosine

T_4: Thyroxine
T_3: Triiodothyronine
DIT: Diiodotyrosine
MIT: Monoiodotyrosine
DI: Deiodinase

Figure 4–9. Thyroid hormone synthesis in a thyroid follicle.

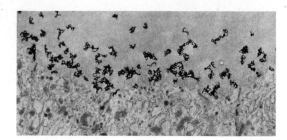

Figure 4–10. Evidence that iodination of thyroglobulin occurs at or near the apical (follicular) border of the thyroid cell. The figure depicts electronmicroscopic autoradiography of part of a rat thyroid cell 30–40 seconds after administration of sodium ^{125}I to the animal in vivo. The radioactive iodine is represented on a photographic emulsion layer by the silver grains. Few radioactive iodine molecules are localized over the thyroid cell itself, but there are many at the junction of the thyroid cell and the follicular colloid. (× 7000.) (Reproduced, with permission, from Ekholm R: *Endocrinology.* DeGroot LJ et al [editors]. Grune & Stratton, 1979.)

suggesting conservation in the evolution of these proteins.

The human thyroglobulin (hTg) gene lies on the long arm of chromosome 8 distal to the c-*myc* oncogene. TSH stimulates the transcription of the thyroglobulin gene, and hypophysectomy or T_3 therapy decreases its transcription. The thyroglobulin gene contains about 8500 nucleotides, which encode the prethyroglobulin (pre-Tg) monomer. The pre-thyroglobulin monomer contains a 19-amino-acid signal peptide, followed by a 2750-amino-acid chain that constitutes the thyroglobulin monomer. The mRNA is translated in the rough endoplasmic reticulum, and thyroglobulin chains are glycosylated during transport to the Golgi apparatus (Figure 4–5). In the Golgi apparatus, the thyroglobulin dimers are incorporated into exocytotic vesicles that fuse with the basement membrane and release the thyroglobulin into the follicular lumen. There, at the apical-colloid border, thyroglobulin is iodinated and stored in colloid (Figure 4–10).

Thyroidal Peroxidase

Thyroidal peroxidase is a membrane-bound glycoprotein with a molecular weight of about 102,000 and a heme compound as the prosthetic group of the enzyme. This enzyme mediates both the oxidation of iodide ions and the incorporation of iodine into tyrosine residues of thyroglobulin. Thyroidal peroxidase is synthesized in the rough endoplasmic reticulum (RER). After insertion into the membrane of its cisternae, it is transferred to the apical cell surface by Golgi elements and exocytic vesicles. Here, at the cell colloid interface, it is available for iodination and hormonogenesis in thyroglobulin. Thyroidal peroxidase biosynthesis is stimulated by TSH.

Iodide Transport
(The Iodide Trap)

I⁻ is transported across the basement membrane of the thyroid cell by an active energy-requiring process that is dependent upon Na⁺-K⁺ ATPase (Figure 4–11). This active transport system allows the human thyroid gland to maintain a concentration of free iodide 30–40 times that in plasma. The thyroiodide trap is markedly stimulated by TSH and by TSH receptor

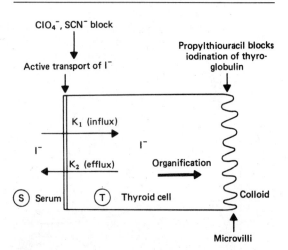

Figure 4–11. The iodide transport mechanism in the thyroid cell. K_1 is the rate constant for iodide being transported from the serum into the thyroid cell and K_2 the diffusion of inorganic iodide from the thyroid cell back into the serum. The iodide transport mechanism involves only inorganic iodide (I⁻). (SCN⁻, thiocyanate; ClO_4^-, perchlorate.)

stimulating antibody (TSH-R Ab [stim]) found in Graves' disease. It is saturable with large amounts of I$^-$ and inhibited by ions such as ClO_4^-, SCN^-, NO_3^-, and TcO_4^-. Some of these ions have clinical utility. Potassium perchlorate has been used clinically with ^{123}I to demonstrate organification defects in the thyroid gland; it will displace and allow the discharge of nonorganified I$^-$ from the iodide trap (Figure 4–12). Potassium perchlorate and potassium thiocyanate have been used to treat iodide-induced hyperthyroidism; both discharge I$^-$ from the trap and prevent further I$^-$ uptake. Sodium pertechnetate Tc 99m, which has a 6-hour half-life and a 140-keV gamma emission, is used for rapid visualization of the thyroid for size and functioning nodules. Although I$^-$ is concentrated by salivary, gastric, and breast tissue, these tissues do not organify or store I$^-$ and are not stimulated by TSH.

Iodination of Tyrosyl in Thyroglobulin

Within the thyroid cell, at the cell-colloid interface, iodide is rapidly oxidized by H_2O_2, catalyzed by thyroperoxidase, and converted to an active intermediate which is incorporated into tyrosyl residues in thyroglobulin. H_2O_2 is probably generated by a dihydronicotinamide adenine dinucleotide phosphate (NADPH) oxidase in the presence of Ca^{2+}; this process is stimulated by TSH. The iodinating intermediate may be iodinium ion (I$^+$), hypoiodate, or an iodine-free radical. The site of iodination at the apical (colloid) border of the thyroid cell can be demonstrated by autoradiography (Figure 4–10).

Thyroidal peroxidase will catalyze iodination of tyrosyl molecules in proteins other than thyroglobulin, such as albumin or thyroglobulin fragments. However, no thyroactive hormones are formed in these proteins. The metabolically inactive protein may be released into the circulation, draining thyroidal iodide reserves.

Coupling of Iodotyrosyl Residues in Thyroglobulin

The coupling of iodotyrosyl residues in thyroglobulin is also catalyzed by thyroidal peroxidase. It is thought that this is an intramolecular mechanism involving three steps: (1) oxidation of iodotyrosyl residues to an activated form by thyroidal peroxidase; (2) coupling of activated iodotyrosyl residues within the same thyroglobulin molecule to form a quinol ether intermediate; and (3) splitting of the quinol ether to form iodothyronine, with conversion of the alanine side chain of the donor iodotyrosine to dehydroalanine (Figure 4–13). For this process to occur, the dimeric structure of thyroglobulin is essential: Within the thyroglobulin molecule, two molecules of DIT may couple to form T_4, and an MIT and a DIT molecule may couple to form T_3. Thiocarbamide drugs—particularly propylthiouracil, methimazole, and carbimazole—are potent inhibitors of thyroidal peroxidase and will block thyroid hormone synthesis (Figure 4–14). These drugs are clinically useful in the management of hyperthyroidism.

Proteolysis of Thyroglobulin & Thyroid Hormone Secretion

The pattern of proteolysis of thyroglobulin and secretion of thyroid hormones is illustrated in Figure 4–5. Lysosomal enzymes are synthesized by the rough endoplasmic reticulum and packaged by the Golgi apparatus into lysosomes. These structures, surrounded by membrane, have an acidic interior and are filled with proteolytic enzymes, including proteases, endopeptidases, glycoside hydrolyases, phosphatases, and other enzymes. At the cell-colloid interface, colloid is engulfed into a colloid vesicle by a process of macropinocytosis or micropinocytosis and is absorbed into the thyroid cell. The lysosomes then fuse with the colloid vesicle and hydrolysis of thyroglobulin occurs, releasing T_4, T_3, DIT, MIT, peptide fragments, and amino acids. T_3 and T_4 are released into the circulation, while DIT and MIT are deiodinated and the I$^-$ is conserved. Thyroglobulin with a low iodine content is hydrolyzed more rapidly than thyroglobulin with a high iodine content, which may be beneficial in geographic areas where natural iodine intake is low. The mechanism of transport of

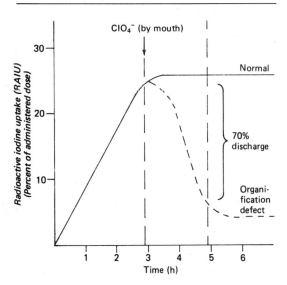

Figure 4–12. Perchlorate discharge of thyroidal inorganic iodine. Two to 3 hours after administration of a tracer dose of radioactive iodide, perchlorate is administered orally, blocking further active transport of iodide into the thyroid cell. In the normal subject (solid line), no significant decrease in radioactivity is detectable over the thyroid gland. In the representative example shown by the dashed line, there is a significant discharge of thyroidal iodide, indicating that iodide organification has been incomplete. (ClO_4^-, perchlorate.)

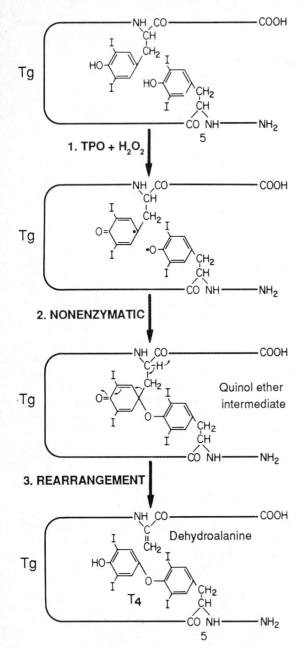

Figure 4–13. Hypothetical coupling scheme for intramolecular formation of T_4 within the thyroglobulin molecule. The major hormonogenic site at tyrosyl residue 5 is indicated. (Reproduced, with permission, from Taurog A: Thyroid hormone synthesis. Thyroid iodine metabolism. In: *Werner and Ingbar's The Thyroid,* 6th ed. Braverman LE, Utiger RD (editors). Lippincott, 1991.)

T_3 and T_4 through the thyroid cell is not known, but it may involve a specific hormone carrier. Thyroid hormone secretion is stimulated by TSH, which activates adenylyl cyclase, and by the cAMP analogue $(Bu)_2cAMP$, suggesting that it is cAMP-dependent. Thyroglobulin proteolysis is inhibited by excess iodide (see below) and by lithium, which, as lithium carbonate, is used for the treatment of manic-depressive states. A small amount of unhydrolyzed thyroglobulin is also released from the thyroid cell; this is markedly increased in certain situations such as subacute thyroiditis, hyperthyroidism, or TSH-induced goiter (Figure 4–9). Thyroglobulin (perhaps modified) may also be synthesized and released by certain thyroid malignancies such as papillary or follicular thyroid cancer and may be useful as a marker for metastatic disease.

Intrathyroidal Deiodination

MIT and DIT formed during the synthesis of thyroid hormone are deiodinated by intrathyroidal deiodinase (Figure 4–9). This enzyme is a an NADPH-dependent flavoprotein found in mitochondria and microsomes. It acts on MIT and DIT but not on T_3 and T_4. The iodide released is mostly reutilized for hormone synthesis; a small amount leaks out of the thyroid into the body pool (Figure 4–7). The 5'-deiodinase that converts T_4 to T_3 in peripheral tissues is also found in the thyroid gland. In situations of iodide deficiency, the activity of this enzyme may increase the amount of T_3 secreted by the thyroid gland, increasing the metabolic efficiency of hormone synthesis.

ABNORMALITIES IN THYROID HORMONE SYNTHESIS & RELEASE

Inherited Metabolic Defects (Dyshormonogenesis)

Inherited metabolic defects may involve any phase of hormonal biosynthesis. These result in "dyshormonogenesis," or impaired hormonal synthesis. Patients present with thyroid enlargement, or goiter, mild to severe hypothyroidism, low serum T_3 and T_4, and elevated serum TSH. The defects are described in more detail in the section on nontoxic goiter, below.

Effect of Iodide Deficiency on Hormone Biosynthesis

A diet very low in iodine reduces intrathyroidal iodine content, increases the intrathyroidal ratio of MIT to DIT, increases the ratio of T_3 to T_4, decreases the secretion of T_4, and increases serum TSH. In the adult, this results in goiter, with a high iodine uptake and mild to severe hypothyroidism; in the neonate, it may result in cretinism (see below). The adaptations that occur involve the increased synthesis of T_3 rela-

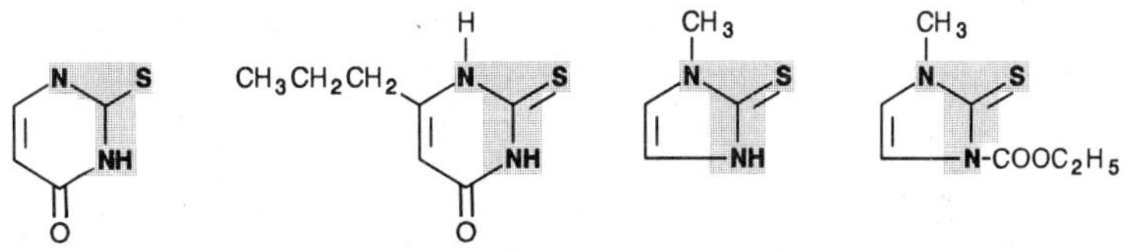

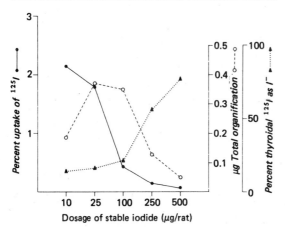

Figure 4–14. Thiocarbamide inhibitors of thyroidal iodide organification.

tive to T_4 and the increased intrathyroidal 5'-deiodination of T_4 to T_3 to produce a more active hormone mixture.

Effect of Iodine Excess on Hormone Biosynthesis

Increasing doses of iodide given to iodide-deficient rats initially induce increased iodide organification and hormone formation until a critical level is reached. At that point, inhibition of organification occurs and hormonogenesis decreases. This **Wolff-Chaikoff effect** (Figure 4–15) is probably due to inhibition of H_2O_2 generation by the high intrathyroidal I^- content. The most striking observation was that the effect is transient and that the normal thyroid gland "escapes" from the I^- effect. This is due to inhibition of the trapping of I^- with reduction in intrathyroidal

iodide, allowing hormonogenesis to proceed. If the gland is unable to make this adaptation—as may occur in patients with autoimmune thyroiditis or in some patients with dyshormonogenesis—iodide-induced hypothyroidism will ensue. In some patients, an iodide load will induce hyperthyroidism ("jod-basedow" effect). This may develop in patients with latent Graves' disease, in those with multinodular goiters, or occasionally in those with previously normal thyroid glands.

THYROID HORMONE TRANSPORT

Thyroid hormones are transported in serum bound to carrier proteins. Although only 0.04% of T_4 and 0.4% of T_3 are "free," it is the free fraction that is responsible for hormonal activity (Figure 4–16). There are three major thyroid hormone transport proteins: thyroxine-binding globulin (TBG); thyroxine-binding prealbumin (TBPA), or transthyretin; and albumin (Figure 4–17).

Thyroxine-Binding Globulin (TBG)

TBG, a single 54-kDa polypeptide chain, is synthesized in the liver. It contains four carbohydrate chains, representing 23% of the molecule by weight, and has homology with α_1-antichymotrypsin and α_1-antitrypsin. Normally, there are about ten sialic acid residues per molecule. Pregnancy or estrogen therapy increases the sialic acid content of the molecule, resulting in decreased metabolic clearance and elevated serum levels of TBG. Each molecule of TBG has a single binding site for T_4 or T_3. The serum concentration of TBG is 15–30 $\mu g/mL$, or 280–560 nmol/L. The affinity constant (K_a) for T_4 is 1×10^{10} M^{-1}, and for T_3 it is 5×10^8 M^{-1}. The high affinity for T_3 and T_4 allows TBG to carry about 70% of the circulating thyroid hormones. When fully saturated, TBG can carry about 20 μg of T_4 per deciliter.

Congenital TBG deficiency is an X-linked trait with a frequency of 1:2500 live births. One variant occurs in African Pygmies, Panamanians, African blacks, Micronesians, and Indonesians. Another variant occurs in 40% of Australian aborigines. Despite the low circulating T_4 and T_3 levels, the free hormone levels are normal and the patients are not hypothyroid. Congenital TBG deficiency is often asso-

Figure 4–15. The Wolff-Chaikoff block. As increasing doses of iodide are administered to rats, there is an initial increase in iodide organification. At a critical concentration, however, higher doses of iodide given to the animals block iodide organification. The effect of increasing doses of iodide on thyroid hormone synthesis is therefore biphasic. Concomitantly with the increase in the organification block, the intracellular inorganic iodide concentration rises. As the amount of stable iodide injected is increased, there is a decrease in thyroidal uptake of radioactive iodide. (Reproduced, with permission, from De-Groot LJ, Stanbury JB: *The Thyroid and Its Diseases,* 4th ed. Wiley, 1975.)

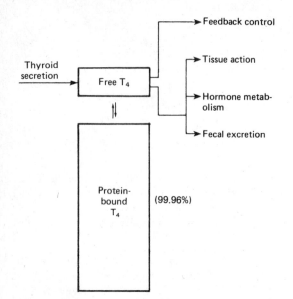

Figure 4–16. Representation of free T_4 (and free T_3) as the biologically active hormone at the level of the pituitary and the peripheral tissues. Most of the thyroid hormones circulating in plasma are protein-bound and have no biologic activity. This pool of bound hormone is in equilibrium with the free hormone pool. (Reproduced, with permission, from DeGroot LJ, Stanbury JB: *The Thyroid and Its Diseases,* 4th ed. Wiley, 1975.)

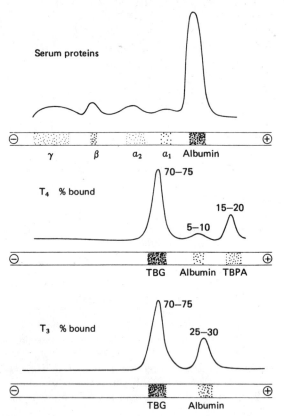

Figure 4–17. Diagrammatic representation of the distribution of radioactive T_4 and T_3 among serum thyroid hormone-binding proteins. *Top:* Paper electrophoretic pattern of serum proteins. *Middle:* Radioactive T_4 was added to serum and was then subjected to paper electrophoresis. The peaks represent the mobility of radioactive T_4 bound to different serum proteins. (TBG, thyroid hormone-binding globulin; TBPA, thyroxine-binding prealbumin.) *Bottom:* Radioactive T_3 was added to serum and subjected to paper electrophoresis. The peaks indicate the relative distribution of protein-bound radioactive T_3. The figures above each peak indicate the relative hormone distribution among the binding proteins in a normal adult. (Reproduced, with permission, from Rosenfield RL et al: *Pediatric Nuclear Medicine.* James AE Jr, Wagner HN Jr, Cooke RE [editors]. Saunders, 1974.)

ciated with congenital CBG deficiency (see Chapter 6). Congenital TBG excess is rare; it presents with elevated total T_4 and T_3 concentrations but normal free hormone levels and normal TSH.

Androgenic steroids and glucocorticoids lower TBG levels, as does major systemic illness (Table 4–1). Drugs such as salicylates, phenytoin, phenylbutazone, and diazepam may bind to TBG, displacing T_4 and T_3, in effect producing a low-TBG state. Heparin stimulates lipoprotein lipase, releasing free fatty acids, which displace T_3 and T_4 from TBG. This can occur in vivo and also in vitro, where even minute quantities of heparin will increase the measured levels of free T_4 and T_3.

Thyroxine-Binding Prealbumin

Transthyretin, or thyroxine-binding prealbumin (TBPA), is a 55-kDa globular polypeptide consisting of four identical subunits, each containing 127 amino acids. It binds about 10% of circulating T_4. Its affinity for T_3 is about tenfold lower than for T_4, so that it mostly carries T_4. The dissociation of T_4 and T_3 from TBPA is very rapid, so that TBPA is a source of rapidly available T_4. There are binding sites of TBPA for retinol-binding protein, but the transport of T_4 is independent of the transport of retinol-binding protein. The concentration of TBPA in serum is 120–240 mg/L, or 2250–4300 nmol/L.

Increased levels of TBPA may be familial and may occur in patients with glucagonoma or pancreatic islet cell carcinoma. These patients have an elevated total T_4 but a normal free T_4. Abnormal TBPA has been described in familial amyloidotic polyneuropathy, associated with a low total T_4 but normal free hormone levels.

Albumin

Albumin has one strong binding site for T_4 and T_3 and several weaker ones. Because of its high concen-

Table 4–1. Factors influencing the concentration of protein-bound thyroid hormones in serum.

A. Increased TBG concentration
1. Congenital
2. Hyperestrogenic states: pregnancy, estrogen therapy
3. Diseases: acute infectious hepatitis, hypothyroidism

B. Decreased TBG concentration
1. Congenital
2. Drugs: androgenic steroids, glucocorticoids
3. Major systemic illness: Protein malnutrition, nephrotic syndrome, cirrhosis, hyperthyroidism

C. Drugs affecting thyroid hormone binding to normal concentrations of binding protein
1. Phenytoin
2. Salicylates
3. Phenylbutazone
4. Mitotane (Lysodren)
5. Diazepam
6. FFA released by heparin stimulation of lipoprotein lipase

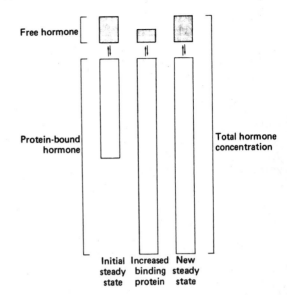

Figure 4–18. The effect of an increase in thyroid hormone-binding protein concentration on the free and protein-bound hormone concentrations. The initial increase in binding protein concentration (as may occur with estrogen administration) increases the amount of bound hormone and transiently decreases the free hormone concentration. There follows a transient increase in thyroid hormone secretion under the stimulus of TSH to replenish the free hormone pool. Another contributing factor is a transient decrease in the metabolic clearance rate of thyroid hormone. A new steady state is attained in which the free hormone secretion, metabolism, and plasma concentration are the same as initially except that the free hormone is now in equilibrium with a larger pool of bound hormone. In subjects receiving thyroid hormone medication, the same daily dose of thyroid hormone is necessary to maintain euthyroidism irrespective of the size of the bound hormone pool.

tration in serum, albumin carries about 15% of circulating T_4 and T_3. The rapid dissociation rates of T_4 and T_3 from albumin make this carrier a major source of free hormone to tissues. Hypoalbuminemia, as occurs in nephrosis or in cirrhosis of the liver, is associated with a low total T_4 and T_3, but the free hormone levels are normal.

Familial dysalbuminemic hyperthyroxinemia is an autosomal dominant inherited disorder in which 25% of the albumin exhibits high-affinity T_4 binding, resulting in an elevated total T_4 level, but normal free T_4 and euthyroidism. Affinity for T_3 may be elevated but is usually normal.

Kinetics of Thyroid Hormone Binding to Transport Proteins

The kinetics of thyroid hormone binding to the thyroid binding proteins can be expressed by conventional equilibration equations. Thus, for T_4:

$$(T_4) + (TBG) \rightleftharpoons (TBG - T_4)$$

where (T_4) represents free (unbound) hormone, (TBG) is TBG not containing T_4, and $(TBG-T_4)$ is TBG-bound T_4. This can be expressed by the mass action relationship:

$$kT_4 = \frac{(TBG - T_4)}{(T_4)(TBG)}$$

where k is the equilibrium constant for the interaction. Rearranging:

$$(T_4) = \frac{(TBG - T_4)}{kT_4(TBG)}$$

From this equation, it can be seen that T_4 exists in plasma in both free and bound forms, and the free hormone level is inversely proportionate to the free binding sites on TBG and the binding affinity for the hormone. The same relationships exist for the other thyroid hormone-binding proteins.

The effect of a change in the concentration of thyroid hormone-binding protein is shown in Figure 4–18. The levels of free thyroid hormone are normal in states where there are primary or secondary changes in plasma binding, because TSH release is controlled by the free thyroid hormone level and adjusts to normalize it irrespective of how much hormone is bound by the plasma proteins.

There has been much speculation on the role of the thyroid hormone transport proteins. The three major hypotheses are as follows: (1) they form a storage pool of readily available free hormone; (2) they allow the delivery of T_3 and T_4 to all tissues because the tiny free hormone pool is continually replenished as the hormones are absorbed by tissues; and (3) they protect tissues from massive hormone release. Thus, although the transport proteins are not essential for thyroid hormone activity, they may make the system more efficient.

METABOLISM OF THYROID HORMONES

The daily secretion of the normal thyroid gland is about 100 nmol of T_4, about 5 nmol of T_3, and less than 5 nmol of metabolically inactive reverse T_3 (rT_3) (Figure 4–19). Most of the plasma pool of T_3 is derived from peripheral metabolism (5'-deiodination) of T_4. The biologic activity of thyroid hormones is greatly dependent on the location of the iodine atoms (Table 4–2). Deiodination of the *outer ring* of T_4 (5'-deiodination) produces 3,5,3'-triiodothyronine (T_3), which is three to eight times more potent than T_4. On the other hand, deiodination of the *inner ring* of T_4 (5-deiodination) produces 3,3',5'-triiodothyronine (reverse T_3, or rT_3), which is metabolically inert. The deiodinative pathways of thyroxine metabolism are presented in Figure 4–20. Monodeiodination of the outer ring of thyroxine is a "step up" process, increasing the metabolic activity of the resultant compound, while monodeiodination of the inner ring is a "step down" or inactivation process. Further deiodination of the molecule abolishes hormonal activity.

At least three enzymes catalyze these monodeiodination reactions: type 1, 5'-deiodinase; type 2, 5'-deiodinase; and type 3, tyrosyl ring deiodinase, or 5-deiodinase. They differ in tissue localization, substrate specificity, and effect of disease. The properties of these deiodinases are summarized in Table 4–3.

Type 1 5'-deiodinase is the most abundant deiodinase and is found largely in liver and kidney and in lesser quantity in the thyroid gland, skeletal muscle, heart muscle, and other tissues. Molecular cloning of type 1 5'-deiodinase has revealed that it contains selenocysteine and that this is probably the active deiodinating site. The major function of type 1 5'-deiodinase is to provide T_3 to the plasma. It is increased in hyperthyroidism and decreased in hypothyroidism. The increased activity in hyperthyroidism accounts in part for the high T_3 levels in this syndrome. The enzyme is inhibited by propylthiouracil but not methimazole, which explains why propylthiouracil is more effective than methimazole in reducing T_3 levels in severe hyperthyroidism. Inhibition of type 1 5'-deiodinase activity results in impaired conversion of T_4 to T_3. Some conditions associated with decreased conversion of T_4 to T_3 are listed in Table 4–4. Note that only propylthiouracil and ipodate impair intracellular conversion of T_4 to T_3; the other conditions may modify the ratio of T_4 to T_3 in serum, requiring interpretation of thyroid tests (see below), but they do not change intracellular T_3 production. Dietary deficiency of selenium also impairs conversion of T_4 to T_3. In the presence of iodine deficiency, repletion of selenium causes increased type 1 5'-deiodinase activity, an acceleration of T_4 metabolism, and a worsening of hypothyroidism, since the iodine-deficient gland cannot compensate for the increased T_4 metabolism.

Type 2 5'-deiodinase is found largely in the brain and pituitary gland. It is resistant to propylthiouracil but very sensitive to circulating T_4. The major effect of the enzyme is to maintain a constant level of intracellular T_3 in the central nervous system. Reduction in circulating T_4 results in a rapid increase in the amount of the enzyme in brain and pituitary cells, probably by altering the rate of enzyme degradation and inactivation, maintaining the level of intracellular T_3 and cellular function. High levels of serum T_4 reduce type 2 5'-deiodinase, protecting brain cells from excessive T_3. This may be the mechanism whereby the hypothalamus and pituitary monitor the levels of circulating T_4. Other metabolic products of T_4 metabolism such as rT_3 can also modify the levels of type 2 5'-deiodinase in the brain and the pituitary gland, and alpha-adrenergic compounds stimulate type 2 5'-deiodinase in brown fat. The physiologic significance of these reactions is not clear.

Type 3 5-deiodinase, or tyrosyl ring deiodinase, is found in placental chorionic membranes and glial cells in the central nervous system. It inactivates T_4 by converting it to rT_3 and T_3 by converting it to 3,3'-diiodothyronine (3,3'-T_2 (Figure 4–20). It is elevated in hyperthyroidism and decreased in hypothyroidism. Thus, it may help to protect the fetus and the brain from excess or deficiency of T_4.

About 80% of T_4 is metabolized by deiodination, 35% to T_3 and 45% to rT_3 (Figure 4–19). The remainder is inactivated mostly by glucuronidation in the liver and secretion into bile, or to a lesser extent by sulfonation and deiodination in the liver or kidney. Other metabolic reactions include deamination

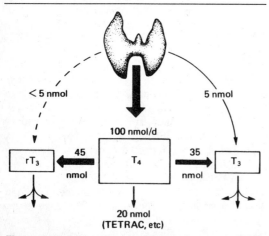

Figure 4–19. Major pathways of thyroxine metabolism in normal adult humans. Rates are expressed in nmol/24 h and are approximations based upon available data. 100 nmol of T_4 is equivalent to approximately 75 μg. (rT3, reverse T3; TETRAC, tetraiodothyroacetic acid.) (Reproduced, with permission, from Cavalieri RR, Rapoport B: Impaired peripheral conversion of thyroxine to triiodothyronine. Ann Rev Med 1977;28:5765.)

Table 4–2. Chemical structures and biologic activity of thyroid hormones.

	Hormone	Common Name	Biologic Activity
	L-3,5,3',5'-Tetraiodothyronine	L-Thyroxine; T_4	100
	L-3,5,3'-Triiodothyronine	T_3	300–800
	L-3,3',5'-Triiodothyronine	Reverse T_3; rT_3	< 1
	DL-3,3'-Diiodothyronine	3,3'-T_2	< 1–3
	DL-3,5-Diiodothyronine	3,5-T_2	7–11
	DL-3',5'-Diiodothyronine	3'5'-T_2	0
	L-3,5,3',5'-Tetraiodothyroacetic acid	Tetrac	? 10–50
	L-3,5,3'-Triiodothyroacetic acid	Triac	? 25–35

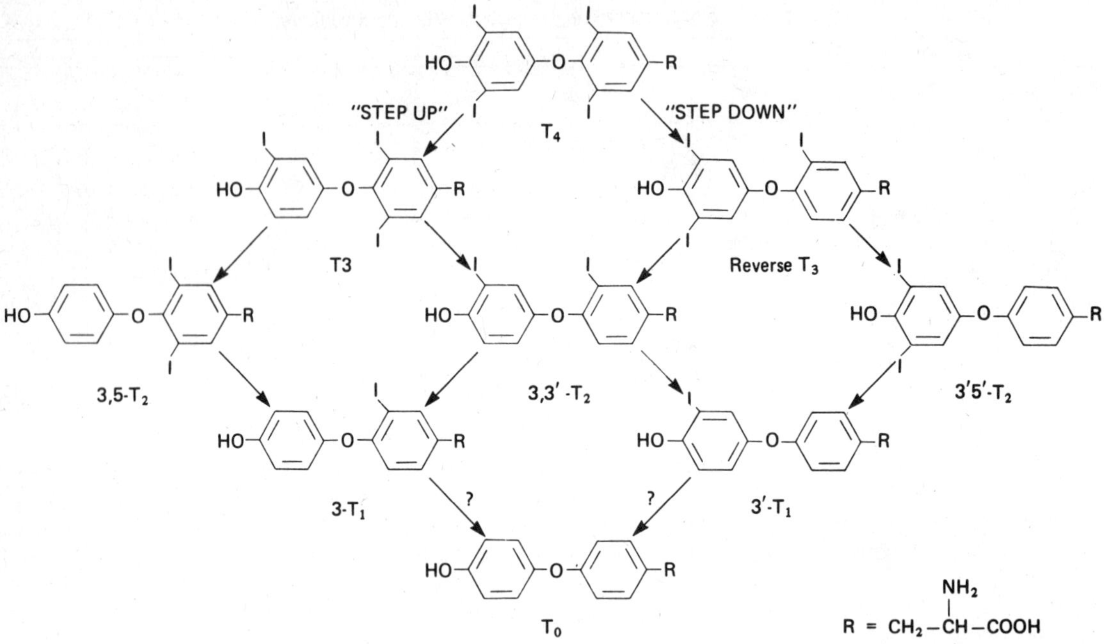

Figure 4–20. The deiodinative pathway of thyroxine metabolism. The monodeiodination of T_4 to T_3 represents a "step up" in biologic potency, whereas the monodeiodination of T_4 to reverse T_3 has the opposite effect. Further deiodination of T_3 essentially abolishes hormonal activity.

of the alanine side chain, forming thyroacetic acid derivatives of low biologic activity (Table 4–2); or decarboxylation or cleavage of the ether bridge, forming inactive compounds.

Representative iodothyronine kinetic values are summarized in Table 4–5. The volume of distribution is the quantity of plasma that would contain the equivalent of the total extrathyroidal pool of the compound. Thus, for T_4, the serum concentration is about 100 nmol/L, the volume of distribution is about 10 L, and the body pool is about 1000 nmol. The metabolic clearance rate for T_4 is only about 10% per day (100 nmol), and the half-life of T_4 in plasma is about 7 days. The body pool of T_3 is much smaller and the turnover more rapid, with a plasma half-life of 1 day. The total body pool of rT_3 is about the same

Table 4–3. Iodothyronine deiodinases.[1]

Parameter	Type 1 (5′)	Type 2 (5′)	Type 3 (5)
Physiologic role	Provide T_3 to plasma	Provide intracellular T_3	Inactivate T_3 and T_4
Tissue location	Liver, kidney, muscle, thyroid	CNS, pituitary, brown fat, placenta	Placenta, CNS, skin, fetal liver
Substrate	$rT_3 \gg T_4 > T_3$	$T_4 = rT_3$	$T_3 > T_4$
K_m for T_4	1×10^{-6} M	1×10^{-9} M	6×10^{-9} M (T_3), 37×10^{-9} M (T_4)
Deiodination site	Outer and inner ring	Outer ring	Inner ring
Kinetic mechanism	Ping-pong	Sequential	Sequential
Dithiothreitol	Stimulates	Stimulates	Stimulates
K_i for PTU	5×10^{-7} M sensitive	4×10^{-3} M resistant	?($> 10^{-3}$ M) resistant
Active site	Selenocysteine	Cysteine	?Cysteine
Ipanoic acid	Inhibits	Inhibits	Inhibits
Hypothyroidism	Decrease	Increase	Decrease
Hyperthyroidism	Increase	Decrease	Increase

[1] Adapted and modified, with permission, from Larsen PR, Ingbar SH. The thyroid gland. In: *Williams Textbook of Endocrinology,* 8th ed. Wilson JW, Foster DW (editors). Saunders, 1992.

Table 4–4. Conditions or factors associated with decreased conversion of T_4 to T_3.

1. Fetal life.
2. Caloric restriction.
3. Hepatic disease.
4. Major systemic illness.
5. Drugs:
   Propylthiouracil
   Glucocorticoids
   Propranolol (mild effect)
   Iodinated x-ray contrast agents (iopanoic acid, ipodate sodium)
   Amiodarone
6. Selenium deficiency

size as that of T_3, but it has a much more rapid turnover, with a plasma half-life of only 0.2 day. The rapid clearance of T_3 and rT_3 is due to lower binding affinity for thyroid binding proteins.

CONTROL OF THYROID FUNCTION

The growth and function of the thyroid gland is controlled by at least four mechanisms: (1) the classic hypothalamic-pituitary-thyroid axis (Figure 4–21), in which hypothalamic thyrotropin-releasing hormone (TRH) stimulates the synthesis and release of anterior pituitary thyroid-stimulating hormone (TSH), which in turn stimulates growth and hormone secretion by the thyroid gland; (2) the pituitary and peripheral deiodinases, which modify the effects of T_4 and T_3; (3) autoregulation of hormone synthesis by the thyroid gland itself in relationship to its iodine supply; and (4) stimulation or inhibition of thyroid function by TSH receptor autoantibodies.

Thyrotropin-Releasing Hormone

Thyrotropin-releasing hormone (TRH) is a tripeptide, pyroglutamyl-histidyl-prolineamide, synthesized by neurons in the supraoptic and supraventricular nuclei of the hypothalamus (Figure 4–22). It is stored in the median eminence of the hypothalamus and then transported via the pituitary portal venous system down the pituitary stalk to the anterior pituitary gland, where it controls synthesis and release of TSH. TRH is also found in other portions of the hypothalamus, the brain, and the spinal cord, where it may function as a neurotransmitter. The gene for human preproTRH contains a 3.3-kb transcription unit that encodes six TRH molecules. The gene also encodes other neuropeptides that may be biologically significant. In the anterior pituitary gland, TRH binds to specific membrane receptors on thyrotropes and prolactin-secreting cells, stimulating synthesis and release of both TSH and prolactin. Thyroid hormones cause a slow depletion of pituitary TRH receptors, diminishing TRH response; estrogen increases TRH receptors, increasing pituitary sensitivity to TRH.

The response of the pituitary thyrotrope to TRH is bimodal: First, it stimulates release of stored hormone; and second, it stimulates gene activity, which increases hormone synthesis. TRH binds to its receptor on the thyrotrope and activates a G protein, which in turn activates phospholipase c to hydrolyze phosphatidylinositol-4,5-bisphosphate (PIP2) to inositol-1,4,5-triphosphate (IP3). IP3 stimulates the release of intracellular Ca^{2+}, which causes the first burst response of hormone release. Simultaneously, there is generation of 1,2-diacylglycerol (1,2-DG), which activates protein kinase C, thought to be responsible for the second and sustained phase of hormone secretion. The increases in intracellular Ca^{2+} and in protein kinase C may be involved in increased transcription (see Figure 1–25). TRH also stimulates the glyco-

Table 4–5. Representative iodothyronine kinetic values in a euthyroid human.

	T_4	T_3	rT_3
Serum levels			
Total, μg/dL (nmol/L)	8 (103)	0.12 (1.84)	0.04 (0.51)
Free, ng/dL (pmol/L)	2.1 (27)	0.28 (4.3)	0.24 (3.69)
Body pool, μg (nmol)	800 (1023)	46 (70.7)	40 (61.5)
Distribution volume (L)	10	38	98
Metabolic clearance rate (MCR) (L/d)	1	22	90
Production (disposal) rate. MCRX serum concentration, μg/d (nmol/d)	80 (103)	26 (34)	36 (46)
Half-life in plasma ($t_{1/2}$) (days)	7	1	0.2

(**Note**: T_4 μg/dL × 12.87 = nmol/L; T_3 μg/dL × 15.38 = nmol/L)

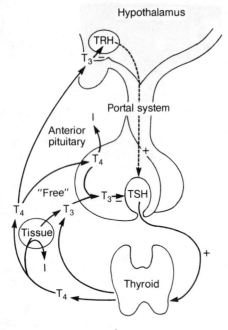

Hypothalamus

Portal system

Anterior pituitary

"Free"

Tissue

Thyroid

Figure 4–21. The hypothalamic-hypophysial-thyroid axis. TRH produced in the hypothalamus reaches the thyrotropes in the anterior pituitary by the hypothalamic-hypophysial-portal system and stimulates the synthesis and release of TSH. In both the hypothalamus and the pituitary, it is primarily T_3 that inhibits TRH and TSH secretion. T_4 undergoes monodeiodination to T_3 in neural and pituitary as well as in peripheral tissues.

Table 4–6. Factors controlling the secretion of thyroid hormones.

1. HYPOTHALAMIC: Synthesis and release of TRH
   Stimulatory:
       Decreased serum T_4 and T_3, and intraneuronal T_3
       Neurogenic: Pulsatile secretion and circadian rhythm
       Exposure to cold (animals and human newborn)
       Alpha-adrenergic catecholamines
       Arginine vasopressin
   Inhibitory:
       Increased serum T_4 and T_3, and intraneuronal T_3
       Alpha-adrenergic blockers
       Hypothalamic tumors
2. ANTERIOR PITUITARY: Synthesis and release of TSH
   Stimulatory:
       TRH
       Decreased serum T_4 and T_3, and intrathyrotrope T_3
       Decreased activity Type 2 5'-deiodinase
       Estrogen: increased TRH binding sites
   Inhibitory:
       Increased serum T_4 and T_3, and intrathyrotrope T_3
       Increased activity Type 2 5'-deiodinase
       Somatostatin
       Dopamine, dopamine agonists: bromocriptine
       Glucocorticoids
       Chronic illness
       Pituitary tumors
3. THYROID: Synthesis and release of thyroid hormones
   Stimulatory:
       TSH
       TSH-R stimulating antibodies
   Inhibitory:
       TSH-R blocking antibodies
       Iodide excess
       Lithium therapy

sylation of TSH, which is necessary for full biologic activity of the hormone. Thus, patients with hypothalamic tumors and hypothyroidism may have measurable TSH, which is biologically inactive.

Elegant studies in vitro and in vivo demonstrated that T_3 directly inhibits the transcription of prepro-TRH gene and thus the synthesis of TRH in the hypothalamus. Since T_4 is converted to T_3 within peptidergic neurons, it is also an effective inhibitor of TRH synthesis and secretion (Table 4–6).

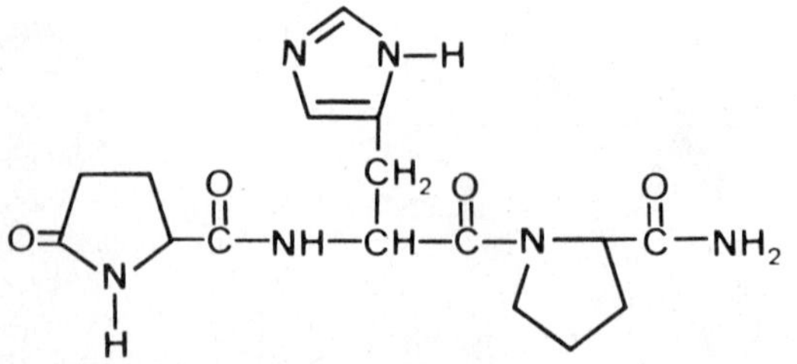

Figure 4–22. Chemical structure of thyrotropin-releasing hormone (TRH).

(pyro)Glu-His-Pro-(NH$_2$)

TRH is rapidly metabolized, with a half-life of intravenously administered hormone of about 5 minutes. Plasma TRH levels in normal subjects are very low, ranging from 25 to 100 pg/mL.

TRH-stimulated TSH secretion occurs in a pulsatile fashion throughout the 24 hours (Figure 4–23). Normal subjects have a mean TSH pulse amplitude of about 0.6 μU/mL and an average frequency of one pulse every 1.8 hours. In addition, normal subjects show a circadian rhythm, with a peak serum TSH at night, usually between midnight and 4 AM. This peak is unrelated to sleep, eating, or the secretion of other pituitary hormones. This rhythm is presumably controlled by a hypothalamic neuronal "pulse generator" driving TRH synthesis in the supraoptic and supraventricular nuclei. In hypothyroid patients, the amplitude of the pulses and the nocturnal surge are much larger than normal, and in patients with hyperthyroidism both the pulses and the nocturnal surge are markedly suppressed.

In experimental animals and in the newborn human, exposure to cold increases TRH and TSH secretion, but this is not noted in the adult human.

Certain hormones and drugs may modify TRH synthesis and release. TRH secretion is stimulated by decreased serum T_4 or T_3 (with decreased intraneuronal T_3), by alpha-adrenergic agonists, and by argi-

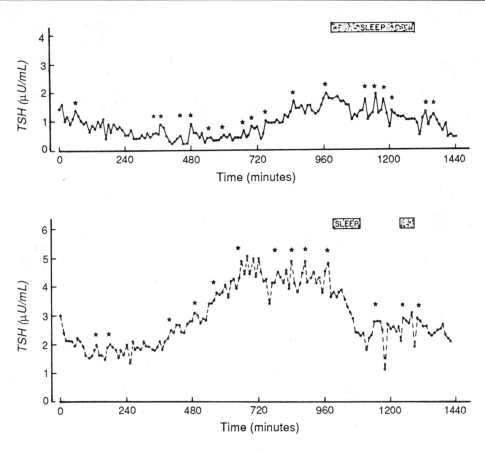

Figure 4–23. Serum TSH in two normal subjects demonstrating spontaneous pulses and the circadian rhythm of TSH secretion. (Reproduced, with permission, from Greenspan SL et al: Pulsatile secretion of TSH in man. J Clin Endocrinol Metabol 1986;63:664. Copyright © 1986 by The Endocrine Society.)

nine vasopressin. Conversely, TRH secretion is inhibited by increased serum T_4 or T_3 (with increased intraneuronal T_3) and alpha-adrenergic blockade (Table 4–6).

TRH administered intravenously to humans in a bolus dose of 200–500 μg results in a rapid rise in serum TSH, peaking at about 30 minutes and lasting for 2–3 hours. Typical responses to TRH in various clinical conditions are presented in Figures 4–24 and 4–25. Note the exaggerated response of pituitary TSH to TRH in patients with primary hypothyroidism and the suppressed response in patients with hyperthyroidism, nodular goiter with autonomously functioning nodules, or pituitary hypothyroidism. TRH and its dipeptide metabolite cyclo(HisPro) are also found in the islet cells of the pancreas, but its function there is not yet established.

Thyrotropin

Thyroid-stimulating hormone, or thyrotropin (TSH), is a glycoprotein synthesized and secreted by the thyrotropes of the anterior pituitary gland. It has a molecular weight of about 28,000 and is composed of two noncovalently linked subunits, α and β. The α subunit is common to the two other pituitary glyco proteins, FSH and LH, and also to the placental hormone hCG; the β subunit is different for each glycoprotein hormone and confers specific binding properties and biologic activity. The human α subunit has an apoprotein core of 92 amino acids and contains two oligosaccharide chains; the TSH β subunit has an apoprotein core of 112 amino acids and contains one oligosaccharide chain. Glycosylation takes place in the rough endoplasmic reticulum and the Golgi of the thyrotrope, where glucose, mannose, and fucose residues and terminal sulfate or sialic acid residues are linked to the apoprotein core. The function of these carbohydrate residues is not entirely clear, but it is likely that they enhance TSH biologic activity and modify its metabolic clearance rate. For example, deglycosylated TSH will bind to its receptor, but its biologic activity is markedly decreased and its metabolic clearance rate is markedly increased.

The gene for the human α subunit is located on chromosome 6 and the gene for the human β subunit

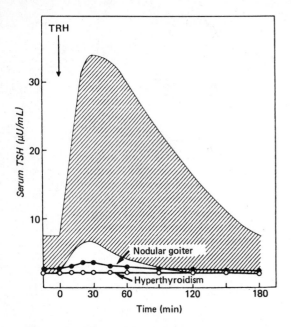

Figure 4–24. Typical serum TSH responses to TRH in patients with hyperthyroidism or toxic nodular goiter. The hatched area indicates normal range. (Reproduced, with permission, from Utiger RD: *The Thyroid,* 4th ed. Werner SC, Ingbar SH [editors]. Harper & Row, 1978.)

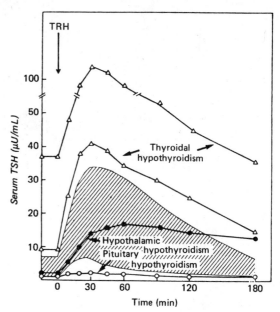

Figure 4–25. Typical serum TSH responses to TRH in patients with thyroid (primary), pituitary (secondary), and hypothalamic (tertiary) hypothyroidism. The hatched area indicates the normal range. (Reproduced, with permission, from Utiger RD: *The Thyroid,* 4th ed. Werner SC, Ingbar SH [editors]. Harper & Row, 1978.)

on chromosome 1. A schematic representation of the α and β subunit genes is presented in Figure 4–26. Several kindreds have been reported with a point mutation in the TSH β gene, resulting in a TSH-β subunit that did not combine with the α subunit to produce biologically active TSH. The disorders were autosomal recessive, and the clinical picture was that of nongoitrous hypothyroidism.

TSH is the primary factor controlling thyroid cell growth and thyroid hormone synthesis and secretion. It achieves this effect by binding to a specific **TSH receptor** (TSH-R) on the thyroid cell membrane and activating both the G protein-adenylyl cyclase-cAMP and the phospholipase C signaling systems. The TSH receptor has been cloned and is a single-chain glycoprotein containing 744 amino acids; the molecular weight of the glycosylated molecule is about 100. It has an intracellular domain of 346 amino acids, with seven transmembrane loops, and an extracellular domain of 398 amino acids containing six glycosylation sites and three disulfide bonds (Figure 4–27). The TSH receptor differs from the other glycoprotein hormone receptors (eg, LH and hCG) by the insertion of an eight-amino-acid sequence (amino acid residues 38–45) and a 50-amino-acid sequence (amino acid residues 317–366). It is thought that the former area (38–45) is the TSH binding site and that the latter area (317–366) contains the binding site for the TSH receptor-stimulating antibody (TSH-R Ab [stim])

characteristic of Graves' disease (see below). The human TSH-R gene is located on chromosome 14q31. TSH upregulates TSH-R mRNA, increasing the number of TSH receptors on the thyroid cell membrane.

Effects of TSH on the Thyroid Cell

TSH has many actions on the thyroid cell. Most of its actions are mediated through the G protein-adenylyl cyclase-cAMP system, but activation of the phosphatidylinositol (PIP2) system with increase in intracellular calcium may also be involved. The major actions of TSH include the following:

A. Changes in Thyroid Cell Morphology: TSH rapidly induces pseudopods at the cell-colloid border, accelerating thyroglobulin resorption. Colloid content is diminished. Intracellular colloid droplets are formed and lysosome formation is stimulated, increasing thyroglobulin hydrolysis (Figure 4–5).

B. Cell Growth: Individual thyroid cells increase in size (Figure 4–4); vascularity is increased; and, over a period of time, thyroid enlargement, or goiter, develops.

C. Iodine Metabolism: TSH stimulates all phases of iodide metabolism, from increased iodide uptake and transport to increased iodination of thyroglobulin and increased secretion of thyroid hormones. The increase in cAMP mediates increased iodide transport, while PIP2 hydrolysis and increased intracellular Ca^{2+} stimulate the iodination of thyroglobulin. The

Common α subunit gene

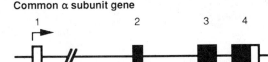

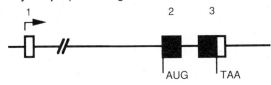

Thyrotropin β subunit gene

Figure 4–26. Schematic representation of the human TSH subunit genes. The human common α subunit gene (on chromosome 6) and the TSH β subunit gene (on chromosome 1) have four and three exons, respectively, represented by boxes separated by introns (thin lines). Point mutations in the TSH β subunit gene have been found in patients with nongoitrous hypothyroidism. (Reproduced, with permission, from Wondisford FE et al: Chemistry and biosynthesis of thyrotropin. In: *Werner and Ingbar's The Thyroid,* 6th ed. Braverman LE, Utiger RD [editors]. Lippincott, 1991.)

TSH effect on iodide transport is biphasic: Initially, it is depressed (iodide efflux); and then, after a lag of several hours, iodide uptake is increased. The efflux of iodide may be due to the rapid increase in hydrolysis of thyroglobulin with release of hormone and leakage of iodide out of the gland.

D. Increase in mRNA for thyroglobulin and thyroidal peroxidase, with an increase in incorporation of I⁻ into MIT, DIT, T_3 and T_4.

E. Increased lysosomal activity, with increased secretion of T_4 and T_3 from the gland. There is also increased activity of type 1 5'-deiodinase, conserving intrathyroidal iodine.

F. TSH has many other effects on the thyroid gland, including stimulation of glucose uptake, oxygen consumption, CO_2 production, and an increase in glucose oxidation via the hexosemonophosphate pathway and the Krebs cycle. There is accelerated turnover of phospholipids and stimulation of synthesis of purine and pyrimidine precursors, with increased synthesis of DNA and RNA.

Serum TSH

Normally, only α subunit and intact TSH are present in the serum. The level of α subunit is about 0.5–2.0 µg/L; it is elevated in postmenopausal women and in patients with TSH-secreting pituitary tumors (see below). The serum level of TSH is about 0.5–5 mU/L; it is increased in hypothyroidism and decreased in hyperthyroidism, whether endogenous or from excessive oral intake of thyroid hormones. The plasma half-life of TSH is about 30 min-

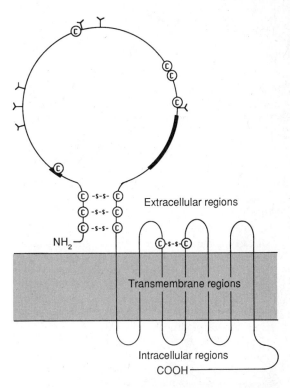

Figure 4–27. Proposed model of the human TSH receptor. The thick black segments represent the regions unique to the TSH-R between amino acids 39–45 and 317–366. The former area is thought to be the TSH binding site and the latter area the binding site for the TSH receptor-stimulating antibody characteristic of Graves' disease. (Reproduced, with permission, from Nagayama Y, Rapoport B: The thyrotropin receptor 25 years after its discovery: New insights after its molecular cloning. Mol Endocrinol 1992;6:145. Copyright © 1992 by The Endocrine Society.)

utes, and the daily production rate is about 40–150 mU/d.

Control of Pituitary TSH Secretion

The two major factors controlling the synthesis and release of TSH are the level of intrathyrotrope T_3, which controls mRNA for TSH synthesis and release, and TRH, which controls glycosylation, activation, and release of TSH (Table 4–6).

TSH synthesis and release are inhibited by high serum levels of T_4 and T_3 (hyperthyroidism) and stimulated by low levels of thyroid hormone (hypothyroidism). In addition, certain hormones and drugs inhibit TSH secretion. These include somatostatin, dopamine, dopamine agonists such as bromocriptine, and glucocorticoids. Acute or chronic disease may cause inhibition of TSH secretion during active illness, and there may be a rebound rise in TSH as the patient recovers. The magnitude of these effects is variable; thus, the drugs mentioned above will suppress serum TSH, but it will usually be detectable. In contrast, hyperthyroidism will turn off TSH secretion entirely. These observations are important clinically in interpreting serum TSH levels in patients receiving these medications.

Destructive lesions or tumors of the hypothalamus or anterior pituitary gland may impair TRH and TSH secretion by destruction of secretory cells. This will result in "secondary hypothyroidism" due to pituitary thyrotrope destruction or "tertiary hypothyroidism" due to destruction of TRH-secreting neurons. Differential diagnosis of these lesions is discussed below (see Thyroid Tests).

Other Thyroid
Stimulators & Inhibitors

The thyroid follicle has a rich supply of capillaries that carry noradrenergic nerve fibers from the superior cervical ganglion and acetylcholine esterase-positive nerve fibers derived from the vagal nodose and thyroid ganglia. The parafollicular "C" cells secrete both calcitonin and calcitonin gene-related peptide (CGRP). In experimental animals, these and other neuropeptides modify thyroid blood flow and hormone secretion. In addition, growth factors such as insulin, IGF-1, and EGF and the autocrine actions of prostaglandins and cytokines may modify thyroid cell growth and hormone production. However, it is not yet clear how important these effects are in clinical situations.

Role of Pituitary
& Peripheral Deiodinases

Pituitary type 2 5'-deiodinase converts T_4 to T_3 in the brain and pituitary, providing the main source of intracellular T_3. Its increased activity in hypothyroidism helps to maintain intracellular T_3 in the presence of falling serum T_4 concentrations. In hyperthyroidism, the decrease in its activity helps to prevent overloading of pituitary and neural cells with thyroid hormone. In contrast, type 1 5'-deiodinase is decreased in hypothyroidism, conserving T_4, and increased in hyperthyroidism, accelerating T_4 metabolism (Table 4–3).

Thyroidal Autoregulation

Autoregulation may be defined as the capacity of the thyroid gland to modify its function to adapt to changes in the availability of iodine, independent of pituitary TSH. Thus, humans can maintain normal thyroid hormone secretion with iodide intakes varying from 50 μg to several milligrams per day. Some of the effects of iodide deficiency or excess are discussed above. The major adaptation to low iodine intake is the preferential synthesis of T_3 rather than T_4, increasing the metabolic effectiveness of the secreted hormone. Iodide excess, on the other hand, inhibits many thyroidal functions, including I^- transport, cAMP formation, H_2O_2 generation, hormone synthesis and secretion, and the binding of TSH and TSH-R

Ab to the TSH receptor. Some of these effects may be mediated by the formation of intrathyroidal iodinated fatty acids. The ability of the normal thyroid to "escape" from these inhibitory effects (Wolff-Chaikoff effect) allows the gland to continue to secrete hormone despite a high dietary iodide intake. It is important to note that this is different from the therapeutic effect of iodide in the treatment of Graves' disease. Here, the high levels of iodide inhibit thyroglobulin endocytosis and lysosomal activity, decreasing thyroid hormone release and lowering circulating hormone levels. In addition, the inhibition of TSH-R Ab [stim] activity reduces the vascularity of the gland, with beneficial consequences during surgery. This effect is also transient, lasting about 10 days to 2 weeks.

Autoimmune Regulation

The ability of B lymphocytes to synthesize TSH receptor antibodies that can either block the action of TSH or mimic TSH activity by binding to different areas on the TSH receptor provides a form of thyroid regulation by the immune system.

Thus, the synthesis and secretion of thyroid hormones are controlled at three different levels: (1) the level of the hypothalamus, by modifying TRH secretion; (2) the pituitary level, by inhibition or stimulation of TSH secretion; and (3) the level of the thyroid, by autoregulation and blockade or stimulation of the TSH receptor (Table 4–6).

THE ACTION OF THYROID HORMONES

1. THE THYROID HORMONE RECEPTOR

Thyroid hormones, T_3 and T_4, circulate in plasma largely bound to protein but in equilibrium with the free hormone. It is the free hormone that is transported either by passive diffusion or by specific carriers through the cell membrane, through the cell cytoplasm, to bind to a specific receptor in the cell nucleus. Within the cell, T_4 is converted to T_3 by 5' deiodinase, suggesting that T_4 is a prohormone and T_3 the active form of the hormone. The nuclear receptor for T_3 has been cloned. It is one of a "family" of receptors, all similar to the receptor for the retrovirus that causes erythroblastosis in chickens, v-*erb* A, and to the nuclear receptors for glucocorticoids, mineralocorticoids, estrogens, progestins, vitamin D_3, and retinoic acid (Figure 4–28 and Figure 1–20). Human thyroid hormone receptor (hTR) exists in at least three forms: hTR-α 1 and 2 and hTR-β1. hTR-α contains 410 amino acids, has a molecular weight of about 47,000, and its gene is located on chromosome 17. hTR-β contains 456 amino acids, with a molecular weight of about 52,000, and its gene is on chromosome 3. Each receptor molecule contains three

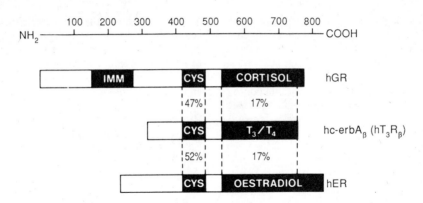

Figure 4–28. Schematic comparison of the steroid and thyroid hormone receptors. IMM, immunogenic region of the human glucocorticoid receptor; CYS, the cysteine-rich region encoding the putative DNA binding domain. Cortisol, T_3/T_4, oestradiol represent hormone-binding regions. The numbers separating the boxes represent the percentage amino acid identities between receptor species. (hGR, human glucocorticoid receptor; hc-erbA$_\beta$ (hT$_3$R$_\beta$, human thyroid hormone receptor; hER, human estrogen receptor.) (Reproduced, with permission, from Weinberger C et al: The c-*erb*-A gene encodes a thyroid hormone receptor. Nature 1986;324:641. © 1986 by Macmillan Magazines.)

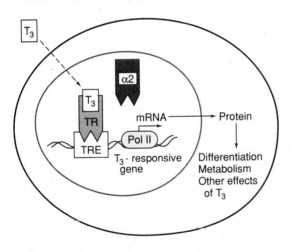

Figure 4–29. Model of the mediation of T_3 action by nuclear thyroid hormone receptors. T_3 either enters the cell (as depicted) or is derived from intracellular deiodination of T_4. Nuclear interaction between a T_3-bound TR and a thyroid hormone-responsive element (TRE) results in increased or decreased activity of RNA polymerase II (pol II) on a T_3-responsive gene. The TRE is indicated as containing two half-sites, and the TR may bind as a dimer. Effects on mRNA levels are translated into increased or decreased cellular concentrations of proteins so as to promote differentiation, metabolic processes, and other cell-specific effects of T_3. In the absence of T_3, the TRE-bound TR may repress basal transcription. c-*erb*A$_a$2 ("a2"), the non-T_3-binding splice variant, can inhibit the effects of T_3-bound TRs by a mechanism that has not yet been established, probably involving heterodimer formation or competition for the TRE. A similar mechanism is likely to explain the dominant negative effect of the v-erbA oncoprotein and mutated TRs, as in the syndromes of generalized resistance to T_3. (Reproduced, with permission, from Lazar MA, Chin WW: Nuclear thyroid hormone receptors. J Clin Invest 1990;86:1777. © 1990 by The American Society for Clinical Investigation.)

specific domains: an amino terminal domain that enhances receptor activity; a central DNA-binding domain with two cysteine-zinc "fingers"; and a carboxyl terminal hormone-binding domain. It is likely that hTR-β1 and hTR-α1 are the biologically active forms of the receptor; hTR-α2 lacks hormone binding capacity, but it does bind to the thyroid hormone response element (TRE) on DNA and thus may act in some instances to inhibit the activity of T_3 (Figure 4–29). The binding affinity of T_3 analogues to the T_3 receptors is directly proportionate to the biologic activity of the analogue. Point mutations in the hTR-β gene, resulting in abnormal T_3 receptors, are responsible for the syndrome of generalized resistance to thyroid hormone (Refetoff's syndrome; see below).

The thyroid hormone receptors bind to the specific TRE sites on DNA in the absence of T^3 (Figure 4–29)—unlike the case with the steroid hormone receptors. The TREs are located near, generally upstream with respect to the start of transcription, to the promoters where transcription of specific thyroid hormone responsive genes is initiated. T_3 binding to the receptors results in stimulation, or in some cases inhibition, of the transcription of these genes with consequent changes in the levels of the mRNAs transcribed from them. The changes in mRNA levels alter the levels of the protein product of these genes. These proteins then mediate the thyroid hormone response. These receptors often function as heterodimers with other transcription factors such as the retinoic X receptor and the retinoic acid receptor.

2. PHYSIOLOGIC EFFECTS OF THYROID HORMONES

The transcriptional effects of T_3 characteristically demonstrate a lag time of hours or days to achieve full effect. These genomic actions result in a number of effects, including those on tissue growth, brain maturation, and increased heat production and oxygen consumption due in part to increased activity of Na^+-K^+ ATPase, production of increased beta-adrenergic receptors. Some actions of T_3 are not genomic, such as reduction of pituitary type 2 5'-deiodinase and increase in glucose and amino acid transport. Some specific effects of thyroid hormones are summarized in what follows.

Effects on Fetal Development

The thyroid and the anterior pituitary TSH system begin to function in the human fetus at about 11 weeks. Prior to this time, the fetal thyroid does not concentrate ^{123}I. Because of the high placental content of type 3 5-deiodinase, most maternal T_3 and T_4 are inactivated in the placenta, and very little free hormone reaches the fetal circulation. Thus, the fetus is largely dependent on its own thyroidal secretion. Although some fetal growth occurs in the absence of fetal thyroid hormone secretion, brain development and skeletal maturation are markedly impaired, resulting in cretinism (mental retardation and dwarfism).

Effects on Oxygen Consumption, Heat Production, & Free Radical Formation

T_3 increases O_2 consumption and heat production in part by stimulation of Na^+-K^+ ATPase in all tissues except the brain, spleen, and testis. This contributes to the increased basal metabolic rate (O_2 consumption by the whole animal at rest) and the increased sensitivity to heat in hyperthyroidism, and the converse in hypothyroidism. Thyroid hormones also decrease superoxide dismutase levels, resulting in increased superoxide anion free radical formation. This may contribute to the deleterious effects of chronic hyperthyroidism.

Cardiovascular Effects

T_3 stimulates transcription of myosin heavy chain α and inhibits myosin heavy chain β, improving cardiac muscle contractility. T_3 also increases transcription of Ca^{2+} ATPase in the sarcoplasmic reticulum, increasing diastolic contraction of the heart; alters isoforms of Na^+-K^+ ATPase genes; and increases beta-adrenergic receptors and the concentration of G proteins. Thus, thyroid hormones have marked positive inotropic and chronotropic effects on the heart. This accounts for the increased cardiac output and marked increase in heart rate in hyperthyroidism and the reverse in hypothyroidism.

Sympathetic Effects

As noted above, thyroid hormones increase the number of beta-adrenergic receptors in heart muscle, skeletal muscle, adipose tissue, and lymphocytes. They also decrease myocardial alpha-adrenergic re-ceptors. In addition, they may amplify catecholamine action at a postreceptor site. Thus, sensitivity to catecholamines is markedly increased in hyperthyroidism, and therapy with beta-adrenergic blocking agents may be very helpful in controlling tachycardia and arrhythmias.

Pulmonary Effects

Thyroid hormones maintain normal hypoxic and hypercapnic drive in the respiratory center. In severe hypothyroidism, hypoventilation occurs, occasionally requiring assisted ventilation.

Hematopoietic Effects

The increased cellular demand for O_2 in hyperthyroidism leads to increased production of erythropoietin and increased erythropoiesis. However, blood volume is usually not increased because of hemodilution and increased red cell turnover. Thyroid hormones increase the 2,3-diphosphoglycerate content of erythrocytes, allowing increased O_2 dissociation from hemoglobin and increasing O_2 availability to tissues. The reverse occurs in hypothyroidism.

Gastrointestinal Effects

Thyroid hormones stimulate gut motility, which can result in increased motility and diarrhea in hyperthyroidism and slowed bowel transit and constipation in hypothyroidism. This may also contribute to the modest weight loss in hyperthyroidism and weight gain in hypothyroidism.

Skeletal Effects

Thyroid hormones stimulate increased bone turnover, increasing bone resorption and, to a lesser degree, bone formation. Thus, hyperthyroidism may result in significant osteopenia and, in severe cases, modest hypercalcemia, hypercalciuria, and increased excretion of urinary hydroxyproline and pyridinium cross-links.

Neuromuscular Effects

Although thyroid hormones stimulate increased synthesis of many structural proteins, in hyperthyroidism there is increased protein turnover and loss of muscle tissue, or myopathy. This may be associated with spontaneous creatinuria. There is also an increase in the speed of muscle contraction and relaxation, noted clinically in the hyperreflexia of hyperthyroidism—or the reverse in hypothyroidism. Thyroid hormones are essential for normal development and function of the central nervous system, and hyperactivity in hyperthyroidism and sluggishness in hypothyroidism can be striking.

Effects on Lipid & Carbohydrate Metabolism

Hyperthyroidism increases hepatic gluconeogenesis and glycogenolysis as well as intestinal glucose absorption. Thus, hyperthyroidism will exacerbate underlying diabetes mellitus. Cholesterol synthesis and degradation are both increased by thyroid hormones. The latter effect is due largely to an increase in the hepatic low-density lipoprotein (LDL) receptors, so that cholesterol levels decline with thyroid overactivity. Lipolysis is also increased, releasing fatty acids and glycerol. Conversely, cholesterol levels are elevated in hypothyroidism.

Endocrine Effects

Thyroid hormones increase the metabolic turnover of many hormones and pharmacologic agents. For example, the half-life of cortisol is about 100 minutes in the normal individual, about 50 minutes in a hyperthyroid patient, and about 150 minutes in a hypothyroid patient. The production rate of cortisol will increase in the hyperthyroid patient, with normal adrenal function thus maintaining a normal circulating hormone level. However, in a patient with adrenal insufficiency, the development of hyperthyroidism or thyroid hormone treatment of hypothyroidism may unmask the adrenal disease. Ovulation may be impaired in both hyperthyroidism and hypothyroidism, resulting in infertility, which will be corrected by restoration of the euthyroid state. Serum prolactin levels are increased in about 40% of patients with hypothyroidism, presumably a manifestation of increased TRH release; this will revert to normal with T_4 therapy. Other endocrine effects will be discussed in appropriate sections elsewhere in this chapter.

PHYSIOLOGIC CHANGES IN THYROID FUNCTION

Thyroid Function in the Fetus

As noted above, the fetal hypothalamic-pituitary-thyroid system develops and functions completely independently of maternal function. By the 11th week of gestation, the hypophysial portal system has developed, and measurable TSH and TRH are present. At about the same time, the fetal thyroid begins to trap iodine. However, secretion of thyroid hormone probably begins in mid gestation (18–20 weeks). TSH increases rapidly to peak levels at 24–28 weeks, and T_4 levels peak at 35–40 weeks. T_3 levels remain low during gestation; T_4 is converted to rT_3 by type 3 5-deiodinase during fetal development. At birth, there is a sudden marked rise in TSH, a rise in T_4, a rise in T_3, and a fall in rT_3 (see Chapter 13). These parameters gradually return to normal over the first month of life.

Thyroid Function in Pregnancy

The striking change in thyroid parameters during pregnancy is the rise in TBG and consequent rise in total T_4 and total T_3 in the serum. The rise in TBG is due to estrogen-induced hepatic glycosylation of TBG with N-acetylgalactosamine, which prolongs the metabolic clearance rate of TBG. There is usually no change in thyroxine-binding prealbumin and little change in albumin. Although total T_4 and T_3 are increased, a new equilibrium develops between free and bound thyronines, and the levels of free T_4 and free T_3 are normal. Other changes in pregnancy include an increase in iodide clearance, which, in areas of low iodine intake, may result in a fall in T_4, a rise in TSH, and thyroid enlargement. hCG, which peaks near the end of the first trimester, has a weak TSH agonist activity and may be responsible for the slight thyroid enlargement that occurs at that time. Maternal I^- crosses the placenta and supplies the fetal requirement; in large amounts, I^- can inhibit fetal thyroid function. Maternal TSH-R Ab [stim] and TSH-R Ab [block] can also cross the placenta and may be responsible for thyroid dysfunction in the fetus. As noted above, most maternal T_3 and T_4 are deiodinated by placental type 3 5-deiodinase and do not reach the fetus. However, antithyroid drugs such as propylthiouracil and methimazole do cross the placenta and in large doses will block fetal thyroid function.

Changes in Thyroid Function With Aging

Thyroxine turnover is highest in infants and children, and gradually falls to adult levels after puberty. The T_4 turnover rate is then stable until after age 60, when it again drops slightly. Thus, replacement doses of levothyroxine will vary with age and other factors, and patients taking the drug must be monitored regularly (see below and Chapter 22).

Effects of Acute & Chronic Illness on Thyroid Function (Euthyroid Sick Syndrome)

Acute or chronic illness may have striking effects on circulating thyroid hormone levels by modifying the peripheral metabolism of T_4 or by interference with T_4 binding to TBG. These effects can be classified as (1) the low T_3 syndrome or (2) the low T_3-T_4 syndrome.

The peripheral metabolism of T_4 is diagrammed in Figure 4–20. Inhibition of outer ring type 1 5′-deiodinase or activation of type 3 5-deiodinase accelerates conversion of T_4 to rT_3 and conversion of T_3 to 3,3′-T_2. These reactions will markedly lower the circulating level of T_3, resulting in the low T_3 syndrome. This occurs physiologically in the fetus and pathologically in circumstances of carbohydrate restriction, as in malnutrition, starvation, anorexia nervosa, and diabetes mellitus, and in patients with hepatic disease or major acute or chronic systemic illnesses (Table 4–4). Drugs that inhibit type 1 5′-deiodinase also lower the circulating levels of T_3; cortico-

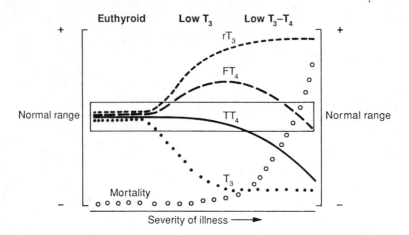

Figure 4–30. A schematic representation of the changes in serum thyroid hormone values with increasing severity of nonthyroidal illness. A rapidly rising mortality rate accompanies the fall in serum total T_4 (TT_4) and free T_4 (FT_4) values. (Reproduced, with permission, from Nicoloff JT: Abnormal measurements in nonendocrine illness. In: *Medicine for the Practicing Physician,* 2nd ed. Hurst JW [editor]. Butterworth-Heinemann, 1991.)

steroids, amiodarone, and iodinated dyes are the most effective, and propylthiouracil and propranolol are relatively weak. The pathogenesis of the low T_3 syndrome when associated with acute or chronic illness is thought to involve cytokines such as tumor necrosis factor, secreted by inflammatory cells, which inhibit type 1 5′-deiodinase, accelerating inner ring deiodination of T_4.

Serum thyroid hormone levels in the low T_3 syndrome are presented diagrammatically in Figure 4–30. T_3 levels are low; total T_4 levels are normal or slightly elevated; free T_4 (by dialysis) often is slightly elevated; and rT_3 is elevated. TSH is normal. True hypothyroidism can be ruled out by the normal T_4, FT_4, and TSH and by the elevated rT_3.

Patients with the low T_3-T_4 syndrome are usually much sicker, and indeed the mortality rate in this group of patients may approach 50%. Serum T_3 and T_4 levels are both low; FT_4 (by dialysis) is usually normal; and rT_3 is elevated. TSH is usually normal, though it may be low if the patient is receiving dopamine or corticosteroids, which suppress TSH. The pathogenesis of this syndrome is thought to involve the liberation of unsaturated fatty acids, such as oleic acid, from anoxic or injured tissue, which inhibits the binding of T_4 to TBG. The syndrome can be differentiated from true hypothyroidism by the normal levels of free T_4 and TSH.

These abnormalities subside when the patient recovers. Recovery is frequently accompanied by a transient elevation of the serum TSH that may be misinterpreted as hypothyroidism. In this setting, in the absence of clinically apparent hypothyroidism, it is best to avoid thyroid hormone therapy and to reevaluate at a later time following recovery. It is possible that intracellular hypothyroidism exists in these patients, but administration of T_3 or T_4 does not

benefit the patient and may worsen the situation. Thus, these changes may represent a protective adaptation on the part of the organism to severe illness. For example, one effect would be to reduce oxygen and other metabolic demands.

THYROID AUTOIMMUNITY

Autoimmune mechanisms are involved in the pathogenesis of many thyroid diseases, including the hyperthyroidism, ophthalmopathy, and dermopathy associated with Graves' disease; the nontoxic goiter or atrophic hypothyroidism associated with Hashimoto's thyroiditis; neonatal Graves' disease and some forms of neonatal hypothyroidism; and postpartum hyperthyroidism or hypothyroidism. Thus, it is important that we understand how the immune system works and how thyroid disease develops. Excellent reviews are available (Volpé, 1991).

Immunologic defense against foreign substances and neoplastic cells involves macrophages that ingest and digest the foreign material and present peptide fragments on the cell surface in association with a class II protein coded by the HLA-DR region of the MHC gene complex. This complex is recognized by a T cell receptor on a CD4 "helper" T cell, which stimulates the release of cytokines such as interleukin 2 (IL-2). These cytokines amplify the response by inducing T cell activation and division, induction of "killer cell activity" in CD8 suppressor cells, and stimulation of antibody formation against the foreign antigen by B lymphocytes. Eventually, the activation process is muted by the action of the CD8 suppressor cells.

Table 4–7. Thyroid autoantigens.[1]

Antigen	Molecular Weight (kD$_a$)	Structure	Function	Comment
Thyroglobulin (Tg)	660	5496-amino acid dimer	Prothyroid hormone	Major colloid component.
Thyroid peroxidase (TPO)	102	926 amino acids	Catalyzes T$_3$ and T$_4$ synthesis	Membrane-bound.
TSH receptor (TSH-R)	100	744 amino acids sage	Transduction of TSH message	Antibodies can stimulate or block.
64-kDa antigen	64	Unknown	Unknown	Antigen common to thyroid and orbital membranes.

[1] Adapted and modified, with permission, from Mariotti S, Pinchera P: Role of the immune system in the control of thyroid function. In: *The Thyroid Gland.* Greer MA (editor). Raven, 1990.

In 1956, three major observations suggested the possibility that immunologic reactions could develop involving the thyroid gland: (1) Rose and Witebsky produced thyroiditis in one lobe of a rabbit thyroid by immunization of the animal with a suspension of the other lobe in Freund's adjuvant; (2) Roitt and Doniach demonstrated the presence of precipitating human thyroglobulin antibodies in the serum of patients with thyroiditis; and (3) Adams and Purves demonstrated the presence of a long-acting thyroid stimulator (later proved to be an antibody to the TSH receptor) in the serum of patients with Graves' disease. Thus, the concept of autoimmune thyroid disease was born.

There are three major thyroidal autoantigens: thyroglobulin (Tg), thyroidal peroxidase (TPO), and the TSH receptor (TSH-R). In addition, a 64-kDa protein expressed on thyroid membranes and on orbital cell membrancs may account for the involvement of both the orbital contents and the thyroid in patients with Graves' disease. The properties of some of these antigens are summarized in Table 4–7. Autoantibodies to these antigens are useful as markers for the presence of autoimmune thyroid disease . However, the pathogenesis of the thyroid disease probably involves lymphocyte sensitization to these and possibly other thyroidal antigens. Thyroid cells have the capacity to ingest antigen (eg, thyroglobulin) and, when stimulated by cytokines such as gamma interferon, will express cell surface class II molecules (eg, DR4) to present these antigens to T lymphocytes. Whereas the presence of both the antigen and the class II molecule may be required for autoimmune thyroid disease to develop, other unknown factors also are critical. Active inquiry is under way into whether the process is initiated or promoted either by external antigens that lead to antibody and cellular immune responses through cross-reactivity with thyroid gland antigens or by primary or secondary immunologic imbalances—or by both mechanisms. Clues to the pathogenesis may come from understanding the roles of both genetic and environmental factors now know to be associated with autoimmune thyroid disease.

Genetic factors play a large role in the autoimmune process. HLA typing in patients with Graves' disease reveals a high incidence of HLA-B8 and HLA-DR3 in Caucasians, HLA-Bw46 and HLA-B5 in Chinese, and HLA-B17 in blacks. In Caucasians, atrophic thyroiditis has been associated with HLA-B8 and goitrous Hashimoto's thyroiditis with HLA-DR5. These associations are of limited diagnostic or prognostic value but illustrate the genetic predisposition to autoimmune thyroid disease. Volpé has suggested that a genetically induced antigen-specific defect in suppressor T lymphocytes may be the basis for autoimmune thyroid disease.

Environmental factors may also play a role in the pathogenesis of autoimmune thyroid disease. Viruses infecting human thyroid cell cultures induce the expression of DR4 on the follicle cell surface, probably as an effect of a cytokine such as alpha interferon. The increased incidence of autoimmune thyroid disease in postpubertal and premenopausal women, as well as the occurrence of postpartum thyroiditis, implies a role for sex hormones in the pathogenesis of autoimmune thyroid disease. The gram-negative bacillus *Yersinia enterocolitica,* which can cause chronic enterocolitis in humans, has a saturable binding site for mammalian thyrotropin as well antigens that cross-react with human thyroid antigens. It has been postulated that antibodies against *Y enterocolitica* could cross-react with the TSH-R on the thyroid cell membrane and trigger an episode of Graves' disease. A high iodine intake may result in more highly iodinated thyroglobulin, which is more immunogenic and would favor the development of autoimmune thyroid disease. Therapeutic doses of lithium, used for the treatment of manic-depressive psychoses, can interfere with suppressor cell function and precipitate autoimmune thyroid disease. Thus, there are a number of environmental and genetic factors that could contribute to the development of this disorder.

TESTS OF THYROID FUNCTION

The function of the thyroid gland may be evaluated in many different ways: (1) tests of thyroid hormones in blood, (2) evaluation of the hypothalamic-pituitary-thyroid axis, (3) assessment of iodine metabolism, (4) estimation of gland size, (5) thyroid biopsy, (6) observation of the effects of thyroid hormones on peripheral tissues, and (7) measurement of thyroid autoantibodies.

TESTS OF THYROID HORMONES IN BLOOD

The total serum T_4 and total serum T_3 are measured by radioimmunoassay or immunofluorescent assay. If the concentration of serum thyroid hormone binding proteins is normal, these measurements provide a reasonably reliable index of thyroid gland activity. However, changes in serum concentration of thyroid-binding proteins or the presence of drugs that modify the binding of T_4 or T_3 to TBP (Table 4–1) will modify the total T_4 and T_3 but not the amount of free hormone. Thus, further tests must be performed to assess the *free* hormone level that determines biologic activity (Figure 4–16).

The free T_4 level can be estimated using the **free thyroxine index** (FT_4I), or it can be measured directly by dialysis (free thyroxine by dialysis; FT_4D).

FT_4I is the product of the total T_4 multiplied by the percentage of labeled T_4 taken up by a resin, charcoal, or antibody added to the serum. Thus, if the range of total serum T_4 is 5–12 μg/dL (64–154 nmol/L) and resin T_4 uptake (RT_4U) is 25–35%, the normal range of the calculated FT_4I ($T_4 \times RT_4U$) will be 1.3–4.2 in arbitrary units (16–54 in arbitrary SI units). The method can be improved by using the ratio of counts taken up by the resin divided by counts remaining in the serum (free:bound ratio); this is called the **thyroid hormone-binding ratio** (THBR). The patient's THBR is "normalized" by dividing it by the THBR of a normal or reference serum. The patient's total T_4 is then multiplied by this ratio, producing an "adjusted FT_4I," in which the total T_4 is adjusted downward if TBG is high and upward if TBG is low. The normal range for the FT_4I as calculated by this method will then be the same as the normal range for total T_4 in a patient with normal TBP, ie, 5–12 (USA units) or 64–154 (SI units).

Although the FT_4I has been very useful as an estimate of the free T_4 level, a direct measure of the free hormone would be much more precise. Analogues of T_4 and T_3 have been prepared which theoretically bind to specific antibodies but not to TBG—and thus could be used to measure, by displacement, the binding of FT_4 to a T_4 antibody. Unfortunately, some of these analogues will bind to serum albumin, limiting the reliability of the test. However, a reliable microdialysis method for determination of FT_4 is available. The levels of free T_4 in normal adults are 0.9–2 ng/dL (12–26 pmol/L).

The FT_4I is valid for most patients except those with marked dysproteinemia or severe illness. In patients with very high or very low thyroid-binding proteins, the THBR may not completely correct for the abnormal binding protein, and in severely ill patients there may be factors that interfere with T_4 binding to thyroid-binding proteins or to the resin or charcoal matrix. In these situations, FT_4D is more reliable. Both FT_4I and FT_4D will be inappropriately low in patients receiving replacement therapy with liothyronine or in patients with early Graves' disease or toxic nodular goiter, in whom hyperthyroidism is associated with overproduction of T_3 rather than T_4 (T_3 toxicosis). Antiepileptic drugs such as phenytoin and carbamazepine and the antituberculosis drug rifampin increase hepatic metabolism of T_4, resulting in a low total T_4, a low free T_4, and a low FT_4I. However, serum T_3 and serum TSH levels are normal, indicating that patients receiving these drugs are euthyroid. As noted above, T_4 and FT_4I may be low in severe illness, but FT_4D and TSH are usually normal, which will distinguish these very ill patients from patients who are hypothyroid.

At times, FT_4I and FT_4D will be inappropriately elevated. For example, drugs such as iodinated contrast media, amiodarone, glucocorticoids, and propranolol (see Table 4–4) inhibit type 1 5′-deiodinase and the conversion of T_4 to T_3 in peripheral tissues, resulting in elevation of total T_4, FT_4I, and FT_4D and depression of T_3. Hyperthyroidism is ruled out by the low T_3 and normal TSH. FT_4I and FT_4D are inappropriately elevated in the rare syndrome of generalized resistance to thyroid hormone (see below). The presence of heparin in serum, even in the tiny amounts that would be found in a patient with a "heparin lock" indwelling intravenous catheter, will cause a spurious increase in FT_4D. This occurs in the test tube, since heparin activates lipoprotein lipase, releasing free fatty acids that displace T_4 from TBG.

Total T_3 can be measured in serum by immunoassay with specific T_3 antisera. The normal range in adults is 95–190 ng/dL (1.5–2.9 nmol/L). The measurement of total T_3 is most useful in the differential diagnosis of hyperthyroidism, because T_3 is preferentially secreted in early Graves' disease or toxic nodular goiter. For example, the normal ratio of serum T_3 in ng/dL to T_4 in μg/dL is less than 20 (eg, T_3 120 ng/dL, T_4 8 μg/dL: ratio = 15). In hyperthyroidism, this ratio will usually be well over 20, and it will be even higher in T_3 thyrotoxicosis. T_3 levels are often maintained in the normal range in hypothyroidism because TSH stimulation increases the relative secretion of T_3; thus, serum T_3 is not a good test for hypothyroidism.

T_3 is bound to TBG, and the total T_3 concentration in serum will vary with the level of TBG (Table 4–1). Serum free T_3 (FT$_3$) can be measured by equilibrium dialysis; the normal adult FT$_3$ is 0.2–0.52 ng/dL (3–8 pmol/L). However, this method is technically difficult, and for clinical purposes FT$_3$ is best estimated by a free T_3 index (FT$_3$I). This is obtained by multiplying the normalized THBR by the total T_3 as measured by immunoassay. The adjusted FT$_3$I in the normal adult is the same as the total T_3.

Reverse T_3 (rT$_3$) can be measured by radioimmunoassay. The serum concentration of rT$_3$ in adults is about one-third of the total T_3 concentration, with a range of 25–75 ng/dL (0.39–1.15 nmol/L). rT$_3$ can be used to differentiate chronic illness from hypothyroidism because rT$_3$ levels are elevated in chronic illness and low in hypothyroidism. However, this differential diagnosis can be made by determination of TSH (see below), so that it is rarely necessary to measure rT$_3$.

Thyroglobulin (Tg) can be measured in serum by double antibody radioimmunoassay. The normal range will vary with method and laboratory, but generally the normal range is less than 40 ng/mL (< 40 µg/L) in the euthyroid individual and less than 5 ng/mL (< 5 µg/L) in a thyroidectomized individual. The major problem with the test is that endogenous thyroglobulin antibodies interfere with the assay procedure and, depending on the method, may result in spuriously low or spuriously high values. Serum thyroglobulin is elevated in situations of thyroid overactivity such as Graves' disease and toxic multinodular goiter; in subacute or chronic thyroiditis, where it is released as a consequence of tissue damage; and in patients with large goiters, in whom the thyroglobulin level is proportionate to the size of the gland. Thyroglobulin has been most useful in the management of patients with papillary or follicular thyroid carcinoma. Following thyroidectomy and ^{131}I therapy, thyroglobulin levels should be very low. In such a patient, serum thyroglobulin greater than 10 ng/dL (> 10 µg/L) indicates the presence of metastatic disease, and a rise in serum thyroglobulin in a patient with known metastases indicates progression of the disease.

EVALUATION OF THE HYPOTHALAMIC-PITUITARY-THYROID AXIS

The hypothalamic-pituitary-thyroid axis is illustrated in Figure 4–21. It has not been clinically feasible to measure TRH in the peripheral circulation in humans. However, very sensitive methods for the measurement of TSH have been developed using monoclonal antibodies against human TSH. The general principle is this: one monoclonal TSH antibody is fixed to a solid matrix to bind serum TSH, and a second monoclonal TSH antibody labeled with iso-

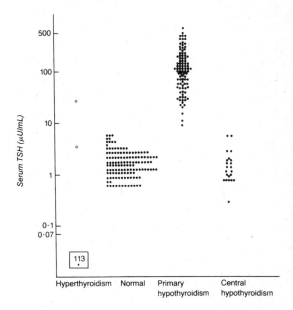

Figure 4–31. Serum TSH concentrations in normal (133) subjects, untreated overt hyperthyroidism (115), and primary (96) and central (22) hypothyroidism. Undetectable values were observed in all hyperthyroid subjects except for two patients (open circle) with hyperthyroidism due to TSH-secreting pituitary tumor. Note logarithmic scale for TSH. (Reproduced, with permission, from Martino E et al: Human serum thyrotrophin measurement by ultrasensitive immunoradiometric assay as a first-line test in the evaluation of thyroid function. Clin Endocrinol 1986;24: 141.)

tope or enzyme or fluorescent tag will bind to a separate epitope on the TSH molecule. The quantity of TSH in the serum is thus proportionate to the quantity of bound second antibody. The earlier TSH radioimmunoassays, which could detect about 1 µU of TSH/mL, were adequate for the diagnosis of elevated TSH in hypothyroidism but could not detect suppressed TSH levels in hyperthyroidism. The "second generation" of "sensitive" TSH assays, using monoclonal antibodies, can detect about 0.1 µU/mL, and the "third generation" of "supersensitive" assays are sufficiently sensitive to detect about 0.01 µU/mL. This has allowed measurement of TSH well below the normal range of 0.5–5 µU/mL (0.5–5 mU/L) and has enabled the clinician to detect partially and totally suppressed serum TSH levels (Figure 4–31). Serum TSH below 0.1 µU/mL (0.1 mU/L) and an elevated FT$_4$D or FT$_4$I is indicative of hyperthyroidism. This may be due to Graves' disease, toxic nodular goiter, or high-dose thyroxine therapy. In the rare case of hyperthyroidism due to a TSH-secreting pituitary tumor, FT$_4$I or FT$_4$D will be elevated and TSH will not be suppressed but will actually be normal or slightly elevated. An elevated TSH (> 10 µU/mL; 10 mU/L) and a low FT$_4$D or FT$_4$I is diagnostic of hypothyroidism. In patients with hypothyroidism due to a pituitary or hypothalamic tumor, FT_4I or FT_4D will be low and TSH will not be elevated. This diagnosis can be confirmed by demonstrating the failure of serum TSH to increase following an injection of TRH (TRH test; Figure 4–25). Note that corticosteroids and dopamine inhibit TSH secretion (Table 4–6), which will modify the interpretation of serum TSH levels in patients taking these drugs.

Serum TSH levels reflect the anterior pituitary gland sensing the level of circulating FT_4. High FT_4 levels suppress TSH and low FT_4 increases TSH release. Thus, the ultrasensitive measurement of TSH has become the most sensitive, most convenient, and most specific test for the diagnosis of both hyperthyroidism and hypothyroidism. Indeed, a suppressed TSH correlates so well with impaired pituitary response to TRH that the simple measurement of serum TSH has replaced the TRH test in the diagnosis of hyperthyroidism.

IODINE METABOLISM & BIOSYNTHETIC ACTIVITY

Radioactive iodine allows assessment of the turnover of iodine by the thyroid gland in vivo. Iodine-123 is the ideal isotope for this purpose: It has a half-life of 13.3 hours and releases a 28-keV x-ray and a 159-keV gamma photon but no beta emissions. Thus, it is easily measured and causes little tissue damage. It is usually administered orally in a dose of 100–200 µCi, and radioactivity over the thyroid area is measured with a scintillation counter at 4 or 6 hours and again at 24 hours (Figure 4–8). The normal **radioactive iodine uptake** (RAIU) will vary with the iodide intake. In areas of low iodide intake and endemic goiter, the 24-hour RAIU may be as high as 60–90%. In the USA—a country with a relatively high iodide intake—the normal uptake at 6 hours is 5–15% and at 24 hours 8–30%. In thyrotoxicosis due to Graves' disease or toxic nodular goiter, 24-hour RAIU is markedly elevated, although if the iodide turnover is very rapid, the 5-hour uptake may be even higher than the 24-hour uptake (Figure 4–8). Thyrotoxicosis with a very low thyroidal RAIU occurs in the following situations: (1) in subacute thyroiditis; (2) during the active phase of Hashimoto's thyroiditis, with release of preformed hormone, causing "spontaneously resolving thyrotoxicosis"; (3) in thyrotoxicosis factitia due to oral ingestion of a large amount of thyroid hormone; (4) as a result of excess iodide intake, inducing thyrotoxicosis in a patient with latent Graves' disease or multinodular goiter, the low uptake being due to the huge iodide pool; (5) in struma ovarii; and (6) in ectopic functioning metastatic thyroid carcinoma after total thyroidectomy.

In normal individuals, administration of 75–100 µg of T_3 in divided doses daily for 5 days will reduce the 24-hour RAIU by more than 50% (suppression test). Failure of the thyroid to suppress on this treatment indicates autonomous thyroid function, as in Graves' disease, or autonomously functioning thyroid nodules.

The efficiency of the thyroid organification process may be tested with the "perchlorate discharge test." As noted above, $KClO_4$ will displace I^- from the iodide trap. Thus, oral administration of 0.5 g $KClO_4$ to a normal individual will block further uptake of ^{123}I, but not more than 5% of the previously accumulated radioiodine will be released. Conversely, if there is an organification defect, not only is further uptake blocked but I^- diffuses out of the gland or is "discharged" (Figure 4–12). Positive tests are seen in some patients with congenital iodide organification defects, Hashimoto's thyroiditis, Graves' disease after ^{131}I therapy, or patients receiving inhibitors of iodide organification such as methimazole or propylthiouracil. The perchlorate discharge test is rarely used clinically, but it can be very helpful in understanding the pathophysiology of some of the above illnesses.

THYROID IMAGING

1. RADIONUCLIDE IMAGING

^{123}I or technetium Tc 99m pertechnetate (^{99m}Tc as TcO_4) is useful for determining the *functional* activity of the thyroid gland. ^{123}I is administered orally in a dose of 200–300 µCi, and a scan of the thyroid is obtained at 8–24 hours. $^{99m}TcO_4$ is administered intravenously in a dose of 1–10 mCi, and the scan is

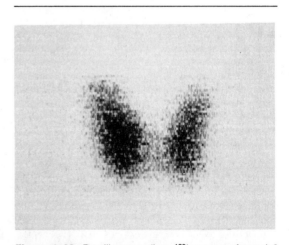

Figure 4–32. Rectilinear sodium ^{123}I scan performed 6 hours after the ingestion of 100 µCi of sodium ^{123}I. (Courtesy of RR Cavalieri.)

Figure 4–33. Scintiphoto (pinhole collimator) thyroid scan performed 6 hours after the ingestion of 100 μCi of sodium ^{123}1. (Courtesy of RR Cavalieri.)

obtained at 30–60 minutes. Images can be obtained with either a rectilinear scanner or a gamma camera. The rectilinear scanner moves back and forth over the area of interest; it produces a life-size picture, and special areas, such as nodules, can be marked directly on the scan (Figure 4–32). The gamma camera has a pinhole collimator, and the scan is obtained on a fluorescent screen and recorded on Polaroid film. The camera has greater resolution, but special areas must be identified with a radioactive marker for clinical correlation (Figure 4–33). Radionuclide scans provide information about both the size and shape of the thyroid gland and the geographic distribution of functional activity in the gland. Functioning thyroid nodules are called "hot" nodules, and nonfunctioning ones are called "cold" nodules. The incidence of malignancy in hot nodules is about 1%, but they may become toxic, producing enough hormone to suppress the rest of the gland and induce thyrotoxicosis. About 16% of surgically removed cold nodules have been malignant. Occasionally, a nodule will be hot with $^{99m}TcO_4$ and cold with ^{123}I, and a few of these nodules have been malignant. For large substernal goiters or for distant metastases from a thyroid cancer, ^{131}I is the preferred isotope because of its long half-life (8 days) and its 0.72 MeV gamma emission.

Fluorescent Scanning

The iodine content and an image of the thyroid gland can be obtained by fluorescent scanning without administration of a radioisotope. An external source of Americium-241 is beamed at the thyroid gland, and the resulting emission of 28.5 keV x-ray from iodide ions is recorded, producing an image of the thyroid gland similar to that obtained with ^{123}I (Figure 4–32). The advantage of this procedure is that the patient receives no radioisotope and the gland can be imaged even when it is loaded with io-

dine—as, for example, after intravenous contrast media. The disadvantage of this study is that it requires specialized equipment that may not be generally available.

THYROID ULTRASONOGRAPHY OR MAGNETIC RESONANCE IMAGING

A rough estimate of thyroid size and nodularity can be obtained from radionuclide scanning, but much better detail can be obtained by thyroid ultrasonography or MRI.

Thyroid ultrasonography is particularly useful for measuring the size of the gland or individual nodules and for evaluating the results of therapy. It is useful also for differentiating solid from cystic lesions and to guide the operator to a deep nodule during fine-needle thyroid aspiration biopsy (see below). Thyroid ultrasonography is limited to thyroid tissue in the neck, ie, it cannot be used for substernal lesions.

MRI provides an excellent image of the thyroid gland, including posterior or substernal extension of a goiter or malignancy. Both transverse and coronal images of the gland can be obtained, and lymph nodes as small as 1 cm can be visualized. MRI is invaluable for the demonstration of tracheal compression from a large goiter, tracheal invasion or local extension of a thyroid malignancy, or metastases to local or mediastinal lymph nodes.

THYROID BIOPSY

Fine-needle aspiration biopsy of a thyroid nodule has proved to be the best method for differentiation of benign from malignant thyroid disease. It is performed as an outpatient procedure and requires no preparation. The skin over the nodule is cleansed with alcohol, and, if desired, a small amount of 1% lidocaine can be injected intracutaneously for local anesthesia. A No. 25 1 1/2-inch needle is then inserted into the nodule and moved in and out until a small amount of bloody material is seen in the hub of the needle; the needle is then removed, and with a syringe, the contents of the needle are expressed onto a clean slide. A second clean slide is placed on top of the first slide, and a thin smear is obtained by drawing the slides apart quickly. Alternatively, a 10 mL or 20 mL syringe in an appropriate syringe holder can be used with a No. 23 1-inch needle to sample the nodule or to evacuate cystic contents.

The slides are fixed—either dry and stained with Wright's or Giemsa's stain, or fixed in alcohol and stained with Papanicolaou's stain. The sensitivity (true-positive results divided by total cases of disease) is about 95%, and the specificity (true-negative results divided by total cases of no disease) is also about 95%. For best results, fine-needle aspiration biopsy requires an adequate tissue sample and a specially trained cytologist to interpret it.

EFFECTS OF THYROID HORMONES ON PERIPHERAL TISSUES

The definitive test of thyroid function would be a test of the effect of thyroid hormones on body tissues. Thyroid hormones increase heat production and oxygen consumption. A measurement of this basal oxygen in the intact organism became one of the first tests of thyroid function, the **basal metabolic rate** (BMR). However, this test is nonspecific and insensitive and is rarely used today. The speed of muscle contraction and relaxation is increased in hyperthyroidism and decreased in hypothyroidism. The contraction and relaxation time of the Achilles tendon has been standardized and measured by an instrument called the **photomotogram.** However, there is considerable overlap between normal subjects and patients with thyroid dysfunction, limiting the usefulness of this procedure.

Cardiac muscle contractility can also be measured as an index of thyroid hormone action. With echocardiography, it is relatively easy to measure such indices as the preejection period (PEP), the time from onset of the QRS complex to the opening of the aortic valve; or the left ventricular ejection time (LVET). These are prolonged in hypothyroidism and shortened in hyperthyroidism. Although these measurements are modified by coexistent cardiac disease, they may be the best objective tests for measuring the peripheral effects of thyroid hormone action.

Thyroid hormones influence the concentration of a number of enzymes and blood constituents. For example, serum cholesterol is usually elevated in hyperthyroidism and lowered in hypothyroidism. Serum creatine kinase and lactic dehydrogenase, probably of skeletal muscle origin, are elevated in hypothyroidism—and indeed, isoenzyme determination may be required to differentiate the enzyme changes occurring in myocardial infarction from those occurring in myxedema.

Sex hormone-binding globulin (SHBG) and angiotensin-converting enzyme are also increased in hyperthyroidism and decreased in hypothyroidism. However, none of these biochemical or enzyme changes are sensitive or specific enough for diagnostic use.

MEASUREMENT OF THYROID AUTOANTIBODIES

Thyroid autoantibodies include (1) thyroglobulin antibody (Tg Ab); (2) thyroid peroxidase antibody (TPO Ab), formerly called microsomal antibody; and (3) TSH receptor antibody, either stimulating (TSH-R Ab [stim]) or blocking (TSH-R Ab [block]). Tg Ab and TPO Ab have been measured by hemagglutination, enzyme-linked immunoassay (ELISA), or radioimmunoassay (RIA). The hemagglutination technique is much less sensitive than the ELISA or RIA methods. For example, in the Whickham study of a normal population in northeastern England, TPO antibodies were found in about 8% of young women (aged 18–24) and 13.7% of older women (aged 45–54). In a similar study of normal blood donors and using radioimmunoassay, TPO antibodies were found in 10.6% of younger and in 30.3% of older women. The incidence of positive TPO antibodies in normal men (by hemagglutination) was low—about 2%—and did not increase with age. On the other hand, high Tg Ab and TPO Ab titers by RIA are found in 97% of patients with Graves' disease or Hashimoto's thyroiditis. Thyroglobulin antibodies are often high early in the course of Hashimoto's thyroiditis and decrease with time; TPO antibodies are usually measurable for the life of the patient. The titers of both Tg and TPO antibodies will decrease with time following institution of T_4 therapy in Hashimoto's thyroiditis or with antithyroid therapy in Graves' disease. A strongly positive test for either of these antibodies is an indication of the presence of autoimmune thyroid disease but is not specific for the type of disease, ie, hyperthyroidism, hypothyroidism, or goiter.

The thyroid receptor stimulating antibody (TSH-R Ab [stim]) is characteristic of Graves' disease (see above). It was originally measured by demonstrating prolonged discharge of radioiodine from the thyroid gland of the mouse after injection of serum from a patient with Graves' disease; it was then called long-acting thyroid stimulator (LATS). This laborious assay has been replaced by a bioassay using human thyroid cells in culture and measuring the increase in thyroid cAMP following incubation with serum or IgG. The test is positive in 90% of patients with Graves' disease and undetectable in healthy subjects or patients with Hashimoto's thyroiditis (without ophthalmopathy), nontoxic goiter, or toxic nodular goiter. It is most useful for the diagnosis of Graves' disease in patients with euthyroid ophthalmopathy or in predicting neonatal Graves' disease in the newborn of a mother with active or past Graves' disease.

The same type of assay can be used to detect TSH receptor-blocking antibody (TSH-R Ab [block]). In this assay, the increase in cAMP induced by TSH added to a human thyroid cell culture is blocked by concurrent incubation with the patient's serum. The TSH-binding inhibition assay measures the ability of serum IgG to inhibit the binding of labeled TSH to a thyroid cell membrane preparation containing the TSH receptor. This technique is not as satisfactory as the bioassay because there are a variety of nonspecific interfering substances, such as thyroglobulin, which inhibit TSH binding. However, a modification of the TSH-binding inhibition assay using recombinant human TSH receptor has proved to be more reliable. Detection of a TSH receptor-blocking antibody in maternal serum may be very helpful in predicting the occurrence of congenital hypothyroidism in newborns of mothers with autoimmune thyroid disease.

SUMMARY: CLINICAL USE OF THYROID FUNCTION TESTS

The diagnosis of thyroid disease has been greatly simplified by the development of sensitive assays for TSH and free thyroxine. The estimate of free thyroxine, either FT_4I or FT_4D, and a sensitive TSH determination are used both for the diagnosis of thyroid disease and for following patients receiving T_4 replacement or antithyroid drug therapy. An elevated TSH and low free thyroxine establish the diagnosis of hypothyroidism, and a suppressed TSH and elevated FT_4 establish the diagnosis of hyperthyroidism.

Other tests are available for special uses. In hypothyroidism, Tg Ab or TPO Ab tests will clarify the etiology of the illness, and in hyperthyroidism elevation of free T_3, abnormal radioiodine uptake and scan, and a positive test for TSH-R Ab [stim] may be useful. In patients with nodules or goiter, fine-needle aspiration biopsy will rule out malignancy; radioiodine scan may help to determine function; and thyroid ultrasound or MRI may be helpful in following the size or growth of the goiter. Patients with known thyroid cancer are followed with serial thyroglobulin determinations, and ^{131}I scan or MRI may be useful for detection of metastatic disease.

DISORDERS OF THE THYROID

Patients with thyroid disease will usually complain of (1) thyroid enlargement, which may be diffuse or nodular; (2) symptoms of thyroid deficiency, or hypothyroidism; (3) symptoms of thyroid hormone excess, or hyperthyroidism; or (4) complications of a specific form of hyperthyroidism—Graves' disease—which may present with striking prominence of the eyes (exophthalmos) or, rarely, thickening of the skin over the lower legs (thyroid dermopathy).

History

The history should include evaluation of symptoms related to the above complaints, discussed in more detail below. Exposure to ionizing radiation in childhood has been associated with an increased incidence of thyroid disease, including cancer. Iodide ingestion in the form of kelp or iodide-containing cough preparations may induce goiter, hypothyroidism, or hyperthyroidism. Lithium carbonate, used in the treatment of manic-depressive psychiatric disorder, can also induce hypothyroidism and goiter. Residence in an area of low dietary iodide is associated with iodine deficiency goiter ("endemic goiter"). Although dietary iodide is generally adequate in developed countries, there are still areas low in natural iodine (ie, developing countries in Africa, Asia, South America, and inland mountainous areas). Finally, the family history should be explored with particular reference to goiter, hyperthyroidism, or hypothyroidism as well as immunologic disorders such as diabetes, rheumatoid disease, pernicious anemia, alopecia, vitiligo, or myasthenia gravis, which may be associated with an increased incidence of autoimmune thyroid disease. Multiple endocrine neoplasia type IIa (Sipple's syndrome) with medullary carcinoma of the thyroid gland is an autosomal dominant condition.

Physical Examination

Physical examination of the thyroid gland is illustrated in Figure 4–34. The thyroid is firmly attached to the anterior trachea midway between the sternal notch and the thyroid cartilage; it is often easy to see and to palpate. The patient should have a glass of water for comfortable swallowing. There are three maneuvers: (1) With a good light coming from behind the examiner, the patient is instructed to swallow a sip of water. Observe the gland as it moves up and down. Enlargement and nodularity can often be noted. (2) Palpate the gland anteriorly. Gently press down with one thumb on one side of the gland to rotate the other lobe forward, and palpate as the patient swallows. (3) Palpate the gland from behind the patient with the middle three fingers on each lobe while the patient swallows. An outline of the gland can be traced on the skin of the neck and measured (Figure 4–34D). Nodules can be measured in a similar way. Thus, changes in the size of the gland or in nodules can easily be followed.

On physical examination, the palpable bulbous portion of each lobe of the normal thyroid gland measures about 2 cm in vertical dimension and about 1 cm in horizontal dimension above the isthmus. An enlarged thyroid gland is called **goiter.** Generalized enlargement is termed diffuse goiter; irregular or lumpy enlargement is called nodular goiter.

HYPOTHYROIDISM

Hypothyroidism is a clinical syndrome resulting from a deficiency of thyroid hormones, which in turn results in a generalized slowing down of metabolic processes. Hypothyroidism in infants and children results in marked slowing of growth and development,

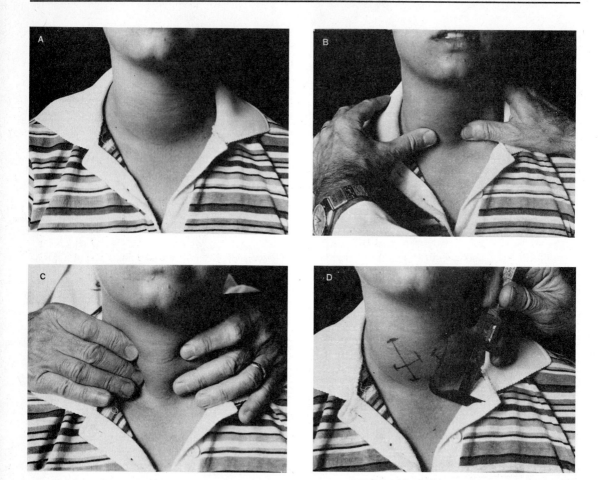

Figure 4–34. Examination of the thyroid gland. **A:** Observe the neck, especially as the patient swallows. **B:** Examine from the front, rotating the gland slightly with one thumb while palpating the other lobe with the other thumb. **C:** Examine from behind, using three fingers and the same technique. **D:** The size of each lobe or of thyroid nodules can be measured by first drawing an outline on the skin.

with serious permanent consequences including mental retardation. Hypothyroidism with onset in adulthood causes a generalized slowing down of the organism, with deposition of glycosaminoglycans in intracellular spaces, particularly in skin and muscle, producing the clinical picture of **myxedema.** The symptoms of hypothyroidism in adults are largely reversible with therapy.

Etiology & Incidence (Table 4–8)

Hypothyroidism may be classified as (1) primary (thyroid failure), (2) secondary (to pituitary TSH deficit), or (3) tertiary (due to hypothalamic deficiency of TRH)—or may be due to (4) peripheral resistance to the action of thyroid hormones. Hypothyroidism can also be classified as goitrous or nongoitrous, but this classification is probably unsatisfactory, since Hashimoto's thyroiditis may produce hypothyroidism with or without goiter.

The incidence of various causes of hypothyroidism will vary depending on geographic and environmental factors such as dietary iodide and goitrogen intake, the genetic characteristics of the population, and the age distribution of the population (pediatric or adult). The causes of hypothyroidism, listed in approximate order of frequency in an adult population in the USA, are presented in Table 4–8. Hashimoto's thyroiditis is probably the most common cause of hypothyroidism. In younger patients, it is more likely to be associated with goiter; in older patients, the gland may be totally destroyed by the immunologic process, and the only trace of the disease will be a persistently positive test for TPO (thyroid microsomal) autoantibodies. Similarly, the end stage of Graves' disease may be hypothyroidism. This is accelerated by destructive therapy such as administration of radioactive iodine or subtotal thyroidectomy. Thyroid glands involved in autoimmune disease are particularly susceptible to excessive iodide intake (eg, in-

Table 4–8. Etiology of hypothyroidism.

Primary:
1. Hashimoto's thyroiditis:
   a. With goiter.
   b. "Idiopathic" thyroid atrophy, presumably end-stage autoimmune thyroid disease, following either Hashimoto's thyroiditis or Graves' disease.
2. Radioactive iodine therapy for Graves' disease.
3. Subtotal thyroidectomy for Graves' disease or nodular goiter.
4. Excessive iodide intake (kelp, radiocontrast dyes).
5. Subacute thyroiditis.
6. Rare causes in the USA:
   a. Iodide deficiency.
   b. Other goitrogens such as lithium; antithyroid drug therapy.
   c. Inborn errors of thyroid hormone synthesis.

Secondary: Hypopituitarism due to pituitary adenoma, pituitary ablative therapy, or pituitary destruction.

Tertiary: Hypothalamic dysfunction (rare).

Peripheral resistance to the action of thyroid hormone.

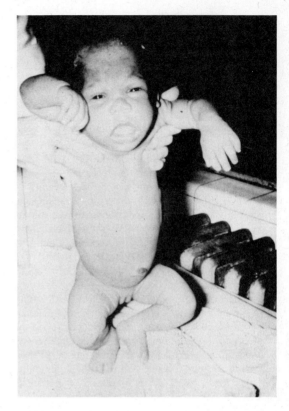

Figure 4–35. A 9-month-old infant with hypothyroidism (cretinism). Note the puffy face, protuberant abdomen, umbilical hernia, and muscle weakness (infant cannot sit up unassisted).

gestion of kelp tablets, iodide-containing cough preparations, or the antiarrhythmic drug amiodarone) or administration of iodide-containing radiographic contrast media. The large amounts of iodide block thyroid hormone synthesis, producing hypothyroidism with goiter in the patient with an abnormal thyroid gland; the normal gland usually "escapes" from the iodide block (see above). Although the process may be temporarily reversed by withdrawal of iodide, the underlying disease will often progress, and permanent hypothyroidism will usually supervene. Hypothyroidism may occur during the late phase of subacute thyroiditis; this is usually transient, but it is permanent in about 10% of patients. Iodide deficiency is rarely a cause of hypothyroidism in the USA but may be more common in developing countries. Certain drugs can block hormone synthesis and produce hypothyroidism with goiter; at present, the most common pharmacologic causes of hypothyroidism (other than iodide) are lithium carbonate, used for the treatment of manic-depressive states, and amiodarone. Chronic therapy with the antithyroid drugs propylthiouracil and methimazole will do the same. Inborn errors of thyroid hormone synthesis result in severe hypothyroidism if the block in hormone synthesis is complete, or mild hypothyroidism if the block is partial. Pituitary and hypothalamic deficiencies as causes of hypothyroidism are quite rare and are usually associated with other symptoms and signs of pituitary insufficiency (see Chapter 2). Peripheral resistance to thyroid hormones is discussed below.

Pathogenesis

Thyroid hormone deficiency affects every tissue in the body, so that the symptoms are multiple. Pathologically, the most characteristic finding is the accumulation of glycosaminoglycans—mostly hyaluronic acid—in interstitial tissues. Accumulation of this hydrophilic substance and increased capillary permeability to albumin account for the interstitial edema that is particularly evident in the skin, heart muscle, and striated muscle. The accumulation is due not to excessive synthesis but to decreased destruction of glycosaminoglycans.

Clinical Presentations & Findings

A. Newborn Infants (Cretinism): The term cretinism was originally applied to infants—in areas of low iodide intake and endemic goiter—with mental retardation, short stature, a characteristic puffy appearance of the face and hands, and (frequently) deaf mutism and neurologic signs of pyramidal and extrapyramidal tract abnormalities (Figure 4–35). In the USA, neonatal screening programs have revealed that in the white population the incidence of neonatal hypothyroidism is 1:5000, while in the black population the incidence is only 1:32,000. Neonatal hypothyroidism may result from failure of the thyroid to descend during embryonic development from its origin at the base of the tongue to its usual site in the lower anterior neck, which results in an "ectopic thyroid" gland that functions poorly. Placental transfer to the embryo of TSH-R Ab [block] from a mother with Hashimoto's thyroiditis, may result in agenesis of the thyroid gland and "athyreotic cretinism." Inherited defects in thyroid hormone biosynthesis induce neonatal hypothyroidism and goiter. Rare causes of neonatal hypothyroidism include administration during pregnancy of iodides, antithyroid drugs, or radioactive iodine for thyrotoxicosis.

The symptoms of hypothyroidism in newborns include respiratory difficulty, cyanosis, jaundice, poor feeding, hoarse cry, umbilical hernia, and marked retardation of bone maturation. The proximal tibial epiphysis and distal femoral epiphysis are present in almost all full-term infants with a body weight of over 2500 g. Absence of these epiphyses strongly suggests hypothyroidism. The introduction of routine screening of newborns for TSH or T_4 has been a major achievement in the early diagnosis of neonatal hypothyroidism. A serum T_4 under 6 μg/dL or a serum TSH over 30 μU/mL is indicative of neonatal hypothyroidism. The diagnosis can then be confirmed by radiologic evidence of retarded bone age.

B. Children: Hypothyroidism in children is characterized by retarded growth and evidence of mental retardation. In the adolescent, precocious puberty may occur, and there may be enlargement of the sella turcica in addition to short stature. This is not due to pituitary tumor but probably to pituitary hypertrophy associated with excessive TSH production.

C. Adults: In adults, the common features of hypothyroidism include easy fatigability, coldness, weight gain, constipation, menstrual irregularities, and muscle cramps. Physical findings include a cool, rough, dry skin, puffy face and hands, a hoarse, husky voice, and slow reflexes (Figure 4–36). Reduced conversion of carotene to vitamin A and increased blood levels of carotene may give the skin a yellowish color.

1. Cardiovascular signs– Hypothyroidism is manifested by impaired muscular contraction, bradycardia, and diminished cardiac output. The ECG reveals low voltage of QRS complexes and P and T waves, with improvement in response to therapy. Cardiac enlargement may occur, due in part to interstitial edema, nonspecific myofibrillary swelling, and left ventricular dilation but often to pericardial effusion (Figure 4–37). The degree of pericardial effusion can easily be determined by echocardiography. Although cardiac output is reduced, congestive heart failure and pulmonary edema are rarely noted. There is controversy about whether myxedema induces coronary artery disease, but coronary artery disease is more common in patients with hypothyroidism, particularly in older patients. In patients with angina pectoris, hypothyroidism may protect the heart from ischemic stress, and replacement therapy may aggravate the angina.

2. Pulmonary function– In the adult, hypothyroidism is characterized by shallow, slow respirations and impaired ventilatory responses to hypercapnia or

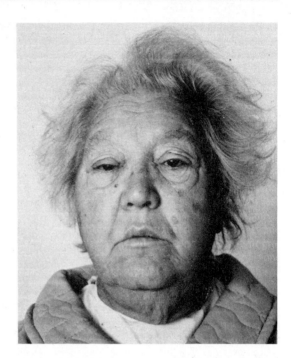

Figure 4–36. Hypothyroidism in adult (myxedema). Note puffy face, puffy eyes, frowsy hair, and dull and apathetic appearance.

hypoxia. Respiratory failure is a major problem in patients with myxedema coma.

3. Intestinal peristalsis is markedly slowed, resulting in chronic constipation and occasionally severe fecal impaction or ileus.

4. Renal function is impaired, with decreased glomerular filtration rate and impaired ability to excrete a water load. This predisposes the myxedematous patient to water intoxication if excessive free water is administered.

5. Anemia– There are at least four mechanisms that may contribute to **anemia** in patients with hypothyroidism: (1) impaired hemoglobin synthesis as a result of thyroxine deficiency; (2) iron deficiency from increased iron loss with menorrhagia, as well as impaired intestinal absorption of iron; (3) folate deficiency from impaired intestinal absorption of folic acid; and (4) pernicious anemia, with vitamin B_{12}-deficient megaloblastic anemia. The pernicious anemia is often part of a spectrum of autoimmune diseases, including myxedema due to chronic thyroiditis associated with thyroid autoantibodies, pernicious anemia associated with parietal cell autoantibodies, diabetes mellitus associated with islet cell autoantibodies, and adrenal insufficiency associated with adrenal autoantibodies (Schmidt's syndrome; see Chapter 21).

6. Neuromuscular system– Many patients complain of symptoms referable to the neuromuscular system, eg, severe muscle cramps, paresthesias, and muscle weakness.

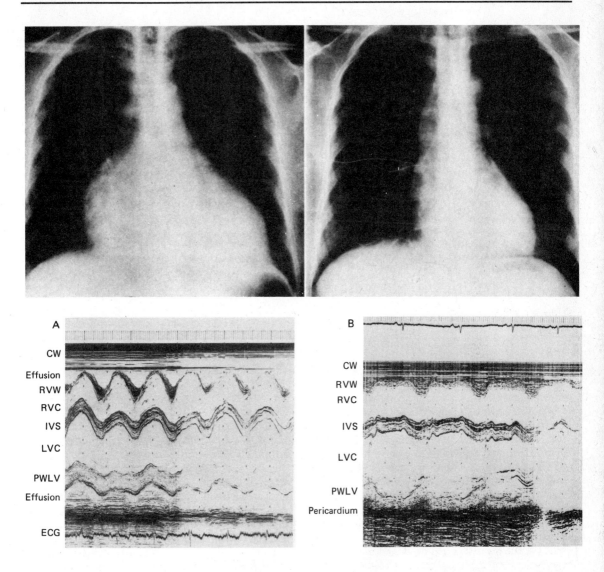

Figure 4–37. *Top:* Chest x-ray studies of patient with hypothyroid cardiomyopathy. **Left:** Before therapy, showing pronounced cardiomegaly. **Right:** Six months after institution of thyroxine therapy, the heart size has returned to normal (Reproduced, with permission, from Reza MJ, Abbasi AS: Congestive cardiomyopathy in hypothyroidism. West J Med 1975;123:228). **Bottom:** Echocardiogram of a 29-year-old woman with hypothyroidism *(A)* before and *(B)* after 2 months of therapy with levothyroxine sodium. (CW, chest wall; RVW, right ventricular wall; RVC, right ventricular cavity; IVS, interventricular septum; LVC, left ventricular cavity; PWLV, posterior wall left ventricle.) Note disappearance of pericardial effusion following levothyroxine therapy. (Reproduced, with permission, from Sokolow M, McIlroy MB: *Clinical Cardiology,* 4th ed. Lange, 1986.)

7. Central nervous system symptoms may include chronic fatigue, lethargy, and inability to concentrate. Hypothyroidism impairs the conversion of peripheral metabolism of estrogen precursors to estrogens, resulting in altered FSH and LH secretion and in anovulatory cycles and infertility. This may also be associated with severe menorrhagia. Patients with myxedema are usually quite placid but can be severely depressed or even extremely agitated ("myxedema madness").

Diagnosis

The combination of a low serum FT_4 or FT_4I and an elevated serum TSH is diagnostic of primary hypothyroidism (Figure 4–38). Serum T_3 levels are variable and may be within the normal range. A positive test for thyroid autoantibodies suggests underlying Hashimoto's thyroiditis. In patients with pituitary myxedema, the FT_4I or FT_4 will be low but serum TSH will not be elevated. It may then be necessary to differentiate pituitary from hypothalamic disease,

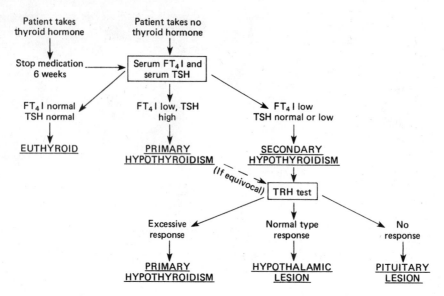

Figure 4–38. Diagnosis of hypothyroidism. Either free thyroxine (FT$_4$) or free thyroxine index (FT$_4$I) may be used with TSH for evaluation.

and for this the TRH test is most helpful (Figure 4–25). Absence of TSH response to TRH indicates pituitary deficiency. A partial or "normal" type response indicates that pituitary function is intact but that a defect exists in hypothalamic secretion of TRH. The patient may be taking thyroid medication (levothyroxine or desiccated thyroid tablets) when first seen. A palpable or enlarged thyroid gland and a positive test for thyroid autoantibodies would suggest underlying Hashimoto's thyroiditis, in which case the medication should be continued. If antibodies are absent, the medication should be withdrawn for 6 weeks and determinations made for FT$_4$I or FT$_4$ and for TSH. The 6-week period of withdrawal is necessary because of the long half-life of thyroxine (7 days) and to allow the pituitary gland to recover after a long period of suppression. The pattern of recovery of thyroid function after withdrawal of T$_4$ is noted in Figure 4–39. In hypothyroid individuals, TSH becomes markedly elevated at 5–6 weeks and T$_4$ remains subnormal, whereas both are normal after 6 weeks in euthyroid controls.

The clinical picture of fully developed myxedema is usually quite clear, but the symptoms and signs of mild hypothyroidism may be very subtle. Patients with hypothyroidism will at times present with unusual features: neurasthenia with symptoms of muscle cramps, paresthesias, and weakness; anemia; disturbances in reproductive function, including infertility, delayed puberty, or menorrhagia; idiopathic edema or pleuropericardial effusions; retarded growth; obstipation; chronic rhinitis or hoarseness due to edema of nasal mucosa or vocal cords; and severe depression progressing to emotional instability or even frank paranoid psychosis. In such cases, the

diagnostic studies outlined above will confirm or rule out hypothyroidism as a contributing factor.

Complications

A. Myxedema Coma: Myxedema coma is the end stage of untreated hypothyroidism. It is characterized by progressive weakness, stupor, hypothermia, hypoventilation, hypoglycemia, hyponatremia, water intoxication, shock, and death. Although rare now, in the future it may occur more frequently in association with the increasing use of radioiodine for the treatment of Graves' disease, with resulting permanent hypothyroidism. Since it occurs most frequently in older patients with underlying pulmonary and vascular disease, the mortality rate is extremely high.

The patient (or a family member if the patient is comatose) may recall previous thyroid disease, radioiodine therapy, or thyroidectomy. The medical history is of gradual onset of lethargy progressing to stupor or coma. Examination reveals bradycardia and marked hypothermia, with body temperature as low as 24 °C (75 °F). The patient is usually an obese elderly woman with yellowish skin, a hoarse voice, a large tongue, thin hair, puffy eyes, ileus, and slow reflexes. There may be signs of other illnesses such as pneumonia, myocardial infarction, cerebral thrombosis, or gastrointestinal bleeding. Laboratory clues to the diagnosis of myxedema coma include lactescent serum, high serum carotene, elevated serum cholesterol, and increased cerebrospinal fluid protein. Pleural, pericardial, or abdominal effusions with high protein content may be present. Serum tests will reveal a low FT$_4$ and a markedly elevated TSH. Thyroidal radioactive iodine uptake is low, and thyroid

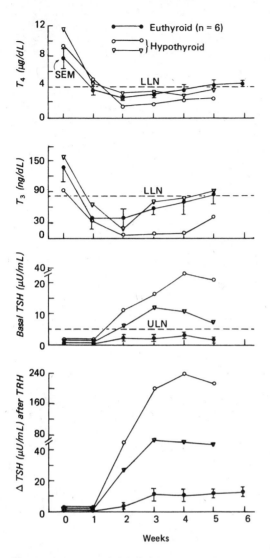

Figure 4–39. Changes in T_4, T_3, TSH, and TRH response following abrupt withdrawal of suppressive thyroxine therapy. Note that in euthyroid individuals the T_4 may not return to normal until 6 weeks after withdrawal of therapy and that serum TSH is never elevated. In hypothyroid patients, TSH may be elevated as early as 2 weeks after withdrawal of therapy, and TRH response is exaggerated. (LLN, lower limit of normal; ULN, upper limit of normal.) (Reproduced, with permission, from Wood LC: Controversial questions in thyroid disease. Workshop in the Thyroid, American Thyroid Association, Nov 1979, as adapted from Vagenakis AG et al: Recovery of pituitary thyrotropic function after withdrawal of prolonged thyroid suppression therapy. N Engl J Med 1975;293: 681.)

autoantibodies are usually strongly positive, indicating underlying chronic thyroiditis. The ECG shows sinus bradycardia and low voltage. If laboratory studies are not readily available, which is frequently the case, the diagnosis must be made clinically.

The pathophysiology of myxedema coma involves three major aspects: (1) CO_2 retention and hypoxia, (2) fluid and electrolyte imbalance, and (3) hypothermia. CO_2 retention and hypoxia are probably due in large part to a marked depression in the ventilatory responses to hypoxia and hypercapnia, though factors such as obesity, heart failure, ileus, immobilization, pneumonia, pleural or peritoneal effusions, central nervous system depression, and weak chest muscles may also contribute. The failure of the myxedema patient to respond to hypoxia or hypercapnia may be due to the hypothermia. Impairment of ventilatory drive is often severe, and assisted respiration is almost always necessary in patients with myxedema coma. Thyroid hormone therapy in patients with myxedema corrects the hypothermia and markedly improves the ventilatory response to hypoxia. The major fluid and electrolyte disturbance is water intoxication due to the syndrome of inappropriate secretion of vasopressin (SIADH). This presents as hyponatremia and is managed by water restriction. Hypothermia is frequently not recognized, because the ordinary clinical thermometer only goes down to about 34 °C (93 °F); a laboratory type thermometer that registers a broader scale must be used to obtain accurate body temperature readings. Active rewarming of the body is contraindicated, because it may induce vasodilation and vascular collapse. A rise in body temperature is a useful indication of therapeutic effectiveness of thyroxine.

Disorders that may precipitate myxedema coma include heart failure, pneumonia, pulmonary edema, pleural or peritoneal effusions, ileus, excessive fluid administration, or administration of sedative or narcotic drugs to a patient with severe hypothyroidism. Adrenal insufficiency occurs occasionally in association with myxedema coma, but it is relatively rare and usually associated with either pituitary myxedema or concurrent autoimmune adrenal insufficiency (Schmidt's syndrome). Seizures, bleeding episodes, hypocalcemia, or hypercalcemia may be present. It is important to differentiate *pituitary* myxedema from *primary* myxedema. In pituitary myxedema, adrenal insufficiency may be present, and glucocorticoid replacement is essential. Clinical clues to the presence of pituitary myxedema include the following: a history of amenorrhea or impotence; scanty pubic or axillary hair; and normal serum cholesterol and normal or low TSH levels. CT scan or MRI may reveal an enlarged sella turcica. The treatment of myxedema coma is discussed below.

B. Myxedema and Heart Disease: In the past, treatment of patients with myxedema and heart disease, particularly coronary artery disease, was very difficult, because levothyroxine replacement was frequently associated with exacerbation of angina, heart failure, or myocardial infarction. Now that coronary angioplasty and coronary artery bypass surgery are available, patients with myxedema and coronary artery disease can be treated surgically first, and more rapid thyroxine replacement therapy will then be tolerated.

C. Hypothyroidism and Neuropsychiatric Disease: Hypothyroidism is often associated with depression, which may be quite severe. More rarely, myxedematous patients may become confused, paranoid, or even manic ("myxedema madness"). Screening of psychiatric admissions with FT_4 and TSH is an efficient way to find these patients, who will frequently respond to levothyroxine therapy alone or in combination with psychopharmacologic agents. The effectiveness of levothyroxine therapy in disturbed hypothyroid patients has given rise to the hypothesis that the addition of T_3 or T_4 to psychotherapeutic regimens for depressed patients may be helpful in patients without demonstrable thyroid disease. Further work needs to be done to establish this concept as standard treatment.

Treatment

A. Treatment of Hypothyroidism: Hypothyroidism is treated with levothyroxine (T_4), which is available in pure form and is stable and inexpensive. Intracellularly, levothyroxine is converted to T_3, so that both hormones become available even though only one is administered. Desiccated thyroid is unsatisfactory because of its variable hormone content, and triiodothyronine (as liothyronine) is unsatisfactory because of its rapid absorption, short half-life, and transient effects. The half-life of levothyroxine is about 7 days, so it need be given only once daily. It is well absorbed, and blood levels are easily monitored by following FT_4I or FT_4 and serum TSH levels. There is a rise in T_4 or FT_4I of about 1–2 μg/dL

(13–26 nmol/L) and a concomitant fall in TSH of 1–2 μU/mL (1–2 mU/L) beginning about 2 hours and lasting about 8–10 hours after an oral dose of 0.1–0.15 mg of levothyroxine (Figure 4–40). It is best, therefore, to take the daily dose of levothyroxine in the morning to avoid symptoms such as insomnia if the medication is taken at bedtime. In addition, when monitoring serum thyroxine levels, it is important that blood be drawn fasting or before the daily dose of the hormone in order to obtain consistent data.

Dosage of levothyroxine: Replacement doses of levothyroxine in adults range from 0.05 to 0.2 mg/d, with a mean of 0.125 mg/d. The dose of levothyroxine varies according to the patient's age and body weight (Table 4–9). Young children require a surprisingly high dose of levothyroxine compared with adults. In adults, the mean replacement dose of T_4 is about 1.7 μg/kg/d, or about 0.8 μg/lb/d. In older adults, the replacement dose is lower, about 1.6 μg/kg/d, or about 0.7 μg/lb/d. For TSH suppression in patients with nodular goiters or cancers of the thyroid gland, the average dose of levothyroxine is about 2.2 μg/kg/d (1 μg/lb/d). Malabsorptive states or concurrent administration of aluminum preparations or cholestyramine will modify T_4 absorption, and in these patients larger doses of T_4 may be necessary. Levothyroxine has a sufficiently long half-life (7 days) so that if the patient is unable to take medications by mouth for a few days, omitting levothyroxine therapy will not be detrimental. However, if the patient is being managed by sustained parenteral therapy, the parenteral dose of T_4 is about 75–80% of the usual oral dose.

B. Treatment of Myxedema Coma: Myxedema coma is an acute medical emergency and should be treated in the intensive care unit. Blood gases must be monitored regularly, and the patient usually requires intubation and mechanical ventilation. Associated illnesses such as infections or heart failure must

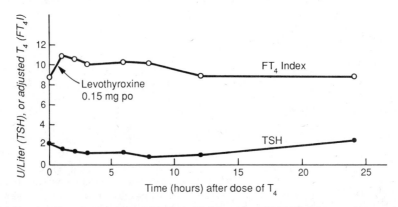

Figure 4–40. Rise in serum free thyroxine index (FT_4I) and fall in serum TSH following an oral dose of 0.15 mg levothyroxine.

Table 4–9. Replacement doses of levothyroxine.[1]

Age	Dose of Levothyroxine (μg/kg/d)
0–6 mo	8–10
7–11 mo	6–8
1–5 yr	5–6
6–10 yr	3–4
11–20 yr	2–3
Adult	1–2

[1] Adapted and modified, with permission, from Dussault J, Fisher DE: Hypothyroidism in infants and children. In: *Werner and Ingbar's The Thyroid,* 6th ed. Braverman LE, Utiger RD (editors). Lippincott, 1991.

be sought and treated by appropriate therapy. Intravenous fluids should be administered with caution, and excessive free water intake must be avoided. Because patients with myxedema coma absorb all drugs poorly, it is imperative to give levothyroxine intravenously. These patients have marked depletion of serum thyroxine with a large number of empty binding sites on thyroxine-binding globulin and therefore should receive an initial loading dose of thyroxine intravenously, followed by a small daily intravenous dose. An initial dose of 300–400 μg of levothyroxine is administered intravenously, followed by 50 μg of levothyroxine intravenously daily. The clinical guides to improvement are a rise in body temperature and the return of normal cerebral and respiratory function. If the patient is known to have had normal adrenal function before the coma, adrenal support is probably not necessary. If, however, no data are available, the possibility of concomitant adrenal insufficiency (due to autoimmune adrenal disease or pituitary insufficiency) does exist. In this case, the plasma cortisol should be measured or, if time permits (30 minutes), a cosyntropin stimulation test should performed (see Chapter 6). Then, full adrenal support should be administered, eg, hydrocortisone hemisuccinate, 100 mg intravenously, followed by 50 mg intravenously every 6 hours, tapering the dose over 7 days. Adrenal support can be withdrawn sooner if the pretreatment plasma cortisol is 20 μg/dL or greater or results of a cosyntropin stimulation test are within normal limits. When giving levothyroxine intravenously in large doses, there is an inherent risk of precipitating angina, heart failure, or arrhythmias in older patients with underlying coronary artery disease. Thus, this type of therapy is not recommended for ambulatory patients with myxedema; in these patients, it is better to start slowly and build up the dose as noted below.

C. Myxedema With Heart Disease: In long-standing hypothyroidism or in older patients—particularly those with known cardiovascular disease—it is imperative to start treatment slowly. Levothyroxine is given in a dosage of 0.025 mg/d for 2 weeks, in-creasing by 0.025 mg every 2 weeks until a daily dose of 0.1 mg or 0.125 mg is reached. It usually takes about 2 months for a patient to come into equilibrium on full dosage. In these patients, the heart is very sensitive to the level of circulating thyroxine, and if angina pectoris or cardiac arrhythmia develops, it is essential to reduce the dose of thyroxine immediately. In younger patients or those with mild disease, full replacement may be started immediately.

Toxic Effects of Levothyroxine Therapy

There are no reported instances of allergy to pure levothyroxine, though it is possible that a patient may develop an allergy to the coloring dye or some component of the tablet. The major toxic reactions to levothyroxine overdosage are symptoms of hyperthyroidism—particularly cardiac symptoms—and osteoporosis. The most common thyrotoxic cardiac symptom is arrhythmia, particularly paroxysmal atrial tachycardia or fibrillation. Insomnia, tremor, restlessness, and excessive warmth may also be troublesome. Simply omitting the daily dose of levothyroxine for 3 days and then reducing the dosage will correct the problem.

Increased bone resorption and severe osteoporosis have been associated with long-standing hyperthyroidism and will develop in patients chronically overtreated with levothyroxine. This can be prevented by regular monitoring and by maintaining normal serum FT_4 and TSH in patients receiving long-term replacement therapy. In patients receiving TSH-suppressive therapy for nodular goiter or thyroid cancer, if FT_4I or FT_4 is kept in the upper range of normal—even if TSH is suppressed—the adverse effects of T_4 therapy on bone will be minimal (Table 22–3).

Course & Prognosis

The course of untreated myxedema is one of slow deterioration, leading eventually to myxedema coma and death. With appropriate treatment, however, the long-term prognosis is excellent. Because of the long half-life (7 days) of thyroxine, it takes time to establish equilibrium on a fixed dose. Therefore, it is important to monitor the FT_4I or FT_4 and the serum TSH every 4–6 weeks until equilibrium is reached. Thereafter, FT_4 and TSH can be monitored once a year. The dose of T_4 must be increased about 25% during pregnancy and lactation. Older patients metabolize T_4 more slowly, and the dose will gradually decrease with age (see Chapter 22).

The mortality rate of myxedema coma was about 80% at one time. The prognosis has been vastly improved as a result of recognition of the importance of mechanically assisted respiration and the use of intravenous levothyroxine. At present, the outcome probably depends upon how well the underlying disease problems can be managed.

Table 4–10. Conditions associated with thyrotoxicosis.

1. Diffuse toxic goiter (Graves' disease)
2. Toxic adenoma (Plummer's disease)
3. Toxic multinodular goiter
4. Subacute thyroiditis
5. Hyperthyroid phase of Hashimoto's thyroiditis
6. Thyrotoxicosis factitia
7. Rare forms of thyrotoxicosis: ovarian struma, metastatic thyroid carcinoma (follicular), hydatidiform mole, "hamburger thyrotoxicosis," TSH-secreting pituitary tumor, pituitary resistance to T_3 and T_4

HYPERTHYROIDISM & THYROTOXICOSIS

Thyrotoxicosis is the clinical syndrome that results when tissues are exposed to high levels of circulating thyroid hormone. In most instances, thyrotoxicosis is due to hyperactivity of the thyroid gland, or hyperthyroidism. Occasionally, thyrotoxicosis may be due to other causes such as excessive ingestion of thyroid hormone or excessive secretion of thyroid hormone from ectopic sites. The various forms of thyrotoxicosis are listed in Table 4–10. These syndromes will be discussed individually below.

1. DIFFUSE TOXIC GOITER
(Graves' Disease)

Graves' disease is the most common form of thyrotoxicosis and may occur at any age, more commonly in females than in males. The syndrome consists of one or more of the following features: (1) thyrotoxicosis, (2) goiter, (3) ophthalmopathy (exophthalmos), and (4) dermopathy (pretibial myxedema).

Etiology

Graves' disease is currently viewed as an autoimmune disease of unknown cause. There is a strong familial predisposition in that about 15% of patients with Graves' disease have a close relative with the same disorder, and about 50% of relatives of patients with Graves' disease have circulating thyroid autoantibodies. Females are involved about five times more commonly than males. The disease may occur at any age, with a peak incidence in the 20- to 40-year age group. (See section on thyroid autoimmunity, above.)

Pathogenesis

In Graves' disease, T lymphocytes become sensitized to antigens within the thyroid gland and stimulate B lymphocytes to synthesize antibodies to these antigens (see section on thyroid autoimmunity, above, and Figure 4–41). One such antibody is directed against the TSH receptor site in the thyroid cell membrane and has the capacity to stimulate the thyroid cell to increased growth and function (TSH-R

Ab [stim]; see Table 4–7). The presence of this circulating antibody is positively correlated with active disease and with relapse of the disease. There is an underlying genetic predisposition, but it is not clear what "triggers" the acute episode. Some factors that may incite the immune response of Graves' disease are (1) pregnancy, particularly the postpartum period; (2) iodide excess, particularly in geographic areas of iodide deficiency, where the lack of iodide may hold latent Graves' disease in check; (3) lithium therapy, perhaps by modifying immune responsiveness; (4) viral or bacterial infections; and (5) glucocorticoid withdrawal. It has been postulated that "stress" may trigger an episode of Graves' disease, but there is no evidence to support this hypothesis. The pathogenesis of ophthalmopathy may involve cytotoxic lymphocytes (killer cells) and cytotoxic antibodies sensitized to a common antigen (perhaps a 64-kDa antigen) in orbital fibroblasts, orbital muscle, and

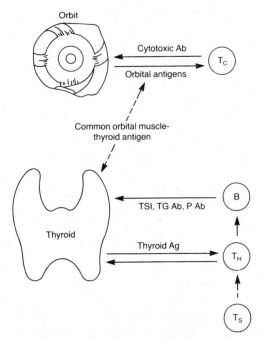

Figure 4–41. One theory of the pathogenesis of Graves' disease. There is a defect in suppressor T lymphocytes (T_s) that allows helper T lymphocytes (T_H) to stimulate B lymphocytes (B) to synthesize thyroid autoantibodies. The thyroid-stimulating immunoglobulin (TSI) is the driving force for thyrotoxicosis. The inflammatory process in the orbital muscles may be due to sensitization of cytotoxic T lymphocytes (T_c), or killer cells, to orbital antigens in association with cytotoxic antibodies. The thyroid and the eye may be linked by a common antigen in thyroid and orbital muscle. It is not yet clear what triggers this immunologic cascade. (Tg Ab, thyroglobulin antibody; P Ab, Peroxidase or microsomal antibody; Ag, antigen; Ab, antibody.)

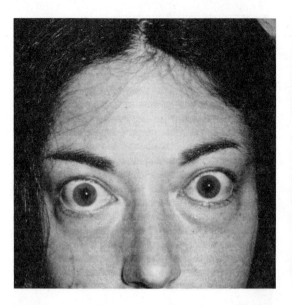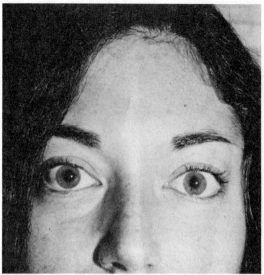

Figure 4–42. Patient with mild ophthalmopathy of Graves' disease. **Left:** Before radioactive iodine therapy. Note white sclera visible above and below the iris as well as mild periorbital edema. **Classification** (see Table 4–11): class 1, mild; class 2, mild: class 3, mild. **Right:** After radioactive iodine therapy. Marked improvement is noted.

thyroid tissue (Figure 4–41). Cytokines from these sensitized lymphocytes would cause inflammation of orbital fibroblasts and orbital myositis, resulting in swollen orbital muscles, proptosis of the globes, and diplopia as well as redness, congestion, and conjunctival and periorbital edema (thyroid ophthalmopathy; Figures 4–42 and 4–43). The pathogenesis of thyroid dermopathy (pretibial myxedema) (Figure 4–44) and the rare subperiosteal inflammation on the phalanges of the hands and feet (thyroid osteopathy) (Figure

Figure 4–43. Severe ophthalmopathy of Graves' disease. Note marked periorbital edema, injection of corneal blood vessels, and proptosis. There was also striking limitation of upward and lateral eye movements and reduced visual acuity. **Classification** (see Table 4–11): class 1, severe; class 2, severe; class 3, severe; class 4, severe; class 5, none; class 6, mild.

4–45) may also involve lymphocyte cytokine stimulation of fibroblasts in these locations.

Many symptoms of thyrotoxicosis suggest a state of catecholamine excess, including tachycardia, tremor, sweating, lid lag, and stare. Circulating levels of epinephrine are normal; thus, in Graves' disease, the body appears to be hyperreactive to catecholamines. This may be due in part to a thyroid hormone-mediated increase in cardiac catecholamine receptors.

Clinical Features

A. Symptoms and Signs: In younger individuals, common manifestations include palpitations, nervousness, easy fatigability, hyperkinesia, diarrhea, excessive sweating, intolerance to heat, and preference for cold. There is often marked weight loss without loss of appetite. Thyroid enlargement, thyrotoxic eye signs (see below), and mild tachycardia commonly occur. Muscle weakness and loss of muscle mass may be so severe that the patient cannot rise from a chair without assistance. In children, rapid growth with accelerated bone maturation occurs. In patients over age 60, cardiovascular and myopathic manifestations predominate; the most common presenting complaints are palpitation, dyspnea on exertion, tremor, nervousness, and weight loss (see Chapter 22).

The eye signs of Graves' disease have been classified by the American Thyroid Association as set forth in Table 4–11. This classification is useful in describing the extent of the eye involvement, though it is not helpful in following the progress of the ill-

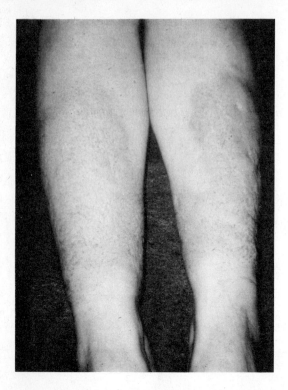

Figure 4–44. Dermopathy of Graves' disease. Marked thickening of the skin is noted, usually over the pretibial area. Thickening will occasionally extend downward over the ankle and the dorsal aspect of the foot but almost never above the knee.

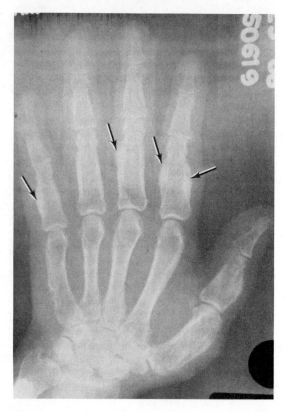

Figure 4–45. X-ray of hand of patient with thyroid osteopathy. Note marked periosteal thickening of the proximal phalanges.

ness since one class does not always progress into the next. The first letters of each class form the mnemonic "NO SPECS." Class 1 involves spasm of the upper lids associated with active thyrotoxicosis and usually resolves spontaneously when the thyrotoxicosis is adequately controlled. Classes 2–6 represent true infiltrative disease involving orbital muscles and orbital tissues (Figures 4–42 and 4–43). Class 2 is characterized by soft tissue involvement with periorbital edema, congestion or redness of the conjunctiva, and swelling of the conjunctiva (chemosis). Class 3 consists of proptosis as measured by the Hertel exophthalmometer. This instrument consists of two prisms with a scale mounted on a bar. The prisms are placed on the lateral orbital ridges, and the distance from the orbital ridge to the anterior cornea is measured on the scale (Figure 4–46). The upper limits of normal according to race are listed in the footnote to Table 4–11. Class 4 consists of muscle involvement. The muscle most commonly involved in the infiltrative process is the inferior rectus, limiting upward gaze. The muscle next most commonly involved is the medial rectus, impairing lateral gaze. Class 5 is characterized by corneal involvement (keratitis) and class 6 loss of vision from optic nerve involvement. As noted above, thyroid ophthalmopathy

is due to infiltration of the extraocular muscles with lymphocytes and edema fluid in an acute inflammatory reaction. The orbit is a cone enclosed by bone, and swelling of the extraocular muscles within this closed space causes proptosis of the globe and impaired muscle movement, resulting in diplopia. Ocular muscle enlargement can be demonstrated by orbital CT scanning or MRI (Figure 4–47). When muscle swelling occurs posteriorly, toward the apex of the orbital cone, the optic nerve is compressed, which may cause loss of vision.

Thyroid dermopathy consists of thickening of the skin, particularly over the lower tibia, due to accumulation of glycosaminoglycans (Figure 4–44). It is relatively rare, occurring in about 2–3% of patients with Graves' disease. It is usually associated with ophthalmopathy and with a very high serum titer of TSH-R Ab [stim]. The skin is markedly thickened and cannot be picked up between the fingers. Sometimes the dermopathy involves the entire lower leg and may extend onto the feet. Bony involvement (osteopathy), with subperiosteal bone formation and swelling, is particularly evident in the metacarpal bones (Figure 4–45). This too is a relatively rare finding. A more common finding in Graves' disease

Table 4–11. Classification of eye changes in Graves' disease.[1]

Class	Definition
0	*No signs or symptoms.*
1	*Only signs, no symptoms. (Signs limited to upper lid retraction, stare, lid lag.)*
2	*Soft tissue involvement (symptoms and signs).*
3	*Proptosis (measured with Hertel exophthalmometer).*[2]
4	*Extraocular muscle involvement.*
5	*Corneal involvement.*
6	*Sight loss (optic nerve involvement).*

[1] Reproduced, with permission, from Werner SC: Classification of the eye changes of Graves' disease. J Clin Endocrinol Metab 1969;29:782 and 1977;44:203.
[2] Upper limits of normal according to race: Oriental, 18 mm; white, 20 mm; black, 22 mm. Increase in proptosis of 3–4 mm is mild involvement; 5–7 mm, moderate involvement; and over 8 mm, severe involvement. Other classes can be similarly graded as mild, moderate, or severe.

is separation of the fingernails from their beds, or onycholysis (Figure 4–48).

B. Laboratory Findings: The laboratory findings in hyperthyroidism have been reviewed in the section on thyroid tests. Essentially, the combination of an elevated FT_4I or FT_4D and a suppressed TSH makes the diagnosis of hyperthyroidism. In early and recurrent Graves' disease, T_3 may be secreted in excess before T_4, so that the serum T_4 may be normal while the T_3 is elevated. Thus, if TSH is suppressed and FT_4I is not elevated, serum T_3 should be measured. Thyroid autoantibodies are usually present, particulary TSH-R Ab [stim]. This may be a useful diagnostic test in the "apathetic" hyperthyroid patient or in the patient who presents with unilateral exophthalmos without obvious signs or laboratory manifestations of Graves' disease. Radioiodine uptake is helpful when low-uptake hyperthyroidism is suspected; this may occur as a phase of subacute or Hashimoto's thyroiditis. This type of hyperthyroidism frequently resolves spontaneously. The ^{123}I or technetium scan may be helpful when it is necessary to demonstrate the size of the gland and to detect the presence of "hot" or "cold" nodules. Since the ultrasensitive TSH test will detect TSH suppression, the TRH test and the TSH suppression test (see above) are rarely indicated. Echography, CT, and MRI of the orbit have revealed muscle enlargement in most patients with Graves' disease even when there is no clinical evidence of ophthalmopathy. In patients with clinical evidence of ophthalmopathy, orbital muscle enlargement is frequently striking (Figure 4–47).

Differential Diagnosis

Graves' disease occasionally presents in an unusual or atypical fashion, in which case the diagnosis may not be obvious. Marked muscle atrophy may suggest severe myopathy that must be differentiated from primary neurologic disorder. Thyrotoxic periodic paralysis usually occurs in Oriental males and presents with a sudden attack of flaccid paralysis and hypokalemia. The paralysis usually subsides spontaneously and can be prevented by K^+ supplementation and beta-adrenergic blockade. The illness is cured by appropriate treatment of the thyrotoxicosis. Patients with thyrocardiac disease present primarily with symptoms of heart involvement—especially refractory atrial fibrillation insensitive to digoxin—or with high-output heart failure. About 50% of these patients have no evidence of underlying heart disease, and the cardiac problems are cured by treatment of the thyrotoxicosis. Some older patients will present

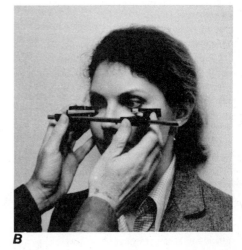

A   *B*

Figure 4–46. A: Hertel exophthalmometer. **B:** Proper use of the exophthalmometer. The edges of the instrument are placed on the lateral orbital ridges, and the distance from the orbital bone to the anterior cornea is read on the scale contained within the prisms.

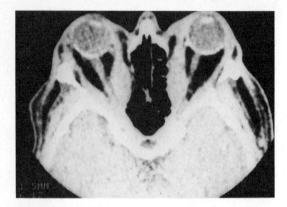

Figure 4–47. Orbital CT scan in a patient with severe ophthalmopathy and visual failure. Note the marked enlargement of extraocular muscles posteriorly, with compression of the optic nerve at the apex of the orbital cone.

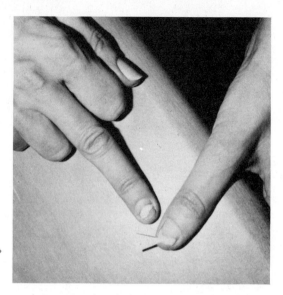

Figure 4–48. Onycholysis (separation of the nail from its bed) in Graves' disease usually resolves spontaneously as the patient improves.

with weight loss, small goiter, slow atrial fibrillation, and severe depression, with none of the clinical features of increased catecholamine reactivity. These placid patients have "apathetic hyperthyroidism." Finally, some young women may present with amenorrhea or infertility as the primary symptom. In all of these instances, the diagnosis of hyperthyroidism can usually be made on the basis of the clinical and laboratory studies described above.

In the syndrome called "familial dysalbuminemic hyperthyroxinemia" (see above), an abnormal albumin-like protein is present in serum that preferentially binds T_4 but not T_3. This results in elevation of serum T_4 and FT_4I, but free T_4, T_3, and TSH are normal. It is important to differentiate this euthyroid state from hyperthyroidism. In addition to the absence of clinical features of hyperthyroidism, a normal serum T_3 and a normal TSH level will rule out hyperthyroidism.

Complications

Thyrotoxic crisis ("thyroid storm") is the acute exacerbation of all of the symptoms of thyrotoxicosis, often presenting as a syndrome that may be of life-threatening severity. Occasionally, thyroid storm may be mild and present simply as an unexplained febrile reaction after thyroid surgery in a patient who has been inadequately prepared. More commonly, it occurs in a more severe form after surgery, radioactive iodine therapy, or parturition in a patient with inadequately controlled thyrotoxicosis or during a severe, stressful illness or disorder such as uncontrolled diabetes, trauma, acute infection, severe drug reaction, or myocardial infarction. The clinical manifestations of thyroid storm are marked hypermetabolism and excessive adrenergic response. Fever ranges from 38 to 41 °C (100–106 °F) and is associated with flushing and sweating. There is marked tachycardia,

often with atrial fibrillation and high pulse pressure and occasionally with heart failure. Central nervous system symptoms include marked agitation, restlessness, delirium, and coma. Gastrointestinal symptoms include nausea, vomiting, diarrhea, and jaundice. A fatal outcome will be associated with heart failure and shock.

At one time it was thought that thyroid storm was due to sudden release or "dumping" of stored thyroxine and triiodothyronine from the thyrotoxic gland. Careful studies have revealed, however, that the serum levels of T_4 and T_3 in patients with thyroid storm are not higher than in thyrotoxic patients without this condition. There is no evidence that thyroid storm is due to excessive production of triiodothyronine. There is evidence that in thyrotoxicosis the number of binding sites for catecholamines increases, so that heart and nerve tissues have increased sensitivity to circulating catecholamines. In addition, there is decreased binding to TBG, with elevation of free T_3 and T_4. The present theory is that in this setting, with increased binding sites available for catecholamines, an acute illness, infection, or surgical stress triggers an outpouring of catecholamines which, in association with high levels of free T_4 and T_3, precipitates the acute problem.

The most striking clinical diagnostic feature of thyrotoxic crisis is hyperpyrexia out of proportion to other findings. Laboratory findings include elevated serum T_4, FT_4, and T_3 as well as a suppressed TSH.

Treatment of Graves' Disease

Although autoimmune mechanisms are responsible for the syndrome of Graves' disease, management has been largely directed toward controlling the hyperthyroidism. Three good methods are available: (1) antithyroid drug therapy, (2) surgery, and (3) radioactive iodine therapy.

A. Antithyroid Drug Therapy: In general, antithyroid drug therapy is most useful in young patients with small glands and mild disease. The drugs (propylthiouracil or methimazole) are given until the disease undergoes spontaneous remission. This occurs in 20–40% of patients treated for 6 months to 15 years. Although this is the only therapy that leaves an intact thyroid gland, it does require a long period of observation, and the incidence of relapse is high, perhaps 60–80% even in selected patients. The relapse rate may be decreased using the regimen of total thyroid block described below. Antithyroid drug therapy is generally started with large divided doses; when the patient becomes clinically euthyroid, maintenance therapy may be achieved with a lower single morning dose. A common regimen consists of giving propylthiouracil, 100–150 mg every 6 hours initially, and then in 4–8 weeks reducing the dose to 50–200 mg once or twice daily. Propylthiouracil has one advantage over methimazole in that it partially inhibits the conversion of T_4 to T_3, so that it is effective in bringing down the levels of activated thyroid hormone more quickly. However, methimazole has a longer duration of action and is more useful if a single daily dose is desirable. A typical program would start with a 40-mg dose of methimazole each morning for 1–2 months; this dose would then be reduced to 5–20 mg each morning for maintenance therapy. The laboratory tests of most value in monitoring the course of therapy are serum FT_4 and TSH.

An alternative method of therapy utilizes the concept of a total block of thyroid activity. The patient is treated with methimazole until euthyroid (about 3–6 months), but instead of continuing to taper the dose of methimazole, at this point levothyroxine is added in a dose of about 0.1 mg/d. The patient then continues to receive the combination of methimazole 10 mg/d and levothyroxine 0.1 mg/d for another 12–24 months. At the end of this time, or when the size of the gland has returned to normal, methimazole is discontinued and levothyroxine continued for another year. With this therapy, the fall in antithyroid antibody titer is striking, and long-term remissions occur in 60–80% of treated patients.

1. Duration of therapy– The duration of therapy with antithyroid drugs in Graves' disease is quite variable and can range from 6 months to 20 years or more. A sustained remission may be predicted in about 80% of treated patients in the following circumstances: (1) if the thyroid gland returns to normal size; (2) if the disease can be controlled with a relatively small dose of antithyroid drugs; (3) if TSH-R Ab [stim] is no longer detectable in the serum; and (4) if the thyroid gland becomes normally suppressible following the administration of liothyronine.

2. Reactions to antithyroid drugs– Allergic reactions to antithyroid drugs involve either a rash (about 5% of patients) or agranulocytosis (about 0.5% of patients). The rash can be managed by simply administering antihistamines, and unless it is severe it is not an indication for discontinuing the medication. Agranulocytosis requires immediate cessation of all antithyroid drug therapy, institution of appropriate antibiotic therapy, and shifting to an alternative therapy, usually radioactive iodine. Agranulocytosis is usually heralded by sore throat and fever. Thus, all patients receiving antithyroid drugs are instructed that if sore throat or fever develops, they should stop the drug, obtain a white blood cell and differential count, and see their physician. If the white blood cell count is normal, the antithyroid drug can be resumed. Cholestatic jaundice, angioneurotic edema, hepatocellular toxicity, and acute arthralgia are serious but rare side effects that also require cessation of drug therapy.

B. Surgical Treatment: Subtotal thyroidectomy is the treatment of choice for patients with very large glands or multinodular goiters. The patient is prepared with antithyroid drugs until euthyroid (about 6 weeks). In addition, starting 2 weeks before the day of operation, the patient is given saturated solution of potassium iodide, 5 drops twice daily. This regimen has been shown empirically to diminish the vascularity of the gland and to simplify surgery.

There is disagreement about how much thyroid tissue should be removed. Total thyroidectomy is usually not necessary unless the patient has severe progressive ophthalmopathy (see below). However, if too much thyroid tissue is left behind, the disease will relapse. Most surgeons leave 2–3 g of thyroid tissue on either side of the neck. Many patients, however, require thyroid supplementation following thyroidectomy for Graves' disease.

Hypoparathyroidism and recurrent laryngeal nerve injury occur as complications of surgery in about 1% of cases.

C. Radioactive Iodine Therapy: In the USA, sodium iodide I 131 is the preferred treatment for most patients over age 21. In many patients without underlying heart disease, radioactive iodine may be given immediately in a dosage of 80–120 µCi/g of thyroid weight estimated on the basis of physical examination and sodium ^{123}I rectilinear scan. The dosage is corrected for iodine uptake according to the following formula:

$$^{131}I\,(\mu Ci/g) \times \frac{\text{Estimated thyroid weight (g)}}{} \times \frac{100}{\text{24-hour RAI uptake}} = \frac{\text{Therapeutic dose of }^{131}I}{\text{in }\mu Ci}$$

In patients with underlying heart disease, severe thyrotoxicosis, or large glands (> 100 g), it is desirable to achieve a euthyroid state before radioactive iodine is started. These patients are treated with antithyroid drugs (as above) until they are euthyroid; medication is then stopped for 5–7 days; radioactive iodine uptake and scan are done; and a dose of 100–150 μCi/g of estimated thyroid weight is calculated on the basis of this uptake. A slightly larger dose is necessary in patients previously treated with antithyroid drugs. Following the administration of radioactive iodine, the gland will shrink, and the patient will usually become euthyroid over a period of 6–12 weeks.

The major complication of radioactive iodine therapy is hypothyroidism, which ultimately develops in 80% or more of patients who are adequately treated. However, this complication may indeed be the best assurance that the patient will not have a recurrence of hyperthyroidism. Serum FT_4 and TSH levels should be followed, and when hypothyroidism develops, prompt replacement therapy with levothyroxine, 0.05–0.2 mg daily, is instituted.

Hypothyroidism may occur after any type of therapy for Graves' disease—even after antithyroid drug therapy; in some patients, "burned–out" Graves' disease may be an end result of autoimmune thyroid disease. Accordingly, all patients with Graves' disease require lifetime follow-up to be certain that they remain euthyroid.

D. Other Medical Measures: During the acute phase of thyrotoxicosis, beta-adrenergic blocking agents are extremely helpful. Propranolol, 10–40 mg every 6 hours, will control tachycardia, hypertension, and atrial fibrillation. This drug is gradually withdrawn as serum thyroxine levels return to normal. Adequate nutrition, including multivitamin supplements, is essential. Barbiturates accelerate T_4 metabolism, and phenobarbital may be helpful both for its sedative effect and to lower T_4 levels. Ipodate sodium or iopanoic acid has been shown to inhibit both thyroid hormone synthesis and release as well as peripheral conversion of T_4 to T_3. Thus, in a dosage of 1 g daily, this drug may help to rapidly restore the euthyroid state. It leaves the gland saturated with iodide, so it should not be used before ^{131}I therapy or antithyroid drug therapy with propylthiouracil or methimazole. In a patient with a large toxic goiter and a severe allergic reaction to antithyroid drugs, ipodate sodium and beta blockade can be used effectively as preparation for surgery.

Choice of Therapy

Choice of therapy will vary with the nature and severity of the illness and prevailing customs. For example, in the USA, radioiodine therapy has been the preferred treatment for the average patient, whereas in Europe and Asia, antithyroid drug therapy is preferred. In the opinion of this author, most patients should be treated with antithyroid drugs until euthyroid. If there is a prompt response and the gland begins to shrink, the option of long-term antithyroid drug therapy with or without simultaneous levothyroxine therapy should be considered. If large doses of antithyroid drugs are required for control and the gland does not shrink in response to therapy, radioiodine would be the treatment of choice. If the gland is very large (> 150 g) or multinodular—or if the patient wishes to become pregnant very soon—thyroidectomy is a reasonable option. A serious allergic reaction to an antithyroid drug is an indication for radioiodine therapy.

Treatment of Complications

A. Thyrotoxic Crisis: Thyrotoxic crisis (thyroid storm) requires vigorous management. Propranolol, 1–2 mg slowly intravenously or 40–80 mg every 6 hours orally, is helpful in controlling arrhythmias. In the presence of severe heart failure or asthma and arrhythmia, cautious intravenous administration of verapamil in a dose of 5–10 mg may be effective. Hormone synthesis is blocked by the administration of propylthiouracil, 250 mg every 6 hours. If the patient is unable to take medication by mouth, methimazole in a dose of 25 mg every 6 hours can be given by rectal suppository or enema. After administration of an antithyroid drug, hormone release is retarded by the administration of sodium iodide, 1 g intravenously over a 24-hour period, or saturated solution of potassium iodide, 10 drops twice daily. Ipodate sodium, 1 g daily given intravenously or orally, may be used instead of sodium iodide, but this will block the definitive use of radioiodine therapy for 3–6 months. The conversion of T_4 to T_3 is partially blocked by the combination of propranolol and propylthiouracil, but the administration of hydrocortisone hemisuccinate, 50 mg intravenously every 6 hours, is additive. Supportive therapy includes a cooling blanket and acetaminophen to help control fever. Aspirin is probably contraindicated because of its tendency to bind to TBG and displace thyroxine, rendering more thyroxine available in the free state. Fluids, electrolytes, and nutrition are important. For sedation, phenobarbital is probably best because it accelerates the peripheral metabolism and inactivation of thyroxine and triiodothyronine, ultimately bringing these levels down. Oxygen, diuretics, and digitalis are indicated for heart failure. Finally, it is essential to treat the underlying disease process that may have precipitated the acute exacerbation. Thus, antibiotics, anti-allergy drugs, and postoperative care are indicated for management of these problems. As an extreme measure (rarely needed) to control thyrotoxic crisis, plasmapheresis or peritoneal dialysis may be used to remove high levels of circulating thyronines.

B. Ophthalmopathy: Management of ophthalmopathy due to Graves' disease involves close cooperation between the endocrinologist and the ophthalmologist. The thyroid disease may be managed as outlined above, but in the opinion of this author, total surgical excision of the thyroid gland or total ablation of the thyroid gland with radioactive iodine is indicated. Although there is controversy over the need for total ablation, removal or destruction of the thyroid gland certainly prevents exacerbations and relapses of thyrotoxicosis, which may reactivate residual ophthalmopathy. A course of prednisone following radioactive iodine therapy will prevent the transitory rise in thyroid antibodies following radioiodine ablation of the gland. Keeping the patient's head elevated at night will diminish periorbital edema. For the severe acute inflammatory reaction, a short course of corticosteroid therapy is frequently effective, eg, prednisone, 100 mg daily orally in divided doses for 7–14 days, then every other day in gradually diminishing dosage for 6–12 weeks. If corticosteroid therapy is not effective, external x-ray therapy to the retrobulbar area may be helpful. The dose is usually 2000 cGy in ten fractions given over a period of 2 weeks. The lens and anterior chamber structures must be shielded.

In very severe cases where vision is threatened, orbital decompression can be used. One type of orbital decompression involves a transantral approach through the maxillary sinus, removing the floor and the lateral walls of the orbit. In the alternative anterior approach, the orbit is entered under the globe, and portions of the floor and the walls of the orbit are removed. Both approaches have been extremely effective, and exophthalmos can be reduced by 5–7 mm in each eye by these techniques. After the acute process has subsided, the patient is frequently left with double vision or lid abnormalities owing to muscle fibrosis and contracture. These can be corrected by cosmetic lid surgery or eye muscle surgery.

C. Thyrotoxicosis and Pregnancy: Thyrotoxicosis during pregnancy presents a special problem. Radioactive iodine is contraindicated because it crosses the placenta freely and may injure the fetal thyroid. Two good alternatives are available. If the disease is detected during the first trimester, the patient can be prepared with propylthiouracil, and subtotal thyroidectomy can be performed safely during the mid trimester. It is essential to provide thyroid supplementation during the balance of the pregnancy. Alternatively, the patient can be treated with antithyroid drugs throughout the pregnancy, postponing the decision regarding long-term management until after delivery. The dosage of antithyroid drugs must be kept to the minimum necessary to control symptoms, because these drugs cross the placenta and may affect the function of the fetal thyroid gland. If the disease can be controlled by initial doses of propylthiouracil of 300 mg or less and maintenance doses of 50–150 mg/d, the likelihood of fetal hypothyroidism is extremely small. The FT_4I or FT_4 should be maintained in the upper range of normal by appropriately reducing the propylthiouracil dosage. Supplemental thyroxine is not necessary. Breast feeding is not contraindicated, because propylthiouracil is not concentrated in the milk.

Graves' disease may occur in the newborn infant. There seem to be two neonatal forms of the disease. In both types, the mother has a current or recent history of Graves' disease. In the first type, the child is born small, with weak muscles, tachycardia, fever, and frequently respiratory distress or neonatal jaundice. Examination reveals an enlarged thyroid gland and occasionally prominent, puffy eyes. The heart rate is rapid, temperature is elevated, and heart failure may ensue. Laboratory studies reveal an elevated FT_4I or FT_4, a markedly elevated T_3, and usually a low TSH—in contrast to normal infants, who have elevated TSH at birth. Bone age may be accelerated. TSH-R Ab [stim] is usually found in the serum of both the infant and the mother. The pathogenesis of this syndrome is thought to involve transplacental transfer of TSH-R Ab [stim] from mother to fetus, with subsequent development of thyrotoxicosis. The disease is self-limited and subsides over a period of 4–12 weeks, coinciding with the fall in the child's TSH-R Ab [stim]. Therapy for the infant includes propylthiouracil in a dose of 5–10 mg/kg/d (in divided doses at 8-hour intervals); strong iodine (Lugol's) solution, 1 drop (8 mg potassium iodide) every 8 hours; and propranolol, 2 mg/kg/d in divided doses. In addition, adequate nutrition, antibiotics for infection if present, sedatives if necessary, and supportive therapy are indicated. If the child is very toxic, corticosteroid therapy (prednisone, 2 mg/kg/d) will partially block conversion of T_4 to T_3 and may be helpful in the acute phase. The above medications are gradually reduced as the child improves and can usually be discontinued by 6–12 weeks.

A second form of neonatal Graves' disease occurs in children from families with a high incidence of that disorder. Symptoms develop more slowly and may not be noted until the child is 3–6 months old. This syndrome is thought to be a true genetic inheritance of defective lymphocyte immunoregulation. It is much more severe, with a 20% mortality rate and evidence of persistent brain dysfunction even after successful treatment. The hyperthyroidism may persist for months or years and requires prolonged therapy.

Maternal sera may contain TSH-R blocking antibodies that can cross the placenta and produce transient hypothyroidism in the infant. This condition may need to be treated with T_4 supplementation for a short time.

Course & Prognosis

In general, the course of Graves' disease is one of remissions and exacerbations over a protracted period of time unless the gland is destroyed by surgery or radioactive iodine. Although some patients may remain euthyroid for long periods after treatment, many eventually develop hypothyroidism. Lifetime

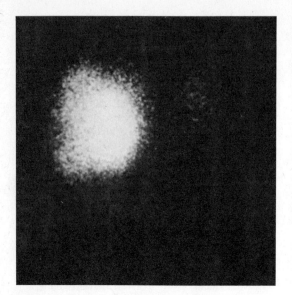

Figure 4–49. Toxic nodule of the right lobe of the thyroid gland as it appears on ^{99m}Tc pertechnetate scan. Note that the left lobe of the gland has been almost completely suppressed. (Courtesy of JM Lowenstein.)

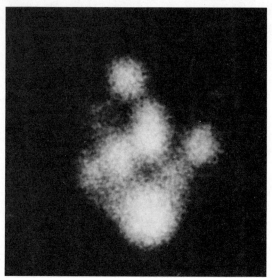

Figure 4–50. Toxic multinodular goiter as it appears on ^{99m}Tc pertechnetate scan. Note multiple functioning thyroid nodules. (Courtesy of JM Lowenstein.)

follow-up is therefore indicated for all patients with Graves' disease.

2. OTHER FORMS OF THYROTOXICOSIS

Toxic Adenoma
(Plummer's Disease)

A functioning adenoma hypersecreting T_3 and T_4 will cause hyperthyroidism. These lesions start out as a "hot nodule" on the thyroid scan, slowly increase in size, and gradually suppress the other lobe of the gland (Figure 4–49). The typical patient is an older individual (usually over 40) who has noted recent growth of a long-standing thyroid nodule. Symptoms of weight loss, weakness, shortness of breath, palpitation, tachycardia, and heat intolerance are noted. Infiltrative ophthalmopathy classes 2–6 (Table 4–11) is never present. Physical examination reveals a definite nodule on one side, with very little thyroid tissue on the other side. Laboratory studies usually reveal suppressed TSH and marked elevation in serum T_3 levels, often with only borderline elevation of thyroxine levels. The scan reveals that the nodule is "hot." Toxic adenomas are almost always follicular adenomas and almost never malignant. They are easily managed by administration of antithyroid drugs such as propylthiouracil, 100 mg every 6 hours, or methimazole, 10 mg every 6 hours, followed by treatment with radioactive iodine or unilateral lobectomy. Sodium ^{131}I in doses of 20–30 mCi is usually required to destroy the benign neoplasm. Radioactive iodine is preferable for smaller toxic nodules, but larger ones are best managed surgically.

Toxic Multinodular Goiter

This disorder usually occurs in older patients with long-standing multinodular goiter. Ophthalmopathy is extremely rare. Clinically, the patient presents with tachycardia, heart failure, or arrhythmia and sometimes weight loss, nervousness, weakness, tremors, and sweats. Physical examination reveals a multinodular goiter that may be small or quite large and may even extend substernally. Laboratory studies reveal a suppressed TSH and striking elevation in serum T_3 levels, with less striking elevation of serum T_4. Radioiodine scan reveals multiple functioning nodules in the gland or occasionally an irregular, patchy distribution of radioactive iodine (Figure 4–50).

Hyperthyroidism in patients with multinodular goiters can often be precipitated by the administration of iodides ("jodbasedow" effect, or iodide-induced hyperthyroidism). Some thyroid adenomas do not develop the Wolff-Chaikoff effect (see above) and cannot adapt to an iodide load. Thus, they are driven to excess hormone production by a high level of circulating iodide. This is the mechanism for the development of hyperthyroidism after administration of the antiarrhythmic drug amiodarone (see below).

The management of toxic nodular goiter is difficult. Control of the hyperthyroid state with antithyroid drugs followed by subtotal thyroidectomy would seem to be the therapy of choice, but often these patients are elderly and have other illnesses that make them poor candidates for surgery. The toxic nodules can be destroyed with ^{131}I, but the multinodular goiter will remain, and other nodules may become toxic, requiring repeated doses of ^{131}I.

Amiodarone is an antiarrhythmic drug that contains 37.3% iodine. In the body, it is stored in fat, myocardium, liver and lung and has a half-life of about 50 days. About 2% of patients treated with amiodarone develop iodine-induced thyrotoxicosis. This presents a most difficult problem. Patients taking amiodarone have serious underlying heart disease, and in many cases the amiodarone cannot be discontinued. If the thyrotoxicosis is mild, it can often be controlled with methimazole, 40–60 mg daily, while amiodarone therapy continues. If the disease is severe, $KClO_4$ in a dose of 250 mg every 6 hours may be added to saturate the iodide trap and prevent further uptake of iodide. Long-term $KClO_4$ has been associated with aplastic anemia and requires monitoring. The only way to eliminate the large store of intrathyroidal hormone would be to surgically remove the goiter. This would be feasible only if the patient could withstand the stress of thyroidectomy.

Subacute or Chronic Thyroiditis

These entities will be discussed in a separate section, but it should be mentioned here that thyroiditis, either subacute or chronic, may present with an acute release of T_4 and T_3, producing symptoms of mild to severe thyrotoxicosis. These illnesses can be differentiated from other forms of thyrotoxicosis in that the radioiodine uptake is markedly suppressed, and the symptoms usually subside spontaneously over a period of weeks or months.

Thyrotoxicosis Factitia

This is a psychoneurotic disturbance in which the patient ingests excessive amounts of thyroxine or thyroid hormone, usually for purposes of weight control. The individual is often someone connected with the field of medicine who can easily obtain thyroid medication. Features of thyrotoxicosis, including weight loss, nervousness, palpitation, tachycardia, and tremor, may be present, but no goiter or eye signs. Characteristically, TSH is suppressed, serum T_4 and T_3 levels are elevated, serum thyroglobulin in low, and radioactive iodine uptake is nil. Management requires careful discussion of the hazards of long-term thyroxine therapy, particularly cardiovascular damage, muscle wasting, and osteoporosis. Formal psychotherapy may be necessary.

Rare Forms of Thyrotoxicosis

A. Struma Ovarii: In this syndrome, a teratoma of the ovary contains thyroid tissue that becomes hyperactive. Mild features of thyrotoxicosis result, such as weight loss and tachycardia, but there is no evidence of goiter or eye signs. Serum FT_4 and T_3 are mildly elevated, serum TSH is suppressed, and radioiodine uptake in the neck is nil. Body scan reveals uptake of radioiodine in the pelvis. The disease is curable by removal of the teratoma.

B. Thyroid Carcinoma: Carcinoma of the thyroid, particularly follicular carcinoma, may concentrate radioactive iodine, but only rarely does it retain the ability to convert this iodide into active hormone. Only a few cases of metastatic thyroid cancer have presented with hyperthyroidism. The clinical picture consists of weakness, weight loss, palpitation, and a thyroid nodule but no ophthalmopathy. Body scan with ^{131}I reveals areas of uptake usually distant from the thyroid, eg, bone or lung. Treatment with large doses of radioactive iodine may destroy the metastatic deposits.

C. Hydatidiform Mole: Hydatidiform moles produce chorionic gonadotropin, which has intrinsic TSH-like activity. This may induce thyroid hyperplasia, increased iodine turnover, suppressed TSH, and mild elevation of serum T_4 and T_3 levels. It is rarely associated with overt thyrotoxicosis and is totally curable by removal of the mole.

D. "Hamburger Thyrotoxicosis": An epidemic of thyrotoxicosis in midwestern United States was traced to hamburger made from "neck trim," the strap muscles from the necks of slaughtered cattle that contained beef thyroid tissue. The United States Department of Agriculture has now prohibited the use of this material for human consumption.

E. Syndrome of Inappropriate TSH Secretion: A group of patients have been reported with elevated serum free thyroxine concentrations in association with elevated serum immunoreactive TSH. This has been called the "syndrome of inappropriate TSH secretion." Two types of problems are found: (1) TSH-secreting pituitary adenoma and (2) nonneoplastic pituitary hypersecretion of TSH.

Patients with TSH-secreting pituitary adenomas usually present with mild thyrotoxicosis and goiter, often with evidence of gonadotropic hormone deficiency such as amenorrhea or impotence. There are no eye signs of Graves' disease. Study reveals elevated total and free serum T_4 and T_3. Serum TSH, usually undetectable in Graves' disease, is within the normal range or even elevated. The TSH α subunit secretion from these tumors is markedly elevated; a molar ratio of α subunit:TSH greater than 1 is usually diagnostic of the presence of a TSH-secreting pituitary adenoma. In addition, there is no hormonal response to TRH, and the increased radioactive iodine uptake is not suppressible with exogenous thyroid hormone. Visual field examination may reveal temporal defects, and CT or MRI of the sella usually reveals a pituitary tumor. Management usually involves control of the thyrotoxicosis with antithyroid drugs and removal of the pituitary tumor via transsphenoidal hypophysectomy. These tumors are often quite aggressive and may extend widely out of the sella. If the tumor cannot be completely removed, it may be necessary to treat residual tumor with radiation therapy and to control thyrotoxicosis with radioactive iodine. Long-acting somatostatin (octreotide) will suppress TSH secretion in many of these patients and may even inhibit tumor growth in some.

Nonneoplastic pituitary hypersecretion of TSH is essentially a form of pituitary (and occasionally peripheral) resistance to T_3 and T_4. This is discussed below.

THYROID HORMONE RESISTANCE SYNDROMES

Several forms of resistance to thyroid hormones have been reported: (1) generalized resistance to thyroid hormones (GRTH), (2) selective pituitary resistance to thyroid hormones (PRTH), and possibly (3) a selective peripheral resistance to thyroid hormones.

Generalized resistance to thyroid hormones was first described in 1967 by Refetoff et al as a familial syndrome of deaf mutism, stippled epiphyses, goiter, and abnormally high thyroid hormone levels with normal TSH. The clinical presentation in the more than 200 families that have been reported has been variable; while most patients are euthyroid, many present with stunted growth, delayed bone maturation, goiter, and behavioral problems. These include a poor attention span suggestive of hypothyroidism; in addition, some patients display tachycardia. Inheritance is usually autosomal dominant, though it was recessive in 10% of the families studied. Laboratory tests reveal elevated T_4, FT_4, T_3, and normal or elevated TSH. Dynamic tests to distinguish generalized resistance to thyroid hormones from TSH-secreting adenomas usually reveal an increase in TSH after administration of TRH, a fall in TSH with T_3 suppression, and a molar ratio of α subunit:TSH of less than 1. In addition, in patients with GRTH, pituitary MRI fails to demonstrate a microadenoma. Molecular studies have revealed point mutations in the human thyroid receptor beta gene (hTR-β), which produces a defective thyroid hormone receptor (TR) that fails to bind T_3 (Figure 4–28). Although this is a recessive mutation, the abnormal receptor may partially block the action of normal receptors, so that it appears to be inherited in an autosomal dominant mode (a "dominant recessive mutation"). Different point mutations in different families may account in part for the differences in clinical expression of the syndrome. Furthermore, identification of the mutation may allow the use of molecular screening methods for the diagnosis of the syndrome in some families.

In most patients with generalized resistance to thyroid hormones, the increased levels of T_3 and T_4 will compensate in part for the receptor defect, and treatment is not necessary. In some children, administration of thyroid hormone may be necessary to correct defects in growth or mental development.

Selective pituitary resistance to thyroid hormones is less common and usually presents with symptoms of mild hyperthyroidism, goiter, elevated serum T_4 and T_3, and normal or elevated serum TSH. In this syndrome, T_3 receptors in peripheral tissues are normal, but there is a failure of T_3 to inhibit pituitary TSH secretion, resulting in inappropriate TSH secretion and TSH-induced hyperthyroidism. Differentiation from TSH-secreting pituitary adenoma can be made using the dynamic tests and MRI of the pituitary as outlined above.

This syndrome may be due in part to some abnormality in the pituitary type 2 5′ deiodinase with failure to convert intrapituitary T_4 to T_3, leading to PTHR. Ablation of the thyroid gland with ^{131}I or treatment with antithyroid drugs may lead to pituitary hyperplasia. However, administration of T_3 or triiodothyroacetic acid (TRIAC) has been reported to suppress TSH, reduce the size of the goiter, lower serum T_4, and correct the hyperthyroidism.

Only one case of suspected selective peripheral resistance to T_3 has been reported, and it is not yet clear that this is a distinct entity.

NONTOXIC GOITER

Etiology

Nontoxic goiter usually represents enlargement of the thyroid gland from TSH stimulation, which in turn results from inadequate thyroid hormone synthesis. Table 4–12 lists some of the causes of nontoxic goiter.

Iodine deficiency was the most common cause of nontoxic goiter or "endemic goiter"; with the widespread use of iodized salt and the introduction of iodides into fertilizers, animal feeds, and food preservatives, iodide deficiency in developed countries is relatively rare. It does not exist in the USA. However, there are large areas such as central Africa, the mountainous areas of central Asia, the Andes of central South America, and Indonesia (particularly New Guinea), where iodine intake is still markedly deficient. Optimal iodine requirements for adults are in the range of 150–300 μg/d. In endemic goiter areas, the daily intake (and urinary excretion) of iodine falls below 50 μg/d; in areas where iodine is extremely scarce, excretion falls below 20 μg/d. It is in these areas that 90% of the population will have goiters,

Table 4–12. Etiology of nontoxic goiter.

1. Iodine deficiency.
2. Goitrogen in the diet.
3. Hashimoto's thyroiditis.
4. Subacute thyroiditis.
5. Inadequate hormone synthesis due to inherited defect in thyroidal enzymes necessary for T_4 and T_3 biosynthesis.
6. Inherited deficiency in T_4 receptor in cell membrane (rare).
7. Neoplasm, benign or malignant.

and 5–15% of infants will be born with myxedematous or neurologic changes of cretinism. The variability in the extent of goiter in these areas may be related to the presence of other, unidentified goitrogens.

Dietary goitrogens are a rare cause of goiter, and of these the most common is iodide itself. Large amounts of iodide, as in amiodarone or kelp tablets, may in susceptible individuals produce goiter and hypothyroidism (see above). Withdrawal of iodide reverses the process. Other goitrogens include lithium carbonate and some vegetable foodstuffs such as goitrin, found in certain roots and seeds; and cyanogenic glycosides, found in cassava and cabbage, that release thiocyanates which may cause goiter, particularly in the presence of iodide deficiency. In addition, compounds such as phenols, phthalates, pyridines, and polyaromatic hydrocarbons found in industrial waste water are weakly goitrogenic. The role of these vegetable and pollutant goitrogens in the production of goiter is not clearly established.

The most common cause of thyroid enlargement in developed countries is chronic thyroiditis (Hashimoto's thyroiditis; see below). Subacute thyroiditis causes thyroid enlargement with exquisite tenderness (see below).

Nontoxic goiter may be due to impaired hormone synthesis resulting from genetic deficiencies in enzymes necessary for hormone biosynthesis (thyroid dyshormonogenesis, or familial goiter). These effects may be complete, resulting in a syndrome of cretinism with goiter; or partial, resulting in nontoxic goiter with mild hypothyroidism. At least five separate biosynthetic abnormalities have been reported: (1) impaired transport of iodine; (2) deficient peroxidase with impaired oxidation of iodide to iodine and failure to incorporate iodine into thyroglobulin; (3) impaired coupling of iodinated tyrosines to triiodothyronine or tetraiodothyronine; (4) absence or deficiency of iodotyrosine deiodinase, so that iodine is not conserved within the gland; and (5) excessive production of metabolically inactive iodoprotein by the thyroid gland (Figure 4–9). The latter may involve impaired or abnormal thyroglobulin synthesis. In all of these syndromes, impaired production of thyroid hormones presumably results in TSH release and goiter formation.

Finally, thyroid enlargement can be due to a benign lesion, such as adenoma, or to a malignant one such as carcinoma.

Pathogenesis

The development of nontoxic goiter in patients with dyshormonogenesis or severe iodine deficiency involves impaired hormone synthesis and, secondarily, an increase in TSH secretion. TSH induces diffuse thyroid hyperplasia, followed by focal hyperplasia with necrosis and hemorrhage, and finally the development of new areas of focal hyperplasia. Focal or nodular hyperplasia usually involves a clone of cells that may or may not be able to pick up iodine or synthesize thyroglobulin. Thus, the nodules will vary from "hot" nodules that can concentrate iodine to "cold" ones that cannot, and from colloid nodules that can synthesize thyroglobulin to microfollicular ones that cannot. Initially, the hyperplasia is TSH-dependent, but later the nodules become TSH-independent, or autonomous. Thus, a diffuse nontoxic TSH-dependent goiter progresses over a period of time to a multinodular toxic or nontoxic TSH-independent goiter.

The mechanism for the development of autonomous growth and function of thyroid nodules may involve mutations that occur with TSH-induced cell division in an oncogene that activates the G_s protein in the cell membrane. Mutations of this oncogene, called the *gsp* oncogene, have been found in a high proportion of nodules from patients with multinodular goiter. Chronic activation of the G_s protein would result in thyroid cell proliferation and hyperfunction even when TSH is suppressed.

Clinical Features

A. Symptoms and Signs: Patients with nontoxic goiter usually present with thyroid enlargement, which, as noted above, may be diffuse or multinodular. The gland may be relatively firm but is often extremely soft. Over a period of time, the gland becomes progressively larger, so that in long-standing multinodular goiter, huge goiters may develop and extend inferiorly to present as substernal goiter. The patient may complain of pressure symptoms in the neck, particularly on moving the head upward or downward, and of difficulty in swallowing. Vocal cord paralysis due to recurrent laryngeal nerve involvement is rare. There may be symptoms of mild hypothyroidism, but most of these patients are euthyroid. Thyroid enlargement probably represents compensated hypothyroidism.

B. Laboratory Findings: Laboratory studies will reveal a low or normal free thyroxine and, usually, normal levels of TSH. The increased mass of thyroid tissue compensates for inefficient synthesis of hormone. In patients with dyshormonogenesis due to abnormal iodoprotein synthesis, PBI may be elevated out of proportion to serum T_4, because of secretion of nonhormonal organic iodide compounds. Radioiodine uptake may be high, normal, or low, depending upon the iodide pool and the TSH drive.

C. Imaging Studies: Isotope scanning usually reveals a patchy uptake, frequently with focal areas of increased uptake corresponding to "hot" nodules and areas of decreased uptake corresponding to "cold" nodules. Radioactive iodine uptake of the "hot" nodules may not be suppressible on administration of thyroid hormones such as liothyronine. Thyroid ultrasound is a simple way to follow the growth of the goiter and in addition may reveal cystic changes in one or more of the nodules, representing previous hemorrhage and necrosis.

Differential Diagnosis

The major problem in differential diagnosis is to rule out cancer. This will be discussed in the section on thyroid carcinoma.

Treatment

With the exception of those due to neoplasm, the current management of nontoxic goiters consists simply of giving thyroid hormones until TSH is completely suppressed. Levothyroxine in doses of 0.1–0.2 mg (approximately 2.2 µg/kg, or 1 µg/lb) daily to suppress pituitary TSH will correct hypothyroidism and often result in slow regression of the goiter. Long-standing goiters may have areas of necrosis, hemorrhage, and scarring as well as autonomously functioning nodules that will not regress on thyroxine therapy. However, the lesions will usually grow more slowly while the patient is taking thyroxine. In older patients with multinodular goiters, administration of levothyroxine must be done very cautiously since the "hot" nodules are usually autonomous and the combination of endogenous and exogenous hormone will rapidly produce toxic symptoms.

Surgery is indicated for goiters that continue to grow despite TSH suppression with T_4 or those that produce obstructive symptoms. Substernal extension of a goiter is usually an indication for surgical removal. The gross appearance of a multinodular goiter at the time of surgery is presented in Figure 4–51. Note that the left lobe of the gland extends downward from the middle of the thyroid cartilage to just above the clavicle. The pressure of this enlargement has caused deviation of the trachea to the right. The surface of the gland is irregular, with many large and small nodules. Although these multinodular goiters are rarely malignant, the size of the mass with resulting pressure symptoms requires subtotal thyroidectomy.

Course & Prognosis

Patients with nontoxic goiter must usually take levothyroxine for life. They should avoid iodides, which may induce either hyperthyroidism or, in the absence of thyroxine therapy, hypothyroidism. Occasionally, single adenomas or several adenomas will become hyperfunctional, producing a toxic nodular goiter (discussed above). Nontoxic goiter is often familial, and other members of the family should be examined and observed for the possible development of goiter.

THYROIDITIS

1. SUBACUTE THYROIDITIS

Subacute thyroiditis (De Quervain's thyroiditis, or granulomatous thyroiditis) is an acute inflammatory disorder of the thyroid gland most likely due to viral infection. A number of viruses, including mumps virus, coxsackievirus, and adenoviruses, have been implicated, either by finding the virus in biopsy specimens taken from the gland or by demonstration of rising titers of viral antibodies in the blood during the course of the infection. Pathologic examination reveals moderate thyroid enlargement and a mild inflammatory reaction involving the capsule. Histologic features include destruction of thyroid parenchyma and the presence of many large phagocytic cells, including giant cells.

Clinical Features

A. Symptoms and Signs: Subacute thyroiditis usually presents with fever, malaise, and soreness in the neck, which may extend up to the angle of the jaw or toward the ear lobes on one or both sides of the neck. Initially, the patient may have symptoms of hyperthyroidism, with palpitations, agitation, and sweats. There is no ophthalmopathy. On physical examination, the gland is exquisitely tender, so that the patient will object to pressure upon it. There are no signs of local redness or heat suggestive of abscess formation. Clinical signs of toxicity, including tachycardia, tremor, and hyperreflexia, may be present.

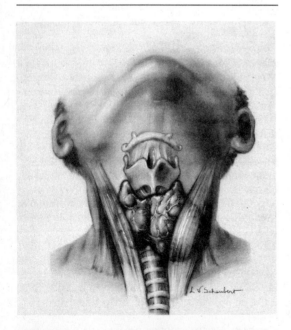

Figure 4–51. Multinodular goiter at the time of surgery. The asymmetric enlargement and the nodularity are apparent, as is the rightward deviation of the trachea resulting from marked enlargement of the lobe.

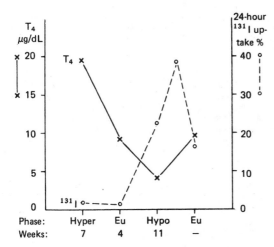

Figure 4–52. Changes in serum T4 and radioactive iodine uptake in patients with subacute thyroiditis. In the initial phase, serum T4 is elevated and the patient may have symptoms of thyrotoxicosis, but radioactive iodine uptake is markedly suppressed. The illness may pass through phases of euthyroidism and hypothyroidism before remission. (Data adapted, with permission, from Woolf PD, Daly R: Thyrotoxicosis with painless thyroiditis. Am J Med 1976;60:73.)

B. Laboratory Findings: Laboratory studies will vary with the course of the disease (Figure 4–52). Initially, T_4 and T_3 are elevated, whereas serum TSH and thyroid radioactive iodine uptake are extremely low. The erythrocyte sedimentation rate is markedly elevated, sometimes as high as 100 mm/h by the Westergren scale. Thyroid autoantibodies are usually not detectable in serum. As the disease progresses, T_4 and T_3 will drop, TSH will rise, and symptoms of hypothyroidism are noted. Later, radioactive iodine uptake will rise, reflecting recovery of the gland from the acute insult.

Differential Diagnosis

Subacute thyroiditis can be differentiated from other viral illnesses by the involvement of the thyroid gland. It is differentiated from Graves' disease by the presence of low thyroid radioiodine uptake associated with elevated serum T_3 and T_4 and suppressed serum TSH and by the absence of thyroid antibodies.

Treatment

In most cases, only symptomatic treatment is necessary, eg, acetaminophen, 0.5 g four times daily. If pain, fever, and malaise are disabling, a short course of a nonsteroidal anti-inflammatory drug or a glucocorticoid such as prednisone, 20 mg three times daily for 7–10 days, may be necessary to reduce the inflammation. Levothyroxine, 0.1–0.15 mg once daily, is indicated during the hypothyroid phase of the ill-

ness in order to prevent reexacerbation of the disease induced by the rising TSH levels. In about 10% of patients, permanent hypothyroidism ensues and long-term levothyroxine therapy is necessary.

Course & Prognosis

Subacute thyroiditis usually resolves completely and spontaneously over weeks or months. Occasionally, the disease may begin to resolve and then suddenly get worse, sometimes involving first one lobe of the thyroid gland and then the other (migrating thyroiditis). Exacerbations often occur when the T_4 levels have fallen, TSH has risen, and the gland is starting to recover function. Rarely, the course may extend over several years, with repeated bouts of inflammatory disease.

2 . CHRONIC THYROIDITIS

Chronic thyroiditis (Hashimoto's thyroiditis, lymphocytic thyroiditis) is probably the most common cause of hypothyroidism and goiter in the USA. It is certainly the major cause of goiter in children and young adults and is probably the major cause of "idiopathic myxedema," which represents an end stage of Hashimoto's thyroiditis, with total destruction of the gland. **Riedel's struma** is probably a variant of Hashimoto's thyroiditis, with extensive fibrosis extending outside the gland and involving overlying muscle and surrounding tissues. Riedel's struma presents as a stony-hard mass that must be differentiated from thyroid cancer.

Etiology & Pathogenesis

Hashimoto's thyroiditis is thought to be an immunologic disorder in which lymphocytes become sensitized to thyroidal antigens and autoantibodies are formed that react with these antigens (see thyroid autoimmunity, above). In Hashimoto's thyroiditis, the three most important thyroid autoantibodies are thyroglobulin antibody (Tg Ab), thyroid peroxidase antibody (TPO Ab), formerly called microsomal antibody, and TSH receptor blocking antibody (TSH-R Ab [block]) (Table 4–7). During the early phases of Hashimoto's thyroiditis, Tg Ab is markedly elevated and TPO Ab is slightly elevated. Later, Tg Ab may disappear, but TPO Ab will be present for many years. TSH-R Ab [block] is found in patients with **atrophic thyroiditis** and myxedema and in mothers giving birth to infants with no detectable thyroid tissue (**athyreotic cretins**). The pathology of Hashimoto's thyroiditis involves a heavy infiltration of lymphocytes totally destroying normal thyroidal architecture. Lymphoid follicles and germinal centers may be formed. The follicular epithelial cells are frequently enlarged and contain a basophilic cytoplasm (Hurthle cells). Destruction of the gland results in a fall in serum T_3 and T_4 and a rise in TSH. Initially,

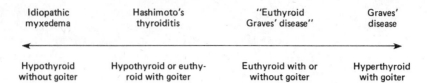

Figure 4–53. Spectrum of autoimmune disease of the thyroid gland. The clinical manifestations of autoimmune disease of the thyroid gland range from idiopathic myxedema, through nontoxic goiter, to diffuse toxic goiter, or Graves' disease. Progression of autoimmune disease from one form to another in the same patient can occasionally occur.

TSH may maintain adequate hormonal synthesis by the development of thyroid enlargement or goiter, but often the gland fails, and hypothyroidism with or without goiter ensues.

Hashimoto's thyroiditis is part of a spectrum of thyroid diseases that includes Graves' disease at one end and idiopathic myxedema at the other (Figure 4–53). It is familial and may be associated with other autoimmune diseases such as pernicious anemia, adrenocortical insufficiency, idiopathic hypoparathyroidism, myasthenia gravis, and vitiligo. **Schmidt's syndrome** consists of Hashimoto's thyroiditis, idiopathic adrenal insufficiency, hypoparathyroidism, diabetes mellitus, ovarian insufficiency, and (rarely) candidal infections. Schmidt's syndrome represents destruction of multiple endocrine glands on an autoimmune basis (see Chapter 21).

Clinical Features

A. Symptoms and Signs: Hashimoto's thyroiditis usually presents with goiter in a patient who is euthyroid or has mild hypothyroidism. The sex distribution is about four females to one male. The process is painless, and the patient may be unaware of the goiter unless it becomes very large. Older patients may present with severe hypothyroidism with only a small, firm atrophic thyroid gland (idiopathic myxedema).

B. Laboratory Findings: There are multiple defects in iodine metabolism. Peroxidase activity is decreased, so that organification of iodine is impaired. This can be demonstrated by a positive perchlorate discharge test (Figure 4–12). In addition, iodination of metabolically inactive protein material occurs, so that there will be a disproportionately high serum PBI compared to serum T_4. Radioiodine uptake may be high, normal, or low. Circulating thyroid hormone levels are usually normal or low, and if low, TSH will be elevated.

The most striking laboratory finding is the high titer of autoantibodies to thyroidal antigens in the serum. Serum tests for either Tg Ab or TPO Ab are positive in most patients with Hashimoto's thyroiditis. Another diagnostic test that may be helpful is the fine-needle aspiration biopsy, which reveals a large infiltration of lymphocytes as well as the presence of Hurthle cells.

Differential Diagnosis

Hashimoto's thyroiditis can be differentiated from other causes of nontoxic goiter by serum antibody studies and if necessary by fine-needle aspiration biopsy.

Complications & Sequelae

The major complication of Hashimoto's thyroiditis is progressive hypothyroidism. Although only 10–15% of young patients presenting with goiter and hypothyroidism seem to progress to permanent hypothyroidism, the high incidence of permanent hypothyroidism in older patients with positive antibody tests and elevated TSH levels suggests that long-term treatment is desirable. Rarely, a patient with Hashimoto's thyroiditis may develop lymphoma of the thyroid gland, but whether the two conditions are causally related is not clear. Thyroid lymphoma is characterized by rapid growth of the gland despite continued thyroid hormone therapy; the diagnosis of lymphoma must be made by surgical biopsy (see below).

There is no evidence that adenocarcinoma of the thyroid gland occurs more frequently in patients with Hashimoto's thyroiditis, but the two diseases—chronic thyroiditis and carcinoma—can coexist in the same gland. Cancer must be suspected when a solitary nodule or thyroid mass grows or fails to regress while the patient is receiving maximal tolerated doses of thyroxine. Fine-needle aspiration biopsy is helpful in this differential diagnosis.

Treatment

The indications for treatment of Hashimoto's thyroiditis are goiter or hypothyroidism; a positive thyroid antibody test does not require therapy. Sufficient levothyroxine is given to suppress TSH and allow regression of the goiter. Surgery is rarely indicated.

Course & Prognosis

Without treatment, Hashimoto's thyroiditis will usually progress from goiter and hypothyroidism to myxedema. The goiter and the myxedema are totally corrected by adequate thyroxine therapy. Hashimoto's thyroiditis may go through periods of activity when large amounts of T_4 and T_3 are released or "dumped," resulting in transient symptoms of thyrotoxicosis. This syndrome, which has been called **spontaneously resolving hyperthyroidism,** is characterized by low radioiodine uptake. However, it can be differentiated from subacute thyroiditis in that the gland is not tender, the erythrocyte sedimentation rate is not elevated, autoantibodies to thyroidal antigens are strongly positive, and fine-needle aspiration biopsy reveals lymphocytes and Hurthle cells. Therapy is symptomatic, usually requiring only propranolol, until symptoms subside; T_4 supplementation may then be necessary.

Because Hashimoto's thyroiditis may be part of a syndrome of multiple autoimmune diseases (see Chapter 21), the patient should be monitored for other autoimmune diseases such as pernicious anemia, adrenal insufficiency, ovarian insufficiency, or diabetes mellitus. Patients with Hashimoto's thyroiditis may also develop true Graves' disease, occasionally with severe ophthalmopathy or dermopathy (Figure 4–53). The chronic thyroiditis may blunt the severity of the thyrotoxicosis, so that the patient may present with eye or skin complications of Graves' disease without marked thyrotoxicosis, a syndrome often called euthyroid Graves' disease. The thyroid gland will invariably be nonsuppressible, and this, plus the presence of thyroid autoantibodies, will help to make the diagnosis. The ophthalmopathy and dermopathy are treated as if thyrotoxic Graves' disease were present.

3. OTHER FORMS OF THYROIDITIS

The thyroid gland may be subject to acute abscess formation in patients with septicemia or acute infective endocarditis. Abscesses cause symptoms of pyogenic infection, with local pain and tenderness, swelling, and warmth and redness of the overlying skin. Needle aspiration will confirm the diagnosis and identify the organism. Treatment includes antibi-

otic therapy and occasionally incision and drainage. A thyroglossal duct cyst may become infected and present as acute suppurative thyroiditis. This too will respond to antibiotic therapy and occasionally incision and drainage.

EFFECTS OF IONIZING RADIATION ON THE THYROID GLAND

Ionizing radiation can induce both acute and chronic thyroiditis. Thyroiditis may occur acutely in patients treated with large doses of radioiodine and may be associated with release of thyroid hormones and an acute thyrotoxic crisis. Such an occurrence is extremely rare, however, and pretreatment with antithyroid drugs to bring the patient to a euthyroid state prior to ^{131}I therapy will completely prevent this type of radiation thyroiditis.

External radiation was used many years ago for the treatment of respiratory problems in the newborn, thought to be due to thymic hyperplasia, and for the treatment of benign conditions such as severe acne and chronic tonsillitis or adenoiditis. This treatment was often associated with the later development of nodular goiter, hypothyroidism, or thyroid cancer. Another source of radiation exposure is fallout from atomic bomb testing or a nuclear reactor accident.

The incidence of thyroid lesions after irradiation is summarized in Table 4–13. As little as 6.5 cGy (1 cGy = 1 rad) to the thyroid gland received during the radiation treatment of tinea capitis has been reported to cause cancer in 0.11% of exposed children; the incidence of thyroid cancer in sibling controls was 0.02%. Radiation therapy to the thymus delivered to the thyroid dosages of 100–400 cGy, and the incidence of thyroid cancer attributed to this source ranged from 0.8% to 5%. X-ray therapy to the neck and chest given to children or adolescents for acne or chronic upper respiratory infections delivered thyroid

Table 4–13. Thyroid lesions after irradiation.

Areas Treated	Estimated Dose to Thyroid (cGy)	Incidence (%) Nodular Goiter	Cancer	Source
Scalp	6.5	. . .	0.11	Modan et al (1974)
Thymus Total group	119	1.8	0.8	Hemplemann et al (1975)
Subgroup	399	7.6	5.0	
Neck, chest	807 180–1500	27.2 26.2	5.7 6.8	Favus et al (1975) Refetoff et al (1975)
Radiation fallout	<50 >50 175 (γ) and 700–1400 (β)	. . . . . . 39.6	0.4 6.7 5.7	Parker et al (1974) Sampson et al (1969) Conrad et al (1970)
[131]I therapy	±10,000	0.17	0.08	Dobyns et al (1974)

doses ranging from 200 cGy to 1500 cGy, resulting in the development of nodular goiter in about 27% and thyroid cancer in 5–7% of the patients so treated. These tumors developed 10–40 years after radiation was administered, with a peak incidence at 20–30 years. Radiation fallout with a thyroid dose of 700–1400 cGy has produced nodular goiter in approximately 40% of exposed victims and thyroid cancer in about 6%. However, radioiodine therapy, which exposes the thyroid to a dosage of around 10,000 cGy, was rarely associated with the development of thyroid cancer, presumably because the thyroid gland is largely destroyed by these doses of radioiodine, so that—although the incidence of postradiation hypothyroidism is high—the incidence of thyroid cancer is extremely low. Ninety percent of patients with radiation-induced thyroid cancer develop papillary carcinoma; the remainder develop follicular carcinoma. Medullary carcinoma and anaplastic carcinomas have been rare following radiation exposure. Although the overall incidence of thyroid carcinoma in irradiated patients is low, data from several large series suggest that the incidence of cancer in a patient who presents with a solitary coldnodule of the thyroid gland and a history of therapeutic radiation of the head, neck, or chest is around 50%.

Patients who have been exposed to ionizing radiation should be followed carefully for life. Annual studies should include physical examination of the neck for goiter or nodules, and FT_4 or TSH to rule out hypothyroidism. Periodic thyroid ultrasound may detect nodules that are not palpable. If a nodule is found, it should be scanned with ^{123}I, and if cold, fine-needle aspiration biopsy should be done. If the nodule is malignant, the patient should have total thyroidectomy; if benign, the patient should be treated with levothyroxine in a dose sufficient to suppress TSH. If the nodule persists or grows while T_4 therapy is being given, the thyroid gland should be surgically removed.

THYROID NODULES & THYROID CANCER

In 95% of cases, thyroid cancer presents as a nodule or lump in the thyroid. In occasional instances, particularly in children, enlarged cervical lymph nodes are the first sign of the disease, though on careful examination a small primary focus in the form of a thyroid nodule can often be felt. Rarely, distant metastasis in lung or bone is the first sign of thyroid cancer. Thyroid nodules are extremely common, particularly among women. The prevalence in the USA has been estimated to be about 4% of the adult population, with a female:male ratio of 4:1. In young children, the incidence is less than 1%; in persons aged 11–18 years, about 1.5%; and in persons over age 60, about 5%.

In contrast to thyroid nodules, thyroid cancer is a

Table 4–14. Etiology of benign thyroid nodules.

1. Focal thyroiditis.
2. Dominant portion of multinodular goiter.
3. Thyroid, parathyroid, or thyroglossal cysts.
4. Agenesis of a thyroid lobe.
5. Postsurgical remnant hyperplasia or scarring.
6. Postradioiodine remnant hyperplasia.
7. Benign adenomas:
   a. Follicular:
      Colloid or macrofollicular.
      Fetal.
      Embryonal.
      Hurthle cell.
   b. Rare: Teratoma, lipoma, hemangioma.

rare condition—0.004% per year according to the Third National Cancer Survey. Thus, most thyroid nodules are benign, and it is important to identify those that are likely to be malignant.

1. BENIGN THYROID NODULES

Etiology

Benign conditions that can produce nodularity in the thyroid gland are listed in Table 4–14. They include focal areas of chronic thyroiditis, a dominant portion of a multinodular goiter, a cyst involving thyroid tissue, parathyroid tissue, or thyroglossal duct remnants, and agenesis of one lobe of the thyroid, with hypertrophy of the other lobe presenting as a mass in the neck. It is usually the left lobe of the thyroid that fails to develop, and the hypertrophy occurs in the right lobe. Scarring in the gland following surgery—or regrowth of the gland after surgery or radioiodine therapy—can present with nodularity. Finally, benign neoplasms in the thyroid include follicular adenomas such as colloid or macrofollicular adenomas, fetal adenomas, embryonal adenomas, and Hurthle cell or oxyphil adenomas. Rare types of benign lesions include teratomas, lipomas, and hemangiomas. Except for thyroid hyperplasia of the right lobe of the gland in the presence of agenesis of the left lobe—and some follicular adenomas—all of the above lesions present as "cold" nodules on isotope scanning.

Differentiation of Benign & Malignant Lesions

Risk factors that predispose to benign or malignant disease are set forth in Table 4–15 and discussed below.

A. History: A family history of goiter suggests benign disease, as does residence in an area of endemic goiter. However, a family history of medullary carcinoma or a history of recent thyroid growth, hoarseness, dysphagia, or obstruction strongly suggests cancer. The significance of exposure to ionizing radiation is discussed above.

Table 4–15. Risk factors useful in distinguishing benign from malignant thyroid lesions.

	More Likely Benign	More Likely Malignant
History	Family history of benign goiter. Residence in endemic goiter area.	Family history of medullary cancer of thyroid. Previous therapeutic irradiation of head or neck. Recent growth of nodule. Hoarseness, dysphagia, or obstruction.
Physical characteristics	Older woman. Soft nodule. Multinodular goiter.	Child, young adult, male. Solitary, firm nodule clearly different from rest of gland ("dominant nodule"). Vocal cord paralysis, firm lymph nodes, distant metastases.
Serum factors	High titer of thyroid autoantibodies.	Elevated serum calcitonin. Elevated serum thyroglobulin (?).
Scanning techniques ^{123}I or ^{99m} TcO$_4$	"Hot nodule."	"Cold nodule."
Echo scan	Cyst (pure).	Solid or semicystic.
Biopsy (needle)	Benign appearance on cytologic examination.	Malignant or suggestion of malignancy.
Levothyroxine therapy (0.2 mg/d or more for 3 months or longer)	Regression.	No regression.

B. Physical Characteristics: Physical characteristics associated with a low risk for thyroid cancer include older age, female sex, soft thyroid nodules, and the presence of a multinodular goiter. Individuals at higher risk for thyroid cancer include children, young adults, and males. A solitary firm or dominant nodule that is clearly different from the rest of the gland signifies an increased risk of malignancy. Vocal cord paralysis, enlarged lymph nodes, and suspected metastases are strongly suggestive of malignancy.

C. Serum Factors: A high titer of thyroid autoantibodies in serum suggests chronic thyroiditis as the cause of thyroid enlargement. However, an elevated serum calcitonin, particularly in patients with a family history of medullary carcinoma, strongly suggests the presence of thyroid cancer. Elevated serum thyroglobulin titers following total thyroidectomy for papillary or follicular thyroid cancer usually indicate metastatic disease, but serum thyroglobulin is not usually helpful in determining the nature of a thyroid nodule.

D. Imaging Studies: Scanning procedures can be used to identify "hot" or "cold" nodules, ie, those that take up more or less radioactive iodine than surrounding tissue. Hot nodules are almost never malignant, whereas cold ones may be. Scintillation camera photographs with ^{99m}Tc pertechnetate give the best

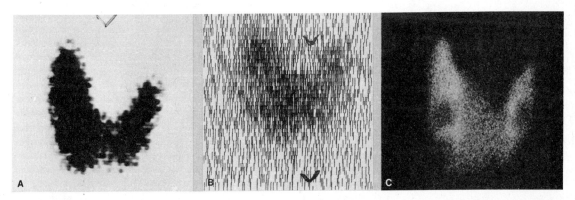

Figure 4–54. Demonstration of resolution obtained utilizing different scanning techniques: **A:** ^{123}I scintiscan with rectilinear scanner. **B:** Fluorescent scan with rectilinear scanner. **C:** ^{99m}Tc pertechnetate scan with the pinhole collimated gamma camera. Note the presence of two "cold" nodules, one in each lobe of the thyroid, easily detected in **C** but not clearly delineated in the other two scans. The lesion in the right lobe was palpable, about 1 cm in diameter, and was shown to be follicular carcinoma on needle biopsy. The lesion in the left lobe was either a metastatic tumor or a second primary follicular carcinoma. (Courtesy of MD Okerlund.)

resolution (Figure 4–54). Thyroid ultrasound can distinguish cystic from solid lesions. A pure cyst is almost never malignant. Cystic lesions that have internal septa or solid lesions on ultrasound may be benign or malignant. CT scanning or MRI may be helpful in defining substernal extension or deep thyroid nodules in the neck.

E. Needle Biopsy: The major advance in management of the thyroid nodule in recent years has been the fine-needle aspiration biopsy (see above). Large-needle core aspiration biopsies of thyroid nodules have been available since about 1930, but they are limited to large nodules and are relatively traumatic. Söderström in 1952 introduced the technique of fine-needle aspiration biopsy, which is simple, safe, reliable, and well-tolerated. Fine-needle aspiration biopsy separates thyroid nodules into three groups: (1) Malignant thyroid nodules: The technique is about 95% diagnostic for all types of thyroid malignancies. (2) Follicular neoplasms: About 15% of these lesions are malignant and about 85% are benign, but these two groups cannot be distinguished by cytology. Thus, a diagnosis of follicular neoplasm is always suspicious for malignancy. On isotope scan, a "hot" follicular neoplasm is benign, and a "cold" follicular neoplasm may be benign or malignant. (3) Benign thyroid nodules: The results with fine-needle aspiration biopsy are about 5% false-negative and about 5% false-positive. Thus, results are accurate in about 90% of cases, as demonstrated by subsequent surgery or long-term follow-up of patients with lesions originally reported to be benign. The results of the biopsy study must be interpreted by the clinician but are extremely useful for the diagnosis of malignancy in thyroid nodules.

F. Suppressive Therapy: Benign lesions may undergo spontaneous involution and regression, and some may be sufficiently TSH-dependent to shrink on thyroxine therapy. One study found no significant difference in nodule size (confirmed by thyroid sonography) between thyroxine- or placebo-treated controls during a 6-month period. In both groups, about half of the benign nodules decreased in size. However, malignant lesions are unlikely to regress either spontaneously or on T_4 therapy.

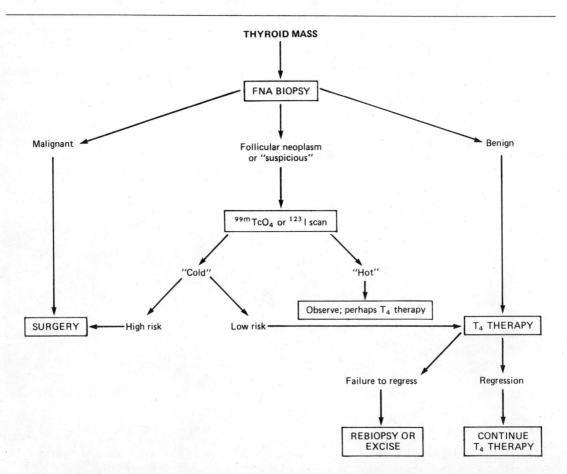

Figure 4–55. Decision matrix for workup of a thyroid nodule. See text for details. (FNA, fine-needle aspiration.)

Management of Thyroid Nodules

A decision matrix for management of a thyroid nodule is presented in Figure 4–55. A patient with a thyroid nodule should have fine-needle aspiration biopsy as the initial screening test for a thyroid mass. If the nodule is malignant, the patient is referred directly to the surgeon. If the cytologic report shows that the nodule is benign, the patient is given thyroxine, and if the lesion regresses, the patient is maintained on thyroxine indefinitely at a dose sufficient to suppress serum TSH. If there is no regression, the lesion is biopsied again—or, if it grows or changes in consistency, it may be excised. In patients who are reported to have follicular neoplasms, radionuclide scan is obtained. If the scan reveals the nodule to be hot, the patient is simply observed, at times with thyroxine therapy. If the lesion is cold and there is an increased chance of malignancy (large lesion over 2 cm in diameter, firm nodule, young patient), the patient might be referred directly to the surgeon. If the risk is low (small lesion 1 cm or less in diameter, soft nodule, older patient), the patient is given thyroxine. If thyroxine does not induce regression in the latter case, the lesion should probably be excised.

There are two groups that represent special problems: patients with thyroid cysts and patients who have received radiation therapy. Although thyroid cysts are almost always benign, cancer is occasionally found in the wall of the cyst. For this reason, recurrent cysts should be studied with ultrasonography, and if there is evidence of a septate lesion or growth in the wall of the lesion, surgical removal is indicated. In patients who have received radiation therapy, there may be multiple lesions, some benign and some malignant. Therefore, in the presence of a cold nodule in a patient who has had radiation exposure, surgery is recommended directly.

If this protocol is followed, there will be a marked reduction in surgery for benign thyroid nodules, and the incidence of malignancy at the time of surgery will be about 40%. The cost savings is enormous, since unnecessary surgery is eliminated and the cost of the thyroid nodule workup is cut in half. In addition, there is no delay in making the diagnosis and referring the patient with thyroid cancer for appropriate therapy.

Table 4–16. Approximate frequency of malignant thyroid tumors.

Papillary carcinoma (including mixed papillary and follicular)	75%
Follicular carcinoma	16%
Medullary carcinoma	5%
Undifferentiated carcinomas	3%
Miscellaneous (including lymphoma, fibrosarcoma, squamous cell carcinoma, malignant hemangioendothelioma, teratomas, and metastatic carcinomas)	1%

2. THYROID CANCER

Pathology

The types and approximate frequency of malignant thyroid tumors are listed in Table 4–16.

A. Papillary Carcinoma: Papillary carcinoma of the thyroid gland usually presents as a nodule that is firm, solitary, "cold,"on isotope scan, solid on thyroid ultrasound, and clearly different from the rest of the gland. In multinodular goiter, the cancer will usually be a "dominant nodule"—larger, firmer, and (again) clearly different from the rest of the gland. About 10% of papillary carcinomas, especially in children, present with enlarged cervical nodes, but careful examination will often reveal a "cold" nodule in the thyroid. Rarely, there will be hemorrhage, necrosis, and cyst formation in the malignant nodule, but on thyroid ultrasound of these lesions, clearly defined internal echoes will differentiate the semicystic malignant lesion from the nonmalignant "pure cyst." Finally, papillary carcinoma may be found incidentally as a microscopic focus of cancer in the middle of a gland removed for other reasons such as Graves' disease or multinodular goiter.

Microscopically, the tumor consists of single layers of thyroid cells arranged in vascular stalks, with papillary projections extending into microscopic cyst-like spaces. The nuclei of the cells are large and pale and frequently contain clear, glassy intranuclear inclusion bodies. About 40% of papillary carcinomas form laminated calcified spheres—often at the tip of a papillary projection—called "psammoma bodies," which are usually diagnostic of papillary carcinoma. These cancers usually extend by intraglandular metastasis and by local lymph node invasion. They grow very slowly and remain confined to the thyroid gland and local lymph nodes for many years. In older patients, they may become more aggressive and invade locally into muscles and trachea. In later stages, they can spread to the lung. Death is usually due to local disease, with invasion of deep tissues in the neck; less commonly, death may be due to extensive pulmonary metastases. In some older patients, a long-standing, slowly growing papillary carcinoma will begin to grow rapidly and convert to undifferentiated or anaplastic carcinoma. This "late anaplastic shift" is another cause of death from papillary carcinoma. Many papillary carcinomas secrete thyroglobulin, which can be used as a marker for recurrence or metastasis of the cancer.

B. Follicular Carcinoma: Follicular carcinoma is characterized by the presence of small follicles, though colloid formation is poor. Indeed, follicular carcinoma may be indistinguishable from follicular adenoma except by capsular or vascular invasion. The tumor is somewhat more aggressive than papillary carcinoma and can spread either by local invasion of lymph nodes or by blood vessel invasion with distant metastases to bone or lung. Microscopically, the cells are cuboidal, with large nuclei, arranged around follicles that frequently contain dense colloid. These tumors often retain the ability to concentrate radioactive iodine, to form thyroglobulin, and, rarely, to synthesize T_3 and T_4. Thus, the rare "functioning thyroid cancer" is almost always a follicular carcinoma. This characteristic makes these tumors more likely to respond to radioactive iodine therapy. In untreated patients, death is due to local extension or to distant bloodstream metastasis with extensive involvement of bone, lungs, and viscera.

A variant of follicular carcinoma is the "Hurthle cell" carcinoma, characterized by large individual cells with pink-staining cytoplasm filled with mitochondria. They behave like follicular cancer except that they rarely take up radioiodine. Mixed papillary and follicular carcinomas behave more like papillary carcinoma. Thyroglobulin secretion by follicular carcinomas can be used to follow the course of disease.

C. Medullary Carcinoma: Medullary cancer is a disease of the C cells (parafollicular cells) derived from the ultimobranchial body and capable of secreting calcitonin, histaminase, prostaglandins, serotonin, and other peptides. Microscopically, the tumor consists of sheets of cells separated by a pink-staining substance that has characteristics of amyloid. This material stains with Congo red. Amyloid consists of chains of calcitonin laid down in a fibrillary pattern—in contrast to other forms of amyloid, which may have immunoglobulin light chains or other proteins deposited in a fibrillary pattern.

Medullary carcinoma is somewhat more aggressive than papillary or follicular carcinoma but not as aggressive as undifferentiated thyroid cancer. It extends locally into lymph nodes and into surrounding muscle and trachea. It may invade lymphatics and blood vessels and metastasize to lungs and viscera. Calcitonin and carcinoembryonic antigen (CEA) secreted by the tumor are clinically useful markers for diagnosis and follow-up. About one-third of medullary carcinomas are familial, involving multiple endocrine glands (multiple endocrine neoplasia, type II (MEN II; Sipple's syndrome) (see Chapter 21). MEN IIa is characterized by medullary carcinoma, pheochromocytoma, and parathyroid adenomas; and MEN IIb is characterized by medullary carcinoma, pheochromocytomas, and multiple neuromas of the tongue, lip, and bowel. About one-third of medullary

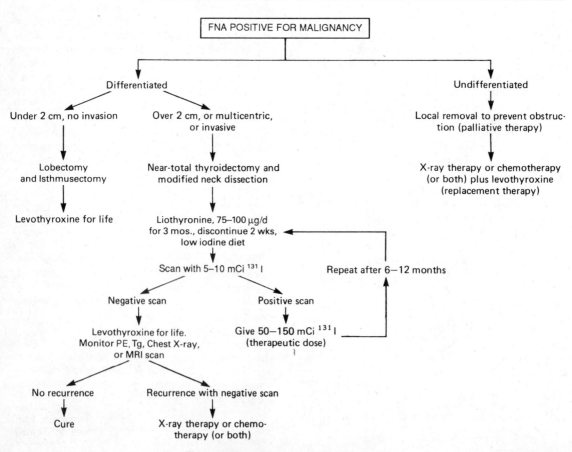

Figure 4–56. Management of thyroid cancer.

carcinomas are familial, involving only the thyroid cancer, and about one-third are isolated instances of the malignancy. If medullary carcinoma is diagnosed by fine-needle aspiration biopsy or at surgery, it is essential that the patient be screened for the other endocrine abnormalities found in MEN II and that family members be screened for medullary carcinoma and MEN II as well. The measurement of serum calcitonin after pentagastrin stimulation or calcium infusion can be used to screen for medullary carcinoma. Pentagastrin is administered intravenously in a bolus of 0.5 μg/kg, and venous blood specimens are drawn at 1, 3, 5, and 10 minutes. An abnormal rise in serum calcitonin at 3 or 5 minutes is indicative of the presence of the malignancy (see Chapter 5). The gene for MEN IIa has been localized to chromosome 10, and it is now possible to use polymorphic DNA probes and restriction fragment length polymorphism (RFLP) to identify carriers of the gene for this syndrome. Thus, family members carrying the gene can be identified and studied as persons at high risk for the development of the syndrome.

D. Undifferentiated (Anaplastic) Carcinoma: Undifferentiated thyroid gland tumors include small cell, giant cell, and spindle cell carcinomas. They usually occur in older patients with a long history of goiter in whom the gland suddenly—over weeks or months—begins to enlarge and produce pressure symptoms, dysphagia, or vocal cord paralysis. Death from massive local extension usually occurs within 6–36 months. These tumors are very resistant to therapy.

E. Miscellaneous Types:

1. Lymphoma– The only type of rapidly growing thyroid cancer that is responsive to therapy is the lymphoma, which may develop as part of a generalized lymphoma or may be primary in the thyroid gland. Thyroid lymphoma occasionally develops in a patient with long-standing Hashimoto's thyroiditis and may be difficult to distinguish from chronic thyroiditis. It is characterized by lymphocyte invasion of thyroid follicles and blood vessel walls, which helps to differentiate thyroid lymphoma from chronic thyroiditis. If there is no systemic involvement, the tumor may respond dramatically to radiation therapy.

2. Cancer metastatic to the thyroid– Systemic cancers that may metastasize to the thyroid gland include cancers of the breast and kidney, bronchogenic carcinoma, and malignant melanoma. The primary site of involvement is usually obvious. Occasionally, the diagnosis is made by needle biopsy or open biopsy of a rapidly enlarging cold thyroid nodule. The prognosis is that of the primary tumor.

Management of Thyroid Cancer (Figure 4–56)

A. Papillary and Follicular Carcinoma: Lobectomy is satisfactory for small (< 2 cm) papillary and follicular thyroid carcinomas, but total thyroidectomy is required for larger lesions or for cancers with evidence of intrathyroidal or extrathyroidal extension. Modified neck dissection is indicated if there is evidence of lymph node metastases. Prophylactic neck dissections are not recommended. Postoperative radioiodine scan and therapy are indicated for patients with large papillary or follicular carcinomas (> 2 cm) or with evidence of intra- or extrathyroidal extension. Postoperatively, the patient receives liothyronine, 50–100 μg daily in divided doses for

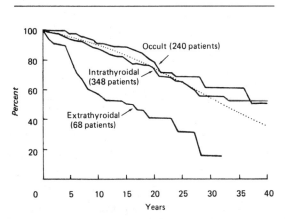

Figure 4–57. Papillary carcinoma. Survivorship curves for occult, intrathyroidal, and extrathyroidal lesions. Dotted line is curve for normal persons of comparable age and sex. (Reproduced, with permission, from Woolner LB et al: Long term survival rates. In: *Thyroid Cancer,* vol 12. Hedinger CE [editor]. UICC Monograph Series. Springer, 1969.)

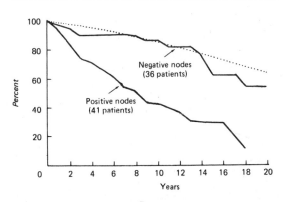

Figure 4–58. Follicular carcinoma. Survivorship curves (six operative deaths excluded) for patients with slight or equivocal capsular invasion and those with moderate or marked invasion (including recurrent and inoperable tumors). Dotted line is curve for normal persons of comparable age and sex. (Reproduced, with permission, from Woolner LB et al: Long term survival rates. In: *Thyroid Cancer,* vol 12. Hedinger CE [editor]. UICC Monograph Series. Springer, 1969.)

about 3 months; the medication is then stopped for 2 weeks, and the patient is placed on a low-iodine diet. The patient is scanned at 24 and 72 hours after a dose of 5–10 mCi of ^{131}I. Liothyronine is used for replacement therapy because it is cleared from the blood rapidly; after 2 weeks off therapy, serum TSH is usually over 50 mU/L, which is necessary for good scanning studies. If there is evidence of residual radioactive iodine uptake in the neck or elsewhere, radioactive iodine (^{131}I) is effective treatment. The scan is repeated at intervals of 6–12 months until no further uptake is observed; the patient is then maintained on maximum replacement therapy with levothyroxine, 0.15–0.3 mg daily, to suppress serum TSH to undetectable levels.

Follow-up at intervals of 6–12 months should include careful examination of the neck for recurrent masses. If a lump is noted, needle biopsy examination is indicated to confirm or rule out cancer. Serum thyroglobulin will usually be less than 5 ng/mL (5 µg/L) after total thyroidectomy and levothyroxine therapy. A rise in serum thyroglobulin to more than 10 ng/mL (10 µg/L) suggests recurrence of thyroid cancer. Chest x-ray, thyroid ultrasound, or MRI every 2–3 years may reveal local or pulmonary metastases, though a rising serum thyroglobulin concentration is a more sensitive indicator. If the patient does develop a mass in the neck, a rise in serum thyroglobulin, or a mass on chest x-ray, thyroid ultrasound, or MRI, ^{131}I scan should be repeated following the technique outlined above. If the lesions concentrate ^{131}I, the patient can be treated with the isotope; if they do not, local excision or local x-ray therapy may be useful. For recurrences that cannot be

managed by these modalities, chemotherapy should be considered.

B. Medullary Carcinoma: Patients with medullary carcinoma should be followed in a similar way, except that the marker for recurrent medullary cancer is serum calcitonin or carcinoembryonic antigen (CEA). Histaminase and other peptides are also secreted by these tumors, but assays for these substances are not generally available. If a patient has a persistently elevated serum calcitonin concentration after total thyroidectomy and regional node dissection, MRI of the neck and chest or selective venous catheterization and sampling for serum calcitonin may reveal the location of the metastases. If this fails to localize the lesion (as is often the case), the patient must be followed until the metastatic lesion shows itself as a palpable mass or a shadow on chest x-ray or MRI. Metastatic medullary carcinoma cannot be treated with ^{131}I; therefore, initial thorough surgical excision and postoperative levothyroxine therapy are essential. Chemotherapy for medullary carcinoma has not been effective.

C. Anaplastic Carcinoma: Anaplastic carcinoma of the thyroid has a very poor prognosis. Treatment consists of isthmusectomy (to confirm the diagnosis and to prevent tracheal compression) and palliative x-ray therapy. Thyroid lymphomas are quite responsive to x-ray therapy; giant cell, squamous cell, spindle cell, and anaplastic carcinomas are unresponsive. Chemotherapy is not very effective for anaplastic carcinomas. Doxorubicin, 75 mg/m^2 as a single injection or divided into three consecutive daily injections repeated at 3-week intervals, has been useful in some patients with disseminated thyroid cancer unresponsive to surgery, TSH suppression, or radiation therapy. This drug is quite toxic; side effects include cardiotoxicity, myelosuppression, alopecia, and gas-

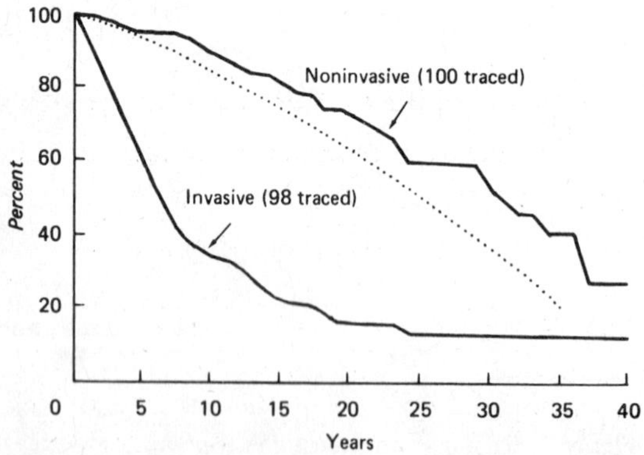

Figure 4–59. Medullary carcinoma. Survivorship curves for patients with metastatic involvement of cervical lymph nodes at time of initial surgery and those without such involvement. Dotted line is curve for normal persons of comparable age and sex. (Reproduced, with permission, from Woolner LB et al: Long term survival rates. In: *Thyroid Cancer,* vol 12. Hedinger CE [editor]. UICC Monograph Series. Springer, 1969.)

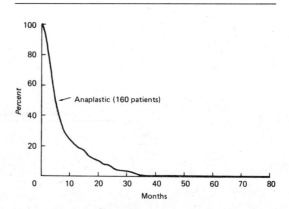

Figure 4–60. Anaplastic carcinoma. Survivorship curve, plotted in months. (Reproduced, with permission, from Woolner LB et al: Long term survival rates. In: *Thyroid Cancer,* vol 12. Hedinger CE [editor]. UICC Monograph Series. Springer, 1969.)

trointestinal symptoms.

D. X-Ray Therapy: Local x-ray therapy has been useful in the treatment of solitary metastatic lesions, particularly follicular or papillary tumors, that do not concentrate radioactive iodine. It is particularly effective in isolated nonfunctional bone metastases.

Course & Prognosis

Papillary carcinoma of the thyroid (the most common type) may exist as a microscopic focus in the gland. The incidence of microscopic foci of thyroid cancer at autopsy has varied from 4% in several series in the USA to as high as 25% in persons of Japanese descent living in the Hawaiian Islands. The lesion does not shorten life and is probably of no clinical significance. Woolner et al have shown that in patients with "occult" or microscopic papillary carcinoma—or small intrathyroidal papillary carcinoma—the survival rate is about the same as that of individuals without thyroid cancer. However, if there is evidence of extrathyroidal extension of the cancer, life expectancy is markedly affected (Figure 4–57). Similarly, in persons with small, noninvasive follicular carcinoma, the survival rate does not differ from that of control groups, whereas in the case of follicular carcinoma that has invaded blood vessels or in which there is evidence of extrathyroidal extension, survival is poor (Figure 4–58). Medullary carcinoma shows a similar pattern, with good survival for intrathyroidal small lesions and impaired survival for

patients with extrathyroidal extension (Figure 4–59). Patients with anaplastic carcinomas have a very poor prognosis; almost all are dead within 3 years (Figure 4–60).

Statistical studies of the factors related to prognosis in patients with papillary or follicular carcinoma have revealed the following:

(1) Age at diagnosis: Patients over 40 generally have a worse prognosis than younger patients.

(2) Sex: Males have a lower survival rate than females.

(3) Size of primary tumor: Patients with tumors over 4 cm have a worse prognosis.

(4) Degree of differentiation of the primary tumor: This is reflected in tumor cell DNA or "ploidy." The less well differentiated tumors with an "aneuploid" or abnormal tumor nuclear DNA content have a poor prognosis.

(5) Extent of local spread at time of initial surgery: Local invasion implies a worse prognosis than nodal involvement.

(6) Extent of initial surgery: Although young patients with small lesions of papillary carcinoma may do well after lobectomy, if cervical lymph nodes are positive, total thyroidectomy and modified neck dissection yield the best survival rates.

(7) Postoperative ^{131}I therapy for residual tumor greatly improves the prognosis.

(8) Postoperative T_4 therapy with TSH suppression also greatly improves the prognosis.

REFERENCES

General

Braverman LE, Utiger RD (editors): *Werner and Ingbar's The Thyroid: A Fundamental and Clinical Text,* 6th ed. Lippincott,1991.

Burrow GN, Oppenheimer JH, Volpé R: *Thyroid Function and Disease.* Saunders, 1989.

Greenspan FS (editor): Thyroid diseases. Med Clin North Am 1991;75:1.

Greer MA (editor): *The Thyroid Gland.* Comprehensive Endocrinology Series. Martini L (editor). Raven Press, 1990.

Larsen PR, Ingbar SH: The thyroid gland. In: *Williams Textbook of Endocrinology,* 8th ed. Wilson JD, Foster DW. Saunders, 1992.

Lazarus JH, Hall R (editors): *Hypothyroidism and goiter. Bailliere's Clin Endocrinol Metab* 1988;2(3).

Utiger RD, Burrow GN: Thyroid disease. In: *Endocrinology and Metabolism,* 2nd ed. Felig P et al (editors). McGraw-Hill, 1987.

Anatomy

Fujita H: Functional morphology of the thyroid. Int Rev Cytol 113:145,1988.

Hegedus L: Thyroid size determined by ultrasound: Influence of physiological factors and non-thyroidal disease. Dan Med Bull 1990;37:249.

Lindner HH: The thyroid gland. In: *Clinical Anatomy.* Appleton & Lange,1989.

Toda S, Sugahara H: Reconstruction of thyroid follicles from isolated porcine follicle cells in three dimensional collagen gel culture. Endocrinology 1989;126:2027.

Physiology

Berry MJ, Larsen PR: The role of selenium in thyroid hormone action. Endocr Rev 1992;13:207.

Brabant G, von zur Muhlen A: Physiological regulation and biological function of thyrotropin. Supplement Series No. 23 In: *Hormone and Metabolic Research.* Pfeiffer EF, Reaven GM (editors). Thieme, 1990.

Brent GA, Moore DD, Larsen PR: Thyroid hormone regulation of gene expression. Annu Rev Physiol 53:17,1991.

DeGroot, LJ: Thyroid hormone nuclear receptors and their role in the metabolic action of the hormone. Biochimie 1989;71:269.

Dunn JT: Thyroglobulin: Chemistry and biosynthesis. In:

Werner and Ingbar's The Thyroid: A fundamental and Clinical Text, 6th ed. Braverman LE, Utiger RD (editors). Lippincott, 1991.

Eckholm R. Biosynthesis of thyroid hormones. Int Rev Cytol 1990;120:243.

Eggo MC, Burrow GN (editors): *Thyroglobulin, the Prothyroid Hormone.* Vol 2 of *Progress in Endocrine Research and Therapy.* Raven Press, 1985.

Glass CK, Holloway JM: Regulation of gene expression by the thyroid hormone receptor. Biochim Biophys Acta 1990;1032:157.

Glinoer D et al: Regulation of maternal thyroid during pregnancy. J Clin Endocrinol Metab 1990; 71:276.

Goldberg Y et al: Thyroid hormone action and the *erbA* oncogene family. Biochimie 1989;71:279.

Henneman G, Doctor R: Plasma transport proteins and their role in tissue delivery of thyroid hormone. In: *The Thyroid Gland.* Greer MA (editor). Comprehensive Endocrinology Series. Martini L (editor), Raven Press, 1990.

Lazar MA, Chin WW. Nuclear thyroid hormone receptors. J Clin Invest 1990;86:1777.

Leonard JL: Identification and structure analysis of iodothyronine deiodinases. In: *The Thyroid Gland,* Greer MA (editor). Comprehensive Endocrinology Series. Martini L (editor). Raven Press, 1990.

Magner JA: Thyroid-stimulating hormone: Biosynthesis, cell biology and bioactivity. Endocr Rev 1990;11: 354.

Magnusson RP: Thyroid peroxidase. In: *Peroxidases in Chemistry and Biology,* vol 1. Everse J, Grisham MB (editors). CRC Press 1990.

Malthiery Y et al: Thyroglobulin structure and function: Recent advances. Biochimie 1989;71:195.

Mariotti S et al: Recent advances in the understanding of humoral and cellular mechanisms implicated in thyroid autoimmune disorders. Clin Immunol Immunopathol 1989;50:S73.

McLachlan SM, Rapaport B: The molecular biology of thyroid peroxidase: Cloning, expression and role as autoantigen in autoimmune thyroid disease. Endocr Rev 1992;13:1992.

Metcalf G, Jackson IMD (editors): Thyrotropin-releasing hormone: Biomedical significance. Ann N Y Acad Sci 1989;553:1.

Pisarev MA: Thyroid autoregulation. J Endocrinol Invest 1985;8:475.

Rapaport B, Nagayama Y: The thyrotropin receptor 25 years after its discovery: New insights after molecular cloning. Mol Endocrinol 1992;6:145.

Shupnik MA, Ridgeway EC, Chin WW: Molecular biology of thyrotropin. Endocr Rev 1989;4:459.

Surks MI et al: Normal free thyroxine in critical nonthyroidal illnesses measured by ultrafiltration of undiluted serum and equilibrium dialysis. J Clin Endocrinol Metab 1988;67:1031.

Taurog A: Hormone synthesis: Thyroid iodine metabolism. In: *Werner and Ingbar's The Thyroid: A Fundamental and Clinical Text,* 6th ed. Braverman LE, Utiger RD (editors). Lippincott, 1991.

Tibaldi JM, Surks MI: Effects of nonthyroidal illness on thyroid function. Med Clin North Am 1985; 69:899.

Volpé R: Autoimmunity causing thyroid dysfunction. Endocrinol Metab Clin North Am 1991;20:565.

Wall JR (editor): Autoimmune thyroid disease. Endocrinol Metab Clin North Am 1987;229:1.

Weinberger C et al: The c-erb-A gene encodes a thyroid hormone receptor. Nature 1986;324:641.

Wilkin TJ. Mechanisms of disease: Receptor autoimmunity in endocrine disorders. N Eng J Med 1990;323: 1318.

Wolff J. Excess iodide inhibits the thyroid gland by multiple mechanisms. In: *Control of the Thyroid Gland.* Eckholm R, Kohn LD, Wollman SH (editors), Plenum, 1989.

Wolff J: Iodide transport: Anion selectivity and the iodide "trap." In: *Diminished Thyroid Hormone Formation.* Reinwein D, Klein E (editors). Schattauer, 1982

Tests of Thyroid Function

Bayer MF: Effective laboratory evaluation of thyroid status. Med Clin North Am 1991;75:1.

Cavalieri RR: The effects of nonthyroid disease and drugs on thyroid function. Med Clin North Am 1991;75:27.

Davies PH, Franklyn JA: The effect of drugs on tests of thyroid function. Eur J Clin Pharmacol 1991;40:439.

Ekins R: Measurement of free hormones in blood. Endocr Rev 1990;11:5.

Helfand M, Crapo LM: Screening for thyroid disease. Ann Intern Med 1990;112:841.

Liewendahl K: Assessment of thyroid status by laboratory methods: Developments and perspectives. Scand J Clin Lab Invest 1990;201(Suppl):83.

Nicoloff JT, Spencer CA: The use and misuse of sensitive thyrotropin assays. Clinical review 12. J Clin Endocrinol Metab 1990;71:553.

Prentice LM et al: Geographical distribution of subclinical autoimmune thyroid disease in Britain: A study using highly sensitive direct assays for autoantibodies to thyroglobulin and thyroid peroxidase. Acta Endocrinol (Copenh) 1990;123:493.

Rees Smith B, McLachlan SM, Furmaniak J: Autoantibodies to the thyrotropin receptor. Endocr Rev 1988;9:106.

Surks MI et al: American Thyroid Association guidelines for use of laboratory tests in thyroid disorders. JAMA 1990;263:1529.

Tunbridge WMG et al: The spectrum of thyroid disease in a community: The Whickham survey. Clin Endocrinol (Oxf) 1977;7:481.

Hypothyroidism

Fisher DA: Management of congenital hypothyroidism. Clinical review 19. J Clin Endocrinol Metab 1991; 72:523.

Greenspan SL et al: Skeletal integrity in premenopausal and postmenopausal women receiving long-term l-thyroxine therapy. Am J Med 1991;91:5.

Holvey DN et al: Treatment of myxedema coma with intravenous thyroxine. Arch Int Med 1964; 113:89.

Lazarus JH, Hall R (editors): Hypothyroidism and goiter. Baillieres Clin Endocrinol Metab 1988;2:531.

Mandel SJ et al: Increased need for thyroxine during pregnancy in women with primary hypothyroidism. N Eng J Med 1990;323:91.

Martino E et al: Amiodarone iodine-induced hypothyroidism: Risk factors and follow-up in 28 cases. Clin Endocrinol 1987;26:227.

Ross DS: Subclinical Hyperthyroidism: Possible danger of overzealous thyroxine replacement therapy. Mayo Clin Proc 1988;63:1223.

Toft AD: Thyroxine replacement therapy. Clin Endocrinol 1991;34:103.

Zwillich CW et al: Ventilatory control in myxedema and hypothyroidism. N Engl J Med 1975; 292:662.

Hyperthyroidism

Bahn RS et al: Diagnosis and management of Graves' ophthalmopathy. Clinical review 13. J Clin Endocrinol Metab 1990;71:559.

Becks GP, Burrow GN: Thyroid disease and pregnancy. Med Clin North Am 1991;75:121.

Bradley EL III et al: Modified subtotal thyroidectomy in the management of Graves' disease. Surgery 1980; 7:623.

Carter JA, Utiger RD: The ophthalmopathy of Graves' disease. Ann Rev Med 1992;43:487.

Char DH: *Thyroid Eye Disease,* 2nd ed. Churchill Livingston, 1990.

Farrar JJ, Toft AD: Iodine-131 treatment of hyperthyroidism: Current issues. Clin Endocrinol 1991;35: 207.

Franklyn JA et al: Long-term follow-up of treatment of thyrotoxicosis by three different methods. Clin Endocrinol 1991;34:71.

Gavin LA: Thyroid crises. Med Clin North Am 1991;75:179.

Hashizume K et al: Administration of thyroxine in treated Graves' disease: Effects on the level of antibodies to thyroid stimulating hormone receptors and on the risk of recurrence of hyperthyroidism. N Eng J Med 1991;324:947.

Hedley AJ et al: Antithyroid drugs in the treatment of hyperthyroidism of Graves' disease: Long-term follow-up of 434 patients. Clin Endocrinol 1989; 31:209.

McDougall IR: Graves' disease: Current concepts. Med Clin North Am 1991;75:79.

Nabil N et al: Methimazole: An alternative route of administration. J Clin Endocrinol Metab 1982;54: 180.

Nademanee K et al: Amiodarone and thyroid function. Prog Cardiovasc Dis 1989;21:427.

Nagayama Y et al: The management of hyperthyroidism due to Graves' Disease in Japan in 1988. Endocrinol Jpn 1989;36:299.

Solomon B et al: Current trends in the management of Graves' disease. J Clin Endocrinol Metabol 1990;70: 1518.

Weetman AP: Thyroid associated eye disease: Pathophysiology. Lancet 1991;338:25.

Thyroid Hormone Resistance Syndromes

Franklyn JA: Syndromes of thyroid hormone resistance. Clin Endocrinol 1991;34:237.

Refetoff S: The syndrome of generalized resistance to thyroid hormone (GRTH). Endocr Res 1989;15:717.

Takeda K et al: Rapid localization of mutations in the thyroid hormone receptor-b gene by denaturing gradient gel electrophoresis in 18 families with thyroid hormone resistance. J Clin Endocrinol Metabol 1992; 74:712.

Usala SJ, Weintraub BD: Thyroid hormone resistance syndromes. Trends Endocrinol Metab 1991;2: 140.

Weiss RE, Refetoff S: Thyroid hormone resistance. Ann Rev Med 1992;43:363.

Syndrome of Inappropriate TSH Secretion

Beckers A et al: Thyrotropin-secreting pituitary adenomas: Report of seven cases. J Clin Endocrinol Metab 1991;72:477.

Chayen SD et al: TSH producing pituitary tumor: Biochemical diagnosis and long-term management with octreotide. Horm Metabol Res 1992;24:34.

Gesundheit N et al: Thyrotropin-secreting pituitary adenomas: Clinical and biochemical heterogeneity. Ann Int Med 1989;111:827.

Hermus A et al: Hyperthyroidism due to inappropriate secretion of thyroid stimulating hormone: Diagnosis and management. Neth J Med 1991;38:193.

Wynne AG et al: Hyperthyroidism due to inappropriate secretion of thyrotropin in 10 patients. Am J Med 1992;92:15.

Nontoxic Goiter

Fenzi G et al: Clinical approach to goiter. Baillieres Clin Endocrinol Metab 1988;2:671.

Gaitan E, Nelson NC, Poole GV: Endemic goiter and endemic thyroid disorders. World J Surg 1991; 15:205.

Greenspan FS: The problem of the nodular goiter. Med Clin North Am 1991;75:195.

Lamberg BA: Endemic goiter-iodine deficiency disorders. Ann Med 1991;23:367.

Thyroiditis

Amino N: Autoimmunity and hypothyroidism. Baillieres Clin Endocrinol Metab 1988;2:591

Rapoport B: Pathophysiology of Hashimoto's thyroiditis and hypothyroidism. Ann Rev Med 1991; 42:91.

Roti E, Emerson CH: Postpartum thyroiditis. Clinical review 29. J Clin Endocrinol Metab 1992;74:3.

Singer PA: Thyroiditis, acute, subacute and chronic. Med Clin North Am 1991;75:61.

Radiation Exposure

DeGroot LJ: Diagnostic approach and management of patients exposed to irradiation to the thyroid. Clinical review 2. J Clin Endocrinol Metabol 1989;69:925.

Mehta MP et al: Radiation induced thyroid neoplasms 1920 to 1987: A vanishing problem? Int J Radiat Oncol Biol Phys 1989;16:1471.

Sako K: Head and neck irradiation in childhood: Increased risk of developing thyroid disease. Semin Surg Oncol 1991;7:112.

Thyroid Nodules & Thyroid Cancer

Cady B: Papillary carcinoma of the thyroid. Semin Surg Oncol 1991;7:81.

Clark OH et al: Thyroid cancer: The case for total thyroidectomy. Eur J Cancer Clin Oncol 1988;24: 305.

Frauman AG, Moses AC: Oncogenes and growth factors in thyroid carcinogenesis. Endocrinol Metab Clin North Am 1990;19:479.

Harvey HK: Diagnosis and management of the thyroid nodule: An overview. Otolaryngol Clin North Am 1990;23:303.

Hung W: Nodular thyroid disease and thyroid carcinoma. Pediatr Ann 1992;21:50.

Kaplan M: Thyroid carcinoma. Endocrinol Metab Clin North Am 1990;19:469.

Mazzaferri EL et al: Solitary thyroid nodule: Diagnosis and management. Med Clin North America 1988;72:1177

Nelkin BD et al: The molecular biology of medullary thyroid carcinoma: A model for cancer development and progression. JAMA 1989;261:3130.

Ridgway EC: Clinician's evaluation of a solitary thyroid nodule. Clinical review 30. J Clin Endocrinol Metabol 1992;74:231.

Robbins J et al: Thyroid cancer, a lethal endocrine neoplasm. Ann Intern Med 1991;115:133.

Ross DS: Evaluation of the thyroid nodule. J Nucl Med 1991;32:2181.

Simpson WJ: Radioiodine and radiotherapy in the management of thyroid cancer. Otolaryngol Clin North Am 1990;23:509.

Thomas CG Jr: Role of thyroid stimulating hormone suppression in the management of thyroid cancer. Semin Surg Oncol 1991;7:115.

Woolner LB et al: Long term survival rates. In: *Thyroid Cancer,* vol 12. Hedinger CE [editor]. UICC Monograph Series. Springer, 1969.

The Calciotropic Hormones & Metabolic Bone Disease

Claude D. Arnaud, MD

EXTRACELLULAR & BONE MINERAL HOMEOSTASIS

A highly integrated and complex endocrine system maintains calcium, phosphate, and magnesium homeostasis in all vertebrates. It involves an interplay between the actions of two polypeptide hormones, parathyroid hormone (PTH) and calcitonin (CT), and a sterol hormone, 1,25-dihydroxycholecalciferol, or $1,25(OH)_2D_3$.* Biosynthesis and secretion of the polypeptide hormones are regulated by a negative feedback mechanism that involves the activity of ionic calcium in the extracellular fluid (Figure 5–1). The biosynthesis of $1,25(OH)_2D_3$ from the major circulating metabolite of vitamin D, 25-hydroxycholecalciferol ($25OHD_3$), takes place in the kidney and is regulated by PTH and CT, as well as by the extracellular fluid concentrations of calcium and phosphate. Other hormones such as insulin, cortisol, growth hormone (GH), thyroxine, epinephrine, estrogen, and testosterone; growth factors such as the insulin-like growth factors and transforming growth factor; and ions such as inorganic phosphate and magnesium—together with some compounds not yet identified and certain physical phenomena—all undoubtedly have roles in modifying and regulating organ responses to PTH, CT, and $1,25(OH)_2D_3$.

PTH, CT, and $1,25(OH)_2D_3$ regulate the flow of minerals into and out of the extracellular fluid compartment through their actions on intestine, kidney, and bone (Table 5–1; Figure 5–2). The target cells of these organs function as a cellular barrier between the extracellular fluid compartment and the intestinal lumen, the renal tubular lumen, and the bone fluid compartment (adjacent to mobilizable bone mineral)

---

*The nomenclature of the calciotropic hormones and vitamin D metabolites discussed in this chapter is generally in agreement with the recommendations of the Endocrine Society and conforms to the editorial practices of the Journal of Clinical Endocrinology and Metabolism. Note especially the following: vitamin D_3, cholecalciferol; vitamin D_2, ergocalciferol; 25-hydroxycholecalciferol, $25OHD_3$; 25-hydroxyergocalciferol, $25OHD_2$; 1,25-dihydroxycholecalciferol (often written 1α,25-dihydroxy . . . in other texts), $1,25(OH)_2D_3$;24,25-dihydroxycholecalciferol, $24,25(OH)_2D_3$. A few others of lesser importance are mentioned briefly in the section entitled Vitamin D.

ACRONYMS USED IN THIS CHAPTER

ACTH	Adrenocorticotropic hormone
ATP	Adenosine triphosphate
cAMP	Cyclic adenosine monophosphate
CGRP	Calcitonin gene-related peptide
CT	Calcitonin
DER (DEX)	Dual-energy radiography
DPA	Dual-photon absorptiometry
ERT	Estrogen replacement therapy
GFR	Glomerular filtration rate
GH	Growth hormone
Gpp (NH)p	5′-Guanyl-imidodiphosphate
HAM	Hypoparathyroidism-Addison's disease-mucocutaneous candidiasis (syndrome)
iCT	Immunoreactive calcitonin
iPTH	Immunoreactive parathyroid hormone
MEDAC	Multiple endocrine deficiency-autoimmune candidiasis (syndrome)
MEN	Multiple endocrine neoplasia
MRI	Magnetic resonance imaging
OAF	Osteoclast-activating factor
OC	Osteocalcin
PYD	Pyridinoline collagen cross-links
PRL	Prolactin
PTH	Parathyroid hormone
QCT	Quantitative computer-assisted tomography
RNA	Ribonucleic acid

(Figure 5–3). These target cells are highly specialized for solute transport against a concentration gradient and thus are often described as being polarized.

Role of Parathyroid Hormone

Under normal circumstances, PTH prevents serum calcium from falling below physiologic concentrations by stimulating calcium movement from intestinal and renal tubular lumens and from the bone fluid compartment into the blood. Whereas its effects on bone and kidney are direct, PTH acts indirectly on the intestine, through the mediation of vitamin D. The hormone stimulates (directly and through its hypophosphatemic effects) the conversion of $25OHD_3$ to $1,25(OH)_2D_3$ in the kidney via a $25OHD_3$ 1α-hy-

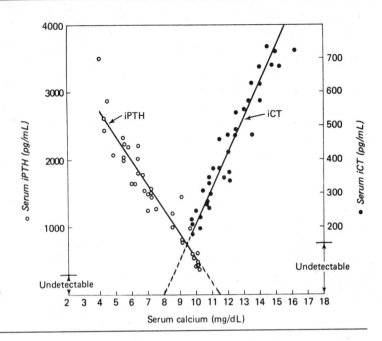

Figure 5–1. Plasma immunoreactive PTH (iPTH) and CT (iCT) as a function of plasma total calcium in pigs given EDTA to decrease plasma calcium or given calcium infusions to increase plasma calcium. Note that as serum calcium increases, serum iPTH falls and serum iCT rises; as serum calcium decreases, the reverse occurs. (r = −0.942 for iPTH and 0.964 for iCT; p for both is < .001.) (Reproduced, with permission, from Arnaud CD et al: Calcium homeostasis and the simultaneous measurement of calcitonin and parathyroid hormone in the pig. In: *Calcitonin: Proceedings of the Second International Symposium.* Taylor S [editor]. Heinemann, 1970.)

droxylase in the mitochondria of the renal tubule. The $1,25(OH)_2D_3$ thus formed stimulates intestinal calcium absorption. PTH also prevents serum phosphate levels from rising above normal physiologic concentrations by increasing renal tubular excretion of phosphate. This regulatory action is important because phosphate, like calcium, is also released into the blood by PTH-induced bone resorption. This function can be particularly appreciated in patients with end-stage renal failure associated with severe hyperparathyroidism. These patients develop hyperphosphatemia because the kidney can no longer excrete the large quantities of phosphate that are released from bone.

Role of Calcitonin

Calcitonin prevents abnormal increases in both serum calcium and serum phosphate. It decreases the translocation of calcium from the renal tubule and bone fluid compartment into the blood and thus can be considered as a counterregulator of PTH. The effects of CT on vitamin D metabolism and on the intestinal absorption of calcium are uncertain.

Integrated Actions of PTH, CT, & $1,25(OH)_2D_3$

It is likely that PTH and CT regulate the entry of calcium into polarized cells of the surface membrane of bone and the renal tubular lumen. $1,25(OH)_2D_3$

Table 5–1. Actions of major calcium-regulating hormones.

	Bone	**Kidney**	**Intestine**
Parathyroid hormone (PTH)	Increases resorption of calcium and phosphate.	Increases reabsorption of calcium; decreases reabsorption of phosphate; decreases reabsorption of bicarbonate; increases conversion of $25OHD_3$ to $1,25(OH)_2D_3$.	No direct effects.
Calcitonin (CT)	Decreases resorption of calcium and phosphate.	Decreases reabsorption of calcium and phosphate. Questionable effect on vitamin D metabolism.	No direct effects.
Vitamin D	Maintains Ca^{2+} transport system.	Decreases reabsorption of calcium.	Increases absorption of calcium and phosphate.

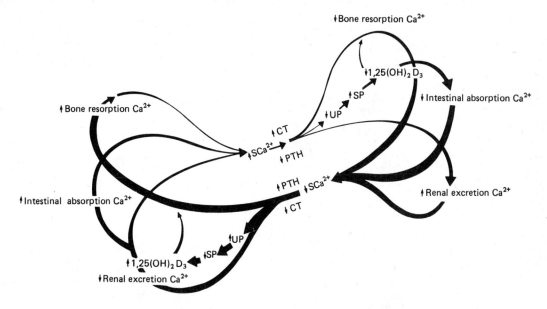

Figure 5–2. Regulation of calcium homeostasis. Three overlapping control loops interlock and relate to one another through the level of blood concentrations of ionic calcium, PTH, and CT. Each loop involves a calciotropic hormone target organ (bone, intestine, kidney). The limbs on the left depict physiologic events that increase the blood concentration of calcium (SCa²⁺), and the limbs on the right, events that decrease this concentration. (UP, urine phosphorus; SP, serum phosphorus.) See text for detailed descriptions. (Modified and reproduced, with permission, from Arnaud CD: Calcium homeostasis: Regulatory elements and their integration. Fed Proc 1978;37:2557.)

acts primarily to maintain the cellular calcium transport system in the intestine, which causes the active extrusion of calcium against a concentration gradient from the interior of the cell (ionized calcium concentration = 10^{-7} to 10^{-6} mol/L), across the antiluminal membrane, and into the extracellular fluid (ionized calcium concentration = 10^{-3} mol/L) (Figure 5–4). Thus, the calciotropic hormones, especially PTH and $1,25(OH)_2D_3$, are interdependent. The renal produc-

tion of $1,25(OH)_2D_3$ depends upon the prevailing concentration of PTH in the blood, and the ability of PTH to increase plasma calcium depends upon a calcium transport system maintained by $1,25(OH)_2D_3$.

Interrelationship of Calcium & the Calciotropic Hormones

The relationships among the several components involved in maintaining mineral homeostasis are il-

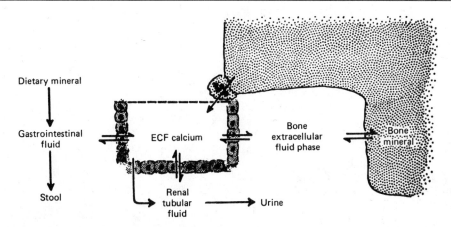

Figure 5–3. Cellular barrier separating the extracellular fluid compartment from the intestinal and renal tubular lumens and from the bone fluid compartment. PTH, CT, and $1,25(OH)_2D_3$ act on these cells (directly or indirectly) to regulate the flow of calcium into and out of the extracellular fluid (ECF) compartments. (See Figure 5–2.) (Reproduced, with permission, from Rasmussen H et al: Effects of ions upon bone cell function. Fed Proc 1970;29:1190.)

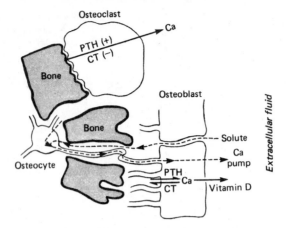

Figure 5–4. Relationships among calciotropic hormones, bone cells, and calcium transport. Bone crystal is represented by the shaded areas. The osteoclast, with an active "ruffled border," is shown resorbing bone—a process stimulated by PTH (+) and inhibited by CT (–). The "osteoblasts" (perhaps better called "surface osteocytes") are not forming bone but are actively extruding calcium from the bone fluid (between cells and crystals) under the influence of hormones. Processes connecting deep osteocytes are shown participating in transport of calcium (dotted arrows).

lustrated in Figure 5–2. Each of the three overlapping feedback loops involves one of the target organs of the calciotropic hormones and the four controlling elements, ie, plasma calcium, PTH, CT, and 1,25 $(OH)_2D_3$. The left limbs of the loops depict physiologic events that increase plasma calcium; the right limbs depict events that decrease plasma calcium. Under physiologic conditions, there are small fluctuations in plasma calcium. Decreases in plasma calcium increase PTH secretion and decrease CT secretion. These changes in hormone secretion lead to increased bone resorption, decreased renal excretion of calcium, and increased intestinal calcium absorption via PTH stimulation of $1,25(OH)_2D_3$ production (left side of Figure 5–2). As a consequence of these events, plasma calcium rises slightly above its physiologic concentrations, inhibiting PTH secretion and stimulating CT secretion. These changes in plasma hormone concentrations decrease bone resorption, increase renal excretion of calcium, and decrease intestinal absorption of calcium (right side of Figure 5–2), causing plasma calcium to fall below the physiologic level. This sequence of events probably occurs within milliseconds, so that plasma calcium is maintained at physiologic levels with minimal oscillation. The "butterfly" scheme in Figure 5–2 not only demonstrates the relationships among elements that control mineral homeostasis under physiologic conditions but also suggests how potential pathogenic mechanisms and adaptive responses elicited by disease or treatment would operate in this system.

Plasma Calcium & Phosphate

A. Calcium: The circulating forms of calcium and phosphorus and their normal ranges are shown in Figure 5–5. Calcium is distributed in three major

fractions: ionized, protein-bound, and complexed. The ionized fraction (Ca^{2+}), which is the only biologically active form, constitutes 46–50% of the total calcium. The protein-bound fraction, roughly equivalent to the ionized fraction in amount, is biologically inert. However, the calcium bound to albumin (80%) and globulin (20%) is an important source of readily available Ca^{2+}; since the binding of calcium to these proteins obeys the mass-law equation, calcium can dissociate from its binding sites as a first line of defense against hypocalcemia. Moreover, hyperproteinemia (eg, hyperglobulinemia in myelomatosis)

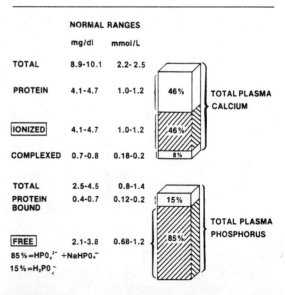

Figure 5–5. Distribution and normal ranges of calcium and phosphorus in the plasma.

can increase, and hypoproteinemia (eg, hypoalbuminemia in cirrhosis of liver and nephrosis) can decrease total plasma calcium without changing the concentration of ionized calcium. Formulas such as the following have been developed to estimate the percentage of calcium bound to the plasma proteins based on the differential binding affinities of albumin and globulin: Such formulas permit the calculation of diffusible calcium (see below) by subtracting protein-bound from total calcium. Estimates of this type can be inadequate, however, especially in patients with low plasma protein concentrations. The only means of accurately determining the plasma concentration of ionized calcium in hypo- or hyperproteinemic states is to measure it directly using an ion-sensitive electrode procedure. The fraction of calcium that is complexed to organic (eg, citrate) and inorganic (eg, phosphate or sulfate) acids is small (approximately 8%) and, like the ionized fraction, it is ultrafiltrable (diffusible). Complexed calcium probably has little quantitative importance as a reservoir for ionized calcium, but excessive complexing of calcium with phosphate may contribute to the decrease in plasma ionized calcium observed in states of hyperphosphatemia such as may exist in chronic renal failure.

The normal range for the serum calcium (Figure 5–5) is small (1.2 mg/dL; 0.3 mmol/L)) compared with the total serum calcium (8.9–10.1 mg/dL; 2.2–2.5 mmol/L), and the same is true for the ionized fraction. Assuming that plasma protein concentrations are normal, values for total calcium below 8.9 mg/dL (2.2 mmol/L) reflect clinically significant hypocalcemia, and values above 10.1 mg/dL (2.5 mmol/L) reflect hypercalcemia. In recent years, serum calcium has been measured with reasonable accuracy in most clinical laboratories. However, stored plasma samples may yield artifactual decreases in circulating calcium concentrations, and contaminated serum samples may yield artifactual increases. Thus, in order to obtain reliable measurements of calcium, it is important to use fresh serum and to eliminate sources of contamination (eg, chalk writing boards) from the laboratory.

The plasma calcium concentration varies little in spite of major changes in dietary calcium because of the adaptive alterations made by the endocrine system regulating this mineral (Figure 5–2). Minor diurnal changes (decreases in the afternoon) have been recorded. In addition, plasma calcium decreases with age in men but not in women, probably owing to a decrease in the serum albumin in men. Total (but not ionized) serum calcium also decreases in pregnancy; this change may be due to the decrease in the serum albumin concentration in this condition.

1. Hypocalcemia– Hypocalcemia produces a myriad of symptoms; severe hypocalcemia can result in tetany and, occasionally, convulsions (see Hypoparathyroidism).

2. Hypercalcemia– Hypercalcemia can produce functional changes in most organ systems, and these changes may lead to a variety of symptoms and objective findings (see Hyperparathyroidism).

B. Phosphorus: Only 15% of the plasma phosphate is bound to proteins in the blood (Figure 5–5). The rest is ultrafiltrable and consists mainly of free HPO_4^{2-} and $NaHPO_4^-$ (85%), with free $H_2PO_4^-$ making up the remainder (15%). By convention, plasma phosphate is expressed in terms of the amount of elemental phosphorus measured.

Compared with calcium concentration, the serum phosphorus concentration has a wider range of normal (2.5–4.5 mg/dL; 0.81–1.45 mmol/L)) (Figure 5–5). Moreover, increases or decreases in dietary phosphorus are promptly reflected in corresponding increases or decreases in serum phosphorus and urinary phosphorus excretion. Marked diurnal variations in serum and urinary phosphorus excretion occur (both may as much as double in the afternoon and evening), even in fasting subjects. These variations are caused in part by diurnal changes in plasma cortisol. Serum phosphorus concentrations in young children are almost double those in adults, and in women they increase slightly with age. The reason for these differences in children and in aging women is poorly understood but may be associated with the increased bone turnover present in both of these groups.

Serum phosphorus can be measured accurately and precisely in most laboratories. However, artifactually high levels may be obtained (1) if serum extracts or dialysates are exposed to acid longer than is prescribed (resulting in the hydrolysis of organic compounds containing phosphorus), or (2) if hemolyzed serum is used (red blood cells contain phosphorus).

1. Hypophosphatemia– Acute respiratory alkalosis, the administration of a large quantity of carbohydrate, and the administration of insulin all cause a rapid decrease in serum phosphorus. Severe hypophosphatemia (< 1.5 mg/dL; 0.48 mmol/L) may occur during the treatment of diabetic ketoacidosis or during forced nutrition of undernourished patients and can cause both skeletal myopathy and cardiomyopathy. Hypophosphatemia may lead to rhabdomyolysis, as evidenced by increases in serum creatine kinase. The levels of 2,3-diphosphoglyceric acid and ATP in erythrocytes may also decrease; the decrease in 2,3-diphosphoglyceric acid in turn may decrease oxygen delivery to tissues, and the decrease in ATP may cause hemolytic anemia. Chronic moderate hypophosphatemia frequently results in osteomalacia or rickets, as seen in X-linked hypophosphatemia, a genetic disorder (see Osteomalacia). Generally, restoration of serum phosphate concentrations to normal levels corrects the abnormal organ function caused by hypophosphatemic conditions, except in X-linked hypophosphatemic rickets, which requires individualized treatment regimens.

2. Hyperphosphatemia– Acute, severe hyperphosphatemia—as might be induced by intravenous phosphate infusion—can cause hypocalcemia severe enough to result in tetany and even death. The less severe hyperphosphatemia induced by phosphate ingestion rarely causes symptoms; however, if patients have associated disorders in which there is a tendency toward hypocalcemia (eg, mild hypoparathyroidism or chronic renal failure), frank hypocalcemia may be precipitated.

Interrelationship of Plasma Calcium & Phosphate

The physiologic importance of the relationship between the circulating concentrations of ionized calcium and diffusible (free) phosphate is poorly understood, especially with regard to the formation and dissolution of amorphous calcium phosphate (Ca_3 $[PO_4]_2$) and hydroxyapatite ($Ca_{10}[PO_4]_6[OH]_2$) in bone. However, available evidence indicates that the ion product of normal plasma concentrations of calcium and phosphate (the calcium $\times$ phosphate product) is considerably higher than that necessary to form these two compounds. Thus, compared with bone, plasma is supersaturated with calcium and phosphate, and this can be considered an important driving force in bone mineralization. The positive effect of vitamin D on bone mineralization is probably indirect and resides in its ability to maintain the calcium $\times$ phosphate product in the normal range by increasing absorption of calcium and phosphate in the gut and resorption of calcium and phosphate from bone (Figure 5–2).

The biologic significance of the calcium $\times$ phosphate product has been questioned in recent years, but it is important to recognize that products below 20 mg/dL (0.7 mmol/L) usually reflect a mineralization defect in bone, and products above 70 mg/dL (2.2 mmol/L) reflect a propensity toward soft tissue calcification. There are exceptions to these numerical guidelines, but short of directly measuring changes in bone formation in bone biopsy specimens or changes in calcium content in soft tissues, the calcium $\times$ phosphate product may be the best indirect indicator of the presence of these pathologic changes.

Calcium & Phosphate Economy

The quantitative aspects of calcium and phosphorus metabolism under conditions of metabolic balance (dietary intake equal to urinary and fecal excretion) are illustrated in Figures 5–6 and 5–7, respectively. The amounts of dietary calcium and phosphate required to maintain metabolic balance vary with the physiologic need for these minerals, the ability of the intestine to absorb them, and the ability of the kidneys to conserve them.

Normally, young adults (ages 21–35 years) require a dietary intake of 15–20 mg/kg/d of calcium and 15–20 mg/kg/d of phosphorus. During periods of rapid skeletal growth (eg, in children or during the development of the fetal skeleton in pregnant women) these requirements may double or triple. In adults aged 50 years and older, calcium requirements tend to increase because the efficiency of intestinal calcium absorption declines. Postmenopausal women and most elderly men need to ingest approximately 50% more calcium than do young adults. Unfortunately, even this level of dietary calcium may not compensate for the inefficient intestinal absorption of calcium in many elderly persons.

Dietary deprivation of calcium or phosphorus induces adaptive changes in the production and secretion of the calciotropic hormones that minimize the development of negative metabolic balance of calcium and phosphate ions. Like most adaptive mechanisms in biology, these changes are beneficial over a relatively short period of time but, when present chronically, can have considerable destructive effects. In the case of calcium, only 30–50% of ingested calcium is normally absorbed (Figure 5–6). With decreased intake, serum calcium decreases slightly, and the sequence of events depicted in the left limbs of the feedback loops in Figure 5–2 is activated. In severe, chronic dietary calcium deficiency in normal subjects, PTH stimulates an increase in plasma $1,25(OH)_2D_3$ levels, which can increase fractional intestinal calcium absorption up to 75%. It also reduces renal calcium excretion to low levels, but this response is quantitatively less important because of the relatively small percentage of filtered calcium excreted. Such changes reduce the overall consequences of this perturbation on overall body calcium economy. However, this adaptive response is offset by the development of chronic hyperparathyroidism, a condition that can induce progressive bone demineralization (see Primary Hyperparathyroidism).

Whereas the intestine plays the major role in the body's adaptation to a dietary deficiency of calcium, the kidney plays the major role in maintaining phosphate balance during dietary deficiency of phosphorus. This is because 70–80% of dietary phosphorus is normally absorbed and practically all (80% or more) of absorbed phosphorus is excreted by the kidney (Figure 5–7). Thus, any increase in intestinal absorption of phosphorus in response to dietary deficiency would have little influence in preventing a negative balance, but a decrease in renal excretion of phosphorus by only 50%, for example, would have an effect comparable to that of almost tripling dietary intake. Reductions of this and greater magnitude occur rapidly and are sustained for long periods in response to dietary deficiency of phosphorus. The mechanisms involved in this response are not entirely understood. The hypophosphatemia that occurs in phosphate deficiency is associated with increased production of $1,25(HO)_2D_3$, increased intestinal absorption of calcium, mild hypercalcemia and a decrease in PTH secretion (Figure 5–2, left, middle limb), increased

Calcium Pools at Balance

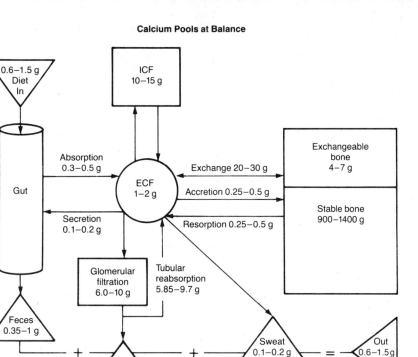

Figure 5–6. Normal distribution of calcium in the body. (ICF, intracellular fluid; ECF, extracellular fluid.)

renal tubular reabsorption of phosphate, and hypophosphaturia. However, it is well established that efficient renal phosphate conservation in response to dietary phosphate deprivation occurs in parathyroidectomized animals; this finding casts doubt upon the hypothesis that the calciotropic hormone response to phosphorus deprivation alone is responsible for the observed hypophosphaturia in hypophosphatemia.

Magnesium Homeostasis

Magnesium is the major intracellular divalent cation. Its extracellular concentration is normally maintained within a reasonably narrow range (1.5–2.2 mg/dL; 0.6–0.9 mmol/L), but, whereas diets low in calcium do not lead to appreciable hypocalcemia, dramatic decreases in serum magnesium can be observed in humans whose diets are deficient in magnesium for as little as 1 week. Thus, despite the presence of appreciable stores of magnesium in cells and bone, it is not readily available; serum concentrations of magnesium are greatly dependent upon adequate dietary supplies and normal intestinal absorption. Increased renal conservation of magnesium is an almost immediate response to dietary deficiency of magnesium. This response is thought to be due to an effect of PTH on the renal tubule similar to that which PTH exerts on the renal tubular reabsorption of calcium. Like hypocalcemia, mild to moderate hy-

pomagnesemia stimulates PTH secretion, albeit to a lesser extent, indicating the presence of at least the rudiments of a negative feedback system that can potentially maintain extracellular magnesium homeostasis. The feedback system is complicated, however, because severe hypomagnesemia (< 1 mg/dL; 0.41 mmol/L) inhibits both PTH secretion and action, causing hypocalcemia and hyperphosphatemia (see Hypoparathyroidism).

PARATHYROID HORMONE

Structure & Biosynthesis

PTH is an 84-amino-acid, linear polypeptide with a molecular weight of 9500. Its biosynthesis and intracellular processing are complex (Figure 5–8). The original gene product of the parathyroid cell is a 115-amino-acid precursor called preproparathyroid hormone (preproPTH). The hydrophobic 23-amino-acid "pre" sequence acts to bind the polyribosome-precursor complex to the endoplasmic reticulum, providing access to the cisternal space and, presumably, to the enzyme ("clipase") that removes the "pre" sequence, leaving the 90-amino-acid proPTH structure. The proPTH is converted to PTH in the Golgi apparatus by proteolytic removal ("tryptic clipase") of the remaining 6-amino-terminal amino acid sequence. Here, the 84-amino-acid polypeptide is readied for

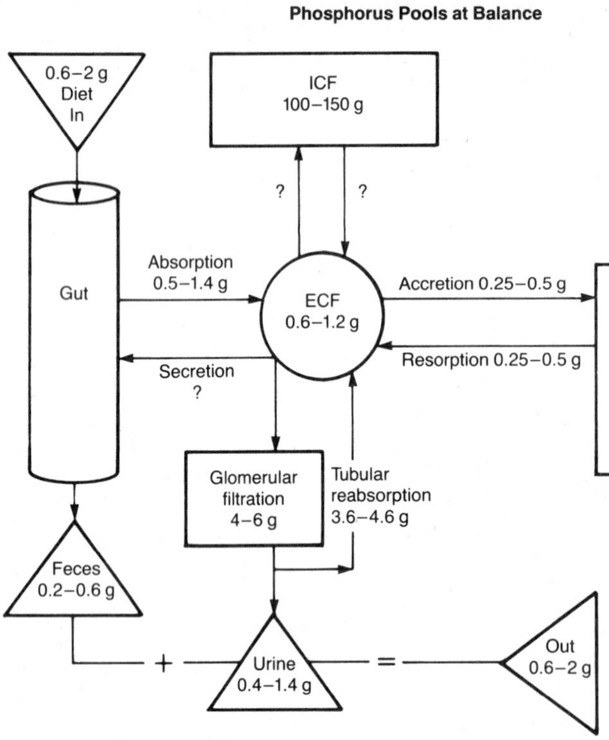

Phosphorus Pools at Balance

Figure 5–7. Normal distribution of phosphorus in the body. (ICF, intracellular fluid; ECF, extracellular fluid.)

secretion either in a secretory granule or in its free form. Interestingly, recent studies indicate that the full 84-amino-acid PTH sequence is essential for efficient prosequence cleavage and for its secretion; this discovery identifies a long-sought-after function for the carboxyl terminal region of the PTH molecule, which appears to have little if any bioactivity. There is no evidence that either of the PTH precursor molecules or the "pre" or "pro" peptide sequences normally find their way into the circulation. In contrast to the rapid regulation of PTH *secretion,* changes in PTH *biosynthesis* occur slowly. PTH gene expression in rats in vivo appears to be fully suppressed at physiologic concentrations of extracellular calcium, but expression is increased threefold with relatively small decreases in extracellular calcium. On the other hand, $1,25(OH)_2D_3$ in the same animal model system dramatically suppresses PTH gene expression from basal levels by 50% within 6 hours and almost completely at 48 hours.

Intracellular stores of PTH may be regulated by a degradative pathway that is stimulated by high and inhibited by low extracellular calcium. Not only may this degradative pathway provide an important mechanism for regulating PTH economy, but the fragments of the hormone produced during intracellular degradation and secreted from the cell may also provide a major source of the multiple immunoreactive

forms of PTH known to circulate in the blood (see below).

The amino acid sequences of bovine, porcine, and human PTH have been determined (Figure 5–9). The differences among them prevent complete immunologic cross-reactivity. This probably accounts for the difficulties encountered in developing radioimmunoassays for the measurement of human PTH using antisera directed against bovine or porcine peptides. All of the structural information required for full biologic activity of native 84-amino-acid PTH lies in the 34 amino acids at the amino terminus. The active fragments of the bovine and human hormones, multiple fragments of the mid and carboxyl regions of the bovine and human hormones, and recently the full sequence of human parathyroid hormone have been synthesized and are available for investigational use. Studies of the mid and carboxyl region fragments have shown them to be biologically inert.

Control of Secretion

PTH is rapidly released from the parathyroid gland in response to decreases in the plasma ionic calcium. It acts on kidney and bone and indirectly on intestine to restore the concentration of this cation to just above the normal set point (Figure 5–1), which in turn inhibits secretion of the hormone. This negative feedback cycle is depicted in Figure 5–2. The con-

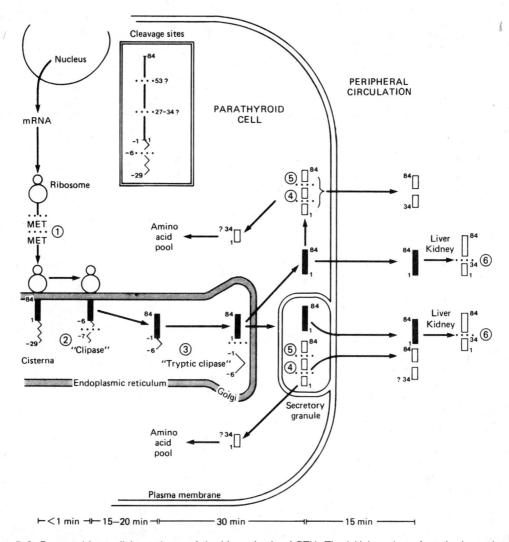

Figure 5–8. Proposed intracellular pathway of the biosynthesis of PTH. The initial product of synthesis on the ribosomes, preproPTH, is converted into proPTH by removal of ① the NH$_2$-terminal methionyl residues (methionyl aminopeptidase) and ② the NH$_2$-terminal sequence (−29 through −7) of 23 amino acids (by "clipase") during synthesis and within seconds afterward, respectively. The conversion of preproPTH to proPTH probably occurs during transport of the polypeptide into the cisterna of the rough endoplasmic reticulum. By 20 minutes after synthesis, proPTH reaches the Golgi region and is converted into PTH by ③ removal of the NH$_2$-terminal hexapeptide. PTH is either stored in secretory granules or released into the cell cytoplasm, where it remains until it is released into the circulation in response to a fall in the blood concentration of calcium. The intact PTH, PTH(1–84), undergoes at least two cleavages while in the secretory granule (and possibly in the cytoplasm) ④ and ⑤. These cleavages generate amino, mid, and carboxyl region fragments. The mid and carboxyl region fragments are secreted into the circulation along with PTH(1–84), whereas the amino region fragments are further degraded by the cell. The PTH(1–84) released into the circulation undergoes metabolic degradation in the liver and kidney ⑥, and this adds to the pool of circulating fragments. The time required for these events to occur is shown. (Modified and reproduced, with permission, from Habener JF et al: Biosynthesis of parathyroid hormone. Recent Prog Horm Res 1977;33:249.)

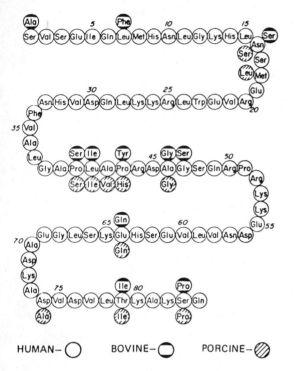

HUMAN— ○   BOVINE— ◐   PORCINE— ◿

Figure 5–9. Parathyroid hormone. The figure shows the structure of human PTH and indicates at which positions the amino acid residues differ for bovine and porcine PTH. (From Keutmann HT et al: Complete amino acid sequence of human parathyroid hormone. Biochemistry 1978;17:5723.)

centration of extracellular ionic calcium is the major regulator of PTH secretion. Other factors influence secretion only indirectly through increasing or decreasing extracellular ionic calcium. The effects of extracellular magnesium concentrations on secretion are qualitatively similar to but physiologically less important than those induced by ionic calcium. Paradoxically, severe, prolonged hypomagnesemia markedly inhibits secretion of PTH and may be associated with hypocalcemia (see above). Known direct PTH secretagogues of questionable physiologic importance include beta-adrenergic agonists, prostaglandins, dopamine, and histamine. These agents, as well as decreased ionic calcium, stimulate the production of cyclic $3',5'$-adenosine monophosphate (cAMP) in parathyroid cells in vitro. cAMP may be a mediator of parathyroid cell secretagogues, but intracellular calcium itself and the phosphoinositol-diacyl-glycerol system appear to be the dominant mediators of extracellular calcium-regulated PTH secretion.

Metabolism & Circulating Forms

Circulating PTH is heterogeneous, consisting of the intact 84-amino-acid polypeptide and multiple fragments of the hormone (Figure 5–10). These frag-

ments are derived from the mid and carboxyl regions of the hormone molecule and thus are likely to be biologically inert. There is no convincing evidence that biologically active fragments are present in the circulation. The relative quantities of intact PTH and its fragments in serum are not known precisely at present, but there are more circulating fragments than intact hormone. This difference is due primarily to the longer survival time of the fragments in the circulation (see Figure 5–10 legend). The fragments are derived both by release from the parathyroid gland and from the degradative metabolism of intact 84-amino-acid PTH (liver and kidney); the quantitative importance of these sources is uncertain. Biologically active PTH normally circulates in the blood at extremely low concentrations (< 50 pg/mL). It is likely that there are individual, constitutionally dependent "set point" values for plasma ionic calcium above which glandular secretion rates are decreased and below which they are increased. However, the steady-state levels of PTH and the size of the glands are probably determined primarily by the degree to which the parathyroid glands must adapt to individual, chronic, environmentally induced changes in the plasma level of ionic calcium (eg, dietary calcium and phosphate). In normal humans, as in lower animals (Figure 5–1), there is an inverse relationship between the fasting levels of serum calcium and serum immunoreactive PTH.

Actions

The major function of PTH is to correct hypocalcemia. As Figure 5–2 shows, it performs this function by (1) conservation of calcium by the kidney, (2) release of calcium from bone, (3) enhanced absorption of calcium from the gut (indirectly via vitamin D), and (4) reduction in plasma phosphate.

A. Effects of PTH on Kidney: PTH acts on the kidney (1) to increase renal tubular reabsorption of calcium and magnesium and (2) to increase phosphate and bicarbonate excretion by inhibiting their proximal tubular resorption. These latter effects have several important indirect effects on the homeostasis of extracellular calcium. Hormone-induced bicarbonaturia tends to produce acidosis, which decreases the ability of circulating albumin to bind calcium, thus increasing ionic calcium by physicochemical means. Hormone-induced phosphaturia ensures that the increased release of phosphate from bone, which occurs obligately during hormone-induced calcium mobilization from bone, does not produce hyperphosphatemia. Increased serum phosphate would tend to complex calcium and thereby counteract the physiologic effect of PTH to increase plasma ionic calcium.

The most important indirect effect of the phosphaturic action of the hormone is illustrated in the intestinal feedback loop in Figure 5–2. PTH, either directly or indirectly by its hypophosphatemic action,

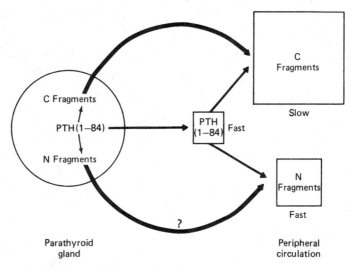

Figure 5–10. Metabolic alterations in PTH(1–84) that result in its immunoheterogeneity in gland extracts and biologic fluids. This scheme is based on study of abnormal parathyroid tissue and hyperparathyroid serum. Data on normal glands and serum are not available. An uncertain proportion of intraglandular PTH(1–84) is proteolytically cleaved into amino-region fragments (N fragments) and carboxyl region fragments (C fragments). All of these PTH molecular species are released into the circulation (approximately 80% PTH[1–84] and 20% fragments). Once in the circulation, PTH(1–84) undergoes proteolytic cleavage in liver and kidney, generating N and C fragments that are added to the circulating pool of hormone fragments. The rate of disappearance of C fragments from the circulation is slow ($t_{1/2}$ 20–40 minutes), whereas that of PTH(1–84) and of N fragments is fast ($t_{1/2}$ < 10 minutes). These differences in metabolic turnover probably account for the large pool of C fragments and small pools of PTH(1–84) and N fragments in the blood under steady-state conditions (see text). (Reproduced, with permission, from DiBella FP et al: Hyperfunctioning parathyroid glands: A major source of immunoheterogeneity of parathyroid in serum. In: Excerpta Medica Int Cong Ser No 421, 1977.)

stimulates renal tubular $25OHD_3$ 1α-hydroxylase to convert the major circulating metabolite of cholecalciferol, $25OHD_3$, to its major biologically active metabolite, $1,25(OH)_2D_3$. This latter compound acts directly on intestinal mucosal cells to increase calcium absorption and on bone to increase resorption.

In the process of stimulating adenylyl cyclase in renal tubular cells (see below), PTH increases urinary excretion of cAMP. Presumably, cAMP is released into the tubular fluid following its intracellular synthesis. Urinary cAMP is increased by administration of other hormones, including epinephrine and glucagon, but its renal production and excretion are almost entirely due to PTH. It can therefore be used as an indirect measure of PTH secretion or action, as noted below.

B. Effects of PTH on Bone: PTH increases the net release of calcium and phosphate from bone into extracellular fluid (Figure 5–4). This is a result of the hormone's effect, direct or indirect, on the differentiation or activities of bone cells (osteogenic precursors, osteoblasts, osteoclasts, and osteocytes). These events appear to depend upon a permissive effect of $1,25(OH)_2D_3$, but the precise cellular mechanism of this important hormonal relationship is poorly understood. The physiology and pathophysiology of mineral metabolism demonstrate a wide range of interactions between PTH (tropic) and vitamin D (per-

missive), and these interactions will be noted below in the sections on hypoparathyroidism, hyperparathyroidism, and metabolic bone disease.

Mechanisms of Action

PTH binds to specific plasma membrane receptors of target cells. These have been cloned recently. The occupied receptors interact with a guanyl nucleotide-regulated membrane-bound protein that in turn activates membrane-bound adenylyl cyclase to convert ATP to cAMP. cAMP, by virtue of its ability to initiate a cascade of enzyme-activated intracellular phosphorylations, is considered to be one of possibly several intracellular "second messengers" responsible for mediating the final expression of the action of the hormone. The details of these enzyme activations and the manner in which they relate to discrete effects of the hormone are unknown. Other potential second messengers of PTH that act in concert with or modulate the actions of cAMP include intracellular free calcium and products of the phosphatidylinositol hydrolysis pathway.

Information concerning the structural requirements for the action of PTH at the site of its receptor is rapidly becoming available. The region of the molecule essential for receptor binding is the amino acid sequence 25–30, and for receptor activation, the 1–7 sequence. Two analogues of bovine PTH that are truncated at the amino terminus have been developed. One of these is ^{8}Nle-^{18}Nle-^{34}Tyr-bPTH(3–34) amide, or bPTH(3–34)amide. This analogue has both agonist and antagonist properties in vitro. It binds to PTH receptors in the kidney to the same degree as bPTH(1–34) but is much less potent in converting the receptor to the high-affinity state necessary to activate adenylyl cyclase. Although bPTH(3–34)amide acts as an antagonist in vitro, it fails to antagonize concomitantly administered PTH in vivo. The other analogue, ^{34}Tyr-bPTH(7–34) amide, has antagonist but no agonist properties in vitro. It antagonizes PTH in vivo, but large doses are required, possibly owing to the fact that its ability to bind to PTH receptors is weak. In spite of this, the development of this analogue represents an important advance in the effort to design a PTH antagonist that can rapidly reverse hypercalcemia in patients with severe hyperparathyroidism.

Assay in Biologic Fluids

A. Immunoassay: At present, all available antisera that have sufficiently high affinity for PTH to be useful in radioimmunoassays are multivalent and contain antibodies directed at multiple regions of the PTH molecule. Whereas antisera directed primarily against the mid or carboxyl region of the PTH molecule recognize both inactive mid- or carboxyl region fragments and intact biologically active PTH, antisera directed against the amino region recognize only amino-region fragments and intact PTH. Because the quantities of mid- and carboxyl region fragments in the circulation are greater than those of amino-region fragments or intact PTH, values for serum iPTH are higher in mid and carboxyl region assays than in amino-region assays.

Mid and carboxyl region assays have provided surprisingly good diagnostic tools in the evaluation of patients suspected of having parathyroid disease, even though the resulting values for serum iPTH primarily reflect circulating biologically inactive hormone (ie, mid and carboxyl region fragments). This is fortunate because concentrations of intact PTH in the circulation are so low that, with rare exception, they are beyond the sensitivity limits of all the amino-region radioimmune assays.

Two-site immunoradiometric or chemiluminometric assays for circulating intact PTH have been reported as having a clinical diagnostic potential similar to that of mid and carboxyl region assays except that, as expected, patients with chronic renal failure have relatively lower values compared to normal subjects than when mid and carboxyl region assays are used. Because of the high sensitivity and ease with which such assays can be performed, it is likely that they will replace classic radioimmunoassay procedures.

B. Bioassay: Until recently, bioassays for PTH lacked sufficient sensitivity for the study of circulating PTH. This obstacle has now been overcome by two novel approaches. One is cytochemical bioassay that is based on the PTH-specific stimulation of glucose 6-phosphate dehydrogenase in guinea pig renal slices. This assay is extremely sensitive, measuring femtogram amounts of PTH. Its disadvantage is its technical complexity. The other assay, which is more convenient, uses a nonhydrolyzable analogue of guanosine triphosphate—ie, 5'-guanyl-imidodiphosphate, or Gpp(NH)p—to greatly augment the sensitivity of adenylyl cyclase to PTH in canine kidneys in vitro. In the presence of Gpp(NH)p, as little as 10 pg/mL of intact PTH elicits significant stimulation. However, even with this sensitivity, the measurement of PTH in normal serum requires the immunoextraction of 3 mL of serum.

CALCITONIN

Structure & Biosynthesis

Calcitonin (CT), a 32-amino-acid polypeptide with a molecular weight of 3700 and a disulfide bridge between residues 1 and 7 (Figure 5–11), is biosynthesized and secreted by the ultimobranchial (parafollicular, "C") cells. Human CT is cleaved from a high-molecular-weight precursor that also contains two other peptides, katacalcin and calcitonin gene-related peptide (CGRP). These peptides circulate in normal subjects in roughly equimolar relationship to CT and, like CT, are secreted in excess in medullary carcinoma of the thyroid. The physiologic roles of these peptides are not known, but CGRP is a potent vasodilator.

The ultimobranchial cells develop from neural crest tissue during embryonic life. They form a discrete organ in submammalian vertebrates called the ultimobranchial gland. In the mammal, the anlage of the cells merges with the embryonic thyroid gland, ultimately becoming dispersed in the central region of each lobe (of the thyroid gland), adjacent to the follicular cells.

The amino acid sequences of CT from many species (porcine, bovine, human, rat, salmon, eel) have been determined (Figure 5–11). They are different enough so that immunologic cross-reactivity between them is incomplete. In fact, radioimmunoassay of human CT was not possible until synthetic human CT became available so that specific antibodies directed against it could be used. The entire CT molecule is required for full biologic activity, as is the intact 1–7 disulfide bridge. Salmon CT has an amino acid sequence markedly different from those of mammalian CTs and is about 30 times more potent. Synthetic salmon and human CTs are commercially available and can be used for treatment of metabolic bone disease (see Osteoporosis and Paget's Disease, below).

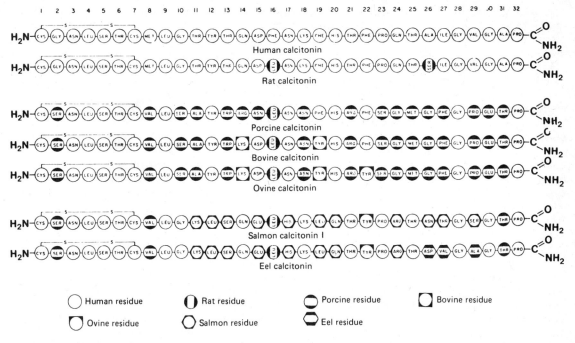

Figure 5–11. Amino acid sequence of CTs. Note the similarity between human and rat CT and the substantial differences in amino acid sequence from the porcine, bovine, and ovine CTs. Salmon and eel CTs are actually more similar to human CT than are hormones from ungulates. In the seven amino acids in the N-terminal ring, the only substitution is serine for glycine. (Modified and reproduced, with permission, from Hirsch PF: Thyrocalcitonin and its role in calcium regulation in mammals. J Exp Zool 1971;178:139.)

Control of Secretion

CT is rapidly released by the "C" cells in response to small increases in plasma ionic calcium. It acts on kidney and bone to restore the level of this cation to just below a normal set point, which in turn inhibits secretion of the hormone (Figure 5–2). CT thus is a physiologic antagonist of PTH. The hormones act in concert to maintain the normal concentration of ionic calcium in extracellular fluid (Figure 5–2).

There is a positive correlation between plasma calcium and plasma immunoreactive CT (iCT) in normal subjects when plasma calcium is increased above the normal range (by oral calcium ingestion). Induced hypercalcemia causes an increase in plasma iCT in about 40–60% of normal women and 70–80% of normal men. Although pentagastrin injection also increases plasma iCT, it is unlikely that gastrin is a physiologic CT secretagogue. Other CT secretagogues of unknown physiologic significance include glucagon, beta-adrenergic agonists, and alcohol.

Metabolism & Circulating Forms

CT exists in several molecular forms both in ultimobranchial tissue and in plasma. In contrast to PTH, however, the major circulating species are not hormone fragments but consist of as many as four or five immunoreactive forms with molecular weights larger than 32-amino-acid CT. It is likely that some

of these forms are polymers of CT with interchain disulfide molecular linkages. The different antisera used in radioimmunoassays recognize these forms differently, and therefore the normal range for plasma CT must be established for each assay. The plasma concentrations of monomeric iCT are extremely low (< 50 pg/mL).

Actions

The importance of CT in the calcium homeostasis of adult humans is not established. An excess or deficiency of PTH or vitamin D produces dramatic clinical disorders. In contrast, an excess or deficiency of CT, as occurs in medullary thyroid carcinoma or postthyroidectomy, respectively, produces few discernible and no serious abnormalities of mineral metabolism. The basal plasma levels of CT and its responsiveness to induced hypercalcemia or pentagastrin injection are lower in women than in men. In adult humans, CT may function primarily to restrain the bone resorptive effects of PTH. When bone turnover rates are high, CT administration rapidly produces hypocalcemia and hypophosphatemia. These effects are largely due to decreased bone resorption secondary to inhibition of activities of bone-resorbing cells (osteoclasts). CT also increases urinary calcium and phosphate, but its action on the kidney is transient and variable. Current evidence does not support a direct effect of CT on the intestinal absorption of calcium. However, several recent reports suggest that the hormone may have a negative influence on the renal production of 1,25 $(OH)_2D_3$. Such an effect would be consistent with the concept of CT as a physiologic antagonist of PTH.

Mechanisms of Action

CT receptors have been cloned and demonstrated in many cell types, including renal tubular cells and osteoclasts. The hormone stimulates adenylyl cyclase in bone and kidney in some species (human and rat), but whether cAMP is a major intracellular mediator of CT action has not been established.

Assay in Biologic Fluids

The major tool for measuring CT in biologic fluids has been radioimmunoassay. Antibodies against human CT generally cross-react with rat CT, but antibodies against porcine or bovine CT cross-react poorly with human and rat CT. Although iCT in human plasma is heterogeneous, synthetic human CT is generally used as an assay standard. As with PTH, most antisera to human CT are multivalent, and assays using them measure the different circulating forms of CT differently. Thus, as noted above, the normal ranges for plasma iCT vary from laboratory to laboratory. An immunoradiometric assay for CT is not available.

The single most important factor determining the clinical utility of a CT radioimmunoassay is its sensitivity. This is because many patients with CT-secreting medullary cancers of the thyroid gland have normal basal levels of plasma iCT and can be identified only with provocative tests (ie, calcium infusion, pentagastrin injection; see below). An assay that cannot measure basal levels of iCT cannot demonstrate an abnormal increase in plasma iCT.

Since the introduction of the original rat hypocalcemic assay for CT, there has been little progress in the development of convenient bioassays for this hormone. Although CT receptors have been demonstrated, radioreceptor assays are too insensitive for the measurement of CT in biologic fluids.

VITAMIN D

Physiology, Metabolism, & Action

It is now firmly established that vitamin D and its metabolites are sterol hormones and that their metabolism and mechanism of action have much in common with those of the other steroid hormones (Figure 5–12). Vitamin D_3 (cholecalciferol) is primarily synthesized in the skin by ultraviolet irradiation of 7-dehydrocholesterol. Vitamin D_2 (ergocalciferol), which is used to fortify dairy products, is produced by ultraviolet irradiation of the plant sterol ergosterol.

A. Activation of Vitamin D: The parent compound, vitamin D, essentially lacks biologic activity and requires metabolic transformation to attain potency.

1. 25-Hydroxylation– The first step in this activation (Figure 5–12) involves 25-hydroxylation by microsomal enzymes–a process that occurs chiefly in the liver. This conversion does not appear to be tightly regulated, and the circulating concentration of 25-hydroxycholecalciferol ($25OHD_3$),* estimated to be about 30 ng/mL in normal individuals, is primarily a function of the bioavailability of vitamin D. Therefore, it is subject to both seasonal and regional variation, owing to differences in both diet and sunlight exposure. $25OHD_3$ is the most abundant circulating form of the hormone, and it is transported in serum bound to a specific globulin (vitamin D-binding protein), as are the other vitamin D metabolites.

2. 1α-Hydroxylation– The next step in the bioactivation of vitamin D, 1α-hydroxylation of $25OHD_3$, occurs in the mitochondria of the renal tubules. This hydroxylation is tightly regulated and constitutes the rate-limiting step in the production of the active metabolite, $1,25(OH)_2D_3$.* Production of $1,25(OH)_2D_3$ is controlled by a number of regulators in accordance with the body's mineral requirements. Hypophosphatemia and hypocalcemia appear to be the primary stimuli for activating renal 1α-hydroxylase. The stimulus created by low calcium levels is probably mediated by PTH, which stimulates 1α-hydroxylase activity either directly or by its hypophosphatemic effects (Figures 5–2 and 5–12). Evidence that CT inhibits the activity of 1α-hydroxylase is less strong. In addition, $1,25(OH)_2D_3$ may regulate its own synthesis directly or by suppressing the parathyroid glands, where receptors for this metabolite have been reported.

B. Concentrations of Vitamin D Metabolites: In normal individuals, $1,25(OH)_2D_3$ is estimated to circulate at concentrations as low as 30 pg/mL. This metabolite is more rapidly cleared from plasma than its more abundant precursor, $25OHD_3$, and is about 100 times more potent in stimulating intestinal calcium absorption. It is thus generally considered to be the major biologic effector of the vitamin D endocrine system. However, the fact that $25OHD_3$ circulates in concentrations 1000 times greater than $1,25(OH)_2D_3$ suggests that $25OHD_3$ may have intrinsic biologic importance as well.

C. Other Hydroxylation Pathways: Hydroxylation of $25OHD_3$ to $24,25(OH)_2D_3$ occurs mainly in the kidney and represents an alternative metabolic fate for $25OHD_3$. The regulation of this pathway generally appears to be reciprocal to that leading to $1,25(OH)_2D_3$: for example, PTH stimulates production of $1,25(OH)_2D_3$ but suppresses that of 24,25

---

*See the footnote at the beginning of this chapter for a comment on the nomenclature of vitamin D metabolites.

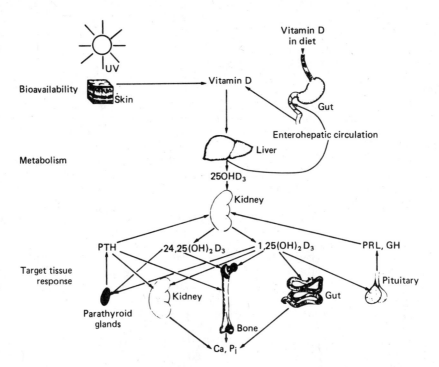

Figure 5–12. The vitamin D endocrine system. **Bioavailability:** Vitamin D is made available to the body by photogenesis in the skin and by absorption from the intestine. Part of the intestinal absorption involves endogenous vitamin D products secreted in bile (enterohepatic circulation). **Metabolism:** Vitamin D must be hydroxylated first in the liver to $25OHD_3$ and then in the kidney to $1,25(OH)_2D_3$ and $24,25(OH)_2D_3$. Other metabolites and other tissues capable of metabolizing the vitamin D metabolites are known. **Target tissue response:** The three principal target tissues are kidney, bone, and intestine, but the parathyroid glands and the anterior pituitary may also be target tissues. Their hormone products (PTH, PRL, and GH) help regulate vitamin D metabolism in the kidney, and PTH, at least, also has independent effects on the regulation of calcium and phosphate homeostasis in bone and kidney. (Reproduced, with permission, from Bikle DD: The vitamin D endocrine system. Adv Intern Med 1982;27:45.)

$(OH)_2D_3$. At present, the physiologic importance of $24,25(OH)_2D_3$ is unclear. It may be involved in normal bone formation, but it is more likely that 24-hydroxylation represents the initial step in the metabolic elimination of $25OHD_3$. Additional vitamin D metabolites have been identified, including $25,26(OH)_2D_3$, $1,24,25(OH)_3D_3$, $1,25,26(OH)_3D_3$, and 25OH-26,23-lactone. Excretion of vitamin D metabolites occurs primarily in the bile, and evidence has been presented for enterohepatic circulation of both $25OHD_3$ and $1,25(OH)_2D_3$.

Role of Vitamin D

It is generally accepted that the principal physiologic role of vitamin D is to increase plasma levels of calcium and phosphate and thus maintain conditions favorable for bone mineralization. The most extensively studied physiologic action of $1,25(OH)_2D_3$, however, is its role in facilitating the absorption of calcium and phosphate by the intestine, and much of our knowledge concerning the molecular mechanism of action of vitamin D has been derived from studies of the intestinal cell. Intestinal cytosolic receptors for

$1,25(OH)_2D_3$ have been demonstrated; they function to translocate the hormone into the cell nucleus, where the association of the hormone-receptor complex with chromatin influences transcription and promotes the production of at least one new protein, calcium-binding protein, which is presumed to facilitate transcellular calcium transport. According to this view, vitamin D acts as a classic steroid hormone; however it has also been suggested that the hormone may have cellular actions independent of de novo protein synthesis.

$1,25(OH)_2D_3$ receptors have also been demonstrated in bone, parathyroid glands, pancreas, pituitary, placenta, and other tissues. It is possible, therefore, that vitamin D acts directly on these tissues. Vitamin D may also have a role, as yet poorly defined, in muscle function. The recent identification of several additional target organs for $1,25(OH)_2D_3$, such as the hematolymphopoietic tissue, suggests a role far beyond its known importance in mineral metabolism. Some lymphomas and granulomatous disorders such as sarcoidosis may show ectopic production of $1,25(OH)_2D_3$ from its precursors, which may explain the hypercalcemia observed in these disorders. $1,25(OH)_2D_3$ may also have a regulatory role in connection with bone marrow stem cells and their progeny, including cells of T lymphocyte lineage.

Assay in Biologic Fluids

Two general approaches using radiolabeled vitamin D derivatives have been developed for measurement of the various vitamin D sterols in vitro: competitive protein-binding analysis and radioimmunoassay. The sensitive technique of competitive protein-binding analysis takes advantage of naturally occurring specific proteins that have high affinity for the vitamin D metabolites and are present either in serum (vitamin D-binding protein) or in intestinal target cells (vitamin D receptors). Both of these techniques involve competition in vitro between a radioligand and the vitamin D sterol of interest for available sites on the binding protein. Antisera for use in radioimmunoassays are developed against immunogenic derivatives of the vitamin D sterol molecule.

Existing competitive protein-binding assays and radioimmunoassays are not inherently specific for a single circulating vitamin D metabolite, because other closely related vitamin D metabolites compete to some extent for available binding sites on the binding protein or antibody. Furthermore, other components of blood, including plasma proteins and lipids, may cause nonspecific interference. To increase the specificity and sensitivity of the assays, it is necessary to first extract the vitamin D sterols from plasma using a suitable lipophilic solvent and then isolate the particular metabolite of interest chromatographically. Simplified, rapid fractionation techniques that have been introduced recently should make the measurement of $25OHD_3$ and $1,25(OH)_2D_3$ more convenient.

A sensitive bioassay for $1,25(OH)_2D_3$ has been developed using the hormone's ability to mobilize calcium in embryonic bone organ cultures in vitro as an index of activity. This assay is comparable in sensitivity to competitive protein-binding assays and radioimmunoassays, but the procedure is tedious and requires experience to perform.

DISORDERS OF PARATHYROID FUNCTION

HYPOPARATHYROIDISM

Deficient secretion of PTH is characterized clinically by symptoms of neuromuscular hyperactivity and biochemically by hypocalcemia, hyperphosphatemia, and diminished to absent circulating iPTH.

Etiology

There are three major categories of PTH-deficient hypoparathyroidism: surgical, idiopathic, and functional.

Surgical hypoparathyroidism is the most common type. It may occur after any surgical procedure in which the anterior neck is explored, including thyroidectomy, removal of abnormal parathyroid glands, and excision of malignant neck lesions. Parathyroid glands need not actually be removed for hypoparathyroidism to ensue; in such cases, it is presumed that the blood supply to the parathyroid glands has been interrupted. Surgical hypoparathyroidism is relatively unusual (0.5–1%) when experienced surgeons perform neck explorations and when such procedures are quick and easy; however, the incidence increases alarmingly with surgical inexperience or with prolonged, extensive procedures requiring frequent blood vessel ligation.

Idiopathic hypoparathyroidism is a broad category of disorders undoubtedly with more than one cause. It can be divided into two subcategories depending on the age at onset: that occurring at an early age and that occurring late in life. Aside from congenital absence of the glands (as in DiGeorge's syndrome), the syndromes occurring at an early age are of genetic origin, usually with an autosomal recessive mode of transmission. This type of hypoparathyroidism is termed "multiple endocrine deficiency-autoimmune-candidiasis (MEDAC) syndrome" or "juvenile familial endocrinopathy" or "hypoparathyroidism-Addison's disease-mucocutaneous candidiasis (HAM) syndrome" (see Chapter 21). Circulating autoantibodies specific for parathyroid and adrenal tissue are frequently present but correlate poorly with clinical manifestations. Candidiasis is usually the first problem to appear (early childhood) and is resistant to both local antifungal measures and treatment of endocrine deficiencies. Hypoparathyroidism generally occurs about 4 years after the onset of candidiasis, at a mean age of 9 years, and Addison's disease about 5 years later, at a mean age of 14 years. Pernicious anemia (with autoantibodies to parietal cells and intrinsic factor), ovarian failure, and autoimmune thyroiditis with hypothyroidism and diabetes mellitus also occur in this category of patients. Sporadic cases of MEDAC syndrome have been reported; in most of these cases, patients are seen at a later age, and some have hypoparathyroidism only.

The late-onset form of idiopathic hypoparathyroidism occurs sporadically without circulating glandular autoantibodies. Except for rare instances of hemochromatotic and metastatic involvement, the cause of parathyroid gland destruction in these cases is unknown.

Functional hypoparathyroidism occurs in patients who have undergone long periods of hypomagnesemia. Such patients include those with selective defects in gastrointestinal magnesium absorption, generalized gastrointestinal malabsorption, or alcoholism. Since magnesium is required for PTH release from the glands, serum iPTH is characteristically low or undetectable. Hypocalcemia is also present. Treatment with magnesium salts is followed within minutes by an increase in serum iPTH and, ultimately, by restoration of eucalcemia. Magnesium is probably also required for the peripheral action of PTH, and hypocalcemia in patients with functional hypoparathyroidism may be partly due to failure of the hormone to act normally on its target tissues.

Less well understood is the neonatal hypoparathyroidism in infants of mothers with primary hyperparathyroidism. It is thought that in utero exposure to maternal hypercalcemia results in prolonged suppression of fetal parathyroid glands and failure of the parathyroid glands to respond to hypocalcemic stimuli after birth.

Pathology

Although it has not been documented, it is likely that small remnants of viable parathyroid tissue are present in many patients with surgical hypoparathyroidism. Patients with MEDAC syndrome may have lymphocytic infiltration and fibrosis of glands. In the few patients with late-onset idiopathic hypoparathyroidism who have been examined, fatty infiltration, fibrosis, and atrophy have been found.

Long-standing cases of hypoparathyroidism have characteristic soft tissue calcifications in the lens and basal ganglia of the brain. All types of bone cells are diminished, and both formation and resorption surfaces in bone are decreased.

Pathologic Physiology

The pathophysiologic and biochemical consequences of parathyroid gland removal can be appreciated by referring to the "butterfly" diagram (Figure 5–2). In this disease, the right limbs of the three feedback loops predominate, with (1) decreased bone resorption; (2) decreased renal phosphate excretion, increased serum phosphate, decreased $1,25(OH)_2D_3$, and decreased intestinal absorption of calcium; and (3) increased renal excretion of calcium for the prevailing serum concentration of calcium. There is hypocalcemia and usually hyperphosphatemia, if dietary phosphate intake has been normal. Urinary calcium is usually low unless eucalcemia has been restored with treatment. In the latter case, urinary calcium is generally higher than it was before the development of hypoparathyroidism, and it occasionally reaches hypercalciuric levels. Nephrogenous cAMP is decreased (Figure 5–19), but it increases promptly following administration of PTH.

Hypocalcemia and alkalosis (due to decreased bicarbonate excretion; see above), if sufficiently severe, cause increased neuromuscular excitability with consequent tetany and, rarely convulsions. Chronic hypocalcemia per se may also cause (1) basal ganglia calcification and occasional extrapyramidal neurologic syndromes; (2) papilledema and increased intracranial pressure; (3) psychiatric disorders; (4) skin, hair, and fingernail abnormalities; (5) candidal infections; (6) inhibition of normal dental development; (7) lenticular cataracts; (8) intestinal malabsorption; (9) prolongation of the QT and ST intervals of the ECG; (10) in rare cases, 2:1 heart block and, even more rarely, heart failure requiring digitalis and diuretics; and finally (11) increased serum concentrations of creatine phosphokinase and lactic dehydrogenase.

Classification

Parfitt has divided clinical hypoparathyroidism into five categories based primarily on the concentration of serum calcium. Grades 1 and 2 represent patients with no hypocalcemia and inconstant spontaneous hypocalcemia, respectively; grades 3, 4, and 5 represent patients whose serum calcium is below 8.5, 7.5, and 6.5 mg/dL, respectively. The clinical manifestations of hypoparathyroidism depend upon the severity and chronicity of the hypocalcemia.

Clinical Features

A. Neuromuscular Manifestations: In general, the rate of decrease in serum calcium appears to be the major determinant for development of neuromuscular complications (see below) of hypocalcemia. Thus, complications are most likely to occur within 1–2 days after parathyroidectomy, when serum calcium decreases acutely, and at serum calcium values that may be considerably higher (eg, 8 mg/dL; 2 mmol/L) than might be found in patients who have had severe hypocalcemia (eg, 6 mg/dL; 1.5 mmol/L) for long periods. Immediately after neck surgery in the region of the parathyroid glands, and for several days afterward, it is important to observe patients carefully for the development of the clinical signs (see below) heralding tetany rather than to rely on the absolute level of serum calcium.

Nerves exposed to low concentrations of calcium show decreased thresholds of excitation, repetitive responses to a single stimulus, reduced accommodation, and, in extreme cases, continuous activity. Such abnormal neural function occurs spontaneously in both sensory and motor fibers in hypocalcemic states and gives rise to neuromuscular manifestations.

1. Paresthesias– Numbness and tingling may occur around the mouth, in the tips of the fingers, and sometimes in the feet.

2. Tetany– An attack of tetany usually begins with prodromal paresthesias and is followed by spasms of the muscles of the extremities and face. The hands (Figure 5–13), forearms, and, less commonly, the feet become contorted in a characteristic way. First, the thumb is strongly adducted, followed by flexion of the metacarpophalangeal joints, extension of the interphalangeal joints (fingers together),

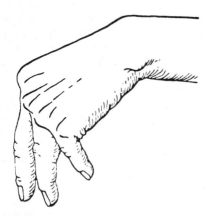

Figure 5–13. Position of hand in hypocalcemic tetany (Trousseau's sign). (Reproduced, with permission, from Ganong WF: *Review of Medical Physiology,* 15th ed. Lange, 1991.)

and flexion of the wrist and elbow joints. This somewhat grotesque spastic condition, although quite painful when full-blown, is more alarming than dangerous.

3. Hyperventilation– Because of the alarm resulting from tetany, patients may hyperventilate and secrete increased amounts of epinephrine. Hyperventilation causes hypocapnia and alkalosis, which in turn worsen hypocalcemia by causing increased binding of ionic calcium to plasma proteins. Prolonged hyperventilation in normal subjects can lower serum ionic calcium and produce tetany, but great care should be exercised in attributing such findings to hyperventilation alone.

4. Adrenergic symptoms– Increased epinephrine secretion produces further anxiety, tachycardia, sweating, and peripheral and circumoral pallor.

5. Convulsions– Patients with hypoparathyroidism may have convulsions. Convulsions are much more common in young people with the disease and are of two types: one is a more generalized form of tetany followed by prolonged tonic spasms; the other is a typical epileptiform seizure (grand mal, jacksonian, focal, or petit mal). The latter type is associated with electroencephalographic findings typical of epilepsy. Because restoration of eucalcemia results in a decrease in the number of seizures without improvement in the electroencephalographic findings associated with seizures, it is thought that hypocalcemia lowers the excitation threshold of preexisting epilepsy. The characteristic electroencephalographic changes associated with hypocalcemia disappear after restoration of eucalcemia. Laryngeal spasm with obstruction may occur during tetany and may precipitate seizures because of hypoxia. The relatively unusual finding of papilledema and increased intracranial pressure resulting from hypocalcemia in association with convulsions mimics the clinical picture of brain tumor.

6. Signs of latent tetany– Latent tetany can be detected by several relatively specific physical signs. **Chvostek's sign** is elicited by tapping the facial nerve just anterior to the ear lobe, just below the zygomatic arch, or between the zygomatic arch and the corner of the mouth. The response ranges from twitching of the lip at the corner of the mouth to twitching of all of the facial muscles on the stimulated side. Simple twitching at the corner of the mouth occurs in 25% of normal subjects, but more extensive muscle contraction (ala nasi and orbital muscles) is a reliable sign of latent tetany.

Trousseau's sign (Figure 5–13) should be sought with a sphygmomanometer cuff. The cuff is inflated to above systolic blood pressure for at least 2 minutes while the hand is observed carefully. A positive response consists of the development of typical carpal spasm (Figure 5–13), with relaxation occurring 5–10 seconds after the cuff is deflated. An apparent spasm that disappears instantly may not be significant. Trousseau's sign is the most reliable sign of latent tetany, and serial tests for it should be performed and the results recorded in the immediate postoperative period after anterior neck surgery.

7. Extrapyramidal signs– Extrapyramidal neurologic syndromes, including classic parkinsonism, occur in patients with chronic hypoparathyroidism. Such manifestations are presumed to be related in some way to the calcification of the basal ganglia that is present in most patients. Many untreated patients without extrapyramidal syndromes are unduly sensitive to the dystonic side effects of phenothiazine drugs, suggesting that basal ganglion calcification may have more general pathologic importance than was once believed. Successful treatment of hypocalcemia may improve the neurologic disorder and is sometimes associated with decreases in basal ganglion calcification on x-ray.

B. Other Clinical Manifestations:

1. Posterior lenticular cataract– This is the most common sequela of hypoparathyroidism. Cataracts must be present and growing for 5–10 years before visual impairment occurs. Fully mature cataracts in hypoparathyroidism are confluent and produce total opacity of the lens. Such cataracts are different from senile cataracts, which are frequently confined to one segment of the lens. Successful treatment of hypocalcemia generally halts the progression of cataracts, and in rare cases the opacities may diminish in size.

2. Cardiac manifestations– Prolongation of the QT interval in the ECG (corrected for rate) is associated with hypocalcemia. Resistance to digitalis, hypotension, and refractory congestive heart failure with cardiomegaly may occur; these are reversed by normalization of the serum calcium.

3. Dental manifestations– Abnormalities in enamel formation, delayed or absent dental eruption, and defective dental root formation with short or blunted roots indicate that hypocalcemia was present during childhood.

4. Malabsorption syndrome– Intestinal malabsorption with steatorrhea is uncommon in hypoparathyroidism but may be present in patients with long-standing untreated disease. It is presumed to be due to decreased serum calcium because it is reversed by successful treatment of hypocalcemia but not by a gluten-free diet. Management is difficult because treatment of hypoparathyroidism largely depends on the ability to increase calcium transport across a normal gastrointestinal tract with drugs.

Diagnosis

A. Serum Calcium: Detection of hypoparathyroidism depends upon being alert to its possible presence in certain clinical situations. Accurate annual measurements of serum calcium are indicated (1) in patients who have had anterior neck surgery or (2) in those suspected of having MEDAC syndrome. Cutaneous candidiasis, cataracts, incidentally discovered calcifications of the basal ganglia, convulsions, numbness and tightening of the fingers, facial muscle spasm (spontaneous or self-induced), delayed dentition, and developmental retardation are all indications for prompt serum calcium measurement.

B. Serum Phosphorus: In the absence of renal failure, the diagnosis of hypoparathyroidism is virtually certain if hypocalcemia and hyperphosphatemia are found. Some patients, however, may be relatively phosphate-depleted because of dietary restriction, malabsorption, or the ingestion of aluminum hydroxide gels. In patients who have undergone parathyroidectomy for primary hyperparathyroidism, osseous avidity for minerals may be so great as to actually produce hypophosphatemia. In the first instance, the exclusion of nonparathyroid disorders as the cause of hypocalcemia becomes important. In the second, the question arises whether hypocalcemia is due to the hypoparathyroidism or to "bone hunger" alone.

C. Serum iPTH: In both circumstances, measurement of serum iPTH is crucial for the correct diagnosis. Increased values in a range appropriate to the degree of hypocalcemia would essentially exclude the presence of hypoparathyroidism and suggest end-organ resistance to PTH (pseudohypoparathyroidism, vitamin D deficiency, vitamin D dependency) or secondary hyperparathyroidism due to such disorders as dietary deficiency of calcium, intestinal malabsorption of calcium, or excessive intake of drugs containing absorbable phosphate (eg, neutral phosphate in the treatment of X-linked hypophosphatemic rickets).

An undetectable serum iPTH confirms the diagnosis of hypoparathyroidism if the assay technique used is sensitive enough to measure serum iPTH in the large majority of normal subjects. Serum iPTH may be detectable in some patients with hypoparathyroidism if the assay employed is very sensitive. Presumably, these patients have grade 1 parathyroid insufficiency. However, it is important to recognize that such low values may be due to nonspecific effects of serum per se in radioimmunoassays that do not adequately control for this factor.

Patients with functional hypoparathyroidism due to hypomagnesemia also have low to undetectable levels of serum iPTH. Identification of these individuals depends upon the measurement of serum magnesium and the demonstration that treatment with magnesium salts restores eucalcemia and increases serum iPTH.

Treatment

A. Rationale: Theoretically, the most appropriate therapy for hypoparathyroidism would be physiologic replacement of PTH. There are practical limitations to this approach, including the need to administer the hormone parenterally and the current high cost of suitable commercial human PTH preparations. Such treatment might become feasible in the future for patients poorly controlled by conventional regimens.

Because of the absence of PTH and the consequent hyperphosphatemia, $25OHD_3$ 1α-hydroxylase, the renal enzyme that converts $25OHD_3$ to $1,25(OH)_2D_3$, is relatively inactive in patients with hypoparathyroidism. Thus, little if any circulating $25OHD_3$ is converted to $1,25(OH)_2D_3$, and there are low to undetectable serum levels of this metabolite. In fact, hypoparathyroid patients are for this reason resistant to pharmacologic doses of vitamin D.

Although lowering of serum phosphate levels with diets low in phosphate (ie, restricting dairy products and meat) and oral aluminum hydroxide gels (to bind intestinal phosphate) might be expected to increase the conversion of $25OHD_3$ to $1,25(OH)_2D_3$, such treatment has received little attention. Rather, treatment with pharmacologic doses of ergocalciferol or its more potent analogue dihydrotachysterol, in combination with oral calcium, has been the mainstay of treatment. Severe hypercalcemia is often a complication of this treatment if serum calcium is not monitored frequently. Serum calcium should be measured weekly at the initiation of treatment with vitamin D, then monthly during dosage adjustment, and at least every 3 months during long-term follow-up. A single episode of vitamin D intoxication can irreversibly impair renal function. Furthermore, toxicity can persist for weeks to months because of the effective tissue storage of vitamin D and its circulating metabolite $25OHD_3$. Treatment of vitamin D intoxication is similar to that described for severe hypercalcemia (discussed below). Hydration is most important, and in some patients corticosteroids (60 mg prednisone or 300 mg cortisone daily in four divided doses), which appear to antagonize vitamin D action, are necessary.

B. Emergency Measures for Tetany: Tetany due to hypoparathyroidism requires emergency treatment with intravenous calcium. The aim is to prevent laryngeal stridor and convulsions. After a patent airway is assured, 10–20 mL of a 10% solution of calcium gluconate (90 mg elemental calcium per 10 mL) should be given slowly (not more than 10 mL/min) until symptoms are relieved or until serum calcium rises above 7 mg/dL (1.75 mmol/L). Hypercalcemia is to be avoided; maintaining calcium at levels between 7.5 and 9 mg/dL (1.9–2.25 mmol/L) is adequate. Caution should be exercised in patients taking digitalis, because calcium potentiates the action of this drug on the heart; electrocardiographic monitoring is thus necessary during intravenous calcium therapy for these patients. Therapy with vitamin D should be initiated as soon as possible (see below). It may be necessary to maintain serum calcium at levels that prevent tetany for several days before vitamin D becomes effective. This is accomplished with the combined administration of oral and intermittent intravenous calcium. Oral calcium is begun as soon as possible, starting with 200 mg of elemental calcium (as calcium carbonate, 40% calcium) every 2 hours and gradually increasing to 500 mg every 2 hours if necessary. If serum calcium falls below 7.5 mg/dL (1.9 mmol/L) after 6 hours of the combined regimen, a continuous calcium infusion should be started. Five hundred milliliters of 5% glucose and water containing 10 mL of 10% calcium gluconate is given over 6 hours initially, with the quantity of calcium increased in increments of 5 mL every 6 hours until satisfactory control is achieved. Anticonvulsive agents (phenytoin, phenobarbital, etc) may be helpful in management of patients with convulsions resistant to calcium therapy and should be given as soon as such resistance is suspected. Phenothiazine drugs should be avoided because they may induce severe dyskinesia.

C. Severe Hypocalcemia ("Hungry Bone" Syndrome): In patients with hyperparathyroidism and bone disease who have undergone successful excision of one or more hyperfunctioning parathyroid glands, hypocalcemia my be profound and resistant to treatment ("hungry bone" syndrome). As much as 10 g of elemental calcium administered intravenously by infusion over 24 hours may be required to increase serum calcium above 7.5 mg/dL (1.9 mmol/L). Such patients are notoriously resistant to vitamin D, but responses are regularly achieved with $1,25(OH)_2D_3$ (calcitriol) in doses ranging from 0.5 to 2 μg daily or with parathyroid hormone (300–1000 units intramuscularly or intravenously). The manufacture of parathyroid extract has been discontinued, but synthetic human PTH(1–34) is now available.

D. Severe Hypoparathyroidism: Most patients with grades 4 and 5 hypoparathyroidism require some form of long-term vitamin D treatment (Table 5–2). Success is usually achieved with the regimen suggested by Parfitt: dihydrotachysterol, 4 mg/d as a single dose for 2 days, then 2 mg/d for 2 days, then 1 mg/d, adjusting this dose as required by serum calcium measurements (1 mg is equivalent to about 120,000 USP units or 3 mg of vitamin D_2). Ideally, serum calcium should be maintained between 8.5 and 9 mg/dL (2.1–2.25 mmol/L). This leaves a margin for an increase in serum calcium to levels that are not dangerous. The major advantage of dihydrotachysterol is its relatively rapid onset of action and short half-life. With regard to the latter, hypercalcemia due to inadvertent overdoses of dihydrotachysterol is relieved within 1–3 weeks after the drug is discontinued, whereas toxicity from vitamin D_2 persists for 6–18 weeks. Dihydrotachysterol offers another advantage in that parathyroid function can be tested relatively soon after withdrawal of the drug. Hypocalcemia within 2 weeks of withdrawal strongly suggests the persistence of hypoparathyroidism. The disadvantage of dihydrotachysterol is that it is more expensive than ergocalciferol.

1. Ergocalciferol (vitamin D_2)– The most commonly available FDA-approved vitamin D preparation is ergocalciferol, or vitamin D_2 (Table 5–2). In initiating treatment with this drug, it is important to prevent hypercalcemia. This can be accomplished consistently by giving small doses in the beginning (0.6 mg/d, or 25,000 units/d) and increasing them gradually after steady-state levels of serum calcium are achieved at each dosage level. However, restoration of eucalcemia in this way sometimes requires an inordinately long time, and it is recommended that high doses (1.25–2.5 mg/d, or 50,000–100,000

Table 5–2. Vitamin D preparations used in the treatment of hypoparathyroidism.

	Potency[1]	How Supplied	Daily Dose (Range)	Time Required for Toxic Effects to Subside
Ergocalciferol (ergosterol, vitamin D_2)	40,000 USP units/mg.	Capsules of 25,000 and 50,000 units; solution, 500,000 units/mL	25,000–200,000 units.	6–18 weeks.
Dihydrotachysterol	120,000 USP units/mg.	Tablets of 0.125, 0.2, and 0.4 mg.	0.2–1 mg.	1–3 weeks.
Calcifediol	. . .	Capsules of 20 and 50 μg.	20–200 μg.	3–6 weeks.
Calcitriol	. . .	Capsules of 0.25 and 0.5 μg.	0.25–5 μg.	½–2 weeks.

[1]Number of units of vitamin D provided by 1 mg of the preparation.

units/d) be given early, tapering to 0.6–1.25 mg/d as serum calcium concentrations approach 9 mg/dL. Most patients can be managed successfully with 1.25–2.5 mg/d. The occasional patient who requires more than 3.75 mg/d (150,000 units/d) is a candidate for the shorter-acting analogues or metabolites of vitamin D.

More information is becoming available concerning the long-term management of hypoparathyroidism with the cholecalciferol metabolites calcifediol and calcitriol. Both appear to be effective and pharmacologically superior to ergocalciferol with respect to rapidity of onset and termination of action, but–except in patients who are particularly difficult to manage–neither seems to offer major advantages over dihydrotachysterol, and both are even more expensive than dihydrotachysterol. The initiation and termination of action appear to be faster for calcitriol than for dihydrotachysterol. Calcitriol has been approved by the FDA for the treatment of hypoparathyroidism.

2. Calcium– Since the major action of vitamin D preparations is to increase intestinal calcium absorption, dietary calcium must be adequate during treatment of hypoparathyroidism. This can be achieved with a total (dietary and supplemental) intake of 1 g or more daily in patients under age 40 and 2 g in patients over age 40. Supplements can be provided by administering calcium as the gluconate, lactate, chloride, or carbonate salt. There are disadvantages for each. Calcium gluconate and lactate tablets contain relatively small quantities of elemental calcium, so that large numbers of tablets must be given. Calcium chloride tablets contain large quantities of calcium but tend to produce gastric irritation. Calcium carbonate (eg, Tums, Oscal) is preferred for most patients. Calcium citrate has been recommended for patients with hypercalciuria, because urinary excretion of the citrate ion may be prophylactic against the development of renal lithiasis.

E. Moderate Hypoparathyroidism: Patients with grade 3 hypoparathyroidism may require only calcium supplementation (1–5 g daily) and moderate degrees of phosphate restriction (combined with aluminum hydroxide gels) to maintain serum calcium in the desired range of 8.5–9 mg/dL. This avoids the risk of vitamin D intoxication and should be tried in appropriate circumstances.

Complications

Apart from hypercalcemia, hypercalciuria may be a complication of successful treatment. Hypercalciuria develops because PTH is no longer maintaining normal renal tubular reabsorption of calcium (Figure 5–2). Accurate measurement of 24-hour urine calcium is therefore necessary to avert possible renal stone formation as serum calcium approaches normal levels during calcium and vitamin D treatment. Thiazide diuretics, which increase renal tubular reab-

sorption of calcium, may be useful in such cases and may have the added advantage of partially restoring eucalcemia. In fact, such treatment has been used successfully without vitamin D in the management of mild hypoparathyroidism.

Prognosis

Long-term restoration of serum calcium to normal or nearly normal ranges usually results in improvement in most manifestations of surgical and idiopathic hypoparathyroidism, including the ocular, neurologic, and dermatologic disorders and associated candidiasis. Unfortunately, the latter appears to persist in MEDAC syndrome, and resolution usually can be achieved only with iodoquinol or with systemic amphotericin B (alone or combined with transfer factor) therapy. Improved surgical techniques and the use of parathyroid autotransplantation in surgery for disorders requiring extensive removal of thyroid or parathyroid tissue may lower the incidence of permanent hypoparathyroidism. Early diagnosis of latent hypoparathyroidism with adequate long-term treatment will lead to a lower incidence of late complications.

PSEUDOHYPOPARATHYROIDISM & PSEUDOPSEUDOHYPO-PARATHYROIDISM

Pseudohypoparathyroidism is a rare familial disorder characterized by target tissue resistance to PTH, hypocalcemia, increased parathyroid gland function, and a variety of congenital defects in the growth and development of the skeleton, including short stature and short metacarpal and metatarsal bones. Patients with pseudopseudohypoparathyroidism have the developmental defects without the biochemical abnormalities of pseudohypoparathyroidism. There are also patients with pseudohypoparathyroidism who have target tissue resistance to the hormone but no developmental abnormalities, and others with developmental abnormalities who experience spontaneous cure of biochemical abnormalities. There are even patients who have developmental abnormalities and clinical hypoparathyroidism in the face of typical osteitis fibrosa cystica. This syndrome is known as pseudohypohyperparathyroidism.

Etiology

Clearly, the complex abnormalities mentioned in the foregoing paragraph cannot be ascribed to a single underlying biochemical defect. Although abnormal target tissue responses to PTH may be the basic disorder, it is likely that defects in any one of a number of limiting steps, from receptor binding of the hormone to final expression of the cellular actions of PTH, could be involved.

At present, the only proved biochemical defect of

this type is one in which the guanyl nucleotide-sensitive regulatory protein that couples PTH-occupied receptors to adenylyl cyclase is decreased by half in the red blood cells, platelets, kidney cells, fibroblasts, and transformed lymphocytes of some patients with pseudohypoparathyroidism (type Ia; see below). In such patients, this defect appears to produce resistance to several other hormones that apparently exert their actions by stimulating the production of increased cellular cAMP (vasopressin, glucagon). Other possible mechanisms, as yet largely untested, include secretion of a biologically inert form of PTH, circulating inhibitors of PTH action, an intrinsic abnormality of PTH receptors, autoantibodies to the PTH receptor, a defect in adenylyl cyclase, a specific and defined disturbance in the process by which PTH alters the distribution of ions across membranes, and abnormalities of cellular protein kinases or other hormone-dependent enzymes (type Ib).

Patients with pseudohypoparathyroidism generally fail to respond normally to the administration of large doses of PTH with an increase in urinary phosphate excretion and in nephrogenous cAMP (type I). A few patients have normal cAMP responses but diminished phosphate responses (type II), whereas others (rarely) may have the reverse. Studies describing these apparently paradoxic findings imply that cAMP may not be involved in all of the biologic actions of PTH. However, these results could also be explained in other ways, including (1) the possibility that urinary excretion of cAMP does not accurately reflect all of the cAMP-related cellular events critical to PTH action and (2) the likelihood that only small changes in intracellular cAMP are required for PTH action.

Serum levels of $1,25(OH)_2D_3$ have been reported to be low in pseudohypoparathyroidism, and defective conversion of $25OHD_3$ to $1,25(OH)_2D_3$ has therefore been suggested as the mechanism involved in abnormal mineral homeostasis in these patients. This argument is supported by reports of success in restoring serum calcium and urinary phosphate excretion to normal levels with administration of $1,25(OH)_2D_3$, but again, other explanations are probably more valid. There is evidence that generation of increased renal tubular cAMP is involved in stimulation of 1α-hydroxylation of $25OHD_3$. If such is the case, one could postulate that normal tissue responsiveness to PTH is necessary for production of $1,25(OH)_2D_3$, and its absence in pseudohypoparathyroidism would account for the low levels of serum $1,25(OH)_2D_3$ in this disease. Furthermore, administration of $1,25(OH)_2D_3$ might be expected to increase the responsiveness of bone to PTH in patients with deficient production of $1,25(OH)_2D_3$ simply because the hypercalcemic action of PTH depends on the presence of biologically active metabolites of vitamin D. Finally, the phosphaturia induced in pseudohypoparathyroidism by $1,25(OH)_2D_3$ administration

could be due to the restoration of eucalcemia; it is well known that phosphaturia occurs when serum calcium is restored toward normal in patients with surgical hypoparathyroidism.

Genetic Basis of Pseudohypoparathyroidism

Although pseudohypoparathyroidism is inherited, its mode of transmission is unclear. The 2:1 female:male ratio of occurrence suggests an X-linked dominant mechanism; however, it is difficult to explain how the developmental defects of pseudohypoparathyroidism can be inherited in the absence of abnormalities in the adenylyl cyclase system. Furthermore, four cases of male-to-male transmission of the developmental defects have been recorded.

Incidence

Pseudohypoparathyroidism and pseudopseudohypoparathyroidism are rare. Most cases are concentrated in a few centers in the USA.

Pathologic Physiology

Qualitatively, the biochemical findings in patients with pseudohypoparathyroidism are identical to those observed in patients with surgical or idiopathic hypoparathyroidism, except that in most patients serum iPTH is increased appropriately for the degree of hypocalcemia. The pathophysiology of the disease is best understood by reference to Figure 5–2. PTH action is blocked in all three of the left limbs of the target tissue feedback loops. The results (in the right limbs) are (1) decreased bone resorption, caused by decreased bone cell responsiveness to PTH; (2) increased serum phosphate, caused by decreased renal tubular responsiveness to the phosphaturic effects of PTH and decreased production of $1,25(OH)_2D_3$ with decreased intestinal calcium absorption; and (3) increased renal excretion of calcium for the degree of hypocalcemia, which is caused again by decreased renal tubular responsiveness to the hypocalciuric effects of PTH. The consequent hypocalcemia stimulates PTH secretion. There is no good explanation for the hypocalcemia in patients with pseudohypohyperparathyroidism who (paradoxically) have osteitis fibrosa cystica and elevated levels of alkaline phosphatase (see below).

In patients with pseudohypoparathyroidism who are hypocalcemic, the parathyroid glands are hyperplastic.

Clinical Features

Most of the symptoms and signs of pseudohypoparathyroidism are the same as those of surgical hypoparathyroidism and idiopathic hypoparathyroidism and are due almost entirely to chronic hypocalcemia. However, there are certain unique developmental features. Many patients are mentally retarded, short and stocky, and obese with rounded faces. Many have one or more short metacarpal or metatarsal bones, which is manifested by formation of a dimple over the head of the involved metacarpals on making a fist. The fingers (especially the fourth and fifth) may be short (Figure 5–14). The calvarium is thickened in one-third of patients, and there may be delayed dentition, defective enamel, and absence of teeth. There may also be exostoses, ectopic ossification, coxa vara or coxa valga, bowing of the radius, tibia, and fibula, and hypothyroidism.

Diagnosis

The diagnosis of pseudohypoparathyroidism is likely when the developmental abnormalities described above are present. When serum calcium and phosphorus are normal in such a patient, the diagnosis of pseudopseudohypoparathyroidism is almost certain, although some of the same abnormalities may be present (occasionally) in patients with Turner's, Gardner's, or basal cell nevus syndrome. If hypocalcemia and hyperphosphatemia are present, the diagnosis of pseudohypoparathyroidism is likely. Increased serum iPTH and markedly diminished phosphaturic and nephrogenous cAMP responses to PTH distinguish pseudohypoparathyroidism from surgical, idiopathic, or functional hypoparathyroidism in patients with equivocal signs or absence of developmental abnormalities. If the serum phosphorus is normal or low in a hypocalcemic patient,

secondary hyperparathyroidism due to vitamin D or dietary calcium deficiency or to intestinal malabsorption of calcium must be excluded. Measurement of serum $25OHD_3$ should be helpful in the first instance, and dietary history or analysis in the second. The third (intestinal malabsorption) may present difficulties because hypocalcemia per se may produce malabsorption, and unless magnesium deficiency is present, patients with primary intestinal malabsorption usually have increased levels of serum iPTH. Therapeutic tests are needed in this situation. When successful treatment of malabsorption with a gluten-free diet restores eucalcemia, the diagnosis is probably gluten-sensitive enteropathy. If correction of hypocalcemia with a regimen used in the treatment of hypoparathyroidism cures the malabsorption syndrome, pseudohypoparathyroidism is a likely diagnosis.

Treatment

The treatment of pseudohypoparathyroidism is identical to that for hypoparathyroidism. No therapy is usually necessary for pseudopseudohypoparathyroidism.

PRIMARY HYPERPARATHYROIDISM

Primary hyperparathyroidism represents an overlapping group of syndromes that are caused by ex-

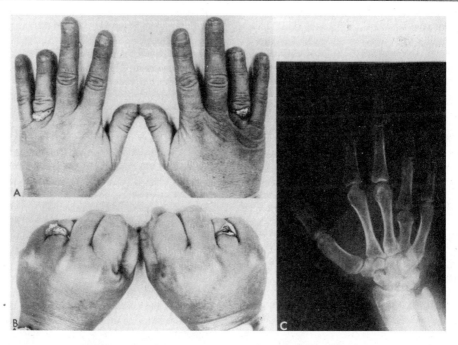

Figure 5–14. Hands of a patient with pseudohypoparathyroidism. **A:** Note the short fourth finger. **B:** Note the "absent" fourth knuckle. **C:** Film shows the short fourth metacarpal. (Reproduced, with permission, from Potts JT: Pseudohypoparathyroidism: Clinical features; signs and symptoms; diagnosis and differential diagnosis. In: The *Metabolic Basis of Inherited Disease,* 4th ed. Stanbury JB, Wyngaarden JB, Frederickson DS [editors]. McGraw-Hill, 1978.)

cessive, relatively uncontrolled secretion of PTH by one or more hyperfunctioning parathyroid glands. Hypercalcemia, the biochemical hallmark of the disorder, fails to inhibit gland activity in the normal manner. Most patients today are relatively asymptomatic and are detected by routine measurements of serum calcium. Symptoms, when present, can be remarkably varied and vague. The classic presentation of nephrolithiasis, osteitis fibrosa cystica, and soft tissue calcification is rare today.

Etiology

The cause of primary hyperparathyroidism is unknown. A genetic factor may be involved, since several families have been described in which the disease is inherited as an autosomal dominant trait. In this regard, a factor with parathyroid mitogenic activity has been reported in the plasma of patients with this genetic disease. Investigations of the incidence of thyroid carcinoma in patients who have had neck irradiation have shown a greater than expected number of cases of primary hyperparathyroidism, implicating this factor as one possible underlying cause. However, it is difficult to interpret such studies because there is little information about the general incidence and natural history of primary hyperparathyroidism.

Calcium infusions in hyperparathyroid patients with mild hypercalcemia incompletely suppress serum iPTH. This strongly suggests that increased hormone secretion in these patients is due, at least in part, to a set point error in the level of ionic calcium at which abnormal tissue is suppressed. This defect has been directly confirmed in vitro. Isolated parathyroid cells from hyperfunctioning glands require higher concentrations of calcium in the medium to decrease PTH secretion than do cells obtained from normal glands.

Incidence

Routine automated measurement of serum calcium has vastly increased detection of primary hyperparathyroidism. In one recent, well-controlled study, the annual rate of disease detection was 3.5 times greater after the introduction of routine screening of serum calcium than it was before. The incidence of primary hyperparathyroidism increases dramatically in both men and women after age 50; it is two to four times more common in women. In a careful epidemiologic study, the age-adjusted incidence was estimated to be 42 per 100,000. However, studies of selected patient populations (with most patients over 40 years of age) have revealed as many as 1:1000 to 1:200 patients with the disease.

Pathology

A. Parathyroid Glands: Histologically, abnormal parathyroid glands from patients with primary hyperparathyroidism have been characterized as being hy-

perplastic, adenomatous, or malignant. Unfortunately, controlled studies of histologic interpretations by pathologists have shown that it is difficult or impossible to distinguish between adenomas and hyperplasia. Furthermore, abnormal but nonmalignant parathyroid tissue may, in rare cases, have many of the histologic features of malignant tissue. Thus, to classify parathyroid lesions, it is generally necessary to rely on gross pathologic features observed during surgery. The surgeon determines the number, size, and gross appearance of abnormal glands present. The pathologist then determines whether biopsy specimens are parathyroid tissue. Single-gland involvement ("adenoma") occurs in about 80% of patients with hyperparathyroidism and multiple-gland involvement ("hyperplasia") in about 20%. The diagnosis of true carcinoma of the gland is based on a combination of gross appearance of the lesion, histologic features, and, ultimately, the biologic behavior of the abnormal tissue. Less than 2% of hyperfunctioning glands are malignant. Familial primary hyperparathyroidism and the hyperparathyroidism associated with multiple endocrine neoplasia almost always involve multiple glands. Abnormal parathyroid glands usually weigh 0.2–2 g (27–75 mg is normal) and have a characteristic yellow-red color and "bulging" appearance in situ. Occasionally, very large glands (> 10 g) are observed. The severity of the clinical manifestations–especially the degree of hypercalcemia–is generally proportionate to the quantity of hyperfunctioning tissue. The predominant cell type in most abnormal glands is the chief cell; it can be arrayed in sheets or cords or may appear in follicles. So-called water-clear cells and oxyphilic cells may be admixed, and in rare cases one of these may predominate. There is no question that the chief cell synthesizes and secretes PTH. The functions of the water-clear and oxyphilic cells are unknown.

B. Bone: In virtually all patients with primary hyperparathyroidism, histomorphometric analysis of bone biopsies of the iliac crest shows the effects of excess PTH on bone. These effects include increased bone resorption surfaces, increased numbers of osteoclasts, osteocytic osteolysis, and, in moderate to severe cases, marrow fibrosis. Only far-advanced disease is associated with classic bone cysts and fractures. These patients have a mineralization defect characterized by large quantities of unmineralized collagen and disorganized (woven rather than lamellar) bone.

C. Kidney: About 20–30% of patients have nephrolithiasis, which is frequently complicated by pyelonephritis. Gross nephrocalcinosis or calcification of the renal papillae is unusual, but microscopic examination of kidneys with special calcium stains has sometimes revealed peritubular and tubular calcifications at autopsy. The incidence of such soft tissue calcification in patients with mild to moderate disease is unknown. However, it may be relatively frequent, since chondrocalcinosis and calcific tendinitis can be demonstrated on x-rays in 7.5–18% of cases.

D. Other Organs: Calcification of other organs such as stomach, lung, and heart and blood vessels has been observed in patients with hyperparathyroid crisis (serum calcium > 15 mg/dL; 3.75 mmol/L).

E. Muscle: Myopathy is relatively common in primary hyperparathyroidism, and muscle biopsy may show neuropathic atrophy of both type I and type II muscle fibers. These histologic changes parallel clinical, neurologic, and neuromuscular dysfunction.

Pathologic Physiology

As might be expected, the constant, incompletely controlled release of PTH from hyperfunctioning parathyroid tissue causes exaggerated physiologic responses in target organs.

A. Hypercalcemia: Because the excess PTH stimulates the transport of calcium into the blood from the intestinal and renal tubular lumens as well as from bone (Figure 5–2), the intestine and kidney are unable to correct the hypercalcemia. Thus, patients with primary hyperparathyroidism, in contrast to those with other (nonparathyroid) hypercalcemic diseases, lack the first lines of defense against hypercalcemia, ie, increased renal and intestinal loss of calcium. Early in the course of the disease, when serum calcium values are less than 11.5 mg/dL (2.88 mmol/L) (normal range, 8.9–10.1 mg/dL [2.23–2.53 mmol/L]), urinary calcium can be relatively low for the degree of hypercalcemia. It is only when serum calcium values are greater than 12 mg/dL (3 mmol/L), when the renal tubular mechanism for resorbing calcium is overwhelmed, or when there is an unrelated decrease in the renal tubular capacity to resorb calcium, that the kidney's adaptive mechanism for correcting hypercalcemia becomes operative and hypercalciuria develops. Unfortunately, this chronic adaptation (hypercalciuria), along with other changes in urine composition that occur in primary hyperparathyroidism (eg, increased pH due to bicarbonaturia), contributes to the urolithiasis and urinary tract infections that are so common in these patients.

Many patients with primary hyperparathyroidism have decreased renal tubular reabsorption of phosphate, hyperphosphaturia, and hypophosphatemia. In normal people or in patients with a diminished capacity to convert $25OHD_3$ to $1,25(OH)_2D_3$, the renal tubular effects of PTH aid mineral homeostasis by stimulating $1,25(OH)_2D_3$ production and by clearing from the blood phosphate that was removed from bone during resorption of calcium. However, in patients with primary hyperparathyroidism, hypercalcemia is aggravated by the increased production of $1,25(OH)_2D_3$ and by a decrease in the amount of serum phosphate available to form complexes with serum ionic calcium.

B. Calcium in Soft Tissues: Other mechanisms for correcting hypercalcemia are required as the disease progresses. These generally result in a "trade-off" between a decrease in serum calcium and the development of organ disease. One such mechanism is the deposition of calcium in soft tissues that occurs because the normal solubility product of $Ca^{2+} \times PO_4^{3-}$ in serum (approximately 40) is exceeded. This may cause joint pain due to calcific tendinitis and chondrocalcinosis, or it may compromise renal function (secondary to nephrocalcinosis).

C. Vitamin D Deficiency: Another adaptive mechanism is the development of vitamin D deficiency, which may render patients with even severe hyperparathyroidism eucalcemic or nearly so. In this instance, a patient with only marginal stores of vitamin D may develop vitamin D deficiency because of the long-term increase in the conversion of $25OHD_3$ to $1,25(OH)_2D_3$ that is caused by the increased circulating levels of PTH. Such patients may have severe osteomalacia.

D. Increased Degradation of PTH: A final adaptive mechanism may be a hypercalcemia-induced increase in the degradation of biologically active forms of PTH peripherally (eg, in the liver and possibly the kidney) and in parathyroid tissue itself. Evidence in support of such effects of ionic calcium is available in both animals and humans. Thus, it is possible that plasma calcium per se may not only regulate PTH secretion but may also be important in determining the relative quantities of biologically active PTH and inactive hormone fragments in the circulation. The one adaptive mechanism that might be expected to play an important role in correcting the hypercalcemia of primary hyperparathyroidism is increased secretion of CT. However evidence indicates that this does not occur in most patients; and in some patients (particularly women), CT reserve actually appears to be diminished.

E. Hyperchloremic Acidosis: Patients with primary hyperparathyroidism generally have mild to moderate hyperchloremic acidosis. This is due chiefly to excess PTH, which decreases the urinary concentration of hydrogen ion and increases urinary bicarbonate excretion. These effects also tend to aggravate existing hypercalcemia, first by impairing the ability of blood albumin to bind ionic calcium and secondly by increasing the dissolution of bone mineral.

F. Increased Urinary cAMP: Urinary cAMP is increased in as many as 80% of patients with primary hyperparathyroidism. This presumably reflects an increase in PTH-stimulated renal cell adenylyl cyclase activity. Interestingly, some studies indicate that the phosphaturic and cAMP responses to exogenously administered PTH are blunted in patients with primary hyperparathyroidism, suggesting a state of refractoriness or "desensitization" of one or more of the cellular components responsible for these effects. This "desensitization" and the increase in urinary cAMP excretion have been used as diagnostic tests for the presence of hyperparathyroidism (see below).

G. Osteitis Fibrosa Cystica: Patients with radiologic evidence of osteitis fibrosa cystica frequently have increased serum concentrations of the bone isoenzyme of alkaline phosphatase. This bone enzyme is produced by osteoblasts and probably is one of several enzymes involved in osseous mineralization. These patients also excrete greater than normal quantities of hydroxyproline in their urine. This amino acid is unique to collagen, the major structural protein in bone. Similarly, pyridinoline, which links the three polypeptide chains of the collagen triple helix and is released when collagen undergoes degradation during osteoclastic bone resorption, is increased in the urine of most patients with primary hyperparathyroidism. Such combined increases in serum alkaline phosphatase and urinary excretion of hydroxyproline and pyridinoline cross-links have been interpreted as reflections of increased bone turnover in primary hyperparathyroidism.

Clinical Features

A. Symptoms: Patients with primary hyperparathyroidism are usually relatively asymptomatic or have nonspecific symptoms such as weakness and easy fatigability. When symptoms do occur, they can generally be attributed to one of two causes: (1) hypercalcemia with associated hypercalciuria or (2) osteitis fibrosa cystica.

1. Hypercalcemia and associated hypercalciuria– The symptoms attributable to hypercalcemia involve a number of systems: (1) central nervous system: impaired mentation, loss of memory for recent events, emotional lability, depression, anosmia, somnolence, and even coma; (2) neuromuscular: weakness (especially of the proximal musculature); (3) rheumatologic: joint pain due to associated gout, intra-articular deposition of calcium pyrophosphate crystals (pseudogout), calcific tendinitis, and chondrocalcinosis; (4) dermatologic: pruritus, probably due to metastatic calcification in the skin; (5) gastrointestinal: anorexia, nausea, vomiting, dyspepsia, and constipation; and (6) renal: polyuria, nocturia, renal colic due to lithiasis, nephrocalcinosis that sometimes leads to renal failure, and associated symptoms of uremia. All of these abnormalities are related to the degree of elevation of ionic calcium in extracellular fluid, but the correlation is a crude one. One patient may be severely incapacitated at a level of serum calcium that produces only moderate symptoms in another.

Severe pancreatitis and intractable peptic ulcer have been observed in individual patients with primary hyperparathyroidism and are thought to be due to hypercalcemia. However, the evidence that these disorders occur with increased frequency in primary hyperparathyroidism is weak. Hypertension occurs with increased frequency, even in patients with mild hyperparathyroidism, but its cause is unknown.

2. Osteitis fibrosa cystica– Symptomatic bone disease (osteitis fibrosa cystica) is now unusual. Patients may complain of diffuse bone pain or, very rarely, may have a pathologic fracture through a bone cyst.

B. Signs: Most patients show no signs of the disorder. Such signs as are present are usually confined to the neuromuscular system or to organ systems in which soft tissue calcification is present. Neurologic abnormalities are nonspecific and include impaired mentation, mental depression, psychosis, hypoactive deep tendon reflexes, joint hyperextensibility, sensory loss for perception of pain and vibration, proximal muscle weakness (particularly the thighs), abnormal tongue movements (resembling fasciculations), lingual atrophy, ataxic gait, and abnormally strong (hard) fingernails.

1. Soft tissue calcification– Soft tissue calcification can result in arthritis (chondrocalcinosis or calcific tendinitis), conjunctivitis (conjunctival calcium phosphate crystals), and "band keratopathy," which is characterized by deposition in the cornea of opaque calcium phosphate in vertical lines parallel to and within the ocular limbus, usually laterally (3 o'clock and 9 o'clock). "Band keratopathy" can best be seen by slit lamp examination. It is rare in hyperparathyroidism unless serum phosphate is also elevated (eg, after the onset of renal failure).

2. Enlarged glands– It is seldom possible to palpate enlarged parathyroid glands. A nodule felt in the neck of a patient with primary hyperparathyroidism is much more likely to be in the thyroid than in the parathyroid gland.

3. Bone tenderness and deformities– Rarely, patients may exhibit bone tenderness on examination. Bone deformities, fractures through an osteoclastic cyst, the presence of an epulis (brown tumor of the jaw), and "pseudoclubbing" due to collapsed terminal phalanges have been described even more rarely.

C. Imaging Studies: The most specific and frequent radiographic sign of osteitis fibrosa cystica is subperiosteal bone resorption. This is best demonstrated in magnified fine-grain industrial x-rays of the fingers (especially the index finger). An example from a patient with severe primary hyperparathyroidism is shown in Figure 5–15A. Note the radial surface of the distal phalanx, where the cortex is almost completely resorbed, leaving only fine wisps of cortical bone. Other radiographic manifestations of the disease range from generalized osteopenia to bone cysts ("brown tumors") and erosion of distal phalangeal tufts or the distal ends of clavicles. Severe osteitis fibrosa cystica involving the skull is shown in Figure 5–15B.

Soft tissue calcifications (eg, calcific tendinitis, chondrocalcinosis, nephrocalcinosis, pulmonary calcifications) may be incidental findings on routine films. The latter two can be well demonstrated with scanning techniques using radioactively labeled bisphosphonate compounds.

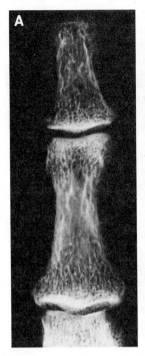
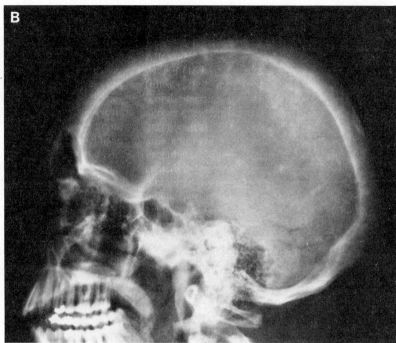

Figure 5–15. *A:* Magnified x-ray of index finger on fine-grain industrial film showing classic subperiosteal resorption in a patient with severe primary hyperparathyroidism. Note the left (radial) surface of the distal phalanx, where the cortex is almost completely resorbed, leaving only fine wisps of cortical bone. ***B:*** Skull x-ray from a patient with severe secondary hyperparathyroidism due to prolonged end-stage renal disease. Extensive areas of demineralization alternate with areas of increased bone density, resulting in an exaggerated picture of the "salt and pepper" skull x-ray, which used to be a classic finding in primary hyperparathyroidism. This is rarely seen now and cannot be visualized easily in x-ray reproductions. Although it is difficult to appreciate at this magnification, the dental lamina dura is absent, another classic x-ray finding in severe hyperparathyroidism. (Both films courtesy of H Genant.)

Nephrocalcinosis is rarely seen on x-ray, but nephrolithiasis is common. The stones are usually radiopaque (ie, calcium oxalate and calcium phosphate stones) and can be seen on plain films. Renal sonograms or nephrotomograms are helpful in identifying, localizing, and measuring them. This latter procedure is important in determining the "activity" of the stone disease. An increase in stone diameter with time can be taken as evidence of "active" stone disease and is probably an indication for treatment of hyperparathyroidism. Primary hyperparathyroidism may also be associated, although less commonly, with uric acid stones (not radiopaque). Thus, renal sonography or x-ray examination of the urinary tract with contrast material is also important.

Differential Diagnosis

In general, the major problem in the differential diagnosis of primary hyperparathyroidism is distinguishing it from other conditions associated with hypercalcemia (Table 5–3). Thiazide diuretic therapy and nonhematologic malignant diseases are the most common ones. Less common but equally important are (1) hematologic malignant diseases involving bone (myeloma, lymphoma, leukemia); (2) granulomatous diseases (sarcoidosis, tuberculosis, berylliosis); (3) endocrine disorders, including thyrotoxicosis and acute adrenal insufficiency; (4) familial hypocalciuric hypercalcemia (benign familial hypercalcemia); (5) intoxication with calcium, vitamin D, vitamin A, or lithium; (6) extensive skeletal immobilization (eg, in a spica body cast) in normal young people and prolonged bed rest in patients with osteolytic or metabolic bone disease; and (7) idiopathic hypercalcemia of infancy. More than one cause of hypercalcemia may coexist in the same patient (eg, hyperparathyroidism and sarcoidosis).

A. Pathogenesis of Hypercalcemia: Hypercalcemic disorders can be divided into those due to excess PTH and those due to other factors. Only primary hyperparathyroidism and a large subgroup of nonhematologic malignant diseases fall into the first category. The remainder fall into the second category and are characterized by suppression of PTH secretion.

B. Nonparathyroid Hypercalcemia: The underlying causes of hypercalcemia in the conditions in the second category are varied and, for the most part,

Table 5–3. Differential diagnosis of hypercalcemia.

Due to increased serum PTH
  Primary and "tertiary" hyperparathyroidism
  Some nonhematologic malignancies
Not due to increased serum PTH
  Drug-induced hypercalcemia (thiazides, furosemide, vitamin D, calcium, vitamin A, lithium)
  Granulomatous diseases (sarcoidosis, tuberculosis, berylliosis)
  Genetic disease (familial hypocalciuric hypercalcemia)
  Immobilization
  "Idiopathic" hypercalcemia
  Some nonhematologic malignancies
  Malignant hematologic diseases
  Nonparathyroid endocrine diseases (Addison's disease, hyper- and hypothyroidism)

uncertain. They will not be discussed here except to show how they can be excluded from the differential diagnosis of primary hyperparathyroidism. The most important ones are the hypercalcemia of cancer and familial hypocalciuric hypercalcemia.

1. Hypercalcemia of cancer– It is unlikely that a bony metastasis produces chronic hypercalcemia simply by physical displacement of bone. Rather, malignant tumors probably produce the same osteolytic humoral factors after metastasis to bone as they do before. These factors include PTH-like substances, prostaglandins, and osteoclast-activating factor (OAF). It is presumed that any one or a combination of these humors might be secreted systemically by parent tumors or released by bony metastases in sufficient quantities to stimulate local osteolysis and produce hypercalcemia. There is little question that OAF is involved in the production of hypercalcemia in patients with hematologic cancers, especially multiple myeloma. Until recently, it was thought that hypercalcemia in patients with nonhematologic cancers was, in large part, due to ectopic secretion of prostaglandins, but studies with inhibitors of prostaglandin synthesis have shown that plasma calcium rarely falls after their administration. This finding suggests that prostaglandins are relatively unimportant in the production of hypercalcemia in cancer.

Fuller Albright in 1941 postulated that PTH was responsible for solid-tumor hypercalcemia in some patients. In the absence of renal failure, many of these patients have the same degree of hypophosphatemia as patients with moderate to severe primary hyperparathyroidism. Normal (80%) to increased (20%) values for serum iPTH have been reported by some laboratories in as many as 70–80% of hypercalcemic patients with nonhematologic cancers. Serum values for iPTH in patients with primary hyperparathyroidism and equal degrees of hypercalcemia are much higher than in patients with the hypercalcemia of cancer. Yet, nephrogenous cAMP excretion in many patients with cancer-associated hypercalcemia is the same as or greater than that in patients

with primary hyperparathyroidism. This paradox led to a search for compounds—in cancer tissue or released into the medium of cultured cancer cells—that bind to the PTH receptor and stimulate adenylyl cyclase in PTH target tissues. This search was rewarded by the identification and chemical characterization of a bioactive peptide that resembles PTH in its N-terminal amino acid sequence but is totally dissimilar in its carboxyl sequence. For a complete discussion of the role this peptide may play in the humoral hypercalcemia of cancer, see Chapter 20.

2. Familial hypocalciuric hypercalcemia (familial benign hypercalcemia)– This syndrome is probably the second most important disorder in the differential diagnosis of primary hyperparathyroidism. It is inherited as an autosomal dominant trait and is characterized usually by asymptomatic or mild hypercalcemia, hypocalciuria, mild hypermagnesemia (variably present), and normal to low levels of serum iPTH. Parathyroid exploration in a number of patients has shown either normal parathyroid glands or equivocal "hyperplasia," and subtotal parathyroidectomy has consistently failed to restore eucalcemia. Recent studies have shown that the nephrogenous cAMP responses to exogenous and endogenous PTH are greater in patients with familial hypocalciuric hypercalcemia than in normal subjects or in patients with primary hyperparathyroidism. These observations suggest that the hypercalcemia in this familial syndrome may be partly due to renal hypersensitivity to the hypocalciuric effects of PTH. However, the persistence of increased renal tubular reabsorption of calcium after parathyroidectomy and the notable absence of the characteristic sequelae of primary hyperparathyroidism (eg, renal stones and osteitis fibrosa cystica) indicate that tissue hypersensitivity to PTH is probably not the sole cause of the disorder. It is likely that this disorder involves an abnormal parathyroid gland "set point" sensitivity to extracellular ionic calcium (as in lithium hypercalcemia).

Severe parathyroid hyperplasia may occur in infants born of parents with this syndrome. Thus, measurement of serum calcium is indicated in all such infants. Hypercalcemia associated with findings compatible with hyperparathyroidism (increased serum iPTH) should be treated promptly by subtotal parathyroidectomy.

Diagnosis

The presence of hypercalcemia is established when at least three measurements of total serum calcium are greater than normal. Venous blood should be drawn in the morning under fasting conditions with minimal venous stasis. The usual normal range for the total serum calcium is 8.9–10.1 mg/dL (2.23–2.53 mmol/L). Laboratories reporting a wider normal range (eg, 9–11 mg/dL [2.25–2.75 mmol/L]) may have based it on measurements of serum calcium in subjects not documented as normal or may have a significant problem with calcium contamination. The latter is frequently due to use of a conventional chalkboard (chalk contains calcium) in the laboratory or to use of contaminated test tubes when drawing blood. Such sources of error must be eliminated, since large numbers of patients with mild hypercalcemia (eg, 10.1–11 mg/dL [2.53–2.75 mmol/L]) will go undetected if the normal range for serum calcium is too wide. In the case of laboratory contamination, wide swings in serum calcium in individual subjects will be observed, leading to diagnostic confusion and to waste of patient and laboratory resources in the further investigation of artifactual hypercalcemia.

Freshly drawn blood specimens adjusted for pH must be used for measurements of serum ionic calcium. In practice, since most calcium is bound to serum albumin, a rough estimate of true calcium can be made by adding or subtracting 0.8 mg/dL (0.2 mmol/L) for each g/dL of albumin that is above or below normal. Special formulas and nomograms are also available. The QT interval in the ECG is shortened (adjusted for heart rate) when serum ionic calcium is significantly elevated.

A. Review of History of Present Illness: Hypercalcemia generally reflects serious underlying disease that may not have been suspected during the initial evaluation. Because of this, the patient with hypercalcemia should first have a repeat history and physical examination with specific objectives in mind. These include detailed evaluations of duration of illness, drug intake, the possible presence of nonmineral-related endocrine disease, a history of nephrolithiasis with documentation (old x-rays), symptoms of cancer, a family history of endocrine and mineral disorders, and the possible presence of palpable lymph nodes or masses, skin pigmentation or lesions (metastases), and thyromegaly, hepatomegaly, or splenomegaly.

1. Nephrolithiasis and body weight– Illness of long duration associated with nephrolithiasis and maintenance of normal weight favors a diagnosis of primary hyperparathyroidism; illness of short duration associated with weight loss without nephrolithiasis favors a nonparathyroid cause of hypercalcemia, particularly cancer.

2. Thiazide drugs– A history of thiazide intake might explain an increase in serum calcium to 11 mg/dL (2.75 mmol/L), but higher values usually indicate that this drug has merely increased the hypercalcemia of another condition (eg, mild primary hyperparathyroidism).

3. Lithium– Lithium carbonate, as administered for a bipolar affective disorder, can cause an increase in serum calcium to 11.5 mg/dL (2.88 mmol/L). The mechanism of this action is likely a drug-induced increase in the parathyroid gland "set point" for suppression by extracellular calcium.

4. Vitamin D intake– This may not have been elicited in the initial history. Vitamin D can cause severe hypercalcemia in adults when taken in doses exceeding 50,000 units/d. Furthermore, patients with any disorder that causes hypercalcemia may be abnormally sensitive to vitamin D. Thus, intake of less than 50,000 units/d may aggravate existing hypercalcemia in sarcoidosis and primary hyperparathyroidism; what may appear initially to be a severe form of the primary disorder may prove ultimately to be relatively mild when vitamin D intake is curtailed.

5. Calcium intake– Excess calcium intake (> 5 g/d) in the form of calcium carbonate antacids can cause severe hypercalcemia in susceptible individuals, especially when coupled with additional intake of alkali (bicarbonate) ("milk-alkali syndrome"). This condition is rare in its pure form. Most patients actually have underlying primary hyperparathyroidism and are taking calcium carbonate and alkali for associated gastric hyperacidity.

6. Family history– The family history may contain important clues to the correct diagnosis and treatment of a hypercalcemic patient. It is essential to inquire about the presence of hypercalcemia, nephrolithiasis, neck exploration, metabolic bone disease, intractable peptic ulcer disease, and endocrine tumors in family members, since primary hyperparathyroidism occurs as part of several familial multiple endocrine neoplasia (MEN) syndromes (see Chapter 21). There are few distinctive laboratory findings in the syndrome of familial hypocalciuric hypercalcemia, and a definitive diagnosis can be made only by documenting hypercalcemia in the patient's immediate relatives. A history of unsuccessful parathyroid surgery in more than one hypercalcemic relative is unfortunately characteristic of this condition. It is helpful if the surgeon is given information regarding possible multiple endocrine neoplasia or familial hyperparathyroidism before neck exploration is undertaken. Multiple parathyroid gland enlargement ("hyperplasia") is almost certain to be present in both of these conditions, and subtotal parathyroidectomy (removal of 3 1/2 glands) rather than single-gland removal would be indicated. Finally, mothers of infants with severe neonatal tetany should be suspected of having primary hyperparathyroidism.

B. Immunologic Measurement of Parathyroid Hormone: There has been a revolutionary change in the laboratory investigation of hypercalcemia in recent years owing to the development of sensitive and specific immunologic measurement techniques for serum PTH. Whereas patients were once extensively evaluated for nonparathyroid disorders that could cause hypercalcemia, the trend now is to use serum iPTH and calcium measurements to assign patients either to a group likely to benefit from surgical resection of parathyroid lesions or to one that requires further diagnostic evaluation for the cause of hypercalcemia (Figure 5–16).

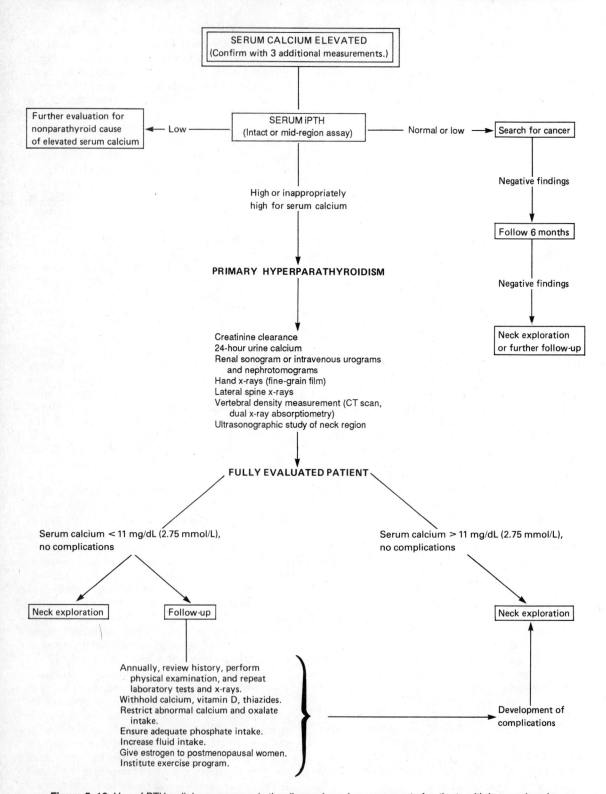

Figure 5–16. Use of PTH radioimmunoassay in the diagnosis and management of patients with hypercalcemia.

1. iPTH in primary hyperparathyroidism– In general, serum iPTH measurements segregate patients with hypercalcemia into two categories. Using a sensitive and specific mid-region assay, serum iPTH is increased in 90% of patients with primary hyperparathyroidism and is inappropriately increased for the level of the serum calcium (upper range of normal) in the remainder (Figure 5–17). In the majority of nonparathyroid disorders causing hypercalcemia, serum iPTH is either undetectable or low unless primary hyperparathyroidism coexists, in which case it is appropriately increased for the level of serum calcium. Thus it is possible, using serum iPTH, to diagnose primary hyperparathyroidism, a surgically curable disease, even in the presence of another nonparathyroid disorder which has the potential to produce hypercalcemia on its own.

2. iPTH in hypercalcemia of cancer– Nonparathyroid tumors seldom produce sufficient native parathyroid hormone to produce hypercalcemia. Yet many patients with malignancy-associated hypercalcemia present with a biochemical syndrome indistinguishable in many respects from primary hyperparathyroidism—ie, they have hypophosphatemia and increased nephrogenous cAMP excretion. This seemingly paradoxic situation was clarified recently when it was shown that a polypeptide (parathyroid hormone-related polypeptide [PTHrP]) could be obtained from the tumors of patients with malignancy-associated hypercalcemia that was immunologically different from PTH but that stimulated adenylyl cyclase in kidney and bone cell preparations. Subse-

quent deduction of the structure of this polypeptide from its cDNA revealed it to be a linear 141-amino-acid polypeptide homologous with authentic PTH in its amino-terminal first 13 amino acids. Little homology was found in the region of the PTH molecule carboxyl terminus to residue 13. However, the biologic effects of synthetic preparations of the human PTHrP(1–34) fragment are essentially identical in vitro and in vivo to human PTH(1–34), and photoaffinity labeling studies show that PTHrP(1–34) binds to an identical plasma membrane (receptor) component as PTH(1–34) (see Chapter 20).

The problem with PTH radioimmunoassays in general is that they cannot always distinguish between primary hyperparathyroidism and malignancy-associated hypercalcemia because values for serum iPTH can be normal or even slightly increased in some patients with that disorder. This is illustrated in Figure 5–17. Even though the distributions of values for serum mid-region iPTH as a function of serum total calcium are different in primary hyperparathyroidism and in malignancy-associated hypercalcemia, there is sufficient overlap in those distributions to cause diagnostic bewilderment in a small percentage of cases. The reason this problem exists with radioimmunoassays of PTH but not with immunometric assays of intact PTH (see below and Figure 5–18B) is not entirely clear.

Utilizing serum immunoextraction procedures and a recently developed radioimmunoassay for PTHrP, increased levels of iPTHrP have been demonstrated in as many as 60–70% of patients with malignancy-associated hypercalcemia, whereas patients with primary hyperparathyroidism had levels within the normal range. With the development of commercially available assays of serum iPTHrP, it will be possible to make the laboratory diagnosis of malignancy-associated hypercalcemia due to excess circulating PTHrP in a direct and specific manner rather than in the way it is done now, namely, on negative grounds based on low or undetectable levels of serum iPTH (Figures 5–17 and 5–18).

3. Comparison of clinical utility of carboxyl (53–84), and mid (44–68) PTH radioimmunoassays with an intact PTH immunometric assay– The clinical utilities of a carboxyl region-specific (53–84) and a mid region-specific (43–68) radioimmunoassay have been compared separately with the same immunochemiluminometric assay (ICMA) for intact PTH in the differential diagnosis of hypercalcemia.

All three assays (53–84, 44–68, intact) were able to measure iPTH in normal sera and showed low or undetectable levels in hypoparathyroid sera. Thirty-five of 36 serum samples from patients with proved primary hyperparathyroidism showed increased levels of intact PTH, whereas only 26 of 36 of those same sera showed increased levels of carboxyl region (53–84)-specific iPTH. By contrast, the intact and the

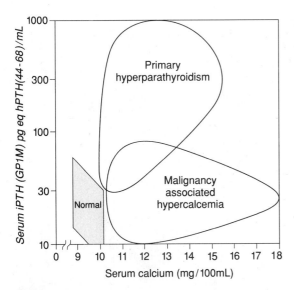

Figure 5–17. Comparison of the distributions of serum mid-region iPTH values as a function of total serum calcium concentration between patients with primary hyperparathyroidism and malignancy-associated hypercalcemia.

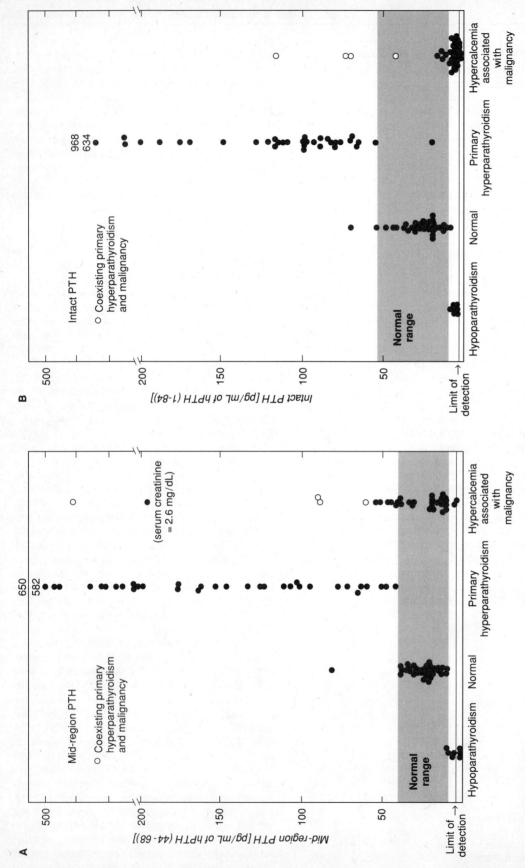

Figure 5–18. Clinical utility of parathyroid hormone immunoassays. Serum mid-region (**A**) and intact (**B**) PTH in normal subjects and patients with hypoparathyroidism, primary hyperparathyroidism, and hypercalcemia associated with malignancy. (Reproduced, with permission, from Endres DB et al: Measurement of parathyroid hormone. Endocrinol Metab Clin North Am 1989;18:611.)

mid region (44–68) PTH assays were essentially equivalent in this regard (Figure 5–18). Moreover, the mid region assay was superior to the intact assay in that PTH levels were more elevated. Whereas 28 of 36 serum samples showed mid region values greater than twice normal, intact PTH was similarly elevated in only 17 of those same 36 samples. These latter observations strongly suggest the glandular secretion of carboxyl fragments contains an epitope within the 44–68 amino acid sequence of PTH and are consistent with the possibility that this epitope is an immunologic marker of abnormal parathyroid tissue.

It is not often that the clinical features of patients with malignancy-associated hypercalcemia fail to distinguish them from patients with primary hyperparathyroidism. However, serious errors in patient management can occur in the small number of patients in whom that uncertainty is encountered. While the relatively lower values for serum mid-region iPTH in malignancy-associated hypercalcemia were noted nearly 2 decades ago to be a powerful means of differentiating those two disease processes (Figure 5–17), it is clear that the intact PTH immunometric assay provides a major improvement in this regard (Figure 5–18).

Lastly, measurements of iPTH in sera taken from various veins potentially draining enlarged parathyroid glands have been used to localize those glands so that they can be surgically removed (see Selective Venous Catheterization, below). Success in these studies depends upon demonstrating "step-up" increases in the concentration of iPTH between peripheral blood and blood draining a parathyroid lesion. Those "step-up" differences are less when iPTH measurements are made with mid or carboxyl region PTH than with intact PTH assays, primarily because of the relatively higher concentrations of mid or carboxyl region iPTH as compared with intact iPTH in the peripheral circulation. Thus, it is generally recommended that intact or NH_2-terminal PTH assays be used for the measurement of serum iPTH in blood obtained during selective venous catheterization to localize parathyroid disease.

C. Serum and Urine Biochemistry: Several serum and urine measurements may be helpful in assigning hypercalcemic patients to parathyroid or nonparathyroid categories. Hyperphosphatemia in the absence of severe renal failure favors a nonparathyroid cause. Hypophosphatemia, when dietary phosphate is adequate and when oral phosphate-binding agents are not being ingested, favors primary hyperparathyroidism but is frequently present in hypercalcemia of malignancy. Increased serum chloride favors primary hyperparathyroidism. Increased serum alkaline phosphatase is more common in patients with cancer than in those with primary hyperparathyroidism and, in the absence of radiographic evidence of osseous hyperparathyroidism, should suggest the possibility of ectopic hyperparathyroidism. Globulin abnormalities in serum protein electrophoresis point toward multiple myeloma or sarcoidosis, but increases in gamma globulin that disappear after parathyroidectomy have been observed in primary hyperparathyroidism. Although increases in the erythrocyte sedimentation rate and anemia have been recorded in primary hyperparathyroidism, these findings suggest a nonparathyroid cause of hypercalcemia, particularly cancer.

Measurement of urine calcium in hypercalcemic patients is generally useful only when it is low. This finding may be the only clue to familial hypocalciuric hypercalcemia. Because of the therapeutic importance of making this diagnosis (ie, avoiding neck exploration), measurement of 24-hour urine calcium is recommended in the routine evaluation of any hypercalcemic patient before exploration is performed.

D. Nephrogenous cAMP: About 40–50% of the cAMP excreted in the urine is derived from renal tubular cells. Its production and cellular release into the urine are almost entirely under the control of PTH. This component of urinary cAMP can be accurately estimated and is termed nephrogenous cAMP. Since it is above normal in about 80% of patients with primary hyperparathyroidism (Figure 5–19) and in a large proportion of patients with ectopic hyperparathyroidism, it is not helpful in distinguishing between these two common disorders. However, because low levels of nephrogenous cAMP are present in patients who have nonparathyroid hypercalcemia but not cancer, the test may be useful in patients with equivocal increases in serum iPTH. In such patients, a low level of nephrogenous cAMP would suggest that the serum iPTH value was artifactual and would argue against primary hyperparathyroidism, whereas a normal or increased level would confirm the validity of the serum iPTH value and favor this condition.

E. Other Diagnostic Tests: The glucocorticoid suppression test may be used in the very unusual circumstance in which the results of all of the tests discussed above are equivocal. It is based on the observation that the hypercalcemia of conditions such as vitamin D intoxication, sarcoidosis, lymphoproliferative syndromes, and myeloma generally responds to the administration of 50–100 mg of cortisone or 40–60 mg of prednisone given daily in divided doses for 10 days, as shown by a decrease in serum calcium. This response is unusual in primary or ectopic hyperparathyroidism. However, results should be interpreted cautiously, since the mechanisms involved in steroid-induced suppression of hypercalcemia are poorly understood, and variables other than steroids (eg, hydration) may influence the level of serum calcium during the test. A positive test result (ie, a significant decrease in serum calcium) is a contraindication to neck exploration and signals the need for investigation for a nonparathyroid cause of hypercalcemia. A negative test result would be consistent

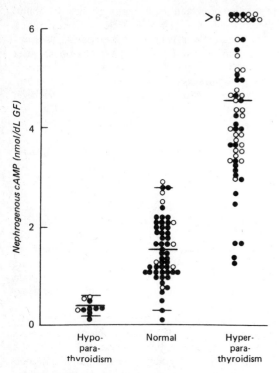

Figure 5–19. Nephrogenous cAMP, expressed as a function of glomerular filtration rate, in control subjects and patients with primary hyperparathyroidism. The open circles represent the subjects and patients with renal impairment (mean creatinine clearance < 80 mL/min). Closed circles represent subjects with normal renal function. The longer horizontal bars represent the mean values; shorter bars show ± 2 SD. (GF, glomerular filtrate.) (Reproduced by copyright permission of the American Society for Clinical Investigation. From Broadus AE et al: Nephrogenous cyclic adenosine monophosphate as a parathyroid function test. J Clin Invest 1977;60:771.)

with a diagnosis of primary or ectopic hyperparathyroidism. Other diagnostic tests used rarely include measurements of phosphate clearance (increased in primary hyperparathyroidism) and of urinary cAMP after PTH administration (usually decreased in primary hyperparathyroidism, most likely because of a "desensitization" mechanism).

F. Radiographs: It is essential to obtain high-quality x-rays of the hands on fine-grain industrial film in all patients whose hypercalcemia is a diagnostic problem. Although the finding of definitive subperiosteal bone resorption is relatively unusual (occurring in about 8–10% of patients with primary hyperparathyroidism), it is diagnostic of hyperparathyroidism and probably represents the most reliable and readily available evidence that neck exploration is needed in patients with severe, life-threatening hypercalcemia.

G. Preoperative Localization of Abnormal Parathyroid Tissue: Abnormal parathyroid tissue that is causing primary hyperparathyroidism will be discovered and excised in over 90% of initial neck explorations performed by a competent parathyroid surgeon. There is no need for invasive procedures to localize glandular tissue prior to first surgery except under unusual circumstances (see below).

With the exception of ultrasonography, localization procedures are generally reserved for patients whose first neck exploration was not successful or who suffer recurrent disease. These procedures can be divided into noninvasive and invasive. Noninvasive procedures include esophagography, ultrasonography, magnetic resonance imaging (MRI), computed tomography, and scanning with ^{201}Tl plus ^{99m}Tc. Invasive procedures include arteriography, differential venous catheterization with measurement of iPTH in the serum samples obtained, and needle aspiration of a mass localized by ultrasonography.

1. Esophagography– Esophagography may occasionally identify a relatively large parathyroid gland deep in the tracheoesophageal groove that was inadvertently missed on first exploration because of its aberrant shape. However, the procedure is usually unrewarding.

2. Ultrasonography, MRI, computed tomography, and scanning with ^{201}Tl plus ^{99m}Tc– Ultrasound technology has improved so rapidly that it is now possible to identify parathyroid lesions in the neck as small as 1 cm in diameter. Further technologic development in this area is expected, and routine ultrasound evaluation prior to initial neck exploration has become accepted practice. Because lesions can be identified in real time with this procedure, it has been possible to obtain needle aspiration biopsies of them. With use of routine and immunohistologic procedures and either immunoassays or bioassays of extracts of aspirated tissue, lesions located by ultrasonography can be identified as parathyroid in origin, thus giving the surgeon a histologic diagnosis preoperatively.

Whereas ultrasonography is generally not useful in identifying mediastinal lesions, MRI or computed tomography should be employed routinely with ultrasonography and esophagography in the patient harboring one or more missed or recurrent parathyroid lesions.

^{201}Tl is avidly concentrated by parathyroid tissue; when it is used in combination with ^{99m}Tc scans of the neck to identify thyroid tissue, parathyroid lesions can be effectively localized. However, the incidence of false-positive and false-negative results obtained with this procedure is a matter of concern. Both false-positive and false-negative results have also been obtained using ultrasonography, MRI, and computed tomography, and at their present stage of development, it is prudent to use more than one of these procedures in patients with recurrent hyperparathyroidism and in patients whose first neck explorations were unsuccessful.

These procedures may also help in the diagnosis of a severely hypercalcemic patient who has not undergone previous neck exploration. In such a case, identification of a mass lesion in a location consistent with normal or aberrant parathyroid tissue strongly suggests the presence of primary hyperparathyroidism and argues for early neck exploration, even before serum iPTH has been measured.

3. Thyroid arteriography– Of the invasive procedures, thyroid arteriography is most useful to the surgeon when a lesion is identified. However, as with the noninvasive procedures, the results are specific only in the sense that the location of an identified lesion is consistent with that of a normal or aberrant parathyroid gland. Neurologic complications such as transient occipital blindness and hemiplegia have been recorded; therefore, the procedure should be avoided in patients at risk for neurovascular disease. Use of small quantities of contrast medium by a radiologist with long experience in the technique minimizes the risk of complications.

4. Selective venous catheterization– Ideally, differential catheterization of the neck and mediastinal veins for the purpose of obtaining serum for iPTH analysis should be performed after veins have been identified by arteriography. The procedure is simple if a lesion has been identified by arteriography. If arteriography has not identified a lesion, all of the accessible small veins of the neck and mediastinum should be entered and sampled. It is often difficult to obtain blood from small veins because the lumens are obstructed by the catheter tip. The blood in the larger veins may be easier to aspirate, but the blood flow is so great that "step-up" increases in serum iPTH can be obliterated even if the catheter tip is near a small vein draining a parathyroid tumor. Venous catheterization studies must be interpreted with caution; because of the distortion in venous anatomy produced by individual variation, previous surgery, and venous anastomoses, the best result that can be obtained is usually lateralization of a parathyroid lesion. In general, less than a two-fold "step-up" should be ignored unless all other values for iPTH are almost identical. It is important to recognize that significant increases in iPTH have been recorded in sera draining normal parathyroid glands. This finding argues against the use of differential venous sampling in the initial diagnosis of hyperparathyroidism.

Treatment of Primary Hyperparathyroidism

A. Natural History: The natural history of primary hyperparathyroidism is not well understood. This is because most patients in whom the diagnosis is made undergo neck exploration and removal of the abnormal glands are and cured.

A large proportion of patients have "biochemical"

hyperparathyroidism—ie, only a slightly increased serum calcium (10.1–11 mg/dL [2.53–2.75 mmol/L]) and no clinical manifestations of the disease. A study of 150 such patients at the Mayo Clinic showed that a minority (10–30%) will develop a more severe form of the disease within 5 years, but no clinical or biochemical measurement was predictive of such progression.

It is presumed that patients with mild to moderately severe primary hyperparathyroidism started with the "biochemical" form of the disease. However, some of these patients attain a degree of disease stability; some have been observed for as long as 10–15 years without apparent progression. Except for a few who progress to severe disease, the remaining patients in this group probably have slow progression with gradual development of osteopenia and deterioration of renal function. Patients with severe primary hyperparathyroidism (serum calcium > 15 mg/dL [3.75 mmol/L]) will almost certainly die of the complications sooner or later unless the disease is diagnosed and appropriately treated.

Resection of benign parathyroid lesions is usually curative. Recurrences are rare in patients with single-gland disease but relatively common in multiple-gland disease. It is unclear whether successful surgical treatment restores impaired renal function. Stone formation generally ceases unless factors other than primary hyperparathyroidism are operative. There have been anecdotal reports of relief of severe psychiatric symptoms after removal of abnormal parathyroid glands. All but the more severe forms of osteitis fibrosa cystica improve within months and resolve completely within a year after parathyroidectomy. Recent studies suggest that surgical treatment of hyperparathyroidism in patients with postmenopausal or senile osteoporosis results in improvement of osteopenia. This is important because as many as 8–10% of patients with age-related osteopenia have increased circulating levels of iPTH and may suffer from some form of curable hyperparathyroidism.

B. Medical Treatment of Hypercalcemia:

1. Chronic moderately severe hypercalcemia (serum calcium 12–15 mg/dL)– Medical management of diseases causing nonparathyroid hypercalcemia generally results in prompt resolution of this biochemical abnormality. Far-advanced malignant disorders (solid or hematologic tumors) are exceptions, and long-term chronic treatment of cancer-related hypercalcemia in such cases is a therapeutic challenge. There is no satisfactory protocol for managing this problem, and it is a fertile area for pharmacologic research.

a. Glucocorticoids– Glucocorticoids have been the major resource for treatment of hypercalcemia associated with hematologic malignant neoplasms. They should be given in relatively high doses (eg, prednisone, 60–120 mg/d given orally in divided doses) and for relatively long periods (1 month) before the treatment is considered a failure. Bisphosphonate drugs are gradually replacing glucocorticoids in the treatment of this important complication of hematologic malignant neoplasms (see below).

b. Plicamycin (mithramycin)– Plicamycin, a toxic antibiotic that inhibits bone resorption, may be useful in the treatment of hypercalcemia due to both hematologic and solid malignant neoplasms. The usual dosage is 25 μg/kg by intravenous push. When hypercalcemia recurs, this same dose may be given again, provided platelet counts have not been dangerously suppressed and renal function has not become impaired. Lower doses (10–15 μg/kg) have been used successfully with fewer side effects. The lower dose is preferred if repeated doses are necessary.

c. Phosphate– Oral phosphate may be used as an antihypercalcemic agent in patients who have not been taking glucocorticoids. (The combination of oral phosphate and glucocorticoids occasionally induces nephrolithiasis, although the cause is unknown.) Either neutral phosphate or potassium phosphate may be given in doses as high as 2–4 g/d orally in divided doses. Initial doses should be relatively low (1–2 g of elemental phosphorus as phosphate per day orally in divided doses every 6 hours), because of gastrointestinal side effects; these disappear with time. Serum calcium, phosphate, and creatinine should be measured regularly to determine if phosphate treatment is effective and to detect the possible development of hyperphosphatemia or renal function impairment. Compliance can be assessed by measurement of 24-hour urine phosphorus. In general, decreases in serum calcium during phosphate therapy do not occur unless serum phosphate concentrations increase. Increases in serum phosphate above 5 mg/dL should be avoided because of the danger of inducing extraskeletal calcifications. Phosphate therapy can be used as a temporary measure during diagnostic studies. Phosphate therapy may cause hypokalemia, requiring administration of potassium supplements.

d. Calcitonin– Although it would seem rational to use CT, normal doses (100 units/d) have been disappointing. However, good results have been obtained with high doses of CT (400–1000 units every 12 hours) or with CT plus glucocorticoids (CT, 100 units twice daily, and prednisone, 60 mg daily).

e. Estrogen– Because estrogens decrease bone resorption and serum calcium in postmenopausal osteoporosis, estrogens have been used successfully to lower serum calcium in primary hyperparathyroidism. In the absence of contraindications (eg, personal or family history of uterine or breast cancer), maintenance doses (eg, 0.625–1.25 mg conjugated estrogens) should be given to all postmenopausal patients with primary hyperparathyroidism under medical management.

f. Intravenous disodium etidronate or pamidronate– These drugs have been used successfully in the acute treatment of hypercalcemia. Etidronate is administered intravenously, in a dose of 7.5 mg/kg in 250 mL saline over 2 hours for 3 successive days. Pamidronate is more potent and is given in doses between 60 and 90 mg (depending on the degree of hypercalcemia) as an intravenous infusion (1000 mL of sterile 0.45% or 0.9% sodium chloride, USP, or 5% dextrose injection, USP, over 24 hours. Re-treatment with pamidronate can be performed after 7 days if hypercalcemia recurs.

g. Other agents– Based on the presence of both adrenergic and histamine receptors on parathyroid cells, alpha- and beta-adrenergic blockers and cimetidine have been tried in primary hyperparathyroidism, with generally negative results.

2. Acute severe hypercalcemia (serum calcium > 15 mg/dL)– The medical therapy of acute severe hypercalcemia is quite different from that of chronic moderate hypercalcemia. Treatment should be started as soon as severe hypercalcemia has been detected, because the condition is life-threatening.

a. Hospitalization– If possible, the patient should remain ambulatory, since immobilization may increase serum calcium in some patients. Serum calcium, magnesium, sodium, and potassium must be monitored every 2–4 hours. In patients with heart disease who are in danger of developing heart failure from volume overload, central venous pressure should be monitored so that appropriate measures can be taken if the pressure increases.

b. Calcium restriction– Dietary calcium should be restricted immediately, and all drugs that might cause hypercalcemia (thiazides, vitamin D, etc) should be discontinued.

c. Reduction of digitalis– If the patient is taking digitalis, it may be wise to reduce the dose because the hypercalcemic patient may be more sensitive to the toxic effects of this drug. Ideally, the patient should be admitted to an intensive care unit for electrocardiographic monitoring while antihypercalcemic measures are being instituted. Beta-adrenergic blocking agents are useful in protecting the heart against the adverse effects of severe hypercalcemia, especially serious arrhythmias.

d. Hydration and diuretics– The mainstay of therapy is a regimen of hydration with saline solutions plus diuresis with furosemide or ethacrynic acid. The objective is to increase the urinary excretion of calcium rapidly, thus decreasing the exchangeable calcium pool and the serum calcium concentration. Saline is given to increase sodium excretion, since sodium clearance and calcium clearance parallel one another during water or osmotic diuresis. Furosemide inhibits the tubular reabsorption of calcium and aids in maintaining diuresis. Approximately 4–6 L of isotonic saline should be given intravenously daily, along with 20–100 mg of furosemide intravenously every 1–2 hours or 10–40 mg of ethacrynic acid intravenously every 1–2 hours. Such a regimen should increase urinary calcium to 500–1000 mg/d and lower serum calcium by 2–6 mg/dL after 24 hours.

e. Potassium and magnesium depletion and dehydration– These complications of therapy must be anticipated and appropriate replacement therapy instituted early.

f. Maintenance regimen– After serum calcium has decreased to a reasonably safe level (< 13 mg/dL), a chronic regimen may be instituted. This should consist of furosemide (40–160 mg/d orally) or ethacrynic acid (50–200 mg/d orally), sodium chloride tablets (400–600 meq/d orally), and at least 3 L of fluid per day. Serum calcium, magnesium, and potassium should be monitored daily at first and then weekly when serum calcium has stabilized. Magnesium and potassium should be replaced as necessary.

g. Other drugs– Two other drugs are used in patients with severe hypercalcemia.

(1) Intravenous disodium etidronate or pamidronate–These drugs are effective in many patients and are safer than plicamycin. They are given as described above.

(2) Plicamycin– Plicamycin is given in two to four doses of 10–15 μg/kg intravenously on alternate days early in the course of treatment of acute hypercalcemia. It is probably unwise to give plicamycin if primary hyperparathyroidism is suspected, because the patient is likely to require surgery and plicamycin can cause marked thrombocytopenia. Patients receiving plicamycin should be followed carefully with platelet counts, serum creatinine, and liver function tests because of its possible toxicity to the liver, kidney, and marrow.

B. Surgery for Removal of Abnormal Parathyroid Tissue: Surgical treatment should be considered in all patients with an established diagnosis of primary hyperparathyroidism. It is not clear that the biochemical form of the disease necessarily progresses to the stage at which clinically significant sequelae develop. However, most of these patients have histologic evidence of hyperparathyroidism on bone biopsy. Age is not a contraindication to neck exploration. Indeed, it is better to perform elective parathyroidectomy and manage hypercalcemia in that way than to deal with it later as a complication of another serious illness (eg, myocardial infarction).

1. Indications for surgery– In the long-term follow-up of biochemical hyperparathyroidism commented upon earlier, a group of arbitrary criteria were developed as indications for neck exploration (Table 5–4): (1) serum calcium higher than 11 mg/d; (2) radiographic evidence of metabolic bone disease; (3) active nephrolithiasis; (4) demonstration of decreased renal function; and (5) development of one or more "complications" of hyperparathyroidism such as se-rious psychiatric disease, peptic ulcer that is resistant to treatment, pancreatitis, and severe hypertension. In any patient in whom long-term medi-

Table 5–4. Categories of treatment for patients with primary hyperparathyroidism.

Criteria	Preferred Treatment
1. One or more of the following: Serum calcium > 11 mg/dL (2.75 mmol/L). Osteitis fibrosa cystica. Progressive osteopenia. Metabolically active nephrolithiasis. Decreased renal function. Intractable peptic ulcer. Pancreatitis. Serious psychiatric disease. Severe hypertension.	Surgical removal of parathyroid lesion.
2. Unsuccessful surgery, or recurrence with manifestations noted in category 1.	Surgical removal of parathyroid lesion; preoperative localization may be indicated.
3. Serum calcium < 11 mg/dL (2.75 mmol/L). Abnormal serum iPTH. Absence of manifestations noted in category 1.	Surgical removal of parathyroid lesion or medical management (see text).
4. Surgery contraindicated.	Medical management for hypercalcemia and prevention of nephrolithiasis (see text).

cal management of the disease is planned, certain studies should be obtained routinely (Figure 5–16). *At a minimum,* these should include a yearly history and physical examination, serum calcium, creatinine clearance, and bone mineral content of the spine and radius; x-rays of the hand on fine-grain industrial film to detect subperiosteal bone resorption; and a plain film of the abdomen to detect renal calcifications. If inactive nephrolithiasis has been found on initial examination, renal sonograms or nephrotomograms should be done to determine if new stones have formed or existing ones have enlarged. By definition, either of the latter would indicate recurrence of active stone disease, which would in turn be an indication for surgery.

2. Parathyroid surgeon– The most critical consideration in the surgical management of primary hyperparathyroidism is selection of a surgeon with extensive experience in parathyroid surgery and the ability to distinguish between an enlarged or abnormal parathyroid gland or lesion and a normal gland.

3. Surgical procedures– Two different procedures are currently used. The most widely accepted procedure consists of identifying all four parathyroid glands (using biopsy if necessary) followed by removal of a single enlarged parathyroid gland or of 3 1/2 glands if multiple glands are involved (Table 5–5). If abnormal parathyroid tissue cannot be identified, hemithyroidectomy should be performed, preferably on the side of a "missing" gland, because an intrathyroidal lesion may be present. All remaining parathyroid glands or remnants are marked with

Table 5–5. Extent of parathyroidectomy.

Number of Glands Involved	Procedure
All 4	Removal of 3 glands and all but 35–50 mg of the fourth gland; suture tagging of remnant or transplant to forearm.
Two or 3	Removal of all but half of a normal gland; suture tagging of remaining half.
One	Removal of involved gland; identification of remaining glands (often by biopsy); suture tagging of remaining glands.

nonabsorbable sutures to facilitate future identification of parathyroid tissue if repeat surgery for recurrent hyperparathyroidism is necessary.

The less commonly used procedure consists of exploring one side of the neck first and removing any single enlarged parathyroid gland. If the second gland on the same side is normal, the other side is not explored. If the second gland is abnormal, it is removed and the other side of the neck is explored and all parathyroid tissue removed except for one-half of a gland. This second approach leaves the unoperated side without scar tissue and makes it easier to explore at some future time for recurrent hyperparathyroidism. However, it fails to establish whether multiple glands are involved, since enlarged glands may be present on the unoperated side.

No matter which approach is taken, it is important to make accurate records of the number and location of glands identified and removed (preferably by detailed diagram). This information is essential in finding the missed glands if hypercalcemia persists or recurs.

4. Parathyroid autotransplantation– Autotransplantation of a portion of an enlarged parathyroid gland to the muscles of the forearm can be beneficial in special circumstances, such as when the last known parathyroid gland is removed because of recurrent primary hyperparathyroidism. Without transplantation, patients of this type may become hypoparathyroid. The functioning of such transplants can be easily assessed by measuring serum iPTH in venous blood from both forearms. A "step-up" in the concentration of serum iPTH in the transplanted forearm in comparison with the nontransplanted one is indicative of a functioning graft. If such patients develop hypercalcemia, portions of the transplanted gland can be removed easily.

5. Ectopic location– About 20% of abnormal parathyroid glands are in the mediastinum. However, 95% of these are in the superior part of the cavity, attached to the thymus or mediastinal fat pad. These abnormal glands are readily identified and removed during routine neck exploration by lifting the contents of the superior mediastinum into the neck incision. The remaining 5% are located elsewhere in the

mediastinum and can only be made accessible for excision by splitting the sternum. Before the advent of localization procedures (see above), the success rate in removing abnormal parathyroid tissue from the mediastinum was only 50%. The success rate is markedly improved if mediastinal lesions can be localized, but they are localized less frequently than are neck lesions (approximately 70+%). The decision to perform mediastinal exploration largely depends on the accuracy and completeness of the information obtained during initial neck exploration. If the exploration was inadequate or the records incomplete, repeat neck exploration is probably indicated. A recent study in which patients of this type were explored again showed an 80% success rate in finding missed abnormal parathyroid glands in the neck or superior mediastinum attached to the thymus. In rare cases, a fifth or sixth parathyroid gland may be present and abnormal.

C. Postoperative Care:

1. Hypocalcemia– If surgery is successful, serum calcium concentrations decrease to the normal range or lower within 24–48 hours. It is possible to determine if all abnormal parathyroid tissue has been removed by measuring decreased cAMP in a "spot" urine collection within 2 hours after parathyroidectomy. Patients with significant bony demineralization may develop severe hypocalcemia postoperatively. This is presumably due to the avidity of demineralized bone for extracellular fluid calcium ("hungry bone syndrome"). It can be distinguished from the development of hypo-parathyroidism by the absence of hyperphosphatemia and the presence of increased serum iPTH. Treatment may be difficult (see Hypoparathyroidism, above) and requires large quantities of intravenous calcium given continuously by infusion plus calcium carbonate given orally in doses of 1–10 g/d, depending upon the serum calcium response. Ergocalciferol (vitamin D_2) (usually 50,000–100,000 units daily) is of uncertain value. In the authors' experience, $1,25(OH)_2D_3$ (calcitriol) in relatively large doses (1–2 μg/d) has been useful.

2. Hypoparathyroidism– Most patients who develop hypocalcemia and mild hyperphosphatemia have temporary hypoparathyroidism, as evidenced by low normal serum levels of iPTH. A few of these patients will develop permanent hypoparathyroidism that requires treatment.

3. Other complications– Worsening of renal function (temporary or permanent), metabolic acidosis, hypomagnesemia, pancreatitis, and gout or pseudogout are other complications that may occur in the postoperative period. The problem of deterioration of renal function should be anticipated in patients who have abnormal renal function before the operation, and prophylactic infusions of mannitol should be given early in the postoperative period to initiate and maintain osmotic diuresis. Likewise, exacerbations of gout or pseudogout should be anticipated in patients with intra-articular calcifications or a history of arthritic attacks.

4. Follow-up– Follow-up is recommended yearly for about 10 years. This is especially important for patients with multiple-gland disease, because of the likelihood of recurrence. Another concern is the rare but real possibility that an excised lesion (in spite of histologic evidence of benignity) may have been malignant. In such cases, early detection of hypercalcemia may permit definitive surgical treatment before the development of local or distant metastases.

SECONDARY HYPERPARATHYROIDISM OF CHRONIC RENAL FAILURE

An increase in PTH secretion that is adaptive and unrelated to intrinsic disease of the parathyroid glands is called secondary hyperparathyroidism. The disorder is associated with prolonged stimulation of the parathyroid glands by chronic decreases in the concentration of ionic calcium in the blood. Several conditions cause chronic hypocalcemia and secondary hyperparathyroidism (Table 5–6). However, except in extreme cases, chronic renal failure is the only one in which secondary hyperparathyroidism produces clinically significant manifestations. Thus, this section will emphasize hyperparathyroidism associated with chronic renal failure.

Interest in the hyperparathyroidism of chronic renal failure and its associated bone disease, **renal osteodystrophy,** is a fairly recent development. Before the advent of hemodialysis, the sequelae of progressive nephron destruction were not studied seriously, because the life expectancy of patients with chronic renal failure was so short. Since these patients are now maintained with dialysis and renal transplantation, the problems of chronic management must be identified and solved.

Pathogenesis of Secondary Hyperparathyroidism in Chronic Renal Failure

Serum iPTH progressively increases in patients with chronic renal failure as glomerular filtration rate (GFR) decreases below 40 mL/min (Figure 5–20).

Table 5–6. Major causes of chronic hypocalcemia other than parathyroprival hypoparathyroidism.

Dietary deficiency of vitamin D or calcium.
Decreased intestinal absorption of vitamin D or calcium due to primary small bowel disease, short bowel syndrome, and post-gastrectomy syndrome.
Drugs that cause rickets or osteomalacia such as phenytoin, phenobarbital, cholestyramine, and laxatives.
States of tissue resistance to vitamin D.
Excessive intake of inorganic phosphate compounds.
Pseudohypoparathyroidism.
Severe hypomagnesemia.
Chronic renal failure.

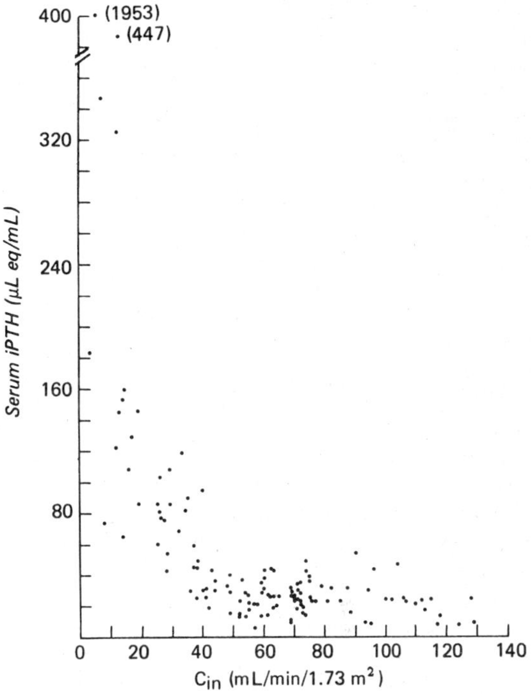

Figure 5–20. Serum iPTH as a function of the renal clearance of inulin in normal subjects and patients with varying degrees of renal failure. The assay used GP1M as the antiserum. (Reproduced, with permission, from Arnaud CD et al: Primary hyperthyroidism, renal lithiasis, and the measurement of parathyroid hormone in serum by radioimmunoassay. In: *Urinary Calculi: Recent Advances in Aetiology, Stone Structure, and Treatment.* International Symposium on Renal Stone Research, 1973.)

This relationship might have been predicted on the basis of older studies that showed increases in serum phosphorus concentrations at this same level of GFR (40 mL/min). However, it was not until the investigations of Bricker et al that the role of decreased renal filtration of phosphate and subsequent hyperphosphatemia in the genesis of renal hyperparathyroidism was appreciated. According to their hypothesis, each decrement in GFR is accompanied by a transient increase in serum phosphorus, which in turn leads to a transient decrease in serum calcium and a compensatory increase in secretion of PTH. Restoration of serum calcium and serum phosphorus toward normal occurs as a result of the effects of increased serum PTH on mobilization of bone mineral and renal tubular reabsorption of phosphate, respectively. As the cycle is repeated, secondary hyperparathyroidism progressively worsens and parathyroid hyperplasia develops.

The evidence in support of the hypothesis of Bricker et al is impressive. First, a reduction in phosphate intake in proportion to the reduction in GFR prevents renal hyperparathyroidism in dogs that have had progressive renal failure for as long as 1 year. Second, there is a consistent positive correlation between serum concentrations of phosphate and iPTH in patients with chronic renal failure (Figure 5–21). Third, reductions in the serum concentrations of phosphate by dietary restriction and administration of aluminum hydroxide gels in patients with chronic renal failure are associated with increases in serum calcium and decreases in serum iPTH.

The hyperphosphatemia of chronic renal failure may also have a negative influence on the production of $1,25(OH)_2D_3$, even before the destruction of nephrons is so complete that the renal $25OHD_3$-converting enzymes are eliminated. As illustrated in Figure 5–2, such an effect would result in a decrease in the intestinal absorption of calcium—a well-established finding in patients with chronic renal failure. This decrease would contribute further to hypocalcemia and secondary hyperparathyroidism. It is well known that serum concentrations of $1,25(OH)_2D_3$ are low in patients with end-stage renal disease, but there have been no systematic studies of the relation between serum concentrations of this vitamin D metabolite and the degree of chronic renal failure.

The osseous manifestations of progressive increases in PTH secretion and decreases in $1,25$ $(OH)_2D_3$ production by the kidney are evident in patients with chronic renal failure. They include classic osteitis fibrosa cystica similar to that seen in primary hyperparathyroidism (Figure 5–15) and osteomalacia (Figure 5–30). In addition, osteosclerosis and osteoporosis are often present at the same time. The causes of those two disorders are unknown and are probably multiple. It is thought that the osteosclerosis is related to the hyperphosphatemia, and the osteoporosis to diminished sex hormone function and the metabolic acidosis of uremia. Finally, there is evidence that the bones of patients with chronic renal failure are resistant to the calcemic actions of PTH. Although there may be several underlying reasons for such resistance, it is commonly thought that the major factors are the decreased serum concentration of $1,25(OH)_2D_3$ and the dependency of PTH on normal vitamin D metabolism for its action on bone.

The pathogenesis of renal hyperparathyroidism during the progressive destruction of nephrons is illustrated in Figure 5–22. The process schematically described results in the classic biochemical and physiologic abnormalities of mineral and bone metabolism observed in patients with chronic renal failure, including hypocalcemia, hyperphosphatemia, decreased intestinal absorption of calcium and negative

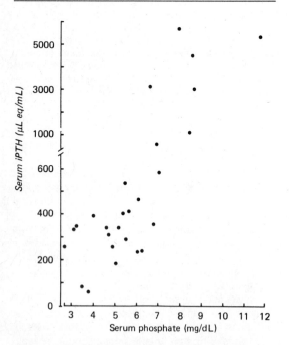

Figure 5–21. Relationship between serum iPTH and serum phosphate in patients with renal failure. (Reproduced, with permission, from Bordier PJ et al: Evolution of renal osteodystrophy: Correlation of bone histomorphometry and serum mineral and immunoreactive parathyroid normal values before and after treatment with calcium carbonate or 25-hydroxycholecalciferol. Kidney Int 1975;7[Suppl 2]:102.)

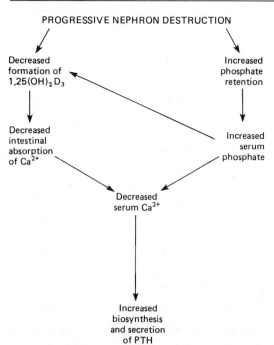

Figure 5–22. Pathogenesis of parathyroid hyperplasia during progressive destruction of nephrons. (Reproduced, with permission, from Arnaud CD: Hyperparathyroidism and renal failure. Kidney Int 1973;4:89.)

calcium balance, marked increases in circulating PTH, and the different bone diseases noted above.

Staging of Renal Osteodystrophy

It is difficult to stage the severity of renal osteodystrophy using any available blood chemistry measurements short of assaying serum mid-region iPTH. For example, serum calcium, phosphorus, magnesium, and alkaline phosphatase are within the reference range early in the course of the development of renal failure (inulin clearance in the range of 20–30 mL/min, stage I; Figure 5–23), yet there is histomorphometric evidence of osteitis fibrosa cystica in trephine biopsies of the iliac crest and increased levels of serum iPTH. Thus, because serum iPTH increases as renal function progressively declines below clearances of 40 mL/min, it is possible to follow patients with compromised renal function with measurements of serum iPTH to determine when to institute therapeutic measures to prevent or treat secondary hyperparathyroidism (eg, dietary phosphorus restriction, calcium supplementation, and vitamin D). In this context, it is important to recognize that increases in serum mid-region iPTH may reflect, in part, impaired clearance of mid and carboxyl PTH fragments from the circulation by failing kidneys. This is supported by reports showing that in patients with renal failure, values for serum bioactive PTH and intact iPTH may be within the normal range while serum mid-region iPTH is increased as much as five- to tenfold. However, the fact that osteitis fibrosa cystica is often present in patients with early renal failure who have increased levels of serum mid-region iPTH strongly suggests that those increases in serum iPTH reflect secondary hyperparathyroidism as well. At this writing, experience with immunometric assays of serum intact PTH are too limited to permit comment upon their application to the problem of staging renal osteodystrophy—although, as with mid-region assays, it has been possible to demonstrate that serum values of intact iPTH correlate highly with quantitative indices of hyperparathyroid bone disease in iliac crest biopsies.

Patients with stage II disease (Figure 5–23) may be easier to identify because they generally have more severe renal functional impairment, hypocalcemia, and hyperphosphatemia. However, hypocalcemia and hyperphosphatemia may be obscured by therapeutic measures, and hyperparathyroidism, detectable only by measurements of serum iPTH, may be of sufficient severity as to warrant more intensive therapy. Untreated stage II hyperparathyroidism is generally identified by serum mid-region iPTH values 20–30 times the upper limit of the reference range. Those patients are generally amenable to medical therapy.

Patients with stage III disease (Figure 5–23) usually have normal levels of total serum calcium but are hyperphosphatemic. They generally have severe

osteodystrophy and the beginnings of soft tissue calcification. The severity of those problems is not generally appreciated until serum iPTH measurements are performed, and they show values 50–100 times the upper limit of normal. It is important to discover such large increases in serum iPTH because they reflect a degree of hyperparathyroidism which is still reversible with medical therapy but is on the verge of transition to stage IV disease, which generally requires operative treatment to reduce parathyroid gland mass so that medical therapy will be effective. Stage IV disease (Figure 5–23) is characterized by hypercalcemia, hyperphosphatemia, severe osteodystrophy, soft tissue calcification, and serum mid-region iPTH levels 200–1000 times the upper limit of the reference range.

Differential Diagnosis of Hypercalcemia in Association With Renal Failure

It is important to recognize that hypercalcemia in patients with chronic renal failure does not always reflect stage IV secondary hyperparathyroidism; it may reflect primary hyperparathyroidism with associated renal failure. Although that diagnosis is difficult to make, it is usually associated with much lower levels of serum iPTH (mid-region assay; unpublished

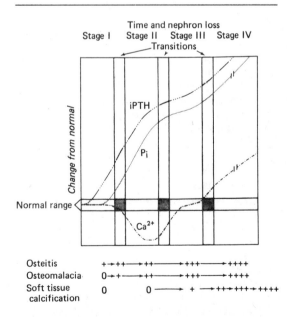

Figure 5–23. Stages of biochemical and osseous abnormalities in renal osteodystrophy as a function of time and nephron loss. (Reproduced, with permission, from Bordier PH et al: Evolution of renal osteodystrophy: Correlation of bone histomorphometry and serum mineral and immunoreactive parathyroid hormone values before and after treatment with calcium carbonate or 25-hydroxycholecalciferol. Kidney Int 1975;7[Suppl 2]:102.)

data) than are found in stage IV renal osteodystrophy, ie, in the range of five to 20 times the upper limit of the reference range. Another alternative that must be considered is "aluminum osteodystrophy" (see below), which is characterized by severe osteodystrophy, hypercalcemia, and lower levels of serum iPTH, also in the range of 5–20 times the upper limit of the reference range. Finally, nonparathyroid causes of hypercalcemia such as sarcoidosis may complicate renal failure. In these instances, serum iPTH will also be lower than expected.

Treatment by subtotal parathyroidectomy is the preferred therapy of stage IV secondary hyperparathyroidism and of primary hyperparathyroidism, but parathyroidectomy tends to make "aluminum osteodystrophy" worse and is inappropriate in patients with nonparathyroid hypercalcemia. It is therefore just as important to specifically identify the underlying causes of hypercalcemia in patients with renal failure as it is in patients with normal renal function (see above). The mid-region PTH radioimmunoassay has provided the author with an invaluable diagnostic aid in this regard. Again, there has been too little experience with serum measurements of intact iPTH to know whether they will be similarly helpful.

Comparison of Clinical Utility of Carboxyl (53–84) and Mid (44–68) PTH Radioimmunoassays With an Intact PTH Immunometric Assay in Chronic Renal Failure

As noted above, serum mid and carboxyl region iPTH may be increased while serum-intact iPTH is within the normal range in the presence of renal failure. Although this phenomenon is apt to be due largely to the diminished ability of diseased kidneys to excrete mid-PTH and carboxyl-PTH fragments, an alternative explanation should be considered. It is possible that appropriate treatment of even severe secondary hyperparathyroidism (eg, high dialysate calcium concentrations, intravenous calcitriol therapy) may dramatically suppress PTH secretion (so that serum-intact iPTH registers in or near the normal range) without altering the size or enormous secretory capacity of greatly enlarged parathyroid glands. In such cases, serum mid or carboxyl region iPTH will not be greatly affected by treatment until gland size is decreased, mostly because of the very long half-life of mid and carboxyl region fragments in patients with renal failure. Thus, it is likely that serum mid-PTH and carboxyl-PTH assays may more consistently reflect the degree of parathyroid hyperplasia in patients with renal failure than intact PTH assays, especially in patients undergoing intensive therapy for secondary hyperparathyroidism. Moreover, physicians not recognizing this might be prompted to decrease the intensity of treatment prematurely based on low or normal levels of serum-intact iPTH. Notwithstanding these considerations, it is fair to say that the interpretation of an elevated serum mid-iPTH or carboxyl-iPTH is not straightforward in patients with impaired renal function; serum intact iPTH is preferable in the diagnostic evaluation of such cases.

"Aluminum" Osteodystrophy

A newly recognized syndrome of osteodystrophy that does not conform to the bone disease characterizing the four stages shown in Figure 5–23 has been described in patients with chronic renal failure. This syndrome is present in an increasing number of patients with renal osteodystrophy. Its cause is unknown, although accumulation of aluminum in bone (especially at the calcification front) due to the aluminum contained in dialysis baths or phosphate-binding agents has been recently implicated. Patients with this disorder have bone pain and multiple fractures and tend to develop hypercalcemia. Thus, superficially at least, they resemble patients with stage III or stage IV disease. However, instead of severe degrees of osteitis fibrosa cystica and hyperparathyroidism, these patients have a bone disease characterized by low-turnover osteomalacia and osteoporosis with only small or moderate increases in serum iPTH. Patients who have been subjected to parathyroidectomy have responded poorly or not at all. This is in striking contrast to patients with true stage IV renal hyperparathyroidism and osteodystrophy, who almost always respond favorably as long as they are carefully managed to prevent recrudescence of hyperparathyroidism after subtotal parathyroidectomy. The effectiveness of deferoxamine, a drug that chelates aluminum, is still being assessed in the treatment of "aluminum" osteodystrophy.

Clinical Features

The clinical manifestations of renal hyperparathyroidism and osteodystrophy are related to hypocalcemia in stage II patients and to soft tissue calcifications, osteodystrophy, and pruritus in stage III and stage IV patients. Although not common, symptoms of neuromuscular irritability and tetany similar to those in hypoparathyroidism may occur. Osteodystrophy may cause bone pain due to either osteitis fibrosa or multiple fractures (frequently of the ribs). Soft tissue calcification of the joints (usually the shoulder) may be evident in rare cases as hard irregular masses over the joints. Pruritus is most debilitating when it occurs, and its cause is poorly understood. However, it routinely abates after successful medical or surgical management of hyperparathyroidism. Radiographs of the skeleton may show the ravages of osteitis fibrosa cystica (Figure 5–15A and 5–15B), osteomalacia (Figure 5–30), and osteosclerosis. This latter condition is classically observed as the "rugger jersey sign" (referring to the striped shirts worn by British rugby teams) and is caused by increased density of the upper and lower margins of vertebral bodies, separated by central horizontal zones of decreased density. Soft tissue calcifications often seen on x-ray in the later stages are most prominent in large vessels and joints but have been observed in extreme cases in lung, stomach, and heart. It is thought that soft tissue calcification of small blood vessels is responsible for the rare development of necrotic skin lesions on legs, abdomen, and fingertips.

Prevention

Little effort has been made to systematically interrupt the adaptive cycle described in the section on pathogenesis. This is probably because patients are generally asymptomatic and reluctant to take medicines early in the course of renal failure. In addition, no long-term prospective studies have been reported showing that appropriate therapy instituted early and directed at preventing the development of positive phosphorus balance, negative calcium balance, and hyperparathyroidism will significantly decrease the incidence or severity of mineral and bone complications that occur in the late stages of renal failure, during hemodialysis, or after kidney transplantation. However, investigations during the past 10 years have shown that restoration of serum calcium and phosphorus levels toward normal by the use of oral phosphate-binding gels and calcium concentrations of 6–7 mg/dL (1.5–1.75 mmol/L) in the dialysate for patients undergoing hemodialysis decreases serum levels of iPTH (Figure 5–24) and causes improvement in established renal osteodystrophy (Figure 5–25). It is therefore likely that the component of renal osteodystrophy that is due to hyperparathyroidism could be prevented if steps were taken *early* in the course of chronic renal failure to avoid adaptive increases in PTH secretion. Since the stimulus of PTH secretion is hypocalcemia induced by hyperphosphatemia and decreased intestinal absorption of calcium, it is logical to assume that a combination of ingestion of a low-phosphate diet, administration of phosphate-binding agents, and treatment with relatively large doses of absorbable calcium and physiologic doses of $1,25(OH)_2D_3$ (calcitriol) might be successful in restoring extracellular calcium and phosphorus homeostasis and preventing secondary hyperparathyroidism.

Treatment

A. Management of Stage I Renal Osteodystrophy:
The major difficulty in this stage is determining when to begin treatment in individual patients, because serum calcium and phosphorus concentrations are usually within the normal range early in the course of chronic renal failure. However, assays specific for the mid or carboxyl region of the PTH molecule show that serum iPTH is increased uniformly in patients with stage I renal failure (Figure 5–23). Although an increased level of serum iPTH may reflect diminished clearance of carboxyl

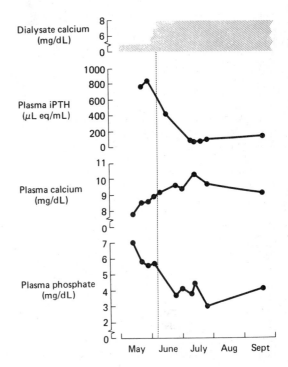

Figure 5–24. Serial values of plasma iPTH, calcium, and phosphate during treatment of a patient with low and then high calcium levels in the dialysate. Plasma phosphate was reduced to 6 mg/dL by oral administration of aluminum hydroxide gel, after which dialysate calcium concentrations were progressively increased to 8 mg/dL. (Reproduced, with permission, from Goldsmith RS et al: Control of secondary hyperparathyroidism during long-term hemodialysis. Am J Med 1971;50:692.)

terminal fragments by diseased kidneys, mid-region assays show that institution of the therapy noted below results in a progressive decline in serum iPTH toward the normal range. This result suggests that there is either a decrease in PTH secretion or improved clearance of carboxyl terminal fragments by the kidney. The latter possibility is remote, and it is likely that the observed decreases in serum iPTH reflect success in directly interrupting the development of adaptive hyperparathyroidism.

1. Dietary restriction of phosphorus– It appears that the single most important marker for stage I renal osteodystrophy—and the major indication for considering a patient with chronic renal failure for treatment with dietary restriction of phosphate, calcium supplementation, and with vitamin D therapy—is an abnormally high serum iPTH value as measured by a mid or carboxyl region assay. Although dietary restriction of phosphate may be sufficient for some patients, others may require the addition of phosphate-binding antacids in order to reduce serum iPTH.

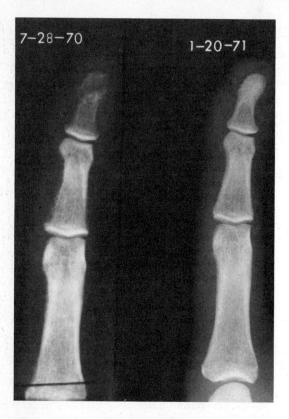

Figure 5–25. X-rays of index finger of a patient before **(left)** and after **(right)** plasma phosphate was reduced to normal with aluminum hydroxide gel and 6 months of dialysis against a bath of 8 mg/dL calcium. (Reproduced, with permission, from Vosik WM et al: Successful medical management of osteitis fibrosa due to tertiary hyperparathyroidism. Mayo Clin Proc 1972:47:110.)

2. Removal of phosphate– Whereas aluminum-based phosphate-binding antacids have been used extensively in the past to reduce intestinal absorption of phosphate, they are used only sparingly now because of their potential for inducing or worsening "aluminum osteodystrophy." Calcium carbonate is being used instead. It is not only effective in reducing serum phosphate but corrects hypocalcemia and improves calcium balance when given in large enough doses (see below). Prolonged hypophosphatemia should be avoided.

3. Calcium supplementation– Because low-phosphate diets are also low in calcium, it is necessary to provide supplementation with some form of absorbable calcium. Calcium carbonate is preferred because it is cheap and well tolerated, it combats renal acidosis, and it is an effective phosphate-binding agent. Calcium supplementation is necessary even when the patient is on a normal diet, because enteral absorption of calcium is usually decreased in chronic renal failure. Calcium as the carbonate should be

given in doses of 1–3 g three times daily with meals. Dose adjustment is done by monitoring serum calcium (maintained at < 11 mg/dL) and serum phosphate (maintained at < 5 mg/dL). If it is not possible to maintain those levels of serum phosphate with calcium carbonate without causing hypercalcemia, low doses of an aluminum-based phosphate binder should be used (Basaljel, Dialume, Alu-Cap, or Amphojel, 1 capsule or tablet three times a day with meals).

4. Vitamin D therapy– It is reasonable to maintain patients with early renal failure on relatively small doses (1000–2000 units/d) of ergocalciferol (vitamin D_2), providing no more than ten times the daily requirement. Experience with $1,25(OH)_2D_3$ (calcitriol) in patients with stage I disease has not yet been reported.

B. Management of Stage II Renal Osteodystrophy: Most patients with end-stage renal failure present with the mineral and osseous abnormalities found in stage II disease. The hallmarks of this stage are hypocalcemia, hyperphosphatemia, and increases in serum iPTH greater than those in stage I. Generally, serum iPTH measured by a mid or carboxyl region assay is 10–20 times normal values.

Since stages III and IV tend to be much less reversible by medical means than stage I or stage II, it is important to manage the patient with stage II disease aggressively. In treating such a patient, one must recognize that the hypocalcemia seen in stage II probably reflects a fortuitous protective adaptation of the organism to severe hyperparathyroidism. In other words, the permissive influence of vitamin D on the bone-resorbing action of PTH has been largely removed by the final destruction of the kidneys, and the devastating effects of enormously high concentrations of circulating PTH have been naturally averted. Thus, it is probably important to delay the introduction of vitamin D or one of its biologically active metabolites or analogues until the hyperparathyroidism has been partially brought under control. This can be done in almost all dialyzed patients by restoring serum calcium and phosphorus to normal levels by the simple manipulation of dietary and dialysate calcium and dietary phosphate described above. Serum phosphate should be reduced to less than 5 mg/dL (1.6 mmol/L) before attempts to increase serum calcium are made; this prevents increases in the calcium × phosphate product greater than 70 and the tendency to soft tissue calcifications. The regimen is most easily initiated in the hospital and should take no longer than 1 week. After serum iPTH begins to decrease, some form of vitamin D therapy may be introduced. The most effective form of vitamin D therapy has not yet been determined. A combination of metabolites may be necessary to restore both intestinal calcium absorption and bone formation processes to normal. Dihydrotachysterol (0.125 mg twice weekly to 1 mg daily) is used extensively. However, the more expensive $1,25(OH)_2D_3$

(calcitriol), at doses of 0.5–2 μg/d, is probably the drug of choice. Equivalent doses of ergocalciferol or any of the available vitamin D metabolites (Table 5–2) may also be used. Recently, intravenous 1,25 $(OH)_2D_3$ (calcitriol), 1–3 μg three times a week, has proved effective in rapidly lowering serum iPTH.

C. Management of Patients on Dialysis: Stage I and II Renal Osteodystrophy: When stage I and II patients who are treated as described in the previous section reach the end stage of renal failure and it becomes necessary for them to begin a hemodialysis program, they will have only minor hyperparathyroidism and renal osteodystrophy. These patients should present few problems in continuing prophylaxis. Although these patients may require only supplements of vitamin D_2 (ergocalciferol) to avoid development of osteomalacia, one or more active vitamin D metabolites is occasionally necessary.

Dialysis patients with stage II renal osteodystrophy should respond to the treatment outlined for patients in stage II who are not on hemodialysis. The important consideration in patients on hemodialysis is to avoid aggravating negative calcium balance, which occurs when dialysate calcium concentrations are below 5.7 mg/dL. In fact, it is possible and probably desirable to use hemodialysis as a means of producing slightly positive calcium balance by employing calcium concentrations of 6.5–8 mg/dL. However, this should not be attempted until serum phosphate concentrations are below 5 mg/dL, because extraosseous mineralization may be induced when the serum calcium × phosphate product is 70 or more. This therapeutic regimen is illustrated in Figure 5–24, where the reduction of plasma phosphate to 3 mg/dL combined with the gradual introduction of dialysate calcium concentrations of 8 mg/dL (2 mmol/L) resulted in an increase in plasma calcium from 8 to 10 mg/dL (2–2.5 mmol/L) and a concomitant and permanent decrease in plasma iPTH from values up to 20 times normal to values just above the upper limits of normal within a period of 2 1/2 months. Once abnormal mineral metabolism is brought under control, dialysate calcium concentrations should be reduced to about 6.5 mg/dL (1.6 mmol/L).

D. Management of Stage III and IV Renal Osteodystrophy: Stage III disease can be identified by the presence of hyperphosphatemia and eucalcemia with serum iPTH values (as measured by mid or carboxyl region assay) from 50 to 100 times normal levels; in stage IV disease, there is hypercalcemia with elevations of serum iPTH to 200–1000 times normal levels. Whether patients with stage III or IV disease should be treated with the regimen illustrated in Figure 5–24 is controversial. It is clear that with heroic effort, it can be successfully applied to these patients. Figure 5–25 shows improvement in bone disease in one such patient. Ordinarily, patients with stage III or IV renal osteodystrophy should probably be treated

initially with subtotal parathyroidectomy in order to decrease the size of the parathyroid gland mass, followed by the regimen described for patients with stage II renal osteodystrophy. This rather radical approach is justified because mineral complications and persistence of hyperparathyroidism after renal transplantation are less severe in patients whose hyperparathyroidism and osteodystrophy were well controlled before transplantation. It generally takes much longer to bring stage III and stage IV patients under control, and success is less common than in patients with stage II disease. Therefore, considering the unpredictable availability of donor kidneys for transplantation and the probable desirability of having hyperparathyroidism and renal osteodystrophy under control prior to transplantation, it is important to decide as soon as possible whether patients have stage III or stage IV renal osteodystrophy. When in doubt, the clinician should institute an intensive regimen of medical treatment, and if marked improvement in hyperparathyroidism and osteodystrophy is not observed within 3–6 months, subtotal parathyroidectomy should be considered.

E. Renal Transplantation: Depending upon the stage of renal hyperparathyroidism and osteodystrophy, successful renal transplantation may reverse the entire course of these complications. Patients who receive transplants during stage I or II achieve normal levels of serum iPTH, calcium, and phosphorus within months. Patients who receive transplants during stage III or IV may never achieve normal levels of serum iPTH and often suffer from hypercalcemia and hypophosphatemia for years, even when the transplanted kidney is functioning normally. Ultimately, some patients in this latter group require subtotal parathyroidectomy, but the indications for the procedure in such patients are poorly defined.

Prognosis & Future Prospects

It is becoming clear that the outcome of the mineral and osseous complications of end-stage renal failure depends upon early recognition and treatment of these complications, particularly before hemodialysis is started. At present, it is uncertain whether such an approach will succeed in the long-term management of patients.

DISORDERS OF CALCITONIN (CT) SECRETION

No clinical disorder has been reported to date in which hypocalcitoninemia plays a definitive role. However, there are a number of conditions in which hypercalcitoninemia is found–most notably medullary carcinoma of the thyroid gland (see also Chapters 4 and 21).

MEDULLARY CARCINOMA OF THE THYROID GLAND

Medullary carcinoma is a malignant tumor of the parafollicular cells of the thyroid gland. It occurs sporadically but may also be inherited as an autosomal dominant trait as part of the type II multiple endocrine neoplasia (MEN) syndrome. This syndrome includes medullary carcinoma of the thyroid gland and pheochromocytoma. There are two variants of the syndrome: type IIa and type IIb. Patients with MEN type IIa have a normal appearance but a high incidence of hyperparathyroidism, most frequently due to enlargement of multiple parathyroid glands. Patients with MEN type IIb have a striking appearance due to labial and mucosal ganglioneuromas, a marfanoid habitus, and other somatic abnormalities. Hyperparathyroidism is unusual in this variant.

Incidence

Medullary carcinoma constitutes 1–3% of all thyroid cancers. The sex incidence is almost equal (male:female ratio of 1.3:1 in sporadic cases and 1:1 in familial cases). In general, familial cases present at a younger age than do sporadic ones.

Pathology

Medullary carcinoma appears as a solid, often hard mass confined to but not encapsulated in the thyroid gland. It is often unilateral in sporadic cases and bilateral in familial cases. The lesion is composed of sheets of cells with granular cytoplasms and usually contains irregular masses of amyloid and fibrous tissue. Most patients who present with a thyroid mass already have metastases to cervical lymph nodes. Some masses spread to the upper mediastinum. Metastases beyond the mediastinum, usually delayed until late in the natural history of the disease, most commonly occur in lungs, liver, bones, and adrenal glands.

Pathophysiology

Medullary carcinomas secrete large quantities of CT and respond to provocative stimuli such as intravenous pentagastrin or hypercalcemia induced by intravenous calcium. Although CT produces hypocalcemia and hypophosphatemia in experimental animals, these biochemical findings are unusual in patients with medullary carcinoma in spite of extremely high levels of immunoreactive calcitonin (iCT). This paradox is probably due to a combination of factors, including homologous desensitization of tissues that normally respond to the actions of CT.

Medullary carcinomas may secrete many other bioactive substances in addition to CT, each with the potential of causing symptoms. These include biogenic amines, ACTH and corticotropin-releasing hormone, prostaglandins, nerve growth factor, and possibly a prolactin-releasing hormone. Diarrhea is present in about 20% of patients. This symptom relents after surgical excision of the tumor and is therefore thought to be humorally mediated. Cushing's syndrome is present in about 5% of cases, secondary to secretion of excessive ACTH.

Clinical Features

Most patients with sporadic medullary carcinoma present with an asymptomatic thyroid mass. Patients with MEN type IIb may complain of neuromas and their marfanoid appearance. Hypercalcemia may be detected in the course of routine blood screening in patients with MEN type IIa with primary hyperparathyroidism. Most importantly, hypertension in patients with MEN type IIa or IIb may reflect the presence of pheochromocytoma, which may be more immediately life-threatening than medullary carcinoma.

Paraneoplastic syndromes (eg, Cushing's syndrome) as well as intractable diarrhea and flushing should alert the physician to the possible existence of medullary carcinoma. A family history of more than one case of thyroid cancer should certainly raise a suspicion of MEN type IIa in a patient with bizarre symptoms.

Other neural manifestations of MEN type IIb include medullated nerves in the cornea on slit lamp examination of the eye and ganglioneuromas of the gastrointestinal tract. The latter may cause gastrointestinal obstruction as well as megacolon. Medullary cancers occasionally calcify. Thus, the discovery of a calcified thyroidal mass does not indicate that it is benign; rather, this is probably an indication for measurement of serum iCT (see below).

Diagnosis

The cornerstone of the laboratory investigation of patients suspected of having medullary carcinoma is radioimmunoassay of plasma CT. Although not absolutely specific for the tumor (see below), increased serum levels of iCT in patients with a thyroid mass, a family history of medullary carcinoma, or pheochromocytoma virtually establish the diagnosis. Other conditions in which increased levels of serum iCT have been reported include (1) ectopic secretion by almost any malignant tumor (especially small cell carcinoma of the lung), (2) chronic renal failure, (3) gastrointestinal disorders such as endocrine tumors of the pancreas and pernicious anemia, (4) subacute Hashimoto's thyroiditis, and (5) pregnancy.

The diagnostic accuracy of CT radioimmunoassay is greatly enhanced when combined with provocative tests. As many as 30% of members of families with MEN type IIa or IIb who harbor small medullary carcinomas will have normal basal levels of plasma iCT.

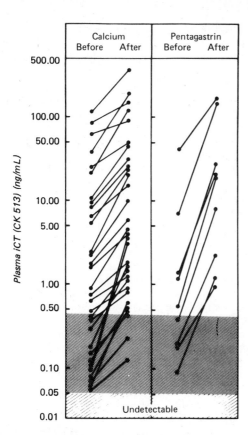

Figure 5–26. Maximal plasma iCT concentrations measured with antiserum CK 513 in patients with histologically proved medullary thyroid carcinoma of C cell hyperplasia before and after administration of calcium (left panel) or pentagastrin (right panel). The upper limit of stimulated plasma iCT concentrations in normal persons (shaded areas) is 0.42 ng/mL. (Reproduced, with permission, from Sizemore GW et al: Epidemiology of medullary carcinoma of the thyroid gland: A 5-year experience (1971–1976). Surg Clin North Am 1977;57:633.)

Their neoplastic disease can only be detected by provocative tests with intravenous administration of pentagastrin, 0.5 μg over 5–10 seconds, or calcium chloride, 150 mg over 10 minutes (Figure 5–26). Plasma iCT increases abnormally in most cases within 2–5 minutes. The CT radioimmunoassay used should be sensitive enough to measure plasma iCT in the normal range. Otherwise, the assay is unlikely to detect relatively small increases above the stimulated normal range, thus making the test impossible to interpret.

To rule out familial medullary carcinoma, iCT should be measured during a provocative test in all available first-degree relatives of patients with medullary carcinoma, regardless of the family history. In a few affected patients with minimal parafollicular cell disease, false-negative results may be obtained with any of the tests mentioned. Provocative

tests should therefore be performed annually in first-degree relatives who have had negative tests. About half of the members of a given family in which one member has MEN type IIa or IIb eventually develop medullary cancer. Early detection will permit definitive surgical treatment.

Treatment

In patients with medullary carcinoma, pheochromocytoma must be excluded or treated first. Medullary carcinoma is then treated by total thyroidectomy. Total thyroidectomy is especially important in patients with MEN type IIa or IIb, because medullary carcinoma is almost always bilateral and polycentric. Lymph nodes in the midline compartment should be removed and those in both internal jugular chains sampled. If jugular lymph nodes are involved, modified neck dissection should be performed. Postoperatively, all patients should be studied with provocative tests to determine if residual tumor is present. They should also be given thyroid hormone replacement. The overall prevalence of residual or metastatic medullary cancer after such surgery is about 35%. Most of these patients are older and have had regional metastases at the time of surgery. Long-term follow-up with provocative tests every year is advised for all patients. Although it is usually difficult to determine the location of metastases that are responsible for a positive test, local recurrences can be suspected and dealt with surgically. There is no known effective chemotherapeutic, radiopharmaceutical, or radiation treatment of medullary carcinoma.

Prognosis

Patients with sporadic medullary carcinoma have the least favorable prognosis because metastases are usually present at the time of diagnosis; only 46% of these patients survive for 10 years. Patients with MEN type IIa appear to fare better, with few deaths reported. Conversely, in a Mayo Clinic series of 107 patients with MEN type IIb, 67% have had residual disease after surgery and 18% died of medullary cancer. The reasons for the apparent difference in prognosis between MEN type IIa and MEN type IIb are unknown.

HYPERCALCIURIA

Hypercalciuria is usually detected in the course of evaluation of a patient with renal stone disease. It is variably defined as excretion of more than 300 mg of calcium per 24 hours in men and 250 mg per 24 hours in women. Urinary calcium excretion depends on many factors, but the most important is dietary intake of calcium. It is the *concentration* of calcium in the urine that determines whether calcium will interact with anionic constituents (particularly oxalate) of the urine to form stones. Thus, prevention of calcium-containing stones requires reduction in urinary concentrations of calcium and oxalate. It has been shown that increased excretion of uric acid in the urine is not only responsible for the formation of uric acid stones but may also be important in the formation of calcium oxalate stones. This means that the clinician should pay careful attention to uric acid excretion in patients with calcium oxalate stones and should attempt to reduce it if it is elevated. Likewise, low urinary levels of citrate should be corrected, because this condition contributes to calcium oxalate precipitation.

The present section will concentrate on evaluation of the metabolic causes of hypercalciuria and calcium-containing stones, with the exception of infection, medullary sponge kidney, and renal tubular acidosis. The reader should consult the references at the end of this chapter for excellent reviews on cystine, uric acid, and magnesium ammonium phosphate stones.

Epidemiologic Considerations

Hypercalciuria appears to be common in the general population, but there is little accurate information about its incidence. The true incidence of stone disease is also unknown, although it is likely that 1–3% of people in most industrialized countries have had or will have a renal stone. Geography, race, and occupation probably have some influence on the incidence of stone disease, but the underlying factors are poorly understood. The frequency of calcium phosphate stones is equal in men and women. They occur in patients with sterile alkaline urines–ie, in cases of renal tubular acidosis, protracted use of carbonic anhydrase inhibitors, or primary hyperparathyroidism. Calcium oxalate stones occur more frequently in men (3–8:1) and in patients with idiopathic hypercalciuria.

Biochemical Characteristics of Calcium Stones

The most common anionic constituent of calcium-containing stones is oxalate. Calcium phosphate is also often present (mixed stones). Urinary saturation with calcium phosphate or calcium oxalate correlates roughly with the stone content of either anion. Hypercalciuria is observed in patients who make either mixed or unmixed stones, regardless of whether urinary calcium excretion is expressed as concentration, quantity per unit of time, or as the ratio of calcium to creatinine. Oxalate excretion is increased in patients who form calcium oxalate stones, and urinary pH is increased in those who form mixed stones.

Pathogenesis of Hypercalciuria

The reader is again referred to the "butterfly" diagram (Figure 5–2) while studying the pathogenetic concepts discussed below.

A. Hypercalcemia: In the presence of a normal rate of renal glomerular filtration, hypercalcemia due to any cause (see section on primary hyperparathyroidism), if sufficiently severe, results in hypercalciuria. One exception is benign familial hypercalcemia (familial hypocalciuric hypercalcemia), in which hypocalciuria is the biochemical hallmark of the disease. Another is mild hyperparathyroidism, in which urinary calcium may be normal in spite of hypercalcemia because of the hypocalciuric effects of excess PTH. However, even in such cases of hyperparathyroidism, calcium stones are common and may be due to the presence of other risk factors, such as hyperoxaluria, hyperuricosuria, and increased urine pH. For the most part, renal stone disease occurs primarily in patients who have had chronic hypercalcemia. In fact, this historical information is sometimes important in making the differential diagnosis of hypercalcemia (Table 5–3). Hypercalcemia in patients with documented stone disease is much more likely to be due to primary hyperparathyroidism than to cancer.

B. Diet: High dietary intake of protein causes both increased intestinal absorption and increased urinary excretion of calcium. These effects are poorly understood, but evidence indicates that dietary protein has a greater influence than dietary calcium on urinary calcium when calcium intake is in the range of 800–1400 mg/d. Urolithiasis has been reported in patients who have inordinately high protein intakes.

Increased dietary carbohydrate increases urinary calcium excretion at least in part because it increases the glomerular filtration rate. The calciuric response to a carbohydrate load is greater in stone-formers and their relatives than in normal subjects, but there is no difference between these groups in fractional urinary calcium excretion.

Lactose ingestion also increases urinary excretion of calcium, but lactose appears to act primarily by facilitating intestinal absorption of calcium. Lactose is known to be highly lithogenic in animals, and milk restriction may be important in the management of some patients with calcium stones (see below).

Urinary calcium increases in parallel with dietary intake of elemental calcium. It is presumed that much of the absorbed calcium is transferred from intestine to blood by a passive transport process, because with a high calcium intake, the hormonal mechanisms that regulate active calcium transport across the intestine adapt to decrease active transport (Figure 5–2). Therefore, decreasing the dietary intake of calcium in patients with hypercalciuric stone disease would seem to be appropriate. However, the situation is not so simple. Although calcium restriction reduces urinary calcium excretion, it also increases intestinal absorption and renal excretion of oxalate and, in the long term, results in secondary hyperparathyroidism and possibly osteopenia. Increased calcium intake, on the other hand, decreases intestinal absorption and renal excretion of oxalate by inducing calcium oxalate precipitation in the gut while increasing urinary calcium. Therefore, either of these dietary manipulations could aggravate calcium stone disease in hypercalciuric patients, and the author cannot recommend them. Instead, a nutritionally adequate intake of calcium (600–800 mg/d) should be maintained in most patients and pharmacologic agents used to lower urinary calcium excretion (see treatment section below).

C. Intestinal Hyperabsorption of Calcium: Most patients with hypercalciuria that is unrelated to chronic states of hypercalcemia, drugs, or diet absorb too much calcium. Many of these patients have decreased serum levels of iPTH and decreased nephrogenous cAMP, presumably reflecting decreased PTH secretion caused by small increases in serum calcium within the normal range. In general, serum phosphorus is below the normal mean; and in one-third of patients, serum levels of $1,25(OH)_2D_3$ are increased. Clearly, in these latter patients, the normal adaptive decrease in $1,25(OH)_2D_3$ production in response to hyperabsorption of calcium and decreased levels of serum PTH fails to occur. It has been suggested that hypophosphatemia due to a renal phosphate leak is responsible (see intestinal loop of Figure 5–2). In this pathogenetic scheme, the renal phosphate leak is postulated to be the primary defect, and hyperabsorption of calcium and hypercalciuria are secondary to the effects of increased serum levels of $1,25(OH)_2D_3$.

The cause of intestinal hyperabsorption of calcium in the remaining two-thirds of patients with hypercalciuria, whose serum concentrations of $1,25(OH)_2D_3$ are normal or low, is unknown. It is possible that endocrine abnormalities not yet identified may be present. On the other hand, these patients may represent a group whose hyperabsorption of calcium is due to an intrinsic defect in the intestine, in which greater than normal quantities of calcium are transported from intestinal lumen to blood.

D. "Renal Leak" of Calcium: It is generally agreed that few patients with hypercalciuria have a true "renal calcium leak." It is possible, however, that some patients with intestinal hyperabsorption of calcium also have a renal tubule defect that permits excessive urinary excretion of calcium. Patients whose hypercalciuria is due solely to a renal leak of calcium have serum concentrations of calcium in the lower range of normal; this results in small increases in serum levels of PTH, which increase bone resorption and the production of $1,25(OH)_2D_3$. The resulting increase in serum levels of $1,25(OH)_2D_3$ causes intestinal hyperabsorption of calcium and produces pathophysiologic changes that superficially resemble

hypercalciuria due to "primary" intestinal hyperabsorption of calcium. Thus, only the increased levels of serum iPTH and increased nephrogenous cAMP distinguish patients with hypercalciuria due to renal calcium leak from those with hypercalciuria due to intestinal hyperabsorption of calcium. A sensitive radioimmunoassay of PTH that can measure serum iPTH in the normal range is required for these diagnostic criteria to be applied systematically. Severe, long-standing hypercalciuria may result in increased bone turnover and osteopenia.

Diagnosis

A. Measurement of Urine Calcium: The diagnosis of hypercalciuria is made by measuring the calcium excreted in the urine over a 24-hour period while the patient is ingesting a diet containing normal amounts of calcium (about 800–1000 mg/d). Values greater than 250 mg/24 h in women and 300 mg/24 h in men indicate the presence of hypercalciuria. Patients who present with renal stone disease should undergo a full evaluation, including measurement of the 24-hour urinary excretion of calcium, phosphate, creatinine, oxalate, uric acid, and citrate. If a renal stone is not available, patients should strain their urine. A biochemical and crystallographic analysis of the stone should be made so that the patient can be instructed in decreasing the urinary concentrations of the stone's constituents. Particular attention should be paid to excluding other metabolic disorders such as primary hyperparathyroidism, which may be primary or contributing factors. When nephrolithiasis is present, it is important to obtain baseline radiographic studies of the kidneys (intravenous urogram and nephrotomograms and sonograms) to identify the number and size (diameter) of stones present. Similar follow-up studies will give an indication of the activity of the stone disease. (Growth of a stone or appearance of a new stone indicates that stone disease is active.) If a patient is in the inactive phase of nephrolithiasis, specific drug therapy is probably not indicated. If the patient is passing gravel, stone disease is active, and intensive therapy is indicated.

B. History: In seeking the underlying cause of hypercalciuria, a careful history, including diet and drug intake, is important. A history of an extremely high intake of protein, dairy products, or carbohydrates may account for hypercalciuria. Excessive self-medication with calcium-containing antacids, low-phosphate diets, or phosphate-binding antacids can also produce hypercalciuria. The mechanism involved in the latter two phenomena is poorly understood. Hypercalciuric patients who are vegetarians may be especially prone to the development of nephrolithiasis, because their diet may be high in oxalate-containing foods or inadequate in phosphate content.

C. Serum iPTH: Although a number of provocative tests of the calciuric and nephrogenous cAMP responses to ingested calcium have been described for distinguishing between intestinal hyperabsorption of calcium and renal leak of calcium, measurement of serum iPTH is the most helpful test available. As noted in the section on pathogenesis, increased serum iPTH in the presence of low normal serum calcium reflects the presence of a renal leak of calcium, whereas normal or decreased serum iPTH in conjunction with high normal serum calcium generally reflects hyperabsorption of calcium. Further study of patients with increased serum iPTH levels may be necessary to distinguish them from patients with primary hyperparathyroidism associated with a renal leak of calcium. For some reason, this latter syndrome occurs most frequently in women, and although unusual, it should be suspected whenever a woman presents with hypercalciuria, because removal of the parathyroid lesion is curative. In most cases, primary hyperparathyroidism can be excluded in patients with increased serum iPTH by determining if serum iPTH decreases during thiazide administration. As will be discussed in the treatment section, thiazide diuretics increase the tubular reabsorption of calcium and thereby increase serum calcium. If serum iPTH decreases with thiazide administration, hyperparathyroidism is probably secondary and due to a renal leak of calcium. If serum iPTH fails to decrease with thiazides, the patient probably has associated primary hyperparathyroidism.

Treatment

A. Hypercalciuria Without Nephrolithiasis: Specific drug therapy (see below) should probably be avoided in patients with hypercalciuria without nephrolithiasis. Excessive intake of protein, carbohydrates, dairy products, antacids, and low-phosphate diets should be discontinued or curtailed. Patients should be instructed to avoid foods high in oxalate and to consume at least 2500–3000 mL of water per day.

B. Hypercalciuria With Nephrolithiasis: Surgical treatment of obstructive uropathy caused by nephrolithiasis is always indicated. Medical management is indicated for prevention of calcium stone disease.

1. Hypercalciuria– All of the therapeutic measures mentioned above should be used, except that

Table 5–7. High-oxalate foods.

Vegetables	Fruits	Miscellaneous
Asparagus	Concord grapes	Almonds
Beans	Cranberries	Cashews
Beets and beet greens	Currants	Cocoa
Brussels sprouts	Oranges	Tea
Potatoes	Pineapple	
Rhubarb	Plums	
Spinach	Strawberries	

water intake should be greater(4000 mL/d). The patient should be instructed to drink one or two glasses of water in the middle of the night because the concentration of urinary solutes is greatest then. If stones contain oxalate, the patient should be instructed in the preparation and planning of a low-oxalate diet. Some foods to be avoided are listed in Table 5–7.

2. Active nephrolithiasis– If nephrolithiasis is active (see above), one or more of six therapeutic agents should be used: (1) thiazide diuretics, (2) orthophosphate, (3) the xanthine oxidase inhibitor allopurinol, (4) magnesium oxide and pyridoxine, (5) potassium citrate, and (6) cellulose phosphate. Thiazide diuretics and orthophosphate have been reported to reduce the rate of stone recurrence. Thiazide diuretics decrease hypercalciuria by increasing the tubular reabsorption of calcium. Medication should be given at 12-hour intervals–eg, 50 mg of hydrochlorothiazide, twice daily. The only significant complications of thiazide therapy are potassium depletion and annoying polyuria; potassium supplements of 20–40 meq/d should be administered to most patients. The potassium-sparing diuretic, amiloride, is an effective substitute, but triamterine should be avoided because it has intrinsic stone-forming potential.

Oral supplements of orthophosphate decrease urinary calcium by an unknown mechanism. One to 1.5 g of elemental phosphorus should be administered in three divided doses daily as neutral phosphate compounds (eg, K-Phos Neutral, 4–6 tablets/d). Few side effects other than occasional diarrhea have been reported with this therapy, and long-term studies have shown no significant changes in serum iPTH. Orthophosphate therapy is indicated only for patients with sterile urines, because it accelerates stone growth in individuals with ammonium phosphate stones caused by urea-splitting organisms. Magnesium oxide (200 mg/d) plus large doses of pyridoxine (100–150 mg/d) may be of value in the treatment of idiopathic calcium oxalate stones, but systematic studies of the efficacy of this regimen have been meager. Potassium citrate given in doses of 30–80 meq/kg, is effective in hypocitraturic calcium oxalate nephrolithiasis (eg, renal tubular acidosis, diarrheal states with hyperoxaluria) and in hyperuricosuria. Cellulose phosphate has been advocated for severe absorptive hypercalciuria. It is expensive and may lead to magnesium depletion and to oxalate hyperabsorption.

3. Uric acid excretion– Many patients with calcium oxalate stones excrete abnormally large quantities of uric acid. Treatment of these patients with allopurinol (100–200 mg twice daily) reduces the urinary excretion of uric acid and the rate of stone formation when combined with thiazide diuretics. The mechanism of this action of allopurinol is unknown.

METABOLIC BONE DISEASE

Functions of Bone

Bone has three major functions: (1) It provides rigid support to extremities and body cavities containing vital organs. In disease situations in which bone is weak or defective, erect posture may be impossible, and vital organ function may be compromised. (An example is the cardiopulmonary dysfunction that occurs in patients with severe kyphosis due to vertebral collapse.) (2) Bones are crucial to locomotion in that they provide efficient levers and sites of attachment for muscles. With bony deformity, these levers become defective, and severe abnormalities of gait develop. (3) Finally, bone provides a large reservoir of ions, such as calcium, phosphorus, magnesium, and sodium, that are critical for life and can be mobilized when the external environment fails to provide them.

Structure of Bone

As a living tissue, bone is unique in that it is not only rigid and resists forces that would ordinarily break brittle materials but is also light enough to be moved by coordinated muscle contractions. These characteristics are functions of the strategic locations of two major types of bone (Figure 5–27). Cortical bone, composed of densely packed, mineralized collagen laid down in layers, provides rigidity and is the major component of tubular bones. Trabecular (cancellous) bone is spongy in appearance, provides strength and elasticity, and constitutes the major portion of the axial skeleton. Disorders in which cortical bone is defective or scanty lead to fractures of the long bones, whereas disorders in which trabecular bone is defective or scanty lead to vertebral fractures. Fractures of long bones may also occur because normal trabecular bone reinforcement is lost.

Two-thirds of the weight of bone is due to mineral; the remainder is due to water and collagen. Minor organic components such as proteoglycans, lipids, acidic proteins containing γ-carboxyglutamic acid, osteonectin, osteopontin, and growth factors are probably important, but their functions are poorly understood.

A. Bone Mineral: The mineral of bone is present in two forms. The major form consists of hydroxyapatite in crystals of varying maturity. The remainder is amorphous calcium phosphate, which lacks a coherent x-ray diffraction pattern, has a lower calcium-to-phosphate ratio than pure hydroxyapatite, occurs in regions of active bone formation, and is present in larger quantities in young bone.

B. Formation and Resorption of Bone: Bone is resorbed and formed continuously throughout life, and these important processes are dependent upon three major types of bone cells, each with different functions (Figure 5–28).

1. Osteoblasts– Osteoblasts form new bone on surfaces of bone previously resorbed by osteoclasts. The osteoblasts are thought to be derived from a population of dividing cells on bone surfaces that arise from mesenchymal cells in bone connective tissue. Osteoblasts are actively involved in the synthesis of matrix components of bone (primarily collagen) and probably facilitate the movement of mineral ions between extracellular fluids and bone surfaces (Figures 5–3 and 5–4). The physiologic importance of such ion transport by osteoblasts—if it occurs at all—is controversial, but there is widespread agreement that osteoblast-mediated deposition of calcium and phosphate is involved in the mineralization of collagen, which in turn is crucial to the formation of bone. In the process of bone formation, osteoblasts gradually become encased in the bone matrix they have produced.

2. Osteocytes– Once osteoblasts are trapped in the mineralized matrix, their functional and morphologic characteristics are changed and they are then called osteocytes. Protein synthetic activity decreases markedly, and the cells develop multiple processes that reach out through lacunae in bone tissue to "communicate" with processes of other osteocytes within a unit of bone (osteon) and also with the cell processes of surface osteoblasts (Figures 5–4, 5–27, and 5–28). The physiologic importance of osteocytes is controversial, but they are believed to act as a cellular syncytium that permits translocation of mineral in and out of regions of bone removed from surfaces.

3. Osteoclasts– The osteoclast is a multinucleated giant cell that is responsible for bone resorption (Figures 5–4 and 5–28). It is probably derived from circulating mononucleated macrophages, which differentiate into the mature osteoclasts by fusion in the bone environment. These cells contain all of the enzymatic components that, when secreted into their environs, are capable of solubilizing matrix and releasing calcium and phosphate. Once released, mineral is transported through the osteoclast into the extracellular fluid and ultimately into blood. Opinion has varied over the years concerning the relative importance of osteoclastic resorption of bone and the translocation of mineral from the surface of bone into the extracellular space by surface osteoblasts in extracellular mineral homeostasis.

C. Structural Features of Bone: Microscopically, there are two types of bone structure: woven and lamellar. Both may be found in either cortical or trabecular bone. However, whereas woven bone is a normal constituent of embryonic bone, it usually reflects the presence of disease in adult bone.

Lamellar bone is stronger than woven bone and is formed more slowly. It progressively replaces woven bone as the skeleton develops after birth. Whereas woven bone is characterized by nonparallelism of

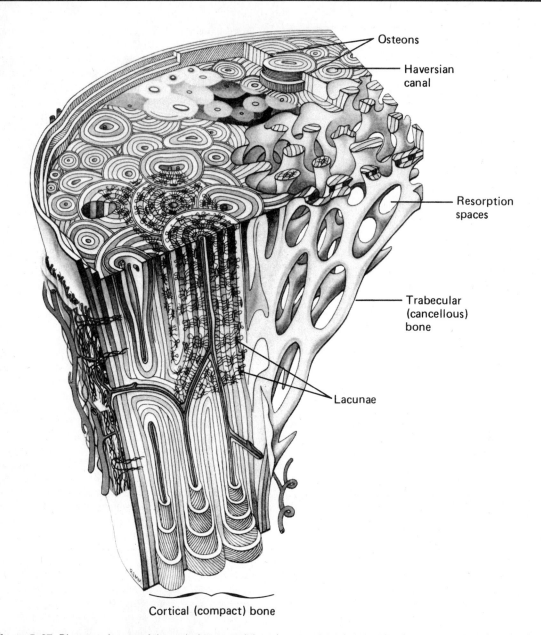

Osteons

Haversian canal

Resorption spaces

Trabecular (cancellous) bone

Lacunae

Cortical (compact) bone

Figure 5–27. Diagram of some of the main features of the microstructure of mature bone seen in both transverse section *(top)* and longitudinal section. Areas of cortical (compact) and trabecular (cancellous) bone are included. The central area in the transverse section simulates a microradiograph, with the variations in density reflecting variations in mineralization. Note the general construction of the osteons, the distribution of the osteocyte lacunae, the haversian canals, resorption spaces, and the different views of the structural basis of bone lamellation. See text for description. (Reproduced, with permission, from *Gray's Anatomy,* 35th ed. Warwick R, Williams PL [editor]. Longman, 1973.)

collagen fibers, with many osteocytes per unit area of matrix and mineral that is poorly incorporated into collagen fibrils, lamellar bone has a parallel arrangement of collagen fibers, few osteocytes per unit area of matrix, and a mineral phase that is within the collagen fibrils. Cortical lamellar bone is present in concentric layers surrounding vascular channels that comprise the haversian systems of cortical bone (os-

teons) (Figure 5–27). By contrast, the lamellar bone of trabeculae is present in layers and is laid down in long sheaves and sheets.

Dynamics of Bone

The term "modeling" as applied to bone denotes processes involved in formation of the macroscopic skeleton. Thus, modeling ceases at maturity (age

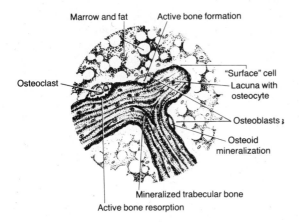

Figure 5–28. Schema of typical microscopic appearance of a section of undemineralized trabecular bone showing bone resorption by osteoclasts and formation by osteoblasts. Note layers of lamellar bone.

18–20). The term "remodeling" denotes those processes occurring at bone surfaces before and after adult development which are required to maintain the structural integrity of bone. Abnormalities of remodeling are responsible for metabolic bone diseases, and these will be discussed in this section. Those abnormalities involve alterations in the balance between bone formation and bone resorption that lead to diminished structural integrity of bone and ultimately compromise its functions.

Normally, in spite of continuous bone remodeling, there is no net gain or loss of skeletal mass after longitudinal growth has ceased. This has led to the view that bone resorption and formation are closely "coupled" and that this coupling is the result of the coordinated activity of "packets" of interacting osteoblasts and osteoclasts. These "packets" have been termed "basic multicellular units." The temporal activity of such a unit is characterized by osteoclastic resorption of a defined quantity of bone (on the surface in trabecular bone and by actual excavation in cortical bone), followed by repair of the defect by osteoblasts. Such repair occurs as a result of laying down of collagen (osteoid) and its subsequent mineralization.

By use of sequential, timed labeling of bone with orally administered tetracycline (which binds to recently mineralized collagen) and quantitative histomorphometric analysis of transiliac bone biopsies from normal adult humans, it has been possible to time the activities of a basic multicellular unit. Such estimates indicate that osteoclastic resorption proceeds for about 1 month in a normal 30-year-old adult, and osteoblastic repair takes about 3 months.

The term "sigma" denotes the total duration of activity of a typical basic multicellular unit (ie, 4 months). This concept of "sigma" has added a new dimension to conventional views about the pathogenesis of metabolic bone disease. Thus, not only might alterations in the relative numbers and activities of osteoblasts and osteoclasts be important in production of an imbalance of bone formation and bone resorption, but abnormalities in the relative durations of activities of these two cell types could underlie such an imbalance.

Analysis of Bone Biopsy

Presently, quantitative histomorphometric analysis of transiliac bone biopsies has achieved almost the status of a fine art. The procedure is employed in centers established to evaluate metabolic bone disease from both diagnostic and therapeutic points of view. The procedure is most useful (1) in establishing a diagnosis of osteomalacia (see below) and (2) in determining if, in a given patient, diminished bone density is associated with quantitatively significant changes in "sigma" and its bone formation and bone resorption components.

OSTEOMALACIA

Osteomalacia is failure of the organic matrix (osteoid) of bone to mineralize normally. Rickets, which will be only briefly discussed in this chapter, is failure of normal mineralization and maturation of the growth plate at the epiphysis in children.

Etiology & Incidence

A number of factors are critical for normal bone mineralization. An absence or defect of any of them may led to osteomalacia. The most frequent underlying biochemical causes of mineralization defects—individually or in combination—are a decrease in the product of the concentrations of calcium and phosphate in the extracellular fluid such that the supply of minerals to bone-forming surfaces is inadequate; abnormal functioning of bone-forming cells; abnormal or defective collagen production; and a decrease in the pH below 7.6 at sites of mineralization.

Table 5–8 lists the major disorders that can lead to osteomalacia, including those due to vitamin D deficiency, phosphate deficiency, systemic acidosis, drug toxicity, and primary defects of bone. Because of the vague symptomatology of osteomalacia (see below), the disease is often not suspected and is probably much more common than is usually thought.

A. Vitamin D Deficiency: Whereas it was formerly thought that vitamin D deficiency due to inadequate sunlight exposure rarely caused osteomalacia, certain social and environmental developments have almost certainly led to an increased incidence of this problem. This is particularly true in the case of the elderly, who are frequently institutionalized or stay indoors at home and fail to receive either adequate sunlight exposure or dietary supplements of vitamin D.

Although the facts are difficult to document, in-

Table 5–8. Etiology of osteomalacia.

Vitamin D deficiency
  Inadequate sunlight exposure without dietary supplementation.
    House- or institution-bound people.
    Atmospheric smog.
    Long-term residence in far northern and far southern latitudes.
    Excessive covering of body with clothing.
  Gastrointestinal disease that interrupts the normal enterohepatic recycling of vitamin D and its metabolites, resulting in their fecal loss.
    Chronic steatorrhea (pancreatic)
    Malabsorption (gluten-sensitive enteropathy).
    Surgical resection of large parts of intestine.
    Formation of biliary fistulas.
  Impaired synthesis of $1,25(OH)_2D_3$ by the kidney.
    Nephron loss, as occurs in chronic kidney disease (see section on renal hyperparathyroidism).
    Functional impairment of $1,25(OH)_2D_3$ hydroxylase (eg, in hypoparathyroidism).
    Congenital absence of $1,25(OH)_2D_3$ hydroxylase (vitamin D-dependency rickets type I).
    Suppression of $1,25(OH)_2D_3$ production by endogenously produced substances (cancer).
  Target cell resistance to $1,25(OH)_2D_3$–eg, absent or diminished number of $1,25(OH)_2D_3$ receptors, as in vitamin D-dependency rickets type II.

Phosphate deficiency
  Dietary.
    Low intake of phosphate.
    Excessive ingestion of aluminum hydroxide.
  Impaired renal tubular reabsorption of phosphate.
    X-linked hypophosphatemia.
    Adult-onset hypophosphatemia.
    Other acquired and hereditary renal tubular disorders associated with renal phosphate loss (Fanconi's syndrome, Wilson's disease).
    Tumor-associated hypophosphatemia.

Systemic acidosis
  Chronic renal failure.
  Distal renal tubular acidosis.
  Ureterosigmoidoscopy.
  Chronic acetazolamide and ammonium chloride administration.

Drug-induced osteomalacia
  Excessive bisphosphonate administration.
  Excessive fluoride administration.
  Anticonvulsant administration.

Toxin-induced osteomalacia
  Aluminum.
  Lead.
  Cadmium.

Primary mineralization defects
  Hypophosphatasia.
  Osteopetrosis.
  Fibrogenesis imperfecta ossium.

dustrialization without adequate smog control will almost certainly result in an increased incidence of osteomalacia and rickets by filtering out the ultraviolet wavelengths of light from the atmosphere. This can be prevented by systematic supplementation with vitamin D.

With the increase in world population, extreme northern and southern latitudes could become more populated. People living there would be susceptible to osteomalacia and rickets because of the diminished amount of ultraviolet irradiation.

In people who habitually cover their bodies with excessive clothing, the migration from areas of intense ultraviolet exposure to areas of marginal ultraviolet exposure can lead to the development of osteomalacia and rickets. This phenomenon has been reported in Great Britain in immigrants from India, Pakistan, and other Commonwealth countries since the 1950s.

1. Malabsorption– One of the most common causes of osteomalacia due to vitamin D deficiency is gastrointestinal disease associated with malabsorption of vitamin D and calcium. This is particularly true of disorders in which the enterohepatic circulation of vitamin D is interrupted. The biologically active metabolites of vitamin D that are normally secreted into the bile are either diverted (biliary fistula) or not reabsorbed (chronic steatorrhea, gluten-sensitive enteropathy, surgical resection of large parts of the distal jejunum and ileum). In these situations, not only is exogenous vitamin D poorly absorbed, but the body's stores of vitamin D and its metabolites that originate from skin biosynthesis are also depleted by biliary or fecal loss.

2. Impaired renal synthesis– As noted in previous sections, impaired synthesis of $1,25(OH)_2D_3$ by the kidney can lead to osteomalacia. This can occur in chronic kidney disease, in which there is extensive nephron loss, or when other conditions are unfavorable for the synthesis of $1,25(OH)_2D_3$, such as in hypoparathyroidism when serum phosphate is increased and the trophic stimulus of PTH is missing (Figure 5–2).

3. Genetic defects– Two recessively inherited vitamin D deficiency states associated with rickets and osteomalacia are characterized by resistance to treatment with large doses of vitamin D. In one, vitamin D-dependency rickets type I, serum concentrations of $1,25(OH)_2D_3$ are very low. This disease is thought to be due to a defect in $1,25(OH)_2D_3$ hydroxylase in the kidney. In the other, vitamin D-dependency rickets type II, serum concentrations of $1,25(OH)_2D_3$ are high. This disease is thought to be due to target cell resistance to the action of $1,25(OH)_2D_3$. Patients have been described recently whose cultured skin fibroblasts are deficient in normal receptors or have abnormal receptors for $1,25(OH)_2D_3$.

4. Oncogenic disease– Osteomalacic syndromes have been associated with certain tumors. Although proof is not yet available, recent findings suggest that the underlying cause of the bone disease is a humoral substance secreted by the tumor that suppresses the synthesis of $1,25(OH)_2D_3$.

B. Lowering of Phosphorus: Any sustained lowering of serum phosphorus will ultimately result in rickets and osteomalacia. Phosphate deficiency can occur as a result of failure of intestinal absorption of phosphate (dietary lack or sequestering of phosphate in the intestine by binding of the mineral to aluminum hydroxide in antacids) or excessive renal excretion of phosphate. Vegetarians who do not include dairy products in their diets are particularly susceptible to phosphate deficiency, as are elderly or debilitated individuals who are fed a diet low in phosphate. Although it is likely that only excessive use of phosphate-binding antacids will result in a deficiency in phosphate severe enough to produce osteomalacia, the potential for this disorder is great because these drugs are widely available.

The classic example of rickets and osteomalacia due to renal phosphate wasting is the heritable disease X-linked hypophosphatemia, in which a renal phosphate transport defect is manifest. Similar renal phosphate wasting and osteomalacia occur in many patients with Fanconi's syndrome and in patients with adult-onset hypophosphatemia.

Severe phosphate wasting is occasionally associated with benign or malignant lesions, such as sclerosing hemangiomas, angiosarcomas, hemangiopericytomas, and nonossifying fibromas. Some of these involve bone and others soft tissues. Surgical removal of these lesions almost always restores serum phosphate and urinary phosphate excretion to normal and heals the osteomalacia, suggesting that the tumors secrete a humoral substance that either promotes phosphaturia or interferes with vitamin D metabolism.

Apart from chronic renal failure, the disorders listed in Table 5–8 that cause systemic acidosis and osteomalacia are uncommon. The evidence that they produce osteomalacia on the basis of systemic acidosis per se is based only on therapeutic responses achieved when blood pH is restored to normal with bicarbonate therapy. Thus, it is possible that the acidosis acts indirectly, by inducing other systemic abnormalities that then produce osteomalacia.

The mechanisms involved in the development of osteomalacia due to drugs and the primary mineralization defects listed in Table 5–8 are largely unknown.

Pathology

There is little (if anything) unusual about the gross characteristics of the bones of patients with osteomalacia, except perhaps that they are easier to biopsy because they are soft. Histomorphometrically, however, there are major deviations from normal, primarily related to the thickness and surface coverage of unmineralized osteoid and the degree of mineralization of osteoid. Characteristically, the average thickness of osteoid exceeds 20 μm (normal, 15 ± 2.3 μm), and over 20% of the bone surface is covered by osteoid (normal, 2.1 ± 1%). The "calcification front" at the junction of mineralized bone and osteoid, which is normally marked intensely by tetracycline labels incorporated into bone prior to biopsy, is

barely visible. These changes in the quantity of osteoid are due not to increased synthesis of collagen by bone-forming cells but rather to failure of collagen mineralization. The rate of collagen synthesis may actually be decreased. Because the rate of mineralization is slowed, "sigma" (see above) is prolonged. Pseudofractures (Figure 5–30), which are characteristic of osteomalacia, are defects in cortical bone that are bordered by osteoid-encased lamellar bone, with interspersed areas of variably mineralized woven bone. Depending upon the stage of development of osteomalacia or rickets, bone resorption surfaces may be increased or decreased. After secondary hyperparathyroidism due to hypocalcemia has been established, increased osteoclastic resorption may be observed. Late in the course of development of the disease, when osteoid covers the greater portion of mineralized surfaces, little exposed mineral is available for osteoclastic attack, and bone resorption surfaces are decreased.

Pathophysiology

A. Vitamin D Deficiency: The most useful information about the pathogenesis of osteomalacia and rickets has been provided by studies of the natural history of these diseases. It has not been possible, because of ethical considerations, to conduct longitudinal investigations of the parameters of calcium metabolism in patients with rickets and osteomalacia. However, measurements of these parameters have been reported in individual patients suffering from rickets or osteomalacia of varying degrees of severity. Figure 5–29, which provides an idealized scheme of the results of these studies, depicts three stages of development of vitamin D-deficiency rickets or osteomalacia. These stages are characterized by unique changes in the serum concentrations of calcium, phosphate, iPTH, and 25OHD$_3$ and the severity of radiographically assessed bone lesions.

B. Stages of Osteomalacia: In the first stage of rickets or osteomalacia, there is mild hypocalcemia, appropriately increased serum iPTH, normal or slightly decreased serum phosphate, and decreased serum 25OHD$_3$, which is approximately half the mean value for age-matched normal controls.

In the second stage, serum 25OHD$_3$ decreases slightly or not at all. The serum calcium concentration is restored to normal, but paradoxically, there is only a small decrease in serum iPTH. Hypophosphatemia and bone lesions worsen.

In the third stage, when florid rickets or osteomalacia becomes manifest, serum 25OHD$_3$ decreases to almost undetectable levels. Hypocalcemia again is apparent and is more severe than in stage I; the degree of hypophosphatemia is the same as for stage II; and serum iPTH increases further and is again appropriate for the degree of hypocalcemia.

The underlying defect leading to these biochemical and osseous changes is the decrease in production

PROGRESSIVE DEPLETION OF 25OHD₃

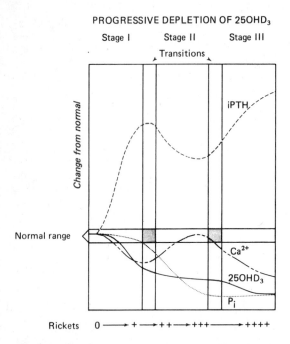

Figure 5–29. Serum biochemical changes and severity of bone disease in the three stages of rickets or osteomalacia. See text for description. (Reproduced, with permission, from Arnaud SB et al: The interrelationships between vitamin D and parathyroid hormone in disorders of mineral metabolism in man. In: *Vitamin D and Problems in Uremic Bone Disease.* Walter de Gruyter, 1975.)

of 1,25(OH)₂D₃, which is due to the diminished availability of the major circulating metabolite of vitamin D, 25OHD₃. As Figure 5–2 shows, decreased 1,25(OH)₂D₃ results in decreased intestinal calcium absorption, decreased bone resorption, hypocalcemia, increased PTH secretion, and hypophosphatemia (stage I). The resulting decreased calcium × phosphate product in serum is insufficient for the normal mineralization of bone, and the osteomalacic process is initiated. The increased PTH secretion and hypophosphatemia represent compensatory phenomena designed to correct the hypocalcemia, but they occur at the expense of osseous demineralization caused by hyperparathyroidism. As stage I shifts to stage II, the severity of the hyperparathyroidism restores serum calcium toward normal. This restoration probably depends upon increased production of 1,25(OH)₂D₃ from residual stores of 25OHD₃; this increased production is the result of the stimulation of renal 1α-hydroxylase by increased serum levels of PTH. The mechanism whereby increased PTH secretion is maintained in spite of normocalcemia in this stage is poorly understood. A negative feedback relationship between vitamin D metabolites and PTH secretion is likely, wherein normal levels of vitamin D metabolites are required for physiologic concentrations of serum calcium to suppress parathyroid gland activity.

During the transition from stage II to stage III, vitamin D stores are depleted, and in spite of the hyperparathyroidism and hypophosphatemia, 1,25(OH)₂D₃ production stops because 25OHD₃, the substrate, is lacking. In stage III, hypocalcemia develops again and is worse than in stage I because of an even greater decrease in intestinal absorption of calcium. PTH secretion increases further in response to hypocalcemia; however, because vitamin D is required for PTH to resorb bone, this compensatory mechanism fails and hypocalcemia persists. In this stage, hypocalcemia and hypophosphatemia become so severe that the serum calcium × phosphate product is too low for normal bond formation, and florid osteomalacia or rickets becomes evident.

C. Phosphate Deficiency: The pathogenesis of the rickets or osteomalacia associated with phosphate deficiency is poorly understood but is presumed to be related to a decrease in the serum calcium × phosphate product below the level required for normal bone formation. Dietary phosphate deficiency is known to be associated with increases in serum concentrations of 1,25(OH)₂D₃ and calcium and in urinary excretion of calcium. Serum concentrations of iPTH are appropriately decreased, and the PTH-induced demineralization of bone seen in vitamin D deficiency is not observed. Thus, as long as phosphate deficiency is not complicated by deficiencies in vitamin D or calcium, the biochemical changes seen in vitamin D deficiency, rickets, or osteomalacia do not occur.

D. Acidosis: The pathogenesis of the rickets and osteomalacia associated with acidosis is also poorly understood. Possible underlying causes include inhibition of mineralization due to a decrease in pH below 7.6 at calcification sites, acidosis-induced hypophosphatemia, and acidosis-induced resistance to the actions of vitamin D. In addition, the hypercalciuria often observed in acidosis may cause hyperparathyroidism, and the combined effects on bone of the excess PTH and negative calcium balance may be important in the ultimate bone disease associated with acidosis.

Clinical Features
A. Symptoms and Signs: The clinical manifestations of osteomalacia in adults often go unrecognized. This is especially true in patients with osteomalacia due to a vitamin D deficiency caused by disorders of the gastrointestinal tract, because the symptoms of the primary disorder are so prominent. Thus, diffuse skeletal pain and muscular weakness without a specific pattern may be overlooked, and the diagnosis of bone disease may not be suspected until roentgenograms reveal osteomalacia as an incidental finding.

There are few if any characteristic clinical signs of osteomalacia, except for deformities caused by fractures in the ribs, vertebrae, and long bones. Such ex-

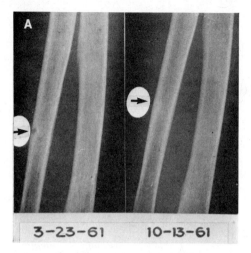 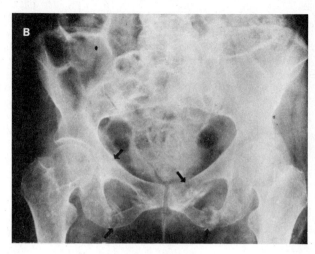

Figure 5–30. A: X-rays of the radius and ulna of a patient with severe osteomalacia, showing healing of a pseudofracture (arrows) during 7 months of treatment with ergocalciferol. **B:** X-ray of the pelvis, showing pseudofractures (Looser's zones, or Milkman's fractures) in a woman with severe osteomalacia. (Courtesy of G Gordan.)

tensive disease is rare. Classically, patients with osteomalacia have a characteristic waddling gait that is due both to proximal muscular weakness and to pain and discomfort during movement of limbs. Some patients have severe muscular hypotonia and paradoxically brisk deep tendon reflexes. This latter finding is probably due to associated hypocalcemia. In contrast to hypoparathyroidism, osteomalacia is rarely associated with hypocalcemia tetanic manifestations. This difference is probably due to the presence of hyperphosphatemia and lower levels of serum ionized calcium in patients with hypoparathyroidism.

B. Laboratory Findings: The serum biochemistry of osteomalacia and rickets is described above. The values of serum calcium, phosphate, iPTH, and $25OHD_3$ clearly depend upon the stage of the disease at the time the patient is seen (Figure 5–29). Generally, low levels of $25OHD_3$ indicate that osteomalacia is severe, but this is not always true. Increased serum alkaline phosphatase is characteristic. The cause of this abnormality is not well understood; it is probably related to increased but ineffective activity of osteoblasts.

C. Imaging Studies: The radiologic features of osteomalacia also depend upon the stage of the disease and may be dramatic. There is usually some decrease in bone density. Cortices may be thinned, and roentgenograms of the vertebrae may reveal both loss of trabeculae and blurring of trabecular markings. In stage I and early stage II osteomalacia, radiologic changes may be indistinguishable from those seen in osteoporosis. The most characteristic finding in osteomalacia–and one that is almost pathognomonic– is the radiolucent band termed a **pseudofracture,** a defect in bone that is perpendicular to the bone surface (Figure 5–30A and 30B). These bands, which may be

present at multiple sites, are usually symmetric and bilateral; the characteristic locations include the inner aspects of the femur, the pubic rami, the outer edges of the scapulas, the upper fibula, and the metatarsals. Pseudofractures almost always occur where major arteries cross bones. It is thought that trauma due to arterial pulsation or other factors is responsible for their location and symmetry. Pseudofractures are also termed Looser's zones or Milkman's fractures, after the individuals who first described them.

Paradoxically, patients with untreated osteomalacia due to specific defects in renal tubular phosphate transport may show increased rather than decreased osseous density and even bony spurs on x-rays. However, such hyperostotic bone is abnormal. It fractures easily and consists of thickened cortices and trabeculae invested in large quantities of thickened osteoid. The cause of this hyperostosis is unknown.

Differential Diagnosis

Osteomalacia and rickets are usually suspected on the basis of the history or the presence of other disorders that frequently cause osteomalacia and rickets. Patients with muscular weakness and skeletal pain should be screened. Children with histories of irritability, poor growth and development, and convulsions should also be investigated. Patients who are taking drugs that have been associated with the development of osteomalacia (Table 5–8) are at risk for this disease and should be evaluated annually for hypocalcemia, hypophosphatemia, and hypocalciuria. Decreased urinary calcium is one of the earliest biochemical signs of osteomalacia and is probably due to increased PTH secretion secondary to mild hypocalcemia. Patients with chronic intestinal disease, particularly those with gluten-sensitive enteropathy or pancreatic insufficiency, should also be considered to have osteomalacia unless this is disproved. Nutritional deprivation and chronic deprivation of sunlight exposure also increase the risk of osteomalacia. Patients with a family history of short stature should be investigated for one of the inherited forms of osteomalacia.

Screening tests for the presence of osteomalacia should include measurements of total serum calcium; serum phosphate, magnesium, iPTH, 25OHD$_3$, alkaline phosphatase, and urinary calcium. The presence of hypocalcemia, hyperphosphatemia, increased iPTH, hyper- or hypophosphatasia, or hypocalciuria should prompt further investigations, including x-rays of the skeleton and a radionuclide bone scan (pseudofractures show increased uptake on bone scan). If these latter procedures do not reveal pseudofractures, a transiliac bone biopsy with double tetracycline labeling should be performed. Patients with full-blown osteomalacia due to vitamin D deficiency will have all of the above biochemical findings as well as pseudofractures, and the bone biopsies only offer confirmation. Measurement of 72-hour excretion of fat in the stool is recommended to exclude intestinal malabsorption as a factor in the development of osteomalacia, because this disease is often unaccompanied by overt symptoms. Serum levels of 25OHD$_3$ are generally low but may be normal in patients whose diets contain vitamin D at the time of investigation. After restoration of serum 25OHD$_3$ concentrations to normal levels, there is a long time lag before the restoration of other important minerals to normal and the healing of bone lesions. Serum concentrations of 1,25(OH)$_2$D$_3$ should be measured in children whose rickets or osteomalacia appears to be resistant to therapeutic doses of vitamin D. Low values will be found in patients with vitamin D-dependency rickets type I and extremely high values in patients with vitamin D-dependency rickets type II.

More often than not, osteomalacia due to mild degrees of vitamin D deficiency is manifested only by small increases in serum iPTH and hypocalciuria. In such cases, only bone biopsy will establish the diagnosis.

A. Hypophosphatemia: Most patients with osteomalacia due to untreated phosphate deficiency (Table 5–8) have normal serum concentrations of calcium, 25OHD$_3$, and iPTH. This distinguishes them from individuals with vitamin D deficiency. However, excessive treatment of these patients with inorganic phosphate frequently produces mild hypocalcemia and increased serum levels of iPTH. Apart from the occasional presence on x-rays of increased bone density in patients with X-linked hypophosphatemic rickets and variable evidence of osteitis fibrosa cystica in patients with vitamin D deficiency, there appears to be no difference between osteomalacic lesions due to vitamin D deficiency and those due to phosphate deficiency.

B. Inherited Osteomalacia: All patients suspected of having an inherited form of osteomalacia should be studied for the presence of renal tubular acidosis using ammonium chloride loading and measurement of urine pH. This is important because successful therapy of renal tubular acidosis depends upon treatment with alkali. Such treatment is not part of the regimen recommended for osteomalacia caused by vitamin D or phosphate deficiencies.

C. Hypoparathyroidism: The differentiation of hypoparathyroidism from osteomalacia is generally not difficult. Patients with hypoparathyroidism usually have hyperphosphatemia (rather than hypophosphatemia) and a history of thyroidectomy. In rare instances, hypoparathyroidism is associated with steatorrhea; in these cases, both hypophosphatemia and osteomalacia may be present, and measurement of serum iPTH may be the key in making the correct diagnosis. Serum concentrations of iPTH are low or undetectable in hypoparathyroidism, but they are generally increased in patients with osteomalacia, unless severe hypomagnesemia is also present.

D. Hypophosphatasia: The finding of a serum alkaline phosphatase at the lower limits of normal should prompt measurement of plasma levels and urinary excretion of phosphorylethanolamine, which are markedly elevated in patients with hypophosphatasia.

E. Tumor: The clinician should search for subcutaneous and bone tumors in all patients with osteomalacia, since such tumors may be the underlying cause of the osteomalacia and their removal may cure the disease.

Treatment

A. Vitamin D: Patients with rickets or osteomalacia due to simple dietary deficiency of vitamin D or lack of exposure to sunlight respond well to small daily supplements of ergocalciferol and calcium or regular periods of exposure to ultraviolet light (artificial or natural). Administration of oral doses of ergocalciferol (0.05 mg [2000 IU] daily) for several months will heal the bone disease and restore serum calcium, phosphate, alkaline phosphatase, and iPTH to normal in most cases. This dose is insufficient to influence the course of rickets or osteomalacia due to any other cause. Although 25OHD$_3$ (calcifediol) and 1,25(OH)$_2$D$_3$ (calcitriol) have been successful in the treatment of simple rickets and osteomalacia due to inadequate sunlight exposure, dihydrotachysterol has not.

Vitamin D treatment usually results in an increase in serum phosphorus within several days, but serum calcium may not increase for a week or more. In fact, in some patients with severe rickets or osteomalacia, serum calcium may actually decrease for a short period, and in children the development of tetany and convulsions has been described. Phosphate supplements are contraindicated during the early stages of treatment with vitamin D because they may aggravate hypocalcemia. Serum alkaline phosphatase and iPTH decrease slowly over a period of several weeks, but improvement in radiographic abnormalities may not be apparent for several months. The previously absent mineralization front in osteoid that underlies osteoblasts appears rapidly. This occurs even before important changes in the serum concentrations of calcium and phosphate and has been interpreted as evidence that vitamin D affects bone mineralization directly.

B. Calcium: Decreases in serum calcium have been ascribed to rapid movement of calcium from the extracellular fluids into bone as a result of its vitamin D-induced mineralization. For this reason–and to provide adequate calcium for bone mineralization–it is important to administer calcium (2 g of elemental calcium daily for children and 1 g for adults) along with vitamin D.

C. Malabsorption Therapy: Patients with rickets or osteomalacia due to intestinal malabsorption may not respond to treatment with vitamin D compounds because the vitamin is poorly absorbed. Those patients with gluten-sensitive enteropathy respond to ingestion of a gluten-free diet if sunlight exposure is adequate or small doses of oral vitamin D are given. Patients with other forms of malabsorption (Table 5–8) may require up to 5 mg (200,000 IU) per day of oral ergocalciferol, and some may require 40,000–80,000 IU of ergocalciferol given intravenously or intramuscularly. Unfortunately, preparations of vitamin D suitable for parenteral use are not generally available. Oral calcifediol and calcitriol in larger-than-usual doses may also be effective.

D. Long-Term Therapy: Patients with impaired synthesis of $1,25(OH)_2D_3$ or target cell resistance to $1,25(OH)_2D_3$ should be treated with calcitriol, although they may respond to large doses of either ergocalciferol or calcifediol. The treatment of patients with renal osteodystrophy or hypoparathyroidism has already been discussed. Patients with vitamin D-dependency rickets types I and II are to be treated with large doses of ergocalciferol. Regimens must be individually tailored and careful lifelong follow-up maintained. Initial doses should be 25 µg (1000 IU) of ergocalciferol per kilogram of body weight per day. After approximately 2 months of treatment, the response to this dose is evaluated with x-rays of bony lesions and measurements of serum calcium, phosphate, iPTH, and alkaline phosphatase. If no improvement is observed, the dose of vitamin D is increased by 25%; if signs of healing are observed, the dose is increased by only 15%. Similar evaluations should be made every 2 months, with appropriate increases in vitamin D dose until a satisfactory maintenance dose has been determined. The requirement for ergocalciferol varies among patients but is usually in the range of 40–50 µg/kg/d. Serum calcium should be measured every 3–4 months for life.

The development of hypercalcemia can be avoided by maintaining serum concentrations of calcium in the low normal range. Vitamin D therapy should be discontinued at the earliest sign of hypercalcemia. If detected early, serum calcium returns to the normal range within a week; if it remains normal for 2 weeks, vitamin D therapy can be reinstituted at a dose 15% lower than that which caused the hypercalcemia. Successful therapy is marked by "catch-up" skeletal growth, followed by normal growth.

Liquid forms of vitamin D should be used in patients with vitamin D-dependency rickets, because precise doses can be metered out to the patient with a small, well-calibrated syringe. Table 5–9 lists available liquid preparations of vitamin D_2.

Calcifediol (100–900 µg/d) has been used successfully in the treatment of vitamin D-dependency rickets, but it is expensive and offers little advantage over ergocalciferol except that hypercalcemia resolves sooner after calcifediol is discontinued. Calcitriol, on the other hand, provides an important advantage because of its rapid onset and termination of action. Long-term experience in the treatment of patients with vitamin D-dependency rickets with calcitriol has not yet accrued. The doses of dihydrotachysterol required for successful treatment of these patients are large, and this drug offers no special advantage over vitamin D.

E. Hypophosphatemic Rickets: The treatment of X-linked hypophosphatemic rickets is extremely challenging and requires persistence and excellent relationships with family members, so that patients will be compliant in their ingestion of phosphate. Lifelong treatment with orthophosphate supplements by mouth in doses ranging from 1 to 5 g of elemental phosphorus per day in divided doses every 5–6 hours will heal the rickets and osteomalacia of this disease. Phosphate supplements (Table 5–10) may be distasteful and can cause diarrhea initially, but with persistence, serum concentrations of phosphorus are restored toward normal (4 mg/dL), and the side effects generally disappear. The only major complication of phosphate therapy is the development of secondary hyperparathyroidism. The reason for this complication is poorly understood, since normal children who maintain similar levels of serum phosphate do not develop secondary hyperparathyroidism. Secondary hyperparathyroidism can be prevented only by coincident treatment with a vitamin D preparation that prevents decreases in ionized calcium that are ordinarily caused by phosphate therapy. Although ergo-

Table 5–9. High-potency ergocalciferol (vitamin D_2) preparations in liquid form.

Ergocalciferol oral solution, 8000 IU vitamin D_2 per milliliter.
Calciferol, 500,000 IU vitamin D_2 per milliliter (should be diluted to 100,000 IU/mL [1:5] with edible vegetable oil before dispensing).

Table 5–10. Phosphate supplements for oral administration in hypophosphatemia.

Acidic phosphate (Joulie's solution)		
Dibasic sodium phosphate ($Na_2HPO_4 \cdot 7H_2O$) (reagent grade)	102	Dissolve the phosphate salt in about 750 mL of warm water to which the phosphoric acid has been added. Make the solution up to 1L with distilled water. Store at room temperature. The concentration of phosphorus in this solution is 2.76 g/dL; the pH is 4.3.
Phosphoric acid NF (85%)	58.8	
Distilled water, qs ad	1000	
Neutral phosphate solution		
$NaH_2PO_4 \cdot H_2O$ (reagent grade)	18.2	Mix the phosphate salts and dispense in dry form as packets. Dissolve the packet of salts in distilled water by gently warming. Store in refrigerator at 4°C. Shake well if precipitate forms. Each batch lasts several days. The concentration of phosphorus in this solution is 2.08 g/dL; the pH is neutral.
$Na_2HPO_4 \cdot 7H_2O$ (reagent grade)	145	
Distilled water, qs ad	1000	
Neutra-Phos-K, K-Phos Neutral; others		
Inorganic phosphorus, 250 mg per capsule or tablet		Dissolve capsules in water and take orally. Take tablets orally with water.

calciferol in doses of 0.1–1.25 mg (4000–50,000 IU) daily was used previously, it has recently been determined that calcitriol is equally effective or even more effective. Calcitriol is recommended in the treatment of patients with X-linked hypophosphatemia because hypercalcemia resolves rapidly after its discontinuation and because it may have specific antirachitic effects.

In following patients with X-linked hypophosphatemia who are under treatment with phosphate supplements and vitamin D, procedures similar to those described in the treatment of vitamin D dependency rickets should be used. Serum calcium, phosphate, and iPTH should be measured at intervals of 3–4 months. If hypercalcemia supervenes, vitamin D should be discontinued and then reinstituted at a lower dose when eucalcemia is restored. If serum iPTH increases much above the upper limit of the normal range, orthophosphate should be withheld temporarily; in some cases, however, it may be necessary to increase the dose of vitamin D. Renal function should be monitored carefully by measuring serum creatinine serially. Twenty-four-hour urinary phosphorus can be monitored to assess patient compliance with the phosphate regimen. Values in excess of 1000–2000 mg/d suggest compliance, but it must be remembered that patients and parents may be interested in pleasing the physician, and patients may take phosphate supplements immediately prior to 24-hour collection of urine but not chronically as prescribed.

F. Renal Tubular Acidosis: Rickets and osteomalacia due to distal renal tubular acidosis are expeditiously treated by correcting the acidosis with sodium bicarbonate, potassium bicarbonate, or potassium citrate. Adults require 5–10 g/d and children 1–5 g/d. Response to therapy should be monitored by measurements of blood pH, with values maintained at nearly physiologic levels. Rickets may heal slowly, and the response may be accelerated by the addition of vitamin D (in relatively high doses) to the treatment regimen. Therapy should be monitored by measuring serum calcium, and the dose of vitamin D should be regulated accordingly. Once rickets has

healed, vitamin D therapy is rarely required, but it is probable that lifelong treatment with alkali will be necessary.

G. Rickets Due to Tumor: The response of tumor-associated rickets and osteomalacia to surgical removal of the offending tumor is dramatic. Serum phosphate increases within 1–2 days, and bone lesions heal within 6 months to 1 year.

H. Hypophosphatasia: In treatment of bone lesions associated with hypophosphatasia, use of conventional drugs (eg, vitamin D and calcium) has been unsatisfactory. Recently, increases in alkaline phosphatase and some degree of healing have been observed with doses of fluoride ion in the range of 40 mg/d. Spontaneous remissions have been reported.

OSTEOPOROSIS

Osteoporosis is an asymptomatic reduction in the quantity of bone. It can now be detected by measuring bone mass using dual-energy x-ray absorptiometry or quantitative computerized tomography. However, the presence of osteoporosis is not usually appreciated until minimal trauma causes a fracture. The most common sites of osteoporotic fracture are the proximal femur, the distal radius (Colles' fractures), the vertebrae, the humerus, the pelvis, and the ribs.

Magnitude of the Problem

Osteoporosis occurs most frequently in postmenopausal white women and in the elderly. The disorder is associated with a high fracture rate. Approximately 20% of women suffer one or more osteoporotic fractures by age 65, and as many as 40% sustain fractures after age 65. Significant osteoporosis is not seen in men and black women until after age 60, when fracture rates progressively increase in these groups.

About 250,000 hip fractures were recorded in Americans over age 45 in 1986. The incidence of hip fracture increases almost logarithmically after age 65, so that by age 80, a white woman has a 1–2% *an-*

nual risk of fracturing her hip. Twelve to 20 percent more women die during the first year after a hip fracture than would be expected on the basis of age and sex alone, and as many as 15–25% of women living independently before hip fracture need institutionalization in a long-term care facility for at least 1 year after hip fracture.

The incidence of Colles' fracture increases in white women after age 50 but plateaus after age 65. Although a 50-year old woman runs a 15% risk of sustaining a Colles fracture during her remaining lifetime, the disability caused by this fracture is generally minimal, and the costs of treatment are less than 10% of those incurred with hip fracture.

About 5% of white women sustain a complete vertebral crush fracture by age 70, and many more have lesser vertebral deformities (wedge) that are attributable to incomplete fractures. Apart from the relatively common kyphotic deformity known as "dowager's hump" and the resulting loss of height caused by multiple vertebral crush and wedge fractures, the prevalence and degree of debility caused by vertebral osteoporosis is not known. (See Chapter 22.)

Etiology

The major types of osteoporosis are listed in Table 5–11 according to frequency of occurrence. The specific cause of the most common form of osteoporosis—that associated with menopause and aging—is unknown, but the major risk and complicating factors are listed in Table 5–12.

A. Calcium Deficiency: Maximum bone mass is achieved by about 25 years of age, is maintained without much change until 35–40 years of age, and is lost at a constant rate of 0.3–0.5% per year in both men and women thereafter. Therefore, the critical point of bone "weakness" that permits fracture with minimal trauma is reached more rapidly in individuals starting with small amounts of bone than in those starting with larger amounts of bone.

Persons under age 25 who do not ingest more calcium than is required to replace obligatory losses in the urine, stool, and sweat (approximately 200–300 mg/d) (Figure 11–6) cannot achieve genetically programmed peak bone mass and are at greater risk for

Table 5–11. Classification of osteoporosis according to frequency of occurrence.

Frequent	Infrequent
Postmenopausal	Juvenile
Senile	Young adult
Hypogonadism (oophorectomy)	Osteogenesis imperfecta
	Chromosomal abnormalities
Corticosteroid-induced	Migratory
Immobilization	Disappearing bones
Neoplasms (eg, myeloma)	Cushing's syndrome
	Hyperthyroidism
	Iron storage disease

Table 5–12. Risk factors and complicating factors in osteoporosis.

Genetic factors
   Nonblack race
   Northern European stock
   Small bone mass
   Defects in collagen synthesis or structure
Nutritional deficiency
   Calcium and phosphate
   Vitamin D (sunlight deprivation without dietary supplementation)
   Vitamin C
   Protein
Hypogonadism
Drugs
   Alcohol
   Corticosteroids
   Thyroid hormone
   Anticonvulsants
   Cancer chemotherapy
   Heparin
   Caffeine
Smoking
Gastrointestinal disease
   Gastric or intestinal resection
   Malabsorption
   Pancreatic insufficiency
   Hepatic disease
Renal disease
Hyperparathyroidism
Hyperthyroidism
Immobilization and lack of exercise
Excessive exercise leading to weight loss, amenorrhea, or both

the development of osteoporosis and fracture. The recommended daily allowance for dietary calcium for ages 10–25 is 1200 mg/d.

Intestinal calcium absorption and the ability to adapt to low-calcium diets are impaired in many postmenopausal women and elderly persons. The pathogenesis of those abnormalities is controversial, but evidence suggests that they may be due to decrease in the ability of the kidney to produce $1,25(OH)_2D_3$ or an intrinsic defect in the intestine to absorb calcium—either or both. The finding that iPTH increases with age implies that those defects in calcium absorption are functionally important in that they result in sufficient degrees of hypocalcemia to produce chronic secondary hyperparathyroidism, a condition that is generally associated with bone demineralization. It appears, therefore, that the ability of the intestine to support calcium homeostasis progressively declines with age and that elderly persons are forced more and more to rely on their own bones rather than the external environment as a source of calcium for maintaining normal extracellular fluid Ca^{2+}. The degree to which this "trade-off" (bone demineralization for calcium homeostasis) is needed depends upon the severity of the described defects in calcium absorption, the level and bioavailability of dietary calcium, and whether specific therapeutic measures are taken to correct defects in calcium absorption. The quantitative contribution of the "trade-off" to decreased bone mass and increased incidence of fractures seen in the elderly is not known, but a dietary calcium intake of 1200 mg/d should be sufficient to prevent it from developing.

B. Estrogen: The loss of bone mass is accelerated after ovariectomy and during the menopause. Physiologic doses of estrogen prevent or retard those losses. The risk of hip and vertebral fracture appears to be reduced by at least 50% for as long as estrogen is taken. Menopause has a greater influence on bone loss than does chronologic age. High parity and long lactation are generally associated with increased bone mass and decreased risk of fracture.

C. Body Build: Thin women have twice the risk of hip and Colles' fractures as obese women. The reason is not known, but it may be that obese women may have a greater supply of estrogen post-menopausally than thin women because the major source of estrogen during that time is from the conversion of androstenedione to estrone in adipose tissue. Another possible explanation is that obese women have more fat "padding" protecting them when they fall.

D. Cigarette Smoking: Most studies show that smoking is associated with reduced bone mass as well as an increased risk of vertebral and hip fracture in women and of vertebral fracture in men. It is thought that the mechanisms of these effects of smoking involve an alteration in the hepatic metabolism of estrogen and a reduction in the amount of adipose tissue in most smokers, both of which factors result in a decrease in circulating concentrations of estrogen.

E. Physical Activity: Immobilization can decrease bone mass. The osteoporosis produced can be localized (eg, associated with fracture casting or painful limbs), generalized (associated with prolonged bed rest or space travel), or neurologic (associated with paraplegia or quadriplegia). The causes are unknown, but it is thought that the absence of stress and muscle pull on bone may be a common etiologic factor.

The results of studies of the influence of increased physical activity on bone mass are mixed. Many studies have shown that exercise sufficient to produce amenorrhea can result in marked decreases in bone mineral density. On the other hand, most controlled trials have shown that postmenopausal bone loss may be prevented by moderate exercise. Unfortunately, none of these latter studies used randomized designs, and sample size and statistical power were inadequate in most of them.

F. Previous Fractures: The occurrence of Colles' fracture in women is associated with only a small increase in the risk for hip fracture. However, women who have had a hip fracture have twice the risk of suffering a contralateral hip fracture. It is not yet established if the incidence of hip fracture risk is increased in patients who have suffered vertebral fractures.

G. Other Medical Conditions: Whereas patients with type II diabetes mellitus are not at increased risk for osteoporotic fracture, those with type I diabetes may have less bone mass than expected for age. Hip fractures are more frequent in patients with significant disability from rheumatoid arthritis.

Similarly, medical problems that increase the risk of falling (eg, neurologic disorders) may also increase the risk of hip fractures, but such associations have not been systematically investigated. Conditions that may aggravate the bone loss associated with aging and the menopause include primary hyperparathyroidism, hyperthyroidism, Cushing's disease, chronic renal failure, hemochromatosis, vitamin D deficiency, vitamin C deficiency, and severe protein deficiency.

H. Medications:

1. Glucocorticosteroids– Glucocorticosteroids cause severe osteoporosis both in patients with hyperadrenocortisolism (Cushing's disease) and in those receiving pharmacologic doses of these drugs. Diminished bone mass can be observed within a few months of the initiation of therapy, and long-term use increases the risk of vertebral and hip fractures. Glucocorticoids have multiple effects on bone and extracellular mineral metabolism. In bone, there is inhibition of the normal production of bone collagen by osteoblasts and an increased sensitivity of cultured bone cells to PTH. Glucocorticoids decrease the intestinal absorption and increase the renal excretion of calcium, thereby causing negative calcium balance, which causes mild hypocalcemia resulting in appropriate increases in serum PTH. The secondary hyperparathyroidism and increased sensitivity of bone to parathyroid hormone are reflected histomorphometrically in increased bone resorptive surfaces. Thus, the combined effects of diminished bone formation and increased bone resorption result in severe negative bone balance and a rapid decrease in bone mass.

2. Thyroid hormone– Dramatic histomorphometric changes occur in the bones of patients with hyperthyroidism and in persons taking pharmacologic doses of thyroid hormones. These are characterized by increased bone resorption and bone formation. Osteoid seams frequently are increased in width owing to accelerated matrix production, and there may be marrow fibrosis. Alterations in extracellular mineral homeostasis are not always obvious, probably because bone formation and bone resorption are equivalently increased. Nevertheless, mild hypercalcemia is occasionally observed and is associated with adaptive decreases in serum iPTH, increases in serum phosphate due to decreased phosphate excretion, hypercalciuria, and decreases in intestinal absorption of calcium. The bone loss occurring in endogenous or exogenous hyperthyroidism rarely achieves clinical significance in the young, but hyperthyroidism may sufficiently aggravate bone loss in postmenopausal individuals to precipitate fractures. Thyroid hormone replacement therapy that does not decrease serum thyrotropin levels below normal (0.3 mU/L) does not appear to increase the risk of fracture, but decreased bone mineral density has been observed in persons taking doses of thyroid hormone that are only slightly greater than physiologic.

Infrequent Causes of Osteoporosis

A. Juvenile Osteoporosis: Juvenile osteoporosis is rare, and its cause is unknown. It occurs in late childhood and adolescence and is self-limited, lasting about 5 years. Young adult osteoporosis is also rare. It occurs at a later age (20–40), but in contrast to juvenile osteoporosis, it may progress rapidly to an almost total collapse of the axial skeleton and death from respiratory failure. Its cause is also unknown.

B. Osteogenesis Imperfecta: Osteogenesis imperfecta is a relatively common heritable disorder of bone that is caused by structural defects in the collagen. The most severely affected individuals suffer multiple fractures early in life that ultimately produce severe deformity and growth retardation. Other manifestations include bluish-gray scleras (an inconstant finding), ligamentous laxity, and hearing loss in adults. It has been suggested that some patients who develop osteoporosis in later life may have mild forms of osteogenesis imperfecta.

C. Chromosomal Abnormalities: Although sex hormone deficiency may be responsible in part for the osteoporosis observed in patients with chromosomal abnormalities (eg, Turner's XO and Klinefelter's XXY syndromes), other unknown factors are probably also involved.

D. Immobilization: The osteoporosis of immobilization can be localized (associated with casts for fractures or with painful limbs), generalized (associated with prolonged bed rest or space travel), or neurologic (associated with paraplegia or quadriplegia). The causes are unknown, but absence of stress and muscle pull on bone is an underlying factor in all of these disorders.

E. Vitamin C Deficiency and Hemochromatosis: Osteoporosis may be associated with severe vitamin C deficiency and hemochromatosis. Vitamin C is a cofactor in the enzymatic hydroxylation of proline and lysine in collagen. Because of this, a deficiency in vitamin C is thought to produce abnormalities in collagen biosynthesis and maturation that interfere with bone formation. A similar mechanism may be involved in the osteoporosis of hemochromatosis; the abnormal accumulation of iron may promote oxidation of vitamin C, resulting in its depletion. Hemochromatosis of the testes or of the pituitary, which causes hypogonadism and sex hormone deficiency, is almost certainly an important

contributing factor in the production of the osteoporosis of this disorder.

F. Migratory Osteoporosis and Sudeck's Atrophy: There are two rare forms of local osteoporosis that appear to be unrelated to immobilization. The first is transitory or regional migratory osteoporosis. It is characterized by painful loss of bone, usually in the upper femoral shafts, which almost always reverses without treatment. The second is the syndrome of "disappearing bones," in which one or more parts of limb bones disappear radiologically and are replaced by fibrous tissue. This disorder probably represents an extreme form of Sudeck's atrophy of bone which occurs after trauma or fracture. It is variably reversible, and no specific treatment is available. The underlying causes of these conditions are unknown.

Anatomic & Chemical Pathology

Osteoporosis can often be detected during transiliac bone biopsy. The biopsy needle saws through the outer table of bone with little difficulty, and extreme care is needed to avoid crushing the specimen. Examination of such a specimen shows that the mass of bone per unit volume of bone tissue is reduced, but its mineral content per unit mass is normal. In contrast, the bone in osteomalacia has a reduced mineral content per unit mass.

Tetracycline labeling of bone in vivo has shown that bone formation decreases with age and bone resorption remains constant or is increased. Microradiographic studies show increases in bone resorption surfaces, probably resulting from the failure of bone formation processes to repair previously resorbed bone. Since it has not yet been possible to investigate the dynamic properties of human bone cells, it is still unknown whether bone cell function in osteoporosis is abnormal.

Pathogenesis of Postmenopausal & Senile Osteoporosis

The pathogenesis of postmenopausal and senile osteoporosis is poorly understood, but important observations during the past decade have led to a hypothesis with therapeutic implications. Although the evidence is incomplete, it is likely that estrogen protects bone against the destructive effects of PTH and inhibits the release of cytokines (interleukins 1 and 6) by osteoblasts that are powerful stimulators of osteoclastic bone resorption. The loss of sex hormone function at the menopause therefore causes marked negative bone balance, which in turn results in small increases in the serum Ca^{2+} (within the normal range) which decrease PTH secretion. The consequences of chronic decreases in PTH secretion are manifest and can be predicted from Figure 5–2. Serum concentrations of phosphate increase because of a decrease in PTH-induced phosphate excretion. The combination of decreased PTH secretion and increased serum phosphate results in diminished $1,25(OH)_2D_3$ production and decreased intestinal calcium absorption. Likewise, urinary calcium excretion is increased as a result of a decrease in PTH-induced renal tubular reabsorption of calcium. These adaptive mechanisms are normally quite effective in preventing increases in serum calcium due to environmental perturbations (eg, increased intestinal absorption of calcium). However, they can only be considered maladaptive when increases in serum calcium are induced by a primary defect in bone that causes a relative increase in resorption over formation (eg, postmenopausal osteoporosis). Thus, if the sequence of events described above is correct, the decrease in intestinal absorption of calcium and increase in renal excretion of calcium observed in postmenopausal osteoporosis represent epiphenomena of negative bone balance that can only aggravate the primary bone lesions by aggravating a negative balance in total body calcium.

Serum iPTH increases with age in apparently normal subjects. Although this could be due to an intrinsic change in the secretory activity of the parathyroid glands, it is likely that a combination of a dietary deficiency in calcium in the aged, diminished intestinal calcium absorption, and possibly decreased renal function is responsible. It is likely, therefore, that the adverse effects of sex hormone deficiency and secondary hyperparathyroidism due to calcium deficiency merge as age progresses and are responsible for the ultimate clinical picture of advanced osteoporosis in the very old (see Figure 22–4). A working classification of the osteoporosis of aging, based on these two pathogenetic schemes, has been proposed, type I denoting osteoporosis due to sex hormone deficiency and type II denoting that due to secondary hyperparathyroidism.

It has been suggested that the chronically decreased secretion of calcitonin in women may be an additional etiologic factor.

Quantitative Measurement of Bone Mass

There are three approaches to quantitative assessment of bone mass. The first uses careful x-rays of the hands and measurements of the periosteal and endosteal diameters of a metacarpal bone (the second, third, or fourth). The thickness of the cortical bone is determined by subtracting the internal diameter from the external diameter. Measurements are best made with a precision caliper. The precision of this measurement is about ± 2%.

The second approach uses photon beam absorptiometry, introduced by Cameron and Sorenson. The single-beam method measures the attenuation by bone (usually the radius) of gamma ray emission from isotopes (^{125}I or ^{247}Am). Commercial instruments are now available, and with careful application the precision of measurements is also about ± 2%. The disadvantage of this technique is that accessible

limb bones have little trabecular bone, and measurements thus reflect chiefly cortical bone. Since most osteoporosis of clinical significance involves principally trabecular bone, there is a large overlap in values for normal subjects and patients with proved osteoporosis.

The recently developed dual-photon absorptiometry (DPA) method can measure mass in almost any bone in the body. Thus, the bones most frequently fractured in patients with osteoporosis (vertebrae and femoral neck) can be assessed directly. The overlap in bone mass values between normal subjects and patients with proved osteoporosis is considerably less than that observed using the single-beam technique.

Another technique, introduced by Genant and Cann, uses quantitative computer-assisted tomography (QCT) to obtain direct measurements of bone mass in the central portion of a given vertebra. This is in contrast with DPA, which measures bone mass in entire vertebrae as well as overlying tissues (eg, calcified aorta). QCT is therefore a more specific measurement of the trabecular bone in the vertebral bodies.

The most recent addition to the technology of bone mineral content measurement is dual-energy radiography (DER, DEX, or DXA), which uses an x-ray source rather than an isotope source to generate photon beams. This method is more rapid, accurate, and precise than DPA and has greater resolution. It therefore has become the standard for measurement of bone mineral content. QCT and DXA can provide the clinician with accurate measurements of changes in bone mass during observation or treatment. They also help in assessing the value of various new treatments for osteoporosis. While there is some controversy as to the cost-effectiveness of bone mineral measurements in patients at risk for the development of osteoporosis, there is little question that they are essential for triaging such patients into groups requiring or not requiring sex hormone prophylaxis against menopausal bone loss.

Clinical Features

A. Symptoms and Signs: Patients with uncomplicated osteoporosis without bone fractures are usually asymptomatic. The first manifestation of reduced bone mass is usually a wrist fracture or a vertebral crush fracture caused by a small amount of force. A fresh vertebral fracture produces severe localized pain in the back that frequently radiates anteriorly into the chest, sometimes resembling the pain of a cardiopulmonary catastrophe. Torso movement aggravates the pain and recumbency relieves it, with improvement occurring within 1–2 months. Subsequent vertebral fractures may occur and may contribute to chronic back pain, but more often the intensity of pain is poorly related to the degree of spinal deformity seen on x-rays. During the acute phase of fracture, spot tenderness occurs over the back, but neurologic signs are rare.

1. Dorsal kyphosis and loss of height– The single most prominent finding in patients with well-established osteoporosis is dorsal kyphosis (so-called dowager's hump) and loss of height. Accurate measurements of height and arm span are most important in assessing the development and progress of osteoporosis in patients who have undergone oophorectomy or orchiectomy or in patients undergoing routine evaluation after the age of 45 years. Normally, total erect height equals arm span but becomes progressively less than arm span with vertebral collapse.

All of the classic signs of hip fracture are present in patients with osteoporosis who are afflicted with this problem, but because most patients are aged, the incidence of fatal complications is increased.

2. Signs of other disorders– Patients with osteoporosis due to causes other than sex hormone deficiency and aging may have symptoms and signs related to the underlying disorder (eg, Cushing's syndrome or thyrotoxicosis).

B. Laboratory Findings: Serum calcium, phosphate, alkaline phosphatase, and iPTH are within normal ranges in patients with osteoporosis due to sex hormone deficiency and aging. In the acute phase of development, urinary calcium and hydroxyproline may be slightly increased, but these indices have little diagnostic value. However, recent reports that the urinary excretion of pyridinoline and deoxypyridinoline collagen cross-links accurately reflects the level of bone resorption suggest that that bone marker could be useful in assessing the likely rate of contemporaneous bone destruction in individual patients. This is in sharp contrast to assessments of bone mass which can provide only a static measurement. Thus, "cross-link" measurements could identify patients with high-turnover osteoporosis and, coupled with bone mass, could help greatly in determining the best form of treatment to offer patients (see below). Serum osteocalcin is a reasonably accurate measure of bone formation, and its measurements may also be helpful in assessing bone turnover. Increased levels are seen in high-turnover states and decreased levels in low-turnover states. Serum osteocalcin is particularly useful in detecting the development of decreased bone formation in corticosteroid-induced bone disease. Significant abnormalities in serum calcium, phosphate, alkaline phosphatase, iPTH, and serum proteins should be regarded with suspicion, and one or more of the complicating factors listed in Table 5–12 should be sought.

C. Imaging Studies: X-rays of the skeleton do not show a decrease in osseous density until at least 30% of bone mass has been lost. Although such a decrease in density may be observed in all bones, the most valuable x-rays for diagnostic purposes are those of the lateral lumbar and thoracic spine. One should look for loss of horizontal trabeculae and prominent end plates of the vertebral bodies (Figure 5–31). Intervertebral disks are more prominent than

is normal, and mechanical failure of vertebrae is manifested by wedging and protrusion of the disk into the body of the vertebra (Figure 5–31). The latter finding has been termed "codfish spine" because this species has biconcave vertebral bodies.

X-rays of the upper part of the femur that are taken so as to accentuate trabecular patterns may be most helpful in assessing the clinical importance of reduced bone mass (Singh index) (Figure 5–32). Disappearance of the superior trabecular pattern that traverses the greater trochanter (arrow in grade 3 sketch) probably indicates that the osteoporosis is severe enough to increase the risk of hip fracture.

Evaluation of Patients With Low Bone Density or Fracture With Minimal Trauma

A. Differential Diagnosis: The most likely reason for low bone mass detected by DXA or QCT measurement or fracture due to minimal trauma is the failure to achieve genetically programmed peak bone mass during adolescence and young adulthood or bone loss due to factors such as estrogen and calcium deficiency. However, there are many disorders that mimic or complicate osteoporosis of those types, and it is essential that they be kept in mind as the evaluation proceeds.

The routine history and physical examination are very useful in discovering these disorders. The history will reveal drug treatment, gastric or intestinal resections, frequent or prolonged episodes of amenorrhea, oophorectomy, sunlight deprivation, and immobilization. Physical examination may reveal the presence of Cushing's syndrome or hyperthyroidism as well as the presence of hepatomegaly or splenomegaly. Liver enlargement suggests liver disease and, in men, the possibility of hemochromatosis. Small, soft testicles should raise suspicions about hypogonadism due to a variety of causes, including Klinefelter's syndrome (see Chapter 9). Short stature in a woman may be a sign of Turner's syndrome (see Chapter 11).

Multiple myeloma and diffuse metastasis of malignant tumors to the vertebrae are commonly misdiagnosed as postmenopausal or senile osteoporosis. These conditions should be suspected when the history indicates that the patient may have cancer. In the absence of historical clues, unusually rapid progression of osseous destruction often indicates the presence of cancer. In such cases, radioactive bisphosphonate bone scan and bone marrow examination or direct biopsy of lesions may be most helpful.

Total serum calcium, phosphate, alkaline phosphatase, protein electrophoresis, iPTH, cortisol, thyroxine, and TSH should be measured in all patients with osteoporosis. In patients with postmenopausal or senile osteoporosis, the values for all of these indices should be within the normal range. Abnormali-

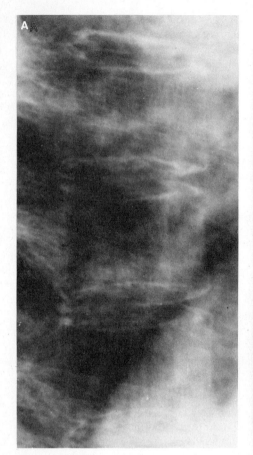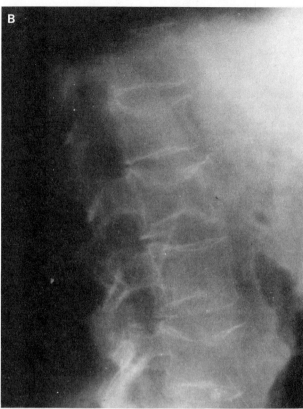

Figure 5–31. A: Magnified x-rays of thoracic vertebrae from a woman with osteoporosis. Note the relative prominence of vertical trabeculae and the absence of horizontal trabeculae. **B:** Lateral x-ray of the lumbar spine of a woman with postmenopausal osteoporosis. Note the increased density of the superior and inferior cortical margins of vertebrae, the marked demineralization of vertebral bodies, and the central compression of articular surfaces of vertebral bodies by intervertebral disks. (Courtesy of G Gordan.)

ties indicate the presence of disorders that mimic or complicate postmenopausal or senile osteoporosis, and a specific diagnosis should be established as soon as possible. Serum $25OHD_2$ and $25OHD_3$ should be measured in patients suspected of sunlight deprivation or malabsorption; and in men, measurement of serum testosterone is indicated to evaluate patients for hypogonadism.

B. Baseline Measurements:

1. Imaging studies– Assuming that multiple myeloma and primary or metastatic malignancy are not discovered, the next step in the evaluation is to establish certain baselines for follow-up. Lateral x-rays of the thoracolumbar spine will determine the number and type of vertebral fractures, and a posteroanterior x-ray of the pelvis and proximal femurs will determine the extent and type of osteoporotic vertebral fractures and the quality and distribution of the trabecular "struts" in the femoral trochanter and neck regions (Singh index; Figure 5–32). The spine

x-ray is particularly important in determining if future episodes of back pain are due to *new* fractures. Bone mineral density measurements of both the proximal femur and the vertebrae should be obtained at a facility that can offer long-term accurate and comparable results.

2. Bone markers– Finally, it is desirable to determine the levels of bone formation and resorption in patients with osteoporosis. For this purpose, serum osteocalcin can be used to assess the level of bone formation and the urinary excretion of pyridinoline collagen cross-links to assess levels of bone resorption. Although those biochemical markers are not as direct as the measurements performed on bone biopsies, they have the great advantage of being noninvasive and accurate, and it is possible to perform them repeatedly.

C. Selection of Patients for Prophylaxis or Therapy: A single determination of low bone mineral density in a perimenopausal woman may result

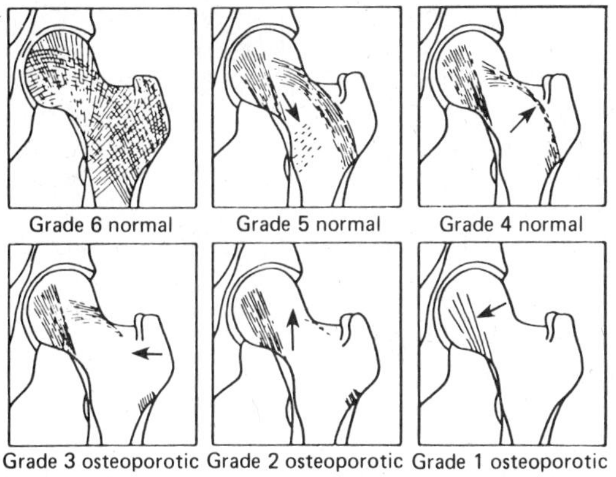

Grade 6 normal | Grade 5 normal | Grade 4 normal

Grade 3 osteoporotic | Grade 2 osteoporotic | Grade 1 osteoporotic

Figure 5–32. The effects of increasingly severe osteoporosis on the pattern of trabecular bone in the upper end of the femur. Arrows show progressive radiologic disappearance of trabecular groups. (Reproduced, with permission, from Singh M et al: Grading of trabecular pattern of proximal femur. Ann Intern Med 1972;77:63.)

from failure to achieve peak bone mass or to contemporaneous bone loss. A history of poor calcium intake and lack of exercise during adolescence and young adulthood suggests a failure to achieve peak bone mass, but it does not exclude bone loss. A small increase in urinary pyridinoline collagen cross-links (PYD cross-links) excretion and in serum osteocalcin (OC) strongly suggests that patients are losing bone, whereas normal or low values for those measurements exclude levels of bone turnover sufficient to produce significant bone loss. Thus, patients with low bone mass and increased levels of PYD cross-links and serum OC need to have prophylactic antiresorptive therapy, whereas those with normal or low levels of those bone markers can be observed safely on a yearly basis for increases in bone marker levels or decreases in bone mineral density.

A similar approach can be taken with perimenopausal women whose bone mineral density values are normal or high. It is anticipated that values for PYD cross-links and serum OC may increase with time in some women even prior to the cessation of menses, signaling the need to initiate antiresorptive therapy early to prevent bone loss.

Low serum OC levels have special significance, especially if they are associated with normal or increased PYD cross-links irrespective of bone mass values. That profile suggests a severe uncoupling of bone formation and bone resorption that will lead, unless antiresorptive therapy is initiated, to a rapid loss of bone. It is likely that glucocorticoid-induced osteoporosis is a classic example of that type of bone loss and represents the form of osteoporosis requiring the most urgent attention.

There are no age restrictions to therapy except in those instances in which the informed older patient has an aversion to a particular treatment. Recent evidence indicates that hormone replacement coupled with calcium and vitamin D supplementation can be effective in preventing bone loss in women older than 70 years of age.

Treatment

A. Endocrine Disease or Drug-Induced Osteoporosis: Patients with endocrine abnormalities can usually be treated by either hormone replacement (eg, hypogonadism) or removal of hyperfunctioning endocrine tissue. In most instances, drugs that induce osteoporosis can be discontinued or replaced by other drugs, or the dosage can be reduced. In the case of corticosteroid therapy, measures designed to help prevent osteoporosis should be considered. Alternate-day corticosteroid therapy in conjunction with oral calcium supplements (1–2 g of elemental calcium daily) and vitamin D (1000–2000 units/d) or $1,25(OH)_2D_3$ (0.25–1 μg/d) to decrease PTH secretion may be helpful in this regard. Alternatively, it may be possible in the future to treat patients with corticosteroid preparations that possess anti-inflammatory activity but have little or no adverse effects on bone. Recent studies suggest that a glucocorticoid analogue called deflazacort may be such a compound. It is not available in the USA.

B. Postmenopausal and Senile Osteoporosis:
1. General measures and fractures– Once it has been established that a patient is at risk or has postmenopausal osteoporosis, the risk factors listed in Table 5–12 should be eliminated whenever possible. Small women of northern European ancestry whose Singh index (Figure 5–32) for the upper femoral trabecular pattern is grade 3 or below or whose bone mineral content at the femur is at or below the fracture threshold should be warned that hip fracture is likely to occur with minimal trauma. These patients should eliminate hazards that might cause them to fall (eg, waxed floors and throw rugs).

In general, fractures heal normally in osteoporotic patients and require no special orthopedic care. However, whereas vertebral fractures tend to reexpand in normal people, they tend to remain compressed in osteoporotic patients because of diminished vertebral trabecular bone content. There is, therefore, a great tendency for kyphotic deformity to develop and progress in osteoporotic patients, all of which contributes to the chronic back pain and weakness that plagues them. The back pain usually requires analgesics, but a more aggressive approach using massage and back extension and water exercises can be extraordinarily effective in patients who are willing to actively pursue such physical therapy. Furthermore, those exercises in conjunction with supervised weight training reverse the muscular deconditioning so many of these patients suffer, resulting in a remarkable improvement in their ability to prevent falls as well as improving their sense of well-being and quality of life.

By contrast, the acute pain due to recent vertebral fracture needs to be treated with analgesics and relatively short periods of bed rest on a hard surface or a very firm mattress. Back pain may be so severe as to require narcotic agents. Mobilization usually requires an especially fitted back brace. The author frequently initiates salmon calcitonin therapy in large doses (200–500 units twice daily subcutaneously or 500–1000 units by continuous intravenous drip over 24 hours) during the first several days of treatment. Calcitonin in those doses seems to have important analgesic properties and serves the purpose of providing specific bone antiresorptive therapy until a long-term regimen can be decided upon.

2. Calcium– After 24-hour urinary calcium is measured (to rule out idiopathic hypercalciuria), oral calcium supplements of 1–2 g of elemental calcium daily–preferably as calcium carbonate or calcium citrate–are begun. Such therapy increases intestinal absorption of calcium, decreases serum levels of iPTH, and decreases resorption surfaces. If undue hypercalciuria is noted, thiazides are indicated.

3. Estrogens– It has been shown that estrogen prevents bone loss in oophorectomized and postmenopausal women, and calcium and estrogen together markedly decrease the fracture rate in osteoporotic women. It is approved by the FDA for those uses. However, estrogen replacement therapy also has significant side effects. The most common and least serious include induction of menstruation and the development of mastodynia and fluid retention. Menstrual bleeding can be avoided in many but not all patients by the constant administration of a progestin with estrogen (see below), but the long-term safety of that regimen has not been fully evaluated. Mastodynia and fluid retention can be controlled in many patients with diuretics, but such treatment trades estrogen side effects for polyuria and the long-term risks of the diuretic used. Much less common but more serious side effects of estrogen replacement therapy include endometrial cancer, breast cancer, venous thrombosis and pulmonary embolism, cholelithiasis, and aggravation of hypertension. Cyclic replacement therapy that includes a progestin (see below) virtually eliminates the risk of endometrial cancer. The evidence supporting estrogen replacement therapy as an important risk factor for breast cancer is less convincing than that for endometrial cancer. In fact. some—not all—think that the increased breast cancer risk in women taking estrogens for this purpose is more apparent than real; it might actually represent an estrogen-induced restoration of postmenopausal women to the state of relatively increased risk experienced by premenopausal women. The increased risk of venous thrombosis and cholelithiasis in women taking oral estrogen is thought to be due to the stimulation of hepatic production of coagulation factors and bile cholesterol, respectively, by the high concentrations of estrogen in the hepatic vein after its absorption from the intestine. It is quite likely that those side effects can be avoided by administering estrogen transdermally (see below). However, it may be that that route of administration represents a questionable trade-off because the beneficial effects of long-term estrogen replacement therapy to prevent cardiovascular disease (estrogen lowers total serum cholesterol and low-density lipoproteins and increases high-density lipoproteins) probably depends to a large extent upon a "first-pass" effect on hepatic lipoprotein metabolism. (See Chapter 10.)

Estrogen replacement therapy is the prime choice for the prevention and treatment of osteoporosis. However, patient compliance with this regimen has been generally poor because of the fear engendered by its well-publicized serious side effects. Therefore, the decision to initiate long term treatment should be made only after the patient has pondered its advantages and disadvantages with the sympathetic support and guidance of her physician. After a positive decision is made, estrogen therapy should never be initiated without a recent clinical examination of the patient's breasts and a mammogram that shows no evidence of malignancy. Recent histories of endometrial or breast cancer (with few exceptions) are contraindications to endocrine replacement therapy.

There are several regimens that can be followed, and the one selected should be individualized to the patients needs and circumstances. The simplest is available only to women who have had a hysterectomy; they can take continuous estrogen (0.625 mg conjugated estrogens daily orally; 0.025 mg ethynyl estradiol daily orally; or 0.05–0.1 mg estradiol-17β daily by transdermal patch). Women who have not had a hysterectomy must take a cyclic estrogen-progestin regimen that ensures periodic and effective endometrial sloughing. The classic regimen involves the daily administration of estrogenic compounds as noted above for 25 days, with the addition of 5 mg of medroxyprogesterone daily during the last 10–14 days of the cycle. Menstrual bleeding can be expected during the week off from estrogen and progesterone. The cycle should then be repeated. Unfortunately, some patients dislike taking progestins because the drug may exacerbate mental depression. A less satisfactory substitute is to give progestin either at lower daily dosage (medroxyprogesterone, 2.5 mg/d) or for 10 days every 2 or 3 months. If the latter regimen is elected, the clinician must be satisfied that a normal menstrual period follows progestin administration. The continuous estrogen and progestin (2.5 mg medroxyprogesterone daily) regimen may result in intermittent uterine bleeding in some women for the first 6–8 months. Eventually, however, such bleeding ceases in many cases, reflecting a quiescent uterine lining. The long-term efficacy or side effects of continuous estrogen-progestin administration have not been fully evaluated. Clearly, any unanticipated uterine bleeding experienced by a woman taking estrogen should be investigated thoroughly by gynecologic examination and endometrial biopsy. That procedure can now be easily performed in an outpatient setting using the recently introduced Pipel aspiration biopsy. Furthermore, breast examination by the patient (monthly) and by her physician (yearly) is the patient's responsibility.

4. Androgens for men– Men with osteoporosis should be treated in a manner similar to that described for women, except that androgens should be given instead of estrogens. This is especially true if hypogonadism can be demonstrated (low total and free serum testosterone levels and increased serum luteinizing hormone levels). Unfortunately, androgens may aggravate prostatic hyperplasia, accelerate the growth of prostatic cancer, adversely influence the serum lipid profile, and induce fluid retention. Thus, the baseline prostate examination, serum prostatic antigen value, and serum lipid profile need to be normal before treatment is begun, and periodic follow-up of those indices is necessary during therapy. Testosterone enanthate therapy may be initiated by determining if doses of 100 mg intramuscularly every 2 weeks produce clinical or biochemical side effects. Provided no serious untoward effects occur, the dose of testosterone is increased progressively each month to a steady state of between 200 and 400 mg intramuscularly every 3 weeks, with continued monitoring for side effects. Transdermal testosterone patches are being developed by several commercial groups, and that route of administration may be available soon. Combined androgen and estrogen therapy may be considered if testosterone side effects develop.

5. Calcitonin– Calcitonin inhibits osteoclastic activity and is an effective antiresorptive therapy for osteoporosis. It differs from estrogen in that there is no evidence that calcitonin decreases fracture incidence. It has been approved by the FDA and is used generally in doses of 100 IU subcutaneously per day. Other regimens (every other day; and daily, 3 months on and 3 months off) have been proved effective in preventing bone loss in postmenopausal women. Calcium supplements need to be provide to prevent secondary hyperparathyroidism. Calcitonin has been given parenterally, but more convenient and equally effective transnasal sprays (not yet FDA-approved) and possibly suppositories should become available in the future. Whichever formulation is used, calcitonin is expensive, but it is the only FDA-approved alternative to estrogen therapy when that drug is contraindicated or not well tolerated.

Salmon and human calcitonin are available in the United States. The salmon form is most frequently used because it is 30–50 times more potent than the human form. However, neutralizing antibodies to salmon calcitonin can develop and can cause resistance, in which case patients need to be switched to human calcitonin.

Calcitonin is an extraordinarily safe drug, but it has side effects that may be debilitating in about 5% of patients. Side effects include nausea and bloating (owing to slowed gastrointestinal motility), upper body flushing, mental confusion, and fatigue. They can be moderated by administering the drug before sleep, and they tend to improve with time. Transnasal administration appears to decrease the incidence of side effects.

6. Bisphosphonate compounds– Bisphosphonates adsorb to bone crystals and inhibit the activities of osteoclasts when they phagocytose those crystals. They are therefore antiresorptive agents similar to calcitonin. The only oral bisphosphonate available in the United States is sodium etidronate. Two long-term studies show that it is as effective in preventing bone loss as calcitonin when given in doses of 400 mg daily by mouth for 2 weeks out of every 3 months. Its effect on fracture incidence was difficult to evaluate because so few fractures occurred in both the treatment and control groups. Osteomalacia was not observed in bone biopsies performed in one of the studies, but it is well established that etidronate can induce osteomalacia when given continuously for more than 4 months at doses exceeding 400 mg daily. Etidronate has not been approved by the FDA for use in osteoporosis.

Other bisphosphonate congeners currently in clinical trial are active at much lower doses than etidronate and do not cause osteomalacia.

7. Fluoride– Sodium fluoride is one of the few agents that is capable of stimulating bone formation sufficiently to have a positive therapeutic effect on established osteoporosis. Unfortunately, two recent randomized long-term studies showed that fluoride, at doses of 50 mg/d, had little effect upon vertebral fracture incidence and actually increased the occurrence of appendicular fractures, even though vertebral bone mass increased dramatically in most patients. Sodium fluoride is not recommended for the treatment of osteoporosis at this time. Other clinical trials are needed using lower doses of fluoride.

8. Parathyroid hormone– Small intermittent doses of the 1–34 fragment of PTH stimulate bone formation in several animal species and can increase vertebral bone density in humans as much as 30%. This is in contrast to its ability to stimulate bone resorption in animals when it is given continuously in large doses. Human PTH(1–34) therefore has been considered as the only available alternative to fluoride as a means of increasing bone mass in osteoporotic patients. The few small clinical trials that have been performed are encouraging, but more definitive and larger studies need to be done before PTH(1–34) can be recommended. It has been given safely in doses of 400–500 units subcutaneously per day, but serum calcium should be monitored to avoid hypercalcemia.

9. Vitamin D and its metabolites– All patients with or at risk for osteoporosis should receive at least the RDA of vitamin D (400 units/d) or somewhat more (800–1200 units/d). The therapeutic use of $1,25(OH)_2D_3$ is controversial. Most clinical trials of $1,25(OH)_2D_3$ in osteoporosis performed in the United States have shown equivocal results, but those done in Europe and New Zealand have shown either prevention of bone loss or increases in vertebral density. The recommended daily dose of $1,25(OH)_2D_3$ is 0.251 μg. Serum calcium monitoring is needed to avoid hypercalcemia.

PAGET'S DISEASE
(Osteitis Deformans)

Although Paget's disease of bone is a disorder of bone remodeling, it cannot be classified strictly as a metabolic bone disease, because the abnormalities are focal. The disease is characterized by histologic and gross osseous deformities due to local uncontrolled bone resorption and bone formation, which is caused by excessive numbers of osteoclasts and osteoblasts and ultimately leads to formation of structurally fragile osseous tissue. Any bone of the body may be involved, but the most frequent sites are the femur, tibia, skull, lumbosacral spine, and pelvis. The disease is usually asymptomatic, and except for a similar bone disease in young children called hereditary bone dysplasia with hyperphosphatasia, or "juvenile Paget's disease," patients generally come to medical attention only after age 40.

Paget's disease occurs in a fairly distinct geographic distribution. About 4% of people over 40 years of age in Germany and England have the disease, whereas it is considerably less common in North America and relatively rare in Scandinavia, Africa, and the Near and Far East. It is likely that fewer than 2% of patients with radiographic evidence of Paget's disease are symptomatic. The disease may occur in families and has been reported in identical twins.

Coexistence of primary hyperparathyroidism and Paget's disease has been noted, but this observation must be interpreted cautiously in light of the fact that both disorders are common, and when one is detected, the usual laboratory investigations will almost certainly reveal the other, if present.

Etiology

Recently, the old idea that Paget's disease may be due to some chronic inflammatory process has been revived. Nuclear inclusions resembling virus particles have been observed in the osteoclasts of patients with Paget's disease, suggesting that its underlying cause may be a slow virus.

Pathology

The gross pathologic features of Paget's disease in its full-blown state consist of diffuse bony deformities, including marked enlargement of the skull, expansion and compression of the vertebrae, platybasia with compression of the cerebellum and spinal cord, anterior and lateral bowing of the extremities, and protrusion of the femoral head into the acetabulum as a result of the pelvic involvement. Histologically, all bone cell types are increased in number and apparently in activity. Lamellar bone in the cortex and trabeculae is progressively replaced by woven bone, so that its gross architecture becomes chaotic. As lesions progress, woven bone is replaced by randomly laid lamellar bone; sections thus present a characteristic mosaic structure when observed under polarized light. Osteoid volume is increased but the calcification front is normal, indicating that new bone formation is occurring at a rapid rate. Osteoclasts show great variation in size and may contain up to 100 nuclei. Osteoblasts may be very large, with irregularly shaped nuclei. Osteocytic osteolysis is a prominent finding. Areas of bone that have undergone a full "pagetic cycle" retain architectural abnormalities, but cell numbers and activity are normal.

Pathogenesis

Although bone mineral turnover may be many times greater than normal in Paget's disease, calcium balance is generally maintained because the rates of bone resorption and formation are similar. Only when Paget's disease is complicated by disorders causing further increases in bone resorption (eg, prolonged immobilization or primary hyperparathyroidism) will abnormalities of extracellular mineral metabolism become evident. The hypercalcemia of immobilization may be extremely severe and lead to suppression of PTH secretion, hypercalciuria, decreased intestinal absorption of calcium, and negative calcium balance. If primary hyperparathyroidism is present, hypercalcemia may be more severe than might be predicted by the levels of serum iPTH.

Characteristically, serum alkaline phosphatase levels are markedly increased. These increased levels are probably due to the increased numbers of osteoblasts present in pagetic bone, since serum alkaline phosphatase activity appears to correlate well with histomorphometric values for active bone formation surface. Serum acid phosphatase activity may also be increased in some patients, and this increase is thought to be due to increased numbers of osteoclasts present in lesions.

Urinary excretion of hydroxyproline and pyridinoline cross-links are increased in most patients, owing to increased rates of destruction of bone collagen.

Clinical Features

A. Symptoms and Signs: Relatively few patients with radiologically proved Paget's disease have significant symptoms. The diagnosis is often made as an incidental finding on x-rays taken for other reasons or with the serendipitous finding of an elevated serum alkaline phosphatase value. The chief symptom is bone pain over lesions. Joint symptoms produced by Paget's disease may be difficult to distinguish from those of arthritis. Deafness in patients with Paget's disease of the skull is usually related to bony abnormalities of the internal and external auditory apparatus rather than compression of the eighth nerve by temporal bone enlargement. Vertebral crush fractures occur frequently. In rare cases, there are severe neurologic complications resulting from spinal cord compression and dislocation of cervical vertebrae.

Fractures of long bones may occur. Incomplete ("fissure") fractures, frequently painful, are usually present on the convex surfaces of lower limb bones and may progress to complete fracture with minimal or no trauma. Fractures usually heal rapidly. Redness with increased skin temperature over pagetic bone is a common finding; rarely, bruits may be heard. Increased cardiac output is common in patients with extensive disease. These vascular manifestations are probably due to increased blood flow in involved areas both in bone and in overlying skin. High-output congestive heart failure may occur in patients with underlying heart disease.

The risk of osteogenic sarcoma is greater in patients with Paget's disease than in the population at large. Its major sites are the humerus and skull.

B. Laboratory Findings: Serum calcium, phosphate, magnesium, and iPTH are usually normal. Abnormalities should be taken as evidence of a superimposed condition, such as immobilization or primary hyperparathyroidism. Serum alkaline phosphatase levels are markedly increased, and acid phosphatase levels may also be increased. Urinary hydroxyproline and pyridinoline cross-links are usually increased except in patients with minimal disease.

C. Imaging Studies: There is a vast spectrum of characteristic radiologic abnormalities, ranging from pure osteolytic lesions to areas that show both osteolysis and sclerosis. Subperiosteal bone resorption has not been noted in Paget's disease; when present, it suggests associated primary hyperparathyroidism. The classic bony abnormality seen in the extremities is a large, uniform resorption front that appears as a V-shaped wedge on x-ray (Figure 5–33). As the front advances along the shaft, sclerotic bone is laid down behind it, resulting in anterior or lateral bowing. Thick bony trabeculae are common and may fill in the medullary cavity of bones. The skull is often grossly enlarged, and the mixture of sclerotic and lytic areas gives rise to the classic "cotton wool" appearance on x-ray. Initially, the skull may show a purely osteolytic lesion (osteoporosis circumscripta). Thickening of long bones and vertebrae occurs frequently, and crush fractures or "disappearing vertebrae" cause varying degrees of kyphosis.

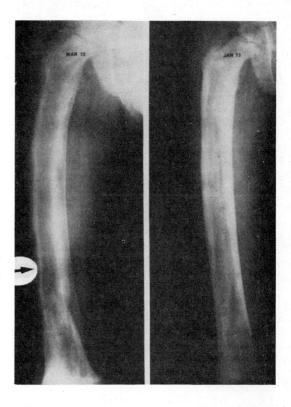

Figure 5–33. X-rays of the right femur in a patient with juvenile Paget's disease before *(left)* and after *(right)* 10 months of treatment with calcitonin. Note the advancing V-shaped resorption front (arrow). A striking improvement in the appearance of diseased bone is seen after treatment. (Reproduced, with permission, from Doyle P et al: Healing of the bone in juvenile Paget's disease treated by human calcitonin. Br J Radiol 1974;47:9.)

The development of radionuclide bone scans using ^{99m}Tc-labeled bisphosphonate or pyrophosphate and ^{67}gallium citrate has aided greatly in documenting the extent of the disease and revealing lesions that may not be apparent radiologically (Figure 5–34).

Differential Diagnosis

The diagnosis of Paget's disease is relatively straightforward. It is based on the presence of typical bone lesions on x-ray or radionuclide bone scans; normal levels of serum calcium, phosphate, and iPTH; increased serum levels of alkaline phosphatase; and increased excretion of total hydroxyproline in the urine. The only major disorder that mimics Paget's disease is cancer that has metastasized to bone. Osteoblastic metastases such as those from the prostate may be indistinguishable from Paget's lesions on x-ray or radionuclide scanning, and alkaline phosphatase may be increased. The only distinguishing feature may be a marked elevation in the serum level of acid phosphatase in prostatic cancer; this en-

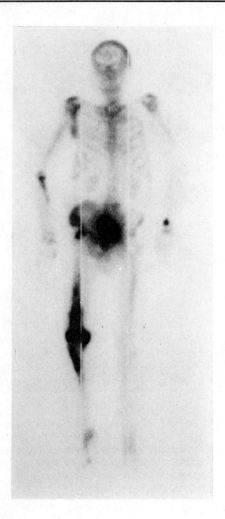

Figure 5–34. Bone scan of patient with severe Paget's disease of the skull, ribs, spine, pelvis, right femur, and acetabulum. Note localization of bone-seeking isotope (^{99m}Tc-labeled bisphosphonate) in these areas.

zyme is only occasionally increased in Paget's disease. In most instances in which metastatic cancer is suspected, confirmation by biopsy either of the primary lesion or of bone metastases is necessary. In contrast, osteolytic lesions such as those that occur in multiple myeloma do not produce markedly abnormal bone scans. Serum alkaline phosphatase may be increased in patients who have metastatic osteolytic lesions due to liver metastases, and specific immunoassay of serum bone alkaline phosphatase will show that the bulk of the enzyme is not derived from bone. Ultimately, lesions must be biopsied to determine whether bone metastases are present. The development of a sarcoma in association with a pagetic bone lesion is suggested by the appearance of a lytic area within dense bone, a marked increase in pain over the lesion, and a rapid unexplained increase in serum alkaline phosphatase levels.

Treatment

The consensus at present is that only patients with symptoms should be treated. However, the underlying cause of symptoms is sometimes difficult to determine because the pain of degenerative arthritis often mimics that of Paget's disease. When doubt exists, a therapeutic trial of nonsteroidal anti-inflammatory agents should be given before therapy for Paget's disease is initiated. In patients who fail to respond to those agents, one of several courses can be followed; each has its advantages and disadvantages. Before any treatment is started, patients with mild disease and without deformity should be reassured that most patients with the disease do not develop the disfiguring deformities they may have read or heard about.

During the last 5 years, calcitonin, bisphosphonates, and plicamycin have become available for treatment. They all suppress the number and activity of the abnormal bone cells, but they act by different mechanisms. As will be noted below, plicamycin is a toxic drug of last resort. Presently, the choice of calcitonin or bisphosphonate treatment in an individual patient is almost arbitrary, although calcitonin is preferred in primarily lytic bone disease. The advantage of calcitonin is that radiologic evidence of healing has been observed in some patients after treatment. The advantage of bisphosphonates is that they can be administered orally. Osteogenic sarcoma developing in pagetic lesions is virtually unresponsive to any form of therapy.

The treatment of juvenile Paget's disease is similar to the treatment of adult Paget's disease, although calcitonin appears to be the drug of choice.

A. Calcitonin: Synthetic salmon calcitonin is most commonly used. Synthetic human calcitonin has recently become available.

The rationale for the use of calcitonin is that it decreases bone resorption. When administered to patients with Paget's disease in doses of about 100 units/d subcutaneously or intramuscularly, it markedly decreases the number of active osteoclasts. Urinary hydroxyproline and pyridinoline cross-links decreases within 24 hours after the initial injection, but serum alkaline phosphatase does not begin to fall until approximately 2 weeks after treatment is started. Brief but significant hypocalcemia and hypophosphatemia occur shortly after administration, and appropriate increases in serum iPTH in response to the hypocalcemia have been observed. Serum calcium, phosphate, and iPTH return to normal within 4–6 hours and remain so until calcitonin is administered again. Negative calcium balance improves, with decreases in urinary and fecal calcium excretion. Radiologic improvement may not occur for months or years; the criteria for healing are decreased bone volume, increased density of cortices with restoration of a normal corticomedullary junction, and restoration of normal trabecular bone. Histomorphometry of bone biopsy specimens is difficult to evaluate because of the dynamics of untreated pagetic lesions. It has been shown, however, that along with a decrease in osteoclast numbers, there is a decrease in the surface of bone covered by osteoblasts, as well as replacement of woven bone by lamellar bone.

Although it is difficult to evaluate pain objectively, there is apparent relief of pain and bone tenderness within weeks following initiation of therapy. Objective signs of response include a decrease in redness and heat of the skin over involved bones and decreases in cardiac output. Neurologic signs (when present) may improve, but hearing rarely improves. Withdrawal of calcitonin treatment usually results in the return of symptoms and progression of bone lesions.

On the basis of decreases in alkaline phosphatase and urinary excretion of hydroxyproline, it appears that most patients given calcitonin have good long-term responses. However, some patients respond only briefly, with the indices returning to previously high levels in months. Others experience prolonged remissions followed by late recrudescence of the disease. There is no rational explanation for these relapses except in a very few patients who develop high titers of calcitonin antibodies when a nonhuman species of calcitonin is used. In such cases, human calcitonin usually produces a remission.

The ideal dose and schedule for treatment of Paget's disease with calcitonin have not been determined. Patients generally administer the drug themselves with a tuberculin syringe after instruction about rotation of injection sites. In patients with Paget's disease who also have hypercalcemia due to immobilization, higher doses (200–400 MRC units) should be given intravenously by slow infusion over 24 hours. A dramatic decrease in serum calcium usually occurs. Treatment is maintained for 2–5 years, depending on the response and on the extent of the disease.

Some patients develop side effects that necessitate discontinuation of treatment. These include flushing, fatigue, nausea, diarrhea, vomiting, pain at the injection site, rash, and a sense of being disconnected from reality. In most cases, these symptoms can be minimized by administering calcitonin at bedtime or lowering the dosage.

B. Bisphosphonate: The bisphosphonates are analogues of pyrophosphate, with a P-C-P rather than a P-O-P structure, and are resistant to enzymatic and chemical hydrolysis. They are adsorbed onto the surface of bone mineral and thus inhibit both bone resorption and formation. Evidence indicates that they also are taken up by osteoclasts and interfere with their activity.

Currently, only etidronate disodium (Didronel) is available in North America. In doses of 5 mg/kg/d

orally, etidronate disodium causes a dramatic decrease in serum alkaline phosphatase and total urinary hydroxyproline and pyridinoline cross-link excretion, as well as symptomatic improvement in most patients with Paget's disease. Unfortunately, the intestinal absorption of this drug is inconstant, so that it must be given after an overnight fast or 2–3 hours after a meal. Most of the drug accumulates in bone and is not metabolized. It is excreted unchanged in the urine. If it is well absorbed, doses higher than 5 mg/kg/d may cause osteomalacia.

Etidronate is given in courses of about 3–6 months and is reinstituted when serum alkaline phosphatase and total hydroxyproline levels increase after remission. Remissions vary in duration but have lasted as long as 2 years or more. Pagetic lesions have been shown to regress histologically in bone biopsies, but radiographic evidence of healing has rarely been reported.

Etidronate causes few side effects. Diarrhea occurs occasionally but can often be prevented by administering the agent with foods low in calcium content; this decreases absorption to a variable degree, but patients still achieve therapeutic effects. Serum concentrations of phosphate increase within a week after starting treatment, especially with doses larger than 5 mg/kg, but serum concentrations of calcium remain normal, and there is no change in serum iPTH. The effect on serum phosphate is probably related to the drug's effect on renal tubular handling of phosphate.

In patients with very severe disease or in those who fail to respond to either drug, larger doses (eg, 10–15 mg/kg/d of etidronate) or alternating or combination therapy with etidronate and calcitonin may produce a biochemical response. Other bisphosphonates as yet not available in the USA (eg, 3-amino-1-hydroxypropylidine-1,1-bisphosphonate [APD]) have been reported to cause remission in patients resistant to etidronate. Rapid responses of severe Paget's disease to intravenous APD with prolonged remissions have also been observed.

C. Plicamycin (Mithramycin): As noted in the discussion of the treatment of hypercalcemia, plicamycin is a cytotoxic antibiotic that inhibits RNA synthesis. It decreases serum alkaline phosphatase levels and urinary hydroxyproline excretion in patients with Paget's disease. It is given intravenously in doses of about 10–15 μg/kg at weekly intervals until biochemical remission occurs or toxic effects appear. Toxicity may be severe and includes liver dysfunction, renal failure, and suppression of platelet production. For this reason, it should be used only under the most desperate circumstances (eg, spinal cord compression). It is possible to obtain long-lasting remissions when this drug is combined with bisphosphonates.

REFERENCES

EXTRACELLULAR & BONE MINERAL HOMEOSTASIS

Arnaud CD: Calcium homeostasis: Regulatory elements and their integration. Fed Proc 1978;37:2557.

Arnaud CD: Minerals. In: *Diet and Health: Implications for Reducing Chronic Disease Risk*. National Academy Press, 1989.

Bringhurst FR, Potts JT: Calcium and phosphate distribution, turnover and metabolic actions. In: *Endocrinology*, 2nd ed. Vol 2. DeGroot LJ et al (editors). Grune & Stratton, 1989.

Canalis E, et al: Growth factors and regulation of bone remodeling. J Clin Invest 1988;81:277.

Favus MJ: Intestinal absorption of calcium, magnesium and phosphorus. In: *Disorders of Bone and Mineral Metabolism*. Coe FL, Favus MJ (editors). Raven Press, 1992.

Neer RM: Calcium and inorganic phosphate homeostasis. In: *Endocrinology*, 2nd ed. Vol 2. DeGroot LJ et al (editors). Grune & Stratton, 1989.

Yanagawa N, Lee DBN: Renal handling of calcium and phosphorus. In: *Disorders of Bone and Mineral Metabolism*. Coe FL, Favus MJ (editors). Raven Press, 1992.

PARATHYROID HORMONE

Structure, Biosynthesis, & Secretion

Anast CS et al: Evidence for parathyroid failure in magnesium deficiency. Science 1972;177:606.

Mallette LE: The parathyroid polyhormones: New concepts in the spectrum of peptide hormone action. Endocr Rev 1991;12:110.

Martin TJ et al: Parathyroid hormone-related protein: isolation, molecular cloning, and mechanism of action. Recent Prog Horm Res 1989;45:467.

Pocotte SL, Ehrenstein G, Fitzpatrick LA: Regulation of parathyroid hormone secretion. Endocr Rev 1991;12:291.

Rosenblatt M et al: Parathyroid hormone: Physiology, chemistry, biosynthesis, secretion, metabolism, and mode of action. In: *Endocrinology*, 2nd ed. Vol 2. DeGroot LJ et al (editors). Grune & Stratton, 1989.

Silver J: Regulation of parathyroid hormone synthesis and secretion. In: *Disorders of Bone and Mineral Metabolism*. Coe FL, Favus MJ (editors). Raven Press, 1992.

Metabolism & Circulating Forms

Arnaud CD, Pun KK: Metabolism and assay of parathyroid hormone. In: *Disorders of Bone and Mineral Metabolism*. Coe FL, Favus MJ (editors). Raven Press, 1992.

Berson SA, Yalow RS: Immunochemical heterogeneity of parathyroid hormone in plasma. J Clin Endocrinol Metab 1968;28:1037.

Flueck JA et al: Immunoheterogeneity of parathyroid hormone in venous effluent serum from hyperfunctioning parathyroid glands. J Clin Invest 1977;60:1367.

Goltzman D et al: Studies of the molecular forms of bioactive parathyroid hormone and parathyroid like substances. Rec Prog Horm Res 1986;42:665.

Martin KV et al: The peripheral metabolism of parathyroid hormone. N Engl J Med 1979;301:1092.

Mayer GP et al: Effects of plasma calcium concentrations on the relative proportion of hormone and carboxyl-terminal fragments in parathyroid venous blood. Endocrinology 1979;104:1778.

Segre GV et al: Parathyroid hormone in human plasma: Immunochemical characterization and biological implications. J Clin Invest 1972;51:3163.

Actions

Donahue HJ et al: Differential effects of parathyroid hormone and its analogues on cytosolic calcium ion and cAMP levels in cultured rat osteoblast-like cells. J Biol Chem 1988;263:13522.

Fitzpatrick LA, Coleman DT, Bilezikian JP: The target tissue actions of parathyroid hormone. In: *Disorders of Bone and Mineral Metabolism*. Coe FL, Favus MJ (editors). Raven Press, 1992.

Juppner H et al: A G-protein-linked receptor for parathyroid hormone and parathyroid hormone-related peptide. Science 1991;254:1024.

Karpf DB et al: Structural properties of the renal parathyroid hormone receptor: Hydrodynamic analysis and protease sensitivity. Endocrinology 1988;123:2611.

Muff R et al: Parathyroid hormone receptors in control of proximal tubule function. Annu Rev Physiol 1992;54:67.

Nissenson RA, Klein RF: Parathyroid hormone receptors. In: *Peptide Hormone Receptors*. Kalimi MY, Hubbard JR (editors). Gruyter, 1987.

Nissenson RA et al: Covalent labeling of a high-affinity, guanyl nucleotide sensitive parathyroid hormone receptor in canine renal cortex. Biochemistry 1987;26:1874.

Pun KK, Arnaud CD, Nissenson RA: Parathyroid hormone receptors in human dermal fibroblasts: Structural and functional characterization. J Bone Min Res 1988;3:453.

Rosenblatt M et al: Parathyroid hormone: Physiology, chemistry, biosynthesis, secretion, metabolism, and mode of action. In: *Endocrinology*, 2nd ed. Vol 2. DeGroot LJ et al (editors). Grune & Stratton, 1989.

Shigeno C et al: Photoaffinity labeling of parathyroid hormone receptors in clonal rat osteosarcoma cells. J Biol Chem 1988;263:3864.

Silve CM et al: Parathyroid hormone receptor in intact embryonic chick bone: Characterization and cellular localization. J Cell Biol 1982;94:379.

Teitelbaum AP, Nissenson RA, Arnaud CD: Coupling of the canine renal parathyroid hormone receptor to adenylate cyclase: Modulation by guanyl nucleotides and N-ethylmaleimide. Endocrinology 1982;111:1524.

Yamaguchi DT et al: Parathyroid hormone-activated calcium channels in an osteoblast-like osteosarcoma cell line. J Biol Chem 1987;262:7711.

Assay in Biologic Fluids

Arnaud CD, Pun KK: Metabolism and assay of parathyroid hormone. In: *Disorders of Bone and Mineral Metabolism*. Coe FL, Favus MT (editors). Raven Press, 1992.

Arnaud C, Tsao HS, Littledike ET: Radioimmunoassay

of human parathyroid hormone in serum. J Clin Invest 1971;50:21.

Endres DB et al: Measurement of parathyroid hormone. Endocrinol Metab Clin North Am 1989;18:611.

Goltzman D et al: Cytochemical bioassay of parathyroid hormone: Characteristics of the assay and analysis of circulating hormonal forms. J Clin Invest 1980;65:1309.

Nissenson RA et al: Endogenous biologically active human parathyroid hormone: Measurement by guanyl nucleotide-amplified renal adenylate cyclase assay. J Clin Endocrinol Metab 1981;52:840.

Nussbaum SR, Potts JT Jr: Immunoassays for parathyroid hormone 1–84 in the diagnosis of hyperparathyroidism. J Bone Min Res 1991;6(Suppl 2):S43.

Segre GV, Potts JT: Differential diagnosis of hypercalcemia: Methods and clinical applications of parathyroid assays. In: *Endocrinology,* 2nd ed. Vol 2. DeGroot LJ et al (editors). Grune & Stratton, 1989.

CALCITONIN

Austin LA et al: Regulation of calcitonin secretion in normal man by changes of serum calcium within the physiologic range. J Clin Invest 1979;64:1721.

Austin LA, Heath HH III: Calcitonin: Physiology and pathophysiology. N Engl J Med 1981;304:269.

Copp DH: Remembrance: Calcitonin: Discovery and early development. Endocrinology 1992;131:1007.

Heath HH III, Sizemore GW: Plasma calcitonin in normal man: Differences between men and women. J Clin Invest 1977;60:1135.

MacIntyre I: Calcitonin: Physiology, biosynthesis, secretion, metabolism, and mode of action. In: *Endocrinology,* 2nd ed. Vol 2. DeGroot LJ et al (editors). Grune & Stratton, 1989.

Talmage RV et al: The physiological significance of calcitonin. In: *Bone and Mineral Research,* Annual 1. Peck WA (editor). Excerpta Medica, 1983.

VITAMIN D

DeLuca HF: The vitamin D story: A collaborative effort of basic science and clinical medicine. FASEB J 1988;2:224.

DeLuca HF, Krisinger J, Darwish H: The vitamin D system: 1990. Kidney Int 1990;29(Suppl 2):S2.

Haussler MR et al: Molecular biology of the vitamin D hormone. Recent Prog Horm Res 1988;44:263.

Hewison M: Vitamin D and the immune system. J Endocrinol 1992;132:173.

Holick MF: Vitamin D: Biosynthesis, metabolism, and mode of action. In: *Endocrinology,* 2nd ed. Vol 2. DeGroot LJ et al (editors). Grune & Stratton, 1989.

Holick MF: The use and interpretation of assays for vitamin D and its metabolites. J Nutr 1990;120(Suppl 11):1464.

Kumar R: Vitamin D metabolism and mechanisms of calcium transport. J Am Soc Nephrol 1990;1:30.

Norman AW: Intestinal calcium absorption: A vitamin D-hormone-mediated adaptive response. Am J Clin Nutr 1990;51:290.

Reichel H, Koeffler HP, Norman AW: The role of the vitamin D endocrine system in health and disease. N Engl J Med 1989;320:980. (See comments.)

Stern PH: Vitamin D and bone. Kidney Int 1990;29(Suppl):S17.

Wasserman RH et al: Recent studies on the biological actions of vitamin D on intestinal transport and the electrophysiology of peripheral nerve and cardiac muscle. Prog Clin Biol Res 1990;332:99.

DISORDERS OF PARATHYROID FUNCTION

Hypoparathyroidism

Ahn TG et al: Familial isolated hypoparathyroidism: A molecular genetic analysis of 8 families with 23 affected persons. Medicine 1986;65:73.

Eastell R, Heath H III: The hypocalcemic states: Their differential diagnosis and management. In: *Disorders of Bone and Mineral Metabolism.* Coe FL, Favus MT (editors). Raven Press, 1992.

Nicar MJ, Pak CYC: Calcium bioavailability from calcium carbonate and calcium citrate. J Clin Endocrinol Metab 1985;61:391.

Nusynowitz ML, Frame B, Kolb FO: The spectrum of the hypoparathyroid states. Medicine 1976;55:105.

Okano K et al: Comparative efficiency of various vitamin D metabolites in the treatment of various types of hypoparathyroidism. J Clin Endocrinol Metab 1982;55:238.

Parfitt AM: The spectrum of hypoparathyroidism. J Clin Endocrinol Metab 1972;34:152.

Parfitt AM: Surgical, idiopathic and other varieties of parathyroid hormone-deficient hypoparathyroidism. In: Endocrinology, 2nd ed. Vol 2. DeGroot LJ et al (editors). Grune & Stratton, 1989.

Porter RH et al: Treatment of hypoparathyroid patients with chlorthalidone. N Engl J Med 1978;298:577.

Rude RK, Oldham SB, Singer FR: Functional hypoparathyroidism and parathyroid hormone end-organ resistance in human magnesium deficiency. Clin Endocrinol 1976;5:209.

Spinner MW et al: Familial distribution of organ-specific antibodies in the blood of patients with Addison's disease and hypoparathyroidism and their relatives. Clin Exp Immunol 1969;5:461.

Suh SM et al: Pathogenesis of hypocalcemia in primary hypomagnesemia: Normal end-organ responsiveness to parathyroid hormone, impaired parathyroid gland function. J Clin Invest 1973;52:153.

Pseudohypoparathyroidism & Pseudopseudohypoparathyroidism

Albright F et al: Pseudohypoparathyroidism: An example of the "Seabright-bantam syndrome." Endocrinology 1942;20:922.

Bell NH et al: Effects of dibutyryl cyclic adenosine 3',5'-monophosphate and parathyroid extract on calcium and phosphorus metabolism in hypoparathyroidism and pseudohypoparathyroidism. J Clin Invest 1972;51:816.

Breslau NA. Pseudohypoparathyroidism: Current concepts. Am J Med Sci 1989;298:130.

Chase LR, Melson GL, Aurbach GD: Pseudohypoparathyroidism: Defective excretion of 3',5'-AMP in response to parathyroid hormone. J Clin Invest 1969;48:1822.

Downs RW et al: Deficient adenylate cyclase regulatory

protein in renal membranes from a patient with pseudohypoparathyroidism. J Clin Invest 1983;71:231.

Drezner M, Neelon FA, Lebavitz HE: Pseudohypoparathyroidism type II: A possible defect in the reception of the cyclic AMP signal. N Engl J Med 1973;289:1056.

Farfel Z et al: Deficiency of receptor cyclase coupling protein in pseudohypoparathyroidism. N Engl J Med 1980;303:237.

Farfel Z et al: Pseudohypoparathyroidism: Inheritance of a deficient receptor-cyclase coupling activity. Proc Nat Acad Sci USA 1981;78:3098.

Kolb FO, Steinbach HL: Pseudohypoparathyroidism with secondary hyperparathyroidism and osteitis fibrosa. J Clin Endocrinol Metab 1962;22:59.

Kooh SW et al: Treatment of hypoparathyroidism and pseudohypoparathyroidism with metabolites of vitamin D: Evidence for impaired conversion of 25-hydroxyvitamin D to 1α,25-dihydroxyvitamin D. N Engl J Med 1975;293:840.

Levine MA, Aurbach GD: Pseudohypoparathyroidism. In: Endocrinology, 2nd ed. Vol 2. DeGroot LJ et al (editors). Grune & Stratton, 1989.

Levine MA et al: Deficient guanine nucleotide regulatory activity in cultured fibroblast membranes from patients with pseudohypoparathyroidism type I: A cause of impaired synthesis of 3′,5′-cyclic AMP by intact and broken cells. J Clin Invest 1983;72:316.

Levine MA et al: Activity of the stimulatory guanine-nucleotide binding protein is reduced in erythrocytes of patients with pseudohypoparathyroidism and pseudopseudohypoparathyroidism: Biochemical, endocrine, and genetic analysis of Albright's hereditary osteodystrophy in six kindreds. J Clin Endocrinol Metab 1986;62:497.

McElduff et al: A 6-hour human parathyroid hormone (1–34) infusion protocol: Studies in normal and hypoparathyroid subjects. Calcif Tissue Int 1987;41:267.

Silve C et al: Selective resistance to parathyroid hormone in cultured skin fibroblasts from patients with pseudohypoparathyroidism type Ib. J Clin Endocrinol Metab 1986;62:640.

Van Dop C: Pseudohypoparathyroidism: Clinical and molecular aspects. Semin Nephrol 1989;9:168.

Primary Hyperparathyroidism

Bilezikian JP: Hypercalcemic states: Their differential diagnosis and acute management. In: Disorders of Bone and Mineral Metabolism. Coe FL, Favus MJ (editors). Raven Press, 1992.

Brandi ML et al: Parathyroid mitogenic activity in plasma from patients with familial multiple endocrine neoplasia type I. N Engl J Med 1986;314:1287

Breslau NA, Pak CYC: Asymptomatic primary hyperparathyroidism. In: Disorders of Bone and Mineral Metabolism. Coe FL, Favus MT (editors). Raven Press, 1992.

Broadus AE: Nephrogenous cyclic AMP. Recent Prog Horm Res 1981;31:667.

Canfield RE (editor): Etidronate sodium: A new therapy for hypercalcemia of malignancy. Am J Med 1987;82:1.

Christianssen T et al: Prevalence of hypercalcemia in health screening in Stockholm. Acta Med Scand 1976;200:131.

Dauphine RT, Riggs BL, Scholz DA: Back pain and vertebral crush fractures: An unemphasized mode of presentation for primary hyperparathyroidism. Ann Intern Med 1975;83:365.

DeSimone DP and Bell NH: Hypercalcemia and abnormal vitamin D metabolism. In: Disorders of Bone and Mineral Metabolism. Coe FL, Favus MJ (editors). Raven Press, 1992.

Fitzpatrick LA, Bilezikian JP: Acute primary hyperparathyroidism. Am J Med 1987;82:275.

Foley TP Jr et al: Familial benign hypercalcemia. J Pediatr 1972;81:1060.

Genant HK et al: Primary hyperparathyroidism: A comprehensive study of clinical, biochemical and radiographic manifestations. Radiology 1973;109:513.

Goldsmith RE et al: Familial hyperparathyroidism: Description of a large kindred with physiological observations and a review of the literature. Ann Intern Med 1976;94:36.

Habener JF, Potts, JT: Primary hyperparathyroidism: Clinical features. In: Endocrinology, 2nd ed. Vol 2. DeGroot LJ et al (editors). Grune & Stratton, 1989.

Harrison BJ, Wheeler MH: Asymptomatic primary hyperparathyroidism. World J Surg 1991;15:724.

Heath H III. Primary hyperparathyroidism: Recent advances in pathogenesis, diagnosis, and management. Adv Intern Med 1992;37:275.

Heath H III, Hodgson SF, Kennedy MA: Primary hyperparathyroidism: Incidence, morbidity, and potential economic impact in a community. N Engl J Med 1980;302:189.

Lambert PW, Heath H III, Sizemore GW: Pre- and postoperative studies of plasma calcitonin in primary hyperparathyroidism. J Clin Invest 1979;63:602.

Levin KE, Clark OH: Localization of parathyroid glands. Annu Rev Med 1988;39:29.

Neer RM, Potts JT: Medical management of hyperparathyroidism and hypercalcemia. In: Endocrinology, 2nd ed. Vol 2. DeGroot LJ et al (editors). Grune & Stratton, 1989.

Norton JA et al: Surgical management of hyperparathyroidism. In: Endocrinology, 2nd ed. Vol 2. DeGroot LJ et al (editors). Grune & Stratton, 1989.

Orloff JJ, Stewart AF: Disorders of serum minerals caused by cancer. In: Disorders of Bone and Mineral Metabolism. Coe FL, Favus MJ (editors). Raven Press, 1992.

Potts JT Jr (editor): Diagnosis and management of asymptomatic hyperparathyroidism. J Bone Min Res 1991;6(Suppl 2):1.

Prinz RA et al: Radiation associated hyperparathyroidism: A new syndrome? Surgery 1977;82:296.

Purnell DC et al: Primary hyperparathyroidism: A prospective clinical study. Am J Med 1971;50:670.

Purnell DC et al: Treatment of primary hyperparathyroidism. Am J Med 1974;56:800.

Ralston SH: The pathogenesis of humoral hypercalcemia of malignancy. Lancet 1987;2:1443.

Scholz DA, Purnell DC: Asymptomatic primary hyperparathyroidism: Ten-year prospective study. Mayo Clin Proc 1981;56:473.

Stewart AF, Insogna KF, Broadus AE: Malignancy associated hypercalcemia. In: Endocrinology, 2nd ed. Vol 2. DeGroot LJ et al (editors). Grune & Stratton, 1989.

Secondary Hyperparathyroidism
of Chronic Renal Failure

Arnaud CD: Hyperparathyroidism and renal failure. Kidney Int 1973;4:80.

Bordier PJ, Marie PJ, Arnaud CD: Evolution of renal osteodystrophy: Correlation of bone histomorphometry and serum mineral immunoreactive parathyroid hormone values before and after treatment with calcium carbonate or 25-hydroxycholecalciferol. Kidney Int 1975;Suppl 2:102.

Bricker NS: On the pathogenesis of the uremic state: An exposition of the "trade-off" hypothesis. N Engl J Med 1972;286:1093.

Coburn JW et al: A skeletal mineralizing defect in dialysis patients: A syndrome resembling osteomalacia but unrelated to vitamin D. Contrib Nephrol 1980;18:172.

Coburn JW, Slatopolsky E: Vitamin D, parathyroid hormone, and renal osteodystrophy. In: *The Kidney,* 3rd ed. Brenner BM, Rector FC (editors). Saunders, 1985.

Fournier AE et al: Etiology of hyperparathyroidism and bone disease during hemodialysis: 2. Factors affecting serum immunoreactive parathyroid hormone. J Clin Invest 1971;50:599.

Fournier A et al: Calcium carbonate, an aluminum-free agent for control of hyperphosphatemia, hypocalcemia and hyperparathyroidism in uremia. Kidney Int 1986;29:S114.

Fournier A et al: Prevention of secondary hyperparathyroidism in chronic renal failure before dialysis. Contrib Nephrol 1989;71:64.

Goodman WG, Coburn JW: The use of 1,25-dihydroxyvitamin D_3 in early renal failure. Annu Rev Med 1992;43:227.

Johnson WJ et al: Prevention and reversal of progressive secondary hyperparathyroidism in patients maintained by hemodialysis. Am J Med 1974;56:827.

Llach F: Parathyroidectomy in chronic renal failure: Indications, surgical approach and the use of calcitriol. Kidney Int 1990;29:S62.

Malluche H, Faugere MC: Renal bone disease 1990: An unmet challenge for the nephrologist. Kidney Int 1990;38:193.

Massry SG et al: Skeletal resistance to parathyroid hormone in renal failure. Ann Intern Med 1973;78:357.

Nebecker HG et al: Aluminum and renal osteodystrophy. Annu Rev Med 1986;37:79.

Parker TF et al: Jejunal absorption and secretion of calcium in patients with chronic renal disease on hemodialysis. J Clin Invest 1974;54:358.

Portale AA et al: Effect of dietary phosphorus on circulating concentrations of 1,25-dihydroxyvitamin D and immunoreactive parathyroid hormone in children with moderate renal insufficiency. J Clin Invest 1984;73:1580.

Salusky IB, Coburn JW: The renal osteodystrophies. In: *Endocrinology,* 2nd ed. Vol 2. DeGroot LJ et al (editors). Grune & Stratton, 1989.

Slatopolsky E et al: On the pathogenesis of hyperparathyroidism in chronic experimental and renal insufficiency in the dog. J Clin Invest 1971;50:492.

Slatopolsky E et al: On the prevention of secondary hyperparathyroidism in experimental chronic renal disease using "proportional reduction" of dietary phosphorus intake. Kidney Int 1972;2:147.

Slatopolsky E et al: Marked suppression of secondary hyperparathyroidism by intravenous administration of 1,25-dihydroxycholecalciferol in uremic patients. J Clin Invest 1984;74:2136.

Slatopolsky E et al: Calcium carbonate as a phosphate binder in patients with chronic renal failure undergoing dialysis. N Engl J Med 1986;315:157.

Stanbury SW, Lumb GA: Parathyroid function in chronic renal failure: A statistical survey of the plasma and biochemistry in azotaemic renal osteodystrophy. Q J Med 1966;35:1.

DISORDERS OF CALCITONIN SECRETION

Austin LA, Health H III: Calcitonin, physiology and pathophysiology. N Engl J Med 1981;304:269.

Block MA: Surgical treatment of medullary carcinoma of the thyroid. Otolaryngol Clin North Am 1990;23:453.

Chong GC et al: Medullary carcinoma of the thyroid gland. Cancer 1975;35:695.

Grauer A, Raue F, Gagel RF: Changing concepts in the management of hereditary and sporadic medullary thyroid carcinoma. Endocrinol Metab Clin North Am 1990;19:613.

Graze K et al: Natural history of familial medullary thyroid carcinoma: Effect of program for early diagnosis. N Engl J Med 1978;299:980.

Saad MF et al: The prognostic value of calcitonin immunostaining in medullary carcinoma of the thyroid. J Clin Endocrinol Metab 1984;59:850.

Schwartz KE et al: Calcitonin in nonthyroidal cancer. J Clin Endocrinol Metab 1979;49:438.

Sizemore GW et al: Epidemiology of medullary carcinoma of the thyroid gland: A 5 year experience (1971–1976). Surg Clin North Am 1977;57:633.

Williams ED: Medullary carcinoma of the thyroid. In: *Endocrinology,* 2nd ed. Vol 2. DeGroot LJ et al (editors). Grune & Stratton, 1989.

HYPERCALCIURIA

Chadwick KS et al: Mechanism for hyperoxaluria in patients with ileal dysfunction. N Engl J Med 1973;289:172.

Coe FL (editor): *Hypercalciuric States: Pathogenesis, Consequences and Treatment.* Grune & Stratton, 1984.

Coe FL, Bushinski DA: Pathophysiology of hypercalciuria. Am J Physiol 1984;247:1.

Danielson BG et al: Treatment of idiopathic calcium stone disease. (Editorial.) Calcif Tissue Int 1983;35:715.

Lemann J Jr: Pathogenesis of idiopathic hypercalciuria and nephrolithiasis. In: *Disorders of Bone and Mineral Metabolism.* Coe FL, Favus MJ (editors). Raven Press, 1992

Lemann J Jr, Worcester EM, Gray RW: Hypercalciuria and stones. Am J Kidney Dis 1991;17:386.

Pak CY: Etiology and treatment of urolithiasis. Am J Kidney Dis 1991;18:624.

Peacock M, Robertson WG: Urinary calcium stone disease. In: *Endocrinology,* 2nd ed. Vol 2. DeGroot LJ et al (editors). Grune & Stratton, 1989.

Smith LH: Hyperoxaluric states. In: *Disorders of Bone and Mineral Metabolism.* Coe FL, Favus MT (editors). Raven Press, 1992.

METABOLIC BONE DISEASE

General

Coe FL, Favus MJ: Clinical and laboratory approach to the patient with disorders of bone and mineral metabolism. In: *Disorders of Bone and Mineral Metabolism.* Coe FL, Favus MT (editors). Raven Press, 1992.

Chesnut CH III: The imaging and quantitation of bone by radiographic and scanning methodologies. In: *Disorders of Bone and Mineral Metabolism.* Coe FL, Favus MT (editors). Raven Press, 1992.

Clarke SE, Fogelman I: Bone scanning in metabolic and endocrine bone disease. Endocrinol Metab Clin North Am 1989;18:977.

Cooper KL: Radiology of metabolic bone disease. Endocrinol Metab Clin North Am 1989;18:955.

Delmas PD: Biochemical markers of bone turnover for, the clinical assessment of metabolic bone disease. Endocrinol Metab Clin North Am 1990;19:1.

Eriksen EF et al: Histomorphometric analysis of bone in metabolic bone disease. Endocrinol Metab Clin North Am 1989;18:919.

Genant HK et al: Quantitative computed tomography in the assessment of osteoporosis. In: *Osteoporosis Update 1987.* Genant HK (editor). Univ California Press, 1987.

Krane SM, Schiller AL: Metabolic bone disease: Introduction and classification. In: *Endocrinology,* 2nd ed. Vol 2. DeGroot LJ et al (editors). Grune & Stratton, 1989.

Malluche HH, Faugere MC: *Atlas of mineralized bone histology.* Karger, 1986.

Marcus R: Normal and abnormal bone remodeling in man. Annu Rev Med 1987;38:129.

Meunier PJ: Histomorphometry of the skeleton. In: *Bone and Mineral Research,* Annual 1. Peck WA (editor). Excerpta Medica, 1983.

Ott DM, Kilcoyne RF, Chesnut CH III: Ability of four different techniques of measuring bone mass to diagnose vertebral fractures in postmenopausal women. J Bone Min Res 1987;2:201.

Parfitt AM: The cellular basis of bone turnover and bone loss. Clin Orthop 1977;127:236.

Parfitt AM: The physiologic and pathogenetic significance of bone histomorphometric data. In: *Disorders of Bone and Mineral Metabolism.* Coe FL, Favus MJ (editors). Raven Press, 1992.

Rasmussen HR, Bordier PJ: *The Physiological and Cellular Basis of Metabolic Bone Disease.* Williams & Wilkins, 1974.

Rodan GA, Martin TJ: Role of osteoblasts in hormonal control of bone resorption: A hypothesis. Calcif Tissue Int 1982;33:349.

Rosenberg AE: The pathology of metabolic bone disease. Radiol Clin North Am 1991;29:19.

Weinstein RS: Clinical use of bone biopsy. In: *Disorders of Bone and Mineral Metabolism.* Coe FL, Favus MJ (editors). Raven Press, 1992.

Osteomalacia

Balsan S, Garabedian M: Rickets, osteomalacia, and osteopetrosis. Curr Opin Rheumatol 1991;3:496.

Bikle DD: Bone disease due to nutritional, gastrointestinal and hepatic disorders. In: *Disorders of Bone and Mineral Metabolism.* Coe FL, Favus MJ (editors). Raven Press, 1992

Eisman JA: Osteomalacia. Baillieres Clin Endocrinol Metab 1988;2:125.

Fraser D et al: Pathogenesis of hereditary vitamin D-dependent rickets: An inborn error of vitamin D metabolism involving defective conversion of 25-hydroxyvitamin D to 1,25-dihydroxyvitamin D. N Engl J Med 1973;289:817.

Glorieux FH et al: Use of phosphate and vitamin D to prevent dwarfism and rickets in X-linked hypophosphatemia. N Engl J Med 1972;287:481.

Glorieux FH (editor): *Rickets,* Nestle Nutrition Workshop, Vol 21. Raven Press, 1991.

Goldring SR, Krane SM: Disorders of calcification: Osteomalacia and rickets. In: *Endocrinology,* 2nd ed. Vol 2. DeGroot LJ et al (editors). Grune & Stratton, 1989.

Haddad JG Jr: Serum 25-hydroxycalciferol levels and bone mass in children on anticonvulsant therapy. N Engl J Med 1975;292:550.

Hutchison FN, Bell NH: Osteomalacia and rickets. Semin Nephrol 1992;12:127.

Marel GM, McKenna MJ, Frame B: Osteomalacia. In: *Bone and Mineral Research,* Annual 4. Peck WA (editor). Elsevier, 1986.

Morgan DB et al: The osteomalacia syndrome after stomach operations. Q J Med 1970;39:395.

Ryan EA, Reiss E: Oncogenic osteomalacia. Am J Med 1984;77:501.

Scriver CR et al: Hereditary rickets. In: *Calcium Disorders.* Heath DA, Marx SJ (editors). Butterworth, 1982.

Steinbach HL, Noetzli M: Roentgen appearance of the skeleton in osteomalacia and rickets. Am J Roentgenol Radium Ther Nucl Med 1964;91:955.

Thakker RV, O'Riordan JL: Inherited forms of rickets and osteomalacia. Baillieres Clin Endocrinol Metab 1988;2:157.

Vitamin D receptor mutations and familial rickets. Nutr Rev 1989;47:179.

Weidner N: Review and update: Oncogenic osteomalacia-rickets. Ultrastruct Pathol 1991;15:317.

Zinc fingers and vitamin D resistance. Lancet 1989;1: 478.

Osteoporosis

Arnaud CD: Osteoporosis. In: *Diet and Health: Implications for Reducing Chronic Disease Risk.* National Academy Press, 1989.

Arnaud CD: Role of dietary calcium in osteoporosis. Adv Intern Med 1990;35:93.

Auwerx J, Boulion R: Mineral and bone metabolism in thyroid disease: A review. Q J Med 1986;232:737.

Avioli LV: Osteoporosis syndromes: patient selection for calcitonin therapy. Geriatrics 1992;47:58,61,67.

Cann CE et al: Decreased spinal mineral content in amenorrheic women. JAMA 1984;251:626.

Christiansen C: Prevention and treatment of osteoporosis: A review of current modalities. Bone 1992;13 (Suppl 1):S35.

Clinical indications for bone mass measurements: A report from the Scientific Advisory Board of the National Osteoporosis Foundation. J Bone Min Res 1989;4(Suppl 2):1.

Consensus development conference: Prophylaxis and treatment of osteoporosis. Am J Med 1991;90:107.

Consensus development conference: Prophylaxis and treatment of osteoporosis. Osteoporos Int 1991;1:114.

Cummings SR et al: Epidemiology of osteoporosis and osteoporotic fractures. Epidemiol Rev 1985;7:178.

Delmas PD: Biochemical markers of bone turnover: methodology and clinical use in osteoporosis. Am J Med 1991;91:59S.

Delmas PD: Clinical use of biochemical markers of bone remodeling in osteoporosis. Bone 1992;13(Suppl 1): S17.

Drinkwater BL et al: Bone mineral content of amenorrheic and eumenorrheic athletes. N Engl J Med 1984;311:277.

Ettinger B, Genant HK, Cann CE: Long term estrogen therapy prevents bone loss and fractures. Ann Int Med 1985;102:319.

Gennari C: Glucocorticoids and bone. In: *Bone and Mineral Research,* Annual 3. Peck WA (editor). Elsevier, 1985.

Gennari C: Salmon calcitonin (Miacalcic) nasal spray in prevention and treatment of osteoporosis. Clin Rheumatol 1989;8(Suppl 2):61.

Gruber HE et al: Long-term calcitonin therapy in postmenopausal osteoporosis. Metabolism 1984;33:295.

Heaney RP: Calcium, bone health and osteoporosis. In: *Bone and Mineral Research,* Annual 4. Peck WA (editor). Elsevier, 1986.

Heaney RP: Calcium in the prevention and treatment of osteoporosis. J Intern Med 1992;231:169.

Hodgson SF: Corticosteroid-induced osteoporosis. Endocrinol Metab Clin North Am 1990;19:95.

Ireland P, Fordtran JS: Effect of dietary calcium and age on jejunal calcium absorption in humans studied by intestinal perfusion. J Clin Invest 1973;52:2672.

Jackson JA, Kleerekoper M: Osteoporosis in men: Diagnosis, pathophysiology, and prevention. Medicine 1990;69:137.

Johnston CC Jr: Studies on prevention of age related bone loss. In: *Bone and Mineral Research,* Annual 3. Peck WA (editor). Elsevier, 1985.

Johnston CC Jr, Slemenda CW: Risk prediction in osteoporosis: A theoretic overview. Am J Med 1991;91: 47S.

Kleerekoper M, Balena R: Fluorides and osteoporosis. Annu Rev Nutr 1991;11:309.

Lang P et al: Osteoporosis: Current techniques and recent developments in quantitative bone densitometry. Radiol Clin North Am 1991;29:49.

Lindsay R et al: Long-term prevention of postmenopausal osteoporosis by estrogen. Lancet 1976;2:1038.

Lindsay R, Cosman F: Primary osteoporosis. In: *Disorders of Bone and Mineral Metabolism.* Coe FL, Favus MJ (editors). Raven Press, 1992.

Marcus R: Rational approaches to osteoporosis therapy. Adv Pharmacol 1991;22:29.

Marcus R: Secondary forms of osteoporosis. In: *Disorders of Bone and Mineral Metabolism.* Coe FL, Favus MJ (editors). Raven Press, 1992.

Marcus R et al: Menstrual function and bone mass in elite women distance runners: Endocrine and metabolic features. Ann Intern Med 1985;102:158.

Marcus R et al: Osteoporosis and exercise in women. Med Sci Sports Exerc 1992;24(6 Suppl):S301.

Mazess RB, Barden HS: Bone densitometry for diagnosis and monitoring osteoporosis. Proc Soc Exper Biol Med 1989;191:261.

Nilas L, Christiansen C: Bone mass and its relationship to age and the menopause. J Clin Endocrinol Metab 1987;65:697.

Paul TL et al: Long-term L-thyroxine therapy is associated with decreased hip bone density in premenopausal women. JAMA 1988;259:3137.

Proceedings of a symposium. Consensus Development Conference on Osteoporosis, October 19–20, 1990, Copenhagen, Denmark. Am J Med 1991;91:1S.

Reid IR et al: Prevention of steroid-induced osteoporosis with (3-amino-1-hydroxypropylidene)-1,1-bisphosphonate (APD). Lancet 1988;1:143.

Riggs BL: Osteoporosis. In: *Endocrinology,* 2nd ed, Vol 2. DeGroot LJ et al (editors). Grune & Stratton, 1989.

Riggs BL: Treatment of osteoporosis with sodium fluoride or parathyroid hormone. Am J Med 1991;91:37S.

Riggs BL, Melton LJ III (editors): *Osteoporosis: Etiology, Diagnosis and Management.* Raven Press, 1988.

Riggs BL, Melton LJ III: Clinical review 8: Clinical heterogeneity of involutional osteoporosis: Implications for preventive therapy. J Clin Endocrinol Metab 1990;70:1229.

Riggs BL, Melton LJ III: The prevention and treatment of osteoporosis. N Engl J Med 1992;327:620.

Riggs BL et al: Effect of the fluoride/calcium regimen on vertebral fracture occurrence in postmenopausal osteoporosis. N Engl J Med 1982;306:446.

Rigotti NA et al: Osteoporosis in women with anorexia nervosa. N Engl J Med 1984;311:1601.

Schapira D: Alcohol abuse and osteoporosis. Semin Arthritis Rheum 1990;19:371.

Seeman E et al: Risk factors for spinal osteoporosis in men. Am J Med 1983;75:977.

Silverman SL: Management of corticosteroid-induced osteoporosis: A clinician's perspective. (Editorial.) Calcif Tissue Int 1992;50:101.

Singh M et al: Femoral trabecular pattern index for evaluation of spinal osteoporosis. Ann Intern Med 1972;77:63.

Slovik DM et al: Restoration of spinal bone in osteoporotic men by treatment with human parathyroid hormone (1–34) and 1,25-dihydroxyvitamin D. J Bone Min Res 1986;1:377.

Tsai K-S et al: Impaired vitamin D metabolism with aging in women: Possible role in pathogenesis of senile osteoporosis. J Clin Invest 1984;73:1668.

Wartofsky L: Use of sensitive TSH assay to determine optimal thyroid hormone therapy and avoid osteoporosis. Annu Rev Med 1991;42:341.

Weisman Y et al: Inadequate status and impaired metabolism of vitamin D in the elderly. Isr J Med Sci 1981; 17:19.

Paget's Disease

Altman RD: Paget's disease of bone. In: *Disorders of Bone and Mineral Metabolism.* Coe FL, Favus MJ (editors). Raven Press, 1992.

Altman RD, Collins-Yudiskas B: Synthetic human calcitonin in refractory Paget's disease of bone. Arch Int Med 1987;147:1305.

Arnold A: Paget's disease of bone: Pathophysiology and diagnosis. In: *Endocrinology,* 2nd ed. Vol 2. DeGroot LJ et al (editors). Grune & Stratton, 1989.

Cawley MI: Complications of Paget's disease of bone. Gerontology 1983;29:276.

Delmas PD et al: Beneficial effects of aminohexane diphosphonate in patients with Paget's disease of bone resistant to etidronate. Am J Med 1987;83:276.

Fleish H: Bisphosphonates: Mechanisms of action and clinical applications. In: *Bone and Mineral Research,* Annual 1. Peck WA (editor). Excerpta Medica, 1983.

Hosking DJ: Advances in the management of Paget's disease of bone. Drugs 1990;40:829.

Huvos AG et al: Osteogenic sarcoma associated with Paget's disease of bone: A clinicopathologic study of 65 patients. Cancer 1983;S2:1489.

Krane SM: Paget's disease of bone. Calcif Tissue Res 1986;38:309.

Rebel A (editor): Symposium: Paget's disease. Clin Orthop 1987;217:1.

Singer FR: *Paget's Disease of Bone.* Plenum Press, 1977.

Singer FR: Clinical efficacy of salmon calcitonin in Paget's disease of bone. Calcif Tissue Int 1991;49 (Suppl 2):S7.

Singer FR, Mills BG: Evidence for a viral etiology of Paget's disease of bone. Clin Orthop 1983;178:245.

Singer FR, Mills BG: Paget's disease of bone: Etiology and therapeutic aspects. In: *Bone and Mineral Research,* Annual 2. Peck WA (editor). Elsevier, 1984.

Strewler GJ: Paget's disease of bone. West J Med 1984;140:763.

Wallach S: Treatment of Paget's disease. Adv Intern Med 1982;27:1.

Glucocorticoids & Adrenal Androgens

6

David C. Aron, MD, & J. Blake Tyrrell, MD

The adrenal cortex produces many steroid hormones of which the most important are cortisol, aldosterone, and the adrenal androgens. Disorders of the adrenal glands lead to classic endocrinopathies such as Cushing's syndrome, Addison's disease, hyperaldosteronism, and the syndromes of congenital adrenal hyperplasia. This chapter describes the physiology and disorders of the glucocorticoids and the adrenal androgens. Disorders of aldosterone secretion are discussed in Chapter 7 and congenital defects in adrenal hormone biosynthesis in Chapters 7 and 11.

Advances in diagnostic procedures have simplified the evaluation of adrenocortical disorders; in particular, the assay of plasma glucocorticoids, androgens, and ACTH has allowed more rapid and precise diagnosis. In addition, advances in surgical and medical treatment have improved the outlook for patients with these disorders.

EMBRYOLOGY & ANATOMY

Embryology

The adrenal cortex is of mesodermal origin and is identifiable as a separate organ in the 2-month-old fetus. At 2 months' gestation, the cortex is composed of a **fetal zone** and a **definitive zone** similar to the adult adrenal cortex. The adrenal cortex then increases rapidly in size; at mid gestation, it is considerably larger than the kidney and much larger than the adult gland in relation to total body mass. The fetal zone makes up the bulk of the weight of the adrenal cortex at this time. Factors other than ACTH, such as insulin-like growth factor II, may be involved in the development of the fetal adrenal cortex.

The fetal adrenal is under the control of ACTH by mid pregnancy, but the fetal zone is deficient in the activity of 3β-hydroxysteroid dehydrogenase (see section on biosynthesis of cortisol and adrenal androgens, below) and thus produces mainly dehydroepiandrosterone (DHEA) and DHEA sulfate, which serve as precursors of maternal-placental estrogen production after conversion in the liver to 16α-hydroxylated derivatives. The definitive zone synthesizes a number of steroids and is the major site of fetal cortisol synthesis.

Anatomy

The anatomic relationship of the fetal and definitive zones is maintained until birth, at which time the fetal zone gradually disappears, with a consequent decrease in adrenocortical weight in the 3 months following delivery. During the next 3 years, the adult adrenal cortex develops from cells of the outer layer of the cortex and differentiates into the three adult zones: glomerulosa, fasciculata, and reticularis.

The adult adrenal glands, with a combined weight of 8–10 g, lie in the retroperitoneum above or medial to the upper poles of the kidneys (Figure 6–1). A fibrous capsule surrounds the gland; the yellowish outer cortex comprises 90% of the adrenal weight, the inner medulla about 10%.

The adrenal cortex is richly vascularized and receives its main arterial supply from branches of the inferior phrenic artery, the renal arteries, and the aorta. These small arteries form an arterial plexus beneath the capsule and then enter a sinusoidal system

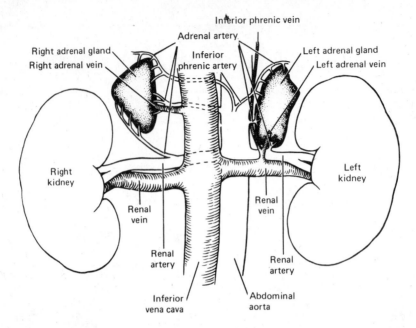

Figure 6–1. Location and blood supply of the adrenal glands (schematic). (Reproduced, with permission, from Baxter JD, Tyrrell JB: The adrenal cortex. In: *Endocrinology and Metabolism*. Felig P et al [editors]. 2nd ed. McGraw-Hill, 1987.)

that penetrates the cortex and medulla, draining into a single central vein in each gland. The right adrenal vein drains directly into the posterior aspect of the vena cava; the left adrenal vein enters the left renal vein. These anatomic features account for the fact that it is relatively easier to catheterize the left adrenal vein than it is to catheterize the right adrenal vein.

Microscopic Anatomy

Histologically, the adult cortex is composed of three zones: an outer zona glomerulosa, a zona fasciculata, and an inner zona reticularis (Figure 6–2). However, the inner two zones appear to function as a unit (see below). The **zona glomerulosa,** which produces aldosterone, is deficient in 17α-hydroxylase activity and thus cannot produce cortisol or androgens (see below and Chapter 7). The zona glomerulosa lacks a well-defined structure, and the small lipid-poor cells are scattered beneath the adrenal capsule. The **zona fasciculata** is the thickest layer of the adrenal cortex and produces cortisol and androgens. The cells of the zona fasciculata are larger and contain more lipid and thus are termed "clear cells." These cells extend in columns from the narrow zona reticularis to either the zona glomerulosa or to the capsule. The inner **zona reticularis** surrounds the medulla and also produces cortisol and androgens. The "compact" cells of this narrow zone lack significant lipid content but do contain lipofuscin granules. The zonae fasciculata and reticularis are regulated by ACTH; excess or deficiency of this hormone alters

their structure and function. Thus, both zones atrophy when ACTH is deficient; when ACTH is present in excess, hyperplasia and hypertrophy of these zones occur. In addition, chronic stimulation with ACTH leads to a gradual depletion of the lipid from the clear cells of the zona fasciculata at the junction of the two zones; these cells thus attain the characteristic appearance of the compact reticularis cells. With chronic excessive stimulation, the compact reticularis cells extend outward and may reach the outer capsule. It is postulated that the zona fasciculata cells can respond acutely to ACTH stimulation with increased cortisol production, whereas the reticularis cells maintain basal glucocorticoid secretion and that induced by prolonged ACTH stimulation.

BIOSYNTHESIS OF CORTISOL & ADRENAL ANDROGENS

Steroidogenesis

The major hormones secreted by the adrenal cortex are cortisol, the androgens, and aldosterone. The carbon atoms in the steroid molecule are numbered as shown in Figure 6–3, and the major biosynthetic pathways and hormonal intermediates are illustrated in Figures 6–4 and 6–5.

The scheme of adrenal steroidogenic synthesis has been clarified by analysis of the steroidogenic enzymes. Most of these enzymes belong to the family of cytochrome P450 oxygenases. In mitochondria, P450scc is responsible for side-chain cleavage of cholesterol. In humans, two separate but closely re-

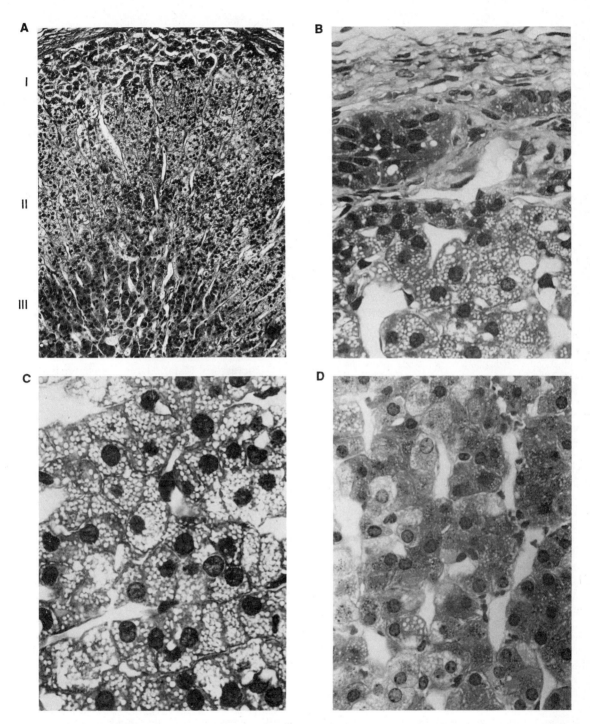

Figure 6–2. Photomicrographs of the adrenal cortex (H&E stain). *A:* A low-power general view. I, the glomerulosa; II, the fasciculata; III, the reticularis. × 80. *B:* The capsule and the zona glomerulosa. × 330. *C:* The zona fasciculata. × 330. *D:* The zona reticularis. × 330. (Reproduced, with permission, from Junqueira LC, Carneiro J: *Basic Histology,* 7th ed. Appleton & Lange, 1992.)

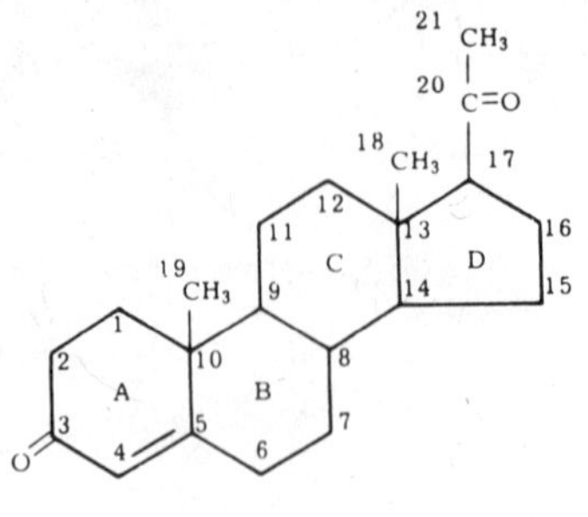

C21 steroid (progesterone)

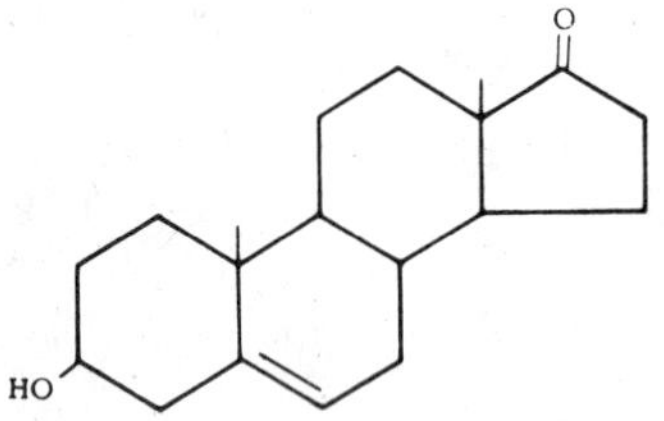

C19 steroid (dehydroepiandrosterone)

Figure 6–3. Structure of adrenocortical steroids. The letters in the formula for progesterone identify the A, B, C, and D rings; the numbers show the positions in the basic C21 steroid structure. The angular methyl groups (positions 18 and 19) are usually indicated simply by straight lines, as in the lower formula. Dehydroepiandrosterone is a "17-ketosteroid" formed by cleavage of the side chain of the C21 steroid 17-hydroxypregnenolone and its replacement by an O atom. (Reproduced, with permission, from Ganong WF: *Review of Medical Physiology,* 14th ed. Appleton & Lange, 1989.)

lated mitochondrial enzymes mediate 11β-hydroxylation, and the biosynthesis of aldosterone. P450c11 in the zona fasciculata and in the zona reticularis mediate conversion of 11-deoxycortisol to cortisol and 11-deoxycorticosterone to corticosterone. In the zona glomerulosa, P450aldo (also known as aldosterone synthase and P450cmo) mediates 11β-hydroxylation, 18-hydroxylation, and 18-oxidation to convert 11-deoxycorticosterone → corticosterone → 18-hydroxycorticosterone → aldosterone. In the endoplasmic reticulum, the single enzyme P450c17 mediates both 17α-hydroxylase activity and 17,20-lyase activity, while P450c21 mediates the 21-hydroxylation of both progesterone and 17-hydroxyprogesterone. The 3β-hydroxysteroid dehydrogenase:$\Delta^{5,4}$-isomerase activities are mediated by a single non-P450 microsomal enzyme.

A. Zones and Steroidogenesis: Because of enzymatic differences between the zona glomerulosa and the inner two zones, the adrenal cortex functions as two separate units, with differing regulation and secretory products. Thus, the zona glomerulosa, which produces aldosterone, lacks 17α-hydroxylase activity and cannot synthesize 17α-hydroxypreg-

nenolone and 17α-hydroxyprogesterone, which are the precursors of cortisol and the adrenal androgens. The synthesis of aldosterone by this zone is primarily regulated by the renin-angiotensin system and by potassium, as discussed in Chapter 7.

The zona fasciculata and zona reticularis (Figure 6–4) produce cortisol, androgens, and small amounts of estrogens. These zones, primarily regulated by ACTH, do not contain the enzyme P450aldo (aldosterone synthase, P450cmo) and therefore cannot convert 11-deoxycorticosterone to aldosterone. (See Chapter 7.)

B. Cholesterol Uptake and Synthesis: Synthesis of cortisol and the androgens by the zonae fasciculata and reticularis begins with cholesterol, as does the synthesis of all steroid hormones. Plasma lipoproteins are the major source of adrenal cholesterol, though synthesis within the gland from acetate also occurs. A small pool of free cholesterol within the adrenal is available for rapid synthesis of steroids when the adrenal is stimulated. When stimulation occurs, there is also increased hydrolysis of stored cholesteryl esters to free cholesterol, increased uptake from plasma lipoproteins, and increased cholesterol synthesis within the gland.

C. Cholesterol Metabolism: The conversion of cholesterol to pregnenolone is the rate-limiting step in adrenal steroidogenesis and the major site of ACTH action on the adrenal. This step occurs in the mitochondria and involves two hydroxylations and then the side-chain cleavage of cholesterol. A single enzyme, P450scc, mediates this process; each step requires molecular oxygen and a pair of electrons. The latter are donated by NADPH to adrenodoxin reductase, a flavoprotein, and then to adrenodoxin, an iron-sulfur protein, and finally to P450scc. Both adrenodoxin reductase and adrenodoxin are also involved in the action of P450c11 (see above). Electron transport to microsomal cytochrome P450 involves P450 reductase, a flavoprotein distinct from adrenodoxin reductase. Pregnenolone is then transported outside the mitochondria before further steroid synthesis occurs.

D. Synthesis of Cortisol: Cortisol synthesis proceeds by P450c17 17α-hydroxylation of pregnenolone within the smooth endoplasmic reticulum to form 17α-hydroxypregnenolone. This steroid is then converted to 17α-hydroxyprogesterone after conversion of its 5,6 double bond to a 4,5 double bond by the 3β-hydroxysteroid dehydrogenase:$\Delta^{5,4}$-oxosteroid isomerase enzyme complex, which is also located within the smooth endoplasmic reticulum. An alternative but apparently less important pathway in the zonae fasciculata and reticularis is from pregnenolone → progesterone → 17α-hydroxyprogesterone (Figure 6–4).

The next step, which is again microsomal, involves the 21-hydroxylation by P450c21 of 17α-hydroxyprogesterone to form 11-deoxycortisol; this

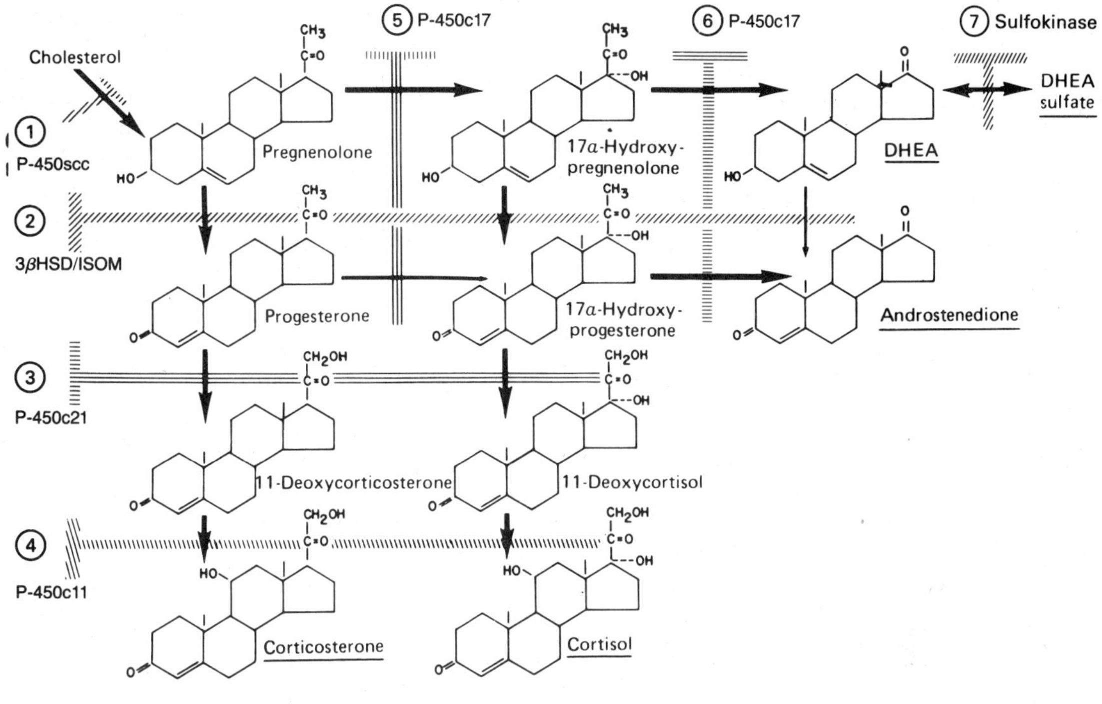

Figure 6–4. Steroid biosynthesis in the zona fasciculata and zona reticularis of the adrenal cortex. The major secretory products are underlined. The enzymes for the reactions are numbered on the left and at the top of the chart, with the steps catalyzed shown by the shaded bars. ① P450scc, cholesterol 20,22-hydroxylase:20,22 desmolase activity; ② 3βHSD/ISOM, 3-hydroxysteroid dehydrogenase:Δ⁵-oxosteroid isomerase activity;③ P450c21, 21α-hydroxylase activity;④ P450c11 = 11β-hydroxylase activity;⑤ P450c17, 17α-hydroxylase activity;⑥ P450c17, 17,20-lyase/desmolase activity;⑦ sulfokinase. (See also Figures 7–1, 9–2, 10–4, and 11–13.) (Modified and reproduced, with permission, from Ganong, WF: *Review of Medical Physiology,* 16th ed. Appleton & Lange, 1993.)

compound is further hydroxylated within mitochondria by 11β-hydroxylation (P450c11) to form cortisol. The zonae fasciculata and reticularis also produce 11-deoxycorticosterone (DOC), 18-hydroxydeoxycorticosterone, and corticosterone. However, as noted above, the absence of the mitochondrial enzyme P450aldo (aldosterone synthase, P450cmo) prevents production of aldosterone by these zones of the adrenal cortex (Figure 6–5).

E. Synthesis of Androgens: The production of adrenal androgens from pregnenolone and progesterone requires prior 17α-hydroxylation (P450c17) and thus does not occur in the zona glomerulosa. The major quantitative production of androgens is by conversion of 17α-hydroxypregnenolone to the 19-carbon compounds (C19 steroids) DHEA and its sulfate conjugate DHEA sulfate. Thus, 17α-hydroxypregnenolone undergoes removal of its two-carbon side chain at the C17 position by microsomal 17,20-desmolase, yielding DHEA with a keto group at C17. DHEA is then converted to DHEA sulfate by a reversible adrenal sulfokinase. The other major adrenal androgen, androstenedione, is produced from 17α-hydroxyprogesterone by 17,20-desmolase and to a lesser extent from DHEA. Androstenedione can be converted to testosterone, though adrenal secretion of this hormone is minimal. The adrenal androgens, DHEA, DHEA sulfate, and androstenedione, have minimal intrinsic androgenic activity, and they contribute to androgenicity by their peripheral conversion to the more potent androgens testosterone and dihydrotestosterone. Although DHEA and DHEA sulfate are secreted in greater quantities, androstenedione is qualitatively more important, since it is more readily converted peripherally to testosterone (see Chapter 9).

Regulation of Secretion

A. Secretion of CRH and ACTH: ACTH is the trophic hormone of the zonae fasciculata and reticularis and the major regulator of cortisol and androgen production by the adrenal cortex. ACTH in turn is regulated by the hypothalamus and central nervous system via neurotransmitters and corticotropin-releasing hormone (CRH). The neuroendocrine control of CRH and ACTH secretion is discussed in Chapter 2 and involves three mechanisms to be discussed below.

B. ACTH Effects on the Adrenal Cortex: The delivery of ACTH to the adrenal cortex leads to the rapid synthesis and secretion of steroids; plasma lev-

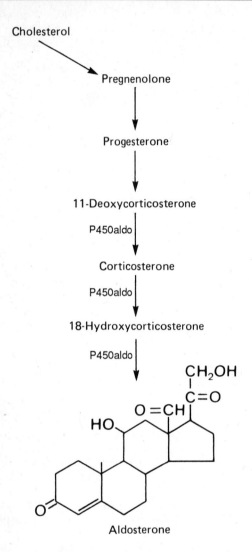

Cholesterol

Pregnenolone

Progesterone

11-Deoxycorticosterone

P450aldo

Corticosterone

P450aldo

18-Hydroxycorticosterone

P450aldo

Aldosterone

Figure 6–5. Steroid biosynthesis in the zona glomerulosa. The steps from cholesterol to 11-deoxycorticosterone are the same as in the zona fasciculata and zona reticularis. However, the zona glomerulosa lacks 17α-hydroxylase activity and thus cannot produce cortisol. Only the zona glomerulosa can convert corticosterone to 18-hydroxycorticosterone and aldosterone. The single enzyme P450aldo catalyses the conversion of 11-deoxycorticosterone → corticosterone → 18-hydroxycorticosterone → aldosterone. (See also Figures 7–1, 9–2, and 10–4.) (Modified and reproduced, with permission, from Ganong, WF: *Review of Medical Physiology*, 16th ed. Appleton & Lange, 1993.)

els of these hormones rise within minutes after ACTH administration. ACTH increases RNA, DNA, and protein synthesis. Chronic stimulation leads to adrenocortical hyperplasia and hypertrophy; conversely, ACTH deficiency results in decreased steroidogenesis and is accompanied by adrenocortical atrophy, decreased gland weight, and decreased protein and nucleic acid content.

C. ACTH and Steroidogenesis: ACTH binds to high-affinity plasma membrane receptors of adrenocortical cells, thereby activating adenylyl cyclase and increasing cAMP, which in turn activates intracellular phosphoprotein kinases (Figure 6–6). This process stimulates the rate-limiting step of cholesterol to Δ^5-pregnenolone conversion and initiates steroidogenesis. The exact mechanisms of ACTH stimulation of the side-chain cleavage enzyme (P450scc) are unknown, as is their relative importance; however, ACTH has a number of effects, including increased free cholesterol formation as a consequence of increased cholesterol esterase activity and decreased cholesteryl ester synthetase; increased lipoprotein uptake by the adrenal cortex; increased content of certain phospholipids, which may increase cholesterol side-chain cleavage; and increased binding of cholesterol to the cytochrome P450scc enzyme in mitochondria.

D. Neuroendocrine Control: Cortisol secretion is closely regulated by ACTH, and plasma cortisol levels parallel those of ACTH (Figure 6–7). There are three mechanisms of neuroendocrine control: (1) episodic secretion and the circadian rhythm of ACTH, (2) stress responsiveness of the hypothalamic-pituitary adrenal axis, and (3) feedback inhibition by cortisol of ACTH secretion.

1. Circadian rhythm– Circadian rhythm is super-

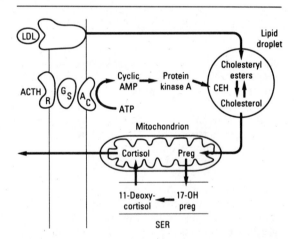

Figure 6–6. Mechanism of action of ACTH on cortisol-secreting cells in the inner two zones of the adrenal cortex. When ACTH binds to its receptor (R), adenylyl cyclase (AC) is activated via Gs. The resulting increase in cAMP activates protein kinase A, and the kinase phosphorylates cholesteryl ester hydrolase (CEH), increasing its activity. Consequently, more free cholesterol is formed and converted to pregnenolone in the mitochondria. Note that in the subsequent steps in steroid biosynthesis, products are shuttled between the mitochondria and the smooth endoplasmic reticulum (SER). (Reproduced, with permission, from Ganong WF: *Review of Medical Physiology*, 16th ed. Appleton & Lange, 1993.)

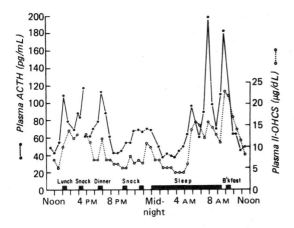

Figure 6–7. Fluctuations in plasma ACTH and glucocorticoids (11-OHCS) throughout the day. Note the greater ACTH and glucocorticoid rises in the morning before awakening. (Reproduced, with permission, from Krieger DT et al: Characterization of the normal temporal pattern of corticosteroid levels. J Clin Endocrinol Metab 1971; 32:266.)

imposed on episodic secretion; it is the result of central nervous system events that regulate both the number and magnitude of CRH and ACTH secretory episodes. Cortisol secretion is low in the late evening and continues to decline in the first several hours of sleep, at which time plasma cortisol levels may be undetectable. During the third and fifth hours of sleep, there is an increase in secretion; but the major secretory episodes begin in the sixth to eighth hours of sleep (Figure 6–7) and then begin to decline as wakefulness occurs. About half of the total daily cortisol output is secreted during this period. Cortisol secretion then gradually declines during the day, with fewer secretory episodes of decreased magnitude; however, there is increased cortisol secretion in response to eating and exercise.

Although this general pattern is consistent, there is considerable intra- and interindividual variability, and the circadian rhythm may be altered by changes in sleep pattern, light-dark exposure, and feeding times. The rhythm is also changed by (1) physical stresses such as major illness, surgery, trauma, or starvation; (2) psychologic stress, including severe anxiety, endogenous depression, and the manic phase of manic-depressive psychosis; (3) central nervous system and pituitary disorders; (4) Cushing's syndrome; (5) liver disease and other conditions that affect cortisol metabolism; (6) chronic renal failure; and (7) alcoholism. Cyproheptadine inhibits the circadian rhythm, possibly by its antiserotonergic effects, whereas other drugs usually have no effect.

2. Stress responsiveness– Plasma ACTH and cortisol secretion are also characteristically responsive to physical stress. Thus, plasma ACTH and cortisol are secreted within minutes following the onset of stresses such as surgery and hypoglycemia (Figure 6–8), and these responses abolish circadian periodicity if the stress is prolonged. Stress responses originate in the central nervous system and increase hypothalamic CRH and thus pituitary ACTH secretion. Stress responsiveness of plasma ACTH and cortisol is abolished by prior high-dose glucocorticoid administration and in spontaneous Cushing's syndrome; conversely, the responsiveness of ACTH secretion is enhanced following adrenalectomy. Regulation of the hypothalamic-pituitary-adrenal axis is linked to that of the immune system. For example, interleukin-1 (IL-1) stimulates ACTH secretion, and cortisol inhibits IL-2 synthesis.

3. Feedback inhibition– The third major regulator of ACTH and cortisol secretion is that of feedback inhibition by glucocorticoids of CRH, ACTH, and cortisol secretion. Glucocorticoid feedback inhibition occurs at both the pituitary and hypothalamus and involves two distinct mechanisms—fast and delayed feedback inhibition (Figure 6–9).

Fast feedback inhibition of ACTH secretion is rate-dependent—ie, it depends on the rate of increase of the glucocorticoid but not the dose administered. This phase is rapid, and basal and stimulated ACTH secretion both diminish within minutes after the plasma glucocorticoid level increases. This fast feedback phase is transient and lasts less than 10 minutes, suggesting that this effect is not mediated via cytosolic glucocorticoid receptors but rather via actions on the cell membrane.

Delayed feedback inhibition after the initial rate-dependent effects of glucocorticoids further suppresses CRH and ACTH secretion by mechanisms

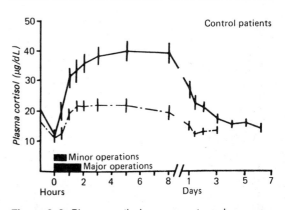

Figure 6–8. Plasma cortisol responses to major surgery (continuous line) and minor surgery (broken line) in normal subjects. Mean values and standard errors for 20 patients are shown in each case. (Reproduced, with permission, from Plumpton FS, Besser GM, Cole PV: Anaesthesia 1969;24:3).

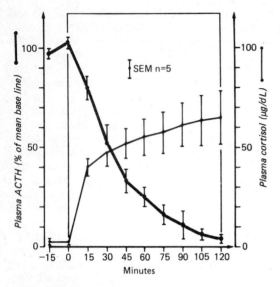

Figure 6–9. Feedback inhibition of plasma ACTH levels during intravenous cortisol infusion at a rate of 50 mg/h in patients with Addison's disease. ACTH values are expressed as percentages of mean basal levels. (Reproduced, with permission, from Fehm HL et al: J Clin Invest 1979;63:247.)

that are both time- and dose-dependent. Thus, with continued glucocorticoid administration, ACTH levels continue to decrease and become unresponsive to stimulation. The ultimate effect of prolonged glucocorticoid administration is suppression of CRH and ACTH release and atrophy of the zonae fasciculata and reticularis as a consequence of ACTH deficiency. The suppressed hypothalamic-pituitary-adrenal axis fails to respond to stress and stimulation. Delayed feedback appears to act via the classic glucocorticoid receptor (see below), thus reducing synthesis of the messenger RNA for pro-opiomelanocortin, the precursor of ACTH.

E. ACTH Effects on Regulation of Androgen Production: Adrenal androgen production in adults is also regulated by ACTH; both DHEA and androstenedione exhibit circadian periodicity in concert with ACTH and cortisol. In addition, plasma concentrations of DHEA and androstenedione increase rapidly with ACTH administration and are suppressed by glucocorticoid administration, confirming the role of endogenous ACTH in their secretion. DHEA sulfate, because of its prolonged metabolic clearance rate, does not exhibit a diurnal rhythm. Thus, adrenal androgen secretion is regulated by ACTH, and, in general, the secretion of these hormones parallels that of cortisol. The existence of a separate anterior pituitary hormone that regulates adrenal androgen secretion has been postulated but not yet proved. Several such factors have been identified in pituitary extracts.

CIRCULATION OF CORTISOL & ADRENAL ANDROGENS

Cortisol and the adrenal androgens circulate bound to plasma proteins. The plasma half-life of cortisol (70–90 minutes) is determined by the extent of plasma binding and by the rate of metabolic inactivation.

Plasma Binding Proteins

Cortisol and adrenal androgens are secreted in an unbound state; however, these hormones bind to plasma proteins upon entering the circulation. Cortisol binds mainly to corticosteroid-binding globulin (CBG, transcortin) and to a lesser extent to albumin, whereas the androgens bind chiefly to albumin. The precise physiologic role of plasma protein binding is unclear, since bound steroids are biologically inactive and the active fraction is that which circulates unbound. Furthermore, CBG is not required for cortisol transport to target tissues or for full biologic activity of the steroid. The plasma proteins may provide a pool of circulating cortisol by delaying metabolic clearance, thus preventing more marked fluctuations of plasma free cortisol levels during episodic secretion by the gland.

Free & Bound Cortisol

In basal conditions, about 10% of the circulating cortisol is free, about 75% is bound to CBG, and the remainder is bound to albumin. The plasma free cortisol level is approximately 1 μg/dL, and it is this biologically active cortisol which is regulated by ACTH.

A. Corticosteroid-Binding Globulin (CBG): CBG has a molecular weight of about 50,000, is produced by the liver, and binds cortisol with high affinity. The CBG in plasma has a cortisol-binding capacity of about 25 μg/dL. When total plasma cortisol concentrations rise above this level, the free concentration rapidly increases and exceeds its usual fraction of 10% of the total cortisol. Other endogenous steroids do not appreciably affect cortisol binding to CBG under usual circumstances; an exception is in late pregnancy, when progesterone may occupy about 25% of the binding sites on CBG. Synthetic steroids do not bind significantly to CBG—with the exception of prednisolone, which has a high affinity. CBG levels are increased in high-estrogen states (pregnancy; estrogen or oral contraceptive use), hyperthyroidism, diabetes, certain hematologic disorders, and on a genetic basis. CBG concentrations are decreased in familial CBG deficiency, hypothyroidism, and protein deficiency states such as severe liver disease or nephrotic syndrome.

B. Albumin: Albumin has a much greater capacity for cortisol binding but a lower affinity. It normally binds about 15% of the circulating cortisol, and this proportion increases when the total cortisol concentration exceeds the CBG binding capacity. Synthetic glucocorticoids are extensively bound to albumin; eg, 77% of dexamethasone in plasma is bound to albumin.

C. Androgen Binding: Androstenedione, DHEA, and DHEA sulfate circulate weakly bound to albumin. However, testosterone is bound extensively to a specific globulin, sex hormone-binding globulin (SHBG). (See Chapters 9 and 10.)

METABOLISM OF CORTISOL & ADRENAL ANDROGENS

The metabolism of the steroids renders them inactive and increases their water solubility, as does their subsequent conjugation with glucuronide or sulfate groups. These inactive conjugated metabolites are more readily excreted by the kidney. The liver is the major site of steroid catabolism and conjugation, and 90% of these metabolized steroids are excreted by the kidney.

Conversion & Excretion of Cortisol

Cortisol is modified extensively before excretion in urine; less than 1% of secreted cortisol appears in the urine unchanged.

A. Hepatic Conversion: Hepatic metabolism of cortisol involves a number of metabolic conversions of which the most important (quantitatively) is the irreversible inactivation of the steroid by Δ^4-reductases, which reduce the 4,5 double bond of the A ring. Dihydrocortisol, the product of this reaction, is then converted to tetrahydrocortisol by a 3-hydroxysteroid dehydrogenase. Cortisol is also converted extensively by 11-hydroxysteroid dehydrogenase to the biologically inactive cortisone, which is then metabolized by the enzymes described above to yield tetrahydrocortisone. Tetrahydrocortisol and tetrahydrocortisone can be further altered to form the cortoic acids. These conversions result in the excretion of approximately equal amounts of cortisol and cortisone metabolites. Cortisol and cortisone are also metabolized to the cortols and cortolones and to a lesser extent by other pathways. Cortisol is also converted to 6β-hydroxycortisol, which is water-soluble and excreted unchanged in the urine.

B. Hepatic Conjugation: Over 95% of cortisol and cortisone metabolites are conjugated by the liver and then reenter the circulation to be excreted in the urine. Conjugation is mainly with glucuronic acid at the 3α-hydroxyl position and to a lesser extent as the sulfate at the 21-hydroxyl group.

C. Variations in Clearance and Metabolism: The metabolism of cortisol is altered by a number of circumstances. It is decreased in infants and in the elderly. It is impaired in chronic liver disease, leading to decreased renal excretion of cortisol metabolites; however, the plasma cortisol level remains normal. Hypothyroidism decreases both metabolism and

excretion; conversely, hyperthyroidism accelerates these processes. Cortisol clearance may be reduced in starvation and anorexia nervosa and is also decreased in pregnancy because of the elevated CBG levels. The metabolism of cortisol to 6β-hydroxycortisol is increased in the neonate, in pregnancy, with estrogen therapy, and in patients with liver disease or severe chronic illness. Cortisol metabolism by this pathway is also increased by drugs that induce hepatic microsomal enzymes, including barbiturates, phenytoin, mitotane, aminoglutethimide, and rifampin. These alterations generally are of minor physiologic importance, since secretion, plasma levels, and cortisol half-life are normal. However, they result in decreased excretion of the urinary metabolites of cortisol measured as 17-hydroxycorticosteroids. These conditions and drugs have a greater influence on the metabolism of synthetic glucocorticoids and may result in inadequate plasma levels of the administered glucocorticoid because of rapid clearance and metabolism.

D. Renal Conversion: Cortisol is also inactivated in the kidney by conversion to cortisone via the action of 11β-hydroxysteroid dehydrogenase. This inactivation is of major physiologic significance because it protects the mineralocorticoid receptor from occupancy by cortisol, and this prevents cortisol from causing a mineralocorticoid excess state. The quantitative role of this enzyme in total cortisol metabolism is unknown, but it has been demonstrated that plasma cortisone levels are reduced in patients with renal disease.

Conversion & Excretion of Adrenal Androgens

Adrenal androgen metabolism results either in degradation and inactivation or the peripheral conversion of these weak androgens to their more potent derivatives testosterone and dihydrotestosterone. DHEA is readily converted within the adrenal to DHEA sulfate, the adrenal androgen secreted in greatest amount. DHEA secreted by the gland is also converted to DHEA sulfate by the liver and kidney, or it may be converted to Δ^4-androstenedione. DHEA sulfate may be excreted without further metabolism; however, both it and DHEA are also metabolized to 7α- and 16α-hydroxylated derivatives and by 17β-reduction to Δ^5-androstenediol and its sulfate. Androstenedione is converted either to testosterone or by reduction of its 4,5 double bond to etiocholanolone or androsterone, which may be further converted by 17α-reduction to etiocholanediol and androstanediol, respectively. Testosterone is converted to dihydrotestosterone in androgen-sensitive tissues by 5β-reduction, and it in turn is mainly metabolized by 3α-reduction to androstanediol. The metabolites of these androgens are conjugated either as glucuronides or sulfates and excreted in the urine. (See Figures 9–2 and 10–5.)

BIOLOGIC EFFECTS

GLUCOCORTICOIDS

Although glucocorticoids were originally so called because of their influence on glucose metabolism, they are currently defined as steroids that exert their effects by binding to specific cytosolic receptors which mediate the actions of these hormones. These glucocorticoid receptors are present in virtually all tissues, and glucocorticoid-receptor interaction is responsible for most of the known effects of these steroids. Alterations in the structure of the glucocorticoids have led to the development of synthetic compounds with greater glucocorticoid activity. The increased activity of these compounds is due to increased affinity for the glucocorticoid receptors and delayed plasma clearance, which increases tissue exposure. In addition, many of these synthetic glucocorticoids have negligible mineralocorticoid effects and thus do not result in sodium retention, hypertension, and hypokalemia. This section describes the molecular mechanisms of glucocorticoid action and the effects on individual metabolic functions and tissues.

Molecular Mechanisms

A. Glucocorticoid Receptors: Glucocorticoid action is initiated by entry of the steroid into the cell and binding to the cytosolic glucocorticoid receptor proteins (Figure 6–10). These proteins probably originate in the nucleus but migrate into the cytosol in the presence of steroids. After binding, activated hormone-receptor complexes enter the nucleus and interact with nuclear chromatin acceptor sites. The 90-kDa heat shock protein hsp90 may be involved in hormone-induced glucocorticoid receptor activity. The DNA binding domain of the receptor is a cysteine-rich region which when it chelates zinc assumes a conformation called a "zinc finger." The receptor-glucocorticoid complex binds to specific sites in nuclear DNA, the glucocorticoid regulatory elements. This results in the expression of specific genes and the transcription of specific mRNAs. The resulting proteins affect the glucocorticoid response, which may be inhibitory or stimulatory depending on the specific tissue affected. Although glucocorticoid receptors are similar in many tissues, the proteins synthesized vary widely and are the result of expression of specific genes in different cell types. The mechanisms of this specific regulation are unknown. Analyses of cloned complementary DNAs for human glucocorticoid receptors have revealed marked structural and amino acid sequence homology between glucocorticoid receptors and receptors for other steroid hormones (eg, mineralocorticoids, estrogen, progesterone) as well as for thyroid hormone and the onco-

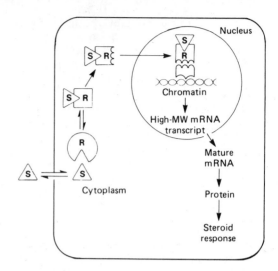

Figure 6–10. Steps in steroid hormone action. Activation of the intracellular receptors by steroid hormones is followed by nuclear binding of the complex and stimulation of mRNA synthesis. (R, receptor; S, steroid hormone.) (Reproduced, with permission, from Catt KJ, Dufau ML: Hormone action: Control of target-cell function by peptide, thyroid, and steroid hormones. In: *Endocrinology and Metabolism.* Felig P et al [editors]. McGraw-Hill, 1981.)

gene v-*erb* A. Although the steroid-binding domain of the glucocorticoid receptor confers specificity for glucocorticoid binding, glucocorticoids such as cortisol and corticosterone bind to the mineralocorticoid receptor with an affinity equal to that of aldosterone. Mineralocorticoid receptor specificity is maintained by the expression of 11β-hydroxysteroid dehydrogenase in classic mineralocorticoid-sensitive tissues. The expression in other tissues of this enzyme that inactivates these glucocorticoids may serve to protect these tissues from excessive glucocorticoid action.

B. Other Mechanisms: Although interaction of glucocorticoids with cytosolic receptors and their subsequent stimulation of gene expression are responsible for most glucocorticoid effects, other effects may occur through different mechanisms. The most significant example is that of glucocorticoid-induced fast feedback inhibition of ACTH secretion (see above). This effect occurs within minutes of glucocorticoid administration, and its rapidity suggests that it is not due to RNA and protein synthesis but rather to glucocorticoid-induced changes in secretory function or cell membranes.

Glucocorticoid Agonists & Antagonists

The study of glucocorticoid receptors has led to the definition of glucocorticoid agonists and antagonists. These studies have also identified a number of steroids with mixed effects termed partial agonist, partial antagonist, or partial agonist-partial antagonist.

A. Agonists: In humans, cortisol, synthetic glucocorticoids (eg, prednisolone, dexamethasone), corticosterone, and aldosterone are glucocorticoid agonists. The synthetic glucocorticoids have substantially higher affinity for the glucocorticoid receptor, and these have greater glucocorticoid activity than cortisol when present in equimolar concentrations. Corticosterone and aldosterone have substantial affinity for the glucocorticoid receptor; however, their plasma concentrations are normally much lower than that of cortisol, and thus these steroids do not have significant physiologic glucocorticoid effects.

B. Antagonists: Glucocorticoid antagonists bind to the glucocorticoid receptors but do not elicit the nuclear events required to cause a glucocorticoid response. These steroids compete with agonist steroids such as cortisol for the receptors and thus inhibit agonist responses. Other steroids have partial agonist activity when present alone; ie, they elicit a partial glucocorticoid response. However, in sufficient concentration, they compete with agonist steroids for the receptors and thus competitively inhibit agonist responses; ie, these partial agonists may function as partial antagonists in the presence of more active glucocorticoids. Steroids such as progesterone, 11-deoxycortisol, DOC, testosterone, and 17β-estradiol have antagonist or partial agonist-partial antagonist effects; however, the physiologic role of these hormones in glucocorticoid action is probably negligible, because they circulate in low concentrations. The antiprogestational agent RU 486 (mifepristone) has substantial glucocorticoid antagonist properties and has been used to block glucocorticoid action in patients with Cushing's syndrome.

Intermediary Metabolism

Glucocorticoids in general inhibit DNA synthesis. In addition, in most tissues they inhibit RNA and protein synthesis and accelerate protein catabolism. These actions provide substrate for intermediary metabolism; however, accelerated catabolism also accounts for the deleterious effects of glucocorticoids on muscle, bone, connective tissue, and lymphatic tissues. In contrast, RNA and protein synthesis in liver is stimulated.

A. Hepatic Glucose Metabolism: Glucocorticoids increase hepatic gluconeogenesis by stimulating the gluconeogenetic enzymes phosphoenolpyruvate carboxykinase and glucose 6-phosphatase. They also have a permissive effect in that they increase hepatic responsiveness to the gluconeogenetic hormones (glucagon, catecholamines), and they also increase the release of substrates from peripheral tissues, particularly muscle. This latter effect may be enhanced by the glucocorticoid-induced reduction in peripheral amino acid uptake and protein synthesis. Glucocorticoids also increase glycerol and free fatty acid release by lipolysis and increase muscle lactate release. These steroids also enhance hepatic glycogen synthesis and storage by stimulating glycogen synthetase activity and to a lesser extent by inhibiting glycogen breakdown. These effects are insulin-dependent.

B. Peripheral Glucose Metabolism: Glucocorticoids also alter carbohydrate metabolism by inhibiting peripheral glucose uptake in muscle and adipose tissue. This effect and the others described above may result in increased insulin secretion in states of chronic glucocorticoid excess.

C. Effects on Adipose Tissue: In adipose tissue, the predominant effect is increased lipolysis with release of glycerol and free fatty acids. This is partially due to direct stimulation of lipolysis by glucocorticoids, but it is also contributed to by decreased glucose uptake and enhancement by glucocorticoids of the effects of lipolytic hormones. Although glucocorticoids are lipolytic, increased fat deposition is a classic manifestation of glucocorticoid excess. This paradox may be explained by the increased appetite caused by high levels of these steroids and by the lipogenic effects of the hyperinsulinemia that occurs in this state. The reason for abnormal fat deposition and distribution in states of cortisol excess is unknown. In these instances, fat is classically deposited centrally in the face, cervical area, trunk, and abdomen; the extremities are usually spared.

D. Summary: The effects of the glucocorticoids on intermediary metabolism can be summarized as follows: (1) Effects are minimal in the fed state. However, during fasting, glucocorticoids contribute to the maintenance of plasma glucose levels by increasing gluconeogenesis, glycogen deposition, and the peripheral release of substrate. (2) Hepatic glucose production is enhanced, as is hepatic RNA and protein synthesis. (3) The effects on muscle are catabolic, ie, decreased glucose uptake and metabolism, decreased protein synthesis, and increased release of amino acids. (4) In adipose tissue, lipolysis is stimulated. (5) In glucocorticoid deficiency, hypoglycemia may result, whereas in states of glucocorticoid excess there may be hyperglycemia, hyperinsulinemia, muscle wasting, and weight gain with abnormal fat distribution.

Effects on Other Tissues & Functions

A. Connective Tissue: Glucocorticoids in excess inhibit fibroblasts, lead to loss of collagen and connective tissue, and thus result in thinning of the skin, easy bruising, stria formation, and poor wound healing.

B. Bone: The physiologic role of glucocorticoids in bone metabolism and calcium homeostasis is unknown; however, in excess, they have major deleterious effects. Glucocorticoids directly inhibit bone formation by decreasing cell proliferation and the synthesis of RNA, protein, collagen, and hyaluronate. Glucocorticoids also directly stimulate bone-resorbing cells, leading to osteolysis and increased urinary hydroxyproline excretion. In addition, they potentiate the actions of PTH and 1,25-dihydroxycholecalciferol $(1,25[OH]_2D_3)$ on bone, and this may further contribute to net bone resorption.

C. Calcium Metabolism: Glucocorticoids also have other major effects on mineral homeostasis. They markedly reduce intestinal calcium absorption, which tends to lower serum calcium. This results in a secondary increase in PTH secretion, which maintains serum calcium within the normal range by stimulating bone resorption. In addition, glucocorticoids may directly stimulate PTH release. The mechanism of decreased intestinal calcium absorption is unknown, though it is not due to decreased synthesis or decreased serum levels of the active vitamin D metabolites; in fact, $1,25(OH)_2D_3$ levels are normal or even increased in the presence of glucocorticoid excess. Increased $1,25 (OH)_2D_3$ synthesis in this setting may result from decreased serum phosphorus levels (see below), increased PTH levels, and direct stimulation by glucocorticoids of renal 1α-hydroxylase. Glucocorticoids also increase urinary calcium excretion, and hypercalciuria is a consistent feature of cortisol excess. They also reduce the tubular reabsorption of phosphate, leading to phosphaturia and decreased serum phosphorus concentrations.

Thus, glucocorticoids in excess result in negative calcium balance, with decreased absorption and increased urinary excretion. Serum calcium levels are maintained, but at the expense of net bone resorption. Decreased bone formation and increased resorption ultimately result in the disabling osteopenia that is often a major complication of spontaneous and iatrogenic glucocorticoid excess (see Chapter 5).

D. Growth and Development: Glucocorticoids accelerate the development of a number of systems and organs in fetal and differentiating tissues, although the mechanisms are unclear. As discussed above, glucocorticoids are generally inhibitory, and these stimulatory effects may be due to glucocorticoid interactions with other growth factors. Examples of these development-promoting effects are increased surfactant production in the fetal lung and the accelerated development of hepatic and gastrointestinal enzyme systems.

Glucocorticoids in excess inhibit growth in children, and this adverse effect is a major complication of therapy. This may be a direct effect on bone cells, although decreased growth hormone (GH) secretion and somatomedin generation also contribute (see Chapter 3).

E. Blood Cells and Immunologic Function:

1. Erythrocytes– Glucocorticoids have little effect on erythropoiesis and hemoglobin concentration. Although mild polycythemia and anemia may be seen in Cushing's syndrome and Addison's disease,

respectively, these alterations are more likely to be secondary to altered androgen metabolism.

2. Leukocytes– Glucocorticoids influence both leukocyte movement and function. Thus, glucocorticoid administration increases the number of intravascular polymorphonuclear leukocytes by increasing PMN release from bone marrow, by increasing the circulating half-life of PMNs, and by decreasing PMN movement out of the vascular compartment. Glucocorticoid administration reduces the number of circulating lymphocytes, monocytes, and eosinophils, mainly by increasing their movement out of the circulation. The converse—ie, neutropenia, lymphocytosis, monocytosis, and eosinophilia—is seen in adrenal insufficiency. Glucocorticoids also decrease the migration of inflammatory cells (PMNs, monocytes, and lymphocytes) to sites of injury, and this is probably a major mechanism of the anti-inflammatory actions and increased susceptibility to infection that occur following chronic administration. Glucocorticoids also decrease lymphocyte production and the mediator and effector functions of these cells.

3. Immunologic effects– Glucocorticoids influence multiple aspects of immunologic and inflammatory responsiveness, including the mobilization and function of leukocytes, as discussed above. They inhibit phospholipase A_2, a key enzyme in the synthesis of prostaglandins. This inhibition is mediated by a class of peptides called lipocortins. They also impair release of effector substances such as the lymphokine interleukin-I, antigen processing, antibody production and clearance, and other specific bone marrow-derived and thymus-derived lymphocyte functions. The immune system, in turn, affects the hypothalamic-pituitary-adrenal axis; interleukin-I stimulates the secretion of CRH and ACTH.

F. Cardiovascular Function: Glucocorticoids may increase cardiac output, and they also increase peripheral vascular tone, possibly by augmenting the effects of other vasoconstrictors, eg, the catecholamines. Glucocorticoids also regulate expression of adrenergic receptors. Thus, refractory shock may occur when the glucocorticoid-deficient individual is subjected to stress. Glucocorticoids in excess may cause hypertension independently of their mineralocorticoid effects. Although the incidence and the precise cause of this problem are unclear, it is likely that the mechanism involves the renin-angiotensin system; glucocorticoids regulate renin substrate, the precursor of angiotensin I.

G. Renal Function: These steroids affect water and electrolyte balance by actions mediated either by mineralocorticoid receptors (sodium and water retention, hypokalemia, and hypertension) or via glucocorticoid receptors (increased glomerular filtration rate due to increased cardiac output or due to a direct renal effect). Thus, corticosteroids such as betamethasone or dexamethasone that have little mineralocorticoid activity increase sodium and water excretion. Glucocorticoid-deficient subjects have decreased glomerular filtration rates and are unable to excrete a water load. This may be contributed to by increased ADH secretion, which may occur in glucocorticoid deficiency.

H. Central Nervous System Function: Glucocorticoids readily enter the brain, and although their physiologic role in central nervous system function is unknown, their excess or deficiency may profoundly alter behavior and cognitive function.

1. Excessive glucocorticoids– In excess, the glucocorticoids initially cause euphoria; however, with prolonged exposure, a variety of psychologic abnormalities occur, including irritability, emotional lability, and depression. Hyperkinetic or manic behavior is less common; overt psychoses occur in a small number of patients. Many patients also note impairment in cognitive functions, most commonly memory and concentration. Other central effects include increased appetite, decreased libido, and insomnia, with decreased REM sleep and increased stage II sleep.

2. Decreased glucocorticoids– Patients with Addison's disease are apathetic and depressed and tend to be irritable, negativistic, and reclusive. They have decreased appetite but increased sensitivity of taste and smell mechanisms.

I. Effects on Other Hormones:

1. Thyroid function– Glucocorticoids in excess affect thyroid function. Although basal TSH levels are usually normal, TSH responsiveness to thyrotropin-releasing hormone (TRH) is frequently subnormal. Serum total thyroxine (T_4) concentrations are usually low normal because of a decrease in thyroxine-binding globulin, but free T_4 levels are normal. Total and free T_3 (triiodothyronine) concentrations may be low, since glucocorticoid excess decreases the conversion of T_4 to T_3 and increases conversion to reverse T_3. TSH synthesis and release are inhibited by glucocorticoids. Despite these alterations, manifestations of hypothyroidism are not apparent.

2. Gonadal function– Glucocorticoids also affect gonadotropin and gonadal function. In males, they inhibit gonadotropin secretion, as evidenced by decreased responsiveness to administered gonadotropin-releasing hormone (GnRH) and subnormal plasma testosterone concentrations. In females, glucocorticoids also suppress LH responsiveness to GnRH, resulting in suppression of estrogens and progestins with inhibition of ovulation and amenorrhea.

J. Miscellaneous Effects:

1. Peptic ulcer– The role of steroid excess in the production or reactivation of peptic ulcer disease is controversial. Ulcers in spontaneous Cushing's syndrome and with modest exposure to glucocorticoid therapy are unusual, although current data suggest that steroid-treated patients with established ulcers and those on high-dose therapy may be at increased risk.

2. Ophthalmologic effects– Intraocular pressure varies with the level of circulating glucocorticoids and parallels the circadian variation of plasma cortisol levels. In addition, glucocorticoids in excess increase intraocular pressure in patients with open-angle glaucoma. Glucocorticoid therapy may also cause cataract formation.

ADRENAL ANDROGENS

The direct biologic activity of the adrenal androgens (androstenedione, DHEA, and DHEA sulfate) is minimal, and they function primarily as precursors for peripheral conversion to the active androgenic hormones testosterone and dihydrotestosterone. Thus, DHEA sulfate secreted by the adrenal undergoes limited conversion to DHEA; this peripherally converted DHEA and that secreted by the adrenal cortex can be further converted in peripheral tissues to androstenedione, the immediate precursor of the active androgens.

The actions of testosterone and dihydrotestosterone are described in Chapter 9. This section will deal only with the adrenal contribution to androgenicity.

Effects in Males

In males with normal gonadal function, the conversion of adrenal androstenedione to testosterone accounts for less than 5% of the production rate of this hormone, and thus the physiologic effect is negligible. In adult males, excessive adrenal androgen secretion has no clinical consequences; however, in boys, it causes premature penile enlargement and early development of secondary sexual characteristics.

Effects in Females

In females, the adrenal substantially contributes to total androgen production by the peripheral conversion of androstenedione. In the follicular phase of the menstrual cycle, adrenal precursors account for two-thirds of testosterone production and one-half of dihydrotestosterone production. During midcycle, the ovarian contribution increases, and the adrenal precursors account for only 40% of testosterone production.

In females, abnormal adrenal function as seen in Cushing's syndrome, adrenal carcinoma, and congenital adrenal hyperplasia results in excessive secretion of adrenal androgens, and their peripheral conversion results in androgen excess, manifested by acne, hirsutism, and virilization.

LABORATORY EVALUATION

Cortisol and the adrenal androgens are measured by specific plasma assays. Certain urinary assays, particularly measurement of 24-hour urine free cortisol, are also useful. In addition, plasma concentrations of ACTH can be determined. The plasma steroid methods commonly used measure the total hormone concentration and are therefore influenced by alterations in plasma binding proteins. Furthermore, since ACTH and the plasma concentrations of the adrenal hormones fluctuate markedly (Figure 6–7), single plasma measurements are frequently unreliable. Thus, plasma levels must be interpreted cautiously, and more specific diagnostic information is usually obtained by performing appropriate stimulation and suppression tests.

Plasma ACTH

A. Methods of Measurement: Plasma ACTH measurements are extremely useful in the diagnosis of pituitary-adrenal dysfunction. The normal range for plasma ACTH, using a sensitive immunoradiometric assay, is 10–50 pg/mL (2.2–11.1 pmol/L).

B. Interpretation: Plasma ACTH levels are most useful in differentiating pituitary causes from adrenal causes of adrenal dysfunction: (1) In **adrenal insufficiency** due to primary adrenal disease, plasma ACTH levels are elevated, usually over 200 pg/mL (44.4 pmol/L). Conversely, in pituitary ACTH deficiency and secondary hypoadrenalism, plasma ACTH levels are less than 20 pg/mL (4.4 pmol/L) and are often below the limit of detection even with sensitive assays. (2) In **Cushing's syndrome** due to primary glucocorticoid-secreting adrenal tumors, plasma ACTH is suppressed, and a level less than 10 pg/mL (2.2 pmol/L) is diagnostic. In patients with Cushing's disease (pituitary ACTH hypersecretion), plasma ACTH levels are normal or only modestly elevated (20–200 pg/mL [4.4–44 pmol/L]). Plasma ACTH levels in the ectopic ACTH syndrome range from the middle of the normal range (eg, 50 mg/mL; 10 mmol/L) to several thousand picograms per milliliter (eg, 600 pmol/L). They are often markedly elevated in patients with ectopic ACTH syndrome due to malignant tumors; however, overlap occurs with levels seen in Cushing's disease. In addition, values lower than expected may be observed occasionally in ectopic ACTH syndrome when the two-site immunoradiometric assay is used; this assay does not detect high-molecular-weight precursors of ACTH. (3) Plasma ACTH levels are also markedly elevated in patients with the common forms of **congenital adrenal hyperplasia** and are useful in the diagnosis and management of these disorders (see Chapters 7 and 11).

Plasma β-Lipotropin & β-Endorphin

β-Lipotropin (β-LPH) is secreted in equimolar amounts with ACTH and is measured by radioimmunoassay. Because of its greater stability and ease of measurement, it has some advantage over the measurement of ACTH. Alterations in β-LPH levels in disease states parallel those of ACTH as described above. Most assays of β-LPH also measure β-endorphin, and thus separation of these hormones is required for precise measurement of β-endorphin. This can be accomplished by chromatography; however, the clinical utility of β-endorphin measurements has not been established.

Plasma Cortisol

A. Methods of Measurement: The most common method of measurement of plasma cortisol is radioimmunoassay. Other methods include high-performance liquid chromatography, competitive protein-binding assay, and fluorimetric assay. All these methods measure total cortisol (both bound and free) in plasma. Methods that measure plasma free cortisol—ie, that not bound to CBG—are not yet clinically available.

Radioimmunoassays of plasma cortisol depend on inhibition of binding of radiolabeled cortisol to an antibody by the cortisol present in a plasma sample. Current assays are very sensitive, so that small plasma volumes can be used. In addition, cross-reactivity of current antisera with other endogenous steroids is minimal, and radioimmunoassay thus gives a reliable measurement of total plasma cortisol levels. Cross-reactivity with some synthetic glucocorticoids, eg, prednisone, is variable. Other commonly used drugs and medications do not interfere with this assay.

B. Interpretation: The diagnostic utility of single plasma cortisol concentrations is limited by the episodic nature of cortisol secretion and its appropriate elevations during stress. As explained below, more information is obtained by dynamic testing of the hypothalamic-pituitary-adrenal axis.

1. Normal values– Normal plasma cortisol levels vary with the method used. With radioimmunoassay and the competitive protein-binding radioassay, levels at 8 AM range from 3 to 20 μg/dL (0.08–0.55 μmol/L) and average 10–12 μg/dL (0.28–0.33 μmol/L). Values obtained later in the day are lower and at 4 PM are approximately half of morning values. At 10 PM to 2 AM, the plasma cortisol concentrations by these methods are usually under 3 μg/dL (0.08 μmol/L).

2. Levels during stress– Cortisol secretion increases in patients who are acutely ill, during surgery, and following trauma. Plasma concentrations may reach 40–60 μg/dL (1.1–1.7 μmol/L).

3. High-estrogen states– The total plasma cortisol concentration is also elevated with increased CBG binding capacity, which occurs most commonly when circulating estrogen levels are high, eg, during pregnancy and when exogenous estrogens or oral contraceptives are being used. In these situations, plasma cortisol may reach levels two to three times normal.

4. Other conditions– CBG levels may be increased or decreased in other situations, as discussed above in the sections on circulation and metabolism. Total plasma cortisol concentrations may also be increased in severe anxiety, endogenous depression, starvation, anorexia nervosa, alcoholism, and chronic renal failure.

Urinary Corticosteroids
A. Free Cortisol:

1. Methods of measurement– The assay of unbound cortisol excreted in the urine is an excellent method for the diagnosis of Cushing's syndrome. Normally, less than 1% of the secreted cortisol is excreted unchanged in the urine. However, in states of excess secretion, the binding capacity of CBG is exceeded, and plasma free cortisol therefore increases, as does its urinary excretion. Urine free cortisol is measured in a 24-hour urine collection by radioimmunoassay or high-performance liquid chromatography.

2. Normal values– The normal range of these assays is 25–95 µg/g creatinine (8–30 µmol/mol creatinine), and elevated concentrations are found in over 90% of patients with spontaneous Cushing's syndrome.

3. Diagnostic utility– This method is particularly useful in differentiating simple obesity from Cushing's syndrome, since levels are not elevated in obesity, as are the urinary 17-hydroxycorticosteroids (see below). The levels may be elevated in the same conditions that increase plasma cortisol (see above), including a slight elevation during pregnancy. This test is not useful in adrenal insufficiency, because of the lack of sensitivity of the method at low levels and because low cortisol excretion is often found in normal persons.

B. 17-Hydroxycorticosteroids:
These urinary steroids are less frequently measured at present, because of the greater utility of plasma cortisol and urine free cortisol measurements.

1. Methods of assay– Urine 17-hydroxycorticosteroids are assayed by the colorimetric Porter-Silber reaction, which detects cortisol and cortisone metabolites.

2. Normal values– Normal values are 3–15 mg/ 24 h (8.3–41.4 µmol/24 h) or 3–7 mg/g (0.9–2.2 mmol/mol) of urine creatinine.

3. Altered excretion– Total excretion is increased in obesity; however, these values are normal when corrected for creatinine excretion. 17-Hydroxy-corticosteroids are increased in hyperthyroidism and decreased in hypothyroidism, starvation, liver disease, renal failure, and pregnancy. Drugs that induce hepatic microsomal enzymes increase cortisol conversion to 6β-hydroxycortisol, which is not measured by the 17-hydroxycorticosteroid method, and therefore reduce 17-hydroxycorticosteroid excretion (see section on metabolism).

d. Drug interference– Direct drug interference with the colorimetric reaction occurs with spirono-

lactone, chlordiazepoxide, hydroxyzine, meprobamate, phenothiazines, and quinine.

Dexamethasone Suppression Tests

A. Low-Dose Tests: These procedures are used to establish the presence of Cushing's syndrome regardless of its cause. Dexamethasone, a potent glucocorticoid, normally suppresses pituitary ACTH release with a resulting fall in plasma and urine corticosteroids, thus assessing feedback inhibition of the hypothalamic-pituitary-adrenal axis. In Cushing's syndrome, this mechanism is abnormal, and steroid secretion fails to be suppressed in the normal way. Dexamethasone in the doses used does not interfere with the measurement of plasma and urinary corticosteroids.

1. Overnight 1-mg dexamethasone suppression test– This is a suitable screening test for Cushing's syndrome. Dexamethasone, 1 mg orally, is given as a single dose at 11 PM, and the following morning a plasma sample is obtained for cortisol determination. Cushing's syndrome is excluded if the plasma cortisol level is less than 5 µg/dL (0.137 µmol/L). If the level is greater than 10 µ/dL (0.276 µmol/L)—in the absence of conditions causing false-positive responses—Cushing's syndrome is the probable cause, and the diagnosis should be confirmed with other procedures.

Over 98% of patients with Cushing's syndrome have abnormal responses. Although false-negative results are rare, they may occur in patients in whom dexamethasone metabolism is abnormally slow, since plasma levels of dexamethasone in these patients are higher than normally achieved and result in apparently normal suppression of cortisol. Simultaneous measurement of plasma dexamethasone and cortisol levels will identify these patients; however, dexamethasone measurements may be available only in a research laboratory.

False-positive results occur in 15% of patients with obesity and in 25% of hospitalized and chronically ill patients. Acute illness, depression, anxiety, alcoholism, high-estrogen states, and uremia may also cause false-positive results. Patients taking phenytoin, barbiturates, and other inducers of hepatic microsomal enzymes may have accelerated metabolism of dexamethasone and thus fail to achieve adequate plasma levels to suppress ACTH.

2. Two-day low-dose test– This test is performed by administering dexamethasone, 0.5 mg every 6 hours for 2 days. Twenty-four-hour urine collections are obtained before and on the second day of dexamethasone administration. The test provides the same information as the overnight 1-mg test but is more time-consuming and requires urine collections. However, it is very useful when the results of other tests are equivocal. In response to this procedure, patients without Cushing's syndrome suppress urine

17-hydroxycorticosteroids to less than 4 mg/24 h (10.1 µmol/24 h) or to less than 1 mg/g (0.3 mmol/mol) of urinary creatinine on the second day of dexamethasone administration. The response of urine free cortisol is less well standardized; however, a reduction in excretion to less than 25 µg/24 h (0.068 µmol/24 h) appears to exclude Cushing's syndrome. Although the plasma cortisol response has been less extensively studied, a morning cortisol level of less than 5 µg/dL (0.137 µmol/L) (obtained 6 hours after the last dose of dexamethasone has been given) is considered a normal response.

About 95% of patients with Cushing's syndrome have abnormal responses. False-positive results occur rarely in patients with obesity and in high-estrogen states. However, false-positive results do occur with acute and chronic illness, depression, alcoholism, and phenytoin therapy.

B. High-Dose Tests: High-dose dexamethasone tests differentiate Cushing's disease (pituitary ACTH hypersecretion) from the ectopic ACTH syndrome and adrenal tumors, since the hypothalamic-pituitary axis in Cushing's disease is suppressible with supraphysiologic doses of glucocorticoids, whereas cortisol secretion is autonomous in patients with adrenal tumors or ectopic ACTH syndrome and is therefore nonsuppressible. Exceptions to these responses are discussed in the section on diagnosis of Cushing's syndrome.

1. Overnight high-dose dexamethasone suppression test– This test is faster and simpler to perform than the 2-day test described below. After a baseline morning cortisol specimen is obtained, a single dose of dexamethasone, 8 mg orally, is administered at 11 PM, and plasma cortisol is measured at 8 AM the following morning. In Cushing's disease, plasma cortisol levels are reduced to less than 50% of baseline values in 95% of patients, whereas steroid secretion in patients with ectopic ACTH syndrome or cortisol-producing adrenal tumors is not suppressed to this extent and is usually unchanged. This single-dose test is more reliable than the 2-day high-dose test and can be regarded as the procedure of choice.

2. Two-day high-dose test– This test is performed by administering dexamethasone, 2 mg orally every 6 hours for 2 days. Twenty-four-hour urine samples are collected before and on the second day of dexamethasone administration. Patients with Cushing's disease have a reduction in urine 17-hydroxycorticosteroid excretion to less than 50% of baseline values, whereas those with adrenal tumors or the ectopic ACTH syndrome usually have little or no reduction in urinary 17-hydroxycorticosteroids. Urine free cortisol or plasma cortisol appears to give equally adequate responses, and the same criteria apply. Regardless of the parameter measured, 15–30% of patients with Cushing's disease fail to achieve 50% suppression of corticosteroid levels, thus limiting the reliability of the procedure.

Pituitary-Adrenal Reserve

Determinations of pituitary-adrenal reserve are used to evaluate the patient's adrenal and pituitary reserve and to assess the ability of the hypothalamic-pituitary-adrenal axis to respond to stress. ACTH administration directly stimulates adrenal secretion; metyrapone inhibits cortisol synthesis, thereby stimulating pituitary ACTH secretion; and insulin-induced hypoglycemia stimulates ACTH release by increasing CRH secretion. More recently, CRH has been utilized to directly stimulate pituitary corticotrophs to release ACTH and β-LPH. The relative utility of these procedures is discussed below in the section on adrenocortical insufficiency and also in Chapter 2.

A. ACTH Stimulation Testing:

1. Procedure and normal values– The rapid ACTH stimulation test measures the acute adrenal response to ACTH and is used to diagnose both primary and secondary adrenal insufficiency. A synthetic human α^{1-24}-ACTH called tetracosactrin or cosyntropin is used. Fasting is not required, and the test may be performed at any time of the day. A baseline cortisol sample is obtained; cosyntropin is administered in a dose of 0.25 mg intramuscularly or intravenously; and additional samples for plasma cortisol are obtained at 30 or 60 minutes following the injection. The normal response is a peak cortisol level greater than 15–18 µg/dL (0.41–0.50 µmol/L), with an increment greater than 5 µg/dL (0.137 µmol/L). If a value of 20 µg/dL (0.55 µmol/L) is obtained, the response is normal regardless of the increment.

2. Subnormal responses– If the cortisol response to the rapid ACTH stimulation test is inadequate, adrenal insufficiency is present. In primary adrenal insufficiency, destruction of cortical cells reduces cortisol secretion and increases pituitary ACTH secretion. Therefore, the adrenal is already maximally stimulated, and there is no further increase in cortisol secretion when exogenous ACTH is given; ie, there is decreased adrenal reserve. In secondary adrenal insufficiency due to ACTH deficiency, there is atrophy of the zonae fasciculata and reticularis, and the adrenal thus is unresponsive to acute stimulation with exogenous ACTH. In either primary or secondary types, a subnormal response to the rapid ACTH stimulation test accurately predicts deficient responsiveness of the axis to insulin hypoglycemia, metyrapone, and surgical stress.

3. Normal responses– A normal response to the rapid ACTH stimulation test excludes both primary adrenal insufficiency (by directly assessing adrenal reserve) and overt secondary adrenal insufficiency with adrenal atrophy. However, a normal response does not rule out partial ACTH deficiency (decreased pituitary reserve) in patients whose basal ACTH secretion is sufficient to prevent adrenocortical atrophy. These patients may be unable to further increase ACTH secretion and thus may have subnormal pituitary ACTH responsiveness to stress or hypoglycemia. In such patients, further testing with metyrapone or hypoglycemia may be indicated. For further discussion, see the section on diagnosis of adrenocortical insufficiency.

4. Aldosterone secretion– The rapid ACTH stimulation test also increases aldosterone secretion and has been used to differentiate primary from secondary adrenocortical insufficiency. In the primary form with destruction of the cortex, both cortisol and aldosterone are unresponsive to exogenous ACTH. However, in secondary adrenal insufficiency, the zona glomerulosa, which is controlled by the renin-angiotensin system, is usually normal. Therefore, the aldosterone response to exogenous ACTH is normal. The normal increment in plasma aldosterone is more than 4 ng/dL (111 pmol/L).

B. Metyrapone Testing: Metyrapone testing is used to diagnose adrenal insufficiency and to assess pituitary-adrenal reserve. The test procedures are detailed in Chapter 2. Metyrapone blocks cortisol synthesis by inhibiting the 11β-hydroxylase enzyme that converts 11-deoxycortisol to cortisol. This stimulates ACTH secretion, which in turn increases the secretion and plasma levels of 11-deoxycortisol. Urinary 17-hydroxycorticosteroid levels also increase because of increased excretion of the metabolites of 11-deoxycortisol that are measured by this method. The overnight metyrapone test is most commonly used and is best suited to patients with suspected pituitary ACTH deficiency; patients with suspected primary adrenal failure are usually evaluated with the rapid ACTH stimulation test as described above and discussed in the section on diagnosis of adrenocortical insufficiency. The normal response to the overnight metyrapone test is a plasma 11-deoxycortisol level greater than 7 μg/dL (0.19 μmol/L) and indicates both normal ACTH secretion and adrenal function. A subnormal response establishes adrenocortical insufficiency but does not differentiate primary and secondary forms. A normal response to metyrapone accurately predicts normal stress responsiveness of the hypothalamic-pituitary axis and correlates well with responsiveness to insulin-induced hypoglycemia.

C. Insulin-Induced Hypoglycemia Testing: The details of this procedure are described in Chapter 2. Hypoglycemia induces a central nervous system stress response, increases CRH release, and in this way increases ACTH and cortisol secretion. It therefore measures the integrity of the axis and its ability to respond to stress. The normal plasma cortisol response is an increment greater than 8 μg/dL (0.22 μmol/L) and a peak level greater than 18–20 μg/dL (0.50–0.55 μmol/L). The plasma ACTH response to hypoglycemia is not well standardized. A normal plasma cortisol response to hypoglycemia excludes adrenal insufficiency and decreased pituitary reserve. Thus, patients with normal responses do not require cortisol therapy during illness or surgery.

D. CRH Testing: The procedure for CRH testing is described in Chapter 2. ACTH responses are exaggerated in patients with primary adrenal failure and absent in patients with hypopituitarism. Delayed responses may occur in patients with hypothalamic disorders.

Androgens

Androgen excess is usually evaluated by the measurement of basal levels of these hormones, since suppression and stimulation tests are not as useful as in disorders affecting the glucocorticoids.

A. Plasma Levels: Assays are available for total plasma levels of DHEA, DHEA sulfate, androstenedione, testosterone, and dihydrotestosterone; these tests are of greater diagnostic utility than the traditional measurement of urinary androgen metabolites measured as urinary 17-ketosteroids.

Because it is present in greater quantities, DHEA sulfate can be measured directly in unextracted plasma. However, because of their similar structures and lower plasma concentrations, the other androgens require extraction and purification steps prior to assay. This is accomplished by solvent extraction followed by chromatography, and the purified steroids are then measured by radioimmunoassay or competitive protein-binding radioassay. These methods allow measurement of multiple steroids in small volumes of plasma.

B. Free Testosterone: Plasma free testosterone (ie, testosterone not bound to SHBG) can be measured and is a more direct measure of circulating biologically active testosterone than the total plasma level. These methods require separation of the bound and free hormone prior to assay and are technically difficult. The plasma free testosterone concentration in normal women averages 5 pg/mL (17.3 pmol/L), representing approximately 1% of the total testosterone concentration. In hirsute women, average levels are 16 pg/mL (55.4 pmol/L), with a wide range (see Chapter 10).

C. SHBG Binding Capacity: The binding capacity of SHBG can be measured, although these methods are not in general use. SHBG binding capacity is higher in women; it is increased in pregnancy, in women receiving exogenous estrogens, in hepatic cirrhosis, and in hyperthyroidism and is decreased in hirsute women with increased androgens and in patients with acromegaly.

DISORDERS OF ADRENOCORTICAL INSUFFICIENCY

Deficient adrenal production of glucocorticoids or mineralocorticoids results in adrenocortical insufficiency, which is either the consequence of destruction or dysfunction of the cortex (primary adrenocortical insufficiency, Addison's disease) or secondary to deficient pituitary ACTH secretion (secondary adrenocortical insufficiency). Secondary adrenocortical insufficiency due to glucocorticoid therapy is the most common cause.

PRIMARY ADRENOCORTICAL INSUFFICIENCY (Addison's Disease)

Etiology & Pathology

The etiology of primary adrenocortical insufficiency has changed over time. Prior to 1920, tuberculosis was the major cause of adrenocortical insufficiency. Since 1950, autoimmune adrenalitis with adrenal atrophy has accounted for about 80% of cases. It is associated with a high incidence of other immunologic and autoimmune endocrine disorders (see below). Tuberculosis of the adrenal gland is responsible for most of the other cases. Rare causes are listed in Table 6–1. Primary adrenocortical insufficiency, or Addison's disease, is rare, with a reported prevalence of 39 per million population in the United Kingdom and 60 per million in Denmark. It is more common in females, with a female:male ratio of 2.6:1. Tuberculous adrenal destruction is most common in males, giving an overall female:male ratio of 1.25:1. Addison's disease is usually diagnosed in the third to fifth decades; mean ages of 34 and 38 years have been reported for the autoimmune and tuberculous types, respectively. As the number of patients with acquired immunodeficiency syndrome (AIDS) increases, and as patients with malignant disease live longer, more cases of adrenal insufficiency will be seen.

Table 6–1. Causes of primary adrenocortical insufficiency.[1]

Major causes
   Autoimmune (about 80%)
   Tuberculosis (about 20%)
Rare causes
   Adrenal hemorrhage and infarction
   AIDS
   Fungal infections
   Metastatic malignancy or lymphomatous replacement
   Amyloidosis
   Sarcoidosis
   Hemochromatosis
   Radiation therapy
   Surgical adrenalectomy
   Enzyme inhibitors (ketoconazole, metyrapone, aminoglutethimide, trilostane)
   Cytotoxic agents (mitotane)
   Congenital enzyme defects, hypoplasia, familial glucocorticoid deficiency, glucocorticoid resistance

[1] Modified and reproduced, with permission, from Baxter JD, Tyrrell JB. in: *Endocrinology and Metabolism.* Felig P et al (editors). McGraw-Hill, 1987.

A. Autoimmune Adrenocortical Insufficiency: Lymphocytic infiltration of the adrenal cortex is the characteristic histologic feature. The adrenals are small and atrophic, and the capsule is thickened. The adrenal medulla is preserved, though cortical cells are largely absent, show degenerative changes, and are surrounded by a fibrous stroma and lymphocytic infiltrates.

Autoimmune Addison's disease is frequently accompanied by other immune disorders. Two distinct polyglandular syndromes involve the adrenal glands: one includes adrenal insufficiency, hypoparathyroidism, and chronic mucocutaneous candidiasis, and the other includes adrenal insufficiency, Hashimoto's thyroiditis, and insulin-dependent diabetes mellitus. Ovarian failure is common in both syndromes. Alopecia, malabsorption syndromes, chronic hepatitis, vitiligo, and pernicious anemia are also found in association with autoimmune Addison's disease— one or more of these associated disorders is found in 40–53% of patients. There is an even higher incidence of antibodies to various endocrine organs and other tissues in the absence of overt clinical disease (see Chapter 21).

B. Adrenocortical Insufficiency Due to Invasive and Hemorrhagic Disorders: Invasive or hemorrhagic disorders causing adrenocortical failure result in total or near-total destruction of both glands. With septicemia or hemorrhage, the adrenal is rapidly destroyed, whereas gradual destruction usually occurs in conditions such as tuberculosis.

1. Adrenal tuberculosis and other destructive causes– Adrenal tuberculosis is due to hematogenous infection of the cortex and usually occurs as a complication of systemic tuberculous infection (lung, gastrointestinal tract, or kidney). The adrenal glands are replaced by caseous necrosis; both cortical and medullary tissue is destroyed. Calcification of the adrenals is frequent and is radiologically demonstrable in about 50% of cases.

2. Bilateral adrenal hemorrhage– Hemorrhage may cause acute adrenal insufficiency. In children, fulminant meningococcemia and *Pseudomonas* septicemia are the most common causes. In adults (mostly > age 50), anticoagulant therapy given for other major illnesses is responsible for one-third of cases. Other causes in adults include septicemia, coagulation disorders, adrenal vein thrombosis, adrenal metastases, trauma, abdominal surgery, and obstetric gestational and postpartum complications. The adrenal glands are often massively enlarged; there is replacement of the medulla and inner cortex by hemorrhage and ischemic necrosis of the outer cortex, so that only a few subcapsular cortical cells survive. Venous thrombosis frequently accompanies the hemorrhage. In surviving patients, the hematomas may calcify.

3. Acquired immunodeficiency syndrome (AIDS)– Postmortem examination reveals the adrenal to be the endocrine gland most commonly affected in AIDS. Although pathologic involvement and subclinical alterations in steroidogenesis are common, clinical adrenal insufficiency is uncommon. Cytomegalovirus involvement of the adrenal cortex is common, but severe necrosis occurs in only a few patients. Other causes of adrenal insufficiency in AIDS include metastatic lesions (Kaposi's sarcoma, lymphomas) and infections (tuberculosis, infections with atypical mycobacteria, mycoses). I Ketoconazole, an antifungal agent frequently used in patients with AIDS, interferes with cytochrome P450 enzymes in several organs, including the adrenal and the gonads, and results in decreased steroidogenesis. Adrenal insufficiency is usually dose-related and reversible, but it may occur with low doses and it may be persistent. Abnormalities of mineralocorticoid secretion in AIDS are discussed in Chapter 7.

4. Adrenal metastases– Although metastases to the adrenals occur frequently with tumors of the lung, breast, stomach, and with melanoma and may occur with many other tumors, frank adrenal insufficiency is relatively uncommon; more than 80–90% of the adrenal must be destroyed before frank insufficiency develops. The adrenals are often massively enlarged, and this may be detected by computed tomography (CT scan). Since the symptoms of adrenal insufficiency may be mistaken for those of the underlying cancer, and since treatment of the adrenal insufficiency may improve the patients' quality of life, a high degree of clinical suspicion should be maintained.

C. Familial Glucocorticoid Deficiency: Familial glucocorticoid deficiency is a rare disorder in which there is hereditary adrenocortical unresponsiveness to ACTH. This leads to adrenal insufficiency with subnormal glucocorticoid and adrenal androgen secretion and elevated plasma ACTH levels.

In this disorder, cortisol secretion is unresponsive to both endogenous and exogenous ACTH stimulation. However, aldosterone secretion responds to both posture change and sodium deprivation, except in a few subjects who have partial aldosterone deficiency. Presentation is usually in childhood and may be accompanied by achalasia. Histologically, there is preservation of the zona glomerulosa, with degenerative changes in the zonae fasciculata and reticularis. These features and the absence of lymphocytic infiltration of the adrenal cortex differentiate this condition from idiopathic adrenocortical insufficiency.

D. Glucocorticoid Resistance: Generalized resistance to the action of glucocorticoids is a rare familial disorder characterized by cortisol excess without clinical features of Cushing's syndrome and varying degrees of mineralocorticoid and adrenal androgen excess. Qualitative and quantitative abnormalities of the glucocorticoid receptor have been described, as well as point mutations in its amino acid sequence. Selective acquired glucocorticoid resistance has been observed in the neoplastic lymphocytes of acute lymphocytic leukemia and correlates with lack of steroid responsiveness.

Pathophysiology

Loss of more than 90% of both adrenal cortices results in the clinical manifestations of adrenocortical insufficiency. Gradual destruction such as occurs in the idiopathic and invasive forms of the disease leads to chronic adrenocortical insufficiency. However, more rapid destruction occurs in many cases; about 25% of patients are in crisis or impending crisis at the time of diagnosis. With gradual adrenocortical destruction, the initial phase is that of decreased adrenal reserve; ie, basal steroid secretion is normal, but secretion does not increase in response to stress. Thus, acute adrenal crisis can be precipitated by the stresses of surgery, trauma, or infection, which require increased corticosteroid secretion. With further loss of cortical tissue, even basal secretion of mineralocorticoids and glucocorticoids becomes deficient, leading to the manifestations of chronic adrenocortical insufficiency. Destruction of the adrenals by hemorrhage results in sudden loss of both glucocorticoid and mineralocorticoid secretion, accompanied by acute adrenal crisis.

With decreasing cortisol secretion, plasma levels of ACTH and β-lipotropin (β-LPH) are increased because of decreased negative-feedback inhibition of their secretion. In chronic states, the elevated ACTH levels cause hyperpigmentation; this is usually absent when adrenal destruction is rapid.

Clinical Features

A. Symptoms and Signs: Cortisol deficiency causes weakness, fatigue, anorexia, nausea and vomiting, hypotension, and hypoglycemia. Mineralocorticoid deficiency produces renal sodium wasting and potassium retention and can lead to severe dehydration, hypotension, hyponatremia, hyperkalemia, and acidosis.

1. Chronic primary adrenocortical insufficiency– The chief symptoms (Table 6–2) are hyperpigmentation, weakness and fatigue, weight loss, anorexia, and gastrointestinal disturbances.

Hyperpigmentation is the classic physical finding, and its presence in association with the above manifestations should suggest primary adrenocortical insufficiency. Generalized hyperpigmentation of the skin and mucous membranes is one of the earliest manifestation of Addison's disease. It is increased in sun-exposed areas and accentuated over pressure areas such as the knuckles, toes, elbows, and knees. It is accompanied by increased numbers of black or dark-brown freckles. The classic hyperpigmentation of the buccal mucosa and gums is preceded by generalized hyperpigmentation of the skin; adrenal insufficiency should also be suspected when there is increased pigmentation of the palmar creases, nail

Table 6–2. Clinical features of primary adrenocortical insufficiency.[1]

	Percent
Weakness, fatigue, anorexia, weight loss	100
Hyperpigmentation	92
Hypotension	88
Gastrointestinal disturbances	56
Salt craving	19
Postural symptoms	12

[1] Reproduced, with permission, from Baxter JD, Tyrrell JB, in: *Endocrinology and Metabolism.* Felig P et al (editors). 2nd Ed. McGraw-Hill, 1987.

beds, nipples, areolae, and perivaginal and perianal mucosa. Scars that have formed after the onset of ACTH excess become hyperpigmented, whereas older ones do not. Although pigmentation of the buccal mucosa, palmar creases, vulva, and anus is a normal phenomenon in dark-skinned races, patients frequently describe increase in pigmentation of these sites. Pigmentation of the tongue is an abnormal finding in all races.

General weakness, fatigue and malaise, anorexia, and weight loss are invariable features of the disorder. Weight loss may reach 15 kg with progressive adrenal failure. Gastrointestinal disturbances, especially nausea and vomiting, occur in most patients; diarrhea is less frequent. An increase in gastrointestinal symptoms during an acute adrenal crisis may confuse the diagnosis by suggesting a primary intra-abdominal process.

Hypotension is present in about 90% of patients and is accompanied by orthostatic symptoms and occasionally syncope. In more severe chronic cases and in acute crises, recumbent hypotension or shock is almost invariably present. Vitiligo occurs in 4–17% of patients with autoimmune Addison's disease but is rare in Addison's disease due to other causes. Salt craving occurs in about 20% of patients.

Severe hypoglycemia may occur in children. This finding is unusual in adults but may be provoked by fasting, fever, infection, or nausea and vomiting, especially in acute adrenal crisis.

Amenorrhea is common in Addison's disease. It may be due to weight loss and chronic illness or to primary ovarian failure. Loss of axillary and pubic hair may occur in women as a result of decreased secretion of adrenal androgens.

2. Acute adrenal crisis– Acute adrenal crisis represents a state of acute adrenocortical insufficiency and occurs in patients with Addison's disease who are exposed to the stress of infection, trauma, surgery, or dehydration due to salt deprivation, vomiting, or diarrhea.

The symptoms are listed in Table 6–3. Anorexia and nausea and vomiting increase and worsen the volume depletion and dehydration. Hypovolemic shock frequently occurs, and adrenal insufficiency should be considered in any patient with unexplained

Table 6–3. Clincial features of acute adrenal crisis.

Hypotension and shock
Fever
Dehydration, volume depletion
Nausea, vomiting, anorexia
Weakness, apathy, depressed mentation
Hypoglycemia

vascular collapse. Abdominal pain may occur and mimic an acute abdominal emergency. Weakness, apathy, and confusion are usual. Fever is usual and may be due to infection or to hypoadrenalism per se. Hyperpigmentation is present unless the onset of adrenal insufficiency is rapid and should suggest the diagnosis.

Additional findings that suggest the diagnosis are hyponatremia, hyperkalemia, lymphocytosis, eosinophilia, and hypoglycemia.

Shock and coma may rapidly lead to death in untreated patients.

3. Acute adrenal hemorrhage– (See Table 6–4.) Bilateral adrenal hemorrhage and acute adrenal destruction in an already compromised patient with major medical illness follow a progressively deteriorating course. The usual manifestations are abdominal, flank, or back pain and abdominal tenderness. Abdominal distention, rigidity, and rebound tenderness are less frequent. Hypotension, shock, fever, nausea and vomiting, confusion, and disorientation are common; tachycardia and cyanosis are less frequent.

With progression, severe hypotension, volume depletion, dehydration, hyperpyrexia, cyanosis, coma, and death ensue.

The diagnosis of acute adrenal hemorrhage should be considered in the deteriorating patient with unexplained abdominal or flank pain, vascular collapse, hyperpyrexia, or hypoglycemia.

Table 6–4. Clinical features of adrenal hemorrhage.[1]

	Percent
General features	
Hypotension and shock	74
Fever	59
Nausea and vomiting	46
Confusion, disorientation	41
Tachycardia	28
Cyanosis or lividity	28
Local features	
Abdominal, flank, or back pain	77
Abdominal or flank tenderness	38
Abdominal distention	28
Abdominal rigidity	20
Chest pain	13
Rebound tenderness	5

[1] Reproduced, with permission, from Baxter JD, Tyrrell JB, In: *Endocrinology and Metabolism.* Felig P et al (editors). 2nd Ed. McGraw-Hill, 1987.

B. Laboratory and Electrocardiographic Findings and Imaging Studies:

1. Gradual adrenal destruction– Hyponatremia and hyperkalemia are classic manifestations of the mineralocorticoid deficiency of primary adrenal insufficiency and should suggest the diagnosis. Hematologic manifestations include normocytic, normochromic anemia, neutropenia, eosinophilia, and a relative lymphocytosis. Azotemia with increased concentrations of blood urea nitrogen and serum creatinine is due to volume depletion and dehydration. Mild acidosis is frequently present. Hypercalcemia of mild to moderate degree occurs in about 6% of patients.

Abdominal radiographs reveal adrenal calcification in half the patients with tuberculous Addison's disease and in some patients with other invasive or hemorrhagic causes of adrenal insufficiency. Computed tomography (CT scan) is a more sensitive detector of adrenal calcification and adrenal enlargement. Bilateral adrenal enlargement in association with adrenal insufficiency may be seen with tuberculosis, fungal infections, cytomegalovirus, malignant and nonmalignant infiltrative diseases, and adrenal hemorrhage.

Electrocardiographic features are low voltage, a vertical QRS axis, and nonspecific ST–T wave abnormalities secondary to abnormal electrolytes.

2. Acute adrenal hemorrhage– Hyponatremia and hyperkalemia occur in only a small number of cases, but azotemia is a usual finding. Increased circulating eosinophils may suggest the diagnosis. The diagnosis is frequently established only when imaging studies reveal bilateral adrenal enlargement.

SECONDARY ADRENOCORTICAL INSUFFICIENCY

Etiology

Secondary adrenocortical insufficiency due to ACTH deficiency is most commonly a result of exogenous glucocorticoid therapy. Pituitary or hypothalamic tumors are the most common causes of naturally occurring pituitary ACTH hyposecretion. These and other less common causes are reviewed in Chapter 2.

Pathophysiology

ACTH deficiency is the primary event and leads to decreased cortisol and adrenal androgen secretion. Aldosterone secretion remains normal except in a few cases. In the early stages, basal ACTH and cortisol levels may be normal; however, ACTH reserve is impaired, and ACTH and cortisol responses to stress are therefore subnormal. With further loss of basal ACTH secretion, there is atrophy of the zonae fasciculata and reticularis of the adrenal cortex; and, therefore, basal cortisol secretion is decreased. At this stage, the entire pituitary adrenal axis is impaired; ie,

there is not only decreased ACTH responsiveness to stress but also decreased adrenal responsiveness to acute stimulation with exogenous ACTH.

The manifestations of glucocorticoid deficiency are similar to those described for primary adrenocortical insufficiency. However, since aldosterone secretion by the zona glomerulosa is usually preserved, the manifestations of mineralocorticoid deficiency are absent.

Clinical Features

A. Symptoms and Signs: Secondary adrenal insufficiency is usually chronic, and the manifestations may be nonspecific. However, acute crisis can occur in undiagnosed patients or in corticosteroid-treated patients who do not receive increased steroid dosage during periods of stress.

The clinical features of secondary adrenal insufficiency differ from those of primary adrenocortical insufficiency in that pituitary secretion of ACTH and β-LPH is deficient and hyperpigmentation is therefore not present. In addition, mineralocorticoid secretion is usually normal. Thus, the clinical features of ACTH and glucocorticoid deficiency are nonspecific.

Volume depletion, dehydration, and hyperkalemia are usually absent. Hypotension is usually not present except in acute presentations. Hyponatremia may occur as a result of water retention and inability to excrete a water load but is not accompanied by hyperkalemia. Prominent features are weakness, lethargy, easy fatigability, anorexia, nausea, and occasionally vomiting. Arthralgias and myalgias also occur. Hypoglycemia is occasionally the presenting feature. Acute decompensation with severe hypotension or shock unresponsive to vasopressors may occur.

B. Associated Features: Patients with secondary adrenal insufficiency commonly have additional features that suggest the diagnosis. A history of glucocorticoid therapy or, if this is not available, the presence of cushingoid features suggests prior glucocorticoid use. Hypothalamic or pituitary tumors leading to ACTH deficiency usually cause loss of other pituitary hormones (hypogonadism and hypothyroidism). Hypersecretion of GH or prolactin (PRL) from a pituitary adenoma may be present.

C. Laboratory Findings: Findings on routine laboratory examination consist of normochromic, normocytic anemia, neutropenia, lymphocytosis, and eosinophilia. Serum sodium, potassium, creatinine, and bicarbonate and blood urea nitrogen are usually normal; plasma glucose may be low, though severe hypoglycemia is unusual.

DIAGNOSIS OF ADRENOCORTICAL INSUFFICIENCY

Although the diagnosis of adrenal insufficiency should be confirmed by assessment of the pituitary-adrenal axis, therapy should not be delayed nor should the patient be subjected to procedures that may increase volume loss and dehydration and further contribute to hypotension. If the patient is acutely ill, therapy should be instituted and the diagnosis established when the patient is stable.

Diagnostic Tests

Since basal levels of adrenocortical steroids in either urine or plasma may be normal in partial adrenal insufficiency, tests of adrenocortical reserve are necessary to establish the diagnosis (Figure 6–11). These tests are described in the section on laboratory evaluation and in Chapter 2.

Rapid ACTH Stimulation Test

The rapid ACTH stimulation test assesses adrenal reserve and is the initial procedure in the assessment of possible adrenal insufficiency, either primary or secondary.

Subnormal responses to exogenous ACTH administration are an indication of decreased adrenal reserve and establish the diagnosis of adrenocortical insufficiency. Further diagnostic procedures are not required, since subnormal responses to the rapid ACTH stimulation test indicate lack of responsiveness to metyrapone, insulin-induced hypoglycemia, or stress. However, this test does not permit differentiation of primary and secondary causes. This is best accomplished by measurement of basal plasma ACTH levels, as discussed below.

A normal response to the rapid ACTH stimulation test excludes primary adrenal failure, since a normal cortisol response indicates normal cortical function. However, normal responsiveness does not exclude partial secondary adrenocortical insufficiency in those few patients with decreased pituitary reserve and decreased stress responsiveness of the hypothalamic-pituitary-adrenal axis who maintain sufficient basal ACTH secretion to prevent adrenocortical atrophy. If this situation is suspected clinically, pituitary ACTH responsiveness may be tested directly with metyrapone or insulin-induced hypoglycemia. (See section on laboratory evaluation and below.)

Plasma ACTH Levels

If adrenal insufficiency is present, plasma ACTH levels are used to differentiate primary and secondary

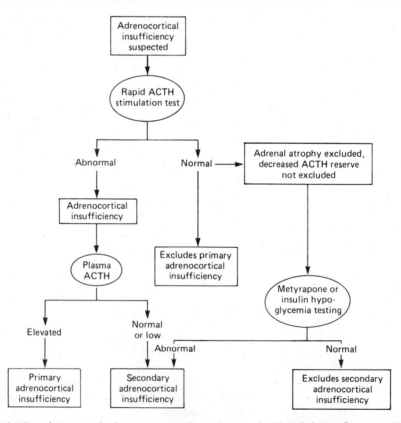

Figure 6–11. Evaluation of suspected primary or secondary adrenocortical insufficiency. Boxes enclose clinical decisions, and circles enclose diagnostic tests. (Redrawn and reproduced, with permission, from Baxter JD, Tyrrell JB: The adrenal cortex. In: *Endocrinology and Metabolism.* Felig P et al [editors]. McGraw-Hill, 1981.)

forms. In patients with primary adrenal insufficiency, plasma ACTH levels are over 240 pg/mL (44.4 pmol/L) and usually range from 400 to 2000 pg/mL (88.8–444 pmol/L). With pituitary ACTH deficiency, plasma ACTH levels are usually less than 20 pg/mL (4.4 pmol/L) (Figure 6–12).

Partial ACTH Deficiency

When partial ACTH deficiency and decreased pituitary reserve are suspected despite normal responsiveness to the rapid ACTH stimulation test, the following procedures may be used for more direct assessment of hypothalamic-pituitary function:

A. Methods of Testing: The overnight metyrapone test is used in patients with suspected hypothalamic or pituitary disorders when hypoglycemia is contraindicated and in those with prior glucocorticoid therapy. Insulin-induced hypoglycemia is used in patients with suspected hypothalamic or pituitary tumors, since both ACTH and GH responsiveness can be assessed (see Chapter 2).

B. Interpretation: A normal response to either metyrapone or hypoglycemia excludes secondary adrenocortical insufficiency. (See section on laboratory evaluation.) Subnormal responses, in the presence of a normal response to ACTH administration,

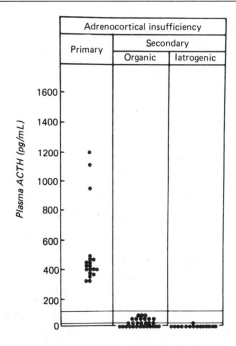

Figure 6–12. Basal plasma ACTH levels in primary and secondary adrenocortical insufficiency. (Reproduced, with permission, from Irvine WJ, Toft AD, Feek CM: Addison's disease. In: *The Adrenal Gland.* James VHT [editor]. Raven Press, 1979.)

establish the diagnosis of secondary adrenal insufficiency.

TREATMENT OF ADRENOCORTICAL INSUFFICIENCY

The aim of treatment of adrenocortical insufficiency is to produce levels of glucocorticoids and mineralocorticoids equivalent to those achieved in an individual with normal hypothalamic-pituitary-adrenal function under similar circumstances.

Acute Addisonian Crisis (Table 6–5)

Treatment for acute addisonian crisis should be instituted as soon as the diagnosis is suspected. Therapy includes administration of glucocorticoids; correction of dehydration, hypovolemia, and electrolyte abnormalities; general supportive measures; and treatment of coexisting or precipitating disorders.

A. Cortisol (Hydrocortisone): Parenteral cortisol in soluble form (hydrocortisone hemisuccinate or phosphate) is the glucocorticoid preparation most commonly used. This agent has sufficient sodium-retaining potency so that additional mineralocorticoid therapy is not required in patients with primary adrenocortical insufficiency who have deficient secretion of both aldosterone and cortisol.

Cortisol in doses of 100 mg intravenously is given every 6 hours for the first 24 hours. The response to therapy is usually rapid, with improvement occurring within 12 hours or less. If improvement occurs and the patient is stable, 50 mg every 6 hours is given on the second day, and in most patients the dosage may then be gradually reduced to approximately 10 mg three times daily by the fourth or fifth day. (See section on maintenance therapy, below.)

1. In severely ill patients, especially in those with additional major complications (eg, sepsis), higher cortisol doses (100 mg intravenously every 6–8 hours) are maintained until the patient is stable.

2. In primary Addison's disease, mineralocorticoid

Table 6–5. Treatment of acute adrenal crises.

Glucocorticoid replacement
   (1) Administer cortisol (as hydrocortisone phosphate or hemisuccinate), 100 mg intravenously every 6 hours for 24 hours.
   (2) When the patient is stable, reduce the dosage to 50 mg every 6 hours.
   (3) Taper to maintenance therapy by day 4 or 5 and add mineralocorticoid therapy as required.
   (4) Maintain or increase the dose to 200–400 mg/d if complications persist or occur.

General and supportive measures
   (1) Correct volume depletion, dehydration, and hypoglycemia with intravenous saline and glucose.
   (2) Evaluate and correct infection and other precipitating factors.

replacement, in the form of fludrocortisone (see below), is added when the total cortisol dosage has been reduced to 50–60 mg/d.

3. In secondary adrenocortical insufficiency with acute crisis, the primary requirement is glucocorticoid replacement and is satisfactorily supplied by the administration of cortisol, as outlined above. If the possibility of excessive fluid and sodium retention in such patients is of concern, equivalent parenteral doses of synthetic steroids such as prednisolone or dexamethasone may be substituted.

4. Intramuscular cortisone acetate is contraindicated in acute adrenal failure for the following reasons: (1) absorption is slow; (2) it requires conversion to cortisol in the liver; (3) adequate plasma levels of cortisol are not obtained; and (4) there is inadequate suppression of plasma ACTH levels, indicating insufficient glucocorticoid activity.

B. Intravenous Fluids: Intravenous glucose and saline are administered to correct volume depletion, hypotension, and hypoglycemia. Volume deficits may be severe in Addison's disease, and hypotension and shock may not respond to vasopressors unless glucocorticoids are administered. Hyperkalemia and acidosis are usually corrected with cortisol and volume replacement; however, an occasional patient may require specific therapy for these abnormalities.

Maintenance Therapy
(Table 6–6)

Patients with Addison's disease require lifelong therapy, usually with both glucocorticoids and mineralocorticoids. Cortisol (hydrocortisone) is the glucocorticoid preparation most often used. The total dosage is usually 25–30 mg/d orally, given as 15–20 mg in the morning on arising and 10 mg at 4–5 PM. Other glucocorticoids such as oral cortisone acetate (37.5 mg/d), which is rapidly absorbed and converted to cortisol, or equivalent doses of synthetic steroids (eg, prednisone or prednisolone) may also be used.

Cortisol in twice-daily doses gives satisfactory responses in most patients; however, some patients may require only a single morning dose, and others may require 3 doses per day to maintain well-being and normal energy levels. Insomnia as a side effect

Table 6–6. Regimen for maintenance therapy of primary adrenocortical insufficiency.[1]

(1) Cortisol, 15–20 mg in AM and 10 mg at 4–5 PM.
(2) Fludrocortisone, 0.05–0.1 mg orally in AM.
(3) Clinical follow-up: Maintenance of normal weight, blood pressure, and electrolytes with regression of clinical features.
(4) Patient education plus identification card or bracelet.
(5) Increased cortisol dosage during "stress."

[1] Reproduced, with permission, from Baxter JD, Tyrrell JB, in: *Endocrinology and Metabolism.* Felig P et al (editors). 2nd Ed. McGraw-Hill, 1987.

of glucocorticoid administration can usually be prevented by administering the last daily dose at 4–5 PM.

Fludrocortisone (9α-fluorocortisol) is used for mineralocorticoid therapy; the usual doses are 0.05–0.2 mg/d orally in the morning. Because of the long half-life of this agent, divided doses are not required. About 10–20% of addisonian patients can be managed with cortisol and adequate dietary sodium intake alone and do not require fludrocortisone.

Secondary adrenocortical insufficiency is treated with the cortisol dosages described above for the primary form. Fludrocortisone is rarely required. The recovery of normal function of the hypothalamic-pituitary-adrenal axis following suppression by exogenous glucocorticoids may take weeks to years, and its duration is not readily predictable. Consequently, prolonged replacement therapy may be required.

Response to Therapy;
Clinical Assessment

There are no currently available biochemical procedures for assessing the response to treatment of adrenocortical insufficiency. Measurement of plasma cortisol and ACTH levels is of no particular value, because of the wide variability in plasma levels in relationship to the timing of the cortisol dose and the time of plasma sampling. Measurement of urine free cortisol levels has been suggested, but a significant advantage has not yet been substantiated.

The adequacy of glucocorticoid and mineralocorticoid replacement is currently best evaluated by the clinical response to therapy. Thus, in appropriately treated patients, there is improvement or resolution of the features of glucocorticoid and mineralocorticoid deficiency, and most patients lead normal lives without significant disability.

A. Cortisol Therapy: Adequate treatment results in the disappearance of weakness, malaise, and fatigue. Anorexia and other gastrointestinal symptoms resolve, and weight returns to normal. The hyperpigmentation invariably improves but may not entirely disappear. Inadequate cortisol administration leads to persistence of these symptoms of adrenal insufficiency, and excessive pigmentation will remain. Greater than physiologic doses of glucocorticoids result in weight gain and may cause cushingoid features.

B. Mineralocorticoid Therapy: This should be monitored by frequent measurement of blood pressure and of serum electrolytes. With adequate treatment, the blood pressure is normal without orthostatic change, and serum sodium and potassium remain within the normal range. Hypertension and hypokalemia result if the fludrocortisone dose is excessive; conversely, undertreatment may lead to fatigue and malaise, orthostatic symptoms, and subnormal supine or upright blood pressure, with hyperkalemia and hyponatremia.

Prevention of Adrenal Crisis

The development of acute adrenal insufficiency in previously diagnosed and treated patients is almost entirely preventable in cooperative individuals. The essential elements are patient education and increased glucocorticoid dosages during illness.

The patient should be informed about the necessity for lifelong therapy, the possible consequences of acute illness, and the necessity for increased therapy and medical assistance during acute illness. An identification card or bracelet should be carried or worn at all times.

The cortisol dose should be increased by the patient to 60–80 mg/d with the development of minor illnesses; the usual maintenance dosage may be resumed in 24–48 hours if improvement occurs. Increased mineralocorticoid therapy is not required.

If symptoms persist or become worse, the patient should continue increased cortisol doses and call the physician.

Vomiting may result in inability to ingest or absorb oral cortisol, and diarrhea in addisonian patients may precipitate a crisis because of rapid fluid and electrolyte losses. Patients must understand that if these symptoms occur, they should seek immediate medical assistance so that parenteral glucocorticoid therapy can be given.

Steroid Coverage for Surgery (Table 6–7)

The normal physiologic response to surgical stress involves an increase in cortisol secretion. Thus, patients with primary or secondary adrenocortical insufficiency scheduled for elective surgery require increased glucocorticoid coverage. This problem is most frequently encountered in patients with pituitary-adrenal suppression due to exogenous glucocorticoid therapy. However, the increased glucocorticoid action may serve primarily to modulate the immunologic response to stress. The principles of management are outlined in Table 6–7. *Note:* Intramuscular

---

Table 6–7. Steroid coverage for surgery.[1]

(1) Correct electrolytes, blood pressure, and hydration if necessary.

(2) Give cortisol (as hydrocortisone phosphate or hemisuccinate), 100 mg intramuscularly, on call to operating room.

(3) Give cortisol, 50 mg intramuscularly or intravenously, in the recovery room and every 6 hours for the first 24 hours.

(4) If progress is satisfactory, reduce dosage to 25 mg every 6 hours for 24 hours and then taper to maintenance dosage over 3–5 days. Resume previous fludrocortisone dose when the patient is taking oral medications.

(5) Maintain or increase cortisol dosage to 200–400 mg/d if fever, hypotension, or other complications occur.

[1] Modified and reproduced, with permission, from Baxter JD, Tyrrell JB, in: *Endocrinology and Metabolism.* Felig P et al (editors). 2nd Ed. McGraw-Hill, 1987.

---

cortisone acetate should not be used, for the reasons discussed above in the section on treatment of acute addisonian crisis.

PROGNOSIS OF ADRENOCORTICAL INSUFFICIENCY

Before glucocorticoid and mineralocorticoid therapy became available, primary adrenocortical insufficiency was invariably fatal, with death usually occurring within 2 years after onset. Survival now depends upon the underlying cause of the adrenal insufficiency. In patients with autoimmune Addison's disease, survival approaches that of the normal population, and most patients lead normal lives. In general, death from adrenal insufficiency now occurs only in patients with rapid onset of disease who may die before the diagnosis is established and appropriate therapy started.

Secondary adrenal insufficiency has an excellent prognosis with glucocorticoid therapy.

Adrenal insufficiency due to bilateral adrenal hemorrhage is still often fatal, with most cases being recognized only at autopsy.

CUSHING'S SYNDROME

Chronic glucocorticoid excess, whatever its cause, leads to the constellation of symptoms and physical features known as Cushing's *syndrome*. It is most commonly iatrogenic, resulting from chronic glucocorticoid therapy. "Spontaneous" Cushing's syndrome is caused by abnormalities of the pituitary or adrenal or may occur as a consequence of ACTH secretion by nonpituitary tumors (**ectopic ACTH syndrome**). Cushing's *disease* is defined as the specific type of Cushing's syndrome due to excessive pituitary ACTH secretion from a pituitary tumor. This section will review the various types of spontaneous Cushing's syndrome and discuss their diagnosis and therapy. (See also Chapter 2.)

Classification & Incidence

Cushing's syndrome is conveniently classified as either ACTH-dependent or ACTH-independent (Table 6–8).

The ACTH-dependent types of Cushing's syndrome—ectopic ACTH syndrome and Cushing's disease—are characterized by chronic ACTH hypersecretion, which results in hyperplasia of the adrenal zonae fasciculata and reticularis and therefore increased adrenocortical secretion of cortisol, androgens, and DOC.

ACTH-independent Cushing's syndrome is due to

Table 6–8. Classification and etiology of Cushing's syndrome.[1]

	Percent
ACTH-dependent	
Cushing's disease	68
Ectopic ACTH syndrome	15
ACTH-independent	
Adrenal adenoma	9
Adrenal carcinoma	8
	100

[1] Reproduced, with permission, from Baxter JD, Tyrrell JB, in: *Endocrinology and Metabolism.* Felig P et al (editors). 2nd Ed. McGraw-Hill, 1987.

autonomous glucocorticoid-secreting adrenocortical adenomas or carcinomas; in these cases, the resulting cortisol excess suppresses pituitary ACTH secretion.

A. Cushing's Disease: This is the most frequent type of Cushing's syndrome and is responsible for about 70% of reported cases. Cushing's disease is much more common in women than in men (female:male ratio of about 8:1) and the age at diagnosis is usually between 20 and 40 years.

B. Ectopic ACTH Hypersecretion: This disorder is said to account for about 15% of cases of Cushing's syndrome. That figure is probably an underestimate, since it is likely that many patients are not diagnosed because they lack the classic features of hypercortisolism. In addition, severe hypercortisolism and rapid death are common. Ectopic ACTH secretion is most common with small cell carcinoma of the lung; this tumor is responsible for about 50% of cases of the syndrome. Ectopic ACTH hypersecretion is estimated to occur in 0.5–2% of patients with this tumor. Other tumors are discussed below. The ectopic ACTH syndrome is more common in men, presumably because of their higher incidence of small-cell carcinoma. The female:male ratio is 1:3, and the peak incidence is at age 40–60 years.

C. Primary Adrenal Tumors: Primary adrenal tumors cause 17–19% of cases of Cushing's syndrome; adenoma and carcinoma occur with about equal frequency in adults. Glucocorticoid-secreting adrenal adenomas are more common in females. Adrenocortical carcinomas causing cortisol excess are also more common in females; however, if all types (including nonsecreting tumors) are considered, the overall incidence is higher in males. Adrenal carcinoma occurs in about two patients per million population per year; the mean age at diagnosis is 38 years; and 75% of cases occur in adults.

D. Childhood Cushing's Syndrome: Cushing's syndrome in childhood and adolescence is distinctly unusual; however, in contrast to the incidence in adults, adrenal carcinoma is the most frequent cause (51%), and adrenal adenomas are present in 14%. These tumors are more common in girls than in boys, and most occur between the ages of 1 and 8 years.

Cushing's disease is more common in the adolescent population and accounts for 35% of cases; most of these patients are over 10 years of age at diagnosis, and the sex incidence is equal.

Pathology

A. Anterior Pituitary Gland:

1. Pituitary adenomas– Pituitary adenomas are present in over 90% of patients with Cushing's disease. These tumors are typically smaller than those secreting GH or PRL; 80–90% are less than 10 mm in diameter. A small group of patients have larger tumors (> 10 mm); these macroadenomas are frequently invasive, leading to extension outside the sella turcica. Malignant pituitary tumors occur rarely.

Microadenomas are located within the anterior pituitary; they are not encapsulated but surrounded by a rim of compressed normal anterior pituitary cells. With routine histologic stains, these tumors are composed of compact sheets of well-granulated basophilic cells in a sinusoidal arrangement. ACTH, β-LPH, and β-endorphin have been demonstrated in these tumor cells by immunocytochemical methods. Larger tumors may appear chromophobic on routine histologic study; however, they also contain ACTH and its related peptides. These ACTH-secreting adenomas typically show Crooke's changes (a zone of perinuclear hyalinization that is the result of chronic exposure of corticotroph cells to hypercortisolism). Electron microscopy demonstrates secretory granules that vary in size from 200 to 700 nm. The number of granules varies in individual cells; they may be dispersed throughout the cytoplasm or concentrated along the cell membrane. A typical feature of these adenomas is the presence of bundles of perinuclear microfilaments (average 7 nm in diameter) surrounding the nucleus; these are responsible for Crooke's hyaline changes visible on light microscopy.

2. Hyperplasia– Diffuse hyperplasia of corticotroph cells has been reported rarely in patients with Cushing's disease. These cases may be the consequence of excessive stimulation of the anterior pituitary by CRH.

3. Other conditions– In patients with adrenal tumors or ectopic ACTH syndrome, the pituitary corticotrophs show prominent Crooke hyaline changes and perinuclear microfilaments. The ACTH content of corticotroph cells is reduced consistent with their suppression by excessive cortisol secretion present in these conditions.

B. Adrenocortical Hyperplasia: Bilateral hyperplasia of the adrenal cortex occurs with chronic ACTH hypersecretion. Three types have been described: simple, that associated with ectopic ACTH syndrome, and bilateral nodular hyperplasia.

1. Simple adrenocortical hyperplasia– This condition is usually due to Cushing's disease. Combined adrenal weight (normal, 8–10 g) is modestly increased, ranging from 12 to 24 g. On histologic study, there is equal hyperplasia of the compact cells of the zona reticularis and the clear cells of the zona fasciculata; consequently, the width of the cortex is increased. Electron microscopy reveals normal ultrastructural features.

2. Ectopic ACTH syndrome– In this disorder, the adrenals are frequently markedly enlarged; combined weights range from 24 g to more than 50 g. The characteristic microscopic feature is marked hyperplasia of the zona reticularis; columns of compact reticularis cells expand throughout the zona fasciculata and into the zona glomerulosa. The zona fasciculata clear cells are markedly reduced.

3. Bilateral nodular hyperplasia– Macronodular hyperplasia occurs in about 20% of cases of adrenocortical hyperplasia. The exact pathogenesis of this lesion is unclear; most cases appear to be secondary to pituitary ACTH excess, but in a minority of cases there may be autonomous function of the adrenals. The adrenals are enlarged; adrenal weight is increased and may be markedly so if large nodules are present. Grossly, there are multiple nodules of various sizes within the adrenal cortices, with widening of the intervening cortex. The nodules are typically yellow and on histologic examination resemble the clear cells of the normal zona fasciculata. The adrenal cortex not involved by the nodules shows the histologic features of simple adrenocortical hyperplasia (see above). Occasionally, large nodules become semiautonomous. Adrenal carcinoma in association with nodular hyperplasia has been described in a few patients. Micronodular hyperplasia occurs less frequently. Both adrenals are involved, and there are multiple small nodules that may be pigmented; the intervening cortex is atrophic. The pathogenesis of this lesion appears to involve an anti-ACTH receptor antibody. This disorder presents at a younger age. It may be familial and may also occur in association with cardiac myxomas, spotty pigmented lesions of the skin, and other endocrine disorders such as growth hormone-producing pituitary tumors.

C. Adrenal Tumors: Adrenal tumors causing Cushing's syndrome are independent of ACTH secretion and are either adenomas or carcinomas.

1. Glucocorticoid-secreting adrenal adenomas– These adenomas are encapsulated, weigh 10–70 g, and range in size from 1 cm to 6 cm. Microscopically, clear cells of the zona fasciculata type predominate, although cells typical of the zona reticularis are also seen.

2. Adrenal carcinomas– Adrenal carcinomas usually weigh over 100 g and may exceed several kilograms. Thus, they are commonly palpable as abdominal masses. Grossly, they are encapsulated and highly vascular; necrosis, hemorrhage, and cystic degeneration are common, and areas of calcification may be present. The histologic appearance of these carcinomas varies considerably; they may appear to be benign or may exhibit considerable pleomor-

phism. Vascular or capsular invasion is predictive of malignant behavior, as is local extension. These carcinomas invade local structures (kidney, liver, and retroperitoneum) and metastasize hematogenously to liver and lung.

3. Uninvolved adrenal cortex– The cortex contiguous to the tumor and that of the contralateral gland are atrophic in the presence of functioning adrenal adenomas and carcinomas. The cortex is markedly thinned, whereas the capsule is thickened. Histologically, the zona reticularis is virtually absent; the remaining cortex is composed of clear fasciculata cells. The architecture of the zona glomerulosa is normal.

Etiology & Pathogenesis

A. Cushing's Disease: The causes and natural history of Cushing's disease are reviewed in Chapter 2. Current evidence is consistent with the view that spontaneously arising corticotroph-cell pituitary adenomas are the primary cause and that the consequent ACTH hypersecretion and hypercortisolism lead to the characteristic endocrine abnormalities and hypothalamic dysfunction. This is supported by evidence showing that selective removal of these adenomas by pituitary microsurgery reverses the abnormalities and is followed by return of the hypothalamic-pituitary-adrenal axis to normal.

Although these primary pituitary adenomas are responsible for the great majority of cases, a few patients have been described in whom pituitary disease has been limited to corticotroph-cell hyperplasia; these may be secondary to excessive CRH secretion by rare, benign hypothalamic gangliocytoma.

B. Ectopic ACTH Syndrome: This syndrome arises when nonpituitary tumors synthesize and hypersecrete biologically active ACTH. The related peptides β-LPH and β-endorphin are also synthesized and secreted, as are inactive ACTH fragments. Production of CRH has also been demonstrated in ectopic tumors secreting ACTH, but whether CRH plays a role in pathogenesis is unclear. A few cases in which nonpituitary tumors produced only CRH have been reported.

Ectopic ACTH syndrome occurs predominantly in only a few tumor types (Table 6–9); small-cell carcinoma of the lung causes half of cases. Other tumors

Table 6–9. Tumors causing the ectopic ACTH syndrome.[1]

Small cell carcinoma of the lung (50% of cases)
Pancreatic islet cell tumors
Carcinoid tumors (lung, thymus, gut, pancreas, ovary)
Medullary carcinoma of the thyroid
Pheochromocytoma and related tumors

[1] Modified and reproduced, with permission, from Baxter JD, Tyrrell JB, in: *Endocrinology and Metabolism.* Felig P et al (editors). 2nd Ed. McGraw-Hill, 1987.

causing the syndrome are carcinoid tumors of lung, thymus, gut, pancreas, or ovary; pancreatic islet cell tumors; medullary thyroid carcinoma; and pheochromocytoma and related tumors. Other rare miscellaneous tumor types have also been reported (see Chapter 20).

C. Adrenal Tumors: Glucocorticoid-producing adrenal adenomas and carcinomas arise spontaneously. They are not under hypothalamic-pituitary control and autonomously secrete adrenocortical steroids. Rarely, adrenal carcinomas develop in the setting of chronic ACTH hypersecretion in patients with either Cushing's disease and nodular adrenal hyperplasia or congenital adrenal hyperplasia.

Pathophysiology

A. Cushing's Disease: In Cushing's disease, ACTH hypersecretion is random and episodic and causes cortisol hypersecretion with absence of the normal circadian rhythm. Feedback inhibition of ACTH (secreted from the pituitary adenoma) by physiologic levels of glucocorticoids is absent; thus, ACTH hypersecretion persists despite elevated cortisol secretion and results in chronic glucocorticoid excess. The episodic secretion of ACTH and cortisol results in variable plasma levels that may at times be within the normal range. However, measurement of the cortisol production rate, urine free cortisol, or sampling of multiple cortisol levels over 24 hours confirms cortisol hypersecretion (see sections on laboratory evaluation and diagnosis of Cushing's syndrome). In addition, because of the absence of diurnal variability, plasma ACTH and cortisol remain elevated throughout the day and night. This overall increase in glucocorticoid secretion causes the clinical manifestations of Cushing's syndrome; however, ACTH and β-LPH secretion are not usually elevated sufficiently to cause hyperpigmentation.

1. Abnormalities of ACTH secretion– Despite ACTH hypersecretion, stress responsiveness is absent; stimuli such as hypoglycemia or surgery fail to further elevate ACTH and cortisol secretion. This is probably due to suppression of hypothalamic function and CRH secretion by hypercortisolism, resulting in loss of hypothalamic control of ACTH secretion (see Chapter 2).

2. Effect of cortisol excess– Cortisol excess not only inhibits normal pituitary and hypothalamic function, affecting ACTH, thyrotropin, GH, and gonadotropin release, but also results in all the systemic effects of glucocorticoid excess described in previous sections and in the section on clinical features below.

3. Androgen excess– Secretion of adrenal androgens is also increased in Cushing's disease, and the degree of androgen excess parallels that of ACTH and cortisol. Thus, plasma levels of DHEA, DHEA sulfate, and androstenedione may be moderately elevated in Cushing's disease; the peripheral conversion of these hormones to testosterone and dihydrotestosterone leads to androgen excess. In women, this causes hirsutism, acne, and amenorrhea. In men with Cushing's disease, cortisol suppression of LH secretion decreases testosterone secretion by the testis, resulting in decreased libido and impotence. The increased adrenal androgen secretion is insufficient to compensate for the decreased gonadal testosterone production.

B. Ectopic ACTH Syndrome: Hypersecretion of ACTH and cortisol is usually greater in patients with ectopic ACTH syndrome than in those with Cushing's disease. ACTH and cortisol hypersecretion is randomly episodic, and the levels are often greatly elevated. With few exceptions, ACTH secretion by ectopic tumors is not subject to negative-feedback control; ie, secretion of ACTH and cortisol is nonsuppressible with pharmacologic doses of glucocorticoids (see section on diagnosis).

Plasma levels, secretion rates, and urinary excretion of cortisol, the adrenal androgens, and DOC are often markedly elevated; despite this, the typical features of Cushing's syndrome are usually absent, presumably because of rapid onset of hypercortisolism, anorexia, and other manifestations of the associated malignant disease. However, features of mineralocorticoid excess (hypertension and hypokalemia) are frequently due to DOC and the mineralocorticoid effects of cortisol.

C. Adrenal Tumors:

1. Autonomous secretion– Primary adrenal tumors, both adenomas and carcinomas, autonomously hypersecrete cortisol. Circulating plasma ACTH levels are suppressed, resulting in cortical atrophy of the uninvolved adrenal. Secretion is randomly episodic, and these tumors are typically unresponsive to manipulation of the hypothalamic-pituitary axis with pharmacologic agents such as dexamethasone and metyrapone.

2. Adrenal adenomas- Adrenal adenomas causing Cushing's syndrome typically present solely with clinical manifestations of glucocorticoid excess, since they usually secrete only cortisol. Thus, the presence of androgen or mineralocorticoid excess should suggest that the tumor is an adrenocortical carcinoma.

3. Adrenal carcinomas- Adrenal carcinomas frequently hypersecrete multiple adrenocortical steroids and their precursors. Cortisol and androgens are the steroids most frequently secreted in excess; 11-deoxycortisol is often elevated, and there may be increased secretion of DOC, aldosterone, or estrogens. Plasma cortisol, urine free cortisol, and urine 17-hydroxycorticosteroids are often markedly increased; androgen excess is usually even greater than that of cortisol. Thus, high levels of plasma DHEA and DHEA sulfate and of urinary 17-ketosteroids typically accompany the cortisol excess. Clinical manifestations of hypercortisolism are usually severe and rapidly progressive in these patients. In women, features of androgen excess are prominent; virilism may occasionally occur. Hypertension and hypokalemia are frequent and most commonly result from the mineralocorticoid effects of cortisol; less frequently, DOC and aldosterone hypersecretion also contribute.

Clinical Features
(Table 6–10)
A. Symptoms and Signs:

1. Obesity– Obesity is the most common manifestation, and weight gain is usually the initial symptom. It is classically central, affecting mainly the face, neck, trunk, and abdomen, with relative sparing of the extremities. Generalized obesity with central accentuation is equally common, particularly in children.

Accumulation of fat in the face leads to the typical "moon facies," which is present in 75% of cases and is accompanied by facial plethora in most patients. Fat accumulation around the neck is prominent in the supraclavicular and dorsocervical fat pads; the latter is responsible for the "buffalo hump."

Obesity is absent in a handful of patients who do not gain weight; however, they usually have central redistribution of fat and a typical facial appearance.

2. Skin changes– Skin changes are frequent, and their presence should arouse a suspicion of cortisol excess. Atrophy of the epidermis and its underlying connective tissue leads to thinning (a transparent appearance of the skin) and facial plethora. Easy bruisability following minimal trauma is present in about 40%. Striae occur in 50–70%; these are typically red to purple, depressed below the skin surface secondary to loss of underlying connective tissue, and

wider (not infrequently 0.5–2 cm) than the pinkish white striae that may occur with pregnancy or rapid weight gain. These striae are most commonly abdominal but may also occur over the breasts, hips, buttocks, thighs, and axillae.

Minor wounds and abrasions may heal slowly, and surgical incisions sometimes undergo dehiscence.

Mucocutaneous fungal infections are frequent, including tinea versicolor, involvement of the nails (onychomycosis), and oral candidiasis.

Hyperpigmentation of the skin is rare in Cushing's disease or adrenal tumors but is common in ectopic ACTH syndrome.

3. Hirsutism– Hirsutism is present in about 80% of female patients owing to hypersecretion of adrenal androgens. Facial hirsutism is most common, but increased hair growth may also occur over the abdomen, breasts, chest, and upper thighs. Acne and seborrhea usually accompany hirsutism. Virilism is unusual except in cases of adrenal carcinoma, in which it occurs in about 20%.

4. Hypertension– Hypertension is a classic feature of spontaneous Cushing's syndrome; it is present in about 75% of cases, and the diastolic blood pressure is greater than 100 mm Hg in over 50%. Hypertension and its complications contribute greatly to the morbidity and mortality rates in spontaneous Cushing's syndrome; in the series of Plotz et al, 40% of those dying with the syndrome did so as a direct result of hypertension or atherosclerosis.

5. Gonadal dysfunction– This is very common as a result of elevated androgens (in females) and cortisol (in males and to a lesser extent in females). Amenorrhea occurs in 75% of premenopausal women and is usually accompanied by infertility. Decreased libido is frequent in males, and some have decreased body hair and soft testes.

6. Psychologic disturbances– Psychologic disturbances occur in the majority of patients. Mild symptoms consist of emotional lability and increased irritability. Anxiety, depression, poor concentration, and poor memory may also be present. Euphoria is frequent, and occasional patients manifest overtly manic behavior. Sleep disorders are present in most patients, with either insomnia or early morning awakening.

Severe psychologic disorders occur in a few patients and include severe depression, psychosis with delusions or hallucinations, and paranoia. Some patients have committed suicide.

7. Muscle weakness– This occurs in about 60% of cases; it is more often proximal and is usually most prominent in the lower extremities.

8. Osteoporosis– Osteoporosis is present in most patients; back pain is an initial complaint in 58% of cases. Pathologic fractures occur in severe cases involving the ribs and vertebral bodies. Compression fractures of the spine are demonstrable radiographically in 16–22%.

Table 6–10. Clinical features of Cushing's syndrome.[1]

	Percent
Obesity	94
Facial plethora	84
Hirsutism	82
Menstrual disorders	76
Hypertension	72
Muscular weakness	58
Back pain	58
Striae	52
Acne	40
Psychologic symptoms	40
Bruising	36
Congestive heart failure	22
Edema	18
Renal calculi	16
Headache	14
Polyuria-polydipsia	10
Hyperpigmentation	6

[1] Reproduced, with permission, from Baxter JD, Tyrrell JB, in: *Endocrinology and Metabolism.* Felig P et al (editors). 2nd Ed. McGraw-Hill, 1987.

9. Renal calculi– Calculi secondary to glucocorticoid-induced hypercalciuria occur in approximately 15% of patients, and renal colic may occasionally be a presenting complaint.

10. Thirst and polyuria– Thirst and polyuria secondary to overt hyperglycemia and diabetes mellitus occur in about 10% of patients, whereas asymptomatic glucose intolerance is much more frequent. Diabetic ketoacidosis is rare, as are diabetic microvascular complications.

B. Laboratory Findings: Routine laboratory examinations are described here. Specific diagnostic tests to establish the diagnosis of Cushing's syndrome are discussed in the section on diagnosis.

High normal hemoglobin, hematocrit, and red cell counts are usual; polycythemia is rare. The total white count is usually normal; however, both the percentage of lymphocytes and the total lymphocyte count may be subnormal. Eosinophils are also depressed, and a total eosinophil count less than 100/μL is present in most patients. Serum electrolytes, with rare exceptions, are normal in Cushing's disease; however, hypokalemic alkalosis occurs when there is marked steroid hypersecretion with the ectopic ACTH syndrome or adrenocortical carcinoma.

Fasting hyperglycemia or clinical diabetes occurs in only 10–15% of patients; postprandial hyperglycemia is more common. Glycosuria is present in patients with fasting or postprandial hyperglycemia. Most patients have secondary hyperinsulinemia and abnormal glucose tolerance tests.

Serum calcium is normal; serum phosphorus is low normal or slightly depressed. Hypercalciuria is present in 40% of cases.

C. Imaging Studies: Routine radiographs may reveal cardiomegaly due to hypertensive or atherosclerotic heart disease. Vertebral compression fractures, rib fractures, and renal calculi may be present.

D. Electrocardiographic Findings: Hypertensive, ischemic, and electrolyte-induced changes may be present on the ECG.

Features Suggesting a Specific Cause

A. Cushing's Disease: Cushing's disease typifies the classic clinical picture: female predominance, onset generally between ages 20 and 40, and a slow progression over several years. Hyperpigmentation and hypokalemic alkalosis are rare; androgenic manifestations are limited to acne and hirsutism. Secretion of cortisol and adrenal androgens is only moderately increased.

B. Ectopic ACTH Syndrome (Carcinoma): In contrast, this syndrome occurs predominantly in males, with the highest incidence between ages 40 and 60. The clinical manifestations of hypercortisolism are frequently limited to weakness, hypertension, and glucose intolerance; the primary tumor is usually apparent. Hyperpigmentation, hypokalemia, and alkalosis are common, as are weight loss and anemia. The hypercortisolism is of rapid onset, and steroid hypersecretion is frequently severe, with equally elevated levels of glucocorticoids, androgens, and DOC.

C. Ectopic ACTH Syndrome (Benign Tumor): A minority of patients with ectopic ACTH syndrome due to more "benign" tumors, especially bronchial carcinoids, present a more slowly progressive course, with typical features of Cushing's syndrome. These patients may be clinically identical with those having pituitary-dependent Cushing's disease, and the responsible tumor may not be apparent. Hyperpigmentation, hypokalemic alkalosis, and anemia are variably present. Further confusion may arise, since a number of these patients with occult ectopic tumors may have ACTH and steroid dynamics typical of Cushing's disease (see below).

D. Adrenal Adenomas: The clinical picture in patients with adrenal adenomas is usually that of glucocorticoid excess alone, and androgenic effects such as hirsutism are usually absent. Onset is gradual, and hypercortisolism is mild to moderate. Urinary 17-ketosteroids and plasma androgens are usually in the low normal or subnormal range.

E. Adrenal Carcinomas: In general, adrenal carcinomas have a rapid onset of the clinical features of excessive glucocorticoid, androgen, and mineralocorticoid secretion and are rapidly progressive. Marked elevations of both cortisol and androgens are usual; hypokalemia is common, as are abdominal pain, palpable masses, and hepatic and pulmonary metastases.

Diagnostic Procedures (Figure 6–13)

A. Diagnosis of Hypercortisolism (Cushing's Syndrome):

1. Overnight dexamethasone and urine free cortisol– Suspected hypercortisolism is investigated by means of the overnight 1-mg dexamethasone suppression test plus measurement of free cortisol in a 24-hour urine specimen collected on an outpatient basis. If the overnight suppression test is normal (plasma cortisol < 5 μg/dL [0.14 μmol/L]), the diagnosis is very unlikely; if the urine free cortisol is also normal, Cushing's syndrome is excluded.

If these two tests are abnormal, hypercortisolism is present and the diagnosis of Cushing's syndrome can be considered established if conditions causing false-positive responses are excluded (see discussion below).

2. Two-day low-dose dexamethasone test– In patients with equivocal or borderline results, a 2-day low-dose dexamethasone suppression test is performed. Normal responses to this test are 17-hydroxycorticosteroid levels less than 4 mg/24 h (11.2 μmol/24 h) (or 1 mg/g of creatinine [0.3 mmol/mol of creatinine]), free cortisol less than 25 μg/24 h (69 nmol/24 h), and plasma cortisol less than 5 μg/dL

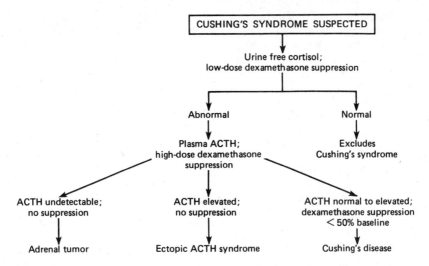

Figure 6–13. Diagnostic evaluation of Cushing's syndrome and procedures for determining the cause. Exceptions and diagnostic difficulties are discussed in the text. (Redrawn and reproduced, with permission, from Baxter JD, Tyrrell JB: The adrenal cortex. In: *Endocrinology and Metabolism.* Felig P et al [editors]. 2nd ed. McGraw-Hill, 1987.)

(0.14 μmol/L). A normal response excludes Cushing's syndrome, and abnormal suppressibility is consistent with the diagnosis, since the incidence of false-positive responses is negligible.

B. Differential Diagnosis of Hypercortisolism: A number of factors may complicate the diagnosis of Cushing's syndrome. These include both rare false-negative results in patients with Cushing's syndrome and, more commonly, false-positive results in those who do not have the disorder.

1. False-negative responses– False-negative results occur rarely in Cushing's syndrome. In these patients, normal suppression of glucocorticoid secretion with low-dose dexamethasone may be due to delayed clearance of dexamethasone and thus higher than usual plasma levels. However, elevated urine free cortisol will establish the diagnosis. Periodic or episodic hormonogenesis in Cushing's syndrome also makes diagnosis difficult. In these unusual patients, hypercortisolism may be cyclic, with regular periodicity of days to weeks, or irregularly episodic; thus, cortisol secretion may be normal or nearly so between cycles or episodes. With spontaneously varying cortisol secretion, adrenal function may be normal at times, and dexamethasone administration during phases of normal secretion may appear to reveal normal suppressibility. In these patients, repeated evaluation is required to establish the diagnosis.

2. False-positive responses– False-positive results are more common:

a. Acute or chronic illness– Especially in hospitalized patients, acute or chronic illness may appropriately elevate glucocorticoid secretion. Patients may have elevated plasma cortisol and urine free cortisol and are frequently nonsuppressible with the 1-mg overnight dexamethasone test. If Cushing's syndrome is suspected, diagnostic evaluation should be repeated when acute stress has resolved.

b. Obesity– Obesity is the most common differential problem in Cushing's syndrome. Urinary 17-hydroxycorticosteroids are often elevated; furthermore, about 15% of obese patients do not adequately suppress plasma cortisol in response to the 1-mg overnight dexamethasone suppression test. However, urine free cortisol excretion is normal in simple obesity, as is normal suppressibility of urine corticosteroids with the 2-day low-dose suppression test.

c. High-estrogen states– Pregnancy, estrogen therapy, and oral contraceptives increase CBG and thus elevate total plasma cortisol levels to 40–60 μg/dL (1.1–1.7 μmol/L). The overnight 1-mg suppression test may be abnormal; however, urine free cortisol is normal, and there is normal suppressibility of urine steroids with the 2-day low-dose test.

d. Drugs– Various drugs, especially phenytoin, phenobarbital, and primidone, cause false-positive low-dose dexamethasone tests; however, urine free cortisol is normal.

e. Alcoholism– A number of alcoholic patients have both clinical and biochemical features of Cushing's syndrome (alcohol-induced pseudo-Cushing's syndrome) with elevated basal plasma cortisol levels, abnormal diurnal variation, increased cortisol production rate, increased urinary corticosteroid excretion, and abnormal dexamethasone suppressibility. These abnormalities revert to normal following abstinence from alcohol.

f. Depression– Endogenous depression frequently causes increased cortisol secretion with elevated plasma levels, absence of diurnal variation, increased urine free cortisol, increased urine 17-hydroxycorticosteroids, and impaired dexamethasone suppressibility in the overnight dexamethasone test. The abnormal steroid dynamics revert to normal upon psychologic recovery. These patients can be differentiated from those with true Cushing's syndrome, since patients with depression alone maintain normal cortisol responsiveness to insulin-induced hypoglycemia, whereas patients with Cushing's syndrome do not. In addition, depressed patients usually maintain normal responses to the 2-day low-dose dexamethasone test.

C. Differential Diagnosis of Cushing's Syndrome: When Cushing's syndrome is present, pituitary ACTH hypersecretion (Cushing's disease) must be differentiated from ectopic ACTH syndrome and primary adrenal tumors.

1. Procedures– Measurement of basal plasma ACTH levels and high-dose dexamethasone suppres-

sion testing (see Laboratory Evaluation, above) will establish the correct diagnosis in most instances, though exceptions are common.

2. Results–

a. Cushing's disease– Patients with Cushing's disease have normal to modestly elevated plasma ACTH levels (Figure 6–14), and the presence of detectable levels is consistent with bilateral adrenocortical hyperplasia. Plasma ACTH levels in Cushing's disease range from 40 to 200 pg/mL (8.8–44.4 pmol/L) and about 50% of patients have values consistently within the normal range. Patients with Cushing's disease characteristically maintain suppressibility of ACTH secretion; ie, cortisol secretion is suppressible to below 50% of basal levels with the high-dose dexamethasone tests.

b. Ectopic ACTH syndrome– In the ectopic ACTH syndrome, plasma ACTH levels are often markedly elevated (500–10,000 pg/mL [111–2222 pmol/L]) and are above 200 pg/mL (44.4 pmol/L) in 65% of patients. However, since at lower levels these overlap with the range seen in Cushing's disease, dexamethasone suppression testing must also be used. Since hypothalamic control of ACTH secretion is absent, cortisol secretion is classically not suppressible with high-dose dexamethasone. In addition, the primary tumor is clinically evident in most patients.

c. Adrenal tumors– Glucocorticoid-secreting adrenal tumors function autonomously, and the resulting suppression of the normal hypothalamic-pituitary axis leads to undetectable plasma ACTH levels (< 10 pg/mL [2.2 pmol/L]) and absent steroid suppression with high-dose dexamethasone.

3. Other tests– CRH testing in Cushing's syndrome reveals that the majority of patients with Cushing's disease respond to CRH, whereas those with ectopic ACTH syndrome do not. However, exceptions have already been reported in both entities, and thus the ultimate clinical utility of this procedure is not yet clear. Metyrapone testing and ACTH stimulation tests do not adequately distinguish the various causes of Cushing's syndrome and are of little diagnostic utility.

D. Problems in Making Etiologic Diagnoses:

1. Episodic hypercortisolism– Problems are encountered in rare patients with periodic, cyclic, or episodic hormonogenesis who may have either Cushing's disease, ectopic ACTH syndrome, or adrenal tumors. Variable responses to high-dose dexamethasone may be observed, and there may be apparent suppressibility if steroid secretion is declining spontaneously at the time of dexamethasone administration. When studied at other times, these patients may be nonsuppressible or even show paradoxic increases during high-dose dexamethasone treatment. Repeated evaluations and use of the localizing procedures described below may be necessary to establish the correct etiologic diagnosis in such patients.

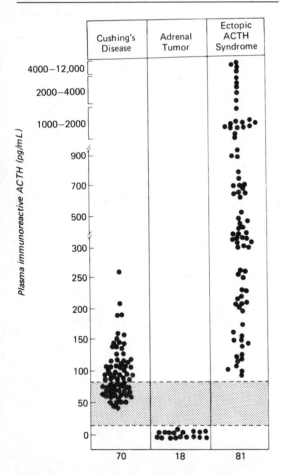

Figure 6–14. Basal plasma ACTH concentrations in patients with spontaneous Cushing's syndrome. (Reproduced, with permission, from Scott AP et al: Pituitary adrenocorticotropin and the melanocyte stimulating hormones. In: *Peptide Hormones.* Parsons JA [editor]. University Park Press, 1979.)

2. Nonsuppressible Cushing's disease and nodular adrenal hyperplasia– About 10–30% of patients with Cushing's disease fail to suppress urinary 17-hydroxycorticosteroids with the standard 2-day high-dose dexamethasone suppression test. This incidence of inadequate suppressibility is less with the overnight 8-mg high-dose dexamethasone suppression test, and the overnight test is therefore preferred. Nonsuppressible Cushing's disease may occur with large pituitary tumors; however, it is also seen in patients with microadenomas and in patients without an obvious pituitary adenoma in whom ACTH is measurable; these findings falsely suggest the ectopic ACTH syndrome.

In these patients, additional procedures are required. Higher doses of dexamethasone (16 or 32 mg) may be administered, and if steroid suppression is demonstrated, Cushing's disease is suggested. The diagnosis is confirmed by demonstration of the pituitary adenoma using high-resolution MRI or the demonstration of pituitary ACTH hypersecretion by selective venous sampling. (See section on tumor localization, below.)

Some of these nonsuppressible patients have macronodular adrenal hyperplasia, which is usually secondary to pituitary ACTH hypersecretion. This disorder frequently causes diagnostic difficulties, since about 75% of these patients are nonsuppressible with the standard 2-day high-dose dexamethasone suppression test. Plasma ACTH levels may be undetectable, normal, or elevated and may vary dramatically in the same patient. These patients should be evaluated with higher doses of dexamethasone (as described above) and pituitary localizing procedures to differentiate them from patients with either the ectopic ACTH syndrome or primary adrenal tumors. In addition, CT scanning of the adrenals may demonstrate nodular hyperplasia.

3. Ectopic ACTH syndrome– Although the ectopic ACTH syndrome is usually easily diagnosed by elevated ACTH levels and nonsuppressible steroid hypersecretion in the presence of an extrapituitary tumor, there are cases in which the tumor is occult, and in these, steroid secretion may be dexamethasone-suppressible and metyrapone-responsive. In addition, the tumor may not make its presence felt for a number of years following the onset of Cushing's syndrome. These occult tumors are usually carcinoids, and the plasma ACTH levels may be in the range of those seen with Cushing's disease. These findings may lead to a mistaken diagnosis of Cushing's disease and inappropriate pituitary therapy. Although it is not possible to make this differentiation with confidence in all cases, certain features should increase the suspicion of ectopic ACTH syndrome: male sex, rapid onset, severe hypercortisolism, hypokalemia, anemia, and weight loss. If ectopic ACTH syndrome is suspected but no tumor is obvious, selective venous ACTH sampling is helpful. Thus, the demonstration of a pituitary ACTH gradient establishes the diagnosis of Cushing's disease. In the absence of a pituitary gradient, ectopic ACTH syndrome is a likely diagnosis, and selective venous sampling may localize the ACTH-secreting ectopic tumor. If localization is not achieved by this method, additional diagnostic and radiologic procedures should be directed to the common sites of ACTH production, ie, the lungs, thymus, pancreas, thyroid, and adrenals.

E. Tumor Localization: The procedures described below are useful in the localization of tumors in Cushing's syndrome, but they should be preceded if possible by a definite biochemical diagnosis, since radiologic procedures may occasionally give misleading results. For example, nodular hyperplasia of the adrenals with a solitary or dominant nodule may be misinterpreted as an autonomous hyperfunctioning adenoma.

1. Neuroradiologic studies– In Cushing's disease, neuroradiologic procedures are used to localize the pituitary adenoma and to define sellar size, anatomy, and extrasellar tumor extension. (See also Chapter 2.)

a. Macroadenomas– In the 10% of patients with larger tumors (macroadenomas), MRI is used to document tumor size, suprasellar extension, lateral expansion, or the presence of a partially empty sella turcica.

b. Microadenomas– The problem of tumor localization in patients with Cushing's disease who have microadenomas has not been solved, necessitating a secure biochemical diagnosis. MRI is the current procedure of choice; however, because of the small size of pituitary adenomas in Cushing's disease, they are detected by current imaging methods in only about 50% of patients. Because of the high prevalence of incidental pituitary microadenomas, the specificity of the MRI procedure is less than 100%. Patients with ACTH-dependent Cushing's syndrome and normal imaging studies should undergo selective venous sampling (see Chapter 2 and below).

2. Selective venous sampling for ACTH determination– This procedure is used when the source of ACTH hypersecretion is in doubt, eg, in patients in whom biochemical data suggest Cushing's disease but MRI does not localize the tumor. This procedure is also very useful in those with suspected dexamethasone-nonsuppressible Cushing's disease, nodular adrenal hyperplasia, or an occult ectopic ACTH-secreting tumor, as discussed above. In these circumstances, venous sampling may establish the pituitary as the source of ACTH and in some cases will localize an ectopic tumor. ACTH samples are obtained from the inferior petrosal sinuses (a major site of venous drainage of the anterior pituitary), from the jugular venous bulb, and from other sites and are compared with simultaneous peripheral vein samples. In patients with Cushing's disease, ACTH levels are higher in the inferior petrosal sinus samples than in the peripheral vein samples (ratios usually > 2:1). In patients with ectopic ACTH syndrome, no inferior petrosal-to-peripheral ACTH gradient is demonstrable, but selective venous sampling may localize the ectopic tumor. Recent studies have established the superiority of this test when the ACTH response of CRH is measured during bilateral simultaneous inferior petrosal sinus sampling. Whether this test should be performed in all cases of ACTH-dependent Cushing's syndrome without an obvious cause is controversial.

3. Adrenal localizing procedures– CT scan (Figure 6–15), MRI, ultrasonography, and isotope scanning with iodocholesterol are used to define adrenal lesions. In patients with ACTH hypersecretion, these procedures exclude an adrenal tumor and confirm bilateral adrenal hyperplasia or nodular adrenal hyperplasia. These procedures also effectively localize adrenal tumors, since these tumors are usually over 2 cm in diameter. Invasive procedures such as arteriography and venography are rarely required.

Treatment

A. Cushing's Disease: The aim of treatment of Cushing's syndrome is to remove or destroy the basic lesion and thus correct hypersecretion of adrenal hormones without inducing pituitary or adrenal damage, which requires permanent replacement therapy for hormone deficiencies.

Treatment of Cushing's disease is currently directed at the pituitary to control ACTH hypersecretion; available methods include microsurgery, various forms of radiation therapy, and pharmacologic inhibition of ACTH secretion. Treatment of hypercortisolism per se by surgical or medical adrenalectomy is less commonly used. These methods are discussed in Chapter 2.

B. Ectopic ACTH Syndrome: Cure of ectopic ACTH syndrome is usually possible only in cases involving the more "benign" tumors such as bronchial or thymic carcinoids, or pheochromocytomas. Treatment is made difficult by the presence of metastatic malignant tumors and accompanying severe hypercortisolism. Therapy directed to the primary tumor is usually unsuccessful, and other means must be used to correct the steroid-excess state.

Severe hypokalemia may require potassium replacement in large doses and spironolactone to block mineralocorticoid effects.

Drugs that block steroid synthesis (ketoconazole, metyrapone, and aminoglutethimide) are useful, but they may produce hypoadrenalism, and steroid secretion must be monitored and replacement steroids given if necessary. The dosage of ketoconazole is 400–800 mg/d in divided doses and is usually well tolerated.

Because of its slow onset of action and its side ef-

fects, mitotane is less useful, and several weeks of therapy may be required to control cortisol secretion (see below).

Bilateral adrenalectomy is rarely required, but it may be necessary if hypercortisolism cannot otherwise be controlled.

C. Adrenal Tumors:

1. Adrenal adenomas– Patients with adrenal adenomas are successfully treated by unilateral adrenalectomy, and the outlook is excellent. Since the hypothalamic-pituitary axis and the contralateral adrenal are suppressed by prolonged cortisol secretion, these patients have postoperative adrenal insufficiency and require glucocorticoid therapy both during and following surgery until the remaining adrenal recovers.

2. Adrenal carcinomas– Therapy in cases of adrenocortical carcinoma is less satisfactory, since the tumor has frequently already metastasized (usually to the retroperitoneum, liver, and lungs) by the time the diagnosis is made.

a. Operative treatment– Surgical cure is rare, but excision serves to reduce the tumor mass and the degree of steroid hypersecretion. Persisting nonsuppressible steroid secretion in the immediate postoperative period indicates residual or metastatic tumor.

b. Medical treatment– Mitotane is the drug of choice. The dosage is 6–12 g/d orally in three or four divided doses. The dose must often be reduced because of side effects in 80% of patients (diarrhea, nausea and vomiting, depression, somnolence). About 70% of patients achieve a reduction of steroid secretion, but only 35% achieve a reduction in tumor size. Since mitotane reduces urinary 17-hydroxycorticosteroid excretion by altering the hepatic metabolism of cortisol, these patients require follow-up by plasma cortisol or urine free cortisol assays.

Ketoconazole, metyrapone, or aminoglutethimide (singly or in combination) are useful in controlling steroid hypersecretion in patients who do not respond to mitotane.

Radiotherapy and conventional chemotherapy have not been useful in this disease.

D. Nodular Adrenal Hyperplasia: When pituitary ACTH dependency can be demonstrated, macronodular hyperplasia may be treated like other cases of Cushing's disease. When ACTH dependency is not present, as in micronodular hyperplasia and in some cases of macronodular hyperplasia, bilateral adrenalectomy is appropriate.

Prognosis

A. Cushing's Syndrome: Untreated Cushing's syndrome is frequently fatal, and death may be due to the underlying tumor itself, as in the ectopic ACTH syndrome and adrenal carcinoma. However, in many cases, death is the consequence of sustained hypercortisolism and its complications, including hypertension, cardiovascular disease, stroke, throm-

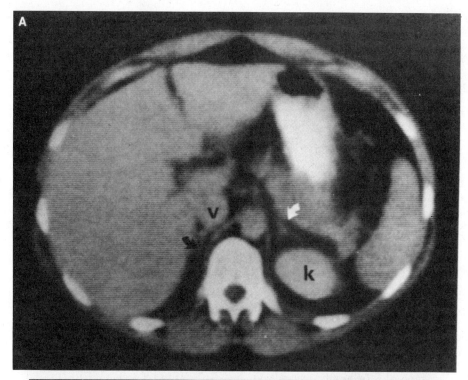

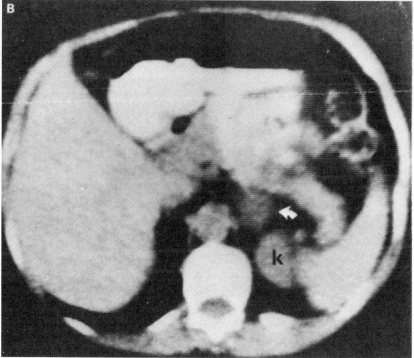

Figure 6–15. Adrenal CT scans in Cushing's syndrome. **A:** Patient with ACTH-dependent Cushing's syndrome. The adrenal glands are not detectably abnormal by this procedure. The curvilinear right adrenal (black arrow) is shown posterior to the inferior vena cava (V) between the right lobe of the liver and the right crus of the diaphragm. The left adrenal (white arrow) has an inverted Y appearance anteromedial to the left kidney (K). **B:** A 3-cm left adrenal adenoma (white arrow) is shown anteromedial to the left kidney (K). (Reproduced, with permission, from Korobkin MT et al: Computed tomography in the diagnosis of adrenal disease. Am J Roentgenol 1979;132:231.)

boembolism, and susceptibility to infection. In older series, 50% of patients died within 5 years after onset.

B. Cushing's Disease: With current refinements in pituitary microsurgery and heavy particle irradiation, the great majority of patients with Cushing's disease can be treated successfully, and the operative mortality and morbidity rates that attended bilateral adrenalectomy are no longer a feature of the natural history of this disease. Survival in these patients is considerably longer than in older series. However, survival is still less than that of age-matched controls; the increased mortality rate is due to cardiovascular causes. Patients with Cushing's disease who have large pituitary tumors at the time of diagnosis have a much less satisfactory prognosis and may die as a consequence of tumor invasion or persisting hypercortisolism.

C. Adrenal Tumors: The prognosis in adrenal adenomas is excellent. In adrenal carcinoma, the prognosis is almost universally poor, and the median survival from the date of onset of symptoms is about 4 years.

D. Ectopic ACTH Syndrome: Prognosis is also poor in patients with ectopic ACTH syndrome due to malignant tumors, and in these patients with severe hypercortisolism, survival is frequently only days to weeks. Some patients respond to tumor resection or chemotherapy. The prognosis is better in patients with benign tumors producing the ectopic ACTH syndrome.

HIRSUTISM & VIRILISM

Excessive adrenal or ovarian secretion of androgens or excessive conversion of androgens in peripheral tissues leads to hirsutism and virilism (see Chapter 10). As previously discussed, the adrenal secretory products DHEA, DHEA sulfate, and androstenedione are weak androgens; however, the peripheral conversion to testosterone and dihydrotestosterone can result in a state of androgen excess.

Excessive androgen production is seen in both adrenal and ovarian disorders. Adrenal causes include Cushing's syndrome, adrenal carcinoma, and congenital adrenal hyperplasia (see previous sections and Chapter 11). Mild adult-onset cases of congenital adrenal enzyme deficiencies have been described; these appear to be relatively uncommon. Biochemical diagnosis of late-onset 21-hydroxylase deficiency is best achieved by measurement of the 17-hydroxyprogesterone response to ACTH. Ovarian causes are discussed in Chapter 10.

In children, androgen excess is usually due to congenital adrenal hyperplasia or adrenal carcinoma. In women, hirsutism accompanied by amenorrhea, infertility, ovarian enlargement, and elevated plasma LH levels is typical of the polycystic ovary syndrome, whereas in Cushing's syndrome hirsutism is accompanied by features of cortisol excess. Late-onset 21-hydroxylase deficiency is accompanied by elevated levels of plasma 17-hydroxyprogesterone. Virilism and severe androgen excess in adults are usually due to androgen-secreting adrenal or ovarian tumors; virilism is unusual in the polycystic ovary syndrome and rare in Cushing's disease. In the absence of these syndromes, hirsutism in women is usually idiopathic or due to milder forms of polycystic ovary syndrome.

The diagnosis and therapy of hirsutism are discussed in Chapter 10.

INCIDENTALLY DISCOVERED ADRENAL MASSES

Unsuspected adrenal masses have been identified in 0.6–2% of abdominal CT scans. These tumors, "incidentalomas," vary in diameter from 0.5 cm to more than 6 cm. Unilateral masses may represent adrenal cortical neoplasms (benign or malignant), metastases, cysts, pheochromocytomas, or myelolipomas. Extensive hormonal screening to determine whether the lesions produce glucocorticoids, mineralocorticoids, sex steroids, or catecholamines has been recommended by many authors. However, benign and clinically silent adrenocortical masses are found frequently at autopsy, and occult adrenal carcinoma is rare. Most authors recommend removal of all functional (eg, hormone-producing) lesions and all masses greater than 3–6 cm in diameter. For nonfunctional lesions smaller than 3 cm (and for some between 3 cm and 6 cm), follow-up with serial CT scan is appropriate, with surgical removal of enlarging lesions.

REFERENCES

General
Baxter JD, Tyrrell JB: The adrenal cortex. In: *Endocrinology and Metabolism,* 2nd ed. Felig P et al (editors). McGraw-Hill, 1987.
James VHT (editor): *The Adrenal Gland,* 2nd ed. Raven Press, 1992.

Milgrom E: Steroid hormones. In: *Hormones: From Molecules to Disease.* Baulieu E-E, Kelly PA (editors). Chapman & Hall, 1990.
Orth DN, Kovacs WJ, DeBold CR: The adrenal cortex. In: *Williams Textbook of Endocrinology,* 8th ed. Wilson JD, Foster DW (editors). Saunders, 1992.

Embryology & Anatomy

McNicol AM: Aspects of structure, function and pathology. In: *The Adrenal Gland,* 2nd ed. James VHT (editor). Raven Press, 1992.

Neville AM, O'Hare MJ: Histopathology of the human adrenal cortex. Clin Endocrinol Metab 1985;14:791.

Saeger W et al: Ultrastructural morphometry of normal adrenal cortex and of hyperplastic adrenals in Cushing's disease. Endocr Pathol 1991;2:40.

Voutilainen R, Miller WL: Developmental and hormonal regulation of mRNAs for insulin-like growth factor II and steroidogenic enzymes in human fetal adrenals and gonads. DNA 1988;7:9.

Biosynthesis, Circulation, & Metabolism of Cortisol & Adrenal Androgens

Ballard PL: Delivery and transport of glucocorticoids to target cells. In: *Glucocorticoid Hormone Action.* Baxter JD, Rousseau GG (editors). Springer-Verlag, 1979.

Brownie AC: The metabolism of adrenal cortical steroids. In: *The Adrenal Gland,* 2nd ed. James VHT (editor). Raven Press, 1992.

Brown MS et al: Receptor-mediated uptake of lipoprotein-cholesterol and its utilization for steroid synthesis in the adrenal cortex. Recent Prog Horm Res 1979;35:215.

Buckingham JC, Smith T, Loxley HD: Control of adrenocortical hormone secretion. In: *The Adrenal Gland,* 2nd ed. James VHT (editor). Raven Press, 1992.

Fraser R: Biosynthesis of adrenocortical steroids. In: *The Adrenal Gland,* 2nd ed. James VHT (editor). Raven Press, 1992.

Gill GN: Biosynthesis, secretion and metabolism of hormones. In: *Endocrinology and Metabolism,* 2nd ed. Felig P et al (editors). McGraw-Hill, 1987.

Hale AC, Rees LH: ACTH and related peptides. In: *Endocrinology,* 2nd ed. DeGroot LJ et al (editors). Saunders, 1989.

Kawamoto T et al: Role of steroid 11β-hydroxylase and steroid 18-hydroxylase in the biosynthesis of glucocorticoids and mineralocorticoids. Proc Natl Acad Sci 1992;89:1458.

Keller-Wood ME, Dallman MF: Corticosteroid inhibition of ACTH secretion. Endocr Rev 1984;5:1.

Malee MP, Mellon SH: Zone-specific regulation of two messenger RNAs for P450cll in the adrenals of pregnant and non pregnant rats. Proc Natl Acad Sci 1991; 88:4731.

Meikle AW, Daynes RA, Araneo BA: Adrenal androgen secretion and biologic effects. Endocrinol Metab Clin North Am 1991;20:381.

Miller, WL: Molecular biology of steroid hormone synthesis. Endocr Rev 1988;9:295.

Parker LN: Control of adrenal androgen secretion. Endocrinol Metab Clin North Am 1991;20:401.

Reed MJ, James VHT: Regulation of steroid synthesis and metabolism by growth factors. Clin Endocrinol 1989;31:511.

Rosner W: Plasma steroid-binding proteins. Endocrinol Metab Clin North Am 1991;20:697.

Sapolsky R et al: Interleukin 1 stimulates the secretion of hypothalamic corticotropin-releasing factor. Science 1987;238:522.

Taylor, AL, Fishman LM: Corticotropin-releasing hormone. N Engl J Med 1988;319:213.

Biologic Effects

Baulieu E-E: The steroid hormone antagonist RU486: Mechanism at the cellular level and clinical applications. Endocrinol Metab Clin North Am 1991;20:873.

Baxter JD: Minimizing the side effects of glucocorticoid therapy. Adv Intern Med 1990;35:173.

Berdanier CD: Role of glucocorticoids in the regulation of lipogenesis. FASEB J 1989;3:2179.

Blalock JE: A molecular basis for bidirectional communication between the immune and neuroendocrine systems. Physiol Rev 1989;69:1.

Blalock JE: New concepts in endocrinology: Neuroendocrine and immune system interactions. In: *Yearbook of Endocrinology.* Yearbook, 1987.

Block NE, Buse MG: Effects of hypercortisolemia and diabetes on skeletal muscle insulin receptor function in vitro and in vivo. Am J Physiol 1989;256(Endocrinol Metab 19):E39.

Bowes SB et al: Glucose metabolism in patients with Cushing's syndrome. Clin Endocrinol 1991;34:311.

Brandon DD et al: Glucocorticoid resistance in humans and nonhuman primates. Cancer Res 1989;49(Suppl): 2203S.

Busbridge NJ, Grossman AB: Stress and the single cytokine; interleukin modulation of the pituitary-adrenal axis. Mol Cell Endocrinol 1991;82:C209.

Chrousos GP et al: Glucocorticoids and glucocorticoid antagonists: Lessons from RU 486. Kidney Int 1988; 34 (Suppl 26):S18.

Chrousos GP et al: Primary cortisol resistance in man: A glucocorticoid receptor-mediated disease. J Clin Invest 1982;69:1261.

Demitrack MA et al: Evidence for impaired activation of the hypothalamic-pituitary-adrenal axis in patients with chronic fatigue syndrome. J Clin Endocrinol Metab 1991;73:1224.

Evans RM: The steroid and thyroid hormone receptor superfamily. Science 1988;240:889.

Farese RV Jr et al: Licorice-induced hypermineralocorticoidism. N Engl J Med 1991;325:1223.

Findling JW et al: Vitamin D metabolites and parathyroid hormone in Cushing's syndrome: Relationship to calcium and phosphorus homeostasis. J Clin Endocrinol Metab 1982;54:1039.

Funder JW et al: Apparent mineralocorticoid excess, pseudohypoaldosteronism, and urinary electrolyte excretion: Toward a redefinition of mineralocorticoid action. FASEB J 1990;4:3234.

Horber FF, Haymond MW: Human growth hormone prevents the protein catabolic side effects of prednisone in humans. J Clin Invest 1990;86:265.

Hyams JS, Carey DE: Corticosteroids and growth. J Pediatr 1988;133:249.

Imura H, Fukata J-I, Mori T: Cytokines and endocrine function: An interaction between the immune and neuroendocrine systems. Clin Endocrinol 1991;35:107.

Joseph-Vanderpool JR et al: Abnormal pituitary-adrenal responses to corticotropin-releasing hormone in patients with seasonal affective disorders: Clinical and pathophysiological implications. J Clin Endocrinol Metab 1991;72:1382.

Katt KJ: Molecular mechanisms of hormone action: Control of target-cell function by peptide, thyroid and steroid hormones. In: *Endocrinology and Metabolism,* 2nd ed. Felig P et al (editors). McGraw-Hill, 1987.

King RJB: Effects of steroid hormones and related compounds on gene transcription. Clin Endocrinol 1992;36:1.

Lacomis D, Samuels MA: Adverse neurologic effects of glucocorticosteroids. J Gen Intern Med 1991;6:367.

Lukert BP, Raisz LG: Glucocorticoid-induced osteoporosis: pathogenesis and management. Ann Intern Med 1990;112:352.

Malerbi D et al: Glucocorticoids and glucose metabolism: Hepatic glucose production in untreated Addisonian patients and on two different levels of glucocorticoid administration. Clin Endocrinol 1988;28:415.

Munch A, Guyre PM, Holbrook NJ: Physiologic functions of glucocorticoids in stress and their relation to pharmacological actions. Endocr Rev 1984; 5:25.

Oikarinen AI, Vitto J, Oikarinen J: Glucocorticoid action on connective tissue: From molecular mechanisms to clinical practice. Med Biol 1986;64:221.

Page R et al: Insulin secretion, insulin sensitivity and glucose-mediated glucose disposal in Cushing's disease: A minimal model analysis. Clin Endocrinol 1991:35:509.

Sakaue M, Hoffman BB: Glucocorticoids induce transcription and expression of the alpha$_1$ β-adrenergic receptor gene in DTT1 MF-2 smooth muscle cells. J Clin Invest 1991:88:385.

Stuck AE, Minder CE, Frey FJ: Risk of infectious complications in patients taking glucocorticoids. Rev Inf Dis 1989;11:954.

Tyrrell JB, Baxter JD: Glucocorticoid therapy. In: *Endocrinology and Metabolism,* 2nd ed. Felig P et al (editors). McGraw-Hill, 1987.

Udelsman R et al: Adaptation during surgical stress: a reevaluation of the role of glucocorticoids. J Clin Invest 1986; 77:1377.

Ulick S et al: Cortisol inactivation overload: A mechanism of mineralocorticoid hypertension in the ectopic adrenocorticotropin syndrome. J Clin Endocrinol Metab 1992;74:963.

Walker BP, Edwards CRW: 11β-Hydroxysteroid dehydrogenase and enzyme-mediated receptor protection: Life after liquorice? Clin Endocrinol 1991;35:281.

Walters MR: Steroid hormone receptors and the nucleus. Endocr Rev 1985;6:512.

Whitworth JA: Mechanisms of glucocorticoid-induced hypertension. Kidney Int 1987;31:1213.

Laboratory Evaluation

APA Task Force on Laboratory Tests in Psychiatry: The dexamethasone suppression test: An overview of its current status in psychiatry. Am J Psychiatry 1987; 144:1253.

Borst GC, Michenfelder HJ, O'Brian JT: Discordant cortisol response to exogenous ACTH and insulin-induced hypoglycemia in patients with pituitary disease. N Engl J Med 1982;306:1462.

Chrousos GP et al: The corticotropin-releasing factor stimulation test: An aid in the evaluation of patients with Cushing's syndrome. N Engl J Med 1984; 310:622.

Cunningham SK, Moore A, Mckenna TJ: Normal cortisol response to corticotropin in patients with secondary adrenal failure. Arch Intern Med 1982;143: 2276.

Doherty GM et al: Time to recovery of the hypothalamic-pituitary-adrenal axis after curative resection of adrenal tumors in patients with Cushing's syndrome. Surgery 1990;108;1085.

Harris MJ, Baker RT, McRoberts JW: The adrenal response to trauma, operation and cosyntropin stimulation. Surg Gyn Ob 1990;170:513.

Liddle GW: Tests of pituitary adrenal suppressibility in the diagnosis of Cushing's syndrome. J Clin Endocrinol Metab 1960;12:1539.

Lindholm J, Kehlet H: Re-evaluation of the clinical value of the 30 min ACTH test in assessing the hypothalamic-pituitary-adrenocortical function. Clin Endocrinol 1987;26:53.

May ME, Carey RM: Rapid adrenocorticotrophic hormone test in practice: Retrospective review. Am J Med 1985;79:679.

Patel SR, Selby C, Jeffcoate WJ: The short Synacthen test in acute hospital admissions. Clin Endocrinol 1991; 35:259.

Streeten DHP et al: Normal and abnormal function of the hypothalamic-pituitary-adrenocortical system in man. Endocr Rev 1984;5:371.

Vermeulen A, Reubens R: Adrenal virilism. In: *The Adrenal Gland,* 2nd ed. James VHT (editor). Raven Press, 1992.

Wade CE et al: Upon admission adrenal steroidogenesis is adapted to the degree of illness in intensive care unit patients. J Clin Endocrinol Metab 1988;67:223.

Disorders of Adrenocortical Insufficiency

Allard P et al: Sensitivity and specificity of computed tomography for the detection of adrenal metastatic lesions among 91 autopsied lung cancer patients. Cancer 1990;66:457.

Best TR et al: Persistent adrenal insufficiency secondary to low dose ketoconazole therapy. Am J Med 1987;82:676.

Burke CW: Adrenocortical insufficiency. Clin Endocrinol Metab 1985;14:947.

Chin R: Adrenal crisis. Crit Care Clin 1991;7:23.

Cutler GB Jr, Laue L: Congenital adrenal hyperplasia due to 21-hydroxylase deficiency. N Engl J Med 1990;323:1806.

Dluhy RG: The growing spectrum of HIV-related endocrine abnormalities. J Clin Endocrinol Metab 1990;70:563.

Gamelin E et al: Non-Hodgkin's lymphoma presenting with primary adrenal insufficiency: A disease with an underestimated frequency? Cancer 1992;69:2333.

Glasgow BJ et al: Adrenal pathology in the acquired immune deficiency syndrome. Am J Clin Pathol 1985; 84:594.

Green LW et al: Adrenal insufficiency as a complication of the acquired immunodeficiency syndrome. Ann Intern Med 1984;101:497.

Leshin M: Polyglandular autoimmune syndromes. Am J Med Sci 1985;290:77.

Membreno L et al: Adrenocortical function in acquired immunodeficiency syndrome. J Clin Endocrinol Metab 1987;65:482.

Moser HW et al: Adrenoleukodystrophy. Endocrinol Metab Clin North Am 1991;20:297.

Neufeld M, Maclaren NK, Blizzard RM: Two types of autoimmune Addison's disease associated with different polyglandular autoimmune (PGA) syndromes. Medicine 1981;60:355.

Rao RH, Vagnucci AH, Amico JA: Bilateral massive adrenal hemorrhage: Early recognition and treatment. Ann Intern Med 1989;110:227.

Redman BG et al: Prospective evaluation of adrenal insufficiency in patients with adrenal metastasis. Cancer 1987;60:103.

Schlaghecke R et al: The effect of long-term glucocorticoid therapy on pituitary adrenal responses to exogenous corticotropin-releasing hormone. N Engl J Med 1992;326:226.

Schulte HM et al: The corticotropin-releasing hormone stimulation test: A possible aid in the evaluation of patients with adrenal insufficiency. J Clin Endocrinol Metab 1984;58:1064.

Stacpoole PW et al: Isolated ACTH deficiency: A heterogeneous disorder. Medicine 1982;61:13.

Thompson DG, Mason AS, Goodwin FJ: Mineralocorticoid replacement in Addison's disease. Clin Endocrinol 1979;10:499.

Vita JA et al: Clinical clues to the cause of Addison's disease. Am J Med 1985;78:461.

Watson CA, Rosenfeld RL, Fang VS: Recovery from glucocorticoid inhibition of the responses to corticotrophin-releasing hormone. Clin Endocrinol 1988;28:471.

Cushing's Syndrome

Aron DC et al: Cushing's syndrome: Problems in diagnosis. Medicine 1981;60:25.

Aron DC et al: Cushing's syndrome: Problems in management. Endocr Rev 1982;3:229.

Aron DC, Findling JW, Tyrrell JB: Cushing's disease. Endocrinol Metab Clin North Am 1987;16:705.

Aron DC, Schnall AM, Sheeler LR: Cushing's syndrome and pregnancy. Am J Obstet Gynecol 1990;162:244.

Asa SL et al: Cushing's disease associated with an intrasellar gangliocytoma producing corticotrophin-releasing factor. Ann Intern Med 1984;101:789.

Atkinson AB: The treatment of Cushing's syndrome. Clin Endocrinol 1991;34:507.

Benecke R et al: Plasma level monitoring of mitotane (*o,p'*-DDD) and its metabolite t (*o,p'*-DDE) during long-term treatment of Cushing's disease with low doses. Eur J Clin Pharmacol 1991;41:259.

Besky JL et al: Cushing's syndrome due to ectopic production of corticotropin-releasing factor. J Clin Endocrinol Metab 1985;60:496.

Decker RA et al: Eastern Cooperative Oncology Group study 1879: Mitotane and Adriamycin in patients with advanced adrenocortical carcinoma. Surgery 1991; 110:1006.

Dickstein G et al: Spontaneous remission in Cushing's disease. Arch Intern Med 1991;151:185.

Dimopoulos MA et al: Paraneoplastic Cushing's syndrome as an adverse prognostic factor in patients who die early with small cell lung cancer. Cancer 1992; 69:66.

Dwyer AJ et al: Pituitary adenomas in patients with Cushing's disease: Initial experience with Gd-DTPA-enhanced MR imaging. Radiology 1987;163:421.

Findling JW, Tyrrell JB: Occult ectopic secretion of corticotropin. Arch Intern Med 1986;146:929.

Fitzgerald PA et al: Cushing's disease: Transient secondary adrenal insufficiency after selective removal of pituitary microadenomas: Evidence for a pituitary origin. J Clin Endocrinol Metab 1982;54:413.

Flack MR et al: Urine free cortisol in the high-dose dexamethasone suppression test for the differential diagnosis of the Cushing syndrome. Ann Intern Med 1992;116:211.

Grua JR, Nelson DH: ACTH-producing pituitary tumors. Endocrinol Metab Clin North Am 1991;20:319.

Howlett TA et al: Diagnosis and management of ACTH-dependent Cushing's syndrome: Comparison of the features in ectopic and pituitary ACTH production. Clin Endocrinol 1986;24:699.

Howlett TA et al: Megavoltage pituitary irradiation in the management of Cushing's disease and Nelson's syndrome: Long-term follow-up. Clin Endocrinol 1989;31:309.

Howlett TA, Rees LH, Besser GM: Cushing's syndrome. Clin Endocrinol Metab 1985;14:911.

Hutter AM, Kayhoe DE: Adrenal cortical carcinoma: Clinical features of 138 patients. Am J Med 1966; 41:572.

Jex RK et al: Ectopic ACTH syndrome: Diagnostic and therapeutic aspects. Am J Surg 1985;149:276.

Kaye TB, Crapo L: The Cushing's syndrome: an update on diagnostic tests. Ann Int Med 1990;112:434.

Larsen JL, Cathey WJ, O'Dell WD: Primary adrenocortical nodular dysplasia: A distinct subtype of Cushing's syndrome. Am J Med 1986;80:976.

Luton J-P et al: Clinical features of adrenocortical carcinoma, prognostic factors, and the effect of mitotane therapy. N Engl J Med 1990;322:1195.

Mampalam TJ, Tyrrell JB, Wilson CB: Transsphenoidal microsurgery for Cushing's disease. Ann Intern Med 1988;109:487.

McNicol AM, Teasdale GM, Beastall GH: A study of corticotroph adenomas in Cushing's disease: No evidence of intermediate lobe origin. Clin Endocrinol 1986;24:715.

Oldfield EH et al: Petrosal sinus sampling with and without corticotropin-releasing hormone for the differential diagnosis of Cushing's syndrome. N Engl J Med 1991;325:897.

Ross EJ, Linch DC: The clinical response to treatment in adult Cushing's syndrome following remission of hypercortisolaemia. Postgrad Med J 1985;61:205.

Sheeler LR: Cushing's syndrome 1988. Cleve Clin J Med 1988;55:329.

Sonino N et al: Prolonged treatment of Cushing's disease by ketoconazole. J Clin Endocrinol Metab 1985; 61:718.

Styne DM et al: Treatment of Cushing's disease in childhood and adolescence by transsphenoidal microadenomectomy. N Engl J Med 1984;310:889.

Tabarin A et al: Use of ketoconazole in the treatment of Cushing's disease and ectopic ACTH syndrome. Clin Endocrinol 1991;34:63.

Trainer PJ, Grossman A: The diagnosis and differential diagnosis of Cushing's syndrome. Clin Endocrinol 1991;34:317.

Tyrrell JB et al: An overnight high-dose dexamethasone

suppression test: Rapid differential diagnosis of Cushing's syndrome. Ann Intern Med 1986;104:180.

Tyrrell JB et al: Cushing's disease: Selective transsphenoidal resection of pituitary adenomas. N Engl J Med 1978;298:753.

Tyrrell JB: Diagnosis of Cushing's disease. In: *Secretory Tumors of the Pituitary Gland.* Black PM et al (editors). Raven Press, 1984.

Watson RGK et al: Results of adrenal surgery for Cushing's syndrome: 10 years' experience. World J Surg 1986;10:531.

Young WF Jr et al: Familial Cushing's syndrome due to primary pigmented nodular adrenocortical disease: Reinvestigation 50 years later. N Engl J Med 1989; 321:1659.

Zeiger MA et al: Primary bilateral adrenocortical causes of Cushing's syndrome. Surgery 1991;110:1106.

Hirsutism & Virilism

Baskin HJ: Screening for late-onset congenital adrenal hyperplasia in hirsutism or amenorrhea. Arch Intern Med 1987;147:847.

Chetkowski RJ et al: The incidence of late-onset congenital adrenal hyperplasia due to 21-hydroxylase deficiency among hirsute women. J Clin Endocrinol Metab 1984;58:595.

Cumming DC et al: Treatment of hirsutism with spironolactone. JAMA 1982;247:1295.

Ehrmann DA, Rosenfield RL: Hirsutism: Beyond the steroidogenic block. N Engl J Med 1990;323:909.

Gabrilove JL et al: Virilizing adrenal adenoma with studies on the steroid content of adrenal venous effluent and a review of the literature. Endocr Rev 1981;2:462.

Killeen AA et al: Prevalence of nonclassical congenital adrenal hyperplasia among women self-referred for electrolytic treatment of hirsutism. Am J Med Genetics 1992;42:197.

Longcope C: Adrenal and gonadal androgen secretion in normal females. Clin Endocrinol Metab 1986;15:213.

Moltz L, Schwartz U: Gonadal and adrenal androgen secretion in hirsute females. Clin Endocrinol Metab 1986;15:229.

Siegel SF et al: ACTH stimulation tests and plasma dehydroepiandrosterone sulfate levels in women with hirsutism. N Engl J Med 1990;323:849.

Incidentally Discovered Adrenal Masses

Copeland PM: The incidentally discovered adrenal mass. Ann Intern Med 1983;98:940.

Gross MD et al: Distinguishing benign from malignant adrenal masses. Ann Int Med 1988;109:613.

Herrera MF et al: Incidentally discovered adrenal tumors: An institutional perspective. Surgery 1991;110: 1014.

McLeod MK et al: Subclinical Cushing's syndrome in patients with adrenal gland incidentalomas: Pitfalls in diagnosis and management. Am Surg 1991;56:398.

Reinig JW et al: Adrenal masses differentiated by MR. Radiology 1986;158:81.

Rosen HN, Swartz SL: Subtle glucocorticoid excess in patients with adrenal incidentaloma. Am J Med 1992;92:213.

Ross NS, Aron DC: Hormonal evaluation of the patient with an incidentally discovered adrenal mass. N Engl J Med 1990; 323:1401.

Thompson NW, Cheung PSY: Diagnosis and treatment of functioning and nonfunctioning adrenocortical neoplasms including incidentalomas. Surg Clin North Am 1987;67:423.

Endocrine Hypertension

7

Edward G. Biglieri, MD, Claudio E. Kater, MD, & David J. Ramsay, MD, DPhil

Endocrine hypertension is prominent in the pathology of primary adrenal disorders (pheochromocytoma, primary hyperaldosteronism, and cortisol- or deoxycorticosterone-producing tumors), pituitary ACTH-producing tumors, and renal disease (renin-secreting tumors, renovascular disease, certain tubulopathies). Arterial hypertension may also be present in endocrine diseases such as acromegaly, thyrotoxicosis, hypothyroidism, hyperparathyroidism, and hyperinsulinism.

MINERALOCORTICOID HORMONES

The biosynthetic pathways of the mineralocorticoid hormones are shown in Figure 7–1 (see also Figure 6–4). The major mineralocorticoids that enter the peripheral circulation from the adrenal cortex are aldosterone and deoxycorticosterone (DOC); the principal mineralocorticoid is aldosterone. Cortisol also has high intrinsic mineralocorticoid activity, but its actions are blunted in the kidney by local degradation. Aldosterone is produced in the zona glomerulosa exclusively and is primarily controlled by the renin-angiotensin system. Other regulators include sodium and potassium levels, ACTH, and adrenergic and dopaminergic stimuli. Although renin and aldosterone move in concert in most situations, aldosterone is also influenced by ACTH, potassium balance and concentration, and probably other factors to maintain homeostasis. With the exception of 18-hydroxycorticosterone, the precursors of aldosterone in this pathway normally are present in very low concentration in the peripheral blood. In the zona fasciculata, there are two steroid pathways—the glucocorticoid (17-hydroxy) and the mineralocorticoid (17-deoxy) pathways—both under the control of ACTH. The glucocorticoid pathway results in the formation of cortisol. The major mineralocorticoid of the zona fasciculata is DOC, but corticosterone and 18-hydroxydeoxycorticosterone are also produced in substantial amounts. The bulk of the circulating levels of DOC, corticosterone, and 18-hydroxydeoxycorticosterone originates from the zona fasciculata. In addition to ACTH, there is probably a second regulator of the 17-deoxy pathway in the zona fasciculata.

ACTIVITIES OF MINERALOCORTICOIDS

Aldosterone and other mineralocorticoids influence certain cell types that have Na^+-K^+ ATPase activity. The principal effects of the mineralocorticoids are on maintenance of normal sodium and potassium concentrations and extracellular volume. Mineralocorticoids cross the cell membrane and combine with an intracellular cytosol mineralocorticoid receptor (see Chapter 1). The active steroid-receptor complex moves into the nucleus of the target cell, where it alters the rate of transcription of mineralocorticoid-responsive genes with subsequent changes in the levels of specific mRNAs and their protein products that regulate the movement of sodium out of the cell. The metabolic effects of aldosterone in the collecting tubule and part of the distal renal tubule result from activation of the Na^+-K^+ ATPase in the serosal membrane to pump passively diffused sodium from the luminal side into the extracellular fluid. A subsidiary mechanism is activation of permease in the luminal membrane, favoring sodium transport into the tubular cell and subsequently to the extracellular fluid. The major effect of this action quantitatively is to increase the difference in potential across the renal tubule. The increased luminal negativity affects tubular secretion of potassium and hydrogen (Figure 7–2). Tubular sodium, via the sodium pump, enters the extracellular fluid and helps maintain its normal composition and volume. All of these events occur in other secretory systems as well and can be measured in saliva, sweat, and feces.

Aldosterone binds weakly to corticosteroid-binding globulin (CBG)—in contrast to the zona fasciculata steroids—and circulates mostly bound to albumin. Free aldosterone comprises 30–50% of its total plasma concentration, whereas the free fractions of the steroids of the zona fasciculata comprise 5–10% of their total concentration. Consequently, aldosterone has a relatively short half-life of 15–20 minutes.

Aldosterone is rapidly inactivated by the liver in a single passage, with the formation of tetrahydroaldosterone. Another metabolite, aldosterone-18-glucuronide, is formed by the kidney and usually represents 5–10% of the secreted aldosterone. A small

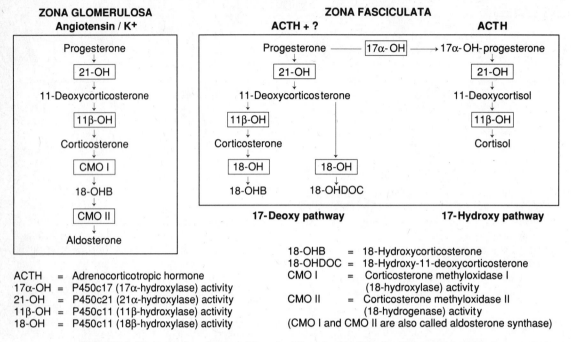

Figure 7–1. Biosynthetic pathways of the mineralocorticoids. See also Figures 6–4 and 6–5.

amount of free aldosterone appears in the urine and can be easily quantitated. Aldosterone secretion rates vary from 50 mg/d to 250 mg/d on relatively normal sodium intakes (8–12 g of NaCl per day).

DOC is secreted at approximately the same rate as aldosterone. However, like cortisol, DOC is almost totally bound to CBG, with less than 5% appearing in the free form. It is metabolized in the liver to tetrahydrodeoxycorticosterone, conjugated with glucuronic acid, and excreted in the urine. There is virtually no detectable free DOC in the urine.

The free hormone can combine with the mineralocorticoid receptor to initiate mineralocorticoid action. The extent of mineralocorticoid action is due to the availability of the free hormone and the affinity of the hormone for the receptor. Aldosterone and DOC have approximately equal and high affinities for the mineralocorticoid receptors and circulate at roughly

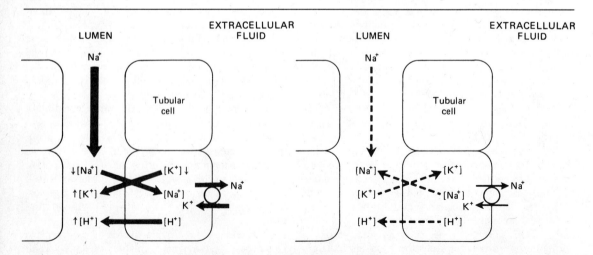

Figure 7–2. Mineralocorticoid action. On the left, high sodium intakes and high tubular sodium with increased mineralocorticoid action lead to K+ and H+ secretion and Na+ movement into extracellular fluid. Similar amounts of mineralocorticoid are ineffective when tubular sodium is reduced (eg, by dietary sodium restriction).

similar concentrations, but aldosterone is quantitatively the most important because much more of it is free. Cortisol has approximately one-tenth the affinity for the receptor as aldosterone and circulates at about 1000-fold higher levels than aldosterone. Because of this, cortisol is the major steroid that occupies the mineralocorticoid receptors in many tissues such as the pituitary; however, at usual levels, cortisol does not contribute much to the mineralocorticoid activity of regulating sodium and potassium balance, because it is degraded to the essentially inactive cortisone in target tissues where these influences occur. Cortisol can lead to mineralocorticoid hypertension when this conversion is blunted (discussed below).

MINERALOCORTICOID HYPERTENSION

Mineralocorticoid hormones produce hypertension by several mechanisms (Figure 7–3). The initiating events are most likely due to mineralocorticoid-induced expansion of plasma and extracellular fluid volume. Insights into these early mechanisms come from studies after spironolactone treatment is withdrawn from a patient with a benign aldosterone-secreting adenoma and from studies with normal subjects given high doses of mineralocorticoids. Initially, sodium and fluid retention occur, with an increase in body weight and extracellular fluid volume. After gaining approximately 2% of previous body weight (1–2 L), the phenomenon of sodium "escape" follows, but renal potassium wasting and arterial blood pressure increase. Chronic mineralocorticoid excess eventually results in an increase in peripheral vascular resistance with normalization of stroke volume and cardiac output. The elevation of peripheral vascular resistance is also in part related to increased sensitivity to catecholamines, even without a distinct increment in epinephrine or norepinephrine plasma levels. An additional mechanism may be the direct central action of aldosterone: Intracerebroventricular infusion of aldosterone to rats produced hypertension that could not be reversed or prevented by infusion, at the same site, of a competitive aldosterone antagonist.

DEFINITION OF TERMS

The terminology for classification of hormone actions is provided in Chapter 1. A mineralocorticoid hormone is one that acts through binding to the mineralocorticoid receptors. As has been said, both the classic mineralocorticoids aldosterone and deoxycor-

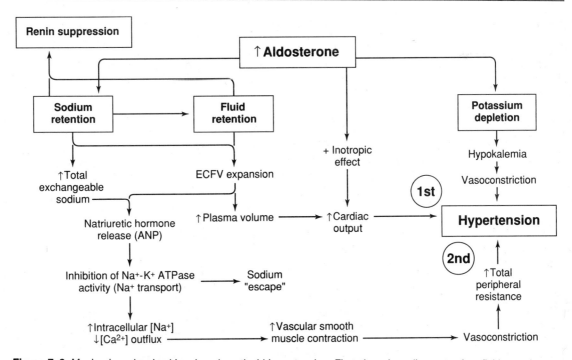

Figure 7–3. Mechanisms involved in mineralocorticoid hypertension. First, there is sodium retention, fluid retention, expansion of extracellular fluid volume and plasma volume, increased cardiac output, and hypertension. Second, there is vasoconstriction and increased total peripheral resistance and hypertension. (ANP, atrial natriuretic peptide; ECFV, extracellular fluid volume.) (See text for details.)

350 / CHAPTER 7

ticosterone and the glucocorticoid cortisol can act through these receptors. Mineralocorticoid receptors mediate the influences on sodium, potassium, and hydrogen ion balance. The terms mineralocorticoid excess and mineralocorticoid deficiency denote an absolute elevation and an absolute diminution, respectively, of the endogenous hormones as reflected by their plasma or urine levels. However, this is not necessarily related to the clinical manifestations of mineralocorticoid activity. A condition characterized by presumed increased mineralocorticoid activity, with salt retention, hypertension, hypokalemia, and metabolic alkalosis, is more appropriately called hypermineralocorticoidism. It can occur in the absence of any mineralocorticoid hormone production, eg, in Liddle's syndrome or chronic ingestion of licorice. In contrast, in the mineralocorticoid resistance syndromes (receptor deficiency, pseudohypoaldosteronism), an excess of circulating mineralocorticoid cannot express its peripheral action and results in a clinical state of hypomineralocorticoidism, presenting with sodium loss, hypotension, hyperkalemia, and metabolic acidosis.

PRIMARY MINERALOCORTICOID EXCESS (Table 7–1)

Disorders in this category are manifested by hypertension, hypokalemia, suppression of the renin system, and normal or low cortisol production.

PRIMARY ALDOSTERONISM

The increased production of aldosterone by abnormal zona glomerulosa tissue (adenoma or hyperplasia) initiates a series of events that result in primary aldosteronism. Increased sodium retention results in expansion of the extracellular fluid volume and increased total body sodium content. Although the effects on the kidney are greatest quantitatively, the other secretory tissues also participate in this event. Fecal excretion of sodium, for example, can be decreased to almost nil. The expanded extracellular fluid and plasma volumes are registered by stretch receptors at the juxtaglomerular apparatus and sodium flux at the macula densa, with resultant suppression of renin secretion, measured as suppressed plasma renin activity. These effects of aldosterone are further manifested by normal or elevated serum sodium concentration and reduced hematocrit. With primary (autonomous) increases in aldosterone production, the renin system is greatly suppressed; this is a main feature of the disorder.

In addition to sodium retention, potassium depletion develops, decreasing the total body and plasma concentration of potassium. The extrusion of potassium from its intracellular reservoir is followed by the intracellular movement of hydrogen ion, and—along with increased renal secretion of hydrogen ion—alkalosis ensues. With moderate potassium depletion, decreased carbohydrate tolerance (shown by an abnormal glucose tolerance test) and resistance to antidiuretic hormone (vasopressin) occur. Severe potassium depletion blunts baroreceptor function, occasionally producing postural hypotension. Because aldosterone biosynthesis is intensified, the entire biosynthetic pathway becomes activated. Precursor

Table 7–1. Biochemical findings in primary hypermineralocorticoidism.

	Plasma Na+	Plasma K+	Aldosterone	Other MCHs	Renin	Cortisol	ACTH	Hematocrit	BUN: Creatinine Ratio
Aldosterone-producing adenoma	N or ↑	↓	↑↑	↑	↓↓	N	N	↓	N
Aldosterone-producing carcinoma	↑	↓	↑↑	↑↑	↓↓	N or ↑	N or ↓	↓	N
Hyperplasia									
Idiopathic hyperaldosteronism	N	↓	↑	N	↓	N	N	N or ↓	N
Indeterminate hyperaldosteronism	N	N or ↓	↑	N	↓	N	N	N or ↓	N
Glucocorticoid-remediable hyperaldosteronism	N	↓	↑	N	↓	N	N	N or ↓	N
"Primary hyperplasia"	N or ↑	↓	↑↑	↑	↓↓	N	N	↓	N
11β-Hydroxylase deficiency	N	N or ↓	↓	↑	N or ↓	N or ↓	↑	N or ↓	N
17α-Hydroxylase deficiency	N or ↑	↓	↓	↑↑	↓↓	↓	↑	N or ↓	N

Key:
BUN = Blood urea nitrogen
MCH = Mineralocorticoid hormone
N = Normal
↑,↓ = Increased, decreased
↑↑, ↓↓ = Markedly increased, decreased

steroids such as DOC, corticosterone, and 18-hydroxycorticosterone are present in increased amounts in the blood of persons with an aldosterone-producing adenoma (Figure 7–1).

Primary aldosteronism is a disease of the zona glomerulosa. Cells of this zone do not have the ability to make cortisol (owing to the absence of the P450c17,17α-hydroxylase system). Thus, there are no abnormalities in cortisol production, plasma cortisol level, or cortisol metabolism.

Clinical Findings

Patients usually come to medical attention because of symptoms of hypokalemia or detection of previously unsuspected hypertension during the course of physical examination. The medical history reveals no characteristic symptoms—often only nonspecific complaints of tiredness, loss of stamina, weakness, nocturia, and lassitude—all symptoms of potassium depletion. If potassium depletion is more severe, with alkalosis, then increased thirst, polyuria (especially nocturnal), and paresthesias may be present. Headaches are frequent. Excessive production of mineralocorticoids produces no characteristic physical findings. Blood pressure in patients with primary aldosteronism can range from borderline to severe hypertensive levels. The mean ± SEM blood pressure in the 136 patients reported by the Glasgow unit was $205 \pm 21/123 \pm 18$ mm Hg, with no significant difference between the group with adenoma and that with hyperplasia. Accelerated (malignant) hypertension is extremely rare. Retinopathy is mild, and hemorrhages are rarely present. Postural falls in blood pressure without reflex tachycardia are observed in the severely potassium-depleted patient because of blunting of the baroreceptors. Clinical edema is rare. A positive Trousseau or Chvostek sign may be suggestive of alkalosis accompanying severe potassium depletion. The heart is usually only mildly enlarged, and electrocardiographic changes are usually those of modest left ventricular hypertrophy and potassium depletion.

Initial Diagnosis
(Figure 7-4)

A. Hypokalemia: Determination of the presence or absence of spontaneous hypokalemia is the most important initial screening procedure in patients with hypertension. During the investigation, a high-potassium diet or potassium chloride supplements should be avoided, and all previous diuretic therapy must be discontinued for at least 3 weeks before a valid potassium measurement is ordered. The most common cause of hypokalemia is diuretic therapy.

Care must also be taken to assess the state of sodium intake or balance in the patient before serum electrolytes are obtained. Serum potassium concentration is closely related to and determined to a great extent by sodium chloride intake. A low-sodium diet, by sparing potassium loss, can correct serum potassium abnormalities, thus masking potassium depletion; as the amount of sodium ion available for reabsorption is reduced, potassium secretion is retarded in the distal tubule.

B. Salt Intake: In the USA, Japan, and many European countries, the average person consumes more than 120 meq of sodium per day—enough to allow hypokalemia to become manifest. If a dietary history of high salt intake is obtained and potassium concentrations are normal, there is no need for further tests. A useful way to demonstrate hypokalemia is to have the patient take an unrestricted diet plus 1 g of sodium chloride (as a 1-g sodium chloride USP tablet, 1/5 tsp of table salt, or packets containing 1 g of salt) with each meal for 4 days; blood samples for fasting electrolyte determinations should be obtained on day 5. This diet is useful because it also prepares the patient for measurement of aldosterone levels. The finding of a low serum potassium concentration warrants further study (Figure 7–4).

In some series, up to 20% of patients with primary aldosteronism have had low-normal serum potassium concentrations, depending on criteria of dietary sodium and laboratory variability. In the presence of normal renal function and aldosterone excess, salt loading will unmask hypokalemia as a manifestation of potassium depletion. Normokalemic hyperaldosteronism under these conditions has been reported but is rare.

C. Plasma Renin Activity: If spontaneous hypokalemia is documented, the renin-angiotensin system must be assessed. This is accomplished by a random plasma renin activity measurement. If plasma renin activity is normal or high in a patient who has been off diuretic therapy for 3 weeks, it is very unlikely that primary aldosteronism is present. If the random plasma renin activity is suppressed, primary aldosteronism is a likely diagnosis.

D. Serum Sodium: Sodium concentrations less than 139 meq/L are rare in patients with primary aldosteronism, but they are common with diuretic therapy. Thus, any lower concentration should suggest secondary hyperaldosteronism. A high serum sodium concentration (142–152 meq/L) in the presence of a reduced hematocrit (due to increased extracellular fluid and plasma volume from sodium retention) is presumptive evidence of mineralocorticoid excess.

1. Measurement of urinary aldosterone– If hypokalemia and suppressed renin activity are detected, both plasma and urinary aldosterone measurements should be performed while the patient is taking an unrestricted salt diet with sodium chloride supplementation, or if the dietary history reveals a high salt intake, as previously described. This is crucial, because with any diminution of salt intake, plasma aldosterone concentration and aldosterone production normally increase.

Assessment of daily aldosterone production can

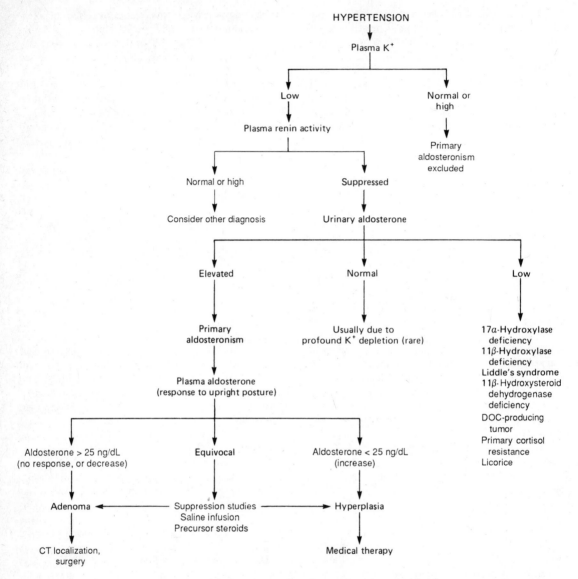

Figure 7–4. Decision diagram for primary mineralocorticoidism.

best be accomplished by measurement of urinary al- dosterone excretion over a 24-hour period. This can be determined by measurement of either the 18-glu- curonide or the tetrahydroaldosterone metabolites.

The normal urinary aldosterone-18-glucuronide values are 5–20 μg/24 h (14–56 nmol/24 h). In one large series, the mean values for patients with aldos- terone-producing adenoma and hyperplasia (idio- pathic hyperaldosteronism) were 45.2 ± 4 μg/24 h (125 ± 9 nmol/24 h) and 27.1 ± 2 μg/24 h (75 ± 5 nmol/24 h), respectively (Table 7–2). Urinary mea- surements are superior for the detection of abnormal production of aldosterone but are not always able to discriminate between adenoma and hyperplasia.

2. Measurement of plasma aldosterone, de- **oxycorticosterone, corticosterone, and 18-hy-** **droxycorticosterone concentrations–** (Table 7–3.) Samples for measurement of the plasma aldos- terone concentration should be obtained at around 8:00 AM after at least 4 hours of recumbency and under the same dietary conditions as described above for measurement of urinary aldosterone. This mea- surement provides not only diagnostic information about hyperaldosteronism but also differential diag- nostic information about the pathologic process. Whereas most adenomas (here referred to as aldos- terone-producing adenomas) show characteristics that differ from most hyperplasias (idiopathic hyper- aldosteronism), there are variants of the syndrome with different characteristics. These include aldos-

Table 7–2. Clinical and preliminary laboratory data in patients with hyperaldosteronism due to tumor and to hyperplasia, subdivided according to their subtypes.

Groups	(n)	Age (years)	Plasma K$^+$ (meq/L)	PRA (ng/mL/h)	Urinary Aldosterone (μg/24 h)	Urinary Aldosterone (nmol/24 h)
Hyperaldosteronism due to tumor						
Adenoma (APA)	94	42.1 (19–64)	2.8 (1.5–3.8)	0.2 (0.1–0.6)	45.2 (16.3–222)	125 (45–612.7)
APA-angiotensin-responsive	5	44.0 (30–57)	3.0 (2.6–3.4)	0.2 (0.1–0.5)	31.8 (17.8–45.0)	87.8 (49.1–124.2)
Carcinoma (APCa)	3	45.0 (32–56)	1.8 (1.4–2.0)	0.2 (0.1–0.4)	96.0 (53.0–178)	265 (136.3–401.3)
Hyperaldosteronism due to hyperplasia						
Idiopathic (IHA)	40	47.1 (32–68)	3.2 (2.5–4.2)	1.0 (0.1–2.1)	27.1 (13.1–51.7)	74.8 (36.2–143.2)
"Primary" (PAH)	8	41.6 (12–60)	3.0 (2.4–3.4)	0.2 (0.1–0.4)	36.0 (12.4–88.9)	99.7 (34.3–143.2)
Normal control subjects						
	55	28.0 (21–52)	4.1 (3.8–4.5)	1.4 (0.5–2.5)	10.3 (5.0–20.0)	28.5 (13.9–55.5)

Key:
PRA = Plasma renin activity
APA = Aldosterone-producing adenoma
APCa = Aldosterone-producing carcinoma
IHA = Idiopathic hyperaldosteronism
PAH = Primary adrenal hyperplasia

terone-producing renin-responsive adenoma, primary adrenal hyperplasia, and dexamethasone-suppressible hyperaldosteronism, which are described later. A plasma aldosterone concentration greater than 25 ng/dL (695 pmol/L) indicates adenoma, and less than 25 ng/dL (695 pmol/L) usually indicates hyperplasia.

The plasma aldosterone level should also be determined after 2 or 4 hours in the upright posture (which normally activates the renin system, with a rise in plasma aldosterone). Plasma aldosterone concentration shows no significant change or diminution in 90% of patients with adenoma (see also Table 7–2; compare also aldosterone-producing adenoma and renin-responsive adenoma in Figure 7–5), but it almost always increases in patients with adrenocortical hyperplasia (Table 7–3; Figure 7–5). This important differential maneuver is extremely accurate in identifying the pathogenetic mechanism. The difference is due to (1) the profound suppression of the renin system by excessive aldosterone production by adenoma; (2) the influence of ACTH, which decreases from 8 AM to 12 noon; and (3) decreased responsiveness of adenomas to angiotensin II. In contrast, in patients with hyperplastic adrenal glands, increased sensitivity of the gland to minute but measurable increases in renin that occur in the upright posture leads to an increased aldosterone level. Serum cortisol levels must be measured simultaneously. An increase in serum cortisol implies an ACTH discharge and invalidates the information obtained from the maneuver.

Additional simultaneous measurements of other precursor steroids will add to the precision of diagnosis. Plasma DOC and corticosterone are frequently increased at 8 AM in patients with adenoma, whereas they are rarely if ever elevated in patients with hyperplasia. 18-Hydroxycorticosterone is invariably increased in patients with adenoma to levels greater than 85 ng/dL (2338 pmol/L) and shows no overlap with the normal or slightly high values of this steroid in patients with hyperplasia. Two recently identified adrenal steroids, 18-hydroxycortisol and 18-oxocortisol, have been found to be frequently increased in the urine of patients with adenoma but not hyperplasia (except in the dexamethasone-suppressible form of hyperaldosteronism).

The procedures just discussed can identify primary aldosteronism and differentiate adenoma from hyperplasia in most cases. Localization studies (discussed below) can provide additional information. However, when uncertainty persists, the saline infusion test can be of further help.

3. Saline infusion test– Saline loading establishes aldosterone unresponsiveness to volume expansion and thereby identifies autonomy in patients with aldosterone-producing adenomas. Two liters of isotonic saline are administered over 2–4 hours. Blood samples for aldosterone and cortisol are obtained before and after the infusion. This expansion of the extracellular fluid volume reduces plasma aldosterone concentration promptly in patients with "essential" hypertension but fails to suppress plasma aldosterone concentration into the normal range in patients with adenoma or hyperplasia. The saline in-

Table 7–3. Simultaneous measurements (±SE) of plasma aldosterone, 18-hydroxycorticosterone, and plasma renin concentration in normal subjects and in primary aldosteronism during postural stimulation.[1,2]

	Normal Subjects (n = 14)			Aldosterone-Producing Adenoma (n = 15)			Idiopathic Hyperaldosteronism (n = 14)		
	Aldosterone ng/dL (pmol/L)	18-Hydroxy-corticosterone ng/dL (pmol/L)	Plasma Renin Concentration ng/mL/h (mg/L/s)	Aldosterone ng/dL (pmol/L)	18-Hydroxy-corticosterone ng/dL (pmol/L)	Plasma Renin Concentration ng/mL/h (mg/L/s)	Aldosterone ng/dL (pmol/L)	18-Hydroxy-corticosterone ng/dL (pmol/L)	Plasma Renin Concentration ng/mL/h (mg/L/s)
8 AM recumbent	8.2 ± 0.6 (228 ± 16.6)	23.5 ± 2.4 (647 ± 66)	3.4 ± 0.7 (0.97 ± .19)	54.7 ± 9.5 (1517 ± 263)	160.0 ± 29.9 (4401 ± 822)	0.49 ± 0.11 (0.14 ± .03)	13.2 ± 1.2 (366 ± 33.3)	24.2 ± 3.7 (666 ± 102)	0.52 ± .08 (0.14 ± .02)
12 noon upright	22.2 ± 2.3 (616 ± 63.8)	48.6 ± 4.9 (1337 ± 134.8)	8.8 ± 1.7 (2.44 ± .47)	49.8 ± 5.8 (1381 ± 161)	136.9 ± 31.8 (3766 ± 875)	0.61 ± .21 (0.17 ± .06)	32.5 ± 4.9 (902 ± 136)	49.0 ± 9.4 (1348 ± 259)	1.13 ± 0.2 (0.31 ± 0.06)

[1] (SI units)

[2] SI unit conversion factors: Aldosterone ng/dL × 27.74 = pmol/L; 18-hydroxycorticosterone ng/dL × 27.51 = pmol/L; plasma renin concentration ng/mL/h × 0.2778 = ng/(L/s).

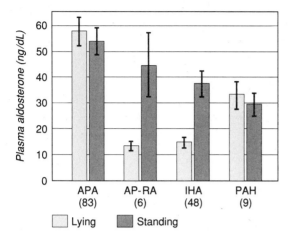

Figure 7–5. Response of plasma aldosterone to postural stimulation in primary aldosteronism. (APA, aldosterone-producing adenoma; AP-RA, renin-responsive APA; IHA, idiopathic hyperaldosteronism; PAH, primary adrenal hyperplasia.)

fusion test clearly distinguishes hyperaldosteronism from low-renin essential hypertension. Both plasma aldosterone and cortisol levels should be obtained before and after the infusion. The ratio of aldosterone to cortisol is greater than 3.0 only in adenoma because of the limited effect of volume expansion in a greatly suppressed renin state.

Identification of Other Types of Aldosteronism (Figure 7–4)

A. Dexamethasone (Glucocorticoid)-Suppressible Aldosteronism: The dexamethasone-remediable form of hyperaldosteronism occurs primarily in young men and is a familial autosomal dominant disorder. The primary defect is due to a gene duplication resulting from unequal crossing over that fuses the regulatory region of the 11β-hydroxylase to the gene coding sequence of aldosterone synthetase in the zona fasciculata. This linkage leads to the elevated levels of aldosterone, 18-oxocortisol, and 18-hydroxycortisol produced in the zona fasciculata. These patients constitute a rare and remarkable subset of hyperaldosteronism with hyperplasia. All of these biochemical abnormalities can be reversed after a 2- to 3-week course of ACTH-suppressive doses of glucocorticoids (1–2 mg of dexamethasone daily). These patients will maintain a normal blood pressure, plasma aldosterone, and other biochemical indices as long as the ACTH suppressant therapy is administered. However, the response to dexamethasone suppression seems to dissipate over the long term in most patients, and additional antihypertensive therapy may be necessary. Plasma aldosterone concentration is moderately elevated in these patients owing to

the increased sensitivity of the aldosterone biosynthetic pathway to normal ACTH levels. Plasma or urinary aldosterone levels are not suppressed in response to saline infusion. Postural stimulation fails to increase plasma aldosterone, similar to aldosterone-producing adenomas, and plasma aldosterone is suppressed by glucocorticoid administration. Since this is an autosomal dominant disorder, when it is found, family studies should be initiated.

B. Aldosterone-Producing Adrenocortical Carcinoma: Malignant tumors producing only aldosterone are rare (less than 3% of cases of primary aldosteronism). The few patients reported have had large tumors with abundant precursor steroids and an absence of circadian rhythm. In general, the biochemical and hormonal features and the response to dynamic tests are similar but much more pronounced in the carcinoma than the adenoma. Association with hypercortisolism or hyperandrogenism or hyperestrogenism is frequently observed during the progression of the disease.

C. Primary Adrenal Hyperplasia: A subset of patients with idiopathic hyperaldosteronism (hyperplasia), when identified, may benefit from surgical reduction of adrenal mass, ie, subtotal or total adrenalectomy. This group uniformly responds to stimulative and suppressive maneuvers in the same way as the aldosterone-producing adenoma and in clear contrast to classic hyperplasia (idiopathic hyperaldosteronism). Pathologic examination of the adrenal tissue discloses micro- or macronodular hyperplasia and occasionally a normal adrenal cortex. This subgroup represents about 6–7% of cases of primary aldosteronism. The autonomy of aldosterone production in this condition is difficult to explain, but the disease may be compared to the autonomy of cortisol production in nodular dysplasia associated with Cushing's syndrome. One might also consider this a form of adenoma without a dominant nodule, whereas the single adenoma usually presents as a dominant nodule in a micronodular gland (see below).

D. Aldosterone-Producing Renin-Responsive Adenoma: A novel group of patients with primary aldosteronism have adenomas whose aldosterone production responds to manipulations in the renin-angiotensin system. Thus, aldosterone levels increase in response to stimulative maneuvers such as the postural test or to prolonged treatment with spironolactone, similar to idiopathic hyperaldosteronism but in contrast to the classic aldosterone-secreting adenoma. This subtype represents about 8% of cases of primary aldosteronism.

Summary of Differential Diagnosis (Table 7–4)

The most important disorder of the mineralocorticoid hormones is primary aldosteronism due to a solitary adenoma. Hypokalemia in a hypertensive pa-

Table 7–4. Biochemical characteristics that permit the differential diagnosis of the subtypes of primary aldosteronism.

Aldosterone	APA	PAH	IHA	AP-RA	DSHA	LREH
Basal production	↑↑↑	↑↑↑	↑↑	↑↑	↑↑	N
Response to posture	↓	↓	↑	↑	↓	↑
Dexamethasone suppression	→	→	→	→	↓	→
Response to SPL	→	→	↑	↑	→	↑
Precursor levels	↑↑	↑	N	↑	N	N
18-OHF/18-OXOF	↑↑	↑	N	N	↑↑	N

Key:
APA   = Aldosterone-producing adenoma
PAH   = Primary adrenal hyperplasia
IHA   = Idiopathic hyperaldosteronism
LREH   = Low-renin essential hypertension
AP-RA   = Angiotensin-responsive aldosterone-producing adenoma
DSHA   = Dexamethasone-suppressible hyperaldosteronism
SPL   = Spironolactone
18-OHF = 18-Hydroxycortisol
18-OXOF = 18-Oxocortisol
N   = Normal
↑   = Increased
↓   = Decreased
→   = No change

tient means hypermineralocorticoidism. The subsequent suppressed plasma renin activity confirms this.

The high urinary aldosterone level identifies the adrenal as the source of the disorder. If the urinary aldosterone level is low, another adrenal mineralocorticoid is operative. Measurement of plasma aldosterone is perhaps the best means of discriminating between adenoma and hyperplasia by both the degree of elevation and the response to postural change.

Suppression studies with dexamethasone and saline in patients with increased aldosterone secretion will rule out low-renin essential hypertension and dexamethasone-suppressible hyperaldosteronism. Measurement of precursor steroids such as DOC, corticosterone, and 18-hydroxycorticosterone helps to distinguish hyperplasia from adenoma, because they are invariably normal in hyperplasia and elevated in adenoma. Markedly elevated levels of plasma or urinary 18-hydroxy- and 18-oxocortisol are found in patients with adenomas and the dexamethasone-suppressible form of hyperaldosteronism.

Management of Aldosterone-Producing Adenomas

A. Location of Adenoma: Once the biochemical diagnosis is secure, lateralization procedures in patients with adenoma become extremely important in determining the surgical approach. A number of techniques have been developed: adrenal venography, ^{131}I iodocholesterol scanning, adrenal vein catheterization and bilateral sampling, and CT or MRI. The diagnostic information provided by CT scanning or MRI in locating adenomas has proved to be the most accurate and practical and is the procedure of choice for adrenal imaging. Adrenal venogra-

phy was associated with a number of problems, such as extravasation of dye, hemorrhage, and adrenal infarction, and in any case this procedure cannot localize tumors smaller than 7 mm. The success rate of adrenal venography in identifying adrenal tumors is only 60–70%.

Scanning using intravenously administered ^{131}I iodocholesterol has located tumors in about 80% of patients, though the success rate drops markedly if tumors are less than 1 cm in diameter. The procedure is tedious and takes several weeks to accomplish. The use of ^{131}I-labeled 6β-iodomethyl-19-norcholesterol reduces the interval between injection and scintiscanning to about 3–7 days.

Adrenal vein catheterization to measure bilateral aldosterone levels continues to be useful in lateralizing tumors only after other lateralizing techniques fail and biochemical evidence still supports the diagnosis of adenoma.

B. Surgical Treatment: Treatment depends for the most part on the accuracy of diagnosis. In patients with an aldosterone-producing adenoma (whether responsive to renin or not) and no contraindication to operation, unilateral adrenalectomy is recommended. The degree of reduction of blood pressure and correction of hypokalemia achieved with spironolactone provides a surprisingly close approximation to the actual response to surgery; in fact, greater reduction often occurs postoperatively, presumably because of a greater reduction of extracellular fluid. The surgical cure rate of hypertension associated with adenoma is excellent—over 70% in several series—with reduction of hypertension in the remainder. Furthermore, subtotal adrenalectomy is recommended for patients with primary adrenal hyperplasia and hyperaldosteronism, since reduction of adrenal mass maintains sustained improvement in hypertension and hypokalemia.

C. Preoperative Preparation: Patients should be treated preoperatively with spironolactone, 200–400 mg/d, until the blood pressure and serum potassium are entirely normal; this may take 1–3 months. This drug is particularly beneficial because of its unique mechanism of action in blocking the mineralocorticoid receptor. Once both blood pressure and serum potassium levels are normal, the dose can be tapered to a maintenance dose of approximately 100 mg/d until the time of surgery. Spironolactone reduces the volume of the expanded extracellular fluid toward normal, promotes potassium retention, and restores normal serum potassium concentration. It often has the additional desirable effect of activating (after 1–2 months) the suppressed renin-angiotensin system in the contralateral adrenal gland. Postoperative hypoaldosteronism with hyperkalemia is unlikely with this treatment. Preoperative treatment will also permit reversal to some extent of some of the changes in target organs that were produced by the hypertensive and hypokalemic states. Spironolactone is usually well tolerated; the side effects of rashes, gynecomastia, impotence, and epigastric discomfort are rare.

As an alternative to spironolactone, the potassium-sparing diuretic amiloride, in doses of 20–40 mg/d, can be used.

D. Surgical and Postoperative Medical Treatment: When the diagnosis and lateralization are certain, surgical removal of the adenoma is advised. Current preoperative lateralization techniques easily identify the site of tumor, and a unilateral posterior approach should be used. Postoperative morbidity is not significant.

If the tumor is identified at surgery, exploration of the contralateral adrenal is not indicated. If surgery is contraindicated or refused, indefinite treatment with spironolactone can be effective. The initial dose of 200–400 mg of spironolactone per day must be continued for 4–6 weeks before the full effect on blood pressure is realized. With prolonged treatment, aldosterone production does not increase even though potassium replenishment, decreased sodium and volume spaces, and activation of the renin-angiotensin system occur. In addition, spironolactone directly inhibits aldosterone synthesis by adenomas. A chronic dose of 75–100 mg is usually sufficient to maintain a normal blood pressure.

Patients who have had unilateral adrenalectomy for removal of an aldosterone-producing tumor occasionally have a transient period of relative hypomineralocorticoidism with negative sodium balance, potassium retention, and mild acidosis. Full recovery of the chronically unstimulated, contralateral zona glomerulosa usually takes place in 4–6 months following surgery, but sometimes it takes as long as 18–24 months, particularly in patients prepared

for surgery without spironolactone. Restitution of the suppressed renin-angiotensin system to normal function usually precedes a completely normal adrenocortical response similar to the recovery of the pituitary-adrenal axis after removal of a cortisol-producing adenoma (Cushing's syndrome). No specific treatment is necessary other than adequate fluid intake and sodium supplementation, except when renal disease is present. A small percentage of patients (1%) do not have normal recovery of their renin-angiotensin-aldosterone system and require mineralocorticoid replacement (fludrocortisone) therapy for life. Preexisting renal disease usually identifies this group.

Subtotal adrenalectomy will correct hypokalemia in patients with idiopathic aldosteronism (hyperplasia), but the blood pressure remains elevated. Therefore, other antihypertensive measures (which should include spironolactone) must be used to control hypertension in patients with hyperplasia. Only in cases of primary adrenal hyperplasia and aldosteronism (Table 7–1) does removal of adrenal mass ameliorate the aldosterone-dependent hypertensive state.

Pathologic Findings

Over 70% of patients with primary aldosteronism who have undergone surgery have had unilateral adenoma. Bilateral tumors are rare. The characteristic adenoma is readily identified by its golden-yellow color. In addition, small satellite adenomas are often found, and distinction from micro- or macronodular hyperplasia is occasionally difficult. In patients with adenoma, the contiguous adrenal gland can show hyperplasia throughout the gland. Hyperplasia is also present in the contralateral adrenal gland but is not associated with aldosterone abnormalities after removal of the primary adenoma.

SYNDROMES WITH DEOXYCORTICOSTERONE EXCESS

Deoxycorticosterone is the second most important naturally occurring mineralocorticoid hormone. Excess DOC production is characteristic of a variety of hypertensive disorders associated with hypokalemia and with renin and aldosterone suppression.

1. 17α-HYDROXYLASE DEFICIENCY

17α-Hydroxylase deficiency syndrome is usually recognized at the time of puberty in young-adults by the presence of hypertension, hypokalemia, and primary amenorrhea (with sexual infantilism) in the female or pseudohermaphroditism in the male. (See Chapter 11.)

In contrast to the 21- and 11β-hydroxylation deficiencies, there is no virilization or restricted growth.

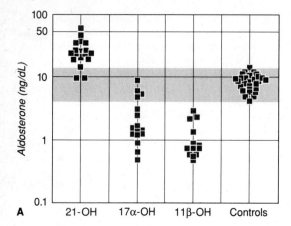

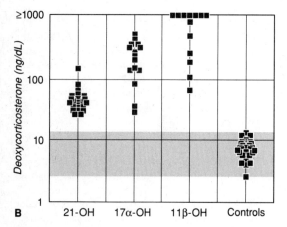

Figure 7–6. Aldosterone and deoxycorticosterone plasma levels in congenital adrenal hyperplasia due to 21-, 17α-, and 11β-hydroxylase deficiencies and in normal control subjects.

Patients often present with eunuchoid proportions and appearance. The virtual absence of 17α-hydroxyprogesterone, pregnanetriol, and 17-ketosteroids is diagnostic of this type of hydroxylase deficiency.

The key location of the 17α-hydroxylating system (cytochrome P450c17α) in the steroid biosynthetic pathway prevents normal production of androgens and estrogens (Figure 6–4). There has been no instance in which the adrenal defect has appeared without a concomitant gonadal defect. The defect occurs in a single gene (in chromosome 10), which codes for the enzyme or the expression of the enzyme. The diminution of cortisol production with this deficiency syndrome induces increased production of ACTH. Initially, the entire biosynthetic pathway of mineralocorticoids (both in the zona glomerulosa and the zona fasciculata) is increased—namely, progesterone, DOC, corticosterone, 18-hydroxydeoxycorticosterone, and aldosterone.

Progressive overproduction of the mineralocorti-

coids in both the zona glomerulosa (aldosterone) and zona fasciculata (DOC) pathways results in expansion of extracellular fluid and blood volumes, hypertension, and subsequent reduction and obliteration, in most cases, of plasma renin activity. Subsequent to this reduction, the plasma aldosterone concentration is virtually absent in most patients. Thus, the principal mineralocorticoids present in great quantities are DOC, corticosterone, 18-hydroxycorticosterone, and 18-hydroxydeoxycorticosterone—all of them ACTH-dependent steroids of the zona fasciculata (the 17-deoxy pathway) (Figures 7–1 and 7–6).

Treatment
See next section.

2. 11β-HYDROXYLASE DEFICIENCY

Congenital adrenal hyperplasia due to 11β-hydroxylase deficiency is usually recognized in newborns and infants because of virilization and the presence of both hypertension and hypokalemia. Plasma androgens, 11-deoxycortisol, 17α-hydroxyprogesterone, urinary 17-ketosteroids, and 17-hydroxycorticosteroids are increased.

The defect (in the gene mapped in chromosome 8) is usually partial, so that some cortisol is produced, but it does not increase with further stimulation by ACTH. Blood levels and production rates of cortisol are usually within normal limits. A partial defect of 11β-hydroxylation results in increased production and blood levels of DOC, 11-deoxycortisol (Figures 7–1 and 7–6), and androgens. Hypertension results from excessive production of DOC by mechanisms previously described for aldosterone.

The blood levels and production rates of aldosterone are low-normal or reduced. Two mechanisms are proposed. Originally, a partial deficiency of the 11β-hydroxylation activity in the zona glomerulosa was postulated, with a block in aldosterone synthesis. This concept was supported by the observation that after normalization of DOC production and correction of the hypertension (by ACTH suppression), aldosterone production remained normal or reduced and a sodium-losing state could be provoked. The current theory is that there is no zona glomerulosa defect but that suppression of renin by the increased production of DOC reduces the production of aldosterone in the zona glomerulosa. Thus, after chronic salt restriction and ACTH suppression, both renin and aldosterone dynamics return to normal, implying an intact zona glomerulosa.

Treatment
Treatment of both of these disorders is similar to that of all non-sodium-losing forms of congenital adrenal hyperplasia. Replacement doses of glucocor-

ticoid, such as hydrocortisone or dexamethasone, restores blood pressure to normal levels, corrects potassium depletion, reduces excessive DOC and corticosterone production in 17α-hydroxylase deficiency, and reduces DOC and 11-deoxycortisol production in 11β-hydroxylase deficiency. In 17α-hydroxylase deficiency syndrome, restoration of normal levels of DOC results in a return of plasma renin activity and aldosterone to normal values. A delay in return of the suppressed renin-aldosterone system toward normal can result in hypovolemic crises with the initial natriuresis and diuresis. It may take several years before the aldosterone and renin systems become normal. The amount of glucocorticoid administered must be carefully determined because of apparently exquisite tissue sensitivity to glucocorticoid hormones. Addition of estrogen-progestogen combined cyclic therapy may be necessary in the adult patient with 17α-hydroxylase deficiency (see Chapter 11).

3. ANDROGEN- & ESTROGEN-PRODUCING ADRENAL TUMORS

Most of the C_{19} steroids produced by the adult adrenocortical zona reticularis have weak androgen activity, especially dehydroepiandrosterone (DHEA) and its sulfate (DHEAS) as well as androstenedione. Disturbances in both internal zona reticularis regulatory mechanisms (ie, enzyme activity) and its extra-adrenal regulators (ACTH and an androgen-stimulating peptide of possible hypothalamic-pituitary origin) may lead to excessive adrenal sex steroid production, resulting in syndromes of hirsutism and virilization in the female or feminization in male adult patients.

Although the zona reticularis has no intrinsic capacity to synthesize any effective glucocorticoid or mineralocorticoid, it has the potential, under conditions of chronic stimulation by ACTH, to transform some cellular function into the fasciculata cell type (by the induction of specific enzyme complexes) and produce cortisol and presumably other typical zona fasciculata steroids.

Some patients with malignancies originating in the zona reticularis (androgen- or estrogen-producing tumors, or both types) may have clinical features of mineralocorticoid excess, with hypertension, hypokalemia, and renin suppression. Aldosterone levels are generally not elevated and are often reduced. Urinary or plasma steroid profiling in some of these patients suggests that there may be inhibition of 11β-hydroxylase activity in association with the increased production of androgens or estrogens. Administration of methylandrostanediol to experimental animals and testosterone to humans suggests that exogenous androgen excess can block the conversion of 11-deoxycortisol and DOC to cortisol and corticosterone, respectively. Excessive secretion of DOC could then

lead to a mineralocorticoid excess state. Elevated urinary DOC metabolites or plasma DOC concentrations have been found in several patients with androgen- or estrogen-producing adrenocortical carcinomas who have hypertension and hypokalemia.

The inhibition of 11β-hydroxylase in these carcinomas may be due to the inactivation of the enzyme cytochrome P450c11 by the high intra-adrenal concentration of androgens (androstenedione) that act as a pseudosubstrate for the reaction. This mechanism is similar to that occurring in Cushing's syndrome, where cortisol is the enzymatic inhibitor.

4. SYNDROME OF PRIMARY CORTISOL RESISTANCE

Peripheral resistance to cortisol action is a very rare condition—reported only in a few families—in which severe hypertension, hypokalemia, and renin suppression are associated with elevated plasma and urinary levels of cortisol without causing clinical manifestations of Cushing's syndrome. The basic defect is at the glucocorticoid receptor level (type II steroid receptor); both the number of receptors and the affinity of the receptors for cortisol are reduced in the target tissues. In this condition, plasma levels of ACTH are elevated as a result of block of cortisol feedback at the corticotroph. Cortisol production is thus increased, but it does not result in the typical clinical stigmas of hypercortisolism. However, chronic stimulation by excess ACTH of the 17-deoxy pathway of the zona fasciculata results in abnormal production of DOC and corticosterone, causing hypertension, hypokalemia, and suppression of renin and aldosterone production. The clinical and biochemical abnormalities are partially relieved by treatment with high doses of dexamethasone.

SYNDROMES WITH SECONDARY MINERALOCORTICOID EXCESS (Table 7–5)

Activation of the zona glomerulosa by the renin-angiotensin system can lead to a variety of conditions in which increased aldosterone production occurs. These conditions include sodium-wasting renal disease, laxative or diuretic abuse, dehydration, cirrhosis with ascites, heart failure, and decrease in intravascular volume; hypertension is typically not a feature. However, direct overproduction of renin, such as in renovascular hypertension and renin-secreting tumors, results in elevated blood pressure.

Renin & the Renin-Angiotensin System

In 1947, Goldblatt noted that reducing the flow of blood to the kidney in experimental animals was fol-

Table 7–5. Biochemical findings in hypertensive syndromes with secondary hypermineralocorticoidism.

	Plasma		Aldos-terone	Other MCHs	Renin	Cortisol	ACTH	Hct	BUN/Creatinine
	Na⁺	K⁺							
Secondary hypermineralocorticoidism									
Renovascular hypertension	N or ↑	N or ↓	↑	N	↑	N	N	↑	N or ↑
Renin-secreting tumor	N or ↑	↓	↑↑	N	↑↑	N	N	↑	N
Accelerated hypertension	N	N or ↓	↑	N	↑	N	N	N or ↑	N or ↑
Estrogen therapy	N	N or ↓	↑	N	N or ↑	N or ↑	N	N or ↓	N
Cushing's disease	N	N or ↓	N or ↓	↑	N	↑	N or ↑	N	N
Disorders simulating mineralocorticoid excess									
Pseudohypoaldosteronism (Liddle's syndrome)	N or ↑	↓	↓	N or ↓	↓	N	N	↓	N
Arnold-Healy-Gordon syndrome	N or ↑	↑	↓	N or ↓	↓	N	N	N or ↓	N
Synthetic MCH administration	N or ↑	↓	↓	N or ↓	↓	N	N	↓	N
Licorice excess	N or ↑	↓	↓	N or ↓	↓	N	N	↓	N
Primary cortisol resistance	N or ↑	↓	N or ↓	↑	N or ↓	↑	↑	N or ↓	N

lowed by an increase in blood pressure. This experiment implicated the kidney in the pathogenesis of hypertension.

As the afferent arteriole enters the glomerulus (Figure 7–7), the smooth muscle cells become modified to perform a secretory function. These **juxtaglomerular cells** produce and secrete renin, a pro-

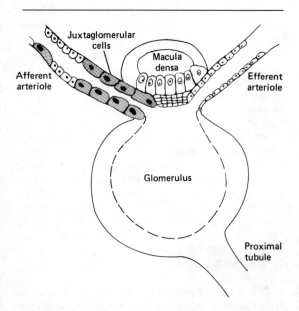

Figure 7–7. Diagram of a glomerulus, showing juxtaglomerular apparatus and macula densa.

teolytic enzyme with a molecular weight of approximately 40,000. It is derived from the proteolysis of its precursor, prorenin. The human kidney secretes both prorenin and renin into the bloodstream. Prorenin (previously called "inactive renin") can be present in the circulation at levels as high as or higher than those of renin. Prorenin can be converted into renin in vitro by a number of methods, but it is unclear whether significant extrarenal conversion of prorenin occurs. Renin reaches the bloodstream, where it acts upon its substrate, angiotensinogen, to form a decapeptide, angiotensin I (Figure 7–8), which is physiologically inert. Angiotensin I is converted to angiotensin II, the biologically active octapeptide, by the action of converting enzyme. The half-life of angiotensin II in plasma is less than 1 minute as a result of the action of multiple angiotensinases located in most tissues of the body.

Angiotensinogen

Angiotensinogen (renin substrate) is an α_2-globulin secreted by the liver. It has a molecular weight of approximately 60,000 and is usually present in human plasma at a constant concentration of 1 μmol/L. Although the rate of production of angiotensin II is normally determined by changes in plasma renin concentration, the concentration of angiotensinogen is below the V_{max} for the reaction. Thus, if angiotensinogen concentration increases, the amount of angiotensin produced at the same plasma renin concentration will increase. Hepatic production of angiotensinogen is increased by glucocorticoids and by

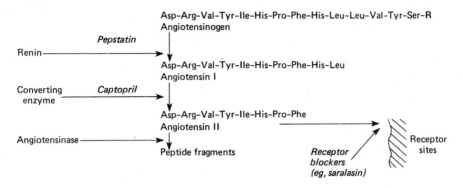

Asp-Arg-Val-Tyr-Ile-His-Pro-Phe-His-Leu-Leu-Val-Tyr-Ser-R
Angiotensinogen

Pepstatin

Renin

Asp-Arg-Val-Tyr-Ile-His-Pro-Phe-His-Leu
Angiotensin I

Converting enzyme   *Captopril*

Asp-Arg-Val-Tyr-Ile-His-Pro-Phe
Angiotensin II

Angiotensinase

Peptide fragments

Receptor blockers (eg, saralasin)

Receptor sites

Figure 7–8. Sequence of formation of angiotensin II. Drugs that can be used to block various steps are shown in italics.

estrogens. Stimulation of angiotensinogen production by estrogen-containing contraceptive pills may contribute to some of the hypertension encountered as a side effect of this treatment.

In situations such as sodium depletion, where there is a sustained high level of circulating angiotensin II, the rate of breakdown of substrate by renin in the plasma is greatly increased. Because the plasma concentration of angiotensinogen remains constant in these situations, hepatic production must increase to match the increased rate of breakdown. The mechanism of this increase is not clear, although angiotensin II itself is a stimulus to substrate production.

Converting Enzyme

Converting enzyme is found in most tissues in the body and circulates in plasma. Thus, theoretically, the conversion of angiotensin I to angiotensin II could take place anywhere in the circulatory system. However, the activity of the enzyme in the lung is particularly high, such that on a single passage, 70–80% of angiotensin I is converted to angiotensin II.

Converting enzyme is a dipeptidyl carboxypeptidase, a glycoprotein of MW 130,000–160,000 that cleaves dipeptides from a number of substrates. In addition to angiotensin I, these include bradykinin, enkephalins, and substance P. Inhibitors of converting enzyme are widely used to prevent the formation of angiotensin II in the circulation and thus block its biologic effects (Figure 7–8). Since converting enzyme acts on a number of substrates, blockade of the enzyme may not always exert its effects solely via the renin-angiotensin system.

Peripheral Effects of Angiotensin II

Angiotensin II is a potent pressor agent, exerting its effects on peripheral arterioles to cause vasoconstriction and thus increasing total peripheral resistance. Vasoconstriction occurs in all tissue beds, including the kidney, and has been implicated in the phenomenon of renal autoregulation. Angiotensin may also increase the rate and strength of cardiac contraction. The possible role of increased circulating levels of angiotensin II in the pathogenesis of hypertension is discussed below.

Angiotensin II acts directly on the adrenal cortex to stimulate aldosterone secretion, and in most situations it is the most important regulator of aldosterone secretion. It thus plays a central role in regulating sodium balance. For example, during dietary sodium depletion, extracellular fluid volume is reduced owing to osmotic transfer of water to the intracellular fluid compartment. Subsequent stimulation of the renin-angiotensin system is important in two ways. Its vasoconstrictor actions help to maintain blood pressure in the face of reduced extracellular fluid volume, whereas its actions to stimulate aldosterone secretion and thus sodium retention allows volume to be conserved.

The intrarenal actions of angiotensin II also promote sodium retention. Angiotensin II preferentially constricts efferent arterioles, thus maintaining the glomerular filtration rate during hypovolemia and arterial hypotension. The subsequent fall in peritubular capillary hydrostatic pressure aids proximal tubule reabsorption of sodium and water. Angiotensin II also stimulates proximal tubule sodium reabsorption. Reduced loop of Henle flow—due to reduced glomerular filtration rate and increased proximal reabsorption—and reduced vasa recta flow aid countercurrent multiplication and urinary concentration mechanisms. Angiotensin II modulates activity at sympathetic nerve endings in peripheral blood vessels and in the heart. It increases sympathetic activity partly by facilitating adrenergic transmitter release and partly by increasing the responsiveness of smooth muscle to norepinephrine. Angiotensin II also stimulates the release of catecholamines from the adrenal medulla.

Blockade of the peripheral effects of angiotensin II is useful therapeutically. For example, in low-output congestive cardiac failure, plasma levels of angiotensin II are high. These high circulating levels promote salt and water retention and—by constricting arterioles—raise peripheral vascular resistance, thus increasing cardiac afterload. Treatment with converting enzyme inhibitors such as captopril results in peripheral vasodilation, thereby improving tissue perfusion and cardiac performance as well as aiding renal elimination of salt and water. The use of converting enzyme inhibitors in the treatment of hypertension is discussed below.

Extrarenal Renin-Angiotensin Systems

Many tissues in the body, including the brain, heart, ovary, adrenal, testis, and peripheral blood vessels, contain the components of the renin-angiotensin system. In some of these tissues, there is evidence that angiotensin can be formed locally and that such formation may have physiologic functions. For example, production of angiotensin II in the brain has been implicated in several models of hypertension.

Effects in the Brain & Central Nervous System

Many actions of angiotensin on the central nervous system have been described. Angiotensin II is a polar peptide that does not cross the blood-brain barrier. Circulating angiotensin II, however, may affect the brain by acting through one or more of the circumventricular organs. These specialized regions within the brain lack a blood-brain barrier, so that receptive cells in these areas are sensitive to plasma composition. Of particular significance to the actions of angiotensin are the subfornical organ, the organum vasculosum of the lamina terminalis, and the area postrema.

The major actions of angiotensin II on the brain are listed in Table 7–6. Angiotensin II is a potent dipsogen when injected directly into the brain or administered systemically. The major receptors for the dipsogenic action of circulating angiotensin II are located in the subfornical organ. Angiotensin II also stimulates vasopressin secretion, particularly in association with raised plasma osmolality. As such, the renin-angiotensin system may have an important part to play in the control of water balance, particularly during hypovolemia.

Angiotensin also acts on the brain to increase blood pressure, though its effects at this site seem to be less potent than those exerted directly in the systemic circulation. In most animals, the receptors are located in the area postrema.

Other central actions of angiotensin II include stimulation of adrenocorticotropic hormone (ACTH) secretion, suppression of plasma renin activity, and stimulation of sodium appetite, particularly in association with raised mineralocorticoid levels. The full implications of these (and other) central actions of angiotensin remain to be elucidated.

RENIN & HYPERTENSION (Table 7–5)

Since the original observation that impaired renal perfusion leads to secretion of renin and an increase in blood pressure, renin has been implicated in the etiology of hypertension. For many years, the evidence linking renin to hypertension was inconclusive, and many investigators discounted the participation of the renin-angiotensin system in all but a few forms of hypertension. For example, rare renin-producing tumors can result in severe hypertension. Renal artery stenosis and coarctation of the aorta above the origin of the renal arteries are associated with renin-dependent hypertension. Similarly, malignant hypertension in end-stage renal disease is associated with increased plasma renin levels.

Renin & Essential Hypertension

Most patients with hypertension have essential hypertension. The connection between renin and essential hypertension has been puzzling because hypertension represents a mixture of clinical entities. At one end of the spectrum lie various causes of hypertension that have in common intense peripheral vasoconstriction ("dry hypertension"). Thus, increased activity of any vasoconstrictor agent—eg, angiotensin in renal vascular hypertension or catecholamines in pheochromocytomas—will cause arteriolar vasoconstriction and an increase in total peripheral resistance and thus an increase in blood pressure. At the other end of the spectrum are increases in blood pressure due to expansion of extracellular fluid volume ("wet hypertension"). Thus, any situation that leads to sodium or water retention can lead to an increase in blood pressure.

Much effort has been expended in defining a normal range for plasma renin activity. It is not easy to assess the state of the renin-angiotensin system from a single blood sample drawn for analysis of plasma renin activity, since the secretion rate may be affected by so many factors. Furthermore, assay methodology varies between laboratories in such important aspects as the pH of the incubation. Of particular importance is the sodium content of the diet. Other factors that affect the interpretation of results include sex, age, race, position (supine, upright, etc),

Table 7–6. Actions of angiotensin on the brain.

Stimulates drinking
Increases vasopressin secretion
Stimulates ACTH secretion
Raises blood pressure
Increases salt appetite

physical activity, severity of hypertension, concurrent medications such as birth control pills and antihypertensive drugs, and illnesses such as diabetes mellitus, congestive heart failure, and cirrhosis. Diuretic therapy is especially important to consider, because it can lead to sodium depletion and elevated plasma renin levels.

Several protocols have been used to standardize the plasma renin activity measurements. These include measurements after normal and low sodium diets, pretreatment with a diuretic, overnight recumbency, and 4 hours of ambulation. Another approach to this problem has been to correlate plasma renin activity with the sodium content of the diet as judged by 24-hour urine collection (Figure 7–9). Investigation of normal subjects has shown that in general, the higher the sodium content of the diet, the lower the plasma renin activity. For instance, when standardized with the latter approach, plasma renin activity in patients with essential hypertension varies considerably. Around 5% of such patients have high levels and around 30% have low levels of plasma renin activity. The significance of these differences is not known. In general, the blood pressure of patients with low plasma renin levels responds better to calcium channel blockers and diuretics and that of patients with higher renin levels responds better to converting enzyme inhibitors and beta-adrenergic blockers. However, even patients with normal plasma renin levels exhibit considerable heterogeneity in response to therapy. Thus, despite the logic of "renin profiling" to decide on an appropriate therapeutic agent, this method has not come into general usage.

Renovascular Hypertension

The most common known cause of renin-dependent hypertension is renovascular hypertension. Various studies have reported it to be present in 1–4% of patients with hypertension. Renovascular hypertension is usually due to either atherosclerosis or fibromuscular hyperplasia of the renal arteries. These result in decreased perfusion in the renal segment distal to the obstructed vessel, resulting in increased renin release and angiotensin II production. Blood pressure increase and high angiotensin II levels suppress renin release from the contralateral kidney. Consequently, total plasma renin activity may be only slightly elevated or even normal.

Other anatomic lesions may cause hypertension as well: renal infarction, solitary cysts, hydronephrosis, and other parenchymal lesions.

A reliable and simple single screening test for renovascular hypertension is unavailable. Because of this and the low incidence of the disorder, screening all hypertensives for renovascular hypertension is generally not recommended. Instead, most physicians look for indications that the hypertension is inappropriate before deciding to evaluate the patient for ren-

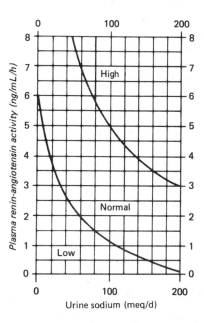

Figure 7–9. Correlation of plasma renin activity with 24-hour sodium excretion in human subjects. (Reproduced, with permission, from Laragh JH, Sealey JE: Renin-sodium profiling: Why, how, and when in clinical practice. Cardiovasc Med 1977;2:1053.)

ovascular hypertension. As a general guideline, any combination of severe hypertension, accelerated hypertension, onset of hypertension before age 20 or after age 50, the presence of abdominal bruit, or hypokalemia in a patient without a family history of hypertension should lead to evaluation for this disorder. Although hypertension in general is more common in blacks, renovascular hypertension is more common in whites.

Renovascular hypertension is diagnosed by tests that demonstrate the anatomic defect and by functional studies that document the abnormal renin release. There is no general agreement about which of the available tests should be performed or the order in which they should be performed. Although the rapid-sequence hypertensive intravenous urogram or pyelogram and radionucleotide renal imaging have been traditionally used for screening, these tests are not frequently used because of their low sensitivity and specificity. The best techniques for defining the renal artery lesion are renal arteriography and CT scanning, which can delineate the anatomic constriction and provide some indication about whether it can be relieved through transluminal angioplasty or other means.

The two most popular methods for documenting the abnormal renin release are selective sampling from the renal veins by renal vein catheterization (selective venous sampling) and blocking angiotensin II production by administration of converting enzyme inhibitor (captopril test). Basal plasma renin levels by themselves do not indicate the diagnosis unless they are extremely low (arguing against the diagnosis), since normal plasma renin levels can be present in renovascular hypertension and elevated levels are present in a significant number of patients with essential hypertension (discussed below) and other forms of renal disease.

In selective venous sampling, plasma samples are taken of the venous effluent from the affected portion of the kidney and from the contralateral kidney. The renin level is ordinarily significantly higher in the sample from the affected kidney than in that from the contralateral kidney. When the value for the affected kidney sample is divided by the value for the unaffected sample, a ratio greater than 1.5 generally indicates a functional abnormality, though a lower ratio does not exclude the diagnosis. In some centers, the results are analyzed by subtracting the arterial value from the venous value and dividing the result by the arterial plasma renin values.

The captopril test involves administering 25 mg of captopril to the patient (on a high- or normal-sodium diet) and measuring the plasma renin levels before and 1 hour after the administration. Captopril induces a reactive hyperreninemia by blocking the negative feedback exerted by intrarenal angiotensin II, and blood pressure falls—often dramatically. This feedback is less pronounced in patients with essential hypertension.

Anatomic correction is the preferred therapy for renovascular hypertension when it is possible and the patient is considered able to tolerate the procedure. Recent advances in transluminal angioplasty have made this the procedure of choice. In special situations, other surgical approaches such as endarterectomy are used. However, renovascular hypertension can be treated medically; this treatment is used when the patient is considered unable to tolerate a surgical procedure or the diagnosis is uncertain. The converting enzyme inhibitors, captopril and enalapril, are particularly effective, though they can lower intrarenal efferent arteriolar resistance and so decrease renal function in patients with bilateral renal artery stenosis. Renovascular hypertension may also respond to beta-adrenergic and calcium channel blockers.

Renin-Secreting Tumors

Renin-secreting tumors are extremely rare and can be mistaken for primary aldosteronism. This is because patients have high plasma levels of aldosterone, marked hypokalemia, and hypertension. However, plasma renin levels are typically elevated. The tumors are usually hemangiopericytomas containing elements of the juxtaglomerular cells. They are located by renal vein catheterization. Other tumors (Wilms' tumor, ectopic tumors) that secrete renin have been reported, including a pulmonary tumor that secreted excessive amounts of renin, producing hypertension and hypokalemia with secondary aldosteronism.

Accelerated Hypertension

Accelerated hypertension is characterized by marked elevations of diastolic blood pressure that can be abrupt in onset. This disorder is associated with progressive arteriosclerosis. The plasma levels of renin and aldosterone may be extremely high. It is believed that the intense vasospastic events that occur and the excessive renal cortical nephrosclerosis lead to hyperreninemia and accelerate the hypertensive process. Vigorous antihypertensive therapy usually mitigates the hyperaldosteronism.

Estrogen Therapy

Aldosterone levels are increased during replacement estrogen therapy or use of oral contraceptives. This is due to increases in plasma renin substrate (angiotensinogen) and plasma renin activity. Angiotensin II levels are increased and thus stimulate aldosterone production. However, hypokalemia rarely occurs during estrogen administration. Total plasma cortisol levels are usually increased due to estrogen-induced increases in CBG concentration.

SYNDROMES OF GLUCOCORTICOID EXCESS & HYPERTENSION

1. CUSHING'S SYNDROME

Hypertension is a common finding of endogenous hypercortisolism (present in more than 80% of cases; see Chapter 6) but occurs in only 10–20% of patients receiving therapy with synthetic glucocorticoids. ACTH-dependent hypercortisolism (Cushing's disease and ectopic ACTH production) is frequently accompanied by increased levels of other ACTH-dependent steroids, especially DOC and corticosterone. Elevated DOC (Figure 7–10) and cortisol levels probably contribute to the mineralocorticoid excess state (see Chapter 6). Plasma renin activity varies but is mostly normal due to increased production of renin substrate. Serum potassium levels are also normal in most patients, implying the absence of a mineralocorticoid excess state. However, a small subset of patients have hypokalemia and suppressed plasma renin levels. Most of these patients have ectopic ACTH hypersecretion or adrenal tumors. Even when there is evidence for mineralocorticoid excess (suppressed plasma renin and hypokalemia), levels of aldosterone and 18-hydroxycorticosterone are consistently within or below the low normal range.

Hypertension in Cushing's syndrome is usually more frequent in patients with adrenocortical hyperplasia (due to ACTH excess) than in patients with cortical adenomas, which implies that in addition to cortisol, other ACTH-dependent steroids, like deoxycorticosterone, corticosterone, or 18-hydroxydeoxy-

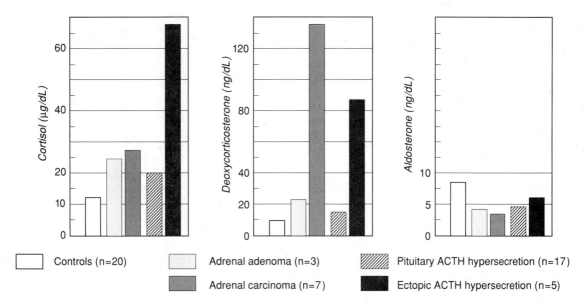

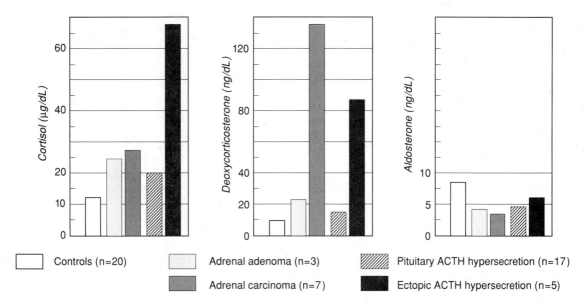

☐ Controls (n=20)	☐ Adrenal adenoma (n=3)	▨ Pituitary ACTH hypersecretion (n=17)
	■ Adrenal carcinoma (n=7)	■ Ectopic ACTH hypersecretion (n=5)

Figure 7–10. Basal cortisol, deoxycorticosterone, and aldosterone levels in patients with Cushing's syndrome according to their etiology.

corticosterone, may contribute to the development or maintenance of hypertension. In addition, urinary excretion of the potent naturally occurring mineralocorticoid 19-nor-DOC, produced in the kidney by the conversion of an oxygenated form of DOC, is elevated in both the primary (adrenal) and secondary (pituitary) forms of Cushing's syndrome. However, since a mineralocorticoid excess state is not apparent in many of these patients, the steroids may be causing hypertension by mineralocorticoid-independent mechanisms (see below).

Pathophysiology & Characteristics of Hypertension in Cushing's Syndrome (Figure 7–11)

The cardiovascular hemodynamics of hypertension in Cushing's syndrome support the participation of both increased total peripheral vascular resistance and increased cardiac output. The following mechanisms may be relatively involved in the pathogenesis of glucocorticoid-induced hypertension of Cushing's syndrome (Figure 7–11).

(1) Increased cortisol inhibits vasodilator systems such as kinins and prostaglandins.

(2) Cortisol increases renin substrate, which may lead to increased angiotensin II levels and increased vasoconstriction.

(3) Cortisol inhibits catecholamine degradation and increases vascular reactivity to vasoconstrictors, increasing total peripheral resistance.

(4) Cortisol increases plasma and extracellular

fluid volume, leading to increased cardiac output.

(5) Other mineralocorticoids such as DOC and 19-nor-DOC increase mineralocorticoid activity, leading to increased blood volume.

(6) A possible contributing mechanism to the elevated cardiac output may be the increased epinephrine formation resulting from enhanced phenylethanolamine-N-methyltransferase (PNMT) activity in the adrenal medulla and also in the myocardium.

2. OTHER HYPERTENSIVE SYNDROMES WITH PSEUDOHYPERALDOSTERONISM (Table 7–5)

Secondary Mineralocorticoid Deficiency

Secondary mineralocorticoid deficiency (pseudohyperaldosteronism) comprises a heterogeneous group of disorders in which endogenous mineralocorticoid secretion is abnormally low owing to suppressed or insufficient renin production. In the former situation, renin is suppressed by increased sodium retention and volume expansion, resulting either from the presence of exogenous mineralocorticoids or mineralocorticoid-like substances or from a renal tubular defect. Hypertension, hypokalemia, and metabolic alkalosis are the usual manifestations. On the other hand, when renin production is insufficient to stimulate mineralocorticoid production, sodium loss, hyperkalemia, and metabolic acidosis occur.

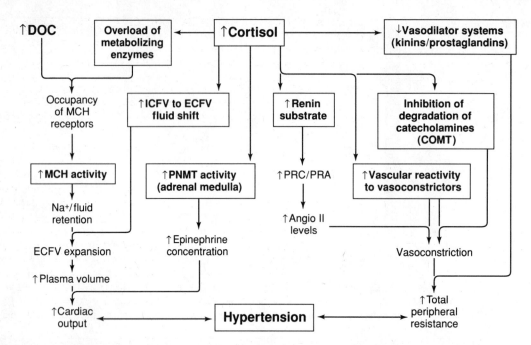

Figure 7–11. Mechanisms involved in glucocorticoid hypertension. (DOC, deoxycorticosterone; MCH, mineralocorticoid hormone; ECFV, extracellular fluid volume; ICFV, intracellular fluid volume; PRC, plasma renin concentration; PRA, plasma renin activity; COMT, catechol-O-methyltransferase; PNMT, phenylethanolamine-N-methyltransferase.)

Syndrome of Apparent Mineralocorticoid Excess (11β-Hydroxysteroid Dehydrogenase Deficiency)

An interesting subgroup of patients with hypertension, hypokalemia, and suppressed renin and aldosterone production but normal cortisol levels has been described primarily in children. The hypertension is sodium-dependent and responds to treatment with spironolactone. However, the steroid abnormality detected in this disorder is the reduced peripheral metabolism of cortisol. There is defective conversion of cortisol to cortisone (Figure 7–12) due to 11β-hydroxysteroid dehydrogenase deficiency. This results in an accumulation of cortisol in renal cells with subsequent occupancy of mineralocorticoid receptors and cortisol-induced mineralocorticoid excess. This is associated with an increase in tetrahydrocortisol (THF) and reduction in tetrahydrocortisone (THE). The disorder can be diagnosed by a high THF/THE ratio (Figure 7–13). Despite normal plasma cortisol levels, urinary cortisol is increased, reflecting impairment of the kidney's ability to convert cortisol to the inactive cortisone. Treatment consists in the administration of dexamethasone (0.75–1 mg/d), which is a weak mineralocorticoid, to suppress ACTH and cortisol production.

Chronic Ingestion of Licorice

Chronic ingestion of large amounts of substances containing "mineralocorticoid-like activity"—eg, certain candies, infusions, and some chewing tobaccos containing licorice—results in a syndrome of hypertension, hypokalemia, renal sodium retention, volume expansion, suppressed plasma renin activity, and metabolic alkalosis that is almost indistinguishable from primary hyperaldosteronism. Aldosterone secretion or excretion is, however, low or undetectable, as are other mineralocorticoid precursors in the aldosterone pathway. The responsible agent for this syndrome is the active principle of licorice, glycyrrhizic acid, and its metabolite glycyrrhetinic acid, that are present in certain commercially available products. They inhibit 11β-hydroxysteroid dehydrogenase in the kidney, which increases free cortisol locally to act as the mineralocorticoid—similar to the syndrome of apparent mineralocorticoid excess. Hypermineralocorticoidism can be induced by licorice and its derivatives such as carbenoxolone (an antigastric ulcer drug), the sodium hemisuccinate of 18β-glycyrrhetinic acid. Electrolyte abnormalities and hypertension disappear within a few weeks upon discontinuation of licorice ingestion or carbenoxolone withdrawal.

Liddle's Syndrome

In 1963, Liddle et al studied a family in which the affected members had clinical manifestations resembling those of classic primary aldosteronism: hypertension, hypokalemia with renal potassium wasting, metabolic alkalosis, and suppressed plasma renin activity. However, aldosterone production was negli-

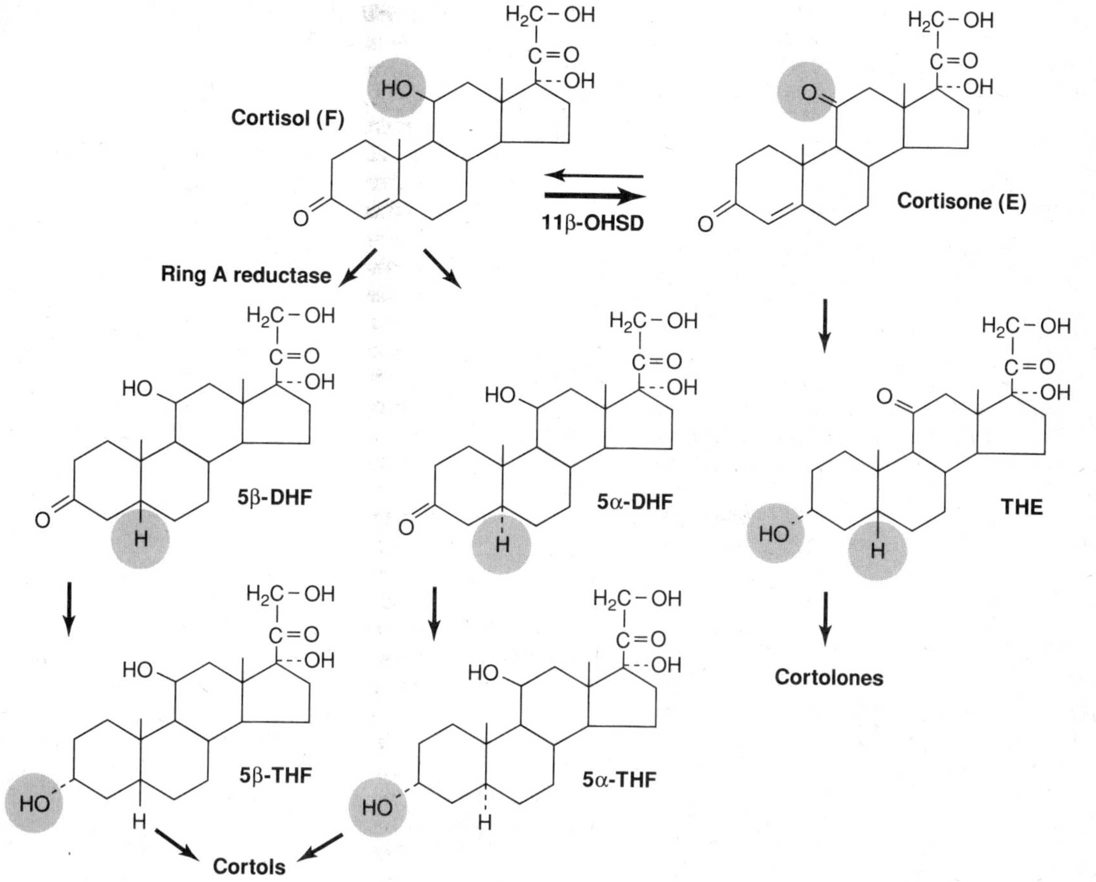

Figure 7–12. Principal pathways of cortisol metabolism. (11β-OHSD, 11β-hydroxysteroid dehydrogenase; DHF, dihydrocortisol; THF, tetrahydrocortisol; THE, tetrahydrocortisone.)

gible. This unusual isolated finding suggested the possibility of excessive production of another unidentified mineralocorticoid to explain the clinical manifestations. However, in contrast to the syndrome of apparent mineralocorticoid excess, administration of spironolactone, a mineralocorticoid antagonist at the distal tubular receptor level, did not correct either the hypertension or the hypokalemia. Furthermore, the adrenocortical synthesis-blocking agent metyrapone, which inhibits 11β- and 18-hydroxylation of aldosterone precursors, also had no effect. In contrast, administration of triamterene, a diuretic agent with potassium-sparing activity acting at a proximal site in the nephron independently of mineralocorticoids, was effective in correcting the abnormalities. The investigators proposed that a primary defect in sodium-potassium transport across membranes in the renal tubule was responsible for the syndrome, though the precise mechanism remains unclear. The defect is probably generalized, since hyperactivity of Na$^+$-K$^+$ ATPase (the sodium-potassium pump) has also been demonstrated in red blood cells.

Arnold-Healy-Gordon Syndrome

Several patients have been reported in whom hypertension is present in association with hyperkalemia, impairment of potassium excretion, hyperchloremic metabolic acidosis, and hyporeninemic hypoaldosteronism in the presence of normal renal function. The aldosterone response to stimulatory maneuvers is normal. Administration of large amounts of mineralocorticoids fails to produce a kaliuretic response and thus correct the hyperkalemia, suggesting a mineralocorticoid-resistant state. Impairment in renal potassium excretion was initially proposed as the primary defect. However, when patients were given a sodium bicarbonate or sulfate load, the increased distal delivery of sodium greatly facilitated potassium excretion and hyperkalemia was virtually corrected, suggesting that the proposed defect in potassium excretion was only secondary. The defect caused increases in chloride reabsorption proximal to the sodium- and mineralocorticoid-dependent driving forces for potassium secretion, resulting in hyperkalemia. By increasing proximal

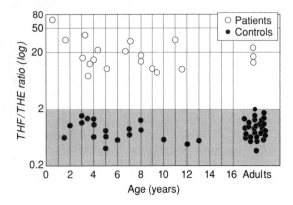

Figure 7–13. Ratio of the urinary metabolites of cortisol (THF, tetrahydrocortisol; 5α-THF, allotetrahydrocortisol) to cortisone (THE, tetrahydrocortisone) in the syndrome of apparent mineralocorticoid excess. (Modified from Shackleton CHL, Stewart PM: The hypertension of apparent mineralocorticoid excess syndrome. In: *Endocrine Hypertension.* Biglieri EG [editor]. Raven Press, 1990.)

sodium reabsorption with consequent volume expansion, hypertension and suppression of renin and aldosterone production occurred.

Abnormalities can be corrected in this syndrome by adding supplementary amounts of sodium bicarbonate, sulfate, or furosemide.

Administration of Synthetic Mineralocorticoid Hormones

In several of the mineralocorticoid deficiency syndromes, the appropriate therapy is mineralocorticoid replacement. The most commonly used synthetic mineralocorticoid is 9α-fluorohydrocortisone (fludrocortisone acetate). Its potent mineralocorticoid activity, which is similar to that of aldosterone, permits it to be used in doses as small as 0.1 mg daily or every other day. Because individual sensitivity to these preparations varies, blood pressure and plasma electrolyte panels should be monitored closely. When used in inappropriately high dosage or in the presence of increased sodium intake or inadequate metabolism, increased mineralocorticoid activity will result in sodium retention, expansion of extracellular fluid volume, hypertension, and hypokalemia.

Also, continuous use of some fluorinated steroids with powerful mineralocorticoid-like activity contained in some topical preparations such as nasal sprays and dermatologic creams can be associated with hypertension, hypokalemia, and renin and aldosterone suppression. Withdrawal of these medica-

tions or adjustment of the dosage easily controls undesirable side effects.

ATRIAL NATRIURETIC PEPTIDE

Extracts of atrial—but not ventricular—tissue cause marked natriuresis when injected into rats. The material is contained in densely staining granules in the atria of most mammalian species. A number of laboratories have sequenced and synthesized several natriuretic peptides containing between 22 and 28 amino acids, and rat and human atrial cDNA clones that encode atrial natriuretic peptides have been isolated and characterized. The 28-amino-acid peptide is probably normally secreted into the bloodstream. Several terms are used to describe these peptides, including atriopeptin, auriculin, cardionatrin, and atrial natriuretic factor. The major effects of administration of atrial natriuretic peptide are natriuresis and a fall in blood pressure. Although the peptide can cause relaxation of smooth muscle, the fall in blood pressure is due to reduction of venous return and depression of cardiac output in intact animals. The natriuresis is associated with a marked increase in filtration fraction without a sustained increase in renal blood flow, which suggests that the peptide may cause efferent arteriolar constriction. There is some evidence that glomerular membrane permeability may be increased and that tubular reabsorption may be reduced. Atrial natriuretic peptide also inhibits secretion of renin and aldosterone. There is also evidence that baroreflex stimulation of the heart rate as well as vasopressin and ACTH secretion is inhibited.

Recently, a number of radioimmunoassays for atrial natriuretic peptide have been developed. Although there are still questions concerning the specificity of these assays, it is clear that there are measurable levels of the material in normal plasma. Maneuvers that expand plasma volume and experiments that increase atrial pressure are associated with increased levels of radioimmunoassayable peptide in plasma. Situations such as congestive heart failure that are associated with chronically raised atrial pressures show raised plasma levels of the peptide. Thus, atrial natriuretic peptide may be involved in the control of sodium balance. When blood volume increases, the associated increase in atrial pressure and atrial stretch may trigger secretion of the peptide and lead to natriuresis and blood pressure reduction. However, the precise role atrial natriuretic peptide plays in the control of sodium balance and blood volume under physiologic conditions is not clear.

REFERENCES

Atlas SA, Maack T: Effects of atrial natriuretic factor on the kidney and the renin-angiotensin-aldosterone system. Endocrinol Metab Clin North Am 1987;16:107.

Baxter JD et al: The endocrinology of hypertension. In: *Endocrinology and Metabolism,* 2nd ed. Felig P et al (editors). McGraw-Hill, 1987.

Biglieri EG: The spectrum of mineralocorticoid hypertension. Hypertension 1991;18:251.

Biglieri EG, Kater CE: Disorders of the adrenal cortex. In: *Internal Medicine,* 2nd ed. Stein JH (editor). Little, Brown, 1987.

Biglieri EG, Kater CE: 17α-Hydroxylation deficiency. Endocrinol Metab Clin North Am 1991;20:257.

Biglieri EG, Kater CE: Mineralocorticoids in congenital adrenal hyperplasia. J Steroid Biochem Molec Biol 1991;40:493.

Carey RM, Sen S: Recent progress in the control of aldosterone secretion. Recent Prog Horm Res 1986;42:251.

Dzau VJ, Burt DW, Pratt RE: Molecular biology of the renin-angiotensin system. Am J Physiol 1988;255:F563.

Falke TH et al: MR imaging of the adrenals: Correlation with computed tomography. J Comput Assist Tomogr 1986;10:242.

Genest J, Cantin M: The atrial natriuretic factor: Its physiology and biochemistry. Rev Physiol Biochem Pharm 1988;110:1.

Gordon RD: Syndrome of hypertension and hyperkalemia with normal glomerular filtration rate. Hypertension 1986;8:93.

Hunt TK, Biglieri EG, Tyrrell JB: Adrenals. In: *Current Surgical Diagnosis & Treatment,* 8th ed. Way LW (editor). Appleton & Lange, 1988.

Irony I et al: Correctable subsets of primary aldosteronism: Primary adrenal hyperplasia and renin responsive adenoma. Am J Hypertens 1990;3:576.

Kater CE et al: Stimulation and suppression of the mineralocorticoid hormones in normal subjects and adrenocortical disorders. Endocr Rev 1989;11:149.

Krieger JE, Dzau VJ: Molecular biology of hypertension. Hypertension 1991;18(Suppl):13.

Laragh JH: Atrial natriuretic hormone, the renin-aldosterone axis, and blood pressure: Electrolyte homeostasis. N Engl J Med 1985;313:1330.

Lifton RP et al: A chimaeric 11β-hydroxylase/aldosterone synthase gene causes glucocorticoid-remediable aldosteronism and human hypertension. Nature 1992;355: 262.

Mantero F et al: New aspects of mineralocorticoid hypertension. Horm Res 1990;34:175.

Melby JC: Diagnosis of hyperaldosteronism. Endocrinol Metab Clin North Am 1991;20:247.

Pickering TG: Renovascular hypertension. Medical evaluation and non-surgical treatment. In: *Hypertension: Pathophysiology, Diagnosis, and Management.* Laragh JH, Brenner BM (editors). Raven Press, 1990.

Rodriguez-Portales JA: 11β-Hydroxylation deficiency. In: *Endocrine Hypertension.* Biglieri EG (editor). Raven Press, 1990.

Schalekamp MA, Wenting GJ, Man in't Veld AJ: Pathogenesis of mineralocorticoid hypertension. Clin Endocrinol Metab 1981;10:397.

Ulick S: Two uncommon causes of mineralocorticoid excess: Syndrome of apparent mineralocorticoid excess and glucocorticoid-remediable aldosteronism. Endocrinol Metab Clin North Am 1991;20:269.

Williams GH: Guardian of the gate: Receptors, enzymes, and mineralocorticoid function. (Editorial.) J Clin Endocrinol Metab 1991;74:961.

Young Jr WF, Klee GG: Primary aldosteronism: Diagnostic evaluation. Endocrinol Metab Clin North Am 1988;17:367.

Adrenal Medulla

8

Alan Goldfien, MD

The adrenal medulla was first distinguished from the adrenal cortex at the beginning of the 19th century. Its major secretory product, **epinephrine,** was isolated, purified, and synthesized a century later. **Norepinephrine** was synthesized in 1904, but not until 1946 was it recognized as a secretory product of the adrenal medulla and as the major neurotransmitter of the postganglionic sympathetic nerves. The adrenal medulla, a highly specialized part of the sympathetic nervous system, functions under stress or whenever marked deviations from normal homeostasis occur—in contrast to the rest of the sympathetic nervous system, which is involved in the minute-to-minute fine regulation of most physiologic processes.

ANATOMY

Embryology
(Figure 8–1)

The sympathetic nervous system arises in the fetus from the primitive cells of the neural crest (sympathogonia). At about the fifth week of gestation, these cells migrate from the primitive spinal ganglia in the thoracic region to form the sympathetic chain posterior to the dorsal aorta. They then begin to migrate anteriorly to form the remaining ganglia.

At 6 weeks, groups of these primitive cells migrate along the central vein and enter the fetal adrenal cortex to form the adrenal medulla, which is detectable by the eighth week. The adrenal medulla at this time is composed of sympathogonia and pheochromoblasts, which then mature into pheochromocytes. The cells appear in rosette-like structures, with the more primitive cells occupying a central position. Storage granules can be found in these cells by electron microscopy at 12 weeks. Pheochromoblasts and pheochromocytes also collect on both sides of the aorta to form the paraganglia. The principal collection of these cells is found at the level of the inferior mesenteric artery. They fuse anteriorly to form the organ of Zuckerkandl, which is quite prominent in fetal life. This organ is thought to be a major source of catecholamines during the first year of life, after which it begins to atrophy. Pheochromocytes (chromaffin cells) also are found scattered throughout the abdominal sympathetic plexuses as well as in other parts of the sympathetic nervous system.

Gross Structure

The anatomic relationships between the adrenal medulla and the adrenal cortex are different in different species. These organs are completely separate structures in the shark. They remain separate but in close contact in amphibians, and there is some intermingling in birds. In mammals, the medulla is surrounded by the adrenal cortex. In humans, the adrenal medulla occupies a central position in the widest part of the gland, with only small portions extending into the narrower parts. It constitutes approximately one-tenth of the weight of the gland, although the proportions vary from individual to individual. There is no clear demarcation between cortex and medulla. The central vein is usually surrounded by a cuff of adrenal cortical cells, and there may be islands of cortex elsewhere in the medulla.

Microscopic Structure

The **chromaffin cells,** or **pheochromocytes,** of the adrenal medulla are large ovoid columnar cells arranged in clumps or cords around blood vessels. They derive their name from the observation that their granules turn brown (*pheo-*) when stained with chromic acid. The color is due to the oxidation of epinephrine and norepinephrine to melanin. These cells have large nuclei and a well-developed Golgi apparatus. They contain large numbers of vesicles or granules containing catecholamines. Vesicles con-

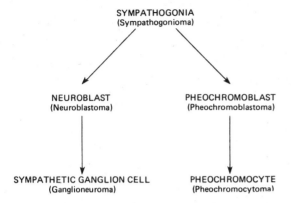

SYMPATHOGONIA
(Sympathogonioma)

NEUROBLAST
(Neuroblastoma)

PHEOCHROMOBLAST
(Pheochromoblastoma)

SYMPATHETIC GANGLION CELL
(Ganglioneuroma)

PHEOCHROMOCYTE
(Pheochromocytoma)

Figure 8–1. The embryonic development of adrenergic cells and tumors that develop from them. Sympathogonia are primitive cells derived from the neural crest. Neuroblasts are also called sympathoblasts; ganglion cells are the same as sympathocytes; and pheochromocytes are mature chromaffin cells.

taining norepinephrine are darker than those containing epinephrine.

The pheochromocytes may be arranged in nests, alveoli, or cords and are surrounded by a rich network of capillaries and sinusoids. The adrenal medulla also contains some sympathetic ganglion cells, singly or in groups. Ganglion cells are also found in association with the viscera, the carotid body, the glomus jugulare, and the cervical and thoracic ganglia.

Nerve Supply

The cells of the adrenal medulla are innervated by preganglionic fibers of the sympathetic nervous system, which release acetylcholine and enkephalins at the synapses. Most of these fibers arise from a plexus in the capsule of the posterior surface of the gland and enter the adrenal glands in bundles of 30–50 fibers without synapsing. They follow the course of the blood vessels into the medulla without branching into the adrenal cortex. Some reach the wall of the central vein, where they synapse with small autonomic ganglia. However, most fibers end in relationship to the pheochromocytes.

Blood Supply

The human adrenal gland derives blood from the superior, middle, and inferior adrenal branches of the inferior phrenic artery, directly from the aorta and from the renal arteries. Upon reaching the adrenal gland, these arteries branch to form a plexus under the capsule supplying the adrenal cortex. A few of these vessels, however, penetrate the cortex, passing directly to the medulla. The medulla is also nourished by branches of the arteries supplying the central vein and cuff of cortical tissue around the central vein. Capillary loops passing from the subcapsular

plexus of the cortex also supply blood as they drain into the central vein. It would appear, then, that most of the blood supply to the medullary cells is via a portal vascular system arising from the capillaries in the cortex. There is also a capillary network of lymphatics that drain into a plexus around the central vein.

In mammals, the enzyme that catalyzes the conversion of norepinephrine to epinephrine (phenylethanolamine-N-methyltransferase, PNMT) is induced by cortisol. The chromaffin cells containing epinephrine therefore receive most of their blood supply from the capillaries draining the cortical cells, whereas cells containing predominantly norepinephrine are supplied by the arteries that directly supply the medulla. (See Biosynthesis, below.)

On the right side, the central vein is short and drains directly into the vena cava, although some branches go to the surface of the gland and reach the azygos system. On the left, the vein is somewhat longer and drains into the renal vein.

HORMONES OF THE ADRENAL MEDULLA

CATECHOLAMINES

Biosynthesis
(Figure 8–2)

Catecholamines are widely distributed in plants and animals. In mammals, **epinephrine** is synthesized mainly in the adrenal medulla, whereas **norepinephrine** is found not only in the adrenal medulla but also in the central nervous system and in the peripheral sympathetic nerves. **Dopamine,** the precursor of norepinephrine, is found in the adrenal medulla and in noradrenergic neurons. It is present in high concentrations in the brain, in specialized interneurons in the sympathetic ganglia, and in the carotid body, where it serves as a neurotransmitter. Dopamine is also found in specialized mast cells and in enterochromaffin cells.

The proportions of epinephrine and norepinephrine found in the adrenal medulla vary with the species (Table 8–1). In humans, the adrenal contains 15–20% norepinephrine.

A. Conversion of Tyrosine to Dopa: The catecholamines are synthesized from **tyrosine,** which may be derived from ingested food or synthesized from phenylalanine in the liver. Tyrosine circulates at a concentration of 1–1.5 mg/dL of blood. It enters neurons and chromaffin cells by an active transport mechanism and is converted to **dihydroxyphen-**

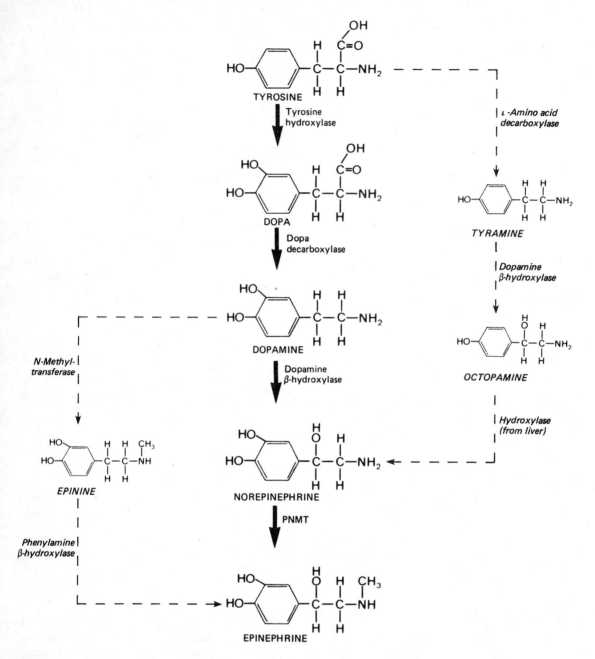

Figure 8–2. Biosynthesis of catecholamines. The alternative pathways shown by the dashed arrows have not been found to be of physiologic significance in humans. (PNMT, phenylethanolamine-N-methyltransferase.)

ylalanine (dopa). The reaction is catalyzed by **tyrosine hydroxylase,** which is transported via axonal flow to the nerve terminal. Tyrosine hydroxylase activity may be inhibited by a variety of compounds. Alpha-methylmetatyrosine is effective and is sometimes used in the therapy of malignant pheochromocytomas (see below). Substances that chelate iron or compete for the pteridine cofactor also inhibit the enzyme but are not useful clinically. Activity of tyro-

sine hydroxylase is a reliable marker of intact sympathetic nerve tissue and neurotransmitter synthesis.

B. Conversion of Dopa to Dopamine: Dopa is converted to dopamine by the enzyme aromatic L-amino acid decarboxylase (dopa decarboxylase). This enzyme is found in all tissues, with the highest concentrations in liver, kidney, brain, and vas deferens. The various enzymes have different substrate specificities depending upon the tissue source. Com-

Table 8–1. Approximate percentages
of total adrenal medullary catecholamines
present as norepinephrine
in various species.

Whale	70	Horse	25
Chicken	70	Squirrel	25
Lion	55	Cow	25
Frog	50	Human	20
Pig	45	Guinea pig	15
Cat	40	Rat	15
Gazelle	35	Zebra	13
Sheep	35	Rabbit	5
Goat	35	Baboon	0
Dog	30		

petitive inhibitors of dopa decarboxylase such as methyldopa are converted to substances (an example is α-methylnorepinephrine) that are then stored in granules in the nerve cell and released in place of norepinephrine. These products (false transmitters) were thought to mediate the antihypertensive action of drugs at peripheral sympathetic synapses but are now believed to stimulate the alpha receptors of the inhibitory corticobulbar system, reducing sympathetic discharge peripherally.

C. Conversion of Dopamine to Norepinephrine: The conversion of dopamine to norepinephrine is catalyzed by dopamine β-hydroxylase, a mixed-function oxidase requiring oxygen and an external electron donor. The enzyme does not occur in tissues outside the neuron. Part of the biologic specificity of dopamine β-hydroxylase may result from its compartmentalization. Newly synthesized dopamine β-hydroxylase is incorporated directly into storage vesicles that take up, synthesize, and store the catecholamines. The membranes of these vesicles contain dopamine β-hydroxylase, ATPase, cytochrome P-561, and cytochrome P-561:NADH reductase. Dopamine β-hydroxylase is also found within the granule and is released with norepinephrine during secretion. Inhibitors of the enzyme, such as disulfuramic and picolinic acid, have no clinical importance.

D. Conversion of Norepinephrine to Epinephrine: PNMT catalyzes the N-methylation of norepinephrine to epinephrine, using S-adenosylmethionine as a methyl donor. It is found only in the adrenal medulla and in a few neurons in the central nervous system. The enzyme is found in the cytosol. Norepinephrine leaves the granule and after methylation reenters different granules. This enzyme is induced by the high levels of glucocorticoids (100 times the systemic concentration) found in the adrenal medulla. The conversion of dopamine to **epinine** is catalyzed by a nonspecific N-methyltransferase.

Catecholamine biosynthesis is coupled to secretion, so that the stores of norepinephrine at the nerve endings remain relatively unchanged even in the presence of marked nerve activity. In the adrenal medulla, it is possible to deplete stores with pro-

longed hypoglycemia. Biosynthesis appears to be increased during nerve stimulation by activation of tyrosine hydroxylase. Prolonged stimulation leads to the induction of increased amounts of this enzyme.

Storage

The catecholamines are found in the adrenal medulla and various sympathetically innervated organs, and their concentration reflects the density of sympathetic neurons. The adrenal medulla contains about 0.5 mg/g; the spleen, vas deferens, brain, spinal cord, and heart contain 1–5 µg/g; liver, gut, and skeletal muscle contain 0.1–0.5 µg/g. The catecholamines are stored in electron-dense granules approximately 1 µm in diameter that contain catecholamines and ATP in a 4:1 molar ratio, several neuropeptides, calcium, magnesium, and water-soluble proteins called **chromogranins.** The ratio of catecholamines to ATP is much higher in granules isolated from pheochromocytomas. The interior surface of the membrane contains dopamine β-hydroxylase and ATPase. The Mg^{2+}-dependent ATPase facilitates the uptake and inhibits the release of catecholamines by the granules. This activity is inhibited by reserpine. Adrenal medullary granules appear to contain and release a number of active peptides including ACTH, vasoactive intestinal polypeptide (VIP), chromogranins, and enkephalins. The peptides derived from the chromogranins are physiologically active and may modulate catecholamine release.

Secretion

Adrenal medullary catecholamine secretion is increased by exercise, angina pectoris, myocardial infarction, hemorrhage, ether anesthesia, surgery, hypoglycemia, anoxia and asphyxia, and many other stressful stimuli. The rate of secretion of epinephrine increases more than that of norepinephrine in the presence of hypoglycemia and most other stimuli (Figure 8–3). However, anoxia and asphyxia produce a greater increase in adrenal medullary release of norepinephrine than is observed with other stimuli (Figure 8–4).

Secretion of the adrenal medullary hormones is mediated by the release of acetylcholine from the terminals of preganglionic fibers. The resulting depolarization of the axonal membrane triggers an influx of calcium ion. The contents of the storage vesicles, including the chromogranins and soluble dopamine β-hydroxylase, are released by exocytosis by the calcium ion increase. Membrane-bound dopamine β-hydroxylase is not released. **Tyramine,** however, releases norepinephrine primarily from the free store in the cytosol. Cocaine and monoamine oxidase inhibitors inhibit the effect of tyramine but do not affect the release of catecholamines by nervous stimulation. The rate of release in response to nerve stimulation is increased or decreased by a wide variety of neurotransmitters acting at specific receptors

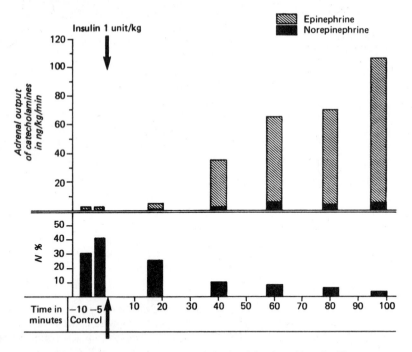

Figure 8–3. Rate of secretion of amines from one adrenal following injection of insulin. The percentage of the total released as norepinephrine is shown below.

on the presynaptic neuron. Norepinephrine has an important role in modulating its own release by activating the alpha receptors on the presynaptic membrane. Alpha$_2$ receptor antagonists inhibit this reaction. Conversely, presynaptic beta receptors enhance norepinephrine release, whereas beta receptor blockers increase it. The effect of such substances are shown in Table 8–2. The accumulation of excess catecholamines that are not in the storage granules is prevented by the presence of intraneuronal monoamine oxidase.

Transport

When released into the circulation, the amines are bound to albumin or a closely associated protein with low affinity and high capacity (K_d 10^{-7}).

Metabolism & Inactivation

The actions of catecholamines are terminated rapidly. Compared to hormones with a more prolonged action they have a relatively low affinity for their receptor and rapidly dissociate from it. The free hormone is removed by several mechanisms. These include reuptake by the sympathetic nerve ending, metabolism by the enzymes catechol-O-methyltransferase (COMT) and monoamine oxidase (Figure 8–5), conjugation with sulfate ion, and direct excretion by the kidney. Estimates of the metabolic clearance rates for epinephrine and norepinephrine are 4000–5000 L/d.

Uptake

A. Neuronal (Uptake 1): A large proportion (85–90%) of the amines released at the synapse are taken up locally by the nerve endings from which they are released (uptake 1). Circulating amines can also be taken up by this mechanism. However, this mechanism plays a less important role in the inactivation of circulating catecholamines. The axonal membrane uptake process is energy-requiring, saturable, stereoselective, and sodium-dependent. It is blocked by cocaine, other sympathomimetic amines such as metaraminol and amphetamine, and agents such as tricyclic antidepressants and phenothiazines. Neither calcium nor magnesium ion has any effect on uptake 1. There is also an uptake process for dopamine in neurons of the central nervous system, but this process is not inhibited by tricyclic antidepressants. After being taken up by the neuron, the amines are reutilized or deaminated by monoamine oxidase and the metabolites are released (Figure 8–6). The intraneuronal monoamine oxidase is a flavoprotein and is localized to the outer mitochondrial membrane. Its substrate specificity favors norepinephrine, which it oxidizes to dihydroxyphenylglycol (DHPG) or dihydroxymandelic acid (DHMA). The major functions of monoamine oxidase are (1) to regulate dopamine and norepinephrine content of the neurons; (2) to destroy ingested amines; and (3) to metabolize the circulating catecholamines and their O-methyl metabolites. Progesterone increases the

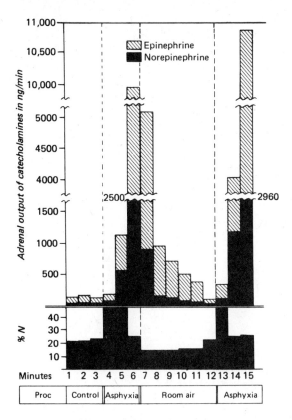

Figure 8–4. Rate of secretion of amines from one adrenal during asphyxia. The percentage of the total released as norepinephrine is shown below.

their O-methyl derivatives by COMT (Figure 8–6). This enzyme is found mainly in the soluble fraction of tissue homogenates, with the highest levels in the liver and kidney. S-Adenosylmethionine is the methyl donor, and divalent ions are required for the reaction. It is predominantly an extraneuronal enzyme and acts on circulating catecholamines as well as on the locally released norepinephrine. It is the most important enzyme in the metabolism of circulating amines. Approximately 70% of circulating epinephrine in humans is methoxylated, and about 24% is also deaminated. These enzymes also metabolize dopamine to homovanillic acid. Although normetanephrine is fairly active at the alpha receptor of the nictitating membrane, the metabolites of the catecholamines are generally devoid of biologic or physiologic activity.

Conjugation

The phenolic hydroxyl group of the catecholamines and their metabolites may be conjugated with sulfate or glucuronide. Liver and gut appear to be important sites of this reaction, and circulating red blood cells are also a significant site of sulfation in humans.

Connective tissue binds catecholamines by a process that is inhibited by oxytetracycline. The significance of this binding is unknown.

Mechanism of Action

The catecholamines exert their physiologic effects by activating signaling pathways in their target cells. The details of the established pathways are discussed in Chapter 1. Early studies of sympathetic activation suggested that there were two classes of responses designated as inhibitory or excitatory. Cannon and his colleagues in the 1930s postulated that this difference was produced by the release of different neurotransmitters: sympathin I and sympathin E. The discovery by von Euler and others that norepinephrine was the neurotransmitter released by peripheral sympathetic nerve endings and was responsible for both types of responses led to the proposal by Ahlquist in 1948 that there were two types of receptors that he designated alpha and beta, based on the relative potencies of a series of adrenergic agonists. The subsequent development of relatively specific antagonists confirmed this hypothesis and allowed the development of binding assays for the alpha, beta, and dopaminergic receptors. Subsequent pharmacologic and biochemical studies indicate that alpha, beta, and dopaminergic receptors can be further divided into subtypes. Although these receptors were first classified by the relative potencies of a series of adrenergic agonists and antagonists, each of the subtypes is now known to be coded for by one or more separate genes. The characteristic interactions of these receptors with various agonists and antagonists are shown in Table 8–3.

level of monoamine oxidase in women, whereas estrogens inhibit the enzyme.

B. Extraneuronal (Uptake 2): Extraneuronal tissues also take up catecholamines. This process, uptake 2, is saturable, is not specific for catecholamines, and is inhibited by various steroids, phenoxybenzamine, and normetanephrine but not by cocaine and other drugs that inhibit neuronal uptake.

At uptake 2, the catecholamines are metabolized to

Table 8–2. Substances altering the release of norepinephrine at nerve endings by binding to specific presynaptic membrane receptors.

Increase	Decrease
Norepinephrine (beta receptor)	[1]Norepinephrine (alpha receptor)
Angiotensin	Serotonin
Epinephrine	Dopamine
	PGE$_2$
	Purines
	Metenkephalin
	Substance P
	Acetylcholine

[1] The alpha receptor-mediated inhibition of norepinephrine release is the dominant effect.

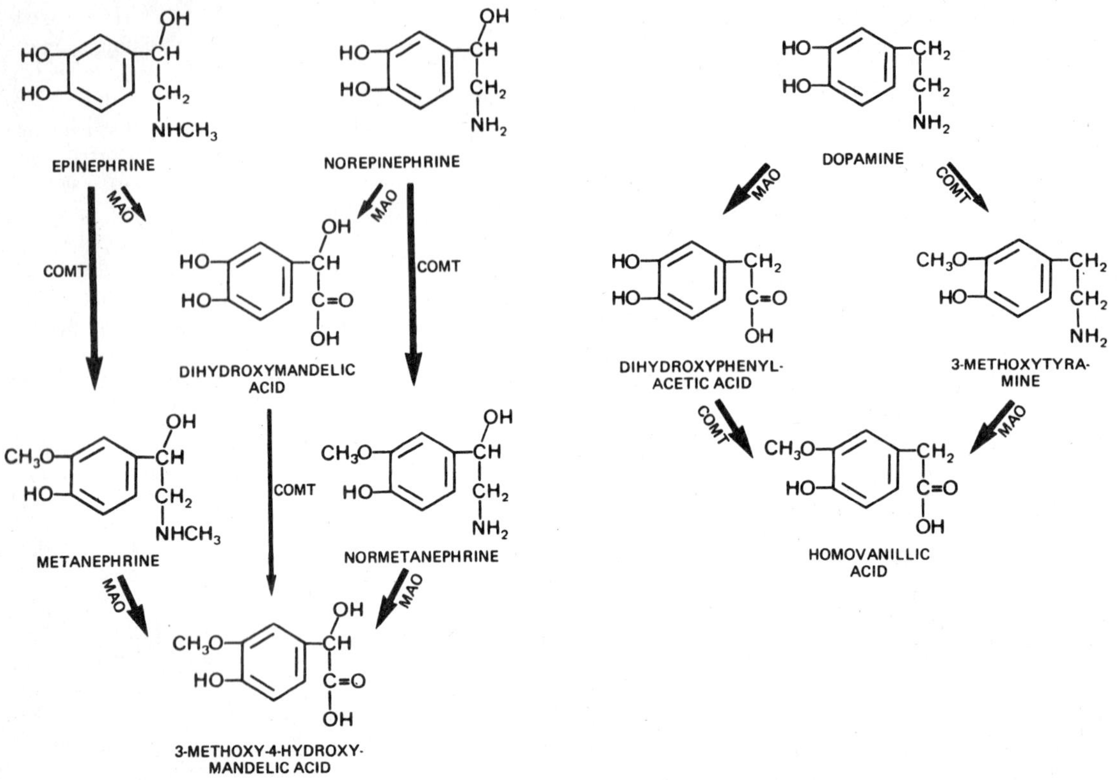

Figure 8–5. Metabolism of catecholamines by catechol-O-methyltransferase (COMT) and monoamine oxidase (MAO).

The physiologic effects mediated by these receptors are summarized in Table 8–4.

The adrenergic receptors are transmembrane proteins with an extracellular amino terminus and an intracellular carboxyl terminus. Each of their seven hydrophobic regions spans the cell membrane. Although these regions of the adrenergic receptor subtypes exhibit significant amino acid homology, differences in the fifth and sixth segments determine the specificity of agonist binding. Differences in the fifth and seventh segments determine whether the receptor is coupled to the stimulatory (G_s) or inhibitory (G_i) guanyl nucleotide binding proteins.

A. Alpha-Adrenergic Receptors: The α_1 subtypes are postsynaptic receptors that typically mediate vascular and other smooth muscle contraction. When agonist binds to this receptor, the alpha subunit of the guanyl nucleotide binding protein G_q is released and activates phospholipase C. This enzyme catalyzes the conversion of phosphatidylinositol phosphate to 1,4,5-inositol trisphosphate (IP_3) and diacylglycerol. IP_3 releases calcium ion from intracellular stores to stimulate physiologic responses. Diacylglycerol activates kinase C, which in turn phosphorylates a series of other proteins that initiate or sustain effects stimulated by the release of IP_3 and calcium ion. Epinephrine and norepinephrine are potent agonists for this receptor, while isoproterenol is weakly active.

Alpha$_2$ receptors were first identified at the presynaptic sympathetic nerve ending and, when activated, served to inhibit the release of norepinephrine. However, these receptors have been found in platelets and postsynaptically in the nervous system, adipose tissue, and smooth muscle.

Agonist binding to the α_2 receptor releases G_i alpha, which inhibits the enzyme adenylyl cyclase and reduces the formation of cAMP. Prazosin is a selective antagonist at the α_1 receptor and yohimbine is selective for the α_2, whereas phentolamine and phenoxybenzamine act at both (Table 8–3).

B. Beta-Adrenergic Receptors: Agonist binding to the beta-adrenergic receptors activates adenylyl cyclase via the G_s alpha subunit to increase the production of cAMP, which in turn converts protein kinase A to its active form. Kinase A then phosphorylates a variety of proteins, including enzymes, ion channels, and receptors (see Chapter 1). There are two major beta-receptor subtypes. The β_1 receptor, which mediates the direct cardiac effects, is more responsive to isoproterenol than to epinephrine or norepinephrine, whose potencies are similar. At the β_2 receptor, which mediates vascular, bronchial, and uterine smooth muscle relaxation, isoproterenol is

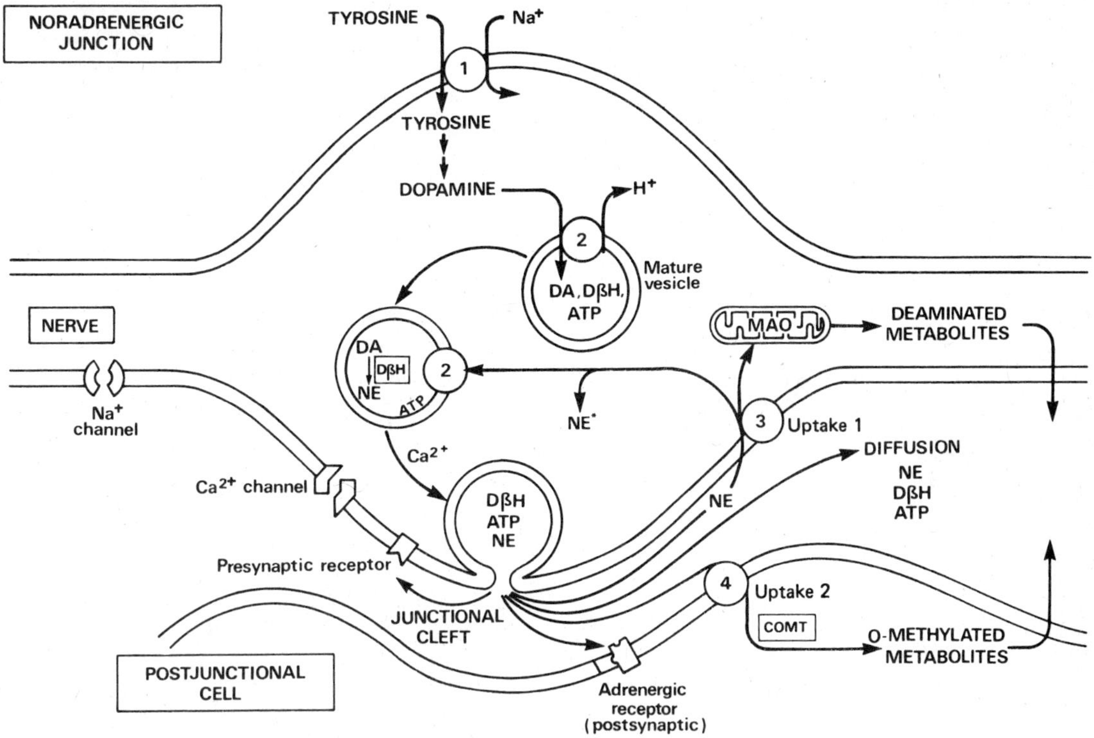

Figure 8–6. Schematic diagram of the neuroeffector junction of the peripheral sympathetic nervous system. The nerves terminate in complex networks with varicosities or enlargements that form synaptic junctions with effector cells. The neurotransmitter at these junctions is norepinephrine, which is synthesized from tyrosine. Tyrosine uptake ① is linked to sodium uptake and transport into the varicosity where the secretory vesicles form. Tyrosine is hydroxylated by tyrosine hydroxylase to dopa, which is then decarboxylated by dopa decarboxylate to dopamine in the cytoplasm. Dopamine (DA) is transported into the vesicle by a carrier mechanism ② that can be blocked by reserpine. The same carrier transports norepinephrine (NE) and several other amines into these granules. Dopamine is converted to norepinephrine through the catalytic action of dopamine β-hydroxylase (DβH). ATP is also present in high concentration in the vesicle. Release of transmitter occurs when an action potential is conducted to the varicosity by the action of voltage-sensitive sodium channels. Depolarization of the varicosity membrane opens voltage-sensitive calcium channels and results in an increase in intracellular calcium. The elevated calcium facilitates exocytotic fusion of vesicles with the surface membrane and expulsion of norepinephrine, ATP, and some of the dopamine β-hydroxylase. Release is blocked by drugs such as guanethidine and bretylium. Norepinephrine reaching either pre- or postsynaptic receptors modifies the function of the corresponding cells. Norepinephrine also diffuses out of the cleft, or it may be transported into the cytoplasm of the varicosity (uptake 1, blocked by cocaine, tricyclic antidepressants) ③ or into the postjunctional cell (uptake 2) ④. (Reproduced, with permission, from Katzung BG [editor]: Basic & Clinical Pharmacology, 5th ed. Appleton & Lange, 1992.)

also most potent, but epinephrine is much more potent than norepinephrine.

C. Dopamine Receptors: Dopaminergic receptors are found in the central nervous system, presynaptic adrenergic nerve terminals, pituitary, heart, renal and mesenteric vascular beds, and other sites. Two subtypes of the dopaminergic receptor, D_1 and D_2, have been identified. The binding affinity of the D_1 receptor is greater for dopamine than for haloperidol; the reverse is true for the D_2 receptor. The effects of the D_1 receptor are mediated by stimulation of the adenylyl cyclase system and are found postsynaptically in the brain. Those in the pituitary are D_2 receptors that inhibit the formation of cAMP.

Regulation of Activity

The major physiologic control of sympathoadrenal activity is exerted by alterations in the rate of secretion of the catecholamines. However, the receptors and postreceptor events serve as sites of fine regulation.

As noted above, presynaptically, norepinephrine released during nerve stimulation binds to alpha receptors and reduces the amount of norepinephrine released. Nerve endings have also been found to have receptors for many other agents presynaptically (Table 8–2).

The number of receptors on the effector cell surface can be reduced by binding of agonist to receptor (antagonists do not have the same effect). This reduc-

Table 8–3. Characteristic interactions of agonists and antagonists at the adrenergic receptors.

Receptor	Agonist Potency[1]	Antagonist Potency	Agonist Effect on Adenylyl Cyclase Activity
Alpha$_1$	Same for α_1 and α_2.	Prazosin > phentolamine >yohimbine.	None
Alpha$_2$	Epinephrine slightly > norepinephrine >> isoproterenol.	Phentolamine slightly >yohimbine >> prazosin.	Decrease
Beta$_1$	Isoproterenol > epinephrine $\cong$ norepinephrine.	Metoprolol > butoxamine.	Increase
Beta$_2$	Isoproterenol > epinephrine >> norepinephrine.	Butoxamine > metoprolol.	Increase

[1] These potencies are defined by studies of binding competition and pharmacologic response.

tion is called "down-regulation." Thyroid hormone, however, has been shown to increase the number of beta receptors in the myocardium. Estrogen, which increases the number of alpha receptors in the myometrium, increases the affinity of some vascular alpha receptors for norepinephrine.

The mechanisms involved in some of these changes are known. For example phosphorylation of the beta-adrenergic receptor by beta-adrenergic receptor kinase results in their sequestration into membrane vesicles, internalization, and degradation. The

Table 8–4. Adrenergic responses of selected tissues.

Organ or Tissue	Receptor	Effect
Heart (myocardium)	β_1	Increased force of contraction Increased rate of contraction
Blood vessels	α	Vasoconstriction
	β_2	Vasodilation
Kidney	β	Increased renin release
Gut	α, β	Decreased motility and increased sphincter tone
Pancreas	α	Decreased insulin release Decreased glucagon release
	β	Increased insulin release Increased glucagon release
Liver	α, β	Increased glycogenolysis
Adipose tissue	β	Increased lipolysis
Most tissues	β	Increased calorigenesis
Skin (apocrine glands on hands, axillae, etc)	α	Increased sweating
Bronchioles	β_2	Dilation
Uterus	α	Contraction
	β_2	Relaxation

phosphorylated receptor also has a greater affinity for β-arrestin, another regulatory protein, which prevents its interaction with G_{sa}.

The finding that most cells in the body have adrenergic receptors has led to an appreciation of the important regulatory role of the peripheral sympathetic nervous system. In contrast, the effects of the adrenal medulla are mediated via the circulating amines and, therefore, are much more generalized in nature. Furthermore, adrenal medullary secretion increases significantly only in the presence of stress or marked deviation from homeostatic or resting conditions. For example, a minor reduction in the available glucose leads to sympathetic activation of fat mobilization from adipose tissue, whereas the adrenal medulla may not release large amounts of epinephrine until the blood sugar falls to 40–50 mg/dL (3 mmol/L) in normal individuals. A summary of physiologic effects of the catecholamines in various tissues is presented in Table 8–4.

Physiologic Effects

A. Cardiovascular Effects: Catecholamines increase the rate and frequency of contraction and increase the irritability of the myocardium by activating myocardial β_1 receptors. The contractile effects of the catecholamines on vascular smooth muscle are mediated via alpha receptors. Although beta receptors are present and cause dilatation, other mechanisms of vascular dilatation are probably more important. The release or injection of catecholamines can therefore be expected to increase heart rate and cardiac output and cause peripheral vasoconstriction—all leading to an increase in blood pressure. These events are modulated by reflex mechanisms, so that, as the blood pressure increases, reflex stimulation may slow the heart rate and tend to reduce cardiac output. Although norepinephrine in the usual doses will have these effects, the effect of epinephrine may vary depending on the smooth muscle tone of the vascular system at the time. For example, in an individual with increased vascular tone, the net effect of small amounts of epinephrine may be to reduce the mean blood pressure while increasing the heart rate and cardiac output. In an individual with a reduction in vascular tone, the mean blood pressure would be expected to increase. In addition to the reflex mechanisms, vascular output is integrated by the central nervous system, so that, under appropriate circumstances, one vascular bed may be dilated while others remain unchanged. The central organization of the sympathetic nervous system is such that its ordinary regulatory effects are quite discrete—in contrast to periods of stress, when stimulation may be rather generalized and accompanied by release of catecholamines into the circulation. The infusion of catecholamines leads to a rapid reduction in plasma volume, presumably to accommodate to the reduced volume of the arterial and venous beds (Figure 8–7).

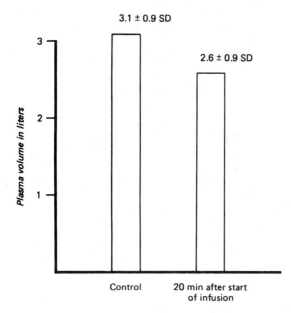

Figure 8–7. Changes in plasma volume produced by infusion of norepinephrine for 20 minutes in a dose sufficient to increase mean arterial pressure from 96 ± 10 mm Hg to 150 ± 16 mm Hg. (Data from Finnerty FA Jr, Buchholz JH, Guillaudeu RL: Blood volumes and plasma protein during arterenol-induced hypertension. J Clin Invest 1958;37:425.)

B. Effects on Extravascular Smooth Muscle: The catecholamines also regulate the activity of smooth muscle in tissues other than blood vessels. These effects include relaxation and contraction of uterine myometrium, relaxation of intestinal and bladder smooth muscle, contraction of the smooth muscle in the bladder and intestinal sphincters, and relaxation of tracheal smooth muscle and pupillary dilatation.

C. Metabolic Effects: The catecholamines increase oxygen consumption and heat production. Although the effects appear to be mediated by the beta receptor, the mechanism is unknown. The catecholamines also regulate glucose and fat mobilization from storage depots. Glycogenolysis in heart

muscle and in liver leads to an increase in available carbohydrate for utilization. Stimulation of adipose tissue leads to lipolysis and the release of free fatty acids and glycerol into the circulation for utilization at other sites. In humans, these effects are mediated by the beta receptor.

The plasma levels of catecholamines required to produce some cardiovascular and metabolic effects in humans are shown in Table 8–5.

The catecholamines have effects on water, sodium, potassium, calcium, and phosphate excretion in the kidney. However, the mechanisms and the significance of these changes are not clear.

The Regulatory Role of Catecholamines in Hormone Secretion

The sympathetic nervous system plays an important role in the regulation and integration of hormone secretion at two levels. Centrally, norepinephrine and dopamine play important roles in the regulation of secretion of the anterior pituitary hormones. Dopamine, for example, has been identified as the prolactin-inhibiting hormone, and the hypothalamic releasing hormones appear to be under sympathetic nervous system control. Peripherally, the secretion of renin by the juxtaglomerular cells of the kidney is regulated by the sympathetic nervous system via the renal nerves and circulating catecholamines. The catecholamines release renin via a beta receptor mechanism. The B cell of the pancreatic islets is stimulated by activation of the beta receptors in the presence of alpha-adrenergic blockade. However, the dominant effect of norepinephrine or epinephrine is inhibition of insulin secretion, which is mediated by the alpha receptor. Similar effects have been observed in the secretion of glucagon by pancreatic A cells. The catecholamines have also been found to increase the release of thyroxine, calcitonin, parathyroid hormone, and gastrin by a beta receptor-mediated mechanism.

OTHER HORMONES

In addition to the catecholamines, the chromaffin cells of the adrenal medulla and peripheral sympathetic neurons synthesize and secrete opiate-like pep-

Table 8–5. Approximate circulating plasma levels of epinephrine and norepinephrine required to produce hemodynamic and metabolic changes during infusions of epinephrine and norepinephrine.[1]

	Norepinephrine	Epinephrine
Systolic blood pressure	↑ at 2500 pg/mL (15 nmol/L)	↑ at 500 pg/mL (3 nmol/L)
Diastolic blood pressure	↑ at 2500 pg/mL (15 nmol/L)	↓ at 500 pg/mL (3 nmol/L)
Pulse	↓ at 2500 pg/mL (15 nmol/dL)	↑ at 250 pg/mL (1.5 nmol/L)
Plasma glucose	↑ at 2500 pg/moL (15 nmol/L)	↑ at 250–500 pg/mL (1.5–3 nmol/L)

[1] Data from Silverberg AB et al: Am J Physiol 1978:234:E252; and from Clutter WE et al: J Clin Invest 1980:66:94.

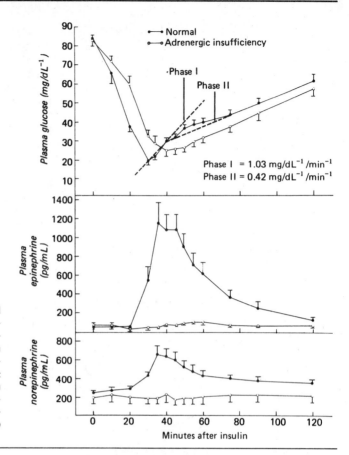

Figure 8–8. Plasma glucose, epinephrine, and norepinephrine levels after insulin administration in 14 normal subjects (•—•) and seven patients with idiopathic orthostatic hypotension (o—o) with low or absent epinephrine responses. Results are expressed as mean ± SEM. (Reproduced, with permission, from Polinsky RJ et al: The adrenal medullary response to hypoglycemia in patients with orthostatic hypotension. J Clin Endocrinol Metab 1980;51:1404.)

tides, including met- and leu-enkephalin (see Chapter 2). They are stored in the large, dense-cored vesicles with the catecholamines in the adrenal medulla and at sympathetic nerve endings. These peptides are also found in the terminals of the splanchnic fibers that innervate the adrenal medulla. The observation that naloxone increases plasma catecholamine levels suggests that these peptides may inhibit sympathetic activity.

Extracts of normal adrenals have also been found to contain corticotropin-releasing factor, growth hormone-releasing hormone, somatostatin, and peptide histidine methionine. Although these and other active peptides are secreted by tumors of the adrenal medulla and contribute to the symptomatology, little is known of their function in the normal gland.

DISORDERS OF ADRENAL MEDULLARY FUNCTION

HYPOFUNCTION

Hypofunction of the adrenal medulla alone probably occurs only in individuals receiving adrenocor-

tical steroid replacement therapy following adrenalectomy. Such individuals with otherwise intact sympathetic nervous systems suffer no clinically significant disability. Patients with autonomic insufficiency, which includes deficiency of adrenal medullary epinephrine secretion, can be demonstrated to have minor defects in recovery from insulin-induced hypoglycemia (Figure 8–8). It should be noted, however, that in patients with diabetes mellitus in whom the glucagon response is also deficient, the additional loss of adrenal medullary response leaves them more susceptible to severe bouts of hypoglycemia. This is the result of a decrease in the warning symptoms as well as an impaired response. Patients with generalized autonomic insufficiency usually have orthostatic hypotension. The causes of disorders associated with autonomic insufficiency are listed in Table 8–6.

When a normal individual stands, a series of physiologic adjustments occur that maintain blood pressure and ensure adequate circulation to the brain. The initial lowering of the blood pressure stimulates the baroreceptors, which then activate central reflex mechanisms that cause arterial and venous constriction, increase cardiac output, and activate the release of renin and vasopressin. Interruption of afferent, central, or efferent components of this autonomic reflex results in autonomic insufficiency.

Table 8–6. Disorders associated with autonomic insufficiency.

Familial dysautonomia
Shy-Drager syndrome
Parkinson's disease
Tabes dorsalis
Syringomyelia
Cerebrovascular disease
Peripheral neuropathy due to diabetes
Idiopathic orthostatic hypotension
Sympathectomy
Drugs: antihypertensives, antidepressants

The treatment of symptomatic orthostatic hypotension is dependent upon maintenance of an adequate blood volume. If physical measures such as raising the head of the bed at night and using support garments do not alleviate the condition, pharmacologic measures may be used. Although agents producing constriction of the vascular bed, including ephedrine, phenylephrine, metaraminol, monoamine oxidase inhibitors, levodopa, propranolol, and indomethacin, have been used, volume expansion with fludrocortisone is the most effective treatment.

HYPERFUNCTION

The adrenal medulla is not known to play a significant role in essential hypertension. However, the role of the sympathetic nervous system in the regulation of blood flow and blood pressure has led to extensive investigations of its role in various types of hypertension. Some of the abnormalities observed, such as a resetting of baroreceptor activity, are thought to be secondary to the change in blood pressure. Others, such as the increased cardiac output found in early essential hypertension, have been thought by some investigators to play a primary role.

Catecholamines can increase blood pressure by increasing cardiac output, by increasing peripheral resistance through their vasoconstrictive action on the arteriole, and by increasing renin release from the kidney, leading to increased circulating levels of angiotensin II. Although many studies show an increase in circulating free catecholamine levels, evidence of increased sympathetic activity has not been a uniform finding in patients with essential hypertension.

PHEOCHROMOCYTOMA

Pheochromocytomas are tumors arising from chromaffin cells in the sympathetic nervous system. They release epinephrine or norepinephrine (or both)—and in some cases dopamine—into the circulation, causing hypertension and other signs and symptoms.

In addition to the catecholamines, pheochromocytomas have been reported to produce a wide variety of active peptides. These include somatostatin, substance P, adrenocorticotropin, β-endorphin, lipotropin, vasoactive intestinal polypeptide, interleukin-6, parathyroid hormone-related protein, neuropeptide Y, calcitonin, calcitonin gene-related peptide, met-enkephalin, serotonin, gastrin, neurotensin, pancreastatin, galanin, insulin-like growth factor II, and others. Secretion of large amounts of these substances may result in atypical clinical presentations.

It is estimated that 0.1% of patients with diastolic hypertension have pheochromocytomas. These tumors are found at all ages and in both sexes and are most commonly diagnosed in the fourth or fifth decades. An analysis of data from the National Cancer Registry in Sweden indicates an incidence of about two per million in that population.

Although uncommon, this disorder is important to diagnose, because undiagnosed it may be fatal in pregnant women during delivery or in patients undergoing surgery for other disorders. However, with early diagnosis and proper management, almost all patients with benign tumors recover completely.

Clinical Features

A. Symptoms and Signs: Although most patients with functioning tumors have symptoms most of the time, these vary in intensity and are perceived to be mainly episodic or paroxysmal by about half of the patients. Most patients with persistent hypertension also have superimposed paroxysms. A few patients are entirely free of symptoms and hypertension between attacks and give no evidence of excessive catecholamine release during these intervals. In some instances, these tumors occur with minimal clinical manifestations and are only found incidentally on CT or MRI scan. Commonly reported symptoms and signs are listed in Table 8–7.

Table 8–7. Common symptoms in patients with hypertension due to pheochromocytoma.

Symptoms during or following paroxysms
    Headache
    Sweating
    Forceful heartbeat with or without tachycardia
    Anxiety or fear of impending death
    Tremor
    Fatigue or exhaustion
    Nausea and vomiting
    Abdominal or chest pain
    Visual disturbances
Symptoms between paroxysms
    Increased sweating
    Cold hands and feet
    Weight loss
    Constipation

B. Description of an Attack: In patients with paroxysmal release of catecholamines, the symptoms resemble those produced by injections of epinephrine or norepinephrine, and the symptom complex is far more consistent than is suggested by the variability of patients' complaints. An episode usually begins with a sensation of something happening deep inside the chest, and a stimulus to deeper breathing is noted. The patient then becomes aware of a pounding or forceful heartbeat, caused by the β_1 receptor-mediated increase in cardiac output. This throbbing spreads to the rest of the trunk and head, causing headache or a pounding sensation in the head. The intense alpha receptor-mediated peripheral vasoconstriction causes cool, moist hands and feet and facial pallor. The combination of increased cardiac output and vasoconstriction causes marked elevation of the blood pressure when large amounts of catecholamines are released. The decreased heat loss and increased metabolism may cause a rise in temperature or flushing and lead to reflex sweating, which may be profuse and usually follows the cardiovascular effects that begin in the first few seconds after onset of an attack. The increased glycolysis and alpha receptor-mediated inhibition of insulin release cause an increase in blood sugar levels. Patients experience marked anxiety during all but the mildest attacks, and when episodes are prolonged or severe, there may be nausea, vomiting, visual disturbances, chest or abdominal pain, paresthesias, or seizures. A feeling of fatigue or exhaustion usually follows these episodes unless they are very mild or of short duration.

C. Frequency of Attacks: In patients with paroxysmal symptoms, attacks usually occur several times a week or oftener and last for 15 minutes or less though they may occur at intervals of months or as often as 25 times daily and may last from minutes to days. As time passes, the attacks usually increase in frequency but do not change much in character. They are frequently precipitated by activities that compress the tumor (eg, changes in position, exercise, lifting, defecation, or eating) and by emotional distress or anxiety.

D. Variability of Manifestations: Although the pattern of the manifestations described above can be elicited in almost all patients capable of clear communication, the variability of presenting complaints may be confusing and is sometimes misleading. Women whose episodes are first noted around the time of menopause may be thought to be experiencing "hot flushes." The diagnosis may only be made when hormonal therapy has failed to alleviate the "hot flush" or the episode is observed and the blood pressure taken during an attack. When a pheochromocytoma causes hypertension late in pregnancy, it may be confused with preeclampsia. As noted above, when tumors secrete other peptides in significant amounts, they may produce atypical manifestations such as fever with leukotrienes, hypercalcemia with

parathyroid hormone-related protein, and Cushing's syndrome with secretion of ACTH or CRH. Other causes of increased sympathetic activity must be distinguished from pheochromocytomas (see below) (Table 8–8).

E. Chronic Symptoms: Patients with persistently secreting tumors and chronic symptoms usually experience the symptom complex described above in response to transient increases in the release of catecholamines. In addition, in these patients the increased metabolic rate usually causes heat intolerance, increased sweating, and weight loss or (in children) lack of weight gain. The effects on glycogenolysis and insulin release can produce hyperglycemia and glucose intolerance, and patients may present with diabetes mellitus. Hypertension is usually present. Wide fluctuations of blood pressure are characteristic, and marked increases may be followed by hypotension and syncope. When pressure is elevated, postural hypotension is present. Typically, the hypertension does not respond to commonly used antihypertensive regimens, and such drugs as guanethidine and ganglionic blockers can induce paradoxic pressor responses. On examination, these patients, usually thin, have a forceful heartbeat that is often visible and easily palpable. They feel warm, may have pallor of the face and chest, perspire, have cool and moist hands and feet, and prefer a cool room. A mass may be palpable in the abdomen or neck, and deep palpation of the abdomen may produce a typical paroxysm. Chronic constriction of the arterial and venous beds leads to a reduction in plasma volume in most of these patients. The inability to further constrict these vessels upon arising causes the postural hypotension that is characteristically observed.

Familial Syndromes & Other Tumors

Pheochromocytoma may also occur as a heritable disorder, either alone or more commonly in association with other endocrine tumors. In one syndrome, multiple endocrine neoplasia (MEN) type IIa (Sip-

Table 8–8. Disorders presenting with features of sympathetic discharge or hypermetabolism.

Angina due to coronary vasospasm
Severe anxiety states
Hypertension
Hypertensive crises associated with—
    Paraplegia
    Tabes dorsalis
    Lead poisoning
    Acute porphyria
Menopausal hot flushes
Autonomic epilepsy
Thyrotoxicosis
Hyperdynamic beta-adrenergic states

ple's syndrome), the patient may also have a calcitonin-producing adenoma of the thyroid, a parathyroid hormone-producing adenoma of the parathyroid, or a pituitary adenoma. In the other group (MEN type IIb), pheochromocytomas occur in association with mucosal neuromas, which are numerous and small and are found around the mouth. Transmission of these disorders follows the pattern of an autosomal dominant gene with incomplete penetrance. (See Chapter 21.)

Pheochromocytomas occurring as part of the familial syndromes appear to be the expression of an as yet unidentified stimulus to tumor formation in patients with genetic abnormalities that predispose them to respond with tumor formation. An abnormal gene on chromosome 10 has been reported in some families. In MEN type IIa, bilateral adrenal tumors, frequently producing epinephrine, are common and may develop from hyperplasia of the adrenal medulla. Medullary carcinoma of the thyroid in these patients is commonly bilateral and associated with parafollicular or "C" cell hyperplasia. Multicentric tumors of the parathyroid gland are also quite typical and are found predominantly in patients with MEN type IIa and rarely in those with MEN type IIb. The thyroid tumors have been reported to secrete ACTH, serotonin, prostaglandins, and kallikreins, which may contribute to the clinical manifestations in these patients. Usually, the thyroid tumor (medullary carcinoma) is diagnosed by finding an elevated serum calcitonin level under basal conditions or after provocative testing with stimuli such as calcium or pentagastrin (see Chapters 4 and 5).

Pathology

A. Location of Tumor: Pheochromocytomas occur wherever chromaffin tissue is found (Figure 8–9). The adrenal medulla contains the largest collection of chromaffin cells. They are also found in the organ of Zuckerkandl, which is very large in the fetus but is gradually replaced by fibrous tissue after delivery and is small in the adult. Chromaffin cells are also found in association with sympathetic ganglia, nerve plexuses, and nerves.

Over 95% of pheochromocytomas are found in the abdomen, and 85% of these are in the adrenal. Common extra-adrenal sites are near the kidney and in the organ of Zuckerkandl. Those found in the chest are in the heart or the posterior mediastinal area. The intracranial lesions reported are thought to be metastatic in origin. The tumors may be multicentric in origin, particularly when they are familial or part of the syndromes of multiple endocrine neoplasia and when they are seen in children. Although fewer than 10% of adults have multiple tumors, they are found in about one-third of affected children.

B. Size of Tumor: Pheochromocytomas vary in size from less than 1 g to several kilograms. However, they are usually small, most weighing under

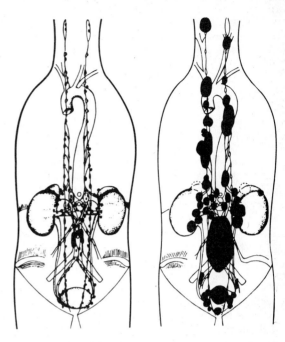

Figure 8–9. *Left:* Anatomic distribution of extra-adrenal chromaffin tissue in the newborn. *Right:* Locations of extra-adrenal pheochromocytomas reported before 1965. (Reproduced, with permission, from Coupland R: *The Natural History of the Chromaffin Cell.* Longmans, Green, 1965.)

100 g. They are vascular tumors and commonly contain cystic or hemorrhagic areas. The cells tend to be large and contain typical catecholamine storage granules similar to those in the adrenal medulla. Multinucleated cells, pleomorphic nuclei, mitoses, and extension into the capsule and vessels are sometimes seen but do not indicate that the tumor is malignant. The incidence of malignant tumors in reported studies varies from less than 5% to more than 10%. These can be recognized during surgery when there is significant local infiltration or when metastases are identified. About 5–10% of patients thought to have been cured will recur later. Using cell sorting and DNA staining methods, it has been found that patients with tumors whose cells contain increased amounts of nuclear DNA and patients with extra-adrenal tumors are at higher risk of recurrence and should be screened at regular intervals following surgery.

Table 8–9. Causes of death in patients with unsuspected pheochromocytomas.

Myocardial infarction
Cerebrovascular accident
Arrhythmias
Irreversible shock
Renal failure
Dissecting aortic aneurysm

C. Adrenal Medullary Hyperplasia: This has also been described as the cause of an indistinguishable clinical picture and is found in the syndrome of multiple endocrine neoplasia (see Chapter 21).

Complications

Patients with persistent symptoms and hypertension may develop hypertensive retinopathy or nephropathy. Postmortem studies indicate that there are a significant number of patients with pheochromocytomas who have myocarditis characterized by focal degeneration and necrosis of myocardial fibers with infiltration of histiocytes, plasma cells, and other signs of inflammation. Platelet aggregates and fibrin deposition are found in pulmonary arterioles. These changes may be associated with abnormal findings on the ECG but may not become apparent until the patient is exposed to marked cardiovascular stress and heart failure results. In patients harboring pheochromocytomas for long periods, the serious sequelae of hypertension are observed. Cerebrovascular accidents, congestive heart failure, and myocardial infarction have been observed. Some of the causes of death in unoperated patients are shown in Table 8–9.

Differential Diagnosis

The diagnosis of pheochromocytoma should be considered in all patients with paroxysmal symptoms; in children with hypertension; in adults with severe hypertension not responding to therapy; in hypertensive patients with diabetes or hypermetabolism; in patients with hypertension in whom symptoms resemble those described above or can be evoked by exercise, position change, emotional distress, or antihypertensive drugs such as guanethidine and ganglionic blockers; and in patients who become severely hypertensive or go into shock during anesthesia, surgery, or obstetric delivery. Patients who have disorders sometimes associated with pheochromocytomas (neurofibromatosis, mucosal adenomas, von Hippel's disease, medullary carcinoma of the thyroid) and those with first-degree relatives who have pheochromocytoma or other manifestations of MEN should be investigated. Other disorders associated with marked sympathetic stimulation are listed in Table 8–8. Levels may also be elevated in patients undergoing severe mental or physical stress or other severe illness. Plasma catecholamine levels at rest and with exercise and various disorders are shown in Table 8–10.

In these and other disorders in which elevated plasma catecholamine levels are under sympathetic nervous system control, it may be possible to reduce catecholamine release by autonomic blockade or sympathetic suppression. Pentolinium and clonidine have been used for this purpose. The reliability and safety of such procedures have not been established.

Ganglioneuromas (which are usually small, well-differentiated tumors arising from ganglion cells) and neuroblastomas (which are highly malignant tumors arising from more primitive sympathoblastic cells) can produce catecholamines and present a similar clinical picture. Dopamine is usually the major active catecholamine produced, and its production leads to elevated concentrations of homovanillic acid in urine.

Incidentally discovered tumors: As noted below, the use of CT and MRI to localize these tumors is indicated only after the diagnosis has been confirmed. However, since these procedures are frequently employed diagnostic tools, masses in the region of the adrenal are diagnosed as incidental findings in approximately 2% of such scans. These images can represent cysts, lipomas, nonfunctioning adenomas, infections, hemorrhage, or metastases as well as pheochromocytomas. These patients should be screened for pheochromocytomas clinically and chemically. The work-up of these patients is discussed in more detail in Chapter 6.

Diagnostic Tests & Procedures

Assay of catecholamines and their metabolites has markedly simplified the diagnosis of this disorder. Operative exploration for pheochromocytoma should not be done in the absence of chemical confirmation of the diagnosis. With currently available methods, it is possible to avoid unnecessary surgery and to successfully locate a tumor in almost all patients.

A. Hormone Assay: In patients with continuous hypertension or symptoms, levels of plasma or urine catecholamines and their metabolites are usually

Table 8–10. Range of plasma catecholamine levels observed in healthy subjects and patients.

	Norepinephrine	Epinephrine
Healthy subjects		
Basal	150–400 pg/mL (0.9–2.4 nmol/L)	25–100 pg/mL (0.1–0.6 nmol/L)
Ambulatory	200–800 pg/mL (1.2–4.8 nmol/L)	30–100 pg/mL (0.1–1 nmol/L)
Exercise	800–4000 pg/mL (4.8–24 nmol/L)	100–1000 pg/mL (0.5–5 nmol/L)
Symptomatic hypoglycemia	200–1000 pg/mL (1.2–6 nmol/L)	1000–5000 pg/mL (5–25 nmol/L)
Patients		
Hypertension	200–500 pg/mL (1.2–3 nmol/L)	20–100 pg/mL (0.1–0.6 nmol/L)
Surgery	500–2000 pg/mL (3–12 nmol/L)	199–500 pg/mL (0.5–3 nmol/L)
Myocardial infarction	1000–2000 pg/mL (6–12 nmol/L)	800–5000 pg/mL (4–25 nmol/L)

Table 8–11. Maximal normal concentrations of the catecholamines and their metabolism in urine.[1] Substances interfering with their measurement are listed.

Compound	Excreted	Interfering Substances
Epinephrine Norepinephrine Dopamine	0.02 mg/24 h (0.1 nmol/24 h) 0.08 mg/24 h (0.5 nmol/24 h) 0.4 mg/24 h (2.5 nmol/24 h)	May be increased by highly fluorescent compounds such as tetracyclines and quinidine; by foods[2] and drugs containing catecholamines; and by levodopa, methyldopa, and ethanol.
Metanephrine Normetanephrine	0.4 mg/24 h (2.5 nmol/24 h) 0.9 mg/24 h (5 nmol/24 h)	Increased by catecholamines, monoamine oxidase inhibitors, and others, depending on the method.
Vanillylmandelic acid Homovanillic acid	8 mg/24 h (7 nmol/24 h) 7 mg/24 h (45 nmol/24 h)	Increased by catecholamines, by foods containing vanillin, or by levodopa. Decreased by clofibrate, disulfiram, and monoamine oxidase inhibitors.

[1] Values may be higher under unusual stress, illness, or strenuous activity.
[2] For example, bananas contain significant amounts of norepinephrine.

clearly increased. Therefore, in the selection of a particular assay, it is more important that the test be performed well by the laboratory than that a particular substance be measured. A reliable assay of the catecholamines, metanephrines, or vanillylmandelic acid (VMA) is usually sufficient to confirm the diagnosis. Patients with large tumors may excrete disproportionately greater amounts of catecholamine metabolites, because the amines can be metabolized by enzymes in the tumor cells prior to their release. Malignant tumors may release large amounts of dopamine, leading to the excretion of large amounts of homovanillic acid in the urine. It is important that the appropriate assay procedure be chosen to avoid misleading results and that drugs and foods that interfere with these assays be eliminated (Table 8–11).

In patients having brief and infrequent paroxysms with symptom-free intervals, confirmation of the diagnosis may be more difficult. Although large amounts of catecholamines are produced during the brief episode, the total amount excreted during the 24-hour urine collection period may not be clearly abnormal—in contrast to patients whose tumors secrete continuously. The latter group will accumulate larger amounts of catecholamines and metabolites in the urine even though secretion rates are lower and symptoms are less severe. Therefore, sampling of blood or timed urine collections during a carefully

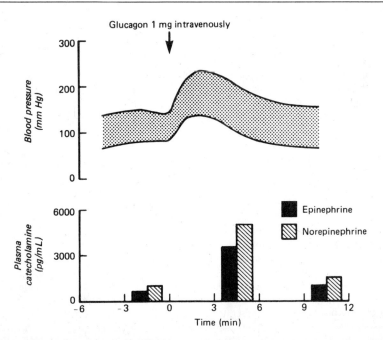

Figure 8–10. Blood pressure and plasma catecholamine levels following glucagon injection in a patient with a paroxysmally secreting pheochromocytoma. The blood sugar at 12 minutes was 180 mg/dL.

Table 8–12. Patients to be screened for pheochromocytoma.

Young hypertensives
Hypertensive patients with–
   Symptoms listed in Table 8–8
   Weight loss
   Seizures
   Orthostatic hypotension
   Unexplained shock
   Family history of pheochromocytoma or medullary carcinoma of thyroid
   Neurofibromatosis and other neurocutaneous syndromes
   Mucosal neuromas
   Hyperglycemia
   Cardiomyopathy
Marked lability of blood pressure
Family history of pheochromocytoma
Shock or severe pressor responses with–
   Induction of anesthesia
   Parturition
   Surgery
   Invasive procedures
   Antihypertensive drugs
Radiologic evidence of adrenal mass

observed episode may be necessary to confirm the diagnosis.

B. Glucagon Test: In patients with infrequent episodes, glucagon can be used to induce a paroxysm. This is rarely necessary and should not be done in patients who have angina, visual changes, or other severe symptoms during spontaneous attacks. Phentolamine should be available to terminate the induced episode. Injection of 1 mg of glucagon intravenously will induce an attack in more than 90% of patients with pheochromocytoma. A typical response in such a patient is shown in Figure 8–10. In those instances in which glucagon has failed to evoke a paroxysm and the clinical suspicion is very strong, histamine given intravenously in doses of 25–50 μg may also be tried. However, histamine injection is associated with flushing and a brief but severe episode of headache. In general, the provoked episodes are no more severe than those occurring spontaneously. Provocative tests should be reserved for patients in whom it is necessary to rule out the presence of pheochromocytoma when they are seen (eg, prior to surgery or obstetric delivery). At all other times, a timed urine collection during an episode can provide the same information.

C. Clonidine Suppression Test: In patients whose catecholamine levels are elevated because of neurogenic stimulation rather than release of catecholamine from a tumor, the administration of 0.3 mg of clonidine 2–3 hours before sampling of blood may be useful in reducing plasma norepinephrine levels. This procedure can be used during an office visit or whenever it is not possible to obtain blood under resting conditions.

D. Trial of Phenoxybenzamine: In the occasional patient in whom the chemical tests are inconclusive, it may be useful or convenient to institute therapy with phenoxybenzamine over a period of 1–2 months to observe effects both on the nature and frequency of attacks and on the blood pressure. A salutary effect will sometimes be observed for a few weeks but seldom longer than that in the absence of pheochromocytoma. A good response indicates the need for reappraisal of the patient.

Screening for Pheochromocytoma

In addition to screening patients with typical clinical manifestations, assays for catecholamines and their metabolites can be used to screen other patients at high risk. The indications for screening are listed in Table 8–12. When the presence of an undetected pheochromocytoma is particularly dangerous, as in pregnancy or prior to surgery, screening should be considered even when clinical manifestations are less typical.

Localization of Tumors

When the diagnosis has been established, the tumor must be located in order to facilitate its surgical removal. CT and MRI are of great value in localizing these tumors (Figure 8–11). MRI is somewhat more successful in locating extra-adrenal tumors and has the advantage of producing brighter images of pheochromocytomas with T2 weighting in contrast to most other adrenal tumors. Only the smallest tumors or those shielded by clips and other metal objects from previous surgery have been elusive.

Analysis of blood samples obtained via percutaneous venous catheterization can be of great value in locating small tumors in unusual locations. An example of the use of this technique is shown in Figure 8–12. Because of a small risk of complications and the discomfort and cost of this procedure, it should be used only after simpler methods fail.

Although not as widely available, scintigrams following the injection of ^{131}I labeled metaiodobenzyl-

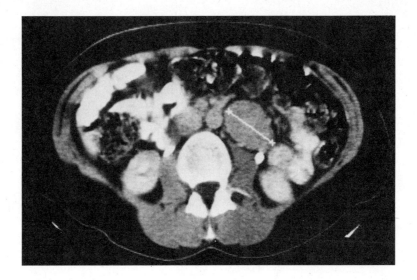

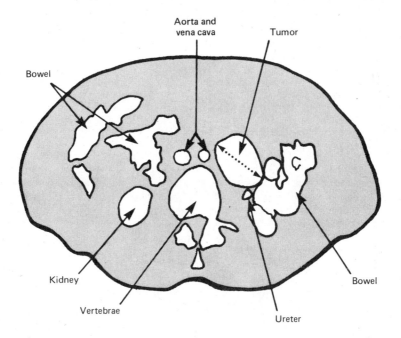

Figure 8–11. Left infrarenal pheochromocytoma shown by CT scanning. The lower diagram identifies many of the visible structures.

guanidine (MIBG) are quite specific for identifying masses producing catecholamines, including neuroblastomas and pheochromocytomas. Administration of MIBG in these patients results in detectable images in 48–72 hours. It is particularly useful in identifying extra-adrenal tumors and metastases. Very small tumors can be safely and conveniently located by this method. Although not all pheochromocytomas will produce detectable images, the specificity of the method seems high, and it has been possible to locate tumors not found by other methods.

Management

Optimal management of patients with pheochromocytomas requires an understanding of the pathophysiology produced by excessive catecholamines and an acquaintance with the action of adrenergic antagonists and other drugs used in the treatment of these patients.

A. Treatment With Adrenergic Antagonists: As soon as the diagnosis has been confirmed, therapy with adrenergic antagonists should be instituted. Treatment is directed toward reduction of symptoms,

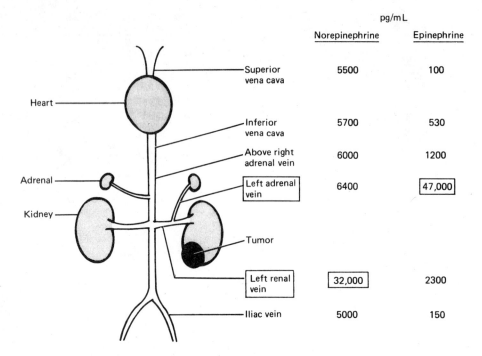

	pg/mL	
	Norepinephrine	Epinephrine
Superior vena cava	5500	100
Inferior vena cava	5700	530
Above right adrenal vein	6000	1200
Left adrenal vein	6400	47,000
Left renal vein	32,000	2300
Iliac vein	5000	150

Figure 8–12. Plasma norepinephrine and epinephrine levels in samples of blood obtained from the vena cava. Note that the level of epinephrine is very high in the left adrenal vein sample, distinguishing it from the drainage of the tumor, which secretes mainly norepinephrine. Note the relatively normal peripheral levels of epinephrine (as seen in the iliac vein or the superior vena cava).

lowering of blood pressure, and amelioration of paroxysms occurring spontaneously or induced by studies undertaken to localize the tumors. Such treatment will allow expansion of the vascular bed and plasma volume and will reduce the amount of transfused blood required for maintenance of blood pressure during surgery.

Although only a few days of therapy are required for preoperative study and preparation of most patients for surgery, prolonged medical therapy is advantageous in patients who have had recent myocardial infarctions, those with electrocardiographic or clinical evidence of catecholamine cardiomyopathy, or those in the last trimester of pregnancy. They can be maintained on this regimen until the infant is delivered or the complication resolved, at which time the tumor can be removed.

Agents commonly used in therapy include phentolamine, prazosin, and phenoxybenzamine. Propranolol is occasionally helpful to control marked tachycardia and arrhythmias, but it should not be given until alpha receptor blockade is established.

In patients with persistent hypertension or frequent paroxysms, **phenoxybenzamine**, a noncompetitive alpha-adrenergic antagonist with a prolonged effect, is indicated. Treatment is begun with doses of 20–40 mg/d orally and can be increased by 10–20 mg every 1–2 days until the desired effect is achieved. Postural hypotension may be marked at the beginning of ther-

apy, and care should be taken to prevent syncope. However, postural hypotension usually disappears when adequate blockade is achieved. Completely normal blood pressures (< 140/90 mm Hg) may not be achieved and are not required. A dose of 60-80 mg daily is usually adequate, but two to three times that amount may be necessary. When marked tachycardia or arrhythmias occur prior to or during surgery, small doses of **propranolol** may be required. Patients with infrequent paroxysms and an absence of interval manifestations can be treated in a similar manner.

Rapid titration of the dose may be difficult using phenoxybenzamine, because of its long half-life (36 hours). However, **prazosin,** an alpha antagonist with a shorter duration of activity, has been found to be useful. Prazosin is predominantly an α_1 antagonist and has not been found to be effective in all patients.

B. Preparation for Surgery: Preparation of the patient as described above minimizes the hazards of anesthesia and surgery. The patient's blood pressure and electrocardiographic patterns should be continuously monitored, and phentolamine and particularly sodium nitroprusside are useful to reduce blood pressure if necessary. Suspected intra-abdominal tumors are usually approached through a transabdominal incision, since this allows exploration of the adrenals, sympathetic ganglia, bladder, and other pelvic structures. However, posterior and flank incisions are preferred by some surgeons for removal of larger tumors. When bilateral adrenal tumors are found and the adrenals removed, adrenocortical steroid replacement is required (see Chapter 6).

C. Postoperative Care: When the tumor is removed, the blood pressure usually falls to about 90/60 mm Hg. Persistence of low blood pressures or poor peripheral perfusion may require blood volume expansion with whole blood, plasma, or other fluids as indicated. Pressor therapy is not usually required and should not be substituted for volume expansion.

Lack of a fall in pressure at the time of tumor removal (even in the presence of adrenergic blockade) indicates the presence of additional tumor tissue.

In patients with tumors producing persistent hypertension, the initial fall in blood pressure may be followed by an elevation of blood pressure in the postoperative period. However, the accompanying symptoms of sympathetic stimulation are gone, and the pressure returns to normal over the next few weeks. If the blood pressure remains elevated but the patient is otherwise asymptomatic, another cause for the elevated blood pressure should be considered. Essential hypertension and renal vascular hypertension have been reported in several patients harboring pheochromocytomas. In patients whose tumors secrete little or no excess of catecholamines and who are free of signs and symptoms other than fixed hypertension, tumor removal will not usually eliminate the elevated blood pressure.

D. Long Term Follow-Up: As noted above, the incidence of malignant tumors in reported studies varies from less than 5% to more than 10%. These can be recognized during surgery only when there is significant local infiltration or when metastases are identified. Since 5–10% of patients thought to have been cured later have recurrences, patients should be followed carefully. Patients with extra-adrenal tumors and those whose tumor cells contain increased amounts of nuclear DNA are at higher risk of recurrence and should be screened at regular intervals for many years.

Table 8–13. Distribution of metastases in 41 cases of malignant pheochromocytoma.[1]

	Autopsy Cases (n = 26)	Nonautopsy Cases (n = 15)	Percentage
Skeleton	12	6	44
Liver	12	3	37
Lymph node	11	4	37
Lungs	9	2	27
Central nervous system	4	0	10
Pleura	4	0	10
Kidneys	2	0	5
Pancreas	1	0	2
Omentum	1	0	2

[1] Reproduced, with permission, from Schönebeck J: Scand J Urol Nephrol 1969;3:66.

E. Treatment of Malignant Tumors: Patients with nonresectable malignant tumors or metastases or those who for other reasons are not amenable to successful surgical treatment can be managed medically for prolonged periods. Phenoxybenzamine and perhaps prazosin can be used chronically as described above. Patients with malignant tumors have also benefited symptomatically from treatment with α-methylmetatyrosine, an inhibitor of tyrosine hydroxylase, the rate-limiting enzyme in the biosynthetic process. Although some patients with malignant pheochromocytomas die early because of disseminated disease, there are long-term survivors. Sites of metastases are shown in Table 8–13. The most common site of metastases is the skeleton, and bone lesions tend to respond well to radiation therapy. The use of combinations of chemotherapeutic agents such as cyclophosphamide, vincristine, and dacarbazine is effective in controlling soft tissue lesions in some patients.

[131]I-labeled metaiodobenzylguanidine has been used in the treatment of malignant pheochromocytomas. Preliminary reports indicate that half of the patients treated have partial remissions and that the side effects of this therapy are acceptable.

REFERENCES

General

Coupland RE: *The Natural History of the Chromaffin Cell.* Longmans, Green, 1965.

Cryer PE: Physiology and pathophysiology of the human sympathoadrenal neuroendocrine system. N Engl J Med 1980;303:436.

Hormones of the Adrenal Medulla

Ahlquist RP: A study of the adrenotropic receptors. Am J Physiol 1948;153:586.

Axelrod J: The metabolism, storage and release of catecholamines. Recent Prog Horm Res 1965;21:597.

Bleasdale J, Eichberg J, Havser G (editors): *Inositol and Phosphoinositides.* Humana Press, 1985.

Brown MR, Fisher LA: Brain peptide regulation of adrenal epinephrine secretion. Am J Physiol 1984; 247:E41.

Clutter WE et al: Epinephrine plasma metabolic clearance rates and physiologic thresholds for metabolic and hemodynamic actions in man. J Clin Invest 1980;66:94.

Eiden LE: Is chromogranin a prohormone? Nature 1987;325:301.

Ganong WF, Reid IA: Role of the sympathetic nervous system and central alpha- and beta-adrenergic receptors in regulation of renin activity. Am J Physiol 1976;230:1733.

Goldfien A: Effects of glucose deprivation on the sympathetic outflow to the adrenal medulla and adipose tissue. Pharmacol Rev 1966;18:303.

Goldstein DS, Eisenhofer G: Plasma catechols: What do they mean? News Physiol Sci 1988;3:139.

Handbook of Psychopharmacology. Section 1, Vol. 3. Plenum Press, 1975.

Mannelli M et al: Endogenous dopamine (DA) and DA2 receptors: A mechanism limiting excessive sympathetic-adrenal discharge in humans. J Clin Endocrinol Metab 1988;66:626.

Murray E et al: Determination of norepinephrine apparent release rate and clearance in humans. Life Sci 1979;25:1461.

Raum WJ: Methods of plasma catecholamine measurement including radioimmunoassay. Am J Physiol 1984;247:E4.

Robertson D et al: Use of alpha$_2$ adrenoceptor agonists and antagonists in the functional assessment of the sympathetic nervous system. J Clin Invest 1986;78: 576.

Seeman P: Dopamine receptors. Pharmacol Rev 1980; 32:230.

Silverberg AB et al: Norepinephrine: Hormone and neurotransmitter in man. Am J Physiol 1978;234:252.

Simon JP, Bader MF, Aunis D: Secretion from chromaffin cells is controlled by chromogranin A-derived peptides. Proc Natl Acad Sci USA 1988;85:1712.

Trendelenburg U, Weiner N (editors): Catecholamines. Vol 90 of Handbook of Experimental Pharmacology. Springer-Verlag, 1988. Annu Rev Pharmacol 1970;10:273.

Woods SC, Porte D Jr: Neural control of the endocrine pancreas. Physiol Rev 1974;54:596.

Disorders of Adrenal Medullary Function; Pheochromocytoma

Averbuch SD et al: Malignant pheochromocytoma: Effective treatment with a combination of cyclophosphamide, vincristine, and dacarbazine. Ann Intern Med 1988;109:267.

Engelman K, Sjoerdsma A: Chronic medical therapy for pheochromocytoma. Ann Intern Med 1964;61:229.

Frohlich ED: The adrenergic nervous system and hypertension: State of the art. Second Pan American Symposium on Hypertension, Part 2. Mayo Clin Proc 1977;52:361.

Gagel RF et al: The clinical outcome of prospective screening for multiple endocrine neoplasia type 2a: An 18-year experience. N Engl J Med 1988;318:478.

Goldfien A: Pheochromocytoma: Diagnosis and anesthetic and surgical management. Anesthesiology 1963;24:462.

Goldstein DS: Plasma norepinephrine in essential hypertension. Hypertension 1981;3:48.

Hosaka Y et al: Pheochromocytoma: Nuclear DNA patterns studied by flow cytometry. Surgery 1986;100: 1003.

Keiser HR et al: Treatment of malignant pheochromocytoma with combination chemotherapy. Hypertension 1985;7(No. 3 Part 2):118.

Krempf M et al: Use of m-[^{131}I]iodobenzylguanidine in the treatment of malignant pheochromocytoma. J Clin Endocrinol Metab 1991;72:455.

Landsberg L: Catecholamines and hyperthyroidism. Clin Endocrinol Metab 1977;6:697.

Manger WM, Gifford RW: Pheochromocytoma. Springer, 1977.

Manger WM: Pheochromocytoma. (Editorial.) West J Med 1986;145:382.

Mathew CG et al: A linked genetic marker for multiple endocrine neoplasia type 2A on chromosome 10. Nature 1987;328:527.

Modlin IM et al: Pheochromocytomas in 72 patients: Clinical and diagnostic features, treatment and long-term results. Br J Surg 1979;66:456.

Ponder BA, Jackson CE (editors): The second international workshop on multiple endocrine neoplasia type 2 syndromes. Henry Ford Hosp Med J 1987;35:1. [Entire 2 issues.]

Proye C et al: Dopamine-secreting pheochromocytoma: An unrecognized entity. Classification of pheochromocytomas according to their type of secretion. Surgery 1986;100:1154.

Ross NS, Aron DC: Hormonal evaluation of the patient with an incidentally discovered adrenal mass. N Engl J Med 1990;323:1401.

Schenker JG, Chowers U: Pheochromocytoma and pregnancy: Review of 89 cases. Obstet Gynecol Surv 1971;26:739.

Schimke NR et al: Syndrome of bilateral pheochromocytoma, medullary thyroid carcinoma and multiple neuromas: A possible regulatory defect in the differentiation of chromaffin tissue. N Engl J Med 1968;279:1.

Shapiro B et al: Iodine-131 metaiodobenzylguanidine for the locating of suspected pheochromocytoma: Experience in 400 cases. J Nucl Med 1985;26:576.

Sheps SG et al: Recent development in the diagnosis and treatment of pheochromocytoma. Mayo Clin Proc 1990;65:88.

Simpson NE et al: Assignment of multiple endocrine neoplasia type 2A to chromosome 10 by linkage. Nature 1987;328:528.

Sisson JC, Wieland DM: Radiolabeled metaiodobenzylguanidine: Pharmacology and clinical studies. Am J Physiol Imaging 1986;1:96.

Sizemore GW, Heath H, Carney JA: Multiple endocrine neoplasia type 2. Clin Endocrinol Metab 1980;9:299.

Sjoerdsma A: Chronic medical therapy for pheochromocytoma. Ann Intern Med 1964;61:229.

Stenström G, Sväurdsudd K: Pheochromocytoma in Sweden 1958-1981: An analysis of the National Cancer Registry data. Acta Med Scand 1986;220:225.

Sutton MGSJ, Sheps SG, Lie JT: Prevalence of clinically unsuspected pheochromocytoma: Review of a 50-year autopsy series. Mayo Clin Proc 1981;56:354.

Troncone L et al: The diagnostic and therapeutic utility of radioiodinated metaiodobenzylguanidine (MIBG). Eur J Nucl Med 1990;16:325.

Visser J, Axt R: Bilateral adrenal medullary hyperplasia: A clinicopathological entity. J Clin Pathol 1975;28: 298.

Yanese T et al: Studies on adrenorphin in pheochromocytoma. J Clin Endocrinol Metab 1987;64:692.

Adrenal Medullary Hypofunction

Robertson D et al: Autonomic insufficiency Isolated failure of autonomic noradrenergic neurotransmission: Evidence for impaired β-hydroxylation of dopamine. N Engl J Med 1986;314:1494.

Schatz IJ: Orthostatic hypotension. Arch Intern Med 1984;144:733.

Testes

9

Glenn D. Braunstein, MD

The testes contain two major components which are structurally separate and serve different functions. The **Leydig cells,** or **interstitial cells,** comprise the major endocrine component. The primary secretory product of these cells, testosterone, is responsible either directly or indirectly for embryonic differentiation along male lines of the external and internal genitalia, male secondary sexual development at puberty, and maintenance of libido and potency in the adult male. The **seminiferous tubules** comprise the bulk of the testes and are responsible for the production of approximately 30 million spermatozoa per day during male reproductive life (puberty to death).

Both of these testicular components are interrelated, and both require an intact hypothalamic-pituitary axis for initiation and maintenance of their function. In addition, several accessory genital structures are required for the functional maturation and transport of spermatozoa. Thus, disorders of the testes, hypothalamus, pituitary, or accessory structures may result in abnormalities of androgen or gamete production, infertility, or a combination of these problems.

ANATOMY & STRUCTURE-FUNCTION RELATIONSHIPS (Figure 9–1)

TESTES

The adult testis is a spheroid with a mean volume of 18.6 ± 4.8 mL. The average length is 4.6 cm (range, 3.6–5.5 cm), and the average width is 2.6 cm (range, 2.1–3.2 cm). The testes are located within the scrotum, which not only serves as a protective envelope but also helps to maintain the testicular temperature approximately 2 °C (3.6 °F) below abdominal temperature. Three layers of membranes—visceral tunica vaginalis, tunica albuginea, and tunica vasculosa—comprise the testicular capsule. Extensions of the tunica albuginea into the testicle as fibrous septa result in the formation of approximately

ACRONYMS USED IN THIS CHAPTER	
ACTH	Adrenocorticotropic hormone
cAMP	Cyclic adenosine monophosphate
DHEA	Dehydroepiandrosterone
FSH	Follicle-stimulating hormone
GnRH	Gonadotropin-releasing hormone
hCG	Human chorionic gonadotropin
LH	Luteinizing hormone
mRNA	Messenger ribonucleic acid
PRL	Prolactin
SHBG	Sex hormone-binding globulin

250 pyramidal lobules each of which contains coiled seminiferous tubules. Within each testis there are almost 200 m of seminiferous tubules, and these structures account for 80–90% of the testicular mass. The approximately 350 million androgen-producing Leydig cells, as well as the blood and lymphatic vessels, nerves, and fibroblasts, are interspersed between the seminiferous tubules.

The blood supply to the testes is derived chiefly from the testicular arteries, which are branches of the internal spermatic arteries. After traversing a complicated capillary network, blood enters multiple testicular veins that form an anastomotic network, the pampiniform plexus. The pampiniform plexuses coalesce to form the internal spermatic veins. The right spermatic vein drains directly into the vena cava; the left enters the renal vein.

The seminiferous tubules in the adult average 165 μm in diameter and are composed of Sertoli cells and germinal cells. The Sertoli cells line the basement membrane and form tight junctions with other Sertoli cells. These tight junctions prevent the passage of proteins from the interstitial space into the lumen of the seminiferous tubules, thus establishing a "blood-testis barrier." Through extension of cytoplasmic processes, the Sertoli cells surround developing germ cells and provide an environment essential for germ cell differentiation. In addition, these cells have been shown to be responsible for the movement of germ cells from the base of the tubule toward the lumen and for the release of mature sperm into the lumen. These cells also actively phagocytose damaged germ cells and residual bodies, which are portions of the

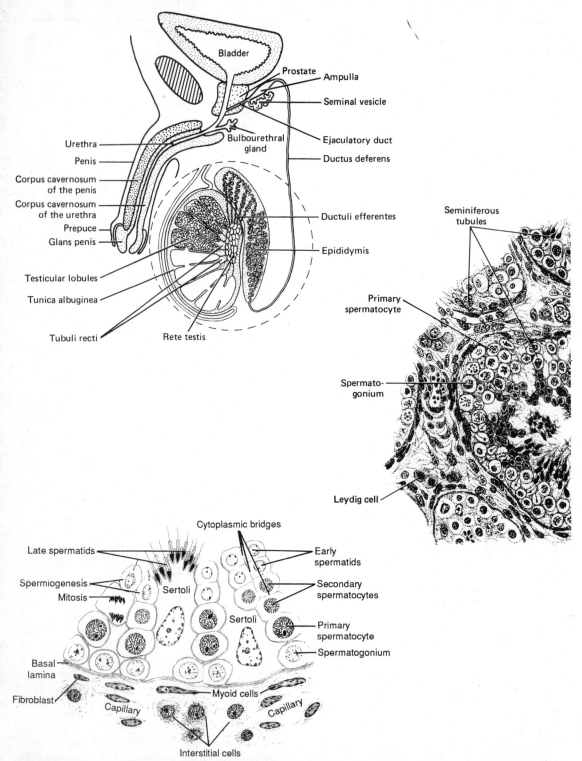

Figure 9–1. Male genital system. ***Top:*** The testis and the epididymis are in different scales from the other parts of the reproductive system. Observe the communication between the testicular lobules. ***Bottom:*** Structural organization of the human seminiferous tubule and interstitial tissue. This figure does not show the lymphatic vessels frequently found in the connective tissue. (Both illustrations reproduced, with permission, from Junqueira LC, Carneiro J, Kelley RO: *Basic Histology,* 7th ed. Appleton & Lange, 1992.) At right: Section of human testis. (Reproduced, with permission, from Ganong WF: *Review of Medical Physiology,* 15th ed. Appleton & Lange, 1991.)

germ cell cytoplasm not used in the formation of spermatozoa. Finally, in response to follicle-stimulating hormone (FSH) or testosterone, the Sertoli cells secrete androgen-binding protein, a molecule with high affinity for androgens. This substance, which enters the tubular lumen, provides a high concentration of testosterone to the developing germinal cells during the process of spermatogenesis.

More than a dozen different types of germ cells have been described in males. Broadly, they can be classified as spermatogonia, primary spermatocytes, secondary spermatocytes, spermatids, and spermatozoa. Spermatogenesis occurs in an orderly fashion, with the spermatocytes being derived from the spermatogonia via mitotic division. Through meiotic (or reduction) division, the spermatids are formed; they contain a haploid number of chromosomes (23). The interval from the beginning of spermatogenesis to release of mature spermatozoa into the tubular lumen is approximately 74 days. Although there is little variation in the duration of the spermatogenic cycle, a cross section of a seminiferous tubule will demonstrate several stages of germ cell development.

ACCESSORY STRUCTURES

The seminiferous tubules empty into a highly convoluted anastomotic network of ducts called the rete testis. Spermatozoa are then transported through efferent ductules and into a single duct, the epididymis, by testicular fluid pressure, ciliary motion, and contraction of the efferent ductules. During the approximately 12 days required for transit through the epididymis, spermatozoa undergo morphologic and functional changes essential to confer upon the gametes the capacity for fertilizing an ovum. The epididymis also serves as a reservoir for sperm. Spermatozoa stored in the epididymis enter the vas deferens, a muscular duct 35–50 cm long that propels its contents by peristaltic motion into the ejaculatory duct.

In addition to the spermatozoa and the secretory products of the testes, retia testis, and epididymides, the ejaculatory ducts receive fluid from the seminal vesicles. These paired structures, 10–20 cm long, are composed of alveolar glands, connective tissue, and muscle. They are the source of seminal plasma fructose, which provides nourishment to the spermatozoa. In addition, the seminal vesicles secrete phosphorylcholine, ergothioneine, ascorbic acid, flavins, and prostaglandins. About 60% of the total volume of seminal fluid is derived from the seminal vesicles.

The ejaculatory ducts terminate in the prostatic urethra. There additional fluid (approximately 20% of total volume) is added by the prostate, a tubuloalveolar gland with a fibromuscular stroma that weighs about 20 g and measures $4 \times 2 \times 3$ cm. The constituents of the prostate fluid include spermine, citric acid, cholesterol, phospholipids, fibrinolysin,

fibrinogenase, zinc, and acid phosphatase. Fluid is also added to the seminal plasma by the bulbourethral (Cowper) glands and urethral (Littre) glands during its transit through the penile urethra.

PHYSIOLOGY OF THE MALE REPRODUCTIVE SYSTEM

GONADAL STEROIDS
(Figure 9–2)

The three steroids of primary importance in male reproductive function are testosterone, dihydrotestosterone, and estradiol. From a quantitative standpoint, the most important androgen is testosterone. Over 95% of the testosterone is secreted by the testicular Leydig cells; the remainder is derived from the adrenals. In addition to testosterone, the testes secrete small amounts of the potent androgen dihydrotestosterone and the weak androgens dehydroepiandrosterone (DHEA) and androstenedione. The Leydig cells also secrete small quantities of estradiol, estrone, pregnenolone, progesterone, 17α-hydroxypregnenolone, and 17α-hydroxyprogesterone. The steps in testicular androgen biosynthesis are illustrated in Figure 9–2.

Dihydrotestosterone and estradiol are derived not only by direct secretion from the testes but also by conversion in peripheral tissues of androgen and estrogen precursors secreted by both the testes and the adrenals. Thus, about 80% of the circulating concentrations of these two steroids is derived from such peripheral conversion. Table 9–1 summarizes the approximate contributions of the testes, adrenals, and peripheral tissues to the circulating levels of several sex steroid hormones in men.

In the blood, androgens and estrogens exist in either a free (unbound) state or bound to serum proteins. Although about 38% of testosterone is bound to albumin, the major binding protein is sex hormone-binding globulin (SHBG), which binds 60% of the testosterone. This glycosylated dimeric protein is homologous to, yet distinct from, the androgen-binding protein secreted by the Sertoli cells. SHBG is synthesized in the liver, with the gene located on the short arm of chromosome 17. The serum concentrations of this protein are increased by estrogen, tamoxifen, phenytoin, or thyroid hormone administration and by hyperthyroidism and cirrhosis, and are decreased by exogenous androgens, glucocorticoids, or growth hormone and by hypothyroidism, acromegaly, and obesity. About 2% of the circulating testosterone is not bound to serum proteins and is able to enter cells and exert its metabolic effects. In

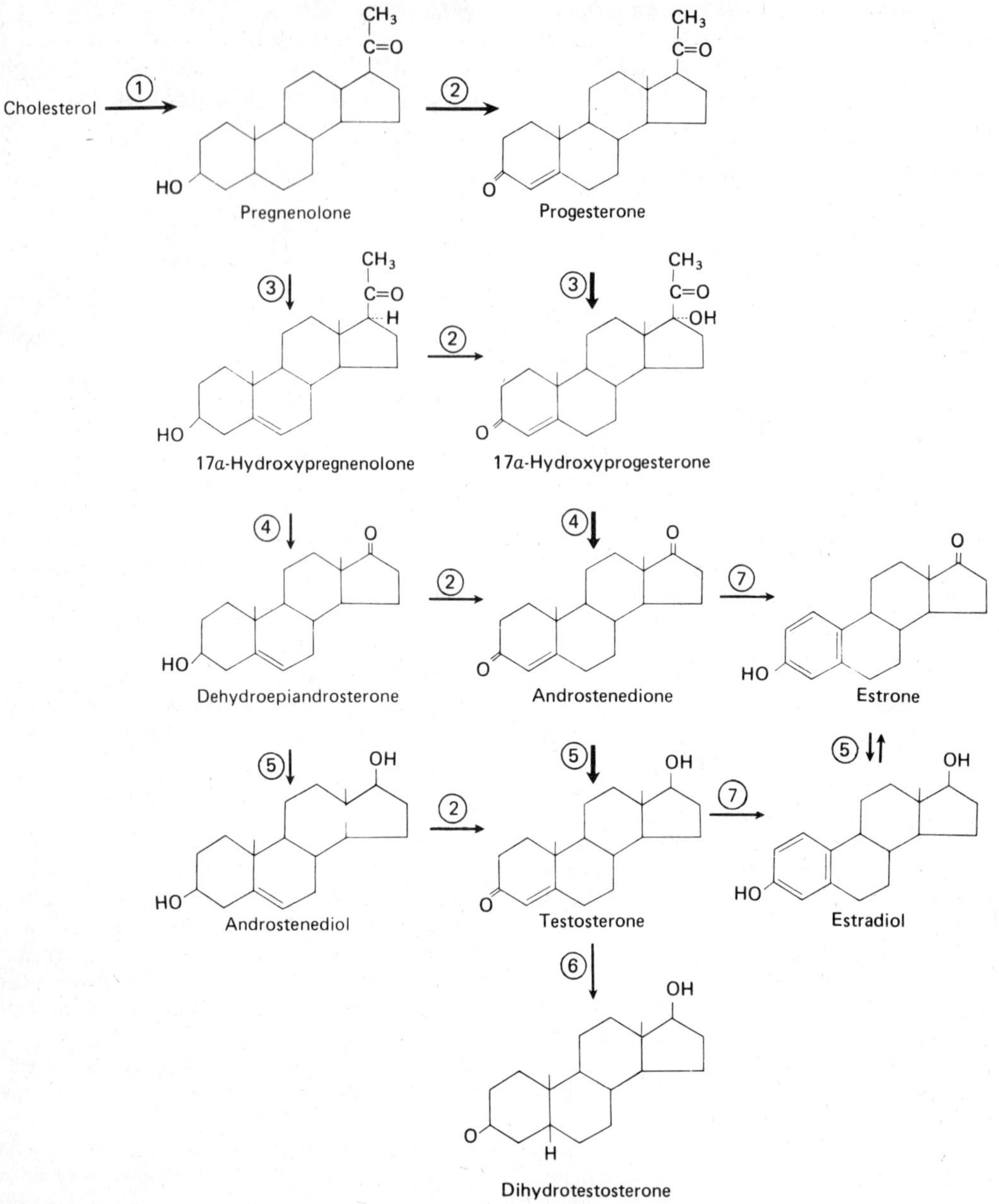

Figure 9–2. Pathways for testicular androgen and estrogen biosynthesis. Heavy arrows indicate major pathways. Circled numbers represent enzymes as follows: ①, 20,22-desmolase (P-450scc); ②, 3β-hydroxysteroid dehydrogenase and Δ⁵,Δ⁴-isomerase; ③, 17-hydroxylase (P-450c17); ④, 17,20-desmolase (P-450c17); ⑤, 17-ketoreductase; ⑥, 5α-reductase; ⑦, aromatase. (See also Figures 6–4, 10–4, and 11–13.)

addition, some of the protein-bound testosterone may dissociate from the protein and enter target tissues; thus, the amount of bioavailable testosterone may be greater than just the amount of non-protein-bound testosterone.

As noted below, testosterone may be converted to dihydrotestosterone within specific androgen target tissues. Most circulating testosterone is converted primarily by the liver into various metabolites such as androsterone and etiocholanolone, which, after conjugation with glucuronic or sulfuric acid, are excreted in the urine as 17-ketosteroids. However, it should be noted that only 20–30% of the urinary 17-ketosteroids are derived from testosterone metabolism. The majority of the 17-ketosteroids are formed from the metabolism of adrenal steroids. Therefore, 17-ketosteroid determinations do not reliably reflect testicular steroid secretion.

Table 9–1. Relative contributions (approximate percentages) of the testes, adrenals, and peripheral tissues to circulating levels of sex steroids in men.

	Testicular Secretion	Adrenal Secretion	Peripheral Conversion of Precursors
Testosterone	95	<1	<5
Dihydrotestosterone	20	<1	80
Estradiol	20	<1	80
Estrone	2	<1	98
DHEA sulfate	<10	90	. . .

Testosterone leaves the circulation and rapidly traverses the cell membrane (Figure 9–3). In most androgen target cells, testosterone is enzymatically converted to the more potent androgen dihydrotestosterone by the microsomal enzyme 5α-reductase. Dihydrotestosterone as well as testosterone then binds to the same specific intracytoplasmic receptor protein (R_c in Figure 9–3) that is distinct from both androgen-binding protein and SHBG. The genes that code for this protein are located on the X chromosome. After binding, the dihydrotestosterone- or testosterone-receptor complex is translocated into the nucleus, where it undergoes transformation (to R_n in Figure 9–3), allowing it to bind to the nuclear chromatin. The DNA-binding domain of the androgen receptor is over 80% identical to that on the progesterone receptor, while the androgen-binding domain shares 50% homology with the hormone-binding domains of the glucocorticoid, mineralocorticoid, and progesterone receptors. The interaction of the androgen-receptor complex with the chromatin results in the synthesis of messenger RNA (mRNA), which is eventually transported to the cytoplasm, where it directs the transcription of new protein synthesis and other changes that together constitute androgen action.

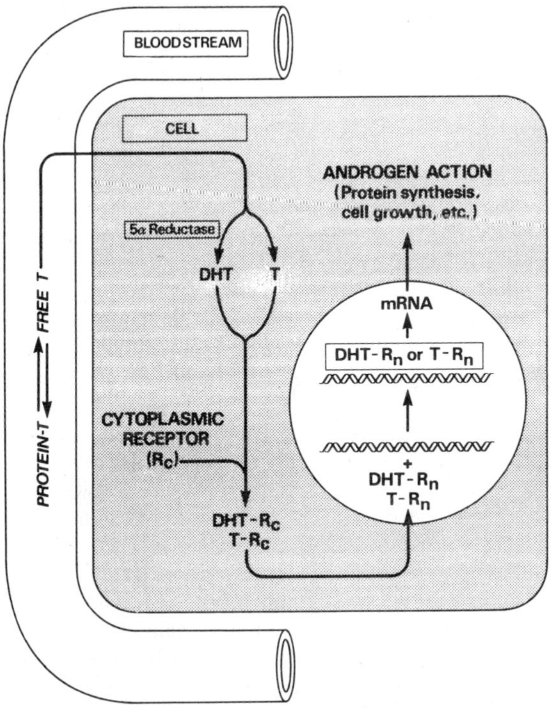

A variety of biologic effects of androgens have been defined in males. As discussed in Chapter 11, they are essential for appropriate differentiation of the internal and external male genital system during fetal development. During puberty, androgen-mediated growth of the scrotum, epididymis, vas deferens, seminal vesicles, prostate, and penis occurs. The functional integrity of these organs requires androgens. Androgens stimulate skeletal muscle growth and growth of the larynx, which results in deepening of the voice; and of the epiphysial cartilaginous plates, which results in the pubertal growth spurt. Both ambisexual (pubic and axillary) hair growth and sexual (beard, mustache, chest, abdomen, and back) hair growth are stimulated, as is sebaceous gland activity. Other effects include stimulation of erythropoiesis and social behavioral changes.

Figure 9–3. Mechanisms of androgen action. T, testosterone; DHT, dihydrotestosterone; R_n, nuclear receptor; mRNA, messenger RNA; R_c, cytoplasmic receptor.

CONTROL OF TESTICULAR FUNCTION

Hypothalamic-Pituitary-Leydig Cell Axis (Figure 9–4)

The hypothalamus synthesizes a decapeptide, gonadotropin-releasing hormone (GnRH), and secretes it in pulses every 90–120 minutes into the hypothalamohypophysial portal blood. After reaching the anterior pituitary, GnRH binds to the gonadotropes and stimulates the release of both lutcinizing hormone (LH) and, to a lesser extent, FSH into the general circulation. LH is taken up by the Leydig cells, where it binds to specific membrane receptors. This leads to activation of adenylyl cyclase and generation of cAMP and other messengers that ultimately result in the secretion of androgens. In turn, the elevation of androgens inhibits the secretion of LH from the anterior pituitary through a direct action on the pituitary and an inhibitory effect at the hypothalamic level. Both the hypothalamus and the pituitary have androgen and estrogen receptors. Experimentally, pure androgens such as dihydrotestosterone (DHT) reduce LH pulse frequency, while estradiol reduces LH pulse amplitude. However, the major inhibitory effect of androgen on the hypothalamus appears to be mediated principally by estradiol, which may be derived locally through the aromatization of testosterone. Leydig cells also secrete small quantities of oxytocin, lipotropin, β-endorphin, dynorphin, an-

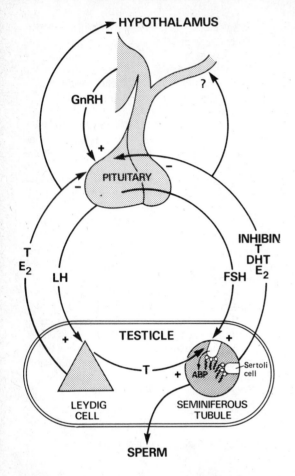

Figure 9–4. Hypothalamic-pituitary-testicular axis. GnRH, gonadotropin-releasing hormone; LH, luteinizing hormone; FSH, follicle-stimulating hormone; T, testosterone; DHT, dihydrotestosterone; ABP, androgen-binding protein; E_2, estradiol; +, positive influence; –, negative influence.

giotensin, and prostaglandins, which may be important for the paracrine regulation of testicular function.

Hypothalamic-Pituitary-Seminiferous Tubular Axis (Figure 9–4)

After stimulation by GnRH, the gonadotropes secrete FSH into the systemic circulation. This glycoprotein hormone binds to specific receptors in the Sertoli cells and stimulates the production of androgen-binding protein. FSH is necessary for the initiation of spermatogenesis. However, full maturation of the spermatozoa appears to require not only an FSH effect but also testosterone. Indeed, the major action of FSH on spermatogenesis may be via the stimulation of androgen-binding protein production, which allows a high intratubular concentration of testosterone to be maintained.

In addition to androgen-binding protein, the Sertoli cell secretes several other substances including GnRH-like peptide, transferrin, plasminogen activator, ceruloplasmin, müllerian duct inhibitory factor, H-Y antigen, and inhibin. At least three genes have been found to direct inhibin synthesis. Two forms of inhibin have been identified, inhibin A and inhibin B. Both are 32-kDa proteins composed of the same alpha subunit cross-linked with different beta subunits, and each can selectively inhibit FSH release from the pituitary without affecting LH release. FSH directly stimulates the Sertoli cells to secrete inhibin, and therefore inhibin is probably a physiologic regulator of pituitary FSH secretion, possibly together with the gonadal steroids.

Two additional inhibin-related proteins that have been identified in porcine follicular fluid may also be present in the testes. These factors, designated follicle regulatory protein and activin, are composed of inhibin beta subunit dimers and can selectively stimulate pituitary secretion in vitro. They are structurally similar to transforming growth factor-β (TGFβ), which can also stimulate pituitary FSH release. The physiologic role, if any, that follicle regulatory protein, activin, and TGFβ have in the regulation of FSH secretion is unknown.

EVALUATION OF MALE GONADAL FUNCTION

CLINICAL EVALUATION

Clinical Presentation

The clinical presentation of patients with deficient testosterone production or action depends upon the age at onset of hypogonadism. Androgen deficiency during the second to third months of fetal development results in varying degrees of ambiguity of the genitalia and male pseudohermaphroditism. These topics are covered in Chapters 11 and 12.

Prepubertal androgen deficiency leads to poor secondary sexual development and eunuchoid skeletal proportions. The penis fails to enlarge, the testes remain small, and the scrotum does not develop the marked rugae characteristic of puberty. The voice remains high-pitched and the muscle mass does not develop fully, resulting in less than normal strength and endurance. The lack of appropriate stimulation of sexual hair growth results in sparse axillary and pubic hair (which receive some stimulation from adrenal androgens) and absent or very sparse facial, chest, upper abdominal, and back hair. Although the androgen-mediated pubertal growth spurt will fail to take place, the epiphysial plates of the long bones will continue to grow under the influence of somatomedins and other growth factors. Thus, the long bones of the upper and lower extremities will grow out of proportion to the axial skeleton. Healthy white men have an average upper segment (crown to pubis) to lower segment (pubis to floor) ratio of >1, whereas prepubertal hypogonadism results in a ratio of <1. Similarly, the ratio of total arm span to total height averages 0.96 in white men. Because of the relatively greater growth in the upper extremities, the arm span of eunuchoid individuals exceeds height by 5 cm or more.

If testosterone deficiency develops after puberty, the patient may complain of decreased libido, impotence, and low energy. Patients with mild androgen deficiency or androgen deficiency of recent onset may not note a decrease in facial or body hair growth; it appears that although adult androgen levels must be achieved to *stimulate* male sexual hair growth, relatively low levels of androgens are required to *maintain* sexual hair growth. With long-standing hypogonadism, the growth of facial hair will diminish, and the frequency of shaving may also decrease (Figure 9–5). In addition, fine wrinkles may appear in the corners of the mouth and eyes and, to-gether with the sparse beard growth, result in the classic hypogonadal facies.

Genital Examination

Adequate assessment of the genitalia is essential in the evaluation of male hypogonadism. The examination should be performed in a warm room in order to relax the dartos muscle of the scrotum. The penis should be examined for the presence of hypospadias, epispadias, and chordee (abnormal angulation of the penis due to a fibrotic plaque), which may interfere with fertility. The fully stretched dorsal penile length should be measured in the flaccid state from the pubopenile skin junction to the tip of the glans. The normal range in adults is 11–16 cm (10th and 90th percentiles, respectively).

Assessment of testicular volume is also vital to the evaluation of hypogonadism. Careful measurement of the longitudinal and transverse axes of the testes may be made and testicular volume (V) calculated from the formula for a prolate spheroid: $V = 0.52 \times$ length $\times$ width^2. The mean volume for an adult testis is 18.6 ± 4.8 mL. Alternatively, volume may be estimated with the Prader orchidometer, which consists

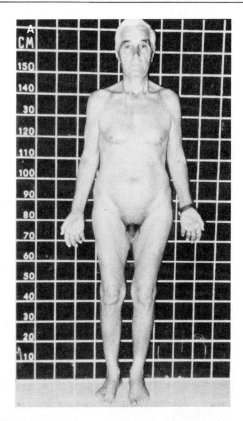

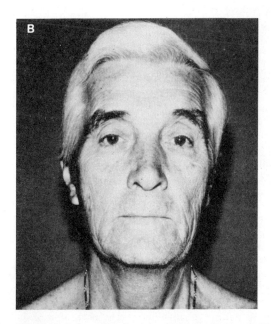

Figure 9–5. ***A:*** Hypogonadal habitus. Note absence of body and facial hair as well as feminine body distribution. ***B:*** Hypogonadal facies. Note absence of facial hair and fine wrinkles around the corners of the eyes and lips.

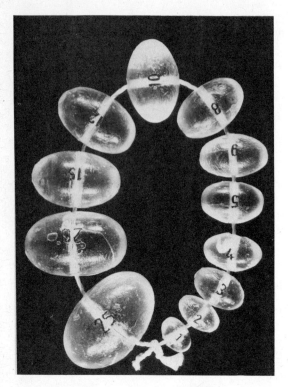

Figure 9–6. Prader orchidometer.

of a series of plastic ellipsoids ranging in volume from 1 mL to 25 mL (Figure 9–6). Each testis is compared with the appropriate ellipsoid. Adults normally have volumes greater than 15 mL by this method.

Since 80–90% of testicular volume is composed of seminiferous tubules, decrease in volume indicates lack of tubular development or regression of tubular size. The consistency of the testicle should be noted. Small, firm testes are characteristic of hyalinization or fibrosis, as may occur in Klinefelter's syndrome. Small, rubbery testes are normally found in prepubertal males; in an adult, they are indicative of deficient gonadotropin stimulation. Testes with a mushy or soft consistency are characteristically found in individuals with postpubertal testicular atrophy.

The epididymis and vas deferens should also be examined. One of the most important parts of the examination is evaluation of the presence of varicocele resulting from incompetence of the internal spermatic vein. As will be discussed later, this is an important and potentially correctable form of male infertility. The patient should be examined in the upright position while performing the Valsalva maneuver. The examiner should carefully palpate the spermatic cords above the testes. A varicocele can be felt as an impulse along the posterior portion of the cord. About 85% of varicoceles are located on the left side, and 15% are bilateral.

LABORATORY TESTS OF TESTICULAR FUNCTION

Semen Analysis

With some exceptions, a normal semen analysis excludes gonadal dysfunction. However, a single abnormal semen analysis is not a sufficient basis for a diagnosis of disturbance of testicular function, since marked variations in several of the parameters may be seen in normal individuals: At least three semen samples must be examined over a 2- to 3-month interval in order to evaluate this facet of male gonadal function. As noted above, approximately 3 months are required for completion of the spermatogenic cycle and movement of the mature spermatozoa through the ductal system. Therefore, when an abnormal semen sample is produced, one must question the patient about prior fever, trauma, drug exposure, and other factors that may temporarily damage spermatogenesis.

The semen should be collected by masturbation after 1–3 days of sexual abstinence. If the patient will not masturbate, a specially designed plastic condom (Mylex Corporation, Chicago) can be used during intercourse. Ordinary condoms cannot be used for this purpose, since they contain spermicidal chemicals. If neither of these methods is satisfactory, coitus interruptus may be used as long as the complete ejaculate is collected. It should be stressed to the patient that the highest concentration of spermatozoa is in the first portion of the ejaculate and that this is the portion most often lost as a result of coitus interruptus.

The specimen should be examined within 2 hours after collection. Normal semen has a volume of 2–5 mL, with 20×10^6 or more sperm per milliliter. Over half of the spermatozoa should exhibit progressive motility, and 30% or more should have normal morphology.

Steroid Measurements

Each of the gonadal steroids may be measured by radioimmunoassay. Although single determinations may distinguish between normal individuals and patients with severe hypogonadism, mild defects in androgen production may be missed. In normal individuals, there are frequent, rapid pulsatile changes in serum testosterone concentration as well as a slight nocturnal elevation. Therefore, at least three separate blood samples should be collected at 20- to 40-minute intervals during the morning for testosterone measurement. The testosterone may be measured in each of the serum samples, or equal aliquots of each of the three serum samples may be combined, mixed, and subjected to testosterone analysis. The latter procedure provides a savings in cost as well as a mean serum testosterone concentration that takes into account the pulsatile release of testosterone.

Androgen and estrogen radioimmunoassays measure total serum steroid concentrations. This is the sum of the free, biologically active hormone and the protein-bound moiety. Although in most circumstances it is not necessary to determine the actual quantity of free steroid hormones, in some situations alterations in the binding protein concentration may occur. Lowered concentrations of SHBG are seen in patients with hypothyroidism, obesity, and acromegaly. In these circumstances, the free testosterone concentration should be directly measured, since it may be normal when the total serum testosterone level is decreased. The normal male serum concentrations of gonadal steroids collected in the basal state are given in Table 9–2.

Gonadotropin & Prolactin Measurements

LH and, to a lesser extent, FSH are released in pulsatile fashion throughout the day. Therefore, as with testosterone, at least three blood samples should be obtained at 20- to 40-minute intervals during the day. FSH and LH may be measured in each of the samples or in a single pooled specimen. Although many laboratories give a numerical value for the lower limits of normal for gonadotropins, some normal males have concentrations of FSH and LH undetectable by presently available radioimmunoassay techniques. Furthermore, the concentrations of gonadotropins measured in one laboratory may not be directly comparable to those measured in another because of differences in the reference preparations used. The primary use of basal FSH and LH concentrations is to distinguish between hypergonadotropic hypogonadism, in which either or both of the gonadotropins are elevated, and hypogonadotropic hypogonadism, in which the gonadotropins are low or inappropriately normal in the presence of decreased androgen production.

Elevations of serum prolactin (PRL) inhibit the normal release of pituitary gonadotropins (shown by a reduced LH pulse frequency), probably through an effect on the hypothalamus. Thus, serum PRL measurements should be performed in any patient with hypogonadotropic hypogonadism. Serum PRL concentrations are generally stable throughout the day; therefore, measurement of this hormone in a single sample is usually sufficient. However, the patient

should abstain from eating for 3 hours before the blood sample is obtained, since a protein meal may acutely stimulate the release of PRL from the pituitary. The normal ranges for serum PRL and gonadotropins are shown in Table 9–2.

Dynamic Tests

A. Chorionic Gonadotropin Stimulation Test: Human chorionic gonadotropin (hCG) is a glycoprotein hormone with biologic actions similar to those of LH. Following an injection of chorionic gonadotropin, this hormone binds to the LH receptors on the Leydig cells and stimulates the synthesis and secretion of testicular steroids. Therefore, the Leydig cells may be directly assessed by the intramuscular injection of 4000 IU of chorionic gonadotropin daily for 4 days. A normal response is a doubling of the testosterone level following the last injection. Alternatively, a single intramuscular dose of chorionic gonadotropin (5000 IU/1.7 m^2 in adults or 100 IU/kg in children) may be given, with blood samples taken for testosterone measurements 72 and 96 hours later. Patients with primary gonadal disease will have a diminished response following administration of chorionic gonadotropin, while patients with Leydig cell failure secondary to pituitary or hypothalamic disease will have a qualitatively normal response.

B. Clomiphene Citrate Stimulation Test: Clomiphene citrate is a nonsteroid compound with weak estrogenic activity. It binds to estrogen receptors in various tissues, including the hypothalamus. By preventing the more potent estrogen estradiol from occupying these receptors, the hypothalamus in effect "sees" less estradiol. As noted above, most if not all of the hypothalamic-pituitary feedback control by testicular androgens is mediated by estradiol, which is derived from the peripheral conversion of androgens. The apparent estradiol deficiency leads to an increase of GnRH release the net result of which is stimulation of the gonadotropes to secrete increased quantities of LH and FSH.

The test is performed by giving clomiphene citrate, 100 mg orally twice daily for 10 days. Three blood samples are collected at 20-minute intervals (see comments above, under Steroid Measurements) 1 day before the drug is administered and again on days 9 and 10 of drug administration. LH, FSH, and testosterone should be measured in pooled aliquots from each of these samples. Healthy men have a 50–250% increase in LH, a 30–200% increase in FSH, and a 30–220% increase in testosterone on day 10 of the test. Patients with pituitary or hypothalamic disease do not show a normal increment in LH or FSH.

C. Gonadotropin-Releasing Hormone Test: The decapeptide GnRH (gonadorelin; Factrel) directly stimulates the gonadotropes of the anterior pituitary to secrete LH and FSH. It was expected that measurement of LH and FSH following the adminis-

Table 9–2. Normal ranges for gonadal steroids, pituitary gonadotropins, and prolactin in men.

	Ranges
Testosterone	300–1100 ng/dL (10.4–38.2 nmol/L)
Free testosterone	50–210 pg/mL (1.7–7.28 pmol/L)
Dihydrotestosterone	27–75 ng/dL (0.9–2.6 nmol/L)
Androstenedione	50–200 ng/dL (1.7–6.9 nmol/L)
Estradiol	15–40 pg/mL (55–150 pmol/L)
Estrone	15–65 pg/mL (55.5–240 pmol/L)
FSH	2–15 mIU/mL (2–15 IU/L)
LH	2–15 mIU/mL (2–15 IU/L)
PRL	4–18 ng/mL (4–18 μg/L)

tration of GnRH would be useful in distinguishing between hypothalamic and pituitary lesions, but this has not proved to be the case. Patients with destructive lesions of the pituitary and those with long-standing hypogonadism due to hypothalamic disorders may not show a response to a GnRH test. However, if the releasing factor is administered by repeated injections every 60–120 minutes or by a programmable pulsatile infusion pump for 7–14 days, patients with hypothalamic lesions may have their pituitary responsiveness to GnRH restored, whereas patients with pituitary insufficiency do not. Conversely, a normal LH and FSH response to GnRH in a hypogonadal male does not eliminate hypopituitarism as the cause of the gonadal failure, since patients with mild hypogonadotropic hypogonadism may demonstrate a normal response.

The test is performed by administering 100 µg of gonadorelin by rapid intravenous bolus. Blood is drawn at –15, 0, 15, 30, 45, 60, 90, 120, and 180 minutes for LH and FSH measurements. Normal adult males have a two- to fivefold increase in LH over baseline concentrations and an approximately twofold rise of FSH. However, some normal males fail to have an increase in FSH following GnRH. Patients with primary testicular disease may respond with exaggerated increases in LH and FSH. If seminiferous tubule damage alone is present, abnormal FSH rise and normal LH response may be seen.

Testicular Biopsy

Testicular biopsy in hypogonadal men is primarily indicated in patients with normal-sized testes and azoospermia in order to distinguish spermatogenic failure and ductal obstruction. Although germinal aplasia, hypoplasia, maturation arrest, and other abnormalities of spermatogenesis may be diagnosed by examination of testicular tissue in oligospermic males, knowledge of the type of defect does not alter therapy. Therefore, testicular biopsy is not usually indicted for evaluation of mild to moderate oligospermia.

Evaluation for Male Hypogonadism

Figure 9–7 outlines an approach to the diagnosis of male gonadal disorders. Semen analysis and determination of the basal concentrations of testosterone, FSH, and LH allow the clinician to distinguish patients with primary gonadal failure who have poor semen characteristics, low or normal testosterone, and elevated FSH or LH from those with secondary gonadal failure and abnormal semen analysis, decreased testosterone, and low or inappropriately normal gonadotropins.

In patients with elevations of gonadotropins resulting from primary testicular disease, chromosomal analysis will help to differentiate between genetic abnormalities and acquired testicular defects. Since no

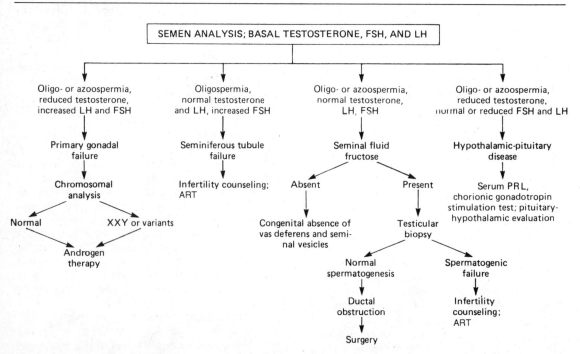

Figure 9–7. Scheme for evaluation of clinical hypogonadism. (ART, assisted reproductive technologies such as in vitro fertilization and sperm injection into ova.)

therapy exists that will restore spermatogenesis in an individual with severe testicular damage, androgen replacement is the treatment of choice. Patients with isolated seminiferous tubule failure may have normal or elevated FSH concentrations in association with normal LH and testosterone levels and usually severe oligospermia. Patients with azoospermia require evaluation for the possible presence of ductal obstruction, since this defect may be surgically correctable. Fructose is added to seminal plasma by the seminal vesicles, and an absence of fructose indicates that the seminal vesicles are absent or bilaterally obstructed. The combination of a poor semen analysis with low testosterone, FSH, and LH is indicative of a hypothalamic or pituitary defect. Such patients need further evaluation of anterior and posterior pituitary gland function with appropriate pituitary function tests, as well as neuroradiologic and neuro-ophthalmologic studies (see Chapter 2).

PHARMACOLOGY OF DRUGS USED TO TREAT MALE GONADAL DISORDERS

ANDROGENS

A variety of drugs are available for the treatment of androgen deficiency. Preparations for sublingual or oral administration such as methyltestosterone, oxymetholone, and fluoxymesterone have the advantage of ease of administration but the disadvantage of erratic absorption, potential for cholestatic jaundice, and decreased effectiveness when compared to the intramuscular preparations. Testosterone propionate is a short-acting androgen. Its main use is in initiating therapy in older men, whose prostate glands may be exquisitely sensitive to testosterone. A dose of 50 mg two or three times per week is adequate. Obstructive symptoms due to benign prostatic hypertrophy following therapy with this androgen usually resolve rapidly because of its short duration of action.

Androgen deficiency is currently best treated with testosterone enanthate or cyclopentylpropionate (cypionate) given intramuscularly. The duration of action of these preparations is usually 2 weeks, although some patients note an effect for up to 4 weeks. Unlike the oral androgen preparations, both of these agents are capable of completely virilizing the patients. Therapy may be initiated with 200 mg intramuscularly every 1–2 weeks for 1–2 years. After adequate virilization has been achieved, the androgen effect may be maintained by doses of 100–200 mg every 2–3 weeks. Testosterone pellets may be implanted subcutaneously for a longer duration of effect. However, this therapy has not enjoyed much

popularity. Transcrotal delivery via a polyethylene-derived membrane impregnated with testosterone is a new investigational method of replacement therapy. The patches must be placed on the scrotum, since this site allows the greatest degree of androgen adsorption through the skin (40 times greater than adsorption through forearm skin). The patches, which must be replaced daily, provide physiologic levels of testosterone that closely mimic the normal diurnal testosterone fluctuation. Elevated serum concentrations of dihydrotestosterone—a finding of unknown clinical significance—have been noted in patients using these patches. However, another type of transdermal delivery system has been developed which provides normal androgen concentrations without elevation in dihydrotestosterone.

Androgens, both oral and intramuscular, have been used (illegally) by some athletes to increase muscle mass and strength. Although this may achieve the anticipated result in some individuals, adverse effects include oligospermia and testicular atrophy—in addition to some of the complications noted below.

Androgen therapy is contraindicated in patients with prostatic carcinoma. About 1–2% of patients receiving oral methyltestosterone or fluoxymesterone develop intrahepatic cholestatic jaundice that resolves when the drug is discontinued. Rarely, these methylated or halogenated androgens have been associated with benign and malignant hepatocellular tumors.

Androgen therapy may also cause premature fusion of the epiphyses in an adolescent, and this may result in some loss of potential height. Therefore, androgen therapy is usually withheld until a hypogonadal male reaches 13 years of age. Water retention may be associated with hypertension or congestive heart failure in susceptible individuals. Since androgens stimulate erythropoietin production, erythrocytosis may occur during therapy. This is not usually clinically significant. Inhibition of spermatogenesis is mediated through suppression of gonadotropins by the androgens. Gynecomastia may develop during initiation of androgen therapy but usually resolves with continued administration of the drug. Priapism, acne, and aggressive behavior are dose-related adverse effects and generally disappear after reduction of dosage. Androgens decrease the production of thyroxine-binding globulin and corticosteroid-binding globulin by the liver. Therefore, total serum thyroxine and cortisone concentrations may be decreased though the free hormone concentrations remain normal.

GONADOTROPINS

In patients with hypogonadism due to inadequate gonadotropin secretion, spermatogenesis and virilization may be induced by exogenous gonadotropin injections. Since the gonadotropins are proteins with short half-lives, they must be administered parenterally two or three times a week.

The expense and inconvenience of this type of therapy preclude its routine use for the treatment of androgen deficiency. The two major indications for exogenous gonadotropins are treatment of cryptorchidism (see below) and induction of spermatogenesis in hypogonadal males who wish to father children.

To induce spermatogenesis, 2000 IU of chorionic gonadotropin may be given intramuscularly three times a week for 12–18 months. In some individuals with partial gonadotropin deficiencies, this may induce adequate spermatogenesis. In patients with more severe deficiencies, menotropins (Pergonal), available in bottles containing 75 IU each of FSH and LH, is added to chorionic gonadotropin therapy after 12–18 months and is administered in a dosage of one vial intramuscularly three times a week.

Adverse reactions with such therapy are minimal. Acne, gynecomastia, or prostatic enlargement may be noted due to excessive Leydig cell stimulation. Reduction of the chorionic gonadotropin dosage or a decrease in the frequency of chorionic gonadotropin injections generally result in resolution of the problem.

GONADOTROPIN-RELEASING HORMONE

GnRH (gonadorelin acetate), administered in pulses every 60–120 minutes by portable infusion pumps, effectively stimulates the endogenous release of LH and FSH in hypogonadotropic hypogonadal patients. This therapy does not currently appear to offer any major advantage over the use of exogenous gonadotropins for induction of spermatogenesis or the use of testosterone enanthate or cypionate for virilization. A long-acting analogue of GnRH, leuprolide acetate, is available for the treatment of prostatic carcinoma. Daily subcutaneous administration of 1 mg or monthly intramuscular injections of 7.5 mg of a depot preparation results in desensitization of the pituitary GnRH receptors, which reduces LH and FSH levels and so ultimately testosterone concentrations. Similar results are produced with a 3.6 mg subcutaneous injection of the depot form of the GnRH analogue, Goserelin. With these therapies, initial remission rates for prostatic carcinoma are similar to those found with orchiectomy or treatment with diethylstilbestrol (about 70%). In patients with benign prostatic hypertrophy, prostate size has been reduced with this therapy. Another potent intranasally administered GnRH analogue, nafarelin acetate, is available for the treatment of endometriosis. Long-acting GnRH agonists combined with testosterone have been studied as a possible male contraceptive, but they do not uniformly induce azoospermia.

CLINICAL MALE GONADAL DISORDERS

Hypogonadism may be subdivided into three general categories (Table 9–3). A thorough discussion of the hypothalamic-pituitary disorders that cause hypogonadism is presented in Chapters 2 and 12. The defects in androgen biosynthesis and androgen action are described in Chapter 11. The following section emphasizes the primary gonadal abnormalities.

KLINEFELTER'S SYNDROME (XXY Seminiferous Tubule Dysgenesis)

Klinefelter's syndrome is the most common cause of male hypogonadism. An extra X chromosome is present in about 0.2% of live-born males. Sex chromosome surveys of mentally retarded males have revealed an extra X chromosome in 0.45–2.5% of such individuals. Patients with an XXY genotype have classic Klinefelter's syndrome; those with an XXXY, XXXXY, or XXYY genotype or with XXY/chromosomal mosaicism are considered to have variant forms of the syndrome.

Etiology & Pathophysiology

The XXY genotype is usually due to maternal meiotic nondisjunction, which results in an egg with two X chromosomes. Meiotic nondisjunction during spermatogenesis has also been documented. Both ob-

Table 9–3. Classification of male hypogonadism.

Hypothalamic-pituitary disorders
Panhypopituitarism
Isolated LH deficiency (fertile eunuch)
LH and FSH deficiency
   a. With normal sense of smell
   b. With hyposmia or anosmia (Kallmann's syndrome)
Prader-Willi syndrome
Laurence-Moon-Biedl syndrome
Cerebellar ataxia
Biologically inactive LH
Gonadal abnormalities
Klinefelter's syndrome
Other chromosomal defects (XX male, XY/XXY, XX/XXY, XXXY, XXXXY, XXYY, XYY)
Bilateral anorchia (vanishing testes syndrome)
Leydig cell aplasia
Cryptorchidism
Noonan's syndrome
Myotonic dystrophy
Adult seminiferous tubule failure
Adult Leydig cell failure
Defects in androgen biosynthesis
Defects in androgen action
Complete androgen insensitivity (testicular feminization)
Incomplete androgen insensitivity
   a. Type I
   b. Type II (5α-reductase deficiency)

servations correlate positively with the epidemiologic findings that both the mother and the father tend to be older than average at the time of the patient's birth.

At birth there are generally no physical stigmas of Klinefelter's syndrome, and during childhood there are no specific signs or symptoms. The chromosomal defect is expressed chiefly during puberty. As the gonadotropins increase, the seminiferous tubules do not enlarge but rather undergo fibrosis and hyalinization, which results in small, firm testes. Obliteration of the seminiferous tubules results in azoospermia.

In addition to dysgenesis of the seminiferous tubules, the Leydig cells are also abnormal. They are present in clumps and appear to be hyperplastic upon initial examination of a testicular biopsy. However, the Leydig cell mass is not increased, and the apparent hyperplasia is actually due to the marked reduction in tubular volume. Despite the normal mass of tissue, the Leydig cells are functionally abnormal. The testosterone production rate is reduced, and there is a compensatory elevation in serum LH. Stimulation of the Leydig cells with exogenous chorionic gonadotropin results in a subnormal rise in testosterone. The clinical manifestations of androgen deficiency vary considerably from patient to patient. Thus, some individuals have virtually no secondary sexual developmental changes, whereas other are indistinguishable from healthy individuals.

The elevated LH concentrations also stimulate the Leydig cells to secrete increased quantities of estradiol and estradiol precursors. The relatively high estradiol:testosterone ratio is responsible for the variable degrees of feminization and gynecomastia seen in these patients. The elevated estradiol also stimulates the liver to produce SHBG. This may result in total serum testosterone concentrations that are within the low normal range for adult males. However, the free testosterone level may be lower than normal.

The pathogenesis of the eunuchoid proportions, personality, and intellectual deficits and associated medical disorders is presently unclear.

Testicular Pathology

Most of the seminiferous tubules are fibrotic and hyalinized, although occasional Sertoli cells and spermatogonia may be present in some sections. Absence of elastic fibers in the tunica propria is indicative of the dysgenetic nature of the tubules. The Leydig cells are arranged in clumps and appear hyperplastic, although the total mass is normal.

Clinical Features
(Figure 9–8)

A. Symptoms and Signs: There are usually no symptoms before puberty other than poor school performance in some affected individuals. Puberty may be delayed, but not usually by more than 1–2 years.

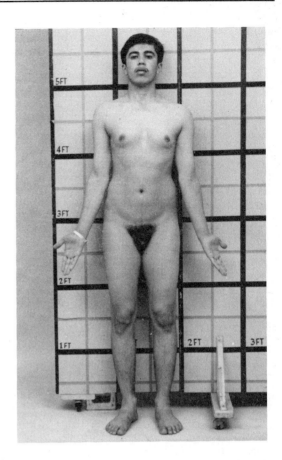

Figure 9–8. Klinefelter's syndrome in a 20-year-old man. Note relatively increased lower/upper body segment ratio, gynecomastia, small penis, and sparse body hair with a female pubic hair pattern.

During puberty, the penis and scrotum undergo varying degrees of development, with some individuals appearing normal. Most patients (80%) have diminished facial and torso hair growth. The major complaint is often persistent gynecomastia, which is clinically present in over half of patients. The testes are uniformly small (< 2 cm in longest axis) and firm as a result of fibrosis and hyalinization. Other complaints include infertility or insufficient libido and potency. The patient may have difficulty putting into words his embarrassment in situations where he must disrobe in the presence of other men, and the subnormal development of the external genitalia along with gynecomastia may lead to feelings of inadequacy that may be partly responsible for the dyssocial behavior some patients exhibit. Osteopenia may be severe in patients with long-standing androgen deficiencies.

Patients with Klinefelter's syndrome have abnormal skeletal proportions that are not truly eunuchoid. Growth of the lower extremities is relatively greater than that of the trunk and upper extremities; therefore, pubis-to-floor height is greater than crown-to-pubis height, and span is less than total height. Thus, the abnormal skeletal proportions are not the result of androgen deficiency per se (which results in span greater than height).

Intellectual impairment is noted in many patients with Klinefelter's syndrome, but the true proportion of affected individuals with subnormal intelligence is not known. Dyssocial behavior is common (see above). Patients generally show want of ambition, difficulties in maintaining permanent employment, and a tendency to ramble in conversations.

Several clinical and genotypic variants of Klinefelter's syndrome have been described. In addition to small testes with seminiferous tubular hyalinization, azoospermia, deficient secondary sexual development, and elevated gonadotropins, patients with three or more X chromosomes uniformly have severe mental retardation. The presence of more than one Y chromosome tends to be associated with aggressive antisocial behavior and macronodular acne. Skeletal deformities such as radioulnar synostosis, flexion deformities of the elbows, and clinodactyly are more commonly seen in Klinefelter variants. Patients with sex chromosome mosaicism (XX/XXY) may have only a few of the Klinefelter stigmas. These patients may have normal testicular size and may be fertile if their testes contain the XY genotype.

Medical disorders found to be associated with Klinefelter's syndrome with greater than chance frequency include chronic pulmonary disease (emphysema, chronic bronchitis), varicose veins, glucose intolerance, primary hypothyroidism, and breast cancer.

B. Laboratory Findings: Serum testosterone is low or normal; FSH and LH concentrations are elevated. Azoospermia is present. The buccal smear is chromatin-positive (>20% of cells having a Barr body), and chromosomal analysis reveals a 47,XXY karyotype.

Differential Diagnosis

Klinefelter's syndrome should be distinguished from other causes of hypogonadism. Small, firm testes should suggest Klinefelter's syndrome. Hypothalamic-pituitary hypogonadism may be associated with small, rubbery testes if puberty has not occurred or atrophic testes if normal puberty has occurred. The consistency of the testes in Klinefelter's syndrome is also different from that noted in acquired forms of adult seminiferous tubular damage. The elevated gonadotropins place the site of the lesion at the testicular level, and chromosomal analysis confirms the diagnosis. Chromosomal analysis is also required to differentiate classic Klinefelter's syndrome from the variant forms.

Treatment

A. Medical: Androgen deficiency should be treated with testosterone replacement. Patients with personality defects should be virilized gradually to decrease the risk of aggressive behavior. Testosterone enanthate or cypionate, 100 mg intramuscularly, may be given every 2–4 weeks initially and increased to 200 mg every 2 weeks if well tolerated. Patients with low normal androgen levels may not require androgen replacement therapy.

B. Surgical: If gynecomastia presents a cosmetic problem, mastectomy may be performed.

Course & Prognosis

Patients generally feel better after androgen replacement therapy has begun. However, the personality defects do not improve, and these patients often require long-term psychiatric counseling. Life expectancy is not affected.

BILATERAL ANORCHIA
(Vanishing Testes Syndrome)

Approximately 3% of phenotypic boys undergoing surgery to correct unilateral or bilateral cryptorchidism are found to have absence of one testis, and in about 1% of cryptorchid males both testes are absent. Thus, bilateral anorchia is found in approximately one out of every 20,000 males.

Etiology & Pathophysiology

Functional testicular tissue must be present during the first 14–16 weeks of embryonic development in order for wolffian duct growth and müllerian duct regression to occur and for the external genitalia to differentiate along male lines. Absence of testicular function before this time will result in varying degrees of male pseudohermaphroditism with ambiguous genitalia. Prenatal testicular injury occurring after 16 weeks of gestation as a result of trauma, vascular insufficiency, infection, or other mechanisms may result in loss of testicular tissue in an otherwise normal phenotypic male; hence the term "vanishing testes syndrome."

Testicular Pathology

In most instances, no recognizable testicular tissue has been identified despite extensive dissections. Wolffian duct structures are generally normal, and the vas deferens and testicular vessels may terminate blindly or in a mass of connective tissues in the inguinal canal or scrotum.

Clinical Features

A. Symptoms and Signs: At birth, patients appear to be normal phenotypic males with bilateral cryptorchidism. Growth and development are normal until secondary sexual development fails to occur at puberty. The penis remains small; pubic and axillary hair does not fully develop despite the presence of adrenal androgens; and the scrotum remains empty.

If the patient does not receive androgens, eunuchoid proportions develop. Gynecomastia does not occur.

An occasional patient will undergo partial spontaneous virilization at puberty. Although anatomically no testicular tissue has been identified in such patients, catheterization studies have demonstrated higher testosterone concentrations in venous blood obtained from the spermatic veins than in the peripheral venous circulation. This suggests that functional Leydig cells are present in some patients, although they are not associated with testicular germinal epithelium or stroma

B. Laboratory Findings: Serum testosterone concentrations are generally quite low, and both LH and FSH are markedly elevated. Serum testosterone concentrations do not rise following a chorionic gonadotropin stimulation test. Chromosomal analysis discloses a 46,XY karyotype.

C. Imaging Studies: Testicular artery arteriograms and spermatic venograms show vessels that taper and end in the inguinal canal or scrotum without an associated gonad.

D. Special Examinations: Thorough inguinal and abdominal laparoscopic examination or retroperitoneal examination at laparotomy may locate the testes. If testicular vessels and the vas deferens are identified and found to terminate blindly together, it may be assumed that the testis is absent.

Differential Diagnosis

Bilateral cryptorchidism must be differentiated from congenital bilateral anorchia. A normal serum testosterone concentration that rises following stimulation with chorionic gonadotropin is indicative of functional Leydig cells and probable bilateral cryptorchidism. Elevated serum LH and FSH and a low testosterone that fails to rise after administration of exogenous chorionic gonadotropin indicate bilateral absence of functional testicular tissue.

Treatment

Androgen replacement therapy is discussed in the section of pharmacology (see Androgens, above).

Implantation of testicular prostheses for cosmetic purposes may be beneficial after the scrotum has enlarged in response to androgen therapy.

LEYDIG CELL APLASIA

Defective development of testicular Leydig cells is a rare cause of male pseudohermaphroditism with ambiguous genitalia.

Etiology & Pathophysiology

Testes are present in the inguinal canal and contain prepubertal-appearing tubules with Sertoli cells and spermatogonia without germinal cell maturation. The interstitial tissue has a loose myxoid appearance with an absence of Leydig cells. The binding of hCG or LH to testicular extracts from these patients is absent. It is not known whether this represents a primary defect in Leydig cell development due to an abnormality in the Leydig cell precursor cells or is the result of a deficiency of Leydig cell receptors for gonadotropins that may be responsible for inducing Leydig cell differentiation. The presence of a vas deferens and epididymis in these patients indicates that the local concentration of testosterone was high enough during embryogenesis to result in differentiation of the wolffian duct structures. However, the ambiguity of the genitalia indicates that the androgen concentration in these patients was insufficient to bring about full virilization of the external genitalia. The absence of müllerian duct structures is compatible with normal fetal secretion of müllerian duct inhibitory factor from the Sertoli cells.

Clinical Features

A. Symptoms and Signs: These patients may present in infancy with variable degrees of genital ambiguity, including a bifid scrotum, clitoral phallus, urogenital sinus, and blind vaginal pouch. Alternatively, they may appear as normal phenotypic females and escape detection until adolescence, when they present with primary amenorrhea, with or without normal breast development. The gonads are generally located in the inguinal canal. Axillary and pubic hair, although present, may be sparse.

B. Laboratory Findings: Serum gonadotropins are elevated, and testosterone levels are below normal limits for a male and within the low normal range for females. There is no increase in testosterone following chorionic gonadotropin administration.

Differential Diagnosis

Leydig cell aplasia should be differentiated from the vanishing testes syndrome, from testosterone biosynthetic defects, from disorders of androgen action, and from 5α-reductase deficiency. The differential diagnostic features of these disorders are discussed in Chapter 11.

Treatment

Patients with Leydig cell aplasia respond well to the exogenous administration of testosterone, and it would be anticipated that they would be fully virilized and even develop some degree of spermatogenesis with exogenous testosterone administration. However, since the few patients that have been reported have been discovered either late in childhood or as adolescents, it would be inappropriate to attempt a gender reversal at such a late period. Removal of the cryptorchid testes and feminization with exogenous estrogens would appear to be the most prudent course of therapy.

CRYPTORCHIDISM

Cryptorchidism is unilateral or bilateral absence of the testes from the scrotum because of failure of normal testicular descent from the genital ridge through the external inguinal ring. About 5% of full-term male infants have cryptorchidism. In most cases of cryptorchidism noted at birth, spontaneous testicular descent occurs during the first year of life, reducing the incidence to 0.2–0.8% by 1 year of age. Approximately 0.75% of adult males are cryptorchid. Unilateral cryptorchidism is five to ten times more common than bilateral cryptorchidism.

Almost 50% of cryptorchid testes are located at the external inguinal ring or in a high scrotal position; 19% lie within the inguinal canal between the internal and external inguinal rings (canalicular); 9% are intra-abdominal; and 23% are ectopic, ie, located away from the normal pathway of descent from the abdominal cavity to the scrotum. Most ectopic testes are found in a superficial inguinal pouch above the external inguinal ring.

Etiology & Pathophysiology

Testicular descent usually occurs between the twelfth week of fetal development and birth. Both mechanical and hormonal factors appear to be important for this process: Cryptorchidism is common in patients with congenital defects in androgen synthesis or action and in patients with congenital gonadotropin deficiency, and experimental studies have demonstrated that dihydrotestosterone is required for normal testicular descent. These observations suggest that prenatal androgen deficiency may be of etiologic importance in the development of cryptorchidism.

It is not known whether pathologic changes in the testes are due to the effects of cryptorchidism or to intrinsic abnormalities in the gonad. Experimental studies in animals have shown that an increase in the temperature of the testes by 1.5–2 °C (2.7–3.6 °F) (the temperature differential between the abdomen and scrotum) results in depression of spermatogenesis. Serial testicular biopsies in cryptorchid patients have demonstrated partial reversal of the histologic abnormalities following surgical correction, suggesting that the extrascrotal environment is partly responsible for the observed pathologic abnormalities.

An intrinsic abnormality in the testes in patients with unilateral cryptorchidism is suggested by the observation that such patients are at increased risk for development of germ cell neoplasms in the scrotal testis. Similarly, the observation that adults with unilateral cryptorchidism surgically corrected before puberty had low sperm counts, high basal serum LH and FSH concentrations, and an exaggerated FSH response to GnRH suggests either that both testes are intrinsically abnormal or that the cryptorchid gonad somehow suppresses the function of the scrotal testis.

Pathology

Histologic studies on cryptorchid testes have demonstrated a decrease in the size of the seminiferous tubules and number of spermatogonia and an increase in peritubular tissue. The Leydig cells usually appear normal. It is unclear at what age these changes first appear. Abnormalities have been detected as early as 18 months to 2 years. It is well established that the longer a testis remains cryptorchid, the more likely it is to show pathologic changes. More severe changes are generally found in intra-abdominal testes than in canalicular testes.

Clinical Features

A. Symptoms and Signs: There are usually no symptoms unless a complication such as testicular torsion, trauma, or malignant degeneration occurs. School-age children may have gender identity problems. Adults may complain of infertility, especially if they have a history of bilateral cryptorchidism.

Absence of one or both testes is the cardinal clinical finding. This may be associated with a small scrotum (bilateral cryptorchidism) or hemiscrotum (unilateral cryptorchidism). Signs of androgen deficiency are not present.

B. Laboratory Findings: Basal or stimulated serum FSH, LH, and testosterone concentrations are not helpful in evaluating prepubertal unilaterally cryptorchid males. However, serum FSH and LH concentrations and the testosterone response to exogenous chorionic gonadotropin are useful in differentiating cryptorchid patients from those with congenital anorchia. The latter have high basal gonadotropins, low serum testosterone, and absent or diminished testosterone rise following chorionic gonadotropin stimulation.

Postpubertal adults may have oligospermia, elevated basal serum FSH and LH concentrations, and an exaggerated FSH increase following GnRH stimulation. Such abnormalities are more prevalent in patients with a history of bilateral cryptorchidism than with unilateral cryptorchidism.

C. Imaging Studies: Intravenous urography will disclose an associated abnormality of the upper urinary tract in 10% of cases—horseshoe kidney, renal hypoplasia, ureteral duplication, hydroureter, and hydronephrosis.

Differential Diagnosis

Retractile testis (pseudocryptorchidism) is due to a hyperactive cremasteric reflex, which draws the testicle into the inguinal canal. Cold temperature, fear, and genital manipulation commonly activate the reflex, which is most prominent between the ages of 5 and 6 years. The child should be examined with warm hands in a warm room. The testis can usually be "milked" into the scrotum with gentle pressure over the lower abdomen in the direction of the inguinal canal.

Bilateral anorchia is associated with elevated gonadotropins, decreased testosterone, and an absent or subnormal response to stimulation with chorionic gonadotropin.

The virilizing forms of congenital adrenal hyperplasia may result in prenatal fusion of the labial-scrotal folds and clitoral hypertrophy (see Chapter 11). Severely affected females have the appearance of phenotypic males with bilateral cryptorchidism. Because of the potentially disastrous consequences (acute adrenal insufficiency) if this diagnosis is missed, a buccal smear should be performed on bilaterally cryptorchid phenotypic male infants.

Complications & Sequelae

A. Hernia: Approximately 90% of cryptorchid males have associated ipsilateral inguinal hernia resulting from failure of the processus vaginalis to close. This is rarely symptomatic.

B. Torsion: Because of the abnormal connection between the cryptorchid testis and its supporting tissues, torsion may occur. This should be suspected in any patient with abdominal or pelvic pain and an ipsilateral empty scrotum.

C. Trauma: Testes that lie above the pubic tubercle are particularly susceptible to traumatic injury.

D. Neoplasms: A cryptorchid testis is 20–30 times more likely to undergo malignant degeneration than are normal testes. The incidence of such tumors is greater in patients with intra-abdominal testes than in patients with canalicular testes. Seminomas are the neoplasms most commonly associated with maldescended testes. Because of the increased risk of neoplasia, many urologists recommend orchiectomy for a unilaterally undescended testicle in a patient first seen during or after puberty. Patients who present with bilateral cryptorchidism after puberty should have bilateral orchiopexy and testicular biopsies to preserve testicular endocrine function and to make palpation for detection of neoplasia easier.

E. Infertility: Over 90% of untreated bilaterally cryptorchid males are infertile. About 30–50% of bilaterally cryptorchid patients who undergo prepubertal orchiopexy have been found to be fertile. About half of patients with untreated unilateral cryptorchidism are infertile, whereas infertility is found in less than one-fourth of such patients whose cryptorchidism is surgically repaired before puberty.

Prevention

Although cryptorchidism cannot be prevented, the complications can. It is clear that the adverse changes that take place in the testes are related in part to the location of the maldescended testis and the duration of the cryptorchidism. Most testes that are undescended at birth enter the scrotum during the first year of life. However, it is rare for a cryptorchid testis to descend spontaneously after the age of 1 year. Since adverse histologic changes have been noted around the age of 2 years, hormonal or surgical correction should be undertaken at or before that time.

Treatment

A. Medical:

1. Intramuscular chorionic gonadotropin therapy– Because growth of the vas deferens and testicular descent are at least partially dependent upon androgens, stimulation of endogenous testosterone secretion by chorionic gonadotropin may correct the cryptorchidism. Cryptorchidism is corrected in less than 25% of patients treated with a course of chorionic gonadotropin, and recent studies suggest that patients with conditions that respond to hormonal therapy may actually have retractile testes rather than true cryptorchidism. Nevertheless, this therapy should be tried prior to orchiopexy, since it is innocuous and may avoid the need for surgery. For bilateral cryptorchidism, give a short course of chorionic gonadotropin consisting of 3300 units intramuscularly every other day over a 5-day period (three injections). For unilateral cryptorchidism, give 500 units intramuscularly three times a week for 6 1/2 weeks (20 injections).

2. Intranasal GnRH therapy– GnRH given three times a day for 28 days by nasal spray has been shown to be as effective as chorionic gonadotropin injections in correcting cryptorchidism in some patients. This preparation of GnRH has not yet been released for clinical use in the USA.

B. Surgical: Several procedures have been devised to place the maldescended testis into the scrotum (orchiopexy). The operation may be performed in one or two stages. Inguinal hernia should be repaired if present.

NOONAN'S SYNDROME
(Male Turner's Syndrome)

Phenotypic and genotypic males with many of the physical stigmas of classic Turner's syndrome have been described under a variety of names, including Noonan's syndrome and male Turner's syndrome. The incidence and cause of this syndrome are unknown. It may occur sporadically or may be familial, inherited in an autosomal dominant fashion with variable penetrance. A number of pathologic features have been noted, including reduced seminiferous tubular size with or without sclerosis, diminished or absent germ cells, and Leydig cell hyperplasia.

Clinical Features

A. Symptoms and Signs: The most common clinical features are short stature, webbed neck, and cubitus valgus. Other somatic defects are variably observed in these patients. Congenital cardiac anomalies are common and involve primarily the right side of the heart—in contrast to patients with XO gonadal dysgenesis.

Cryptorchidism is frequently present. Although some affected individuals are fertile, with normal testes, most have small testes and mild to moderate hypogonadism.

B. Laboratory Findings: Serum testosterone concentrations are usually low or low normal, and serum gonadotropins are high. The karyotype is 46,XY.

Differential Diagnosis

The clinical features of Noonan's syndrome are sufficiently distinct so that confusion with other causes of hypogonadism is usually not a problem. However, a rare individual with XY/XO mosaicism may have similar somatic anomalies requiring chromosomal analysis for differentiation.

Treatment

If the patient is hypogonadal, androgen replacement therapy is indicated.

MYOTONIC DYSTROPHY

Myotonic dystrophy is one of the familial forms of muscular dystrophy. About 80% of affected males have some degree of primary testicular failure.

The disorder is transmitted in an autosomal dominant fashion, with marked variability in expression. The underlying cause is unknown, and no chromosomal abnormalities have been described.

Testicular histology varies from moderate derangement of spermatogenesis with germinal cell arrest to regional hyalinization and fibrosis of the seminiferous tubules. The Leydig cells are usually preserved and may appear in clumps.

The testes are normal in affected prepubertal individuals, and puberty generally proceeds normally. Testosterone secretion is normal, and secondary sexual characteristics develop. After puberty, seminiferous tubular atrophy results in a decrease in testicular size and change of consistency from firm to soft or mushy. Infertility is a consequence of disrupted spermatogenesis. If testicular hyalinization and fibrosis are extensive, Leydig cell function may also be impaired.

Clinical Features

A. Symptoms and Signs: The disease usually becomes apparent in adulthood. Progressive weakness and atrophy of the facial, neck, hand, and lower extremity muscles is commonly observed. Severe atrophy of the temporalis muscles, ptosis due to weakness of the levator muscles of the eye with compensatory wrinkling of the forehead muscles, and frontal baldness comprise the myopathic facies characteristic of the disorder. Myotonia is present in several muscle

groups and is characterized by inability to relax the muscle normally after a strong contraction.

Testicular atrophy is not noted until adulthood, and most patients develop and maintain normal facial and body hair growth and libido. Gynecomastia is usually not present.

Associated features include mental retardation, cataracts, cranial hyperostosis, diabetes mellitus, and primary hypothyroidism.

B. Laboratory Findings: Serum testosterone is normal to slightly decreased. FSH is uniformly elevated in patients with atrophic testes. LH is also frequently elevated, even in patients with normal serum testosterone levels. Leydig cell reserve is generally diminished, with subnormal increases in serum testosterone following stimulation with chorionic gonadotropin. An excessive rise in FSH and, to a lesser extent, LH is found following GnRH stimulation.

Differential Diagnosis

Myotonic dystrophy should be distinguished from forms of muscular dystrophy not associated with hypogonadism.

Treatment

There is no therapy that will prevent progressive muscular atrophy in this disorder. Testosterone replacement therapy is not indicated unless the serum testosterone levels are subnormal.

ADULT SEMINIFEROUS TUBULE FAILURE

Adult seminiferous tubule failure encompasses a spectrum of pathologic alterations of the seminiferous tubules that results in hypospermatogenesis, germinal cell arrest, germinal cell aplasia, and tubular hyalinization. Almost half of infertile males exhibit some degree of isolated seminiferous tubule failure.

Etiology, Pathology, & Pathophysiology

Etiologic factors in seminiferous tubule failure include mumps or gonococcal orchitis, leprosy, cryptorchidism, irradiation, uremia, alcoholism, paraplegia, lead poisoning, and therapy with antineoplastic agents such as cyclophosphamide, chlorambucil, vincristine, methotrexate, and procarbazine. Vascular insufficiency resulting from spermatic artery damage during herniorrhaphy, testicular torsion, or sickle cell anemia may also selectively damage the tubules. Similar pathologic changes may be found in oligospermic patients with varicoceles. In many patients, no etiologic factors can be identified, and the condition is referred to as "idiopathic."

The rapidly dividing germinal epithelium is more susceptible to injury than are the Sertoli or Leydig cells. Thus, pressure necrosis (eg, mumps or gonococcal orchitis), increased testicular temperature (eg, cryptorchidism and perhaps varicocele and paraplegia), and the direct cytotoxic effects of irradiation, alcohol, lead, and chemotherapeutic agents primarily injure the germ cells. Although the Sertoli and Leydig cells appear to be morphologically normal, severe testicular injury may result in functional alterations in these cells.

Several different lesions may be found in testicular biopsy specimens. The pathologic process may involve the entire testes or may appear in patches. The least severe lesion is hypospermatogenesis, in which all stages of spermatogenesis are present but there is a decrease in the number of germinal epithelial cells. Some degree of peritubular fibrosis may be present. Cessation of development at the primary spermatocyte or spermatogonial stage of the spermatogenic cycle is classified as germinal cell arrest. More severely affected testes may demonstrate a complete absence of germ cells with maintenance or morphologically normal Sertoli cells (Sertoli cell only syndrome). The most severe lesion is fibrosis or hyalinization of the tubules. This latter pattern may be indistinguishable from that seen in Klinefelter's syndrome.

Irrespective of the etiologic factors involved in damage to the germinal epithelium, the alterations in spermatogenesis result in oligospermia. If the damage is severe, as in the Sertoli cell only syndrome or tubular hyalinization, azoospermia may be present. Since testicular volume consists chiefly of tubules, some degree of testicular atrophy is often present in these patients. Some patients have elevations in basal serum FSH concentrations and demonstrate a hyperresponsive FSH rise following GnRH, suggesting that the Sertoli cells are functionally abnormal despite their normal histologic appearance.

Clinical Features

A. Symptoms and Signs: Infertility is usually the only complaint. Mild to moderate testicular atrophy may be present. Careful examination should be made for the presence of varicocele by palpating the spermatic cord during Valsalva's maneuver with the patient in the upright position. The patients are fully virilized, and gynecomastia is not present.

B. Laboratory Findings: Semen analysis shows oligospermia or azoospermia, and serum testosterone and LH concentrations are normal. Basal serum FSH levels may be normal or high, and an excessive FSH rise following GnRH may be present.

Differential Diagnosis

Patients with hypothalamic or pituitary disorders may have oligospermia or azoospermia and testicular atrophy. The serum FSH and LH concentrations are often in the low normal range, and the testosterone level is usually (not always) diminished. The presence of neurologic and ophthalmologic abnormalities, diabetes insipidus, anterior pituitary trophic hormone deficiencies, or an elevated serum PRL concentration distinguishes these patients from those with primary seminiferous tubule failure. Other causes of primary testicular failure are associated either with clinical signs and symptoms of androgen deficiency or with enough somatic abnormalities to allow differentiation from isolated seminiferous tubule failure.

Prevention

In many instances, damage to the seminiferous tubules cannot be prevented. Early correction of cryptorchidism, adequate shielding of the testes during diagnostic radiologic procedures or radiotherapy, and limitation of the total dose of chemotherapeutic agents may prevent or ameliorate the adverse effects.

Treatment

A. Medical: Attempts to treat oligospermia and infertility medically have included testosterone rebound therapy, low-dose testosterone, exogenous gonadotropins, thyroid hormone therapy, vitamins, and clomiphene citrate. None of these agents have been found to be uniformly beneficial, and several may actually lead to a decrease in the sperm count.

B. Surgical: Some of the pathologic changes in the testes have been reversed by early orchiopexy in cryptorchid individuals. If a varicocele is found in an oligospermic, infertile male, it should be ligated.

Course & Prognosis

Patients who have received up to 300 cGy of testicular irradiation may show partial or full recovery of spermatogenesis months to years following exposure. The prognosis for recovery is better for individuals who receive the irradiation over a short interval than for those who are exposed over several weeks.

Recovery of spermatogenesis may also occur months to years following administration of chemotherapeutic agents. The most important factor determining prognosis is the total dose of chemotherapy administered.

Improvement in the quality of the semen is found in 60–80% of patients following successful repair of varicocele. Restoration of fertility has been reported in about half of such patients.

The prognosis for spontaneous improvement of idiopathic oligospermia due to infection or infarction is poor.

ADULT LEYDIG CELL FAILURE (Male Climacteric Syndrome)

In contrast to the menopause in women, men do not experience an abrupt decline or cessation of gonadal function. However, a gradual diminution of testicular function does occur in many men as part of the aging process (see Chapter 22). It is not known how many men develop symptoms directly attributable to this phenomenon.

Etiology, Pathology, & Pathophysiology

There have been many studies of the relationships between age and testicular function, often with conflicting results. Several investigators have found that after age 50, there is a gradual decrease in the total serum testosterone concentration, although the actual values remain within the normal range. The levels of free testosterone decrease to a greater extent because of an increase in SHBG. The testosterone production rate declines, and Leydig cell responsiveness to hCG also decreases. A gradual compensatory increase in serum LH levels has also been noted.

Histologic studies of the aging testes have shown patchy degenerative changes in the seminiferous tubules with morphologically normal Leydig cells. The pathologic changes are first noted in the regions most remote from the arterial blood supply. Thus, microvascular insufficiency may be the etiologic basis for the histologic tubular changes and the decrease in Leydig cell function noted with aging. In addition, virtually all of the conditions that cause adult seminiferous tubule failure may lead to Leydig cell dysfunction if testicular injury is severe enough.

Clinical Features

A. Symptoms and Signs: A great many symptoms have been attributed to the male climacteric, including decreased libido and potency, emotional instability, fatigue, decreased concentrating ability, vasomotor instability (palpitations, hot flushes, diaphoresis), and a variety of diffuse aches and pains. There are usually no associated signs unless the testicular injury is severe. In such patients, a decrease in testicular volume and consistency may be present.

B. Laboratory Findings: Serum testosterone may be low or low normal; serum LH concentration is usually high normal or slightly high. Oligospermia is usually present.

C. Special Examinations: Because many men with complaints compatible with Leydig cell failure have testosterone and LH concentrations within the normal adult range, a diagnostic trial of testosterone therapy may be attempted. The test is best performed double-blind over an 8-week period. During the first or last 4 weeks, the patient receives testosterone enanthate, 200 mg intramuscularly per week; during the other 4-week period, placebo injections are administered. The patient is interviewed by the physician 2 weeks after the last course of injections. After the interview, the code is broken; if the patient notes amelioration of symptoms during the period of androgen administration but not during the placebo period, the diagnosis of adult Leydig cell failure is substantiated. If the patient experiences no subjective improvement following testosterone, or if improve-

ment is noted following both placebo and testosterone injections, Leydig cell failure is effectively ruled out.

Differential Diagnosis

Impotence from vascular, neurologic, or psychologic causes must be distinguished from Leydig cell failure. A therapeutic trial of androgen therapy will not help impotence that is not due to androgen deficiency.

Treatment

Androgen replacement therapy is the treatment of choice for symptomatic Leydig cell failure.

IMPOTENCE

Impotence implies erectile dysfunction with or without associated disturbances of libido or ejaculatory ability. The overall prevalence of impotence in the general population is unknown, though it is probable that most men experience occasional episodes of impotence at some time during their lives.

Etiology & Pathophysiology

Penile erection occurs when blood flow to the penile erectile tissue (corpora cavernosa and spongiosum) increases as a result of dilation of the urethral artery, the artery of the bulb of the penis, the deep artery of the penis, and the dorsal artery of the penis. Concurrent contraction of the ischiocavernosus muscle leads to compression of the veins draining the corpora cavernosa and spongiosum. This combination results in the distention, engorgement, and rigidity of the penis that constitute erection. Erection is an involuntary reflex that may occur via two different mechanisms. Psychogenic stimuli transmitted to the limbic system stimulate the thoracolumbar (T12–L2) parasympathetic nerves, and this in turn results in dilation of the arteriolar vessels that supply the corpora cavernosa and spongiosum. In addition to the thoracolumbar center, sacral parasympathetic (S2–4) nerves may be activated by direct genital stimuli. The afferent limb for the spinal reflex arc is located within the pudendal nerves.

Broadly speaking, erectile dysfunction may be divided into psychogenic and organic causes. Table 9–4 lists various pathologic conditions and drugs that may be associated with impotence.

Most organic causes of impotence result from disturbances in the neurologic pathways essential for the initiation and maintenance of erection or in the blood supply to the penis. Many of the endocrine disorders, systemic illnesses, and drugs associated with impotence affect libido, the autonomic pathways essential for erection, or the blood flow to the penis. Local urogenital disorders such as Peyronie's disease (idiopathic fibrosis of the covering sheath of the corpus cavernosum) may mechanically interfere with erec-

Table 9–4. Organic causes of impotence.

Neurologic
Anterior temporal lobe lesions
Spinal cord lesions
Autonomic neuropathy
Vascular
Leriche's syndrome
Pelvic vascular insufficiency
Sickle cell disease
Aging (?)
Endocrine
Diabetes mellitus
Hypogonadism
Hyperprolactinemia
Adrenal insufficiency
Feminizing tumors
Hypothyroidism
Hyperthyroidism
Urogenital
Trauma
Castration
Priapism
Systemic illness
Cardiac insufficiency
Cirrhosis
Uremia
Respiratory insufficiency
Lead poisoning
Postoperative
Aortoiliac or aortofemoral reconstruction
Lumbar sympathectomy
Perineal prostatectomy
Retroperitoneal dissection
Drugs
Alcohol
Barbiturates
Spironolactone
Anticholinergics
Estrogens
Guanethidine
Reserpine
Methyldopa
Ketoconazole
Phenothiazines
Butyrophenones
Thiothixenes
Tricyclic antidepressants
Monoamine oxidase inhibitors
Heroin
Methadone
Morphine
Cocaine
Amphetamines
Diuretics
Antiandrogens

tion. In some patients, the cause of impotence is multifactorial. For example, some degree of erectile dysfunction is reported by over 50% of men with diabetes mellitus. The basis of the impotence is usually autonomic neuropathy. However, vascular insufficiency, antihypertensive medication, uremia, and depression may also cause or contribute to the problem in diabetics.

Clinical Features

A. Symptoms and Signs: Patients may complain of constant or episodic inability to initiate or maintain an erection, decreased penile turgidity, decreased libido, or a combination of these difficulties. Besides the specific sexual dysfunction symptoms, symptoms and signs of a more pervasive emotional or psychiatric problem may be elicited. If an underlying neurologic, vascular, or systemic disorder is the cause of impotence, additional symptoms and signs referable to the anatomic or metabolic disturbances may be present. A history of claudication of the buttocks or lower extremities should direct attention toward arterial insufficiency.

The differentiation between psychogenic and organic impotence can usually be made on the basis of the history. Even though the patient may be selectively unable to obtain or maintain a satisfactory erection to complete sexual intercourse, a history of repeated normal erections at other times is indicative of psychogenic impotence. Thus, a history of erections that occur nocturnally, during masturbation, or during foreplay or with other sexual partners eliminates significant neurologic, vascular, or endocrine causes of impotence. Patients with psychogenic impotence often note a sudden onset of sexual dysfunction concurrently with a significant event in their lives such as loss of a friend or relative, an extramarital affair, or the loss of a job.

Patients with organic impotence generally note a more gradual and global loss of potency. Initially, such individuals may be able to achieve erections with strong sexual stimuli, but ultimately they may be unable to achieve a fully turgid erection under any circumstances. In contrast to patients with psychogenic impotence, patients with organic impotence generally maintain a normal libido. However, patients with systemic illness may have a concurrent diminution of libido and potency. Hypogonadism should be suspected in a patient who has never had an erection (primary impotence).

B. Laboratory Findings and Special Examinations: The integrity of the neurologic pathways and the ability of the blood vessels to deliver a sufficient amount of blood to the penis for erection to occur may be objectively examined by placement of a strain gauge behind the glans penis and at the base of the penis at the time the patient retires for sleep. The occurrence of nocturnal penile tumescence can thus be recorded. Healthy men and those with psychogenic impotence have three to five erections a night associated with rapid eye movement (REM) sleep. Absence or reduced frequency of nocturnal tumescence indicates an organic lesion. Penile rigidity as well as tumescence can be evaluated with an ambulatory monitor called RigiScan (Dacomed Corporation, Minneapolis, MN 55420).

Penile arterial blood pressure may be measured with a small pneumatic cuff wrapped around the base of the penis and connected to a manometer. Penile blood flow is monitored during inflation and deflation of the cuff by a Doppler ultrasound device. Comparison of the ratio of the penile systolic blood pressure with the brachial systolic blood pressure at rest and following exercise of the lower extremities is a useful technique for unmasking pelvic vascular insufficiency.

Neural innervation of the penis may be assessed by measurement of the bulbocavernosus reflex response latency period. This procedure is performed by electrical stimulation of the dorsal nerve to the penis, which evokes contraction of the bulbocavernosus muscle with a normal latency of 30–50 ms. Alternatively, since the autonomic pathways involved in erection and urination are the same, cystometrography with measurement of bladder capacity and residual urine may be used as an indirect measurement of penile innervation.

Serum PRL should be measured in all patients with cryptogenic organic impotence, since hyperprolactinemia, whether drug-induced or due to a pituitary or hypothalamic lesion, appears to inhibit the peripheral effects of androgens. In addition, testosterone measurements may uncover a mild and otherwise asymptomatic androgen deficiency. Because diabetes mellitus is a relatively common cause of impotence and impotence may be the presenting symptom of diabetes, fasting and 2-hour postprandial blood glucose measurements should be ordered. The choice of other laboratory tests depends upon associated organic symptoms or signs.

Treatment

A. Psychogenic Impotence: Simple reassurance and explanation, formal psychotherapy, and various forms of behavioral therapy have a reported 40–70% success rate. Androgen therapy should not be used in patients with psychogenic impotence, since androgens exert no more than a placebo effect and may focus the patient's attention on a nonexistent organic problem.

B. Organic Impotence: Discontinuation of an offending drug usually results in a return of potency. Similarly, effective therapy of an underlying systemic or endocrine disorder may cure the erectile dysfunction.

Patients with permanent impotence due to organic lesions that cannot be corrected should be counseled in noncoital sensate focus techniques. Some patients respond to intracavernous injections of the vasoactive drugs prostaglandin E_1 or papaverine hydrochloride, or papaverine with phentolamine mesylate, although priapism, infection, and bleeding can complicate this type of therapy. Recently, a device has been developed that uses suction to induce penile engorgement and constrictive bands to maintain the ensuing erection (ErecAid System, Osbon Medical Systems, Augusta, Georgia). Patients appear to be quite satisfied with this nonsurgical therapy. Alternatively, a penile prosthesis may be surgically implanted. Two major types of such prostheses have been developed.

These include semirigid silicone rubber rods that are implanted in the corpora (eg, Small-Carrion and Jonas prostheses) or inflatable penile prostheses that allow the penis to remain flaccid until erection is desired. Both types of prostheses have given satisfactory results in 85–90% of cases.

MALE INFERTILITY

About 15% of married couples are unable to produce offspring. Male factors are responsible in about 40% of cases, female factors in about 40%, and couple factors in 20%.

Etiology & Pathophysiology

In order for conception to occur, spermatogenesis must be normal, the sperm must complete its maturation during transport through patent ducts, adequate amounts of seminal plasma must be added to provide volume and nutritional elements, and the male must be able to deposit the semen near the female's cervix. Any defect in this pathway can result in infertility due to a male factor problem. The spermatozoa must also be able to penetrate the cervical mucus and reach the uterine tubes, where conception takes place. These latter events may fail to occur if there are female reproductive tract disorders or abnormalities of sperm motility or fertilizing capacity.

Table 9–5 lists the identified causes of male infertility. Disturbances in the function of the hypothalamus, pituitary, adrenals, or thyroid are found in approximately 4% of males evaluated for infertility. Sex chromosome abnormalities, cryptorchidism,

Table 9–5. Causes of male infertility.

Endocrine
  Hypothalamic-pituitary disorders
  Testicular disorders
  Defects of androgen action
  Hyperthyroidism
  Hypothyroidism
  Adrenal insufficiency
  Congenital adrenal hyperplasia
Systemic illness
Defects in spermatogenesis
  Immotile cilia syndrome
  Drug-induced
  Adult seminiferous tubule failure
Ductal obstruction
  Congenital
  Acquired
Seminal vesicle disease
Prostatic disease
Varicocele
Retrograde ejaculation
Antibodies to sperm or seminal plasma
Anatomic defects of the penis
Poor coital technique
Sexual dysfunction
Idiopathic

adult seminiferous tubule failure, and other forms of primary testicular failure are found in 15% of infertile males. Congenital or acquired ductal problems are found in approximately 6% of such patients, and poor coital technique, sexual dysfunction, ejaculatory disturbances, and anatomic abnormalities such as hypospadias are causative factors in 4–5% of patients evaluated for infertility. Idiopathic infertility, in which no cause can be identified with certainty, accounts for approximately 35% of patients. Autoimmune disturbances that lead to sperm agglutination and immobilization causes infertility in only a small fraction of patients. Varicoceles are found in 25–40% of patients classified as having idiopathic infertility. The significance of this finding is uncertain, since 8–20% of males in the general population have varicoceles.

Clinical Features

A. Symptoms and Signs: The clinical features of the hypothalamic-pituitary, thyroid, adrenal, testicular, and sexual dysfunctional disorders have been discussed in preceding sections of this chapter. Evaluation for the presence of varicocele has also been described.

Patients with immotile cilia syndrome have associated mucociliary transport defects in the lower airways that result in chronic pulmonary obstructive disease. Some patients with this disorder also have Kartagener's syndrome, with sinusitis, bronchiectasis, and situs inversus. Infections of the epididymis or vas deferens may be asymptomatic or associated with scrotal pain that may radiate to the flank, fever, epididymal swelling and tenderness, and urethral discharge. The presence of thickened, enlarged epididymis and vas is indicative of chronic epididymitis. Chronic prostatitis is usually asymptomatic, although a perineal aching sensation or low back pain may be described. A boggy or indurated prostate may be found on rectal palpation. A careful examination for the presence of penile anatomic abnormalities such as chordee, hypospadias, or epispadias should be made, since these defects may prevent the deposit of sperm in the vagina.

B. Laboratory Findings: A carefully collected and performed semen analysis is mandatory. A normal report indicates normal endocrine function and spermatogenesis and an intact transport system. Semen analysis should be followed by a postcoital test, which consists of examining a cervical mucus sample obtained within 2 hours after intercourse. The presence of large numbers of motile spermatozoa in mucus obtained from the internal os of the cervix rules out the male factor as a cause of infertility. If a postcoital test reveals necrospermia (dead sperm), asthenospermia (slow-moving sperm), or agglutination of sperm, examination of the female partner for the presence of sperm-immobilizing antibodies or cervical mucus abnormalities should be carried out.

If semen analysis shows abnormalities, at least two more specimens should be obtained at monthly intervals. Persistent oligospermia or azoospermia should be evaluated by studies outlined in Figure 9–7.

The female partner should be thoroughly examined to verify patency of the uterus and uterine tubes, normal ovulation, and normal cervical mucus. This examination must be done even in the presence of a male factor abnormality, since infertility is due to a combination of male and female factors in about 20% of cases.

Treatment

A. Endocrine Disorders: Correction of hyperthyroidism, hypothyroidism, adrenal insufficiency, and congenital adrenal hyperplasia generally restores fertility. Patients with hypogonadotropic hypogonadism may have spermatogenesis initiated with gonadotropin therapy. Chorionic gonadotropin (2000 units given intramuscularly three times per week) with menotropins (75 units given intramuscularly three times per week) added after 12–18 months if sperm do not appear in the ejaculate, will restore spermatogenesis in most hypogonadotropic men. The sperm count following such therapy usually does not exceed 10 million/mL but may still allow impregnation. Patients with isolated deficiency of LH may respond to chorionic gonadotropin alone. There is no effective therapy for adult seminiferous tubule failure not associated with varicocele or cryptorchidism. However, if the oligospermia is mild (10–20 million/mL), cup insemination of the female partner with concentrates of semen may be tried. In vitro fertilization and other assisted reproductive techniques are increasingly being utilized as a method for achieving pregnancy in couples in which the male is oligospermic.

B. Defects of Spermatogenesis: There is no treatment for immotile cilia syndrome or for chromosomal abnormalities associated with defective spermatogenesis. Drugs that interfere with spermatogenesis should be discontinued. These include the antimetabolites, phenytoin, marihuana, alcohol, monoamine oxidase inhibitors, and nitrofurantoin. Discontinuing use of these agents may be accompanied by restoration of normal sperm density.

C. Ductal Obstruction: Localized obstruction of the vas deferens may be treated by vasovasotomy. Sperm are detected in the ejaculate of 60–80% of patients following this procedure. However, the subsequent fertility rate is only 30–35%; the presence of antisperm antibodies that agglutinate or immobilize sperm probably accounts for the high failure rate.

Epididymovasostomy may be performed for epididymal obstruction. Sperm in the postoperative ejaculate have been found in approximately half of patients treated with this procedure, but subsequent fertility has been demonstrated in only 20% of cases.

D. Genital Tract Infections: Acute prostatitis may be treated with daily sitz baths, prostatic massage, and antibiotics. A combination of trimethoprim (400 mg) and sulfamethoxazole (2000 mg), twice a day for 10 days followed by the same dosage once a day for another 20 days, has been used with some success. Acute epididymitis may respond to injections of local anesthetic into the spermatic cord just above the testicle. Appropriate antibiotic therapy should also be given. The prognosis for fertility following severe bilateral chronic epididymitis or extensive scarring from acute epididymitis is poor.

E. Varicocele: The presence of varicocele in an infertile male with oligospermia is an indication for surgical ligation of the incompetent spermatic veins. Improvement in the semen is noted in 60–80% of treated patients, and about half are subsequently fertile.

F. Retrograde Ejaculation: Ejaculation of semen into the urinary bladder may occur following disruption of the internal bladder sphincter or with neuropathic disorders such as diabetic autonomic neuropathy. Normal ejaculation has been restored in a few patients with the latter problem following administration of phenylpropanolamine, 15 mg orally twice daily in timed-release capsules. Sperm can also be recovered from the bladder following masturbation for the purpose of direct insemination of the female partner.

G. Antibodies to Sperm or Seminal Plasma: Antibodies in the female genital tract that agglutinate or immobilize sperm may be difficult to treat. Older methods such as condom therapy or administration of glucocorticoids have not been uniformly successful. Currently, intrauterine insemination with washed spermatozoa, in vitro fertilization, and gamete intrafallopian transfer are considered the most effective treatments.

H. Anatomic Defects of the Penis: Patients with hypospadias, epispadias, or severe chordee may collect semen by masturbation for use in insemination.

I. Poor Coital Technique: Couples should be counseled not to use vaginal lubricants or postcoital douches. In order to maximize the sperm count in cases of borderline oligospermia, intercourse should not be more frequent than every other day. Exposure of the cervix to the seminal plasma is increased by having the woman lie supine with her knees bent up for 20 minutes after intercourse.

Course & Prognosis

The prognosis for fertility depends upon the underlying cause. It is good for patients with nontesticular endocrine abnormalities, varicoceles, retrograde ejaculation, and anatomic defects of the penis. If fertility cannot be restored, the couple should be counseled regarding artificial donor insemination, in vitro fertilization, or adoption.

GYNECOMASTIA

Gynecomastia is common during the neonatal period and is present in about 70% of pubertal males (see Chapter 12). Clinically apparent gynecomastia has been noted at autopsy in almost 1% of adult males, and 40% of autopsied males have histologic evidence of gynecomastia.

Etiology & Pathophysiology

The causes of gynecomastia are listed in Table 9–6. Several mechanisms have been proposed to account for this disorder. All involve a relative imbalance between estrogen and androgen concentrations or action at the mammary gland level. Decrease in free testosterone may be due to primary gonadal disease or an increase in SHBG as is found in hyperthyroidism and some forms of liver disease (eg, alcoholic cirrhosis). Acute or chronic excessive stimulation of the Leydig cells by pituitary gonadotropins alters the steroidogenic pathways and favors excessive estrogen and estrogen precursor secretion relative to testosterone production. This mechanism may be responsible for the gynecomastia found with hypergonadotropic states such as Klinefelter's syndrome and adult Leydig cell failure. The rise of gonadotropins during puberty may lead to an estrogen-androgen imbalance by similar mechanisms.

Table 9–6. Causes of gynecomastia.

Physiologic
  Neonatal
  Pubertal
Drug-induced
  Amphetamines
  Androgens
  Chorionic gonadotropin
  Cimetidine
  Digitalis
  Estrogens
  Hydroxyzine
  Isoniazid
  Marihuana
  Meprobamate
  Methadone
  Methyldopa
  Phenothiazines
  Reserpine
  Spironolactone
Endocrine
  Primary hypogonadism with Leydig cell damage
  Hyperprolactinemia
  Hyperthyroidism
  Androgen receptor disorders
Systemic diseases
  Hepatic cirrhosis
  Uremia
  Recovery from malnourishment
Neoplasms
  Testicular germ cell or Leydig cell tumors
  Feminizing adrenocortical adenoma or carcinoma
  hCG-secreting nontrophoblastic neoplasms
Idiopathic

Patients who are malnourished or have systemic illness may develop gynecomastia during refeeding or treatment of the underlying disorder. Malnourishment and chronic illness are accompanied by a reduction in gonadotropin secretion, and during recovery the gonadotropins rise and may stimulate excessive Leydig cell production of estrogens relative to testosterone.

Excessive stimulation of Leydig cells may also occur in patients with hCG-producing trophoblastic or nontrophoblastic tumors. In addition, some of these tumors are able to convert estrogen precursors into estradiol. Feminizing adrenocortical and Leydig cell neoplasms may directly secrete excessive quantities of estrogens. The mechanisms by which PRL-secreting pituitary tumors and hyperprolactinemia produce gynecomastia are unclear. PRL may directly stimulate breast glandular development through its mammotropic action. Elevated serum PRL levels may also diminish the peripheral actions of testosterone, which may result in an excessive estrogen effect on the breast that is not counteracted by androgens.

Drugs such as phenothiazines, methyldopa, and reserpine may induce gynecomastia through elevations of PRL. Other drugs may reduce androgen production (eg, spironolactone), peripherally antagonize androgen action (spironolactone, cimetidine), or interact with breast estrogen receptors (spironolactone, digitalis, phytoestrogens in marihuana).

Finally, it has been proposed that patients with idiopathic gynecomastia have breast glandular tissue that is inordinately sensitive to normal circulating levels of estrogen or excessively converts estrogen precursors to estrogens.

Pathology

Three histologic patterns of gynecomastia have been recognized. The florid pattern consists of an increase in the number of budding ducts, proliferation of the ductal epithelium, periductal edema, and a cellular fibroblastic stroma. The fibrous type has dilated ducts, minimal duct epithelial proliferation, no periductal edema, and a virtually acellular fibrous stroma. An intermediate pattern contains features of both types.

Although it has been proposed that different causes of gynecomastia are associated with either the florid or the fibrous pattern, it appears that the duration of gynecomastia is the most important factor in determining the pathologic picture. Approximately 75% of patients with gynecomastia of 4 months' duration or less exhibit the florid pattern, while 90% of patients with gynecomastia lasting a year or more have the fibrous type. Between 4 months and 1 year, 60% of patients have the intermediate pattern.

Clinical Features

A. Symptoms and Signs: The principal complaint is unilateral or bilateral concentric enlargement of breast glandular tissue. Nipple or breast pain is present in one-fourth of patients and objective tenderness in about 40%. A complaint of nipple discharge can be elicited in 4% of cases. Histologic examination has demonstrated that gynecomastia is almost always bilateral, although grossly it may be detected only on one side. The patient will often complain of discomfort in one breast despite obvious bilateral gynecomastia. Breast or nipple discomfort generally lasts less than 1 year. Chronic gynecomastia is usually asymptomatic, with the major complaint being the cosmetic one.

Symptoms and signs of underlying disorders may be present. Gynecomastia may be the earliest manifestation of an hCG-secreting testicular tumor; therefore, it is mandatory that careful examination of the testes be performed in any patient with gynecomastia. Enlargement, asymmetry, and induration of a testis may be noted in such patients.

B. Laboratory Findings: Serum hCG by the beta subunit radioimmunoassay method is the most sensitive test for detection of hCG-secreting neoplasms. Feminizing tumors of the adrenals or Leydig cells are associated with marked elevations of serum estradiol. However, most patients with gynecomastia not associated with these neoplasms have total serum estradiol levels within the normal range. Serum PRL and thyroid hormones should be measured to detect hyperprolactinemia and hyper- or hypothyroidism. If hyperprolactinemia is found in a patient who has been taking phenothiazines or other drugs that enhance PRL secretion, the drug should be withdrawn and the PRL concentration measured in 2–3 months.

C. Imaging Studies: Chest x-ray may detect metastatic disease or an hCG-secreting primary lung neoplasm. CT scans of the pituitary-hypothalamic region should be performed if hyperprolactinemia is present. If gynecomastia is unilateral and especially if the "glandular" tissue is eccentric, mammograms should be taken to exclude breast carcinoma, which accounts for about 0.2% of all cancers in males.

D. Special Examinations: If small testes are found on physical examination, buccal smear or chromosomal analysis should be done, since Klinefelter's syndrome is one of the more common causes of persistent pubertal gynecomastia.

Differential Diagnosis

Gynecomastia should be differentiated from lipomas, neurofibromas, carcinoma of the breast, and obesity. Breast lipomas, neurofibromas, and carcinoma are usually unilateral, painless, and eccentric, whereas gynecomastia characteristically begins in the subareolar areas and enlarges concentrically. The differentiation between gynecomastia and enlarged breasts due to obesity may be difficult. The patient should be supine. Examination is performed by spreading the thumb and index fingers and gently palpating the breasts during slow apposition of the fingers toward the nipple. In this manner, a concentric ridge of tissue can be felt in patients with gynecomastia but not in obese patients without glandular tissue enlargement. The examination may be facilitated by applying soap and water to the breasts.

Complications & Sequelae

There are no complications other than possible psychologic damage from the cosmetic defect. Patients with gynecomastia may have a slightly increased risk of development of breast carcinoma.

Treatment

A. Medical: The underlying disease should be corrected if possible, and offending drugs should be discontinued. Antiestrogens such as tamoxifen and clomiphene citrate have been found useful for relieving pain and reversing gynecomastia in a few patients. Whether this therapy will be useful in most patients with gynecomastia remains to be seen.

B. Surgical: Reduction mammoplasty should be considered for cosmetic reasons in any patient with long-standing gynecomastia that is in the fibrotic stage.

C. Radiologic: Patients with prostatic carcinoma may receive low-dose radiation therapy (900 rads or less) to the breasts before initiation of estrogen therapy. This may prevent or diminish the gynecomastia that usually results from such therapy. Radiotherapy should not be given to other patients with gynecomastia.

Course & Prognosis

Pubertal gynecomastia usually regresses spontaneously over 1–2 years. Patients who develop drug-induced gynecomastia generally have complete or near-complete regression of the breast changes if the drug is discontinued during the early florid stage. Once gynecomastia from any cause has reached the fibrotic stage, little or no spontaneous regression occurs.

TESTICULAR TUMORS

Testicular neoplasms account for 1–2% of all male-related malignant neoplasms and 4–10% of all genitourinary neoplasms. They are the second most frequent type of cancer in men between 20 and 34 years of age. The incidence is 2–3 per 100,000 men in the USA and 4–6 per 100,000 men in Denmark. The incidence is lower in nonwhite than in white populations. Ninety-five percent of testicular tumors are of germ cell origin; 5% are composed of stromal or Leydig cell neoplasms.

Etiology & Pathophysiology

The cause of testicular tumors is not known. Predisposing factors include testicular maldescent and dysgenesis. About 4–12% of testicular tumors are found in association with cryptorchidism, and such a testicle has a 20- to 30-fold greater risk of developing a neoplasm than does a normally descended one. Almost 20% of testicular tumors associated with cryptorchidism arise in the contralateral scrotal testis, suggesting that testicular dysgenesis may be of etiologic importance in the development of germ cell neoplasms. Although trauma is frequently cited as an etiologic factor in testicular tumors, no causal relationship has been established. What is more likely is that testicular trauma serves to call the patient's attention to the presence of a testicular mass.

Bilateral gynecomastia is uncommon in patients who present with testicular cancer. It is generally associated with production of hCG by the trophoblastic elements in the tumor. The hCG stimulates the Leydig cells to produce excessive estrogens relative to androgen production, resulting in estrogen-androgen imbalance and gynecomastia. In addition, the trophoblastic tissue in some of the tumors may convert estrogen precursors to estrogens.

Pathology

A. Germ Cell Tumors: Seminomas account for 33–50% of all germ cell tumors. They are composed of round cells with abundant cytoplasm, prominent nuclei, and large nucleoli. The cells are arranged in cords and nests and have a thin delicate network of stromal connective tissue. Embryonal cell neoplasms comprise 20–33% of germ cell tumors. These tumors have multiple histologic patterns composed of cuboidal pleomorphic cells. One distinct pattern of cellular arrangement is the endodermal sinus tumor (yolk sac tumor), the most frequent germ cell neoplasm found in infants. Immunohistochemical techniques have localized alpha-fetoprotein to the embryonal cells. About 10% of germ cell tumors are teratomas, which are composed of well-differentiated cells derived from all three germ layers. When one or more of the teratoid elements are malignant or are mixed with embryonal carcinoma cells, the term teratocarcinoma is applied. These tumors account for one-tenth to one-third of germ cell neoplasms. Choriocarcinoma is the rarest form of germ cell tumor (2%) and is composed of masses of large, polymorphic, multinucleated syncytiotrophoblastic cells. Although pure choriocarcinoma is rare, many testicular tumors contain an occasional trophoblastic giant cell. Immunohistochemical techniques have shown that these cells are the source of hCG in such tumors.

B. Leydig Cell Tumors: Leydig cell (interstitial cell) tumors are rare. Most are benign and are composed of sheets of oval to polygonal cells arranged in lobules separated from one another by thin strands of connective tissue. Malignant Leydig cell tumor disseminates by both lymphatic and venous channels, with initial metastatic deposits being found in the regional lymph nodes, followed by metastases to liver, lung, and bone.

Clinical Features

A. Symptoms and Signs:

1. Germ cell tumors– Testicular tumors usually present as painless enlargement of a testicle with an associated feeling of fullness or heaviness in the scrotum. Thus, about 80% of patients note a testicular swelling or mass, whereas only 25% complain of testicular pain or tenderness. About 6–25% of patients give a history of testicular trauma that brought the testicular mass to their attention. Gynecomastia may be present initially in 2–4% of patients and develops subsequently in another 10%. About 5–10% of patients present with symptoms of distant metastatic disease, including backache, skeletal pains, gastrointestinal and abdominal pains, inguinal adenopathy, and neurologic dysfunction.

A testicular mass or generalized enlargement of the testis is often present on examination. In 5–10% of patients, a coexisting hydrocele may be present. In the presence of metastatic disease, supraclavicular and retroperitoneal lymph node enlargement may be present.

2. Leydig cell tumors– In children, Leydig cell tumors of the testes may produce sexual precocity, with rapid skeletal growth and development of secondary sexual characteristics. Adults with such tumors usually present with a testicular mass and occasionally gynecomastia. Decreased libido may also be present in such patients.

B. Laboratory Findings:

1. Germ cell tumors– The tumor markers hCG and alpha-fetoprotein should be measured in every male presenting with a testicular mass. hCG is found in the sera of 5–10% of males with seminoma, over half of patients with teratocarcinoma or embryonal cell carcinoma, and all patients with choriocarcinoma. hCG should be measured by the beta subunit or other hCG-specific radioimmunoassay method. Elevated serum immunoreactive alpha-fetoprotein concentrations are found in almost 70% of patients with nonseminomatous forms of germ cell neoplasms. Both markers are elevated in over 50% of patients with nonseminomatous germ cell tumors, and at least one of the markers is elevated in 85% of such patients. These markers can also be used to monitor the results of therapy.

2. Leydig cell tumors– Urinary 17-ketosteroids and serum DHEA sulfate concentrations are increased. Both urinary and serum estrogen levels may also be increased. Serum testosterone concentrations tend to be low or within the normal adult range.

C. Imaging Studies:
Staging of testicular tumors requires several radiologic procedures, including chest tomograms, intravenous urograms, liver scans, gallium scans, and CT scans of the abdomen and retroperitoneum.

Differential Diagnosis

Testicular tumors are sometimes misdiagnosed as epididymitis or epididymo-orchitis. An inflammatory reaction of the epididymis often involves the vas deferens. Therefore, both the vas and the epididymis will be thickened and tender on examination during the acute disease. Pyuria and fever also help to differentiate between epididymitis and testicular tumor. Because hydrocele may coexist with testicular tumor, the testes should be carefully examined following aspiration of the hydrocele.

Other conditions that can cause confusion with testicular tumors include inguinal hernia, hematocele, hematoma, torsion, spermatocele, varicocele, and (rarely) sarcoidosis, tuberculosis, and syphilitic gumma. Ultrasonic examination of the scrotum may help distinguish between testicular tumors and extratesticular disease such as acute or chronic epididymitis, spermatocele, or hydrocele.

Benign Leydig cell tumors of the testes must be differentiated from adrenal rest tumors in patients with congenital adrenal hyperplasia. Since the testes and the adrenals are derived from the same embryologic source, ectopic adrenal tissue may be found to migrate with the testes. This tissue can enlarge under the influence of ACTH in patients with congenital adrenal hyperplasia or Cushing's disease. Adrenal rest tumors tend to be bilateral, whereas patients with Leydig cell tumors generally have unilateral disease. Both may be associated with elevated urine 17-ketosteroids and elevated serum DHEA sulfate concentrations. Elevated serum and urinary estrogen concentrations are found with both disorders. However, patients with congenital adrenal hyperplasia or Cushing's disease will have a decrease in 17-ketosteroids, DHEA sulfate, and estrogen concentrations, as well as a decrease in tumor size, following administration of dexamethasone.

Treatment

A. Germ Cell Tumors:
Seminomas are quite radiosensitive, and disease localized to the testes is usually treated with orchiectomy and 2000–4000 cGy of conventional radiotherapy delivered to the ipsilateral inguinal-iliac and bilateral para-aortic lymph nodes to the level of the diaphragm. For disease that has spread to the lymph nodes below the diaphragm, additional whole abdominal radiotherapy and prophylactic mediastinal and supraclavicular lymph node irradiation are usually given. Widely disseminated disease is generally treated with a combination of radiotherapy and chemotherapy, especially with alkylating agents.

Nonseminomatous tumors are treated with orchiectomy, retroperitoneal lymph node dissection, and, if necessary, radiotherapy or chemotherapy (or both). Although many chemotherapeutic agents have been used, combinations of etoposide (VP-16), bleomycin, and cisplatin currently appear to produce the best overall results. Patients with nonseminomatous tumors treated by these means should be monitored with serial measurements of serum hCG and alpha-fetoprotein.

B. Leydig Cell Tumors: Benign Leydig cell tumors of the testes are treated by unilateral orchiectomy. Objective remissions of malignant Leydig cell tumors have been noted following treatment with mitotane.

Course & Prognosis

A. Germ Cell Tumors: In patients with seminoma confined to the testicle, the 5-year survival rates after orchiectomy and radiotherapy are 98–100%. Disease in the lymph nodes below the diaphragm also has an excellent prognosis, with 5-year survival rates of 80–85%. Disease above the diaphragm and disseminated disease have 5-year survival rates as low as 18%.

In patients with nonseminomatous germ cell tumors, aggressive surgery and combination chemotherapy have raised the 5-year survival rates from less than 20% to 60–90%.

B. Leydig Cell Tumors: Removal of a benign Leydig cell tumor is accompanied by regression of precocious puberty in children or feminization in adults. The prognosis for malignant Leydig cell tumor is poor, with most patients surviving less than 2 years from the time of diagnosis.

REFERENCES

Physiology

Berger FG, Watson G: Androgen-regulated gene expression. Annu Rev Physiol 1989;51:51.

de Kretser DM, Robertson DM: The isolation and physiology of inhibin and related proteins. Biol Reprod 1989;40:33.

Lazar MA: Steroid and thyroid hormone receptors. Endocrinol Metab Clin North Am 1991;20:681.

Maddocks S et al: Regulation of the testis. J Reprod Immunol 1990;18:33.

Sharpe RM: Intratesticular control of steroidogenesis. Clin Endocrinol 1990;33:787.

Rosner W: Plasma steroid-binding proteins. Endocrinol Metab Clin North Am 1991;4:697.

Vermeulen A: Androgen in the aging male. J Clin Endocrinol Metab 1991;73:221.

Androgen Therapy

Bardin CW, Swerdloff RS, Santen RJ: Androgens: Risks and benefits. J Clin Endocrinol Metab 1991;73:4.

Cunningham GR, Cordero E, Thornby JI: Testosterone replacement with transdermal therapeutic systems. Physiological serum testosterone and elevated dihydrotestosterone levels. JAMA 1989;261:2525.

Cryptorchidism

Hutson JM, Beasley SW: Embryological controversies in testicular descent. Semin Urol 1988;6:68.

Palmer JM: The undescended testicle. Endocrinol Metab Clin North Am 1991;20:231.

Primary Testicular Insufficiency

Lee PA, O'Dea L St L: Primary and secondary testicular insufficiency. Pediatr Clin North Am 1990;37:1359.

Schwartz ID, Root AW: The Klinefelter syndrome of testicular dysgenesis. Endocrinol Metab Clin North Am 1991;20:153.

Whitcomb RW, Crowley WF Jr: Diagnosis and treatment of isolated gonadotropin-releasing hormone deficiency in men. J Clin Endocrinol Metab 1990;70:3.

Vazquez JA et al: Hypothalamic-pituitary-testicular function in 70 patients with myotonic dystrophy. J Endocrinol Invest 1990;13:375.

Infertility

Gangi GR, Nagler HM: Clinical evaluation of the subfertile male. Infertil Reprod Med Clin North Am 1992;3:299.

Howards SS: Varicocele. Infertil Reprod Med Clin North Am 1992;3:429.

Overstreet JW, Davis RO, Katz DF: Semen evaluation. Infertil Reprod Med Clin North Am 1992;3:329.

Silber SJ: Effect of age on male fertility. Semin Reprod Endocrinol 1991;9:241.

Sokol RZ: Medical and endocrine therapy of male factor infertility. Infertil Reprod Med Clin North Am 1992;3:389.

Impotence

Drugs that cause sexual dysfunction: Med Lett Drugs Ther 1987;29:65.

McClure RD, Oses R, Ernest ML: Hypogonadal impotence treated by transdermal testosterone. Urology 1991;37:224.

Junemann K-P, Persson-Junemann C, Alken P: Pathophysiology of erectile dysfunction. Semin Urol 1990;8:80.

Melman A: Evaluation and management of erectile dysfunction. Surg Clin North Am 1988;68:965.

Stine CC, Collins M: Male sexual dysfunction. Prim Care 1989;16:1031.

Whitehead ED et al: Treatment alternatives for impotence. Postgrad Med 1990;88:139.

Gynecomastia

Braunstein GD: Gynecomastia. N Engl J Med 1993:328:490.

Hands LJ, Greenall MJ: Gynaecomastia. Br J Surg 1991;78:907.

Testicular Cancer

Ozols RF, Williams SD: Testicular cancer. Curr Probl Cancer 1989;13:285.

Roth BJ, Nichols CR (editors): Testicular cancer. Semin Oncol 1992;19:117.

Ovaries

10

Alan Goldfien, MD, & Scott E. Monroe, MD

ANATOMY OF THE OVARIES

The mature ovaries are paired nodular structures $2.5–5 \times 2 \times 1$ cm, weighing from 4 to 8 g, the weight varying during the menstrual cycle. They are situated behind the peritoneum attached to the posterior surface of the broad ligament by a fold of the peritoneum called the mesovarium, which contains the blood vessels and nerves leading to the hilum. The ovaries are attached to the uterus by the ovarian ligament and lie in close association with the uterine tubes (oviducts, fallopian tubes) (Figure 10–1).

The ovaries develop from the genital ridges situated between the base of the dorsal mesentery and the mesonephros on either side of the coelomic cavity. The primordial germ cells that originate in the endoderm of the yolk sac at the third week begin to migrate through the hindgut to invade the genital ridges at about the sixth week. These primary oocytes are surrounded by a layer of epithelium and mesenchymal cells that give rise to the primordial follicles. About 1700 germ cells are present before migration to the genital ridge begins; however, these multiply during the process of migration and within the genital ridge, reaching a peak of 7 million oocytes at mid gestation. The primordial germ cells increase in size early in their development and become oogonia. At mid gestation they begin the first meiotic division, becoming primary oocytes. This prophase lasts until just before ovulation, which may occur 12–40 or more years later. In this state, they are no longer capable of multiplication and in fact steadily decline in number (Figure 10–2). About 400 ova are lost through the process of ovulation during a woman's lifetime. The remainder undergo degeneration so that, by the time of the menopause, few are present.

Blood Supply

The arterial vessels supplying the ovary are derived from branches of the ovarian and uterine arteries that enter through the mesovarium and divide into branches leading into the stroma of the medulla and

ACRONYMS USED IN THIS CHAPTER

ACTH	Adrenocorticotropic hormone
ALT	Alanine aminotransferase
BSP	Bromsulphalein
CBG	Corticosteroid-binding globulin
DHEA	Dehydroepiandrosterone
EI	Eosinophilic index
FSH	Follicle-stimulating hormone
GH	Growth hormone
GnRH	Gonadotropin-releasing hormone
hCG	Human chorionic gonadotropin
HDL	High-density lipoprotein(s)
KPI	Karyopyknotic index
LDL	Low-density lipoprotein(s)
LH	Luteinizing hormone
LHRH	Luteinizing hormone-releasing hormone
LRH	Luteotropin-releasing hormone
MCR	Metabolic clearance rate
MI	Maturation index
PMN	Polymorphonuclear neutrophil
PMS	Premenstrual syndrome
PRL	Prolactin
PTH	Parathyroid hormone
RNA	Ribonucleic acid
SHBG	Sex hormone-binding globulin
TBG	Thyroid hormone-binding globulin
VLDL	Very low density lipoprotein(s)

then to the cortex. The small arteries of the ovary are characteristically spiral. The capillary blood gathers in veins that form a large, thin-walled plexus of vessels called the pampiniform plexus, leaving the ovary by way of the ovarian vein at the hilum. Lymphatics arise in the outer or cortical portion of the ovary and anastomose centrally, leaving through the hilum. Although the lymphatic channels are numerous in the theca externa, corpora lutea, and corpora albicantia, they are not seen in the theca interna, granulosa, or tunica albuginea.

Nerve Supply

The ovary has a rich autonomic innervation arising from the intermesenteric nerves and renal plexus; from the superior hypogastric plexus or presacral nerve and the hypogastric nerve; and from the inferior hypogastric plexus or pelvic plexus. The nerves appear to be mainly sympathetic in origin.

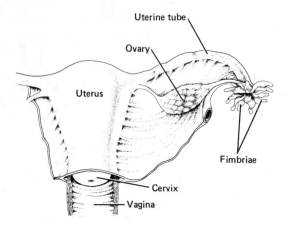

Figure 10–1. Internal organs of the female reproductive system: ovary, fimbriae of infundibulum, uterine tube, uterus, cervix, and vagina. (Reproduced, with permission, from Junqueira LC, Carneiro J, Kelley RO: *Basic Histology,* 6th ed. Appleton & Lange, 1989.)

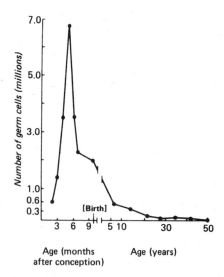

Figure 10–2. Total number of germ cells in the human ovary at different ages. (Reproduced, with permission, from Baker TG: *Reproduction in Mammals.* Austin CR, Short RV [editors]. Cambridge Univ Press, 1972.)

Microscopic Anatomy

As shown in Figure 10–3, the ovary consists of many different structures. The mature ovary is covered by a layer of columnar cells that constitute the **germinal epithelium.** The dense layer of connective tissue under the epithelium is called the tunica albuginea. The remainder of the organ is divided into outer cortical and inner medullary portions, of which the cortex is the larger. The cortex contains follicular structures in all stages of development, surrounded by the connective tissue elements of the stroma and the hilar cells, a group of steroid-secreting cells that histologically resemble the Leydig, or interstitial, cells of the testes. The medulla consists of a connective tissue stroma containing elastic fibers, blood vessels, nerves, lymphatics, and smooth muscle fibers.

The follicular complex contains the ova as well as the cells responsible for production of the ovarian hormones and their precursors. Structural changes and hormonal activity that occur throughout the menstrual cycle are discussed below.

HORMONES OF THE OVARY

The mature ovary actively synthesizes and secretes a variety of hormones. Among these are the sex steroids, which include estrogens, progesterone, androgens, and their precursors. In addition, the ovary produces relaxin, inhibin, prostaglandins, and other substances.

STEROID HORMONES

The ovary is normally the major source of estrogens, although the conversion of androgen precursors in other tissues is clinically important after the menopause and in some women with disorders of ovarian function. The ovary also produces and secretes large amounts of progesterone during the luteal phase of the cycle. It is also the source of small amounts of testosterone and other androgens that serve not only as precursors to estrogen synthesis but also are released into the circulation to act on peripheral tissues.

Biosynthesis of Steroid Hormones

The biochemical pathways, including the major enzymes and their intracellular localizations, are similar in the ovary, testis, and adrenal. The process in the ovary is outlined in Figure 10–4. The steroid hormones are synthesized from cholesterol, which is present in the gland both free and esterified to fatty acids (cholesteryl esters). Cholesterol derived either from circulating lipoproteins or from cholesteryl esters in the gland is converted to pregnenolone by removal of a 6-carbon fragment, isocaproic acid. This reaction or group of reactions is the rate-limiting step in the biosynthetic process and is controlled by luteinizing hormone (LH) from the anterior pituitary.

Pregnenolone formed by this reaction may be converted either to progesterone or to 17α-hydroxypregnenolone. The conversion to progesterone requires the action of 3β-hydroxysteroid dehydrogenase and $\Delta^{5,4}$-ketosteroid isomerase, which shifts the double

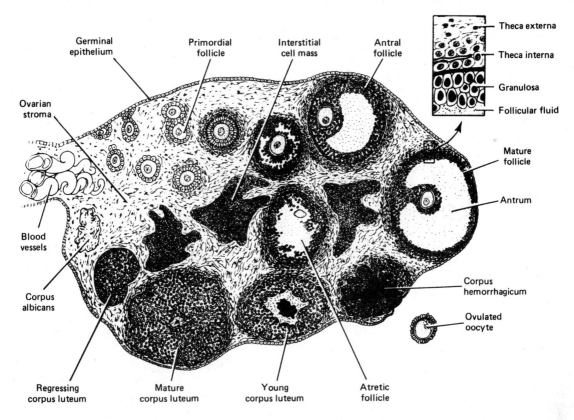

Figure 10–3. Diagram of a mammalian ovary, showing the sequential development of a follicle, formation of a corpus luteum, and, in the center, follicular atresia. A section of the wall of a mature follicle is enlarged at the upper right. The interstitial cell mass is not prominent in primates. (After Patten and Eakin. Reproduced, with permission, from Katzung BG [editor]: *Basic and Clinical Pharmacology*, 3rd ed. Appleton & Lange, 1987.)

bond from the Δ^5 to the Δ^4 position. Progesterone is secreted by the corpus luteum in large amounts following ovulation (see below). However, it also serves as a precursor for androgen and estrogen, since it is a substrate for P450c17 (17α-hydroxylase), which converts it to 17α-hydroxyprogesterone in the endoplasmic reticulum. Following 17α-hydroxylation, the two-carbon (20–21) side chain may be cleaved by the P450c17 (17,20-lyase) enzyme to form androgens (see Figure 10–4).

17α-Hydroxypregnenolone is converted by the P450c17 (lyase) enzyme to dehydroepiandrosterone (DHEA). This compound can then be converted to androstenedione. The relative importance of these pathways to androgen production is not clear. Androstenedione is the major androgen secreted by the ovary, but small amounts of DHEA and testosterone are also released.

Estradiol, the most active estrogen produced by the ovary, is synthesized from androgens by a group of enzymes known as the aromatase complex or system. The process involves 3 steps: hydroxylation of the methyl group at carbon 19, oxidation of this group, and hydroxylation at the 3α position. These steps are thought to occur in the microsomal fraction.

During the menstrual cycle, regulation of biosynthesis and release is controlled by the gonadotropins as well as by local factors.

Secretion of Steroid Hormones

The secretory activity of the steroid-producing granulosa and theca cells is closely coupled to their biosynthetic activity, since little hormone is stored in the cells. Direct measures of secretion rates in humans require an accurate measure of the concentration of the hormone in the effluent blood from the gland and a measure of blood flow through the gland. Such samples and measurements are difficult to obtain without interfering with blood flow and normal gland activity. Therefore, indirect measures have been widely used. Some of the most useful information has been obtained by measuring the metabolic clearance rate (MCR) with an in vivo isotope dilution technique. Multiplying MCR by the concentration of the hormone in blood provides a total production rate for the hormone. However, the production rate also

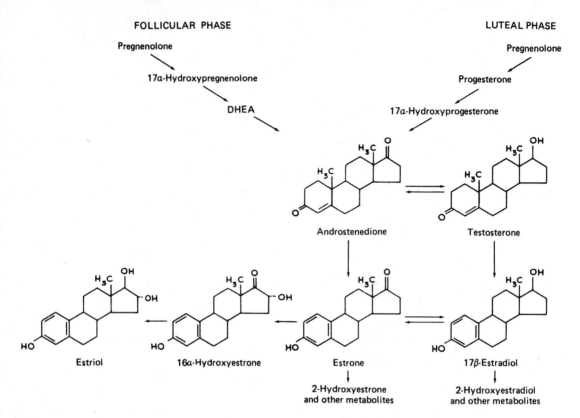

Figure 10–4. Biosynthesis and metabolism of estrogens. (See also Figures 6–4, 9–2, and 11–13.) (Reproduced, with permission, from Katzung BG [editor]: *Basic and Clinical Pharmacology,* 4th ed. Appleton & Lange, 1989.)

includes production of the hormone at other sites from circulating precursors, and it may therefore be greater than the amount secreted by the gland. The production rates, plasma levels, and MCRs of various ovarian steroids are shown in Table 10–1.

During pregnancy, the fetal-placental unit produces a large amount of steroid hormone. The placenta produces progesterone, which is released into the maternal circulation, and large amounts of pregnenolone, which is released into the fetal circulation. Enzymatic conversion of pregnenolone by the fetal adrenal and liver produces steroids, including 16-hydroxydehydroepiandrosterone sulfate, which are subsequently converted to estriol and other estrogens in the placenta and released into the maternal circulation (see Chapter 13).

Transport of Steroid Hormones

When released into the circulation, the gonadal steroids bind to plasma proteins. Estradiol binds avidly to a transport globulin called sex hormone-binding globulin (SHBG) and binds with less affinity to albumin. Progesterone binds strongly to corticosteroid-binding globulin (CBG) and weakly to albumin. The percentages of various steroids that bind to these carrier proteins are listed in Table 10–2. The

concentration of these binding proteins is increased by estrogen and thyroxine and decreased by androgens and progestins. SHBG is synthesized in the liver, and because its synthesis is stimulated by estrogens and inhibited by androgen, levels are twice as high in women as in men. The proportions of free and bound estradiol do not vary significantly during the menstrual cycle. However, differences in binding may assume clinical importance after the menopause or in women with abnormal ovarian function associated with excess androgens.

Metabolism of Steroid Hormones

A. Estrogens: Circulating estradiol is rapidly converted in the liver to estrone by 17β-hydroxysteroid dehydrogenase (Figure 10–5). Some of the estrone reenters the circulation; however, most of it is further metabolized to 16α-hydroxyestrone (which is then converted to estriol) or to 2-hydroxyestrone, a catechol estrogen. Much of the remaining estrone is conjugated to form estrone sulfate. Estriol is converted largely to estriol 3-sulfate-16-glucuronide before excretion by the kidney.

B. Progesterone: Progesterone is rapidly cleared from the circulation, having an initial half-life of about 5 minutes. As indicated by its high clearance

Table 10-1. Approximate concentrations, metabolic clearance rates (MCR), production rates, and ovarian secretion rates of steroids in blood.[1]

	MCR (L/d)	Phase of Menstrual Cycle	Plasma Concentration		Production Rate		Secretion Rate (Both Ovaries)	
			(µg/dL)	(nmol/L)	(mg/d)	(µmol/d)	(mg/d)	(µmol/d)
Estradiol	1350	Early follicular	0.006	(0.22)	0.081	(0.3)	0.07	(0.26)
		Late follicular	0.033–0.07	(1.21–2.57)	0.445–0.945	(1.63–3.47)	0.4–0.8	(1.63–2.93)
		Midluteal	0.02	(0.73)	0.27	(1)	0.25	(0.92)
Estrone	2210	Early follicular	0.005	(0.18)	0.11	(0.41)	0.08	(0.3)
		Late follicular	0.015–0.03	(0.55–1.11)	0.331–0.662	(0.86–2.45)	0.25–0.5	(0.92–1.85)
		Midluteal	0.011	(0.41)	0.243	(0.9)	0.16	(0.59)
Progesterone	2200	Late follicular	0.095	(3.02)	2.1	(6.68)	1.5	(4.77)
		Luteal	1.13	(35.9)	25	(79.5)	24	(76.3)
Androstenedione	2010	...	0.159	(5.1)	3.2	(11.1)	0.8–1.6	(2.77–5.55)
Testosterone	690	...	0.038	(1.32)	0.26	(0.9)	...	...
Dehydroepiandrosterone	1640	...	0.49	(16.8)	8	(27.5)	0.3–3	(1.03–10.3)
Dihydrotestosterone	400	...	0.02	(0.69)	0.05	(0.17)	0.01–0.02	(0.03–0.06)

[1]Modified from Lipsett, MB: Steroid hormones. Page 84 in: *Reproductive Endocrinology.* Yen SSC, Jaffe RB (editors). Saunders, 1978.

Table 10–2. Total plasma concentration and percentage of steroid hormone that is free or bound to plasma transport proteins in healthy women in the early follicular phase. During the luteal phase, the total concentrations of estradiol (0.72 nmol/L) and progesterone (38 nmol/L) are higher, but the distribution is the same.[1]

	Total Plasma Concentration (nmol/L)	Percentage Distribution of Steroid			
		Free	SHBG	CBG	Albumin
Estradiol	0.29	1.8	37.3	0.1	60.8
Estrone	0.23	3.6	16.3	0.1	80.1
Progesterone	0.65	2.4	0.6	17.7	79.3
Testosterone	1.3	1.4	66	2.3	30.4
Dihydrotestosterone	0.65	0.5	78.4	0.1	21
Androstenedione	5.4	7.5	6.6	1.4	84.5
Cortisol	400	3.8	0.2	89.7	6.3

[1]Data from Dunn JF, Nisula BC, Rodbard D: *J Clin Endocrinol Metab* 1981;**53**:58.

rate (Table 10–1), it is rapidly converted to pregnanediol and conjugated to glucuronic acid in the liver. Pregnanediol glucuronide is excreted in the urine and may be used as an index of progesterone production. In addition, small amounts of 20α-hydroxyprogesterone are formed (Figure 10–5). This compound has one-fifth the activity of progesterone.

Physiologic Effects of Steroid Hormones

The biologic effects of the ovarian steroids are mediated by specific hormone receptors. Plasma estradiol is thought to enter its target cell by diffusion and is transported to the nucleus, where it binds to the estrogen receptors. The estrogen receptors are found in the nucleus bound to a number of different heat shock proteins that dissociate from the receptor when it binds to estradiol. The ligand-receptor complex forms a homodimer that binds to the estrogen response element on the gene to activate transcription, leading to the formation of specific messenger RNA (see Chapter 1).

There are estimated to be between 5000 and 20,000 estrogen receptor molecules per cell. These receptors also serve as sites for regulation of hormonal activity. For example, estrogens induce development of increased numbers of estrogen receptors in some tissues and also stimulate the synthesis of progesterone receptors. By contrast, progesterone may cause a reduction in the number of estrogen and progesterone receptors.

Progesterone also enters the cell by diffusion and binds to progesterone receptors, which are distributed between the nucleus and the cytoplasmic domains. The ligand-receptor complex binds to a response element to activate gene transcription. The response element for progesterone appears to be similar to the corticoid response element, and the specificity of the response is determined by which receptor is present in the cell as well as by other cell-specific transcription factors. The progesterone receptor also forms a dimer before binding to DNA. However, in contrast to the estrogen receptor, it can form heterodimers. Although it is clear that these intracellular receptors

mediate many of the important effects of steroid hormones, some effects, such as the anesthetic effect of progesterone and the stimulatory effect of estrogens on uterine blood flow, suggest that these steroids also act at the cell membrane.

A. Estrogens: Estrogens are required for the normal maturation of the female. They stimulate the maturation of the vagina, uterus, and uterine tubes at puberty as well as the secondary sex characteristics. They stimulate stromal development and ductal growth in the breast and are responsible for the accelerated growth phase and the closing of the epiphyses of the long bones that occurs at puberty. They alter the distribution of body fat so as to produce typical female body contours, including some accumulation of body fat around the hips and breasts. Larger quantities also stimulate development of pigmentation in the skin, most prominently in the region of the nipples and areolae and in the genital region.

In addition to its effects on growth of uterine muscle, estrogen also plays an important role in development of the endometrial lining. Continuous exposure to estrogens for prolonged periods leads to an abnormal hyperplasia of the endometrium that is usually associated with abnormal bleeding patterns. When estrogen production is properly coordinated with the production of progesterone during the normal human menstrual cycle, regular periodic bleeding and shedding of the endometrial lining occur.

Estrogens have a number of important metabolic effects. They seem to be partially responsible for maintenance of the normal structure of the skin and blood vessels in women. Estrogens decrease the rate of resorption of bone by antagonizing the effect of parathyroid hormone (PTH) on bone; they do not stimulate bone formation. Estrogens may have important effects on intestinal absorption, because they reduce the motility of bowel. In addition to stimulating the synthesis of enzymes leading to uterine growth, they alter the production and activity of many other enzymes in the body. In the liver, there is an increase in the synthesis of binding or transport proteins, including those for estrogen, testosterone, and thyroxine.

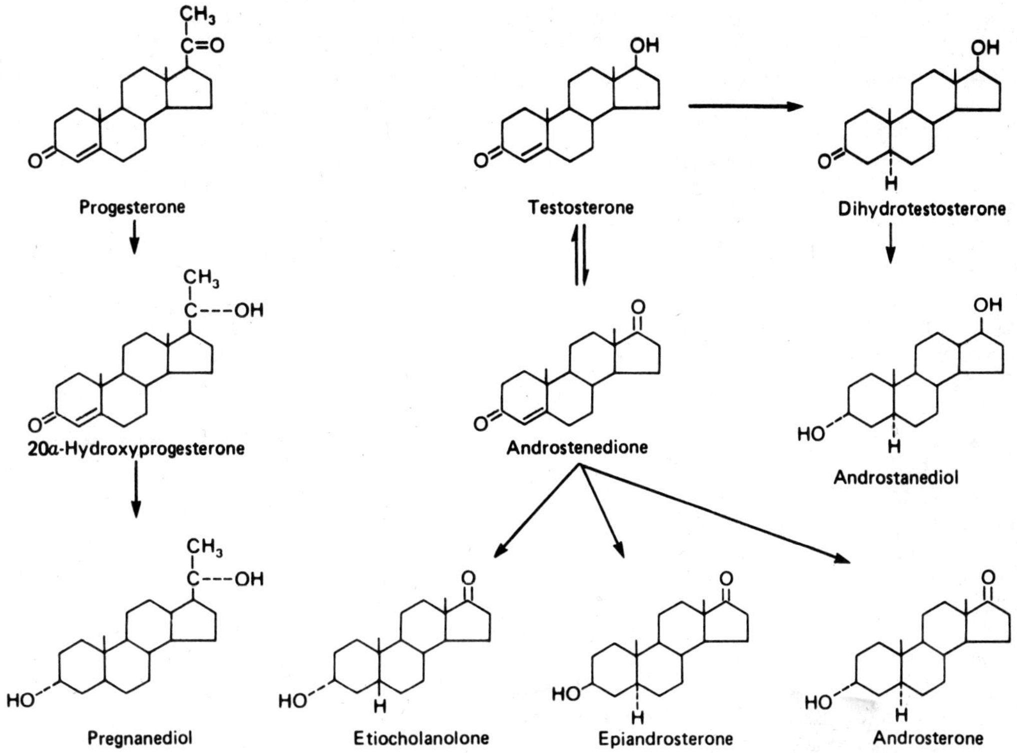

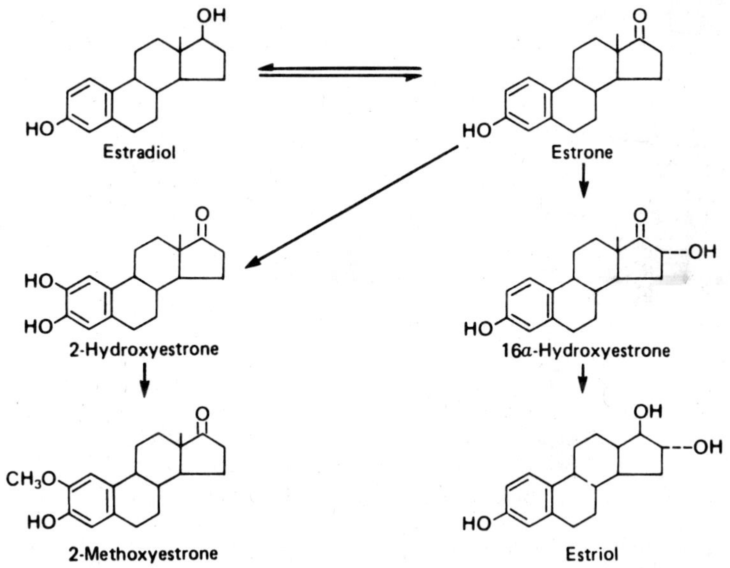

Figure 10–5. Metabolism of ovarian steroid hormones. (See also Figures 9–2 and 11–14.)

Estrogens enhance the coagulability of blood. Many changes in factors influencing coagulation have been reported, including increased circulating levels of factors II, VII, IX, and X and decreased levels of antithrombin III. Increased plasminogen levels and decreased platelet adhesiveness have been reported.

Alterations in the composition of the plasma lipids caused by estrogens include an increase in high-density lipoproteins (HDL), a slight reduction in low-density lipoproteins (LDL), and a reduction in plasma cholesterol levels. Plasma triglyceride levels are increased.

Estrogens have many other effects. They are responsible for estrous behavior in animals and influence libido in humans. They facilitate the loss of intravascular fluid into the extracellular space, producing edema. The resulting decrease in plasma volume causes a compensatory retention of sodium and water by the kidney. Estrogens also modulate sympathetic nervous system control of smooth muscle function.

B. Progesterone: The effects of progesterone on reproductive organs include the glandular development of the breasts and the cyclic glandular development of the endometrium described below (see Menstrual Cycle) and are critical for successful reproduction. However, progesterone exhibits important metabolic effects in other organs and tissues, producing changes in carbohydrate, protein, and lipid metabolism.

A dose of 50 mg of progesterone intramuscularly daily can lead to increased insulin levels and decreased response of blood glucose levels to insulin as observed in normal pregnancy.

Progesterone can compete with aldosterone at the renal tubule, causing a decrease in Na^+ reabsorption. This leads to an increased secretion of aldosterone by the adrenal cortex—eg, in pregnancy. Progesterone increases the body temperature in humans. The mechanism of this effect is not known, but an alteration of the temperature-regulating centers in the hypothalamus has been suggested. Progesterone also alters the function of the respiratory centers. The ventilatory response to CO_2 is increased, leading to a measurable reduction in arterial and alveolar PCO_2 during pregnancy and in the luteal phase of the menstrual cycle. Synthetic progestins with an ethinyl group do not have these respiratory effects. Progesterone and related steroids also have hypnotic effects on the brain.

C. Androgens: The normal ovary produces potent androgens, including testosterone and dihydrotestosterone, as well as androstenedione, Δ^5-androstenediol, and DHEA. Only testosterone and dihydrotestosterone have significant androgenic activity, although androstenedione is converted to testosterone in peripheral tissues. The healthy woman produces less than 300 μg of testosterone in 24

hours, and about one-fourth of this is probably formed in the ovary directly. The physiologic significance of these small amounts of androgens is not established, but they may be partly responsible for normal hair growth at puberty and may have other important metabolic effects. Androgen production by the ovary may be markedly increased in some abnormal states (usually in association with amenorrhea), and less active precursors (eg, androstenedione) may be converted to more active hormones in target tissues such as the hair follicle and sebaceous glands.

Dehydroepiandrosterone (DHEA) and dehydroepiandrosterone sulfate (DHEAS) in large amounts and androstenedione and testosterone in smaller amounts are also secreted by the adrenal cortex. Although they are thought to contribute to the normal maturation process (adrenarche), they do not stimulate or support other androgen-dependent pubertal changes in the human. Recent studies suggest that DHEA and DHEAS may have other important metabolic effects which inhibit atherosclerosis and prolong life in rabbits and perhaps in humans. The therapeutic uses of this hormone are currently being explored.

RELAXIN

Relaxin is a polypeptide that has been extracted from the ovary. In certain animal species, it appears to play an important role at the time of parturition, causing relaxation of the pelvic ligaments and softening of the uterine cervix. The three-dimensional structure of relaxin is similar to that of insulin and related growth-promoting polypeptides, although the amino acid sequences are different. It consists of two chains linked by disulfide bonds, cleaved from a prohormone. It is found in the ovary, placenta, and uterus and in the blood. Relaxin synthesis has been demonstrated in luteinized granulosa cells of the corpus luteum. In addition to changing the mechanical properties of tissues such as the cervix and pubic ligaments, it increases glycogen synthesis and water uptake by the myometrium and decreases its contractility. It may also have mammotropic effects.

In women, relaxin has been measured by immunoassay. During the menstrual cycle, levels were highest immediately after the LH surge and during menstruation. Circulating levels of relaxin are reported to be 25% higher by the end of the first trimester than during the second and third trimesters of pregnancy.

OTHER OVARIAN HORMONES & REGULATORY SUBSTANCES

Several nonsteroidal substances that may be important in the regulation of both intra- and extraovarian processes have been found in follicular fluid. These substances include factors that can decrease (eg, inhibin) or increase (eg, activin) FSH secretion, modulate steroid secretion from granulosa cells, and delay the maturation of the oocyte in the developing preovulatory follicle (oocyte maturation inhibitor). See below for additional information concerning nonsteroidal ovarian regulatory factors.

THE MENSTRUAL CYCLE

The female reproductive system undergoes a series of regular cyclic changes termed the menstrual cycle. The most obvious of these changes is periodic vaginal bleeding, resulting from shedding of the endometrial lining of the uterus. Normal menstrual function results from the interaction of the hypothalamus, pituitary, and ovaries and associated changes in the target tissues of the reproductive tract. Although each component is essential for normal reproductive function, the ovary plays a central role in this process, since it appears to be responsible for regulating both the cyclic changes and the length of the menstrual cycle. In most women in the middle reproductive years, menstrual bleeding recurs every 25–35 days, with a median cycle length of 28 days (Figure 10–6). In women with ovulatory cycles, the interval from the onset of menses to ovulation—the follicular (proliferative) phase—is variable in duration and ac-

counts for the range of cycle lengths observed in ovulating women. The interval from ovulation to the onset of menstrual bleeding—the luteal (secretory) phase—is relatively constant and averages 14 ± 2 days in most women. The greatest variability in cycle length is found in the first few years after menarche and the years immediately preceding the menopause. There is a high incidence of anovulatory vaginal bleeding at these times.

HORMONAL PROFILES DURING THE MENSTRUAL CYCLE

Pituitary Gonadotropins

Luteinizing hormone (LH) and follicle-stimulating hormone (FSH) are glycoproteins with molecular weights of about 28,000 and 33,000, respectively. Each hormone is composed of an alpha subunit and a beta subunit. The alpha subunits have essentially the same amino acid sequences. The beta subunits, however, are unique and are responsible for the characteristic biologic activities of each hormone. The initial plasma half-life of LH is approximately 30 minutes, whereas the half-life of FSH is 3 hours. The profiles of LH and FSH throughout the menstrual cycle are illustrated in Figure 10–7. Because of the diversity of standards used to quantitate gonadotropins, the LH and FSH values for the same serum sample reported by different laboratories may vary 2- or 3-fold. The clinician must therefore be aware of the laboratory's upper and lower limits of normal. Serum FSH levels persistently greater than 40 mIU/mL (mIU of the Second International Reference Preparation of Human Menopausal Gonadotropin; mIU-2nd IRP-HMG) usually indicate declining or absent ovarian follicular activity.

In the normal menstrual cycle, serum concentrations of both LH and FSH begin to increase a few days prior to menses. FSH concentrations initially increase more rapidly than those of LH and attain maximum levels during the first half of the follicular phase. FSH levels gradually decline in the latter half of the follicular phase and, with the exception of a brief peak at midcycle, continue to fall until the lowest concentrations in the cycle are reached during the second half of the luteal phase. The preovulatory decline in serum concentrations of FSH is a consequence of the rising concentration of estradiol in this period. LH levels increase gradually throughout the follicular phase. At midcycle, there is a large peak in serum concentration of LH (midcycle LH surge) lasting 1–3 days. Subsequently, LH levels gradually decline, also reaching their lowest concentrations late in the luteal phase (Figure 10–7). Frequent measurements of serum gonadotropin levels in individual women indicate that gonadotropin secretion—particularly LH—is pulsatile. These pulses of gonadotropins are dependent upon the pulsatile secre-

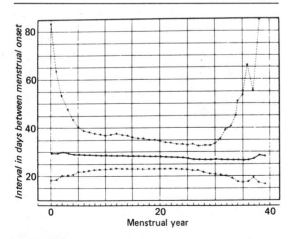

Figure 10–6. Median lengths of menstrual cycles (solid line) throughout reproductive life in women from menarche (year 0) to menopause (year 40). Ninety percent of all cycles fall within the upper and lower dotted lines. (After Treolar AE et al. Reproduced, with permission, from Yen SSC, Jaffe RB [editors]: *Reproductive Endocrinology.* Saunders, 1978.)

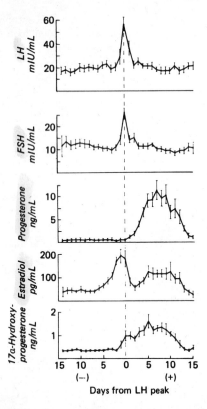

Figure 10–7. Mean values of LH, FSH, progesterone, estradiol, and 17α-hydroxyprogesterone in daily serum samples from 9 women during ovulatory menstrual cycles. Data from different cycles have been combined using the day of the midcycle LH peak as the reference day (day 0). The vertical bars represent one standard error of the mean. (Reproduced, with permission, from Thorneycroft IH et al: Am J Obstet Gynecol 1971;111:947).

tion of gonadotropin-releasing hormone (GnRH) from the hypothalamus. During the follicular phase, pulses of LH occur approximately every hour. During the luteal phase, these pulses gradually decrease in frequency, occurring as infrequently as once every 4–8 hours. The decrease in frequency is secondary to rising levels of progesterone, which slow down the hypothalamic GnRH pulse generator.

Prolactin (PRL)

In contrast to LH and FSH profiles, there are no consistent cyclic changes in individual PRL profiles during the normal menstrual cycle. In studies of large numbers of women, however, mean PRL levels in the preovulatory and luteal phases of the menstrual cycle may be slightly higher than in the follicular phase. There is also a significant diurnal variation in plasma concentrations of PRL, with peak levels during the night and early morning hours. Laboratories vary in their reporting of PRL levels (as they do also in reporting gonadotropin levels) because of the use

of standards with different biologic and immunologic potencies. The upper limit of normal may thus vary from 15 ng/mL to 30 ng/mL (0.68–1.4 nmol/L), depending upon the laboratory.

Ovarian Steroids

The ovary secretes progestins, androgens, and estrogens. Many of these steroids are also secreted by the adrenal gland or can be formed by peripheral conversion of other steroid precursors; consequently, plasma concentrations of these hormones may not directly reflect ovarian steroidogenic activity. Table 10–1 summarizes the plasma concentrations, metabolic clearance rates, and production rates of the major steroids secreted by the ovary in normal women.

A. Estrogens: Estradiol (E_2) is perhaps the most important secretory product of the ovary, because of its biologic potency and diverse physiologic effects on peripheral target tissues. Plasma concentrations of estradiol during the first half of the follicular phase are low, generally less than 50 pg/mL (0.18 nmol/L) (Figure 10–7). About 1 week prior to the midcycle gonadotropin surge, estradiol concentrations begin to increase rapidly, and peak levels of approximately 200–300 pg/mL (0.73–1.1 nmol/L) are attained on the day preceding—or, less commonly, the day of—the LH surge. The rise in plasma estradiol levels correlates closely with the increase in size of the preovulatory follicle. After the LH surge, serum estradiol levels fall rapidly for several days. There is a secondary increase in plasma estradiol levels that reaches a peak in the midportion of the luteal phase, reflecting estrogen secretion by the corpus luteum. Plasma patterns of estrone during the menstrual cycle are similar to those of estradiol, but the changes in concentrations are less than those of estradiol; thus, the ratio of estrone to estradiol varies throughout the cycle. The ratio is highest at the time of menses, when estradiol secretion is minimal, and lowest in the preovulatory period, when estradiol secretion is maximal. While most of the estradiol in the peripheral circulation results from direct ovarian secretion, a significant fraction of the circulating estrone arises from estradiol and the peripheral conversion of androstenedione. Catheterization studies have shown that increased plasma concentrations of estradiol in the preovulatory and midluteal phases of the cycle principally reflect secretion from the ovary containing the dominant or preovulatory follicle, which later becomes the corpus luteum.

B. Progesterone: Throughout the follicular phase, serum concentrations of progesterone are low—less than 1 ng/mL (3.18 nmol/L). At the time of the LH surge, there is a small increase in plasma concentrations of progesterone, followed by a rise over the next 4–5 days (Figure 10–7). Progesterone levels reach a plateau at concentrations between 10 and 20 ng/mL (32–64 nmol/L) during the midportion of the luteal phase. Thereafter, progesterone levels decline rapidly, reaching concentrations of about 1 ng/mL (3.18 nmol/L) by the first day of menses. Although catheterization studies have shown that progesterone is secreted by both ovaries during the first half of the follicular phase, most of the circulating progesterone at this time appears to be derived from the extraglandular conversion of the adrenal steroids, pregnenolone and pregnenolone sulfate, and from the direct secretion of small amounts of progesterone by the adrenal glands.

During the luteal phase of the cycle, virtually all of the circulating progesterone arises by direct secretion from the corpus luteum. Measurement of plasma concentrations of progesterone is widely used to monitor ovulation. Concentrations greater than 4–5 ng/mL (12.7–15.9 nmol/L) suggest that ovulation has occurred.

C. Androgens: In healthy women, circulating androgens can be derived from secretion by the ovaries and the adrenal glands and also by peripheral conversion of steroid precursors of ovarian and adrenal origin. In healthy women, testosterone is secreted in small quantities by the ovaries and adrenal glands. About 50–70% of the circulating testosterone, however, arises primarily from the peripheral conversion of androstenedione. Mean plasma concentrations of testosterone range from 0.2 ng/mL to 0.4 ng/mL (0.69–1.39 nmol/L) during most of the follicular and luteal phases and increase slightly in the preovulatory phase. Androstenedione arises primarily from direct secretion by the ovaries and adrenal glands. Only a small percentage (about 10%) is formed by peripheral conversion. Secretion of androstenedione by the adrenal does not vary significantly during different phases of the menstrual cycle, although there is a diurnal variation in adrenal secretion of androstenedione similar to that of cortisol. Ovarian secretion of androstenedione, however, fluctuates throughout the menstrual cycle, and the pattern of secretion resembles that of estradiol. Serum concentrations of androstenedione increase in the late follicular phase of the cycle and are maximal at the time of the midcycle gonadotropin surge. There is a small secondary peak of androstenedione during the midluteal phase. Plasma concentrations of both DHEA and DHEA sulfate vary independently of the phase of the menstrual cycle. Both hormones are secreted primarily by the adrenal gland.

THE OVARIAN CYCLE

Ovarian Structure

Throughout adult reproductive years, the structural composition and hormonal activity of the ovary are continually changing (Figures 10–3 and 10–8). These changes in composition and activity are responsible for many of the physiologic events in the normal menstrual cycle. The two major functions of the adult ovary—the synthesis and secretion of sex steroids

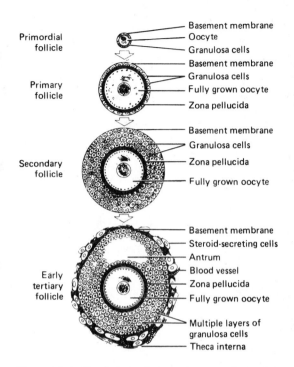

Figure 10–8. Morphologic changes that occur in ovarian follicles during growth and development. (Reproduced, with permission, from Erickson GF: Follicular growth and development. In: *Gynecology and Obstetrics.* Vol 5. Sciarra JJ [editor]. Harper & Row, 1981.)

and the release of a mature ovum every 28–30 days—normally progress in concert with one another and are closely interrelated. The basic reproductive unit of the ovary is the small **primordial follicle,** consisting of (1) a small oocyte (< 25 μm in diameter) arrested in the diplotene stage of meiotic prophase; (2) a few, or a complete ring of, poorly differentiated granulosa cells; and (3) a basement membrane that surrounds the granulosa cells, separating them from the adjacent ovarian stroma. Primordial follicles are found principally in the outer cortex just beneath the fibrous capsule of the ovary. These primordial follicles constitute an inactive or resting pool from which all ovulatory follicles will eventually develop. During late fetal life and throughout the prepubertal years, a small percentage of these small, inactive follicles are continually resuming growth. At an early stage of development and prior to antrum formation, however, growth is arrested and the follicles undergo atresia. Although ovulation does not occur, the continual process of limited growth and atresia in the prepubertal ovary depletes a large portion of the small primordial follicles, so that only about 400,000 primordial follicles remain at puberty (Figure 10–2). Of these follicles, only about 400 will reach full development and release an oocyte during ovulation in the adult.

The earliest morphologic change indicating that

the primordial follicle has left the pool of resting follicles and resumed the process of growth is an increase in size of the oocyte. As the oocyte enlarges, the zona pellucida, a membrane that will eventually surround the oocyte, begins to form. The flat, poorly differentiated granulosa cells, which form a single layer, assume a cuboidal shape as the oocyte approaches its maximum size of 80–100 μm. At this stage of development, the follicular unit is known as a **primary follicle.** Subsequently, the granulosa cells rapidly proliferate, forming a multilayered covering around the oocyte. Small patches of fluid form between the granulosa cells. Blood vessels, however, do not penetrate the basement membrane surrounding the granulosa cells, and the granulosa layer remains avascular until after ovulation has occurred. As the follicle continues to enlarge, cells that are indistinguishable from mesenchymal fibroblasts align themselves concentrically outside the basement membrane. These cells form the thecal layer and complete the formation of the **secondary follicle (preantral follicle).** As the granulosa cells continue to multiply, there is further production and accumulation of fluid within the granulosa cell layer, leading to the formation of a follicular cavity, or **antrum.** The oocyte and a portion of the surrounding granulosa cells (cumulus cells) are gradually displaced to one side of the follicular cavity, and a **tertiary follicle (antral follicle)** is formed. There is both a rapid accumulation of follicular fluid and additional growth of granulosa cells, causing further enlargement of the **preovulatory (graafian) follicle.** The follicle reaches a diameter of 2–2.5 cm shortly before ovulation. Following ovulation, the antrum fills with blood and lymph fluid (Figure 10–3). The wall of the follicle collapses and becomes convoluted, and vessels from the thecal layer invade the granulosa layer. The appearance of the granulosa cells changes markedly after ovulation, and they become luteinized. In conjunction with the contiguous thecal layer or adjacent stromal cells, the luteinized granulosa layer forms the **corpus luteum.** If pregnancy does not follow ovulation, the corpus luteum lasts about 14 days and is gradually replaced by fibrous tissue, forming a **corpus albicans.** The mechanisms responsible for regression (luteolysis) of the corpus luteum after 14 days in humans are incompletely understood. In nonprimates, prostaglandins appear to play an important role in luteolysis.

Control of Growth & Steroidogenesis in Ovarian Follicles

The factors that stimulate resting primordial follicles to resume growth and development are unknown. Pituitary gonadotropins, however, are not involved in initiating these events. Cohorts of primordial follicles in prepubertal girls—in whom LH and FSH levels are undetectable—and in hypophysectomized laboratory animals are continually leaving the large pool of inactive primordial follicles and resuming growth. Development beyond the preantral or early antral stage, however, depends upon the interaction of pituitary gonadotropins, ovarian steroids, and other local factors within the follicle.

Receptors for FSH have been found only in granulosa cells. Each cell is estimated to contain about 1000 receptors. The binding of FSH to its receptor stimulates the synthesis of enzymes which have aromatase activity and which convert androgen precursors to estrogens. Estradiol, in turn, plays a critical role in follicular growth and development both by a local effect on granulosa cells and via positive and negative feedback regulation of FSH and LH secretion (see below). In small follicles, estradiol induces the proliferation of granulosa cells. In the absence of FSH, estradiol per se can stimulate follicular growth to the preantral stage, but further development is dependent upon gonadotropin stimulation. FSH and estradiol, working in concert, also induce the formation of LH receptors in granulosa cells. In contrast to FSH receptors, which are restricted to granulosa cells, LH receptors also have been found in theca, interstitial, and luteal cells.

The cellular origin of estradiol in large ovarian follicles in primates remains controversial. In the rat, granulosa cells lack the enzyme P450c17 (17α-hydroxylase and 17,20-lyase) and thus are unable to directly synthesize androgens or estrogens from C21 precursors—eg, progesterone or pregnenolone. Therefore, estradiol production by granulosa cells is dependent upon the availability of C19 androgenic precursors (testosterone and androstenedione), which can be aromatized to estrogens. These observations have led to the formation of the "two-cell theory" to explain estradiol formation within the follicular complex (Figure 10–9). According to this hypothesis, LH stimulates the synthesis of androgenic precursors, primarily androstenedione and to a lesser extent testosterone, by the theca cells. The androgens diffuse across the basement membrane that separates the theca and granulosa cells. Some of the androstenedione and testosterone enters the antral fluid, while the remainder is converted to estradiol by the granulosa cells. Studies in primates, however, have shown that both the thecal layer and the granulosa cells of antral follicles are able to synthesize estradiol; consequently, it is unclear whether it is the theca cells or the granulosa cells that are the principal site of estradiol synthesis in the mid and late follicular phases of the menstrual cycle. A study in the rhesus monkey suggested that most of the estradiol production in the preovulatory period was of theca cell—not granulosa cell—origin. It is possible that most of the estradiol produced by the granulosa cells remains within the follicular fluid, while estradiol in the serum arises primarily from the thecal layer.

In the normal ovary, androgens produced by the

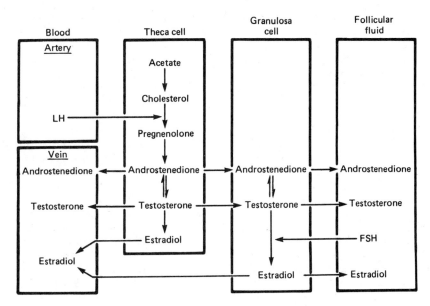

Figure 10–9. Pathways involved in the synthesis and secretion of androgens and estradiol by the preovulatory follicle. In primates, it is not known if the theca cells or granulosa cells are the major source for estradiol in plasma. (Reproduced, with permission, from Peters H, McNatty KP: *The Ovary: A Correlation of Structure and Function in Mammals.* Granada Publishing, 1980.)

thecal layer—particularly androstenedione—serve, in part, as precursors of estrogen synthesis by granulosa cells. Androgens utilized in this fashion thus indirectly facilitate follicular growth via estradiol stimulation. However, high concentrations of testosterone or dihydrotestosterone—or increased ratios of androgen to estrogen—have been found in follicles undergoing atresia, and this suggests an inhibitory action of androgens on follicular development. This could explain, in part, the lack of normal follicular development in polycystic ovary syndrome and other disorders associated with increased androgen levels.. In polycystic ovary syndrome, high levels of LH may promote excessive androgen production by the thecal layer. Since FSH levels are low, granulosa cells may have a reduced capacity to convert these androgens to estrogens.

All of the developing follicles within the ovary are initially exposed to similar concentrations of FSH and LH. Since fewer than 1% of these follicles will eventually reach full maturity and ovulate, local factors must play a critical role in selection of the dominant preovulatory follicle. There are significant differences in the concentrations of protein and steroid hormones in the antral fluid of follicles of differing sizes and at differing stages of the menstrual cycle. The presence of this fluid-filled cavity provides a mechanism by which the granulosa cells and oocyte of one developing follicle can be exposed to a unique microenvironment that differs from that of the other developing follicles within the ovary. Studies have shown that it is the concentrations of pituitary go-

nadotropins and ovarian steroids within the follicular fluid rather than the serum concentrations of these hormones that correlate most closely with both the mitotic and synthetic activity of the granulosa cells as well as with the future viability of the oocyte. The highest concentrations of FSH and LH in antral fluid are found in the largest follicles during the late follicular phase of the menstrual cycle. Prolactin (PRL) levels, in contrast, are highest in small follicles and lower in large follicles in the late follicular phase. The concentrations of LH and FSH in follicular fluid are generally lower than corresponding serum levels, but the concentrations of ovarian steroids—androstenedione, testosterone, dihydrotestosterone, and estradiol—may be 10-40,000 times greater than their serum levels. Although androgen concentrations do not differ greatly in follicular fluid from either small or large follicles, mean estradiol concentrations in antral fluid increase markedly, reaching levels in excess of 1500 ng/mL (5507 nmol/L) in large follicles in the late follicular phase of the menstrual cycle. It is not known at present whether these increases in the absolute concentration of estradiol and the ratio of estradiol to androgen in antral fluid are a consequence of follicular growth and development or play an important role in the process that leads to selection of a single preovulatory follicle.

Nonsteroidal Ovarian Regulatory Factors

Several proteins that can alter the secretion of FSH and/or modify estradiol secretion by granulosa cells have been identified in ovarian follicular fluid. The best characterized of these are the inhibins A and B, which are glycoprotein heterodimers with two subunits. Both inhibins have a common alpha subunit but somewhat different beta subunits, called β_a and β_b. Inhibin preferentially inhibits the secretion of FSH; it is thought to be produced by ovarian granulosa cells. If the beta subunits of inhibin are combined, forming a dimer without the usual alpha subunit, the resultant proteins, known as activins, can stimulate the secretion of FSH. The exact physiologic roles of inhibins and activins during the menstrual cycle remain to be elucidated; however, studies in primates indicate that inhibin has no direct effect on ovarian steroidogenesis but that activin modulates the response to LH and FSH. For example; co-treatment with activin and human FSH enhances FSH stimulation of progesterone synthesis and aromatase activity in granulosa cells. Activin, when combined with LH, suppresses the LH-induced progesterone response by 50% while markedly stimulating basal and LH-stimulated aromatase activity. Activin may also act as a growth factor in other tissues.

HORMONE INTERACTION & REGULATION DURING THE MENSTRUAL CYCLE

Gonadotropin-Releasing Hormone (GnRH)

GnRH (also referred to as luteinizing hormone-releasing hormone [LHRH]; luteotropin-releasing hormone [LRH]; and luteotropin-releasing factor [LRF]) is a decapeptide synthesized by neurosecretory cells located primarily within the hypothalamus. It regulates the secretion of LH and FSH and is essential for their synthesis and release. LH and FSH cannot be detected in serum from peripheral blood of women with congenital absence of hypothalamic GnRH. Ovarian sex steroids are not essential for the synthesis of LH and FSH, but they modulate release of these hormones by altering either gonadotrope response to GnRH or secretion of hypothalamic GnRH. Concentrations of GnRH in serum from peripheral blood are very low, and the pattern of GnRH secretion throughout the menstrual cycle in humans has not been well characterized. However, studies in humans suggest that GnRH secretion may be increased in the preovulatory period. GnRH has been measured in the pituitary portal blood of rhesus monkeys. In these nonhuman primates, GnRH is secreted in pulses every 1–3 hours. Concentrations of GnRH in the portal blood of nonhuman primates during the follicular phase of the menstrual cycle range from less than 10 pg/mL (which is undetectable) to 200 pg/mL. Studies in sheep have shown that each episode of LH release is triggered by a pulse of GnRH from the hypothalamus. Continuous infusions of GnRH initially increase the secretion of LH and FSH. After several hours or days of continuous infusion, desensitization and receptor "down-regulation" occur, and the pituitary gonadotropes become refractory to further stimulation by GnRH.

Regulation of GnRH Secretion

In both rhesus monkeys and humans, intermittent pulses of GnRH every 60–90 minutes stimulate indefinitely the release of LH and FSH. In rhesus monkeys, changes in the frequency of the GnRH pulses can selectively increase or decrease the serum concentration of either LH or FSH. This observation suggests a mechanism by which a single releasing hormone, GnRH, can alter the ratio of LH to FSH in serum and further supports the concept that GnRH is the only hypothalamic hormone required for the regulation of both LH and FSH secretion.

Effects of Ovarian Steroids & Peptides on Gonadotropin Secretion

A. Negative Feedback: Under most conditions, ovarian steroids limit or reduce the secretion of pituitary gonadotropins. Serum concentrations of both FSH and LH increase markedly following ovariectomy or menopause, whereas the administration of estrogen (or estrogen and progesterone) lowers serum gonadotropin levels. Throughout most of the normal menstrual cycle, the negative feedback effects of ovarian steroids predominate and plasma gonadotropin concentrations remain below 25 mIU/mL. The physiologic importance of inhibin and other inhibitory peptides of ovarian origin during the normal menstrual cycle has not yet been determined.

B. Positive Feedback: Estradiol and progesterone, under certain conditions, can induce the release of LH and FSH. During the menstrual cycle, rising concentrations of estradiol in the latter part of the follicular phase initiate the preovulatory surge of LH via this mechanism. This increase in LH secretion in turn stimulates a small but significant increase in the secretion of progesterone that further augments the LH surge and, coupled with estradiol, initiates the midcycle surge of FSH. Although the negative feedback action of ovarian steroids may become apparent within a few hours, positive feedback develops more slowly, and 48–72 hours of sustained estrogen stimulation is generally required before an increase in LH secretion is observed. It is probable that the negative and positive feedback actions of ovarian sex steroids result from both (1) a direct effect of the steroids on the pituitary gonadotropes that alters their sensitivity to GnRH and (2) modulation of the frequency and magnitude of the pulses of hypothalamic GnRH.

Neural Regulation of the Menstrual Cycle

In nonhuman primates—and perhaps in humans as well—the neural components that control both the tonic and surge secretion of gonadotropins are located within the medial basal hypothalamus. When the medial basal hypothalamus, which includes the median eminence, the arcuate nucleus, and portions of the ventromedial nucleus, was surgically isolated from the remainder of the brain without disrupting the hypothalamic-pituitary-portal vasculature, gonadotropin secretion in rhesus monkeys was not significantly altered. Both the negative and positive feedback actions of estradiol remained intact, and many monkeys continued to have spontaneous ovulatory menstrual cycles. It is probable, however, that other neural areas outside the hypothalamus (eg, limbic structures) normally modify gonadotropin secretion.

GnRH plays a permissive, though still essential, role in the regulation of LH and FSH secretion throughout the menstrual cycle. Pulsatile administration of exogenous GnRH every 60–90 minutes induced ovulatory menstrual cycles in monkeys with hypothalamic lesions or in humans with congenital absence of hypothalamic GnRH. In these cycles, the serum profiles of pituitary gonadotropins and ovarian steroids were within normal limits. These observations suggest that the cyclic nature of the menstrual cycle in primates is regulated by the ovary and not by the brain. The length of the menstrual cycle thus is determined by both the time required for development of a mature follicle and by the functional life span of the corpus luteum. Following luteolysis, follicular development resumes, and a new menstrual cycle begins. The major hypothalamic-pituitary-gonadal interactions that regulate the menstrual cycle are summarized in Figure 10–10.

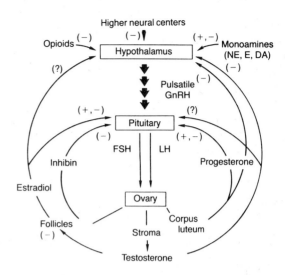

Figure 10–10. The major hypothalamic-pituitary-gonadal interactions thought to regulate the menstrual cycle. Ovarian sex steroids and neural monoamines may exert stimulatory (+) or inhibitory (–) (or both) effects on the secretion of GnRH or pituitary gonadotropins (or both).

CYCLIC CHANGES IN THE FEMALE REPRODUCTIVE TRACT

As a consequence of the changing rates of secretion of estrogen and progesterone throughout the menstrual cycle, the female reproductive tract undergoes a series of regular and cyclic changes. These changes can be recognized by histologic study of the endometrium, the composition and appearance of the cervical mucus, and the cytologic features of the vaginal epithelium. The end of each cycle is marked by uterine bleeding that continues for 3–7 days.

HISTOLOGY OF THE ENDOMETRIUM THROUGHOUT THE MENSTRUAL CYCLE

The endometrium consists of two distinct layers or zones differing in both histologic appearance and functional responsiveness to hormonal stimulation: a **basal layer** and a **functional layer.** The basal layer is in direct contact with the myometrium, undergoes little change throughout the menstrual cycle, and is not sloughed during menses. The functional layer arises from the basal layer and eventually surrounds the entire lumen of the uterine cavity. The functional layer can be subdivided further into two components: a thin superficial **compact layer** and a deeper **spongiosa layer,** of which most of the secretory or fully developed endometrium is composed. The blood supply of the endometrium consists of a highly specialized network of arterial and venous channels. The **spiral arteries** arise within the myometrium from branches of the uterine artery, pass through the basal endometrial layer, and extend into the functional zone. The proximal portion of the spiral artery, the **straight artery,** distributes blood to tissues of the basal layer and is not influenced by changes in estrogen and progesterone secretion. The spiral arteries, however, undergo cyclic regeneration and degeneration during each menstrual cycle in response to hormonal changes.

The endometrial cycle can be subdivided into three major phases: proliferative, secretory, and menstrual. The morphologic changes of the endometrium that occur during the normal menstrual cycle have been described in great detail and are summarized in Figure 10–11. For convenience, the changes described in this figure and the following discussion are based on a hypothetical menstrual cycle of 28 days, in which the follicular and luteal phases are each approximately 14 days in length.

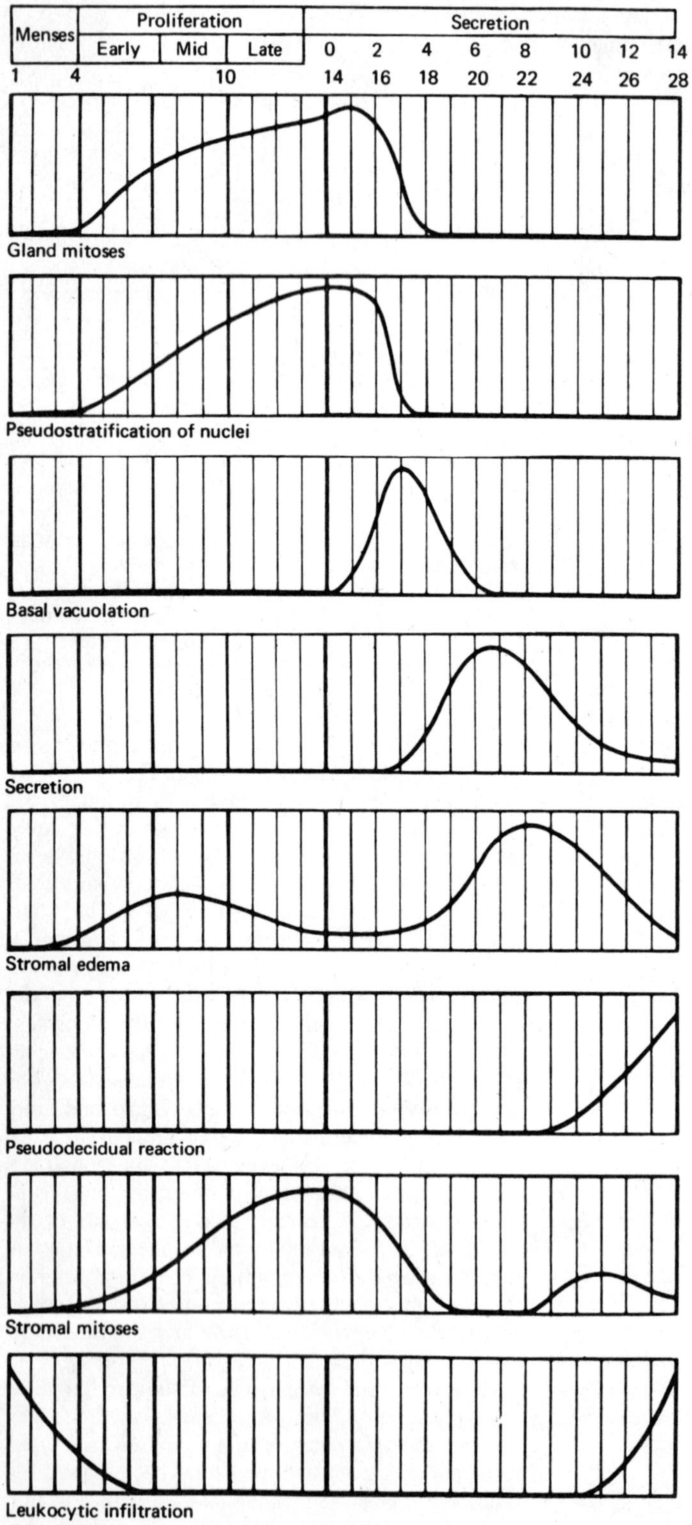

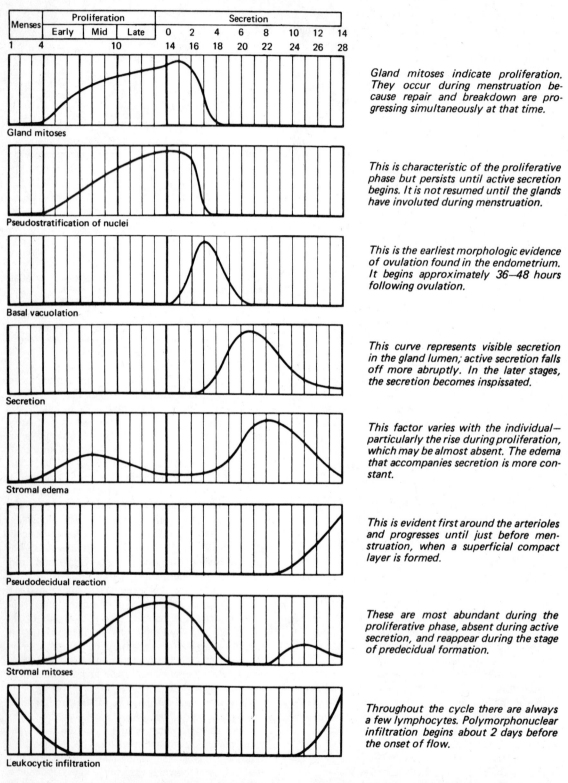

Gland mitoses: *Gland mitoses indicate proliferation. They occur during menstruation because repair and breakdown are progressing simultaneously at that time.*

Pseudostratification of nuclei: *This is characteristic of the proliferative phase but persists until active secretion begins. It is not resumed until the glands have involuted during menstruation.*

Basal vacuolation: *This is the earliest morphologic evidence of ovulation found in the endometrium. It begins approximately 36–48 hours following ovulation.*

Secretion: *This curve represents visible secretion in the gland lumen; active secretion falls off more abruptly. In the later stages, the secretion becomes inspissated.*

Stromal edema: *This factor varies with the individual—particularly the rise during proliferation, which may be almost absent. The edema that accompanies secretion is more constant.*

Pseudodecidual reaction: *This is evident first around the arterioles and progresses until just before menstruation, when a superficial compact layer is formed.*

Stromal mitoses: *These are most abundant during the proliferative phase, absent during active secretion, and reappear during the stage of predecidual formation.*

Leukocytic infiltration: *Throughout the cycle there are always a few lymphocytes. Polymorphonuclear infiltration begins about 2 days before the onset of flow.*

Figure 10–11. Morphologic changes in the endometrium that are useful in determining the stage of the menstrual cycle. (After Noyes, Hertig, and Rock. Reproduced, with permission, from Benson RC [editor]: *Current Obstetric and Gynecologic Diagnosis and Treatment*, 5th ed. Lange, 1984.)

Proliferative Phase

When menstrual flow ceases, a thin layer of basal endometrial tissue remains. This tissue, consisting of the remnants of glands and stroma, grows rapidly. Epithelial cells from the glands proliferate and cover the raw stromal surfaces with a layer of simple columnar epithelium. In the early proliferative phase, most of the glands are straight, short, and narrow. The glandular epithelium exhibits increasing mitotic activity. Throughout the proliferative phase, there is continued and rapid growth of both the epithelial and stromal components of the endometrium. By the late proliferative phase of the menstrual cycle, the surface of the endometrium is somewhat undulant. The glands are becoming tortuous and are lined by tall columnar cells with basal nuclei. Pseudostratification of nuclei is prominent. The stroma at this time is moderately dense, with many mitotic figures.

Secretory Phase

During the secretory phase, histologic changes occur very rapidly. During the first half of this phase, the appearance of the glandular epithelium is most useful in precise dating of the endometrium, whereas in the second half, accurate dating depends largely on the characteristics of the stroma. On the 16th day of the cycle (second postovulatory day), subnuclear glycogen-rich vacuoles become prominent in the glandular epithelium. The vacuoles push the epithelial cell nuclei into a central position within the cells. By the 19th day (fifth postovulatory day), few vacuoles remain within the cells. Acidophilic intraluminal glandular secretory material is most apparent on day 21. Stromal edema, which is variable during the proliferative phase, also becomes prominent at this time and peaks on day 22. By day 24, pseudodecidual or predecidual changes begin to appear within the stroma. These changes are initially most apparent near the spiral arteries and eventually encompass large areas of the stroma. Lymphocytic infiltration of the stroma increases markedly in conjunction with the appearance of pseudodecidual changes, and by day 26, PMN invasion also is apparent.

If the blastocyst implants successfully, serum concentrations of hCG and, secondarily, progesterone begin to increase 7–10 days after ovulation (ie, days 21–24 of the menstrual cycle). The rising levels of progesterone produce a type of endometrial change known as decidualization. The decidua of pregnancy consists primarily of plump, eosinophilic stromal cells that have a pavement-like appearance. In the early stages of pregnancy, the cells of the glandular epithelium become distended with clear cytoplasm and possibly with enlarged and hyperchromatic nuclei, a feature called the Arias-Stella phenomenon. With advancing pregnancy, the endometrial glands gradually atrophy.

Menstrual Phase

In the absence of pregnancy, changes in the endometrium secondary to declining hormone production by the corpus luteum can be observed by day 24. The functional layer of the stroma begins to shrink, and the endometrial glands become more tortuous and saw-toothed in appearance. Intermittent constriction of the spiral arteries leads to stasis within the capillaries of the functional layer, tissue ischemia, and extravasation of blood into the stroma with formation of small hematomas. Eventually, desquamation and sloughing of the entire functional layer of the endometrium occurs.

Endometrial biopsy has been used extensively in the past to assess progesterone secretion in women with menstrual dysfunction and infertility. With the widespread availability of reliable radioimmunoassays to measure serum concentrations of progesterone, the need for endometrial biopsy is limited; it should be used primarily to assess the response of the endometrium to hormonal stimulation. Endometrial biopsy is most informative when performed a few days before the anticipated menstrual period. Although biopsy late in the luteal phase may potentially interrupt a pregnancy if conception has occurred, the risk is minimal.

CERVICAL MUCUS

Cervical mucus is a complex secretion produced by the glands of the endocervix. It is composed of 92–98% water and approximately 1% inorganic salts, of which NaCl is the main constituent. The mucus also contains free simple sugars, polysaccharides, proteins, and glycoproteins. Its pH is usually alkaline and ranges from 6.5 to 9.0. Several physical characteristics of cervical mucus can be evaluated readily by the clinician. Since these characteristics are influenced by serum estrogen and progesterone levels, it is often possible to gain an approximate assessment of the hormonal status of a patient by examination of cervical mucus. Estrogen stimulates the production of copious amounts (up to 700 mg/d) of clear, watery mucus through which sperm can penetrate most readily. Progesterone, however, even in the presence of high plasma levels of estrogen, reduces the secretion of mucus. Both during the luteal phase of the menstrual cycle and during pregnancy, the mucus is scant, viscous, and cellular. During most of the menstrual cycle, 20–60 mg of mucus is produced each day.

Figure 10–12 summarizes those characteristics of cervical mucus that the clinician can readily determine and correlates them with the day of the menstrual cycle.

Spinnbarkeit is the property that allows cervical mucus to be stretched or drawn into a thread. Spinnbarkeit can be estimated by stretching a sample

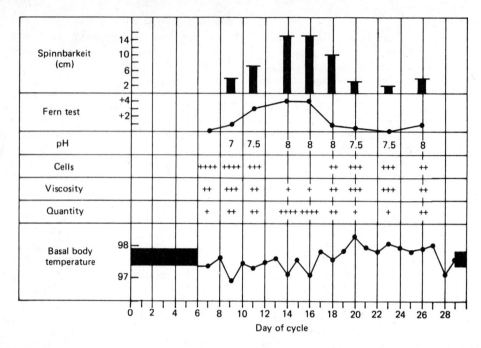

Figure 10–12. Changes in the composition and properties of cervical mucus throughout the menstrual cycle. (Modified and reproduced, with permission, from Moghissi KS: Composition and function of cervical secretion. In: *Handbook of Physiology,* Section 7: Endocrinology, Vol 2, Part 2. Greep RO [editor]. American Physiological Society, 1973.)

of mucus between 2 glass slides and measuring the maximum length of the thread before it breaks. At midcycle, spinnbarkeit usually exceeds 10 cm. **Ferning,** or **arborization,** refers to the characteristic microscopic pattern cervical mucus forms when dried on a slide (Figure 10–13). Ferning results from the crystallization of inorganic salts around small and optimal amounts of organic material present in cervical mucus. As serum concentrations of estradiol increase, the composition of cervical mucus changes, so that dried mucus begins to demonstrate ferning in the latter part of the follicular phase. In the periovulatory interval, when estradiol levels are maximal and prior to significant progesterone secretion, ferning is most prominent and the mucus is thin, watery, and contains few cells. As serum progesterone concentrations increase following ovulation, the quality of the mucus changes and ferning disappears. The absence of ferning can reflect either inadequate stimulation of endocervical glands by estrogen or inhibition by increased secretion of progesterone. Persistent ferning throughout the menstrual cycle suggests anovulatory cycles or insufficient progesterone secretion.

VAGINAL EPITHELIUM

The vaginal mucosa is composed of a stratified squamous epithelium and does not contain glands.

Cells in the outer layer during the reproductive years are flattened and may contain keratohyaline granules, but true cornification does not normally occur. The epithelial cells of the vagina, like other tissues of the female reproductive tract, respond to changing levels of ovarian sex steroids. Estrogen stimulates the proliferation and maturation of the epithelial cells, resulting in a thickening of the vaginal mucosa and increased glycogen content of the epithelial cells. This glycogen is fermented to lactic acid by the normal bacterial flora of the vagina, thus accounting for the mildly acid pH of vaginal fluid. The histologic and cytologic changes of the vaginal epithelium of women during the normal menstrual cycle are less marked than those occurring in the estrous cycle of rodents.

Cytologists describe three types of exfoliated vaginal epithelial cells—superficial, intermediate, and basal-parabasal—which do not refer to the locations of the cells within the epithelium but to their degree of cellular maturity or differentiation. Exfoliated cells, obtained by light scrapings from the midportion of the lateral vaginal wall, are most useful for cytohormonal assessment.

Superficial cells are mature, flat, usually polygonal, squamous epithelial cells with pyknotic, hyperchromatic nuclei. These cells develop in response to high levels of unopposed estrogen stimulation.

Intermediate cells are relatively mature squamous epithelial cells with eosinophilic or cyanophilic cyto-

Normal cycle, 14th day

Midluteal phase, normal cycle

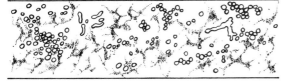

Anovulatory cycle with estrogen present

Figure 10–13. Patterns formed when cervical mucus is smeared on a slide, permitted to dry, and examined under the microscope. Progesterone makes the mucus thick and cellular. In the smear from a patient who failed to ovulate (bottom), there is no progesterone to inhibit the estrogen-induced fern pattern. (Reproduced, with permission, from Ganong WF: *Review of Medical Physiology,* 14th ed. Appleton & Lange, 1989.)

plasm and a vesicular, nonpyknotic nucleus. The appearance of the nucleus is the critical factor in differentiating intermediate cells from superficial cells. Intermediate cells predominate in endocrinologic states in which progesterone levels are high, such as in pregnancy or in the midluteal phase of the menstrual cycle.

Basal-parabasal cells are thick, small, oval or round, immature cells with large vesicular nuclei and cyanophilic cytoplasm. Parabasal cells usually indicate estrogen deficiency and are the predominant cell type in the prepubertal and postmenopausal periods.

Among the various indices that describe the ratio or percentage of superficial, intermediate, and basal-parabasal cells are (1) the karyopyknotic index (KPI), the ratio of superficial cells to intermediate cells; (2) the eosinophilic index (EI), the ratio of mature eosinophilic cells to mature cyanophilic cells; and (3) the maturation index (MI), the percentage of parabasal, intermediate, and superficial cells present, in that order. Since only MI includes as a factor the presence of all three cell types, it may provide more information than the other two indices.

In general, only two diagnostic patterns of vaginal epithelial cells are clinically useful. When the vaginal epithelium has been stimulated by estrogen, MI may range from (0/40/60) at mid cycle, when estradiol concentrations are highest, to (0/70/30) late in the luteal phase, when progesterone effects are most prominent. A finding of parabasal cells with a few intermediate cells and no superficial cells indicates that the vaginal epithelium has received little or no estrogen stimulation. The MI in this instance may be (100/0/0) or (80/20/0). The vaginal smear can be used to provide a qualitative assessment of estrogen production in women with amenorrhea.

EXTRAGENITAL SYMPTOMS ASSOCIATED WITH NORMAL MENSTRUAL FUNCTION

PREMENSTRUAL SYNDROME

Premenstrual syndrome (PMS) is a complex of symptoms occurring in the luteal phase of the cycle in ovulating women. Behavioral symptoms include fatigue, irritability, anxiety, depression, emotional lability, insomnia, increased appetite, and difficulty in working effectively. Physical symptoms may include bloating, breast tenderness, ankle edema, and headaches.

Recent epidemiologic studies indicate that in the populations studied, about 5–10% of women in the reproductive age group have moderate to severe symptoms temporally related to the menstrual cycle, and most of these women seek medical care. Another 20–40% of women feel less well during the late luteal and early menstrual phase of the cycle and for a day or so in mid cycle. PMS appears to be limited to women with ovulatory cycles. In patients with more severe symptoms, interrelationships at home and at work can be disrupted. Among the serious consequences commonly reported are marital discord, parenting problems, poor work or school performance, and social isolation.

Although many theories of causation have been proposed, none account for the entire symptom complex, and the syndrome is probably the result of hormonal as well as environmental and psychologic factors. Women with moderate to severe PMS experience more stressful events than other women. However, it is not clear whether these events are etiologically related nor whether they exacerbate the syndrome or result from it. Studies in twins indicate that genetic factors may also be involved.

Diagnosis

The physician must take a careful history, including detailed inquiry into the stresses associated with the patient's work and family life, and perform a complete physical examination to properly assess the nature and severity of the complaints. It may also be helpful to interview the patient's spouse or housemate. It is important to rule out other causes of the complaints, particularly the somatic complaints, since they may be amenable to therapy.

When symptoms are severe and maneuvers such as ovulation suppression or anxiolytic and antidepressant drugs are contemplated, it is best to document the cyclic nature and severity of the symptoms and behaviors to be treated. Several instruments are available for this purpose; however, it is sufficient to have the patient select the symptoms she finds most bothersome and rate them daily on a calendar through two or more cycles using the following scale:

0 No symptoms.
1+ Changes are noticed by the patient and family, but normal activities are not affected.
2+ Family or occupational relationships and activities are disturbed but functioning.
3+ Family or occupational relationships are seriously disturbed, and normal activities cannot continue.

Treatment

The objective of therapy is to make the patient more comfortable and enable her to function more normally. Simple life-style changes, a diet and exercise program, and stress management strategies are a useful way to begin treatment. Reductions in alcohol and caffeine intake can reduce irritability and anxiety, respectively. Salt restriction may reduce swelling and bloating. Empiric treatment of physical manifestations is helpful. Spironolactone, a potassium-sparing agent, given in doses of 50–100 mg from day 12 to menses, reduces swelling, breast tenderness, and bloating and can be useful when salt restriction and exercise are ineffective in relieving swelling. Naproxen, 550 mg twice daily, or ibuprofen, 600 mg three times daily, taken from onset of symptoms until bleeding commences, is effective for headaches, cramping, and back and muscle aches, and in some patients these agents reduce irritability and depression. Danazol, tamoxifen, and bromocriptine are useful for breast pain. Preliminary studies suggest that danazol in doses of 200 mg/d taken from the onset of symptoms to the start of menses provides modest but significant overall improvement without side effects or ovulation suppression.

When anxiety and irritability are the dominant symptoms, alprazolam in doses of 0.125–0.25 mg three times daily from day 20 to the second day of menses, followed by the same dose twice daily on day 3 and one dose on day 4, is effective and unassociated with withdrawal symptoms. Buspirone is also effective and free of sedative effects in a dose of 25

mg/d from the onset of symptoms until menses. Fluoxetine, 20–60 mg daily, or fenfluramine, 20 mg three times daily, has been found to be helpful when depression is a prominent symptom. Psychiatric referral is advisable when there is a risk of suicide, violence toward others, or exacerbation of psychiatric illness or when the physician requires assistance with the use of psychotropic drugs.

In many studies, women treated with placebos have shown as much as 50% or more improvement for short periods of time. Pyridoxine, vitamin E, evening primrose oil (a rich source of γ-linoleic acid—a precursor of prostenoids), or vitamin and mineral supplements as well as progesterone are commonly used but have not been shown to be more effective than placebo.

When symptoms last more than a week or are unduly severe, ovulation suppression can be tried. Patients responding to ovulation suppression with danazol, gonadotropin-releasing hormone analogues, medroxyprogesterone, depot medroxyprogesterone acetate, or estrogen implants or patches may have relief which continues after a period (1 year) of treatment. If symptoms return and persist, ovariectomy can be discussed with appropriate patients. In a patient with a well-documented symptom complex that responds to induction of anovulation with GnRH analogues, danazol, or estrogen and in whom the syndrome causes a major disruption of the patient's life, ovariectomy is a rational therapeutic option if the desire for further childbearing is not a factor and the patient can anticipate many more years of ovulatory function.

DYSMENORRHEA

Dysmenorrhea unrelated to any identifiable disorder almost always begins before age 20 but seldom within the first year or so after menarche. It is one of the most important causes of lost working hours and failure to attend school. The pain is colicky in nature and thought to be related to uterine contractions caused by prostaglandins released at the time of endometrial breakdown. When severe, the pain may radiate from the pelvic region to the back and thighs and is frequently accompanied by nausea and in some women vomiting and diarrhea. Treatment with aspirin before the onset of pain is effective in milder cases; however, the nonsteroidal anti-inflammatory compounds that are active inhibitors of prostaglandin synthesis are more effective when the pain is severe. Naproxen, 250 mg twice daily, and ibuprofen, 400 mg three times daily, are useful for this purpose, as is indomethacin, 25 mg three or four times daily, or mefenamic acid, 250 mg four times daily. These compounds are often more effective if started before the pain begins. Since dysmenorrhea rarely accompanies bleeding in the absence of ovulation, suppression of ovulation with oral contraceptives is also effective treatment.

DISORDERS OF OVARIAN & MENSTRUAL FUNCTION

Abnormal ovarian endocrine function is manifested by (1) evidence of inappropriate estrogen secretion (eg, precocious puberty); (2) deficient estrogen secretion (eg, delayed puberty); (3) disturbances or alterations of the menstrual cycle in mature women; or (4) evidence of excessive androgen production. In this chapter, emphasis will be placed on disorders occurring in postpubertal adults, since these comprise the vast majority of disorders encountered and because disorders of development and differentiation are described in Chapters 8 and 18 and pituitary disorders in Chapter 6.

The pattern of menstrual bleeding with regard to the frequency, duration, and amount of flow tends to be fairly consistent in most healthy women. Periodic, regular menstrual cycles are usually ovulatory. However, there are a wide variety of organic and functional disturbances of menstrual flow. In general, when the basic pattern of bleeding is undisturbed and there are superimposed episodes of spotting or bleeding, the cause is likely to be a local organic lesion or hematologic disorder. When the basic pattern of bleeding is changed, it is more often due to lack of ovulation and disturbances in the pattern of hormone secretion. Table 10–3 sets forth the terms frequently used to describe abnormalities of menses, their definitions, and some common causes.

The great majority of disorders of ovarian function causing amenorrhea occur without known or identifiable structural changes in the components of the complex system required for normal ovulatory cycles. They can result from abnormalities in function of the central mechanism that regulates the pulsatile secretion of GnRH; from abnormalities in feedback; or from changes in intraovarian regulatory mechanisms. Environmental changes, physical and emotional stress, extreme weight loss, and drugs seem to be able to interfere with the functioning of the hypothalamic centers and their control of GnRH secretion. In such cases, a variety of hormonal abnormalities may be identified. In some patients, follicle stimulation by FSH is insufficient to produce adequate growth and maturation of ovarian follicles, with a resulting decrease in ovarian estradiol secretion. Failure of the preovulatory LH surge to occur even though follicles have developed and produced

Table 10–3. Types of abnormal vaginal bleeding.

	Definition	Causes
Hypermenorrhea (menorrhagia)	Cyclic bleeding in excessive amount.	Uterine myomas and endometrial polyps, hyperplasia, adenomyosis, endometritis, von Willebrand's disease.
Hypomenorrhea	Cyclic bleeding in abnormally small amount	Cervical obstruction, synechia of endometrium, tuberculosis of endometrium.
Polymenorrhea	Frequent periods (cycle length of <21 days).	Shortening of follicular phase, luteal insufficiency, frequent anovulatory bleeding.
Oligomenorrhea	Infrequent periods (cycle length of >35 days).	Anovulation, systemic disturbances.
Amenorrhea	More than 6 months since last menstrual period.	Anovulation or outflow tract disorder.
Metrorrhagia	Bleeding between normal cycles.	Except for ovulatory bleeding or spotting, this symptom usually indicates disease of the vagina, cervix, or uterus.

estrogen will also disrupt normal ovarian and menstrual function. However, the continuous secretion of increased amounts of LH in the absence of normally developing follicles may result in overproduction of androgens and lead to amenorrhea and hirsutism (eg, polycystic ovary syndrome). The role of estrogens, androgens, and other local hormones in the ovary is not presently well delineated, but these hormones may be responsible for abnormalities in ovarian function in some patients. Abnormalities of gonadotropin secretion leading to anovulation are sometimes associated with the release of increased amounts of PRL in the absence of any demonstrable lesion of the pituitary. In such patients, amenorrhea may be associated with galactorrhea.

Treatment of these disorders depends to some extent on their causes and manifestations. However, the desired outcome is the critical consideration. It would be fruitless, for example, to treat hirsutism secondary to excess production of ovarian androgens by suppressing the ovary with oral contraceptives in a patient whose main objective was to achieve a pregnancy.

In considering the possible causes of amenorrhea in a given patient, it is useful to review the requirements for normal cyclic ovarian function: (1) a normal outflow tract, (2) normal ovaries, (3) a normal pituitary gland, and (4) a normal central nervous system. Each of these systems can be examined by means of the history, direct observation, and appropriate laboratory tests or procedures. The problem may be more complex in young women with primary amenorrhea and no evidence of sexual maturation. In women with secondary amenorrhea, however, the process may require very few laboratory tests. By the time one has begun to speak to the patient, one has already observed her approximate age, appearance, stature, and extent of sexual development; this information provides some direction for taking her history and doing the physical examination.

AMENORRHEA IN THE ABSENCE OF SEXUAL MATURATION

The diagnostic considerations for a young, immature woman are quite different from those for a mature woman with secondary amenorrhea. In the otherwise healthy but sexually immature patient over 16 years of age, the first question to resolve is whether normal puberty is merely delayed. This question can sometimes be answered by finding a normal level of gonadotropins and a history of late puberty in the family. No conclusion can be drawn if the levels of gonadotropins are low. In these patients, LH and FSH responses to testing with GnRH or a GnRH agonist analogue may help to differentiate delayed puberty from a more serious disorder.

Elevated concentrations of FSH and LH indicate unresponsiveness or absence of functioning ovarian tissue. If the patient is short in stature and has obvious stigmas of Turner's syndrome (gonadal dysgenesis), gonadotropins will be elevated. Chromosomal analysis will confirm the diagnosis, determine the genotype, and indicate the need for gonadectomy if a Y chromosome mosaicism is found. If the patient is of normal height or has relatively longer arms and legs compared with the length of the trunk (eunuchoid proportions), gonadal absence or agenesis must be differentiated from selective hypogonadotropism. FSH will be elevated in the former and low in the latter. If height and stature are normal and gonadotropins are low, one must also consider a central nervous system defect such as Kallmann's syndrome. These patients also have anosmia, which can be determined by the history or by testing the ability to smell.

Patients with amenorrhea and hypogonadism in whom the levels of gonadotropins are normal or lower than normal may be experiencing a delay in onset of puberty. However, after age 16, this is sufficiently unusual to warrant further investigation. When the cause is craniopharyngioma or pituitary tumor, there is commonly an interference with growth secondary to deficient GH secretion. Clinical or laboratory evidence of thyroid or adrenal insufficiency or decreased reserve also may be present. These and other pituitary disorders causing amenorrhea and

conditions of abnormal pubertal development are discussed in Chapters 2 and 12.

Primary Ovarian Disorders

A. Gonadal Agenesis: Hypogonadism may result from absent or incomplete development of the ovary. This abnormality could result from environmentally induced abnormalities in development early in pregnancy (see Chapter 11).

B. Turner's Syndrome (Gonadal Dysgenesis): Turner's syndrome and related variants of gonadal dysgenesis are the most common cause of congenital hypogonadism. The karyotype in affected patients is most frequently 45,X, showing an absence of the second X chromosome. Clinical features, in addition to the lack of sexual maturation, include short stature, webbed neck, shield chest, and valgus deformity of the elbow. This syndrome and its variants are described in detail in Chapter 11. Gonadal dysgenesis may also occur in the presence of multiple cell lines with varying chromosomal composition. This is called "mosaicism." Many patients with mosaicism have typical phenotypic characteristics of Turner's syndrome, and the diagnosis may be made before puberty. A karyotype should be performed on all of these patients to determine whether or not a Y chromosome is present. Patients having Y chromosomes require laparotomy and excision of the gonadal area to prevent development of gonadoblastomas. It should also be noted that patients having an XX constituent to their mosaicism may have functional ovarian tissue. In some of these, normal puberty (including menses) occurs, and they are able to reproduce. These individuals frequently experience premature menopause.

C. 17α-Hydroxylase (P450c17) Deficiency: Hypogonadism and elevated levels of gonadotropin can be found in patients with 17α-hydroxylase deficiency, a rare form of congenital adrenal hyperplasia in which there is impaired conversion of pregnenolone and progesterone to cortisol and to androgens and estrogens. The impairment leads to increased production of deoxycorticosterone and corticosterone, resulting in hypokalemia and hypertension (see Chapters 7 and 11).

Disorders Due to Central Nervous System Disease

A. Hypogonadotropism and Anosmia: This syndrome, similar to Kallmann's syndrome in the male, is a rare cause of amenorrhea. Patients fail to mature at the expected time for puberty and are found to have low gonadotropins, normal stature, anosmia, and a female karyotype. The disorder is believed to involve failure of development of the olfactory lobe and a deficiency of GnRH. Ovulation can be induced by injection of menopausal gonadotropins and by pulsatile injection of GnRH.

B. Prepubertal Pituitary and Central Nervous

System Tumors: Pituitary and central nervous system disorders which interfere with ovarian function, or tumors such as craniopharyngeomas and pituitary adenomas are discussed in Chapters 2 and 12.

AMENORRHEA IN PATIENTS WITH NORMAL SECONDARY SEX CHARACTERISTICS

The evaluation of women with amenorrhea but otherwise normal sexual development begins with the history and physical examination plus a few laboratory tests (Figure 10–14). This initial evaluation will localize the underlying cause of the amenorrhea to dysfunction of either the outflow tract, the ovary, or the hypothalamic-pituitary complex. In most cases, further diagnostic procedures will not be required. The medical history should include a complete description of prior menstrual patterns, the presence or absence of breast discharge, and any changes that might suggest increased androgen secretion. The possibility of pregnancy should always be considered.

The initial evaluation consists of a qualitative assessment of the patient's endogenous estrogen level and determination of the serum PRL concentration. The presence of endogenous estrogens can be established by attempting to induce withdrawal uterine bleeding by administering progesterone. An oral progestin with no estrogenic activity—eg, medroxyprogesterone, 10 mg daily for 5–7 days—or a single intramuscular injection of 200 mg of progesterone in oil may be used. The presence of vaginal bleeding within 7 days after conclusion of the progesterone treatment indicates that the outflow tract is intact and that the patient is producing sufficient estrogen to stimulate endometrial growth. If the serum PRL concentration is also within normal limits, a pituitary tumor is very unlikely. These patients can be considered to be anovulatory, and in most cases no further evaluation is required. The choice of treatment, if any, will depend upon the objectives of the patient.

Failure to induce menstrual bleeding by exogenous progestin indicates either a defect of the outflow tract with normal estrogen production (an infrequent cause of secondary amenorrhea) or insufficient estrogen production secondary to hypothalamic-pituitary-ovarian dysfunction. To differentiate between these possibilities in women with normal PRL levels, gonadotropin levels are obtained to differentiate between ovarian failure and hypothalamic-pituitary dysfunction. If an abnormality of the outflow tract is suspected, its integrity can be assessed by administering oral estrogen (1.25–2.5 mg of conjugated estrogens or 50 μg of ethinyl estradiol per day) for 21 days. A progestin should be added during the last 5 days of treatment. Lack of withdrawal bleeding following treatment usually indicates an abnormality of the outflow tract. In most instances, however, bleeding will occur and the outflow tract is found to be normal.

To differentiate between ovarian failure and hypothalamic-pituitary dysfunction, gonadotropin levels are obtained. If ovarian failure is the primary cause of amenorrhea, serum FSH and LH levels will be elevated because of the loss of negative feedback by ovarian sex steroids. If serum concentrations of FSH and LH are low or low normal or if prolactin levels are elevated, radiologic or magnetic resonance examination of the pituitary gland is indicated to rule out a pituitary tumor. Therapy for these disorders is discussed below.

Abnormalities of the Outflow Tract

Patients with amenorrhea in whom gonadal tissue is presumed to be present because they have undergone normal sexual maturation may have abnormalities of the outflow tract. Patients who cannot be induced to bleed by treatment with a progestational agent and who fail to bleed following administration of estrogens in conjunction with a progestational agent after several attempts can be presumed to have an abnormality of the outflow tract. In these patients, the presence or absence of ovulation can be determined by following the basal body temperature over a month or more or by measuring serum progesterone levels once a week for several weeks.

A. Müllerian Defects: In women with no history of vaginal bleeding, developmental abnormalities of the müllerian tube must be considered. These abnormalities range from the presence of an imperforate hymen to the total absence of müllerian structures. In the presence of a uterus lined with endometrium, interruption of the outflow tract by an abnormal cervix, interruptions of the vaginal canal, or imperforate hymen may be accompanied by collection of the menstruum proximal to the point of obstruction. This leads to pain and distention of the proximal structures or accumulation of blood in the peritoneal cavity. **Absence of the vagina,** with varying degrees of uterine development associated with normal ovarian function, is one of the more common abnormalities of müllerian development (Mayer-Rokitansky-Küster-Hauser syndrome). Affected patients commonly have developmental abnormalities of the urinary and skeletal systems. Surgical creation of an artificial vagina is indicated when there is evidence that a functioning uterus exists and that fertility might be restored. Otherwise, progressive dilation by the use of vaginal dilators can be used to form a functional vagina.

B. Asherman's Syndrome (Uterine Synechia): In women in whom menses have once been established, destruction of the endometrial cavity by chronic infections such as tuberculosis or destruction of the endometrium by curettage can lead to amenorrhea. Such scarring (Asherman's syndrome) is un-

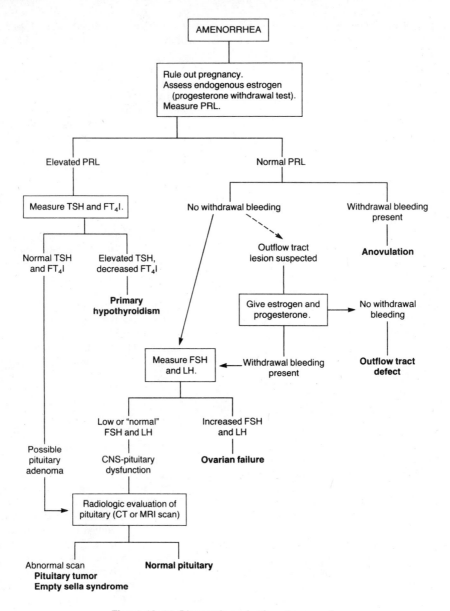

Figure 10–14. Diagnostic evaluation of amenorrhea.

common and can be treated by careful dilatation under hysteroscopic view, followed by insertion of a small Foley catheter or other device to prevent adhesions from recurring. Treatment should include the use of broad-spectrum antibiotics for 10 days following the procedure and cyclic stimulation of endometrial development with large doses of estrogen plus a progestin.

Primary Gonadal Disorders

In patients with amenorrhea and a normal outflow tract, abnormal ovarian function may result from disorders of the ovary itself or disorders of the controlling mechanisms. A plasma FSH of more than 40

mIU/mL accompanied by high levels of LH is evidence of failure of ovarian hormone production. This is a very serious diagnosis, not only because of the hormone deficiency, which is correctable, but also—and more importantly from the patient's point of view—because lack of a functioning follicular apparatus results in sterility. For this reason, it is worth repeating the test to be sure there is no error. In women near menopause, elevated gonadotropin levels are sometimes found in the presence of ovulatory cycles. However, a misdiagnosis in this group of patients is rarely clinically important unless the patient is pregnant.

A. Premature Ovarian Failure: Ovarian failure

occasionally occurs in women under the age of 35 following spontaneous sexual maturation. In some patients, ovarian failure is associated with ovarian autoantibodies and is probably due to autoimmune destruction of the ovary. It is frequently associated with autoantibodies to other glands such as the thyroid and adrenal (Schmidt's syndrome) (see Chapters 4, 6, and 21). In other patients, the ovaries show a few primordial follicles, and in some they resemble menopausal ovaries.

B. Testicular Feminization: This disorder in its classic form is characterized by primary amenorrhea, an absent uterus, and the absence of pubic and axillary hair. Affected patients are male pseudohermaphrodites with testes and an XY karyotype. Incomplete forms of this disorder have also been described. They are discussed in detail in Chapter 11.

C. Resistant Ovary Syndrome: Rarely, women exhibit amenorrhea and elevated gonadotropin levels in the presence of potentially functional ovarian follicles. It may be possible to induce follicular growth and estrogen secretion in these patients by administration of large amounts of exogenous gonadotropins. However, it is usually difficult or impossible to induce ovulation and subsequent pregnancy in these patients. Although this disorder can only be diagnosed with certainty by ovarian biopsy, the infrequency of the disorder and the poor prognosis dictate that ovarian biopsy be performed only rarely in patients with high gonadotropins and normal karyotype.

D. Functioning Ovarian Tumors: Hormone-producing tumors of the ovary presenting clinically as endocrine disorders are uncommon. Classification of these tumors is made difficult by the uncertainty of embryonic origin in some and the lack of correlation between the functional and morphologic characteristics. However, it is convenient to divide them into broad morphologic categories, keeping in mind that the diagnostic approach will be based on the clinical presentation. Detection of androgen-producing tumors is considered in the section on amenorrhea with excess androgen production (see below). The estro-gen-producing tumors cause amenorrhea or anovulatory bleeding in premenopausal women, irregular bleeding after the menopause, and precocious puberty in children. A classification of these tumors is presented in Table 10–4.

1. Germ cell tumors–

a. Germinomas (dysgerminoma, seminoma, gonocytoma, embryonal carcinoma)– These tumors of the ovary are usually found on routine examination in young women. They are generally small and asymptomatic unless associated with teratomatous elements that produce hCG. When hCG is produced, the patient will develop amenorrhea and other signs and symptoms of early pregnancy.

b. Teratomas– Teratomas arising in gonadal tissue are common. Although rarely active hormonally, they may contain hormone-secreting elements. Tumors containing thyroid tissue (struma ovarii) can release thyroxine. Carcinoid tumors producing serotonin have also been reported.

Choriocarcinoma of the ovary is usually secondary to uterine choriocarcinoma and very rarely arises within the ovary. It is composed of trophoblastic tissue, usually with extensive hemorrhage and necrosis. These tumors produce large amounts of hCG. The elevated plasma levels of this hormone are useful in diagnosing the tumor and in monitoring treatment. Treatment is similar to that of tumors of trophoblastic origin in the uterus. However, the prognosis is less favorable.

c. Gonadoblastomas– These rare tumors arise in dysgenetic gonads. They are typically seen in phenotypic females with a Y chromosome. They are morphologically similar to germinomas but also have cells of mesenchymal or sex cord origin. The latter may differentiate into Leydig or granulosa cells and secrete androgens or estrogens. Prophylactic removal of the dysgenetic gonads is recommended in patients with a Y chromosome (see Chapter 11).

2. Sex cord-mesenchymal tumors–

a. Granulosa-theca cell tumors– These tumors constitute 5–10% of ovarian neoplasms. They are

Table 10–4. Classification and clinical features of functioning ovarian tumors.

	Hormones[1]	Usual Age at Onset	Percent Palpable	Percent Bilateral	Percent Malignant
Germ cell tumors					
Germinomas-teratomas					
Struma ovarii	Thyroxine	10–40	90	10	Rare
Carcinoid tumors	Serotonin	10–40	90	10	Rare
Choriocarcinomas	Chorionic gonadotropin	6–15	100	Rare	100
Gonadoblastomas	Androgens, estrogens	10–30		40	50
Sex cord-mesenchymal tumors					
Granulosa-theca cell tumors	Estrogens, androgens, progestins	30–70	90	10	20
Sertoli-Leydig cell tumors (arrhenoblastomas)	Androgens, estrogens	20–50	80	Rare	20
Hilar cell tumors	Androgens, estrogens	45–75	50	Rare	Rare

[1]Steroid-producing tumors may produce estrogens or androgens. The usual hormone released is listed first.

usually associated with some clinical or pathologic evidence of estrogen secretion. Androgen-producing tumors of this type have been reported but are rare. Granulosa cell tumors are unilateral in 90% of patients. They are usually solid and vary in appearance from mature granulosa cells arranged in circumferential rows around spaces ("Call-Exner bodies") to immature cells with a sarcomatous appearance. The cells may take on the polyhedral appearance of the luteinized granulosa cells of the corpus luteum. Although the prognosis following removal of these tumors is better than for ovarian carcinomas, about 20% recur in 5 years and about 40% in 10 years. The recurrences may be circumscribed and can be quite sensitive to radiation.

b. Sertoli-Leydig cell tumors (arrhenoblastoma, androblastoma)– This group of tumors, as noted above, may cause feminization. They more commonly produce virilization and under these circumstances are commonly called arrhenoblastomas or androblastomas. They are not common, accounting for fewer than 5% of ovarian tumors. They vary in size and, although usually small, may become large. The histologic pattern varies from that of well-differentiated testicular tubules (Pick's adenoma) to an undifferentiated sarcomatous appearance and mixtures of both.

Typically, the first manifestation of an androgen-producing tumor is amenorrhea, followed rapidly by hirsutism, acne, and breast atrophy; clitoral hypertrophy, balding, and deepening of the voice occur later. Plasma androgen levels are usually in the normal male range (testosterone ≥ 3 ng/mL) and usually cannot be suppressed by administration of estrogens or estrogen-containing oral contraceptives. Removal of the tumor is followed by a return of menses and partial or complete loss of abnormal hair. The tumors are seldom bilateral and usually benign.

3. Hilar cell (lipoid cell) tumors– These androgen-producing tumors usually occur in older patients and cause severe masculinization, including hirsutism, balding, clitoral enlargement, and deepening of the voice. They are usually small and less likely to be palpated than other ovarian tumors. Histologically, they are typical steroid-producing cells and contain Reinke crystalloids, which are characteristically found in the interstitial cells of the testis. They are almost always benign and are treated by extirpation, which reverses the hirsutism, baldness, and metabolic changes, though clitoral enlargement and voice changes persist.

Disorders of the Pituitary

The anterior pituitary gland plays a key role in normal ovarian function. In adults, the loss of pituitary gonadotropic activity is usually noted before the loss of other pituitary trophic functions when the organ is damaged by vascular, inflammatory, or neoplastic processes.

A. Pituitary Tumors: Most patients with amenorrhea and low gonadotropin levels have decreased or altered secretion of GnRH secondary to altered hypothalamic or central nervous system activity. However, the presence of a pituitary tumor must be considered and excluded. Amenorrhea may be the only clue to a nonfunctioning tumor. Most commonly, however, pituitary tumors in young women with amenorrhea cause hyperprolactinemia, and galactorrhea is found in more than 50% of patients with PRL-secreting adenomas (see Chapter 2). In contrast, GH-secreting tumors are associated with clinical signs of acromegaly. Although this is an unusual cause of amenorrhea, it is important to consider the diagnosis in appropriate clinical circumstances, since early diagnosis and treatment can prevent the permanently disfiguring effects of excessive GH. Amenorrhea may also be the presenting symptom in patients with Cushing's syndrome due to a pituitary tumor (Cushing's disease).

B. Empty Sella Syndrome: Amenorrhea and galactorrhea may occur in the presence of the empty sella syndrome (see Chapter 2). In this condition, there appears to be an extension of the subarachnoid space into the pituitary fossa, which leads to flattening of pituitary tissue against the wall of the sella and may lead to its enlargement. The disorder is found in 5% of patients at autopsy. It is benign and requires no treatment unless associated abnormalities of pituitary function are present. This condition can be differentiated from tumor by CT or MRI scanning.

Disorders Due to Central Nervous System Abnormalities of Regulation of Gonadotropin Secretion

A. Hypothalamic Amenorrhea: This term is used to described amenorrhea due to functional abnormalities in the neural mechanisms that regulate the pulsatile secretion of GnRH. Young women commonly fail to ovulate at times of increased stress such as may be occasioned by academic or career pressures, disruption of personal life-styles, change in residences, or illness. These events may mark the onset of periods of amenorrhea.

In most instances, the period of amenorrhea is self-limited and ovulatory menstrual function returns spontaneously. If this does not occur, treatment is dependent upon the expectations of the patient. If she wishes to become pregnant, induction of ovulation by clomiphene would be the initial treatment. If this does not induce ovulation, treatment with clomiphene plus chorionic gonadotropin, with menotropins (Pergonal), or with pulsatile administration of GnRH will be required. If the patient does not want to become pregnant, her estrogenic status will help to determine treatment. Most of these women will have a positive progesterone challenge test (withdrawal bleeding) and either normal or only moderately reduced levels of estrogen. Cyclic treatment with a progestational agent will prevent endometrial hyperplasia in these women. Rarely, these women will have a negative progesterone challenge test (no withdrawal bleeding) and may have significant loss of calcium with the eventual development of osteoporosis secondary to low levels of estrogen. In these patients, preventative treatment with estrogen and a cyclic progestin should be considered.

B. Amenorrhea in Athletes: Menstrual abnormalities are sufficiently common in female athletes to suggest a causal relationship between vigorous physical effort and amenorrhea. About one-third of long-distance runners experience amenorrhea or oligomenorrhea. The incidence appears to vary with the degree of stress and effort in other activities. The incidence of amenorrhea correlates directly with the amount of weight lost and inversely with the percentage of body weight as fat. It is less frequent in multiparous women. No consistent changes in plasma estradiol, testosterone, or gonadotropin levels have been reported. In general, these menstrual abnormalities disappear with a reduction of physical activity and a return to the individual's natural weight and proportion of body weight as fat. Some of these women with prolonged amenorrhea show excessive bone loss in spite of their intense physical activity, and appropriate hormone replacement therapy should be instituted.

C. Anorexia: Anorexia nervosa in its classic form is a serious but uncommon disorder characterized by extreme malnutrition and hypogonadotropism. It is considered to be a severe behavioral disorder, with endocrine changes secondary to both psychologic and nutritional disturbances. Amenorrhea may precede weight loss. Milder forms of malnutrition and amenorrhea are more commonly seen in formerly overweight women with an abnormal fear of regaining weight lost by dieting. These patients may respond to psychotherapy and antidepressant drug therapy. Malnutrition may result from refusal to eat, induced vomiting (bulimia), and excessive use of laxatives. Psychiatric treatment is required, and hospitalization may be necessary to prevent death from starvation, suicide, or intercurrent illnesses.

D. Post-Pill Amenorrhea: Although it has not been possible to clearly demonstrate an increase in prolactinomas or a reduction in the fertility rate of women following the use of oral contraceptives, studies are available that show a moderate increase in the incidence of amenorrhea in such women. Furthermore, the syndrome of amenorrhea with galactorrhea (see below) is more common in women treated with oral contraceptives. Although the nature of this relationship is not established, it is clear that most women who develop amenorrhea following the use of contraceptive pills would probably have developed amenorrhea without them, and the disorder must be investigated as in other women.

Amenorrhea With Galactorrhea

Galactorrhea may be induced by a wide variety of stimuli ranging from local irritation or stimulation of the chest wall to ingestion of drugs that interfere with the hypothalamic release of dopamine or its binding to the pituitary lactotrophs (see Chapter 2). The expression of even 1 drop of fluid from the nipple is clinically significant and is rarely seen in healthy women who have not taken oral contraceptives or who have not been recently pregnant or exposed to drugs such as phenothiazines (which cause galactorrhea) or to excessive breast stimulation. In women with amenorrhea, an attempt should be made to elicit such a secretion by gentle manual pressure at the base of the breast, working toward the nipple. The secretion may be present in only one breast at any given time.

Whether or not galactorrhea is present, however, prolactin levels should be measured in patients with persistent amenorrhea (Figure 10–14). When a detectable tumor is present, prolactin levels are usually elevated. In the presence of nonsecreting tumors impinging on the pituitary stalk, prolactin levels may be only minimally elevated. It is advisable to obtain CT or MRI studies of the pituitary in most patients with galactorrhea or elevated prolactin levels. Studies of pituitary function, including the gonadotropin response to GnRH and the effect of levodopa and other drugs on prolactin secretion, do not reliably identify patients with pituitary tumors. However, these and other tests of pituitary function are useful in assessing residual pituitary function. CT scanning will detect microadenomas as small as 3–5 mm in size. Bulging and demineralization of the sella turcica usually occur when the tumor exceeds 1 cm in diameter, and larger tumors are usually found in patients presenting with visual field defects.

Criteria for the selection of patients with tumors for surgical treatment or medical treatment with bromocriptine have not been firmly established and may be expected to change over the next few years. About 10–20% of women examined at autopsy show small pituitary adenomas. The natural history of the disorder is not well understood.

Although clomiphene or gonadotropins may induce ovulation in these patients, bromocriptine is more effective. Bromocriptine mesylate is an ergot alkaloid that acts by binding to the dopaminergic receptors in the pituitary, resulting in inhibition of PRL secretion. In 90% or more of these patients, treatment leads to the onset of menses in 3–5 weeks. The usual dose is 2.5 mg two or three times a day. Since there are side effects of nausea and mild dizziness, it is useful to start with a small dose, such as 2.5 mg daily—or half that amount given at bedtime in sensitive patients—and increase to 2.5 mg twice daily. PRL levels should be depressed to normal if treatment is adequate.

The long-term use of bromocriptine to induce regression of pituitary tumors is under study. Preliminary results indicate that at least in some patients tumors can be shown to regress. Even incomplete regression may be useful in patients whose tumors are too large to favor the transsphenoidal approach to the removal of the tumor. As noted above, the indications for surgery in patients with small tumors have not been established. Transsphenoidal tumor removal will restore normal gonadal function and normal PRL levels in the large majority of these patients. However, others have been followed for many years without evidence of tumor enlargement. In any case, patients must be followed carefully with PRL levels. Patients with tumors require radiologic reevaluation of the sella every 1–2 years. (See Chapter 2.)

DISORDERS OF ANDROGEN METABOLISM

Production & Metabolism of Androgens in Women

The major circulating androgens in women are testosterone, dihydrotestosterone, androstenedione, dehydroepiandrosterone (DHEA), and DHEA sulfate. The relative androgenic activity, serum concentrations, and sources of these androgens are summarized in Table 10–5. Testosterone is the principal circulating androgen in normal women. Both the ovaries and the adrenals normally secrete testosterone. Approximately 50% of the testosterone in serum, however, is derived from the peripheral conversion of steroid precursors, principally androstenedione and to a lesser extent DHEA. In many androgen-sensitive tissues, such as hair follicles, the enzyme 5α-reductase converts testosterone to dihydrotestosterone. It is believed that dihydrotestosterone per se (and not testosterone) is mainly responsible for stimulating hair growth in many areas of the body. Virtually all of the dihydrotestosterone in the circulation is formed in androgen-dependent peripheral tissues by 5α-reductase conversion of testosterone and androstenedione. Most of the dihydrotestosterone formed in these target tissues is metabolized further to androstanediols. Circulating androstenedione, in contrast to testosterone and dihy-

drotestosterone, is derived primarily from direct secretion by the ovaries and adrenals. Although androstenedione is a relatively weak androgen, possessing only 10–20% of the biologic activity of testosterone, it can be converted to testosterone and dihydrotestosterone in androgen-sensitive target tissues. Increased production and secretion of androstenedione thus may play a role in promoting the development of hirsutism in many women. DHEA is a very weak androgen with little biologic activity. DHEA sulfate has little or no androgenic activity. Most of the DHEA sulfate in the serum is derived from the adrenal glands. Measurement of serum DHEA sulfate is useful in assessing adrenal androgen production.

Androgen Metabolism in Skin and Hair Follicles: Factors that alter the activity of 5α-reductase can influence the androgenic activity of testosterone. In vitro studies utilizing skin biopsies from hair-bearing regions have demonstrated increased 5α-reductase activity in hirsute women; thus, many women presently thought to have idiopathic hirsutism may actually have increased formation of dihydrotestosterone in hair follicles. This mechanism also is suggested by the relatively high percentage of women with hirsutism and normal levels of testosterone who have been found to have increased serum levels of androstanediol glucuronide, a major metabolite of dihydrotestosterone. The factors responsible for the development of androgen-dependent hirsutism are summarized in Figure 10–15.

Amenorrhea With Androgen Excess

The presence of excessive amounts of circulating androgen is usually associated with oligomenorrhea or amenorrhea. Causes of androgen excess are shown in Table 10–6.

A. Polycystic Ovary Syndrome: Polycystic ovary (Stein-Leventhal) syndrome is a complex of varying symptoms ranging from amenorrhea to anovulatory bleeding often associated with obesity and hirsutism. The term has been used to describe such a variety of symptom complexes (Table 10–7) that it is almost a barrier to communication. In this

Table 10–5. Circulating androgens and their relative androgenic activity, serum concentration, and site of formation in women.

Hormone	Relative Androgenic Activity[1]	Serum Concentration[2]		Source of Circulating Hormone (Percentage of Total)		
		(ng/mL)	(nmol/L)	Adrenal	Ovary	Peripheral Conversion
Testosterone	100	0.2–0.7	(0.69–2.43)	5–25	5–25	50–70
Dihydrotestosterone	250	0.05–0.3	(0.17–1.03)	. . .	. . .	100
Androstenedione	10–20	0.5–2.5	(1.72–8.6)	30–45	45–60	10
DHEA	5	1.3–9.8	(4.5–34)	80	20	. . .
DHEA sulfate	Minimal	400–3200	(790–6318)	>95	<5	. . .

[1]Testosterone has been assigned a potency of 100. Values are approximate and may vary depending upon the biologic system in which the hormones are evaluated.
[2]Normal ranges will vary in different laboratories.

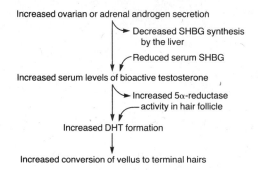

Figure 10–15. Development factors of androgen-dependent hirsutism.

Table 10–7. Incidence of various clinical findings in women with polycystic ovary syndrome. Data are derived from 187 references comprising a total of 1079 cases.[1]

	Incidence (%)	
	Mean	Range
Infertility	74	35–94
Hirsutism	69	17–83
Amenorrhea	51	15–77
Obesity	41	16–49
Functional bleeding	29	6–65
Dysmenorrhea	23	
Corpus luteum at surgery	22	0–71
Virilization	21	0–28
Biphasic basal body temperature	15	12–40
Cyclic menses	12	7–28

[1]Reproduced, with permission, from Goldzieher JW: Polycystic ovarian disease. In: *Progress in Infertility,* 2nd ed. Behrman SH, Kistner RW (editors). Little, Brown, 1975.

discussion, we are referring to patients who are anovulatory with continuous stimulation of the ovary by normal or disproportionately high levels of LH. The chronic stimulation leads to increased ovarian androgen secretion and characteristic morphologic changes in the ovaries. The ovaries are usually (not always) enlarged and may reach several times their normal size; one ovary may be significantly larger than the other. The ovaries typically appear glistening white because of a thickened capsule and show many small follicles in various stages of development and atresia at the surface. They also may appear normal. The theca cells are often hyperplastic and luteinized. The syndrome is also associated with changes in adrenal androgen production in some patients. Estrogen production in these patients is usually a result of the peripheral conversion of androgens to estrogens, predominantly androstenedione to estrone. Increased estrogen effects are secondary to either increased estrogen production or decreased levels of sex hormone-binding globulin. This can produce endometrial hyperplasia and eventually lead to adenocarcinoma of the endometrium, since the estrogen action is unopposed by progesterone. As a

Table 10–6. Causes of increased androgen production, hirsutism, or both.

Ovarian causes
  Polycystic ovary syndrome (LH-dependent androgen excess, hyperandrogenic chronic anovulation)
  Hyperthecosis
  Androgen-producing ovarian tumors
  Virilization of pregnancy (luteoma)
Adrenal causes
  Congenital or adult-onset adrenal hyperplasia
  Androgen-producing adrenal tumors
  Cushing's syndrome
Other
  Idiopathic or familial hirsutism
  Incomplete testicular feminization
  Postmenopausal state
  Iatrogenic (androgens, danazol, diazoxide, minoxidil, phenytoin)

group, patients with polycystic ovarian disease also may have increased secretion of insulin, an increased incidence of diabetes, and hypertension and a late menopause.

1. Etiology– The cause of this syndrome is unknown, and it is possible that there are several causes. Each of the functional changes that occur tends to maintain the cycle of functional abnormalities as shown in Figure 10–16. It has been suggested that in some patients this disorder may be initiated by excessive adrenal androgen production at the time of puberty or by a stress-induced increase in adrenal androgen secretion. The peripheral conversion of androgen to estrogen could facilitate the secretion of increased amounts of LH, leading to increased ovarian androgen production and impaired follicular maturation. In some patients, there is a strong family history, and the pattern of inheritance suggests that the trait is dominant and may be linked to the X chromosome. A group of patients have also been found in whom amenorrhea and androgen excess are associated with acanthosis nigricans and insulin resistance.

This syndrome could also result from central nervous system abnormalities, leading to inappropriate secretion of hypothalamic GnRH. This, in turn, could increase the secretion of LH and reduce the secretion of FSH. High levels of LH may promote excessive androgen production by the thecal layer. Since FSH levels also are low, granulosa cells may have a reduced capacity to convert these androgens to estrogens. High local levels of androstenedione and testosterone in the polycystic ovary may impede normal follicular growth and increase the rate of atresia, resulting in the formation of numerous small cystic follicles. Serum levels of estrone and free estradiol are elevated secondarily to increased peripheral aromatization of the ovarian androgens and reduced SHBG as noted above. The elevated levels of estrogen, in turn, may further sensitize the pituitary gland to hypothalamic GnRH, sustaining the abnormality.

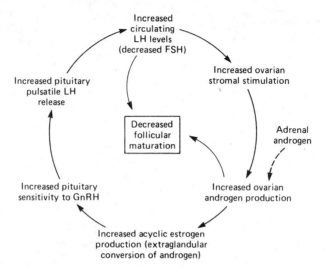

Figure 10–16. Pathophysiology of chronic anovulation in women with polycystic ovary syndrome. (Reproduced, with permission, from Yen SSC, Jaffe RB [editors]: *Reproductive Endocrinology.* Saunders, 1978.)

Although androgen production is quite variable, it seldom reaches the levels seen in the presence of androgen-producing ovarian tumors. As a result, the vast majority of women show hirsutism and increased activity of the sebaceous glands often associated with acne. Signs of more severe virilization, such as male pattern (bitemporal) balding, clitoral hypertrophy, and voice changes, are rare. In general, there is a good correlation between levels of free testosterone and clinical evidence of androgen excess.

2. Management– The major manifestations of polycystic ovary syndrome are hirsutism secondary to increased circulating levels of androgens or increased 5α-reductase activity (or both) in the hair follicles and failure of ovulation causing amenorrhea and infertility. The goals of therapy in the individual patient are of prime importance in determining the appropriate therapeutic program.

Induction of ovulation is required for anovulatory patients who wish to conceive. Most women ovulate in response to clomiphene citrate (see Ovulation Induction, below). In women whose ovaries fail to respond, combined therapy consisting of adrenal suppression and clomiphene may be more successful. The use of pulsatile GnRH to induce ovulation has generally not been effective. Wedge resection of the ovaries is rarely employed today.

In patients who have amenorrhea but do not wish to become pregnant, treatment may not be required. Some obese patients have been reported to resume ovulation and reduce androgen secretion on a program of weight reduction alone. In patients producing moderate to large amounts of estrogen continuously, endometrial hyperplasia with consequent bleeding and even endometrial carcinoma may develop. In such patients, the cyclic administration of a progestational agent may be required (see Anovulatory Bleeding, below). Hirsutism can be treated by suppression of ovarian androgen production or by antiandrogen therapy, as discussed in the Treatment of Hirsutism section, below.

B. Adult-onset Congenital Adrenal Hyperplasia: An infrequent cause of amenorrhea and hirsutism is adult-onset congenital adrenal hyperplasia. The incidence is 1–5% (about 5% in Hispanics, Ashkenazi Jews, and Yugoslavs, and highest in Alaskan Eskimos). These women most often have a reduction in P450c21 (21-hydroxylase) activity (see Chapter 11). This defect in cortisol synthesis leads to an increase in ACTH and 17-hydroxyprogesterone production. The latter is the basis for making the diagnosis (Figure 10–17). Levels of 17-hydroxyprogesterone below 300 ng/dL are normal, and levels of more than 800 ng/dL are considered to be diagnostic. When levels fall between these values, ACTH stimulation is required to make the diagnosis.

C. Other Causes of Androgen Excess: Excessive production of androgens is more commonly of ovarian than adrenal origin. The exact cause needs to be established to rule out androgen-producing adrenal and ovarian tumors, and Cushing's syndrome. Other causes of androgen excess are shown in Table 10–6. The general clinical approach to the evaluation of patients with excess androgen production is discussed above and summarized in Figure 10–17.

HIRSUTISM

Hair can be classified as either vellus or terminal. Vellus hairs are fine, soft, and nonpigmented. They are found over most of the body and predominate prior to puberty. They are often so fine that they are

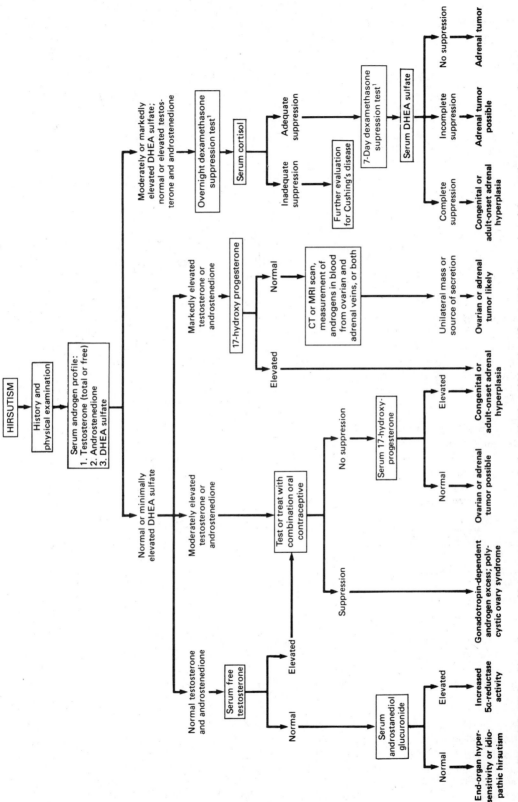

Figure 10–17. A guide to the use of hormone measurements in the evaluation of hirsutism. See text for discussion of dexamethasone suppression tests.

barely visible. Terminal hairs are coarse and pigmented. Before puberty, terminal hairs normally are found only on the scalp and eyebrows. Under the influence of increasing levels of androgen at puberty, vellus hairs are transformed into terminal hairs. In women, this conversion to terminal hairs involves principally the axillary and pubic regions and to a lesser extent the extremities. Under conditions of excessive androgen production or increased 5α-reductase activity (which increases conversion of testosterone to dihydrotestosterone), there is increased conversion of vellus to terminal hairs. Terminal hairs may thus develop in body regions where such hair growth is normally considered to be a male secondary sex characteristic. The presence of increasing numbers of terminal hairs on the face, chest, back, lower abdomen, and inner thighs is referred to as hirsutism. In many women, hirsutism in combination with increased circulating levels of androgen is accompanied by menstrual dysfunction (usually oligomenorrhea but sometimes amenorrhea). Rarely, abnormal androgen production increases to levels normally found only in men. In such instances, the high circulating levels of androgen also produce somatic changes referred to as virilization. These changes include frontal balding, deepening of the voice, breast atrophy, clitoral enlargement, increased muscle mass, and loss of normal female body contours.

Pathophysiology of Hirsutism

A. Increased Androgen Production: Studies in which women with mild to moderate hirsutism have been evaluated with sensitive and specific laboratory techniques have shown that most women with excessive hair growth have increased serum androgen levels (ie, increased concentrations of free testosterone) or increased 5α-reductase activity. Thus, fewer women are currently classified as having "idiopathic" hirsutism. The source (adrenal, ovarian, or both) of the increased production of androgens in women with mild to moderate hirsutism is sometimes difficult to establish. Many published reports support a combined adrenal-ovarian source for the increased serum levels of androgens, with the ovary as the major contributor in most instances. Approximately 1–5% of women with mild hirsutism and menstrual abnormalities have elevated serum levels of 17-hydroxyprogesterone and are thought to have increased androgen production secondary to adult-onset congenital adrenal hyperplasia.

B. Serum Binding Proteins and the Serum Transport of Androgens: As reviewed earlier (Table 10–2), circulating steroid hormones are bound, to varying degrees, to plasma proteins, eg., albumin and specific transport proteins. In normal women, approximately 65% of the circulating testosterone is tightly bound to SHBG, while most of the remaining hormone is loosely bound to albumin.

Only 1–2% of the total testosterone is free (not bound to protein). It is generally thought that testosterone bound to SHBG is not readily available to intracellular androgen receptors at target tissues and therefore has little biologic activity. Factors that can alter the serum concentration of SHBG are shown in Table 10–8. Hirsute women often have reduced serum concentrations of SHBG. Thus, a small increase in total testosterone, accompanied by a decrease in the concentration of SHBG, may result in a significant increase in biologically active hormone. The measurement of free, or non-SHBG bound, testosterone levels in serum is a more sensitive indicator of androgen activity. A greater proportion of women with mild to moderate hirsutism have elevated concentrations of free—as compared to total—plasma testosterone.

Evaluation of Women With Hirsutism

The common causes of increased androgen production and hirsutism are listed in Table 10–6. The initial assessment of hirsute women should include a thorough history and physical examination. Hirsutism is usually secondary to a mild increase in androgen activity. The increase in body hair occurs gradually and may be accompanied by other symptoms of mild androgen excess such as acne, oily skin, and oligomenorrhea or amenorrhea. The sudden appearance of rapid hair growth and amenorrhea associated with virilization, however, suggests an ovarian or adrenal androgen-producing tumor (see Chapter 6 and Table 10–4). The physical examination should detect signs of associated endocrine dysfunction, such as Cushing's syndrome or virilization. The degree and extent of growth of terminal hairs should be carefully recorded. This will help the physician decide if further endocrine investigation is warranted and help assess the effects of any future therapy. A pelvic examination also should be included in the initial evaluation of the patient, especially if she has oligomenorrhea or amenorrhea.

The laboratory evaluation of women with hirsutism is important for ruling out a serious underlying disease process such as an ovarian or adrenal an-

Table 10–8. Conditions affecting SHBG synthesis and therefore the percentage of plasma testosterone that is free.

Decreased SHBG synthesis
Hypothyroidism
Androgen therapy
Corticosteroid therapy
Obesity
Acromegaly
Increased SHBG synthesis
Hyperthyroidism
Pregnancy
Estrogen therapy
Cirrhosis

drogen-producing tumor, steroid enzymatic defect (eg, partial 21-hydroxylase deficiency), or Cushing's syndrome. Once therapy has been initiated, measurement of serum androgen levels also can be used to determine if androgen secretion has been reduced. Suppression of androgen production or action at the hair follicle will, in most women, reduce the extent of excessive hair growth.

A general approach to the hormonal evaluation of women with hirsutism is shown in Figure 10–17. The rate of ovarian and adrenal androgen secretion can be estimated initially by measuring the serum concentrations of testosterone (total or free), androstenedione, and DHEA sulfate. In many women with hirsutism, serum testosterone or androstenedione will be somewhat elevated. Patients with raised levels of these hormones and normal or minimally increased levels of DHEA sulfate can be evaluated further by administering a combination oral contraceptive to suppress pituitary LH and FSH secretion. If the excess production of androgen is gonadotropin-dependent and of ovarian origin (eg, as in polycystic ovary syndrome), serum androgen levels (especially free testosterone levels) also will be suppressed after a 1-month trial of oral contraceptives. Treatment may be continued in those women with LH-dependent androgen secretion. Failure of serum androgens to suppress indicates that the excessive production is either of adrenal origin (eg, a tumor or enzyme defect) or secondary to an ovarian neoplasm. Women with adult-onset adrenal hyperplasia secondary to a 21-hydroxylase deficiency will have elevated serum levels of 17-hydroxyprogesterone, which are readily suppressed by dexamethasone.

Women with initially normal serum levels of total testosterone and androstenedione can be evaluated further by measuring free testosterone. If free testosterone levels also are within normal limits, 5α-reductase activity in the hair follicles can be estimated by measuring serum levels of androstenediol glucuronide (measurement of serum androstenediol glucuronide is rarely justified for clinical management). Only a small percentage of hirsute women eventually will be found to have both normal androgen production and 5α-reductase activity. These women can be diagnosed as having idiopathic hirsutism.

Women with signs or symptoms of virilization generally will have greatly elevated testosterone levels (> 3 ng/mL [10.4 nmol/L]), androstenedione levels above 5 ng/mL (17.3 nmol/L), or both. These women are most likely to have an androgen-producing *ovarian* tumor if DHEA sulfate levels are normal or an androgen-producing *adrenal* tumor if DHEA sulfate levels are elevated. Rarely, an androgen-secreting adrenal tumor can be found in the presence of normal serum DHEA sulfate levels. Women with 21-hydroxylase deficiencies may also have normal or minimally elevated levels of DHEA sulfate. Further evaluation of women with virilization should include

suppression tests (dexamethasone for adrenal suppression and an oral contraceptive for ovarian suppression) as well as CT or MRI scans of the adrenals and ovaries. If the androgens are not suppressible, surgical exploration is required. A few patients have been found to have tumors with LH-dependent androgen secretion.

Moderately to markedly elevated serum levels of DHEA sulfate indicate increased adrenal androgen secretion resulting from excessive stimulation (eg, Cushing's disease) or indicate adrenal hyperplasia secondary to an enzyme defect, stress, or a tumor. In these cases, serum testosterone and androstenedione levels may vary from minimally to markedly elevated. Initially, women in this group should be evaluated by an overnight dexamethasone suppression test (1 mg of dexamethasone given at bedtime, and serum cortisol levels measured in the morning) to rule out Cushing's syndrome. Suppression of serum cortisol levels to less than 5 µg/dL (138 nmol/L) excludes this disorder. If suppression to this level is not achieved, further assessment of adrenal function, as described in Chapter 6, is required. An overnight dexamethasone suppression test, however, is inadequate to assess adrenal androgen production as reflected by levels of DHEA sulfate, since this hormone has a long plasma half-life. In women who have elevated levels of DHEA sulfate but in whom Cushing's syndrome has been excluded, dexamethasone (2 mg/d) given for 4–7 days will differentiate an adrenal tumor (no suppression) from other causes of increased adrenal androgen production.

Treatment of Hirsutism

Medical therapies directed at reducing the production of ovarian or adrenal androgens are effective primarily in reducing or preventing the formation of new hair growth. For the most part, such treatment has limited effect on terminal hairs previously formed, since the cycle of hair growth ordinarily occurs only every 6 months to 2 years. Consequently, an effective approach to the management of hirsutism usually consists of both medical and cosmetic treatment.

A. Suppression of Androgen Production: The reduction of serum levels of androgens by trials with combination oral contraceptives, progestins, or glucocorticoids should provide a rational basis for choosing one or another of these various forms of therapy. However, most women with hirsutism have only slightly increased androgen production, and its precise source or sources cannot be identified readily. In these patients, estrogen-containing oral contraceptives are generally more effective and are most often the initial form of treatment.

1. Oral contraceptives or progestins– Oral contraceptives containing both an estrogen and a progestin suppress the secretion of LH and FSH and reduce LH-dependent ovarian androgen production.

The progestin component also increases the metabolic clearance rate of testosterone, while the estrogen component stimulates the production of SHBG. Although treatment with a progestin alone (ie, oral or injectable medroxyprogesterone acetate) suppresses the secretion of LH and increases the metabolic clearance rate of androgens, there is no concomitant increase in SHBG levels. Progestins are therefore generally less effective than combination oral contraceptives. They may be useful when estrogens are contraindicated.

The available combination oral contraceptives are listed in Table 10–9. In selecting a particular contraceptive for the treatment of hirsutism, the physician should avoid compounds containing the more androgenic progestins, particularly norgestrel. Contraceptives containing a minimum of 35–50 µg of ethinyl estradiol may increase serum concentrations of SHBG and reduce the levels of both total and free testosterone in most patients. If significant clinical improvement—eg, a decrease in acne, skin oiliness, and rate of hair growth—is not apparent after 3 months of treatment, serum androgen levels should be reevaluated to make certain that adequate suppression of ovarian function has occurred. Treatment with oral contraceptives is discussed in a subsequent section of this chapter.

2. Glucocorticoids– If increased androgen production is predominantly or entirely of adrenal origin—such as occurs in adult-onset adrenal hyperplasia—treatment with glucocorticoids is indicated. In these cases, dexamethasone, 0.5–0.75 mg/d, or prednisone, 5–7.5 mg/d, has been used to reduce the production of adrenal androgens. In most women with hirsutism, however, excess androgen secretion is generally of ovarian origin, and glucocorticoids are not effective.

3. Gonadotropin-releasing hormone analogues– GnRH analogues are effective in the management of hirsutism due to excessive ovarian androgens. They inhibit pituitary FSH and LH secretion and thus decrease ovarian androgen production. Since ovarian estradiol production will also be reduced, treatment with GnRH analogues will produce symptoms and other changes of estrogen deficiency. These can be prevented by concurrent low-dose estrogen replacement. A nonandrogenic progestin such as medroxyprogesterone acetate should also be administered.

B. Antiandrogens: Cyproterone acetate was the first antiandrogen to be employed extensively for the treatment of hirsutism. Clinical studies with this drug in Europe have resulted in a high rate of improvement. Cyproterone acetate is a derivative of the progestin chlormadinone acetate and possesses both progestational and antiandrogenic activity. It suppresses the secretion of LH, with a subsequent decrease in ovarian androgen production, and blocks the binding of androgens to receptors in the hair follicles. Estro-

gen is usually administered concurrently, since endogenous estrogen production also is reduced during treatment. Although few serious side effects have been reported, cyproterone acetate is not available in the USA. A commonly used dosage is 2 mg of cyproterone acetate plus 50 µg of ethinyl estradiol daily on days 5–20 of each menstrual cycle.

Spironolactone, a competitive inhibitor of aldosterone, has been shown to possess antiandrogenic properties and competes with dihydrotestosterone for androgenic receptors in target tissues. It also decreases 17α-hydroxylase activity and thus reduces serum levels of testosterone and androstenedione. Doses ranging from 50 to 200 mg/d have been used to treat hirsutism. Spironolactone is especially useful for therapy in women in whom oral contraceptives are contraindicated or ineffective. Irregular uterine bleeding is a common side effect of treatment with spironolactone. Combined therapy consisting of spironolactone and an oral contraceptive may be employed when neither alone has been effective in reducing hair growth.

C. Cosmetic Therapy: The initial response to medical treatment is generally slow, and 3–6 months of therapy may be required before there is noticeable improvement in hirsutism. During the initial period of treatment, the patient can either continue with or start a simple and inexpensive method for the temporary removal of hair, eg, shaving or use of a depilatory or hot wax. After several months of medical treatment, the rate of formation of new terminal hairs will be reduced markedly, and permanent hair removal by electrolysis can be initiated, if desired. If permanent hair removal is tried prior to adequate medical treatment, the results will be transient, since new terminal hairs will continue to be formed.

ANOVULATORY BLEEDING

In the absence of ovulatory cycles, the pattern of bleeding (Table 10–3) is dependent upon the amount and timing of estrogen secretion, since the bleeding is due to estrogen stimulation of the endometrium. When estrogen secretion is low, there is usually no bleeding. However, the heaviest bleeding is observed in association with continuous secretion of substantial amounts of estrogen. In these instances, the estrogen produces proliferation of the endometrium, leading to hyperplasia or adenomatous hyperplasia. In some of these women, endometrial carcinoma will develop over long periods.

When the level of estrogen fluctuates, bleeding will occur during periods of reduced secretion. However, when the secretion is continuous and maturation is not synchronized by progesterone, the tissue is subject to spontaneous breakdown and bleeding of differing portions of the endometrium at different times. Furthermore, local factors such as the coiling

Table 10–9. Oral contraceptive agents in use. The estrogen-containing compounds are arranged in order of increasing content of estrogen (ethinyl estradiol and mestranol have similar potencies). The relative progestational potencies are shown in the last column.[1]

	Estrogen (mg)		Progestin (mg)		pp[2]
Monophasic combination tablets					
Loestrin 1/20	Ethinyl estradiol	0.02	Norethindrone acetate	1.0	4
Desogen	Ethinyl estradiol	0.03	Desogestrel	0.15	
Loestrin 1.5/30	Ethinyl estradiol	0.03	Norethindrone acetate	1.5	6
Lo/Ovral	Ethinyl estradiol	0.03	dl-Norgestrel	0.3	18
Nordette	Ethinyl estradiol	0.03	L-Norgestrel	0.15	18
Brevicon Modicon	Ethinyl estradiol	0.035	Norethindrone	0.5	1
Demulen 1/35	Ethinyl estradiol	0.035	Ethynodiol diacetate	1.0	30
Norinyl 1/35 Ortho-Novum 1/35	Ethinyl estradiol	0.035	Norethindrone	1.0	2
Ortho-Cyclen	Ethinyl estradiol	0.035	Norgestimate	0.25	
Ovcon 35	Ethinyl estradiol	0.035	Norethindrone	0.4	0.8
Demulen 1/50	Ethinyl estradiol	0.05	Ethynodiol diacetate	1.0	30
Norlestrin 1/50	Ethinyl estradiol	0.05	Norethindrone acetate	1.0	4
Norlestrin 2.5/50	Ethinyl estradiol	0.05	Norethindrone acetate	2.5	10
Ovcon 50	Ethinyl estradiol	0.05	Norethindrone	1.0	2
Ovral	Ethinyl estradiol	0.05	dl-Norgestrel	0.5	30
Norinyl 1/50 Ortho-Novum 1/50	Mestranol	0.05	Norethindrone	1.0	2
Enovid 5	Mestranol	0.075	Norethynodrel	5.0	11
Norinyl 1/80 Ortho-Novum 1/80	Mestranol	0.08	Norethindrone	1.0	2
Enovid E	Mestranol	0.1	Norethynodrel	2.5	6
Norinyl-2 Ortho-Novum-2	Mestranol	0.1	Norethindrone	2.0	4
Ovulen	Mestranol	0.1	Ethynodiol diacetate	1.0	30
Biphasic combination tablets					
Ortho-Novum 10/11					
Days 1–10	Ethinyl estradiol	0.035	Norethindrone	0.5	1
Days 11–21	Ethinyl estradiol	0.035	Norethindrone	1.0	2
Triphasic combination tablets					
Triphasil					
Days 1–6	Ethinyl estradiol	0.03	L-Norgestrel	0.05	2
Days 7–11	Ethinyl estradiol	0.04	L-Norgestrel	0.075	3
Days 12–21	Ethinyl estradiol	0.03	L-Norgestrol	0.125	5
Ortho-Novum 7/7/7					
Days 1–7	Ethinyl estradiol	0.035	Norethindrone	0.5	1
Days 8–14	Ethinyl estradiol	0.035	Norethindrone	0.75	1.5
Days 15–21	Ethinyl estradiol	0.035	Norethindrone	1.0	2
Ortho-Tri-Cyclen					
Days 1–7	Ethinyl estradiol	0.035	Norgestimate	0.18	
Days 8–14	Ethinyl estradiol	0.035	Norgestimate	0.215	
Days 15–21	Ethinyl estradiol	0.035	Norgestimate	0.25	
Tri-Norinyl					
Days 1–7	Ethinyl estradiol	0.035	Norethindrone	0.5	1
Days 8–16	Ethinyl estradiol	0.035	Norethindrone	1.0	2
Days 17–21	Ethinyl estradiol	0.035	Norethindrone	0.5	1
Daily progestin tablets					
Micronor	. . .		Norethindrone	0.35	0.7
Nor-QD	. . .		Norethindrone	0.35	0.7
Ovrette	. . .		dl-Norgestrel	0.075	3

[1] Modified and reproduced, with permission, from Katzung BG (editor): *Basic & Clinical Pharmacology,* 4th ed. Appleton & Lange, 1989.
[2] Progestational potency.

and contraction of the spiral vessels do not contribute to the hemostasis, and bleeding may be severe. Such bleeding is more common in postpubertal teenagers and in the premenopausal period in older women. It is also seen in some patients in association with polycystic ovary syndrome and in women receiving estrogen therapy.

OVULATION INDUCTION

CLOMIPHENE CITRATE

Clomiphene citrate is a partial agonist of estrogen that effectively inhibits the action of stronger estrogens and stimulates the secretion of gonadotropins; it is used for the treatment of anovulatory patients in whom ovulation is desired. In general, a single ovulation is induced by a single course of therapy, and the patient must be treated repeatedly until pregnancy is achieved. The compound is of no use in the treatment of ovarian or pituitary failure.

The recommended initial dose of clomiphene citrate is 50 mg/d for 5 days. If ovulation occurs, this same course may be repeated until pregnancy is achieved. If ovulation does not occur, the dose is doubled to 100 mg/d for 5 days. If ovulation and menses occur, the next course can be started on the fifth day of the cycle. About 80% of patients with anovulatory disorders or amenorrhea can be expected to respond to this treatment by having ovulatory cycles. Approximately half of these patients will become pregnant. In patients in whom pregnancy is achieved, the incidence of early abortion seems to be slightly increased, as is the occurrence of multiple pregnancy (10%). Although a variety of congenital defects have been described in the offspring of these pregnancies, the incidence does not appear to be greater than that of the general population. Ovulation can be induced in some of the patients not responding to 50 or 100 mg of clomiphene daily for 5 days by using larger doses (up to 200 mg/d) for longer periods or by injecting 5000 units of chorionic gonadotropin at the time of expected ovulation. The combination of clomiphene and bromocriptine has also been reported to be successful in some patients with normal PRL levels. Clomiphene has also been used in combination with menotropins to reduce the amount of the latter required to induce ovulation.

The effective use of clomiphene is associated with some stimulation of the ovaries and usually with ovarian enlargement. The degree of enlargement tends to be greater and its incidence higher in patients who have enlarged ovaries at the beginning of therapy.

The most common side effects in patients treated with this drug are hot flushes, which resemble those experienced by menopausal patients. These tend to be mild and disappear when the drug is discontinued. There have been occasional reports of visual disturbances consisting of intensification and prolongation of afterimages. These are generally of short duration. Headache, constipation, allergic skin reactions, and reversible hair loss have been reported occasionally.

HUMAN MENOPAUSAL GONADOTROPINS (Menotropins)

Human menopausal gonadotropins, or menotropins, in conjunction with chorionic gonadotropin, are used to stimulate ovulation in anovulatory patients who have potentially functional ovarian tissue. Patients with ovarian failure should not be considered for therapy. Menotropins are generally used only after less complicated therapies, such as clomiphene citrate or bromocriptine, have been unsuccessful. Since therapy is difficult and expensive, it is also important to exclude other factors that might preclude pregnancy (eg, obstruction of the uterine tubes or abnormalities in sperm production by the husband) prior to initiating treatment. The possibility of multiple births must be acceptable to the patient. This treatment has induced ovulation in patients with hypopituitarism and other defects of gonadotropin secretion and in patients with amenorrhea or anovulatory cycles in whom ovulatory disturbances are associated with galactorrhea or hirsutism. In patients undergoing in vitro fertilization, menotropins are used to stimulate the development of multiple large follicles to increase the number of available ova.

Contraindications & Cautions

The most common problem encountered is excessive ovarian stimulation. Ovarian enlargement is common. When marked, as in the ovarian hyperstimulation syndrome, it may be accompanied by pain, ascites, and pleural effusion. A few patients experience fever and swelling along with discomfort at the injection site. Undesirable results of therapy include a high incidence of multiple pregnancy and abortion. The frequency of birth defects has not been increased in the offspring of patients who have succeeded in carrying their pregnancies to term.

The typical outcome of therapy in properly selected patients treated by experienced physicians is shown in Table 10–10. Menotropins are potentially dangerous and should be administered by physicians with experience in endocrine disturbances and problems of reproductive function. This mode of therapy is complicated, time-consuming, and expensive and

Table 10–10. Results of treatment with menotropins.

Pregnancy achieved: 25–40%
Multiple births
Twins, 10–20%
Triplets, etc, 5–10%
Abortions, 20%
Hyperstimulation syndrome: 0.5–1.5%

should not be undertaken unless simpler therapeutic measures have failed.

Dosages

Human menopausal gonadotropins (menotropins, Pergonal) are supplied in lyophilized form in ampules containing 75 units each of FSH and LH and 10 mg of lactose. The usual dosage is one or more ampules intramuscularly daily until estrogen production is optimal—ie, plasma levels of 600–1000 pg/mL (2.2–3.7 nmol/L). Growth of ovarian follicles should also be monitored by ultrasonography to assist in determining the optimal dosage and duration of treatment. Chorionic gonadotropin (see Chapter 13) in doses of 5000–10,000 units intramuscularly is then administered once to induce ovulation from the mature follicle and then several times after ovulation to support corpus luteum function. If estrogen production becomes excessive during the preovulatory treatment phase, chorionic gonadotropin should be withheld to avoid the ovarian hyperstimulation syndrome. Patients must be examined frequently (daily or on alternate days) for 2 weeks following the last injection to detect signs of overstimulation and should be advised to have intercourse at least every other day near the time of expected ovulation.

GONADOTROPIN-RELEASING HORMONE

The pulsatile administration of GnRH in doses of 1–10 μg per pulse at 60- to 120-minute intervals will induce ovulation in most patients with amenorrhea due to hypothalamic dysfunction associated with decreased secretion of endogenous GnRH. GnRH can be given intravenously or subcutaneously using a peristaltic pump. Although the method is somewhat cumbersome, less frequent monitoring of the patient is required and ovarian hyperstimulation is less likely to occur.

BROMOCRIPTINE

Although bromocriptine is occasionally effective in treating patients with amenorrhea in the absence of elevated serum levels of PRL, its use is generally reserved for patients with hyperprolactinemia or galactorrhea. Its use in such patients is described elsewhere in this chapter.

THERAPEUTIC USE OF OVARIAN HORMONES & THEIR SYNTHETIC ANALOGUES

Estrogens are used in combination with progestins by more than 40 million women for contraception and are widely used after the menopause. Estrogens are also used to limit the height of tall girls and to replace absent or deficient endogenous hormone in patients with hypogonadism or after gonadectomy. It is therefore important to understand the effects of these agents and problems engendered by their use.

TREATMENT OF PRIMARY HYPOGONADISM

Treatment of primary hypogonadism is usually begun at 11–13 years of age in order to stimulate the development of secondary sex characteristics and menses and to promote optimal growth. Treatment consists mainly of the administration of estrogens and progestins. Androgens and anabolic agents have also been used in these patients to stimulate growth, but no further increase in final height was achieved. Furthermore, acne, hirsutism, clitoromegaly, and premature closure of the epiphyses have occurred as unwanted effects of androgens and anabolic agents. Progestins are advisable in conjunction with estrogens, because long-term replacement therapy, even when used cyclically in modest doses, has been associated with an increase in the incidence of endometrial hyperplasia and endometrial carcinoma. Oral contraceptives have also been used for replacement therapy.

OVARIAN SUPPRESSION

Estrogen-progestin combinations (oral contraceptives) are used to suppress ovarian function in patients with LH-dependent excess androgen production or endometriosis and are discussed elsewhere in this chapter.

Progestational hormones alone are used to produce long-term ovarian suppression when estrogens are contraindicated. When used parenterally in large doses—eg, medroxyprogesterone acetate, 150 mg intramuscularly every 90 days—prolonged anovulation and amenorrhea are produced. This procedure has been employed in the treatment of dysmenorrhea, endometriosis, hirsutism, and bleeding disorders. The major problem encountered with this regimen is the prolonged time required for ovulatory function to return after cessation of therapy in some patients. Irregular spotting also occurs. This treatment should not be used for patients planning a pregnancy in the near future.

THREATENED ABORTION

Progestins do not appear to have any place in the therapy of threatened or habitual abortion. Early reports of the usefulness of these agents were based on the unwarranted assumption that after several abortions the likelihood of repeated abortions was over 90%. When progestational agents were administered to patients with previous abortions, a salvage rate of 80% was achieved. It is now recognized that similar patients abort only 20% of the time even when untreated.

In some patients with "threatened" abortion, progesterone production is decreased. It is likely that the decrease in progesterone reflects damage to the placenta or fetus and is a result of events leading to abortion rather than a cause of the abortion. Administration of progesterone in these circumstances, especially in the presence of declining serum levels of hCG, does not appear to be useful and may allow retention of the dead fetus, thus delaying recognition of an abortion that has occurred. Prolonged postpartum bleeding has also been reported in some patients treated with repository medroxyprogesterone or hydroxyprogesterone caproate.

INADEQUATE LUTEAL PHASE

Progesterone and medroxyprogesterone have been used in the treatment of women who have difficulty in conceiving and who demonstrate a slow rise in basal body temperature. Some investigators believe that these patients suffer from a relative luteal insufficiency, and progesterone or related compounds are given to replace the deficiency. There is no convincing evidence that this treatment is effective. In the absence of satisfactory controls, the successes reported are impossible to distinguish from placebo effects.

DIAGNOSTIC USES

Progesterone is also used as a test of estrogen secretion. A single intramuscular injection of 200 mg of progesterone in oil or a course of medroxyprogesterone, 10 mg/d for 5–7 days, is followed by withdrawal bleeding in amenorrheic patients only when the endometrium has been stimulated by estrogens. In the absence of withdrawal bleeding, a combination of estrogen and progestin can be given to test the responsiveness of the endometrium in patients with amenorrhea.

INHIBITORS OF OVARIAN FUNCTION

GONADOTROPIN-RELEASING HORMONE ANALOGUES

As noted above, GnRH administered in a pulsatile manner will induce ovulation in patients with amenorrhea. However, when large amounts are administered continuously, inhibition of gonadotropin release occurs. This property has been exploited by the development of highly potent agonist analogues, such as leuprolide, buserelin, and nafarelin. These analogues can be administered subcutaneously or intranasally. In sufficient doses, they can inhibit ovarian function, both reducing the secretion of sex steroids and inhibiting ovulation. GnRH analogues have been used to treat patients with sex hormone-dependent disorders such as precocious puberty, endometriosis, uterine fibroids, and hirsutism secondary to excess ovarian androgen production.

TAMOXIFEN

Tamoxifen, a partial estrogen agonist, is a nonsteroidal competitive inhibitor of estradiol at its receptor. It can be given orally and is being used in the palliative treatment of advanced breast cancer in postmenopausal women (see Chapter 19). Peak plasma levels are reached in a few hours. It has an initial half-life of 7–14 hours in the circulation and is predominantly excreted by the liver. It is dispensed as the citrate in the form of tablets containing the equivalent of 10 mg of tamoxifen. It is used in doses of 10–20 mg twice daily. Hot flushes and nausea and vomiting occur in 25% of patients, and many other adverse effects have been reported.

Studies of patients given tamoxiphen as adjuvant therapy for early breast cancer have shown a 35% decrease in contralateral breast cancer. Prevention of the expected loss of lumbar spine bone density and plasma lipid changes consistent with a reduction in the risk for atherosclerosis have also been reported in these patients following spontaneous or surgical menopause.

DANAZOL

Danazol, an isoxazole derivative of ethisterone (17α-ethinyl testosterone) with weak progestational and androgenic activities, is used to suppress ovarian function. It inhibits the midcycle surge of LH and FSH and can prevent the compensatory increase in LH and FSH following castration in animals, but it does not significantly lower or suppress basal LH or FSH levels in healthy humans. Danazol binds to androgen, progesterone, and glucocorticoid receptors and can initiate androgen-specific RNA synthesis. It does not bind to intracellular estrogen receptors, but it does compete with steroids for binding to sex hormone-binding globulin (SHBG) and corticosteroid-binding globulins (CBG). It inhibits P450scc (the cholesterol side chain-cleaving enzyme), 3β-HSD (3β-hydroxysteroid dehydrogenase), P450c17 (17,20-lyase; 17α-hydroxylase), P450c11 (11β-hydroxylase), and P450c21 (21-hydroxylase), but it does not inhibit aromatase. It increases the mean clearance rate of progesterone, probably by competing with the hormone for binding proteins, and may have similar effects on other active steroid hormones. Ethisterone, a major metabolite, has both progestational and mild androgenic effects.

Danazol has been employed as an inhibitor of gonadal function and has found its major use in the treatment of endometriosis. For this purpose, it can be given in a dose of 600 mg/d. The dose is reduced to 400 mg/d after 1 month and to 200 mg/d in 2 months. About 85% of patients show marked improvement in 3–12 months.

The major side effects are weight gain, edema, decreased breast size, acne and oily skin, mild hirsutism, deepening of the voice, headache, hot flushes, changes in libido, and muscle cramps. Although these side effects do not present any health risks, many women discontinue treatment because of them.

Danazol should be used with great caution in patients with hepatic dysfunction, since it has been reported to produce mild to moderate hepatocellular damage in some patients, as evidenced by enzyme changes. Danazol treatment also markedly decreases the HDL:LDL ratio in most women. It is contraindicated during pregnancy and breast-feeding, as it can produce urogenital abnormalities in the offspring.

ANTIPROGESTINS

Mifepristone (17β-hydroxy-11β[4-dimethylaminophenyl]-17α[1-propynyl]estra-4,9-dien-3-one; RU 486), a 19 norsteroid, binds strongly to the progesterone receptor (in addition to binding to the glucocorticoid receptor) and inhibits the binding and activity of progesterone. Preliminary studies indicate that it has luteolytic properties in many women when given in the midluteal period and may be useful as a contraceptive. The mechanism of this effect is unknown. However, its long half-life and large dose requirement may prolong the follicular phase of the subsequent cycle and make it difficult to use for this purpose. This drug has been used for the termination of early pregnancy. The combination of a single oral dose of 600 mg of mifepristone and a vaginal pessary con-

taining 1 mg of prostaglandin E_1 or oral misoprostol has been found to effectively terminate pregnancy in 95% of patients when administered during the first 7 weeks after conception. The side effects of the medications included vomiting, diarrhea, and abdominal pain. However, the major side effect was prolonged bleeding that did not require treatment. As many as 5% of patients have vaginal bleeding requiring intervention with dilation and curettage.

Preliminary studies have found that epostane, a 3β-hydroxysteroid dehydrogenase inhibitor, decreases the synthesis of progesterone and can terminate early pregnancy.

ANTIANDROGENS

The possibility of using antiandrogens to treat hirsutism and other disorders due to excessive amounts of testosterone has led to a search for effective drugs via two approaches that have met with limited success experimentally. Several compounds have been developed that inhibit the 17-hydroxylation of progesterone or pregnenolone, thereby preventing the action of the side chain-splitting enzyme and the further transformation of these steroid precursors to active androgens. A few of these compounds have been tested clinically but have been too toxic for prolonged use. Another approach has been the development of steroids that are chemically similar and act as competitive inhibitors. A few of them have been tried in patients on a limited basis.

Cyproterone and **cyproterone acetate** are effective antiandrogens that inhibit the action of the androgens at the target organ. The acetate form has a marked progestational effect that suppresses LH and FSH, thus leading to a more effective antiandrogen effect. These compounds have been used to decrease excessive sexual drive in disturbed individuals and are being studied in other conditions in which reduction of androgenic effects would be useful. In Europe, they are used in the treatment of hirsutism (see above). They are not available in the USA.

Ketoconazole, an imidazole derivative used for the treatment of fungal disease, is a potent inhibitor of adrenal and gonadal steroid synthesis. This compound inhibits P450scc (cholesterol side chain cleavage enzyme), P450c17 (17α-hydroxylase and 17,20-lyase), 3β-hydroxysteroid dehydrogenase, and P450c11 (11β-hydroxylase) enzymes. The sensitivity of the P450 enzymes to this compound in mammalian tissues is much lower than that of the fungal enzymes, so that the inhibitory effects are seen only at high doses. Ketoconazole also has other endocrine effects. It displaces estradiol and dihydrotestosterone from SHBG in vitro and increases the estradiol-testosterone ratio in plasma in vivo by a different mechanism. The latter effect may be responsible for the gynecomastia that occurs in men with ketoconazole therapy. This compound has been used with some success for the treatment of Cushing's syndrome. However, it does not appear to be clinically useful in women with increased androgens because of the toxicity associated with prolonged use of the 400–800 mg/d required.

MENOPAUSE

Menopause begins with the last episode of menstrual bleeding induced by the cyclic endogenous secretion of ovarian hormones. It normally occurs between the ages of 42 and 60 years. It occurs prematurely as a result of surgical removal, irradiation, or abnormalities of the ovaries.

HORMONAL CHANGES

The changes in endocrine function are not abrupt in women undergoing spontaneous menopause. The circulating levels of gonadotropins begin to increase several years before ovulation ceases. Production of estrogen and progesterone decreases, and irregular cycles and anovulatory bleeding are not uncommon (Table 10–11). The increase in FSH is greater than that of LH and reflects the lack of feedback inhibition by estrogen or inhibin, or both. The stromal cells of the ovary respond to increased LH stimulation by producing more androstenedione but only tiny amounts of estrogen.

The average production rate of estradiol falls to 12 μg/24 h (44 nmol/24 h), and the clearance rate is reduced. Since very little estradiol is found in ovarian or adrenal veins, most of the circulating estradiol is derived from estrone, which in itself is produced by the peripheral conversion of androstenedione. The average production rate for estrone is 55 μg/24 h

(202 nmol/24 h), and there is a 20% reduction in its clearance.

Progesterone levels are approximately 30% of the concentration seen in young women during the follicular phase. The source of this progesterone appears to be the adrenal.

Androgen levels are also reduced postmenopausally. Androstenedione falls to about half of the concentration found in young women, and most of that apparently comes from the adrenal, as suggested by its peak concentrations at 8 AM and nadir concentrations at 3–4 PM. The clearance rate does not change. The average production rate is about 1.5 mg/24 h (5200 nmol/24 h). About 20% of it is thought to come from the ovary. Testosterone production rates are approximately 150 μg/24 h (520 nmol/24 h), as compared to about 200 μg/24 h (693 nmol/24 h) in younger women. This fall is less than that seen after ovariectomy, indicating that testosterone is produced by conversion of androstenedione as well as being secreted by the adrenal and ovary. It is of interest that DHEA and DHEA sulfate also fall with age, although almost all of these steroids come from the adrenal gland.

CLINICAL MANIFESTATIONS OF MENOPAUSE

1. EARLY MANIFESTATIONS

Menstrual Changes

The interval prior to the menopause is usually characterized sequentially by cycles with a shortening of the follicular phase, an interval of very irregular cycles, and an interval of anovulatory bleeding. Fertility is usually very low during this time. Although menses may cease abruptly, usually there is a gradual diminution in the amount of menstrual flow as well as its duration. However, if secretion of estrogen is prolonged in the absence of ovulation, endometrial hyperplasia may occur and cause heavy bleeding. It is sometimes difficult to clinically distinguish this type of bleeding from that produced by or-

Table 10–11. Serum concentrations (mean ± SEM) of steroids in premenopausal and postmenopausal women.[1]

Steroid	Premenopausal[2]		Postmenopausal	
	(ng/mL)	(nmol/L)	(ng/mL)	(nmol/L)
Progesterone	0.47 ± 0.03	(1.49 ± 0.1)	0.17 ± 0.02	(0.54 ± 0.06)
DHEA	4.2 ± 0.5	(14.5 ± 1.7)	1.8 ± 0.2	(6.2 ± 0.69)
DHEA sulfate	1600 ± 350	(3159 ± 691)	300 ± 70	(592 ± 138)
Androstenedione	1.5 ± 0.1	(5.2 ± 0.35)	0.6 ± 0.01	(2.08 ± 0.03)
Testosterone	0.32 ± 0.02	(1.11 ± 0.07)	0.25 ± 0.03	(0.87 ± 0.1)
Estrone	0.08 ± 0.01	(0.29 ± 0.04)	0.029 ± 0.002	(0.11 ± 0.01)
Estradiol	0.05 ± 0.005	(0.18 ± 0.02)	0.013 ± 0.001	(0.05 ± 0.004)

[1]Reproduced, with permission, from Pernoll ML, Benson RC (editor): *Current Obstetric & Gynecologic Diagnosis & Treatment*, 6th ed. Appleton & Lange, 1987.
[2]Follicular phase concentrations.

ganic diseases, including endometrial carcinoma. Any bleeding that occurs more than a year after the last previous period is likely to be an indication of organic disease.

Vasomotor Symptoms

The most common menopausal complaint is hot flushes, which occur in 75% of women at the menopause. They are due to declining estrogen levels. Women with estrogen deficiency from childhood do not develop hot flushes unless they have been treated with exogenous estrogens and treatment is interrupted. Episodes of flushing are associated with periodic increases in core temperature, causing reflex peripheral vasodilatation, a small increase in pulse rate, and sweating. They are synchronous with the pulsatile release of LH but are not caused by increased secretion of gonadotropins. Rather, they appear to be linked to the central mechanism controlling the release of GnRH. These symptoms occur most frequently in a warm environment and are common at night, contributing to insomnia.

The hot flush often starts with a sensation of pressure in the head, followed by a feeling of warmth in the head and neck and upper thorax. It may be associated with palpitations and gradually spreading waves of heat over the entire body. The feeling of warmth and flushing is quickly followed by sweating. The sweating and vasodilatation lead to heat loss and a decrease in core temperature of approximately 0.2 °C. These episodes last 10–20 minutes.

In 20% of patients, hot flushes are a transient phenomenon lasting for less than 1 year, but 25–50% of women experience them for more than 5 years. Estrogen therapy is remarkably effective in controlling hot flushes in over 90% of patients.

Atrophic Changes in the Genitourinary System

The decline in estrogen production results in reduction in mucus secretion and gradual atrophy of the vaginal and urethral epithelium. The rugae progressively disappear with thinning of the epithelium. The surface may appear vascular at first but then becomes pale. These changes lead to itching, dyspareunia, and burning. Similar changes in the urinary tract may give rise to atrophic cystitis, with symptoms of urgency, incontinence, and frequency. The cervix decreases in size, and the mucus secretion diminishes. The endometrium and myometrium also undergo atrophy. Myomas become smaller and endometriosis less symptomatic. The adverse symptoms can be treated by administration of estrogens locally as well as systemically (see below).

Skin & Hair Changes

At the time of the menopause, changes in the skin due to aging are noticeable. There is some thinning and wrinkling. Although estrogen creams are widely used cosmetically, it is not clear that they have any effects other than enhancement of the dermal water content. Changes in hair include loss of some underarm and pubic hair and occasionally replacement of vellus hair on the chin and upper lip by terminal hairs.

Emotional Changes

Anxiety, depression, and irritability are commonly reported around the time of the menopause. There is no good evidence that these symptoms are directly related to estrogen deficiency. However, sleep disturbances caused by hot flushes may contribute to the irritability. The majority of women treated with estrogens report some improvement in their sense of well-being and relief of insomnia and other symptoms produced by estrogen deficiency.

2. LATER MANIFESTATIONS

In addition to the signs and symptoms that follow closely upon the cessation of normal ovarian function, there are changes which over many years influence the health and well-being of postmenopausal women. These include an acceleration of bone loss, which in susceptible women may lead to vertebral, hip, and wrist fractures, and lipid changes that may contribute to the acceleration of cardiovascular disease noted in postmenopausal women. The effects of estrogens on bone have been extensively studied, and the effects of hormone withdrawal and replacement are well characterized. However, the roles of estrogen and progestins in the cause and prevention of cardiovascular disease, which is responsible for 350,000 deaths per year, and breast cancer, which causes 35,000 deaths per year, are less well understood.

Osteoporosis

Osteoporosis results from a combination of increased bone resorption and decreased bone formation. In its early stages, it is predominantly a disease of trabecular bone. Affected patients show increased calcium loss from bone. The problem is enhanced in winter months because of decreased activity and decreased exposure to sunlight and by the difficulty of maintaining calcium balance at normal levels of intake (see Chapters 5 and 22).

During the first few years following menopause, women lose an average of about 1% of their metacarpal cortical bone mass per year (Figure 10–18). The initial rapid bone loss is inhibited by estrogen. Loss of bone mass leads to reduced skeletal strength and susceptibility to fractures. There is, for example, a tenfold increase in the incidence of Colles' fractures in women between the ages of 35 and 55, although a similar increase is not seen in men (Figure 10–19). Hip fractures, which are ultimately

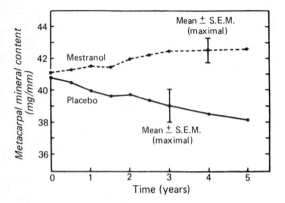

Figure 10–18. Metacarpal mineral content in post-menopausal women treated with mestranol or placebo for 5 years. Note loss of bone density in placebo but not mestranol treatment group. (Reproduced, with permission, from Lindsay R et al: Long-term prevention of post-menopausal osteoporosis by oestrogen. Lancet 1976;1: 1038.)

fatal in about one-third of patients and disable others for life, also occur more frequently.

Studies indicate that bone density decreases in women as the years advance. However, the loss is accelerated at menopause. Other studies indicate that estrogen therapy started at that time can prevent the loss (Figure 10–18). If estrogens are administered subsequently, the process can be arrested. However, when treatment is delayed for 5–6 years, less effect is noted. Treatment with estrogen decreases plasma Ca^{2+} and increases plasma PTH and $1,25(OH)_2D_3$, which, in turn, increases calcium absorption. The risk for osteoporosis is highest in smokers who are thin, Caucasian, inactive, and have a low calcium intake and a strong family history of osteoporosis. (See Chapters 5 and 22.)

Cardiovascular Disease

When normal ovulatory function ceases and the estrogen levels fall after the menopause or oophorectomy, there is an accelerated rise in cholesterol, and LDL and LDL receptors decline. HDL are not much affected, and levels remain higher than in men. VLDL and triglyceride levels are not much different. Since cardiovascular disorders account for most deaths in this age group, the risk for these disorders constitutes a major consideration in deciding whether or not hormonal therapy is indicated and influences the selection of hormones to be administered. The effects of estrogen replacement therapy on circulating lipids and lipoproteins is shown in Figure 10–20. These changes are associated with a reduction in myocardial infarction by about 50% and fatal strokes by as much as 40%. Progestins antagonize the effects on LDL and HDL to a variable extent.

MANAGEMENT OF MENOPAUSE

Optimal management requires careful assessment of the patient's symptoms as well as consideration of her age; the risk for cardiovascular disease, osteoporosis, and breast and endometrial cancer; and knowledge of the effects of the gonadal hormones on each of these disorders. The goals of therapy can then be defined and the risks of therapy assessed and discussed with the patient.

Hormonal Therapy

If the main indication for therapy is hot flushes, therapy with the lowest dose of estrogen required for symptomatic relief is recommended. Treatment may only be required for a limited period of time and the possible increased risk for breast cancer thus avoided. In women who have had hysterectomies, estrogens alone can be given 5 days a week or every

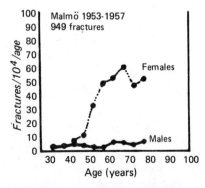

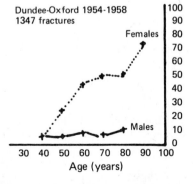

Figure 10–19. Indices of Colles' fracture in relation to age in Malmö and Dundee-Oxford. (Reproduced, with permission, from Cope E: Physical changes associated with post-menopausal years. Page 4 in: Management of the Menopause and Post-Menopause Years. Campbell S [editor]. MTP Press Ltd, 1976.)

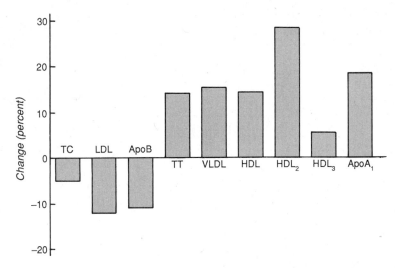

Figure 10–20. Percentage changes in lipids and lipoproteins with the use of oral estrogen (equivalent to 0.625 mg for at least 3 months). (TC, total cholesterol; TT, total triglycerides.) (Redrawn and reproduced, with permission, from Lobo RA: Effects of hormonal replacement on lipids and lipoproteins in postmenopausal women. J Clin Endocrinol Metab 1991;79:925.)

day, since progestins are not required to reduce the risk for endometrial hyperplasia and cancer. In women who have not undergone hysterectomy, estrogen therapy should be given for the first 25 days of each month and a progestational agent administered during the last 10–14 days of estrogen administration. The recommended daily dosage of estrogen is 0.3-1.25 mg of conjugated estrogens or 0.01–0.02 mg of ethinyl estradiol. Doses in the middle of these ranges have been shown to be maximally effective in preventing the decrease in bone density occurring at the menopause. In order to prevent osteoporosis, it is important to begin therapy as soon as possible after the menopause. Studies indicate that addition of 10 mg medroxyprogesterone acetate orally daily for the last 10–14 days of estrogen therapy markedly reduces the risk of endometrial carcinoma.

On this regimen, some women will experience a return of symptoms during the period off estrogen therapy. In these patients, the estrogen can be given every day. If the progestin produces sedation or other undesirable effects, the dose can be reduced to 2.5–5 mg for the last 10 days of the cycle, with a slight increase in the risk for endometrial hyperplasia. These regimens are usually accompanied by bleeding at the end of each cycle.

Women who object to the cyclic bleeding associated with sequential therapy can consider uninterrupted therapy. Therapy with 0.625 mg of conjugated estrogens and 2.5–5 mg of medroxyprogesterone will eliminate cyclic bleeding, control vasomotor symptoms, prevent genital atrophy, maintain bone density, and show a favorable lipid profile with a small decrease in LDL and an increase in HDL. Short-term studies indicate that these women have endometrial

atrophy on biopsy. About half of them experience breakthrough bleeding during the first few months of therapy. After the first 4 months, 70–80% become amenorrheic, and most remain so. The main disadvantage of uninterrupted therapy is the need for uterine biopsy when bleeding occurs after the first few months.

The above combination of hormones can also be given 5 days a week, withholding medication on the weekends. This regimen controls bleeding about as well as daily therapy and results in an increase in HDL with little change in LDL.

Patients at low risk for development of osteoporosis with only mild atrophic vaginitis can be treated with local vaginal preparations. This route of application is also useful in treatment of urinary tract symptoms. It is important to realize, however, that locally administered estrogens are almost completely absorbed into the circulation and should be used intermittently or with a progestin.

Although the estrogens share most, if not all, of their hormonal effects, their relative potencies vary depending on the agent and the route of administration. As noted above, estradiol is the most active endogenous estrogen and has the highest affinity for the estrogen receptor. However, its metabolites estrone and estriol have weak uterotropic effects. 2-Hydroxyestrone, another important metabolite, possesses neurotransmitter activity in the brain. It also competes with catecholamines for catechol-O-methyltransferase and inhibits tyrosine hydroxylase. For a given level of gonadotropin suppression, oral compounds have a greater effect on the circulating levels of corticosteroid and sex hormone-binding proteins. This effect, which is thought to be due to larger concentrations of hormone reaching the liver by this route, has led to the development of transdermal preparations. When administered transdermally, 50–100 µg of estradiol had effects similar to those of 0.625–1.25 mg conjugated oral estrogens on gonadotropin levels, endometrium, and vaginal epithelium. However, only the oral estrogen increased levels of renin substrate, CBG, and TBG and had favorable effects on high- and low-density lipoprotein levels.

In patients in whom estrogen replacement therapy is contraindicated (eg, those with estrogen-sensitive tumors), relief of vasomotor symptoms may be obtained by the use of progestational agents. Medroxyprogesterone acetate, 150 mg intramuscularly once a month, norgestrel, 250 µg orally daily, or medroxyprogesterone, 10 mg orally daily, can be useful. Mild tranquilizers and clonidine are also effective in some patients, as are atropine-barbiturate mixtures. Calcium carbonate supplements (eg, Os-Cal) are useful in bringing the total daily calcium intake up to 1500 mg. Vitamin D therapy may be useful when calcium intake is less than optimal. Preliminary studies show that fluoride in adequate amounts can increase bone density but that it may not reduce the rate of fracture (see Chapter 5).

Adverse Effects of Therapy

Nausea and breast tenderness are common and can be minimized by using the smallest effective dose. These symptoms may be more marked at the beginning of therapy. The presence of cystic mastitis or fibroids that increase in size during treatment may also interfere with the use of estrogen. Hyperpigmentation also occurs. Estrogen therapy is associated with an increase in frequency of hypertension and gallbladder disease. Some women experience migraine headaches during the last few days of the cycle. The use of a continuous estrogen regimen will often prevent their occurrence.

The relationship of hormonal therapy to cancer in postmenopausal women continues to be the subject of active investigation. The risk of endometrial carcinoma is increased in patients taking estrogens without adjunct progestins and varies with the dose and duration of treatment. It increases 15 times in patients taking large doses of estrogen for 5 or more years but only two to four times in patients receiving lower doses for 2 years. The concomitant use of a progestin not only prevents this increased risk but actually reduces the incidence of endometrial cancer below that in the general population.

Although short-term estrogen therapy has not been shown to increase the incidence of breast cancer, a small increase in the incidence of this tumor may occur with prolonged therapy. Although the increased risk factor is small (1.25), the impact is great since this tumor occurs in 10% of women. The effect of progesterone has not been determined as yet. As noted above, studies indicate that following unilateral excision of breast cancer, women receiving tamoxifen show a 35% decrease in contralateral breast cancer compared with controls. These studies also demonstrate that tamoxifen is well tolerated by most patients, produce estrogen-like alterations in plasma lipid levels, and stabilize bone mineral loss. Studies bearing on the possible use of tamoxiphen in postmenopausal women at high risk for breast cancer are under way.

HORMONAL CONTRACEPTION
(Oral Contraceptives)

A large number of oral contraceptives containing estrogens or progestins (or both) are now available for clinical use (Table 10–9). These preparations vary in chemical composition and, as might be expected, have many properties in common, but there are also differences. Two types of preparations are used for oral contraception: (1) monophasic, biphasic, and triphasic combinations of estrogens and progestins; and (2) progestins without concomitant administration of estrogens.

PHARMACOLOGIC EFFECTS OF ESTROGENS & SYNTHETIC PROGESTINS

Mechanisms of Contraceptive Action

Estrogen and progestin combinations inhibit gonadotropin secretion, which prevents ovulation. They also change the cervical mucus, the endometrium, and tubal motility and secretion, all of which decrease the likelihood of conception and implantation. Continuous use of progestins alone does not inhibit ovulation, and the other effects play a major role in prevention of pregnancy when these agents are used.

Genital Effects of Oral Contraceptives

Chronic use of estrogen-progestin combinations depresses ovarian function. The ovary shows minimal follicular development and an absence of corpora lutea and other morphologic features normally seen in ovulating women. Estrogen production is decreased, and progesterone secretion is minimal. The ovaries usually become smaller even when previously enlarged.

Cytologic findings on vaginal smears vary depending on the preparation used. However, with almost all of the combined drugs, a midzone maturation index is found because of the presence of progestational agents.

Effects on the uterus include hypertrophy of the cervix and polyp formation after prolonged use. The cervical mucus becomes thick and less copious and contains much cellular debris. Stromal deciduation occurs toward the end of the cycle. The agents containing 19-nortestosterone derivatives combined with smaller amounts of estrogen tend to produce more glandular atrophy and less bleeding than agents containing progestins that stimulate glandular development.

Stimulation of the breasts occurs in most patients receiving estrogen-containing agents. Some enlargement is generally noted. These agents tend to suppress lactation, but when the doses are small, the effects on breast feeding are not appreciable. Preliminary studies of transport of oral contraceptives into the breast milk suggest that only small amounts of these compounds are found and they have not been considered to be of importance.

Extragenital Effects of Oral Contraceptives

It is important to understand the extragenital effects of oral contraceptives, because of the large and growing number of normal individuals using them.

A. Central Nervous System Effects: The effects of the oral contraceptives on the central nervous system have not been well studied in humans. In animals, estrogens tend to lower the threshold of excitability in the brain, whereas progesterone tends to increase it. In addition, the increased respiration and thermogenic actions of progesterone and some of the synthetic progestins are thought to be due to effects on the central nervous system. The suppression of ovarian function results in part from inhibition of GnRH secretion by the hypothalamus.

It is very difficult to evaluate any behavioral or emotional effects of these compounds. Although there is a low incidence of pronounced changes in mood, affect, and behavior in most studies, milder changes are common.

B. Endocrinologic Effects: The combined agents inhibit the secretion of pituitary gonadotropins, as mentioned above. Estrogens increase the plasma concentration of CBG. This increases plasma cortisol concentrations but does not lead to chronic alteration in the rate of cortisol secretion. It has also been observed that the ACTH response to the administration of metyrapone is attenuated by estrogens and the oral contraceptives.

These preparations alter the angiotensin-aldosterone system, increasing plasma renin activity and therefore aldosterone secretion. The relationship between these alterations and the hypertension that occurs in some patients taking oral contraceptives is not clear.

TBG is increased, resulting in higher circulating

thyroxine levels. However, the free thyroxine level in these patients is normal.

C. Hematologic Effects: Serious thromboembolic phenomena occurring in women taking oral contraceptives have stimulated a great many studies of their effects on blood coagulation. In general, the changes observed are similar to those reported in pregnancy and include an increase in factors VII, VIII, IX, and X. Increased amounts of coumarin derivatives are required to prolong prothrombin time in patients taking oral contraceptives. The platelet aggregation response to catecholamines is also increased.

Oral contraceptives inhibit the conversion of polyglutamic folate found in food to the monoglutamic folate that is absorbed in the gastrointestinal tract, thereby causing folic acid deficiency anemias, which can be reversed by folic acid supplementation or by discontinuing oral contraceptives.

D. Hepatic Effects: The liver plays an important role in the metabolism of the estrogens and progestins used in oral contraceptives. These hormones also affect liver function. (See Adverse Effects of Oral Contraceptives, below.)

Estrogens increase the synthesis of the various transport globulins and fibrinogen and decrease the synthesis of serum haptoglobins.

Important alterations in drug excretion and metabolism also occur in the liver. Estrogens in the amounts present during pregnancy or ingested in oral contraceptive agents delay the clearance of sulfobromophthalein (BSP) and reduce bile flow.

Oral contraceptives increase the saturation of cholesterol in bile, and the ratio of cholic acid to chenodeoxycholic acid is increased. These changes may cause the observed increase in cholelithiasis associated with use of these agents.

E. Effects on Lipid Metabolism: Estrogens increase plasma high-density lipoproteins (HDL) and very low density lipoproteins (VLDL) while lowering low-density lipoproteins (LDL). In young women with normal lipids, this results in higher circulating triglyceride and free and esterified cholesterol levels. In older women with higher cholesterol levels, a reduction is usually observed because of the reduction of LDL. Phospholipid levels are increased. Although the effects are marked with doses of 100 μg of mestranol or ethinyl estradiol, doses of 50 μg or less have minimal effects. The progestins—particularly the 19-nortestosterone derivatives—tend to antagonize the effects of estrogen. Preparations containing small amounts of estrogen and a progestin may slightly decrease triglycerides and high-density lipoproteins.

F. Effects on Carbohydrate Metabolism: The administration of oral contraceptives produces alterations in carbohydrate metabolism similar to those observed in pregnancy (see Chapter 13). There is a reduction in the rate of absorption of carbohydrates from the gastrointestinal tract. These agents antagonize the effects of insulin, causing decreases in glucose tolerance or increased secretion of insulin following administration of glucose. Studies in experimental animals indicate that estrogens enhance islet cell function, whereas progesterone interferes with insulin action. The changes in glucose tolerance are reversible on discontinuing medication.

G. Cardiovascular Effects: These agents cause small increases in cardiac output associated with slightly higher systolic and diastolic blood pressure and heart rate. Pathologic increases in blood pressure occur in a small number of patients, in whom the pressure slowly returns to normal when treatment is terminated. It is important that blood pressure be followed in each patient.

H. Dermatologic Effects: Oral contraceptives have been noted to increase pigmentation of the skin (chloasma). This effect seems to be enhanced in women with dark complexions and by exposure to ultraviolet light. Agents with larger amounts of androgenic progestins may increase the production of sebum and cause acne. However, estrogen-dominant oral contraceptive preparations usually decrease sebum production by suppressing the ovarian production of androgens.

CLINICAL USES OF ORAL CONTRACEPTIVES

The most important use of estrogen and progestin compounds is for prevention of pregnancy. Many preparations are available, and they are packaged to provide for ease of administration. When these agents are taken according to directions, the risk of conception is estimated to be about 0.5–1 per 100 woman years.

These compounds are also used in the treatment of endometriosis. When severe dysmenorrhea is the major symptom of this disorder, suppression of ovulation with estrogen may be followed by painless periods. In some patients, long-term continuous administration of large doses of progestins or estrogen-progestin combinations to prevent cyclic breakdown of the endometrial tissue leads to endometrial fibrosis and prevents the reactivation of implants for prolonged periods.

As is true with most hormonal preparations, many of the adverse effects are physiologic or pharmacologic effects of the drug that are objectionable only because they are not pertinent to the situation for which they are being used. Therefore, the product containing the smallest amounts of hormones should be selected for use.

The differences between preparations can be used to advantage for individualized treatment. These preparations differ in amounts and types of estrogen and progestin (Table 10–11). Preparations containing

larger amounts of estrogen tend to produce more withdrawal bleeding, nausea, and mastalgia. Preparations containing 19-nortestosterone derivatives tend to reduce the amount of withdrawal bleeding and have more anabolic or androgenic effects.

ADVERSE EFFECTS OF ORAL CONTRACEPTIVES

The incidence of serious adverse effects associated with the use of these drugs is low. Minor adverse effects are frequent but transient and may respond to simple changes in pill formulation. Although it is not often necessary to discontinue taking the pills because of these adverse effects, one-third of patients started on oral contraception discontinue therapy for reasons other than a desire to become pregnant.

Mild Adverse Effects

Breakthrough bleeding is the most common problem in the use of progestational agents alone for contraception, occurring in as many as 25% of patients. It also occurs in patients taking combined agents and is more common with preparations containing less than 50 μg of ethinyl estradiol (or equivalent). The newer biphasic and triphasic formulations containing 35 μg of ethinyl estradiol and varying doses of progestin (Table 10–11) reduce breakthrough bleeding without increasing the total amount of hormone administered during a cycle.

Nausea, mastalgia, excessive withdrawal bleeding, and edema are more common with larger amounts of estrogen and can often be alleviated by a shift to a preparation containing smaller amounts of estrogen or more potent progestational compounds.

Psychologic changes are often transient and are not predictable with any of the preparations. In general, most patients "feel better" because they are relieved of anxiety about becoming pregnant. Some patients experience symptoms of irritability and depression throughout the cycle. Depression and fatigue may respond to a reduction in progestin content.

Withdrawal bleeding sometimes fails to occur and may cause confusion with regard to pregnancy. If this is disturbing to the patient, a preparation with higher estrogenic or lower progestational potency may be tried or another method of contraception used. Increased estrogen potency can also reduce early and midcycle spotting.

Moderately Severe Adverse Effects

Any of the following may require discontinuation of oral contraceptives:

Mild and transient headaches may occur. Migraine is often made worse and is associated with an increased frequency of cerebrovascular accidents. Therefore, when migraine becomes more severe or has its onset during therapy with these agents, treatment should be discontinued.

Weight gain is more common with the combination agents containing more potent progestins. It can usually be controlled by shifting to preparations with less progestin effect or by dieting.

Increased skin pigmentation occurs in 5% of women at the end of the first year and about 40% after 8 years. It is thought to be exacerbated by vitamin B deficiency. The condition improves upon discontinuance of medication, but pigmentation may disappear very slowly.

Acne may be exacerbated by agents containing androgenic progestins, whereas agents containing larger amounts of estrogen frequently cause marked improvement in acne in women with androgen excess.

Hirsutism may be aggravated by the 19-nortestosterone derivatives. This effect is seldom seen, because the suppression of ovarian androgens usually causes a net reduction in androgen effect.

Ureteral dilatation similar to that observed in pregnancy has been reported, and bacteriuria is more frequent.

Vaginal infections are more common and more difficult to treat in patients who are receiving oral contraceptives.

When therapy is terminated, the great majority of patients return to normal menstrual patterns. About 75% will ovulate in the first posttreatment cycle and 97% by the third posttreatment cycle. Patients with a history of irregular cycles more commonly develop amenorrhea following cessation of therapy.

About 2% of patients remain amenorrheic for up to several years after stopping the pills, and the prevalence of amenorrhea, often with galactorrhea, is higher in women who have used this form of contraception.

Severe Adverse Effects

A. Vascular Disorders: Thromboembolism was one of the earliest of the serious unanticipated effects to be reported and has been the most thoroughly studied. It should be kept in mind that almost all of these studies have been conducted in Great Britain, the USA, and Scandinavia and that effects in other populations might be somewhat different. During the past 15 years, the amounts of estrogen used in these preparations have been reduced, and this decline has been associated with a reduction in frequency of many of these effects. The most important adverse effect of the oral contraceptives is the increased risk of cardiovascular disease, including venous thromboembolism, myocardial infarction, and stroke.

1. Venous thromboembolic disease– Epidemiologic studies indicate that about one woman per 1000 woman years not using oral contraceptives will develop superficial or deep thromboembolic disease. The overall incidence of these disorders in patients

taking oral contraceptives is about 3 per 1000 woman years. Data obtained by studying changes in plasma fibrinogen or by ^{125}I fibrinogen uptake studies suggest that subclinical thrombosis occurs much more frequently than overt disease. The risk for this disorder is increased during the first month of contraceptive use and remains constant for several years or more. The risk returns to normal within a month when treatment is discontinued. The risk of venous thrombosis or pulmonary embolism among women with predisposing conditions may be higher than that in healthy women.

The incidence of this complication is related to the estrogen content of oral contraceptives. A reduction from 100–150 µg to 50–80 µg reduced the incidence of pulmonary embolism by 50% or more. The most recent studies employing contraceptives containing 30 µg of estrogen indicate that the risk of death from pulmonary embolism is even lower. There is no clear relationship between progestin content and the incidence of this complication. The risk of superficial or deep thromboembolic disease in patients treated with oral contraceptives is not related to age, parity, mild obesity, or cigarette smoking. However, the risk of idiopathic deep venous thromboembolic disease in women with blood types A, B, or AB is twice as great as in those with blood type O who are not taking contraceptives and three times as great in type O women using these compounds. These studies indicate a genetic susceptibility to this disorder and suggest that oral contraceptives magnify the effect. Decreased venous blood flow, endothelial proliferation in veins and arteries, and increased coagulability of blood due to changes in platelet coagulation and fibrinolytic systems contribute to the increased incidence of thrombosis. In general, these changes are similar to those seen in pregnancy. It has been proposed that the main factor responsible is a decrease in the ability to halt the progression of intravenous coagulation and inhibition of fibrin clot dissolution. The major plasma inhibitor of thrombin is antithrombin 3, which is substantially decreased during oral contraceptive use. This change occurs in the first month of treatment and lasts as long as treatment persists.

2. Myocardial infarction– Myocardial infarction occurs more frequently in oral contraceptive users but is unrelated to the duration of use. The attributable risk of myocardial infarction is about 5–7 per 100,000 current user years at age 30–39, rising to approximately 60 at age 40–44. The risk is related to the dose of estrogen and is significantly lower in women using low-dose estrogen compounds. There are also data indicating that the risk is increased in women using oral contraceptives containing 3–4 mg, as compared to 1 or 2 mg, of the progestin norethindrone acetate.

The use of oral contraceptives is associated with a higher risk of myocardial infarction in women who smoke 15 or more cigarettes a day, who have a history of preeclampsia or hypertension, or who have type II hyperlipoproteinemia or diabetes. The risk attributable to oral contraceptives in women 30–39 years of age who do not smoke is about 4 cases per 100,000 users per year, as compared to 185 cases per 100,000 among women 40–44 who smoke heavily. The pathogenesis of myocardial infarction is thought to be related to acceleration of atherogenesis, decreased levels of HDL, and increased platelet aggregation. However, the facilitation of coronary arterial spasm may play a role in some of these patients. The progestational component of oral contraceptives decreases HDL cholesterol, whereas the estrogenic component increases it. The net difference, therefore, will depend entirely on the specific composition of the pill used and the patient's susceptibility to the particular effects. Preparations containing norgestrel, 0.5 mg, or norethindrone acetate, 2.5 mg, have been reported to have strong antiestrogenic effects and to decrease HDL cholesterol, while some of the others have no effect.

3. Cerebrovascular disease– The risk of stroke is concentrated in women over 35. It is increased in current users but not in past users. However, the incidence of subarachnoid hemorrhage is increased among both current and past users and may increase with time. The risk of thrombotic or hemorrhagic stroke attributable to oral contraceptives is about 37 cases per 100,000 users per year. Ten percent of these strokes are fatal, and most of them are due to subarachnoid hemorrhage. Insufficient data are available on which to base an assessment of the effects of smoking and other risk factors.

Elevations in blood pressure may also increase the risk, since there is a three- to sixfold increase in the incidence of overt hypertension in women taking oral contraceptives.

In summary, the information available indicates that oral contraceptives increase the risk of various cardiovascular disorders at all ages and among both smokers and nonsmokers. *However, this risk appears to be concentrated in women 35 years of age or older who are heavy smokers. The presence of these risk factors must be considered in each individual patient for whom oral contraceptives are considered.*

B. Gastrointestinal Disorders: Many cases of cholestatic jaundice have been reported in patients taking progestin-containing drugs. The differences in incidence of these disorders from one population to another suggest that genetic factors are involved. The jaundice caused by these agents is similar to that produced by other 17-alkyl-substituted steroids. It is most often observed in the first 3 cycles and is particularly common in women with a history of cholestatic jaundice during pregnancy. Liver biopsies from such women show bile thrombi in the canaliculi and occasional areas of focal necrosis. Serum alkaline phosphatase and ALT are increased. The BSP retention and serum enzyme changes observed in some patients may indicate liver damage. Jaundice and pruritus disappear 1–8 weeks after the drug is discontinued.

These agents have also been found to increase the incidence of symptomatic gallbladder disease, including cholecystitis and cholangitis. This is probably the result of alterations in bile secretion and content.

It also appears that the incidence of hepatic adenomas is increased in women taking oral contraceptives. Ischemic bowel disease secondary to thrombosis of celiac and superior and inferior mesenteric arteries and veins has also been reported in women using these drugs.

C. Depression: Depression severe enough to require stopping the pills occurs in about 6% of patients taking some preparations.

NONCONTRACEPTIVE ADVANTAGES OF HORMONAL CONTRACEPTION

The advent of oral contraceptives with low hormone content has significantly reduced the incidence of serious adverse effects. Furthermore, it has become apparent that their use is associated with important health benefits such as less risk of developing endometrial cancer, iron deficiency anemia, benign breast disease, functional ovarian cysts, premenstrual syndrome, and dysmenorrhea.

These and other benefits make hormonal contraception with low-dose, low-potency combination pills an excellent contraceptive method for younger women who do not smoke.

CONTRAINDICATIONS & CAUTIONS

Oral contraceptives are contraindicated in patients with thrombophlebitis, thromboembolic phenomena, and cerebrovascular disorders or a past history of these conditions. They should not be used to treat vaginal bleeding when the cause is unknown. They should be avoided in patients known or suspected to have a tumor of the breast or other estrogen-dependent neoplasm. They are contraindicated in adolescents in whom epiphysial closure has not yet been completed, because they may prevent attainment of normal adult height.

Since these preparations have caused aggravation of preexisting disorders, they should be avoided or used with caution in patients with liver disease, hypertriglyceridemia, asthma, eczema, migraine, diabetes, hypertension, congestive heart failure, optic neuritis, retrobulbar neuritis, or convulsive disorders.

Estrogens may increase the rate of growth of fibroids. Therefore, for women with these tumors, agents with the smallest amounts of estrogen and the most potent progestins should be selected. The use of progestational agents alone for contraception might be especially useful in such patients (see below).

CONTRACEPTION WITH PROGESTINS

Small doses of progestins administered orally can be used for contraception (Table 10–9). They are particularly suited for patients who should not take estrogens. They are about as effective as intrauterine devices or combination pills containing 20–30 μg of ethinyl estradiol. There is a high incidence of spotting or irregular bleeding. Effective contraception can also be achieved by injecting 150 mg of depot medroxyprogesterone acetate monthly.

Subcutaneous implants of capsules containing levonorgestrel are extremely effective for 5–6 years. These capsules release one-fifth to one-third the amount of progestin required by oral administration. The low circulating levels of hormone have little effect on blood pressure or carbohydrate and lipid metabolism. The disadvantages of this method include the need for surgical insertion and removal of the capsules and some irregular bleeding.

POSTCOITAL CONTRACEPTIVES

Pregnancy can be prevented following coitus by the administration of estrogens alone or in combination with progestins. Insertion of an intrauterine device within 5 days has also been effective.

A variety of schedules have been tested and found effective, and these are shown in Table 10–12. When treatment is begun within 72 hours, the failure rate is less than 1%. Since 40% of patients treated experience nausea or vomiting, antiemetics are recommended. Headache, dizziness, breast tenderness, and abdominal and leg cramps have also been reported as adverse effects. Because these compounds have serious teratogenic effects early in pregnancy and because vaginal adenosis and cancer, cervical abnormalities, and impairment of reproductive function have been found in the offspring of women treated with diethylstilbestrol during gestation, voluntary termination of pregnancy is advised when conception occurs in these patients.

Mifepristone (see above), when given in the midluteal phase or at intervals during the menstrual cycle, can also prevent pregnancy. Its use for this purpose is under study.

INFERTILITY

Infertility is usually defined as failure of conception by a couple who have been having regular inter-

Table 10–12. Schedules for use of postcoital contraceptives.

Conjugated estrogens: 10 mg 3 times daily for 5 days
Ethinyl estradiol: 2.5 mg twice daily for 5 days
Diethylstilbestrol: 50 mg daily for 5 days
Norgestrel, 0.5 mg, with ethinyl estradiol, 0.05 mg: 2 tablets and 2 in 12 hours

course for 1 year or more without contraception. The intensity of the patients' concern varies, and a physician may be consulted after only a few months or many years of trying to become pregnant. Some of the more common problems encountered are listed in Table 10–13.

SEMEN ABNORMALITIES

Semen analysis is usually performed early in the investigation of infertile couples, because male factors are responsible for 40% of cases of infertility and because the test is relatively simple and inexpensive; furthermore, sperm abnormalities may compound the problem in women who fail to ovulate or have other problems reducing fertility. The characteristics of normal semen and sperm are discussed in Chapter 9. Male infertility is commonly attributed to varicocele of the left internal spermatic vein. Although this hypothesis is controversial, surgical correction of this disorder usually results in marked improvement in sperm motility, and even when lower than normal sperm counts remain, pregnancy is achieved about half the time. The quality and concentration of sperm can also be improved in some men by the use of split ejaculates. In about 90% of men, the first few drops of semen contain a higher concentration of sperm with better motility than the

Table 10–13. Causes of infertility.

Male (40–50%)	Female (50–60%)
Abnormalities of sperm	Tubal disease (20%)
Infection (mumps)	Anovulation (15%)
Failure to liquefy	Cervical factors (5%)
Agglutination	Unknown (10–20%)
Chronic infection (epididymitis, prostatitis)	Immunologic abnormalities[1]
High scrotal temperature	
Varicocele	
Baths	
Jockey shorts	
Prolonged sitting	
Radiation exposure	
Drugs (cimetidine, sulfasalazine, nitrofurantoin, etc)	
Retrograde ejaculation	
Severe allergic reactions (rare)	
Endocrine disorders	
Immunologic abnormalities[1]	

[1]Failure of conception correlates best with agglutinating antibodies to sperm in the male and with agglutinating and immobilizing antibodies in the female.

remainder of the ejaculate. The combination of this technique with artificial insemination increases the chances of pregnancy in some couples.

OVULATORY DISORDERS

Absent or infrequent ovulation accounts for about 15% of infertility problems. Whether ovulation is completely absent or occurs infrequently, the opportunity for conception is diminished, and the patient should be treated by ovulation induction (see above).

Women who have menstrual bleeding at regular intervals preceded by recognizable symptoms or who have dysmenorrhea almost always ovulate regularly. The occurrence of ovulation can be confirmed by the finding of a progesterone level greater than 4 ng/mL. However, it is useful to obtain daily basal body temperatures in order to determine the length of the luteal phase and to find out whether coitus has occurred at the time of ovulation. The timing of coitus is important, since the egg is fertilizable for only 12–24 hours, and sperm retain their ability to fertilize for 24–48 hours. Ideally, coitus should occur every other day for the 3 days preceding and following ovulation.

INFERTILITY IN THE PRESENCE OF OVULATION

When conception has not occurred in spite of a normal sperm analysis in the man and regular ovulation in the woman, a postcoital test of cervical mucus should be done near the time of expected ovulation as indicated by basal body temperature charts, length of cycle, or the patient's observation of increased amounts of clear mucus at an appropriate time of the cycle. The cervical mucus at this time is under the influence of high estrogen levels and is clear and abundant. It can be stretched between a slide and cover slip as much as 10 cm at this time ("spinnbarkeit"). When the mucus is dried on the slide, the interaction of the electrolytes and protein results in a crystalline pattern called "ferning" (Figure 10–13). This mucus contains chains of glycoproteins that form channels through which the sperm can migrate. In order to perform the test, mucus is obtained from the cervix following intercourse, preferably within 8 hours. If the mucus is thick and cloudy, the specimen may have been obtained too late in the cycle, and the test should be repeated. Absence of spermatozoa in the specimen indicates the need for a more careful study of the semen specimen, as does the presence of dead sperm cells without motility. The presence of 20 or more motile sperm per high dry field is associated with a higher fertility rate than when few sperm are found. However, pregnancies occur even when no motile sperm cells are found in this test. The finding of dead cells suggests the use of spermicidal lubricants or may indicate the need for sperm antibody testing.

Tests of Tubal Patency

When there is a history of pelvic infection or pelvic surgery, tubal patency should be examined by hysterosalpingography or at the time of diagnostic laparoscopy. Such examinations are also indicated in patients in whom other factors have not been identified that might explain the infertility. Hysterosalpingography is best performed a few days following cessation of menstrual flow, thus avoiding the disruption of an early pregnancy. It is contraindicated in the presence of active pelvic inflammatory disease, as indicated by the presence of pelvic masses, tenderness, or an elevated sedimentation rate. Radiation should be minimized by the use of image intensification fluoroscopy and by taking the minimum number of films. An increased number of conceptions has been reported following this procedure when oil-based dye is used. The increase has been attributed to various mechanical and chemical effects of lavage with an iodine-containing and possibly bacteriostatic substance.

When semen analysis and the above tests are found to be normal in the infertile couple, the possibility of endometriosis should be considered even in the absence of typical signs and symptoms such as severe dysmenorrhea, dyspareunia, thickening of the broad ligament, nodularity and tenderness, or fixation of the uterus on pelvic examination. In these instances, laparoscopy may detect the presence and indicate the extent of any intrapelvic disease. Surgical treatment of minimal endometriosis established in this manner is followed by conception in half of women so treated. Hormonal treatment (eg, danazol or GnRH analogues) also may be effective in some patients.

IN VITRO FERTILIZATION

In vitro fertilization and transfer of the fertilized ovum into the uterus is now a therapeutic option to achieve pregnancy. After thorough fertility evaluation and study of the patient's menstrual cycles, the patient is given clomiphene citrate, menotropins, or both to increase the number of large mature follicles. Just before ovulation, several ova are obtained by laparoscopy or percutaneously under ultrasound guidance. The ova are incubated for several hours, and washed sperm are added to the culture medium. After 2–3 days of incubation, several four- to six-cell conceptuses are transferred to the uterus via the cervix.

Seventy to 80 percent of mature ova obtained can be fertilized. Early abortion is frequent, and the overall success rate is less than 30% even in experienced hands. The process is very expensive, lengthy, and time-consuming. However, the risks of fetal abnormalities and maternal complications are low and it copes with the problem of tubal obstruction.

GAMETE INTRA-FOLLICULAR TRANSFER (GIFT)

In this process, the fertilized gamete is transferred into the uterine tube. The preparation of the patient and fertilization technique are similar to that for in vitro fertilization. However, the transfer of the gamete takes place shortly after fertilization.

Enormous amounts of money are spent and millions of visits to physicians occur every year for the complaint of infertility. Recent focus on advanced technologies has overshadowed what can be accomplished with less sophisticated management. It is also important to recognize that there is a significant spontaneous cure rate in almost every category of infertility, including failed in vitro fertilization and GIFT. In one study of infertile couples, pregnancy occurred in 41% of treated couples and 35% of untreated couples.

REFERENCES

General

Adashi EY: Intraovarian peptides: Stimulators and inhibitors of follicular growth and differentiation. Endocrinol Metab Clin North Am 1992;21:1.

Carr BR, Blackwell RE (editors): *Textbook of Reproductive Endocrinology.* Appleton & Lange, 1993.

Chen CL: Inhibin and activin as paracrine/autocrine factors. Endocrinology 1993;132:4.

Hodgen GD: The dominant ovarian follicle. Fertil Steril 1982;38:281.

Speroff L, Glass RH, Kase NG: *Clinical Gynecologic Endocrinology and Infertility,* 4th ed. Williams & Wilkins, 1989.

Disorders of Ovarian Function

Conn MP, Crowley WF: Gonadotropin releasing hormone and its analogs. N Engl J Med 1993;324:1001

Griffin JE, Wilson JD: The syndromes of androgen resistance. N Engl J Med 1980;302:198.

Kirschner MA, Samojlik E, Szmal E: Clinical usefulness of plasma androstanediol glucuronide measurements in women with idiopathic hirsutism. J Clin Endocrinol Metab 1987;65:597.

Malkasian GD Jr et al: Functioning tumors of the ovary in women under 40. Obstet Gynecol 1965;26:669.

Prior JC et al: Spinal bone loss and ovulatory disturbances. N Engl J Med 1990;323:1221.

Schlechte J et al: The natural history of untreated hyperprolactinemia: A prospective analysis. J Clin Endocrinol Metab 1989;68:412.

Shangold M et al: Evaluation and management of menstrual dysfunction in athletes. JAMA 1990;263:1665.

Hirsutism

Andreyko JL, Monroe SE, Jaffe RB: Treatment of hirsutism with a gonadotropin-releasing hormone agonist (nafarelin). J Clin Endocrinol Metab 1986;63:854.

Cummings DC et al: Treatment of hirsutism with spironolactone. JAMA 1982;247:1295.

Ferriman D, Gallwey JD: Clinical assessment of body hair growth in women. J Clin Endocrinol Metab 1961;21:1440.

Horton R, Lobo R (editors): Androgen metabolism in hirsute and normal females. Clin Endocrinol Metab 1986;15:213.

Leemay A: Attenuation of mild hyperandrogenic activity in postpubertal acne by a triphasic oral contraceptive containing low doses of ethynyl estradiol and d,l-norgestrel. J Clin Endocrinol Metab 1990;71:8.

Mooradian AD, Morley JD, Korenman SG: Biological action of androgens. Endocr Rev 1987;8:1.

Mortola JF, Yen SSC: The effects of oral dehydroepiandrosterone on endocrine-metabolic parameters in postmenopausal women. J Clin Endocrinol Metab 1990;71:696.

Pittaway DE, Maxson WS, Wentz AC: Spironolactone in combination drug therapy for unresponsive hirsutism. Fertil Steril 1985;43:878.

Raj SG et al: Normalization of testosterone levels using a low estrogen-containing oral contraceptive in women with polycystic ovarian syndrome. Obstet Gynecol 1982;60:15.

Venturoli S et al: Ketoconazole therapy for women with acne and/or hirsutism. J Clin Endocrinol Metab 1990;71:335.

Therapeutic Use of Ovarian & Hypothalamic Hormones & Inhibitors

Andreyko JL et al: Therapeutic uses of gonadotropin-releasing hormone analogs. Obstet Gynecol Surv 1987;42:1.

Chetkowski RJ et al: Biologic effects of transdermal estradiol. N Engl J Med 1986;314:1615.

Christiansen C, Riis BJ: 17β-estradiol and continuous norethisterone: A unique treatment for established osteoporosis in elderly women. J Clin Endocrinol Metab 1990;71:836.

Couzinet B et al: Termination of early pregnancy by the progesterone antagonist RU 486 (mifepristone). N Engl J Med 1986;315:1565.

Crooij MJ et al: Termination of early pregnancy by the 3β-hydroxysteroid dehydrogenase inhibitor epostane. N Engl J Med 1988;319:813.

D'Amato G et al: Serum and bile lipid levels in a postmenopausal woman after percutaneous and oral natural estrogens. Am J Obstet Gynecol 1989;169:600.

Davidson NE: Tamoxifen: Panacea or Pandora's box? N Engl J Med 1992;326:885.

Hill NCW, Furguson J, MacKenzie IZ: The efficacy of oral mifepristone (RU 38,486) with a prostaglandin E_1 analog vaginal pessary for the termination of early pregnancy: Complications and patient acceptability. Am J Obstet Gynecol 1990;162:414.

Love RR et al: Effects of tamoxifen on bone mineral density in postmenopausal women with breast cancer. N Engl J Med 1992;326:852.

Mishell DR (editor): Interdisciplinary review of estrogen replacement therapy. Am J Obstet Gynecol 1989;161 (Suppl Part 2):1825.

Mishell DR Jr: Contraception. N Engl J Med 1989; 320:777.

Nieman LK et al: The progesterone antagonist RU 486: A potential new contraceptive agent. N Engl J Med 1987;316:187.

Reid RL, Fretts R, Van Vugt DA: The theory and practice of ovulation induction with gonadotropin-releasing hormone. Am J Obstet Gynecol 1988;158:176.

Riggs BL: Overview of osteoporosis. West J Med 1991; 154:63.

Sherwin BB: The impact of different doses of estrogen and progestin on mood and sexual behavior in postmenopausal women. J Clin Endocrinol Metab 1991; 72:336.

Speroff L, Diczfalusy E: International symposium on contraception. Am J Obstet Gynecol 1987;157:1019.

Stampfer MJ et al: A prospective study of past use of oral contraceptive agents and risk of cardiovascular diseases. N Engl J Med 1988;319:1313.

Menopause

Baran D et al: Dietary modification with dairy products for preventing bone loss in premenopausal women: A three-year prospective study. J Clin Endocrinol Metab 1990;70:264.

Cann CE et al: Spinal mineral loss by quantitative computed tomography in oophorectomized women. JAMA 1980;244:2056.

Civitelli R et al: Bone turnover in postmenopausal osteoporosis: Effect of calcitonin treatment, J Clin Invest 1988;82:1268.

Godsland IF et al: The effects of different formulations of oral contraceptive agents on lipid and carbohydrate metabolism. N Engl J Med 1990;323:1375.

Henderson BE, Paganini-Hill A, Ross RK: Estrogen replacement therapy and protection from acute myocar-dial infarction. Am J Obstet Gynecol 1988;159:312.

Judd HL: Hormonal dynamics associated with the menopause. Clin Obstet Gynecol 1976;19:775.

Knopp RH, Mishell DR Jr (editors): Prevention and management of cardiovascular risk in women. Am J Obstet Gynecol 1988;158:1551.

Lindsay R et al: Bone response to termination of oestrogen treatment. Lancet 1978;1:1325.

Mishell DR et al: Postmenopausal replacement with a combination estrogen-progestin regimen for five days per week. J Reprod Med 1991;36:351.

Prough SG et al: Continuous estrogen/progestin therapy in menopause. Am J Obstet Gynecol 1987;157:1449.

Rockwell JC et al: Weight training decreases vertebral bone density in premenopausal women: A prospective study. J Clin Endocrinol Metab 1990;71:988.

Sherman BM, West JH, Korenman SG: The menopausal transition: Analysis of LH, FSH, estradiol, and progesterone concentrations during menstrual cycles of older women. J Clin Endocrinol Metab 1976;42:629.

Weinstein L, Bewtra C, Gallagher JC: Evaluation of a continuous combined low-dose regimen of estrogen-progestin for treatment of the menopausal patient. Am J Obstet Gynecol 1990;162:1534.

Williams SR et al: A study of combined continuous ethynyl estradiol and norethindrone acetate for postmenopausal hormone replacement. Am J Obstet Gynecol 1990;162:438.

Wolfe BM, Huff MW: The effects of combined estrogen and progestin administration on plasma lipoprotein metabolism in postmenopausal women. J Clin Invest 1989;83:40.

Hormonal Contraception

Bradley BD et al: Serum high-density-lipoprotein cholesterol in women using oral contraceptives, estrogen and progestins. N Engl J Med 1978;299:17.

Kuhl H, Goethe JW (editors): Pharmacokinetics of oral contraceptive steroids and drug interaction. Am J Obstet Gynecol 1990;163(Suppl Part 2):2113.

Infertility

Collins JA et al: Treatment-independent pregnancy among infertile couples. N Engl J Med 1983;309:1201.

Speroff L, Glass RH, Kase NG: Clinical Gynecologic Endocrinology and Infertility, 4th ed. Williams & Wilkins, 1989.

Abnormalities of Sexual Determination & Differentiation

11

Felix A. Conte, MD, & Melvin M. Grumbach, MD

Advances in molecular genetics, experimental embryology, steroid biochemistry, and methods of evaluation of the interaction between the hypothalamus, pituitary, and gonads have helped to clarify problems of sex determination and differentiation. Anomalies may occur at any stage of intrauterine maturation and lead to gross ambisexual development or to subtle abnormalities that do not become manifest until sexual maturity is achieved.

NORMAL SEX DIFFERENTIATION

Chromosomal Sex

The normal human diploid cell contains 22 autosomal pairs of chromosomes and two sex chromosomes (two X, or one X and one Y). When arranged serially and numbered according to size and centromeric position, they are known as a karyotype. Advances in the techniques of staining chromosomes (Figure 11–1) permit positive identification of each chromosome by its unique "banding" pattern. Bands can be produced in the region of the centromere (C bands), with the fluorescent dye quinacrine (Q bands), and with Giemsa's stain (G bands). Fluorescent banding (Figure 11–2) is particularly useful because the Y chromosome stains so brightly that it can be identified easily in both interphase and metaphase cells. The standard nomenclature for describing the human karyotype is shown in Table 11–1. Recently, a complete clone map of the euchromatic region of the Y chromosome was described. It is the first map of this type for a human chromosome, and spans about 35 million base pairs.

Studies in animals as well as in humans with abnormalities of sexual differentiation indicate that the

This chapter is modified from the author's Chapter 41, in Smith's General Urology, 13th ed., Appleton and Lange, 1992.

Figures 11–1, 11–2, 11–3, 11–7, 11–9 and Tables 11–1, 11–2, 11–3, 11–4, 11–5 reproduced with permission from Grumbach MM, Conte FA: Disorders of sex differentiation, Chapter 14, pp 853–952, in: Williams Textbook of Endocrinology, 8th edition, eds. Wilson JD, Foster DW, WB Saunders Co., 1992.

ACRONYMS USED IN THIS CHAPTER

AMH	Anti-müllerian hormone
DOCA	Deoxycorticosterone acetate
HMG	High-mobility group proteins binding to DNA
RFLP	Restriction fragment length polymorphism
SRY	Sex-determining region on the Y chromosome
TDF	Testis-determining factor
TGFβ	Transforming growth factor beta
WAGR	Wilms' tumor-aniridia-genital anomalies-mental retardation syndrome

---

sex chromosomes (the X and Y chromosomes) and the autosomes carry genes that influence sexual differentiation by causing the bipotential gonad to develop either as a testis or as an ovary. Two intact and normally functioning X chromosomes, in the absence of a Y chromosome (and the genes for testicular organogenesis), lead to the formation of an ovary, whereas a Y chromosome or the presence of the male-determining region of the short arm of the Y chromosome—the "testis-determining factor" (TDF)—will lead to testicular organogenesis.

In humans, there is a marked discrepancy in size between the X and Y chromosomes. Gene dosage compensation is achieved in all persons with two or more X chromosomes in their genetic constitution by partial inactivation of all X chromosomes except one. This phenomenon is thought to be a random process that occurs in each cell in the late blastocyst stage of embryonic development in which either the maternally or the paternally derived X chromosome undergoes heterochromatinization. The result of this process is formation of an X chromatin body (Barr body) in the interphase cells of persons having two or more X chromosomes (Figure 11–3).

The distal portion of the short arm of the X chromosome escapes inactivation and has a short (2.5 megabase) segment homologous to a segment on the distal portion of the short arm of the Y chromosome. This segment is called the "pseudoautosomal" region; it is these two limited regions of the X and Y that pair during meiosis, undergo obligatory chiasm formation, and allow for exchange of DNA between

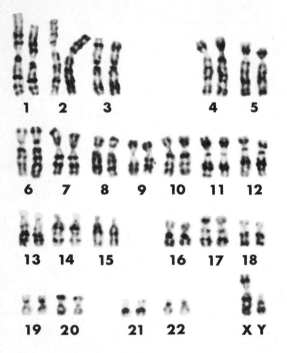

Figure 11–1. A normal 46,XY karyotype stained with Giemsa's stain to produce G bands. Note that each chromosome has a specific banding pattern.

this specific region of the X and Y chromosomes. MIC2, a gene coding for a cell surface antigen recognized by the monoclonal antibody, 12E7, the gene for the granulocyte-macrophage colony-stimulating factor receptor (GM-CSF), and a gene affecting short stature have been localized to the pseudoautosomal region of the X and Y chromosomes (Figures 11–4 and 11–5).

In buccal mucosal smears of 46,XX females, a sex chromatin body is evident in 20–30% of the inter-

phase nuclei examined, whereas in normal 46,XY males, a comparable sex chromatin body is absent. In patients with more than two X chromosomes, the maximum number of sex chromatin bodies in any diploid nucleus is one less than the total number of X chromosomes. Using sex chromatin and Y fluorescent staining, one can determine indirectly the sex chromosome complement of an individual (Table 11–2).

Sex Determination
(*SRY* = Testis-Determining Factor)

Over the past 20 years, interest has focused on several proteins as candidates for the "testis-determining factor" produced by a gene on the Y chromosome. Experimental and clinical data do not support the candidacy of H-Y antigen or zinc finger Y (ZFY) as the testis-determining factor. In studies of 46,XX males with very small Y-to-X translocations, a gene was localized to the region just proximal to the pseudoautosomal boundary of the Y chromosome (Figure 11–5). This gene has been cloned, expressed, and named sex-determining region Y (*SRY*). *Sry* (the murine analogue of the human *SRY* gene) is expressed in the embryonic genital ridge of the mouse between days 10.5 and 12.5, just prior to and during the time at which testis differentiation first occurs. Furthermore, deletions or mutations of the human *SRY* gene occur in about 15–20% of 46,XY females with gonadal dysgenesis. However, the most compelling evidence to indicate that *SRY* is the testis-determining factor is that transfection of the *Sry* gene into 46,XX mouse embryos results in transgenic 46,XX mice with testes and male sex differentiation.

Molecular studies have revealed that the *SRY* gene codes for a DNA-binding protein that has an 80-amino-acid domain similar to that found in "high-mobility group" (HMG) proteins. This domain binds to DNA in a sequence-specific manner (AA-

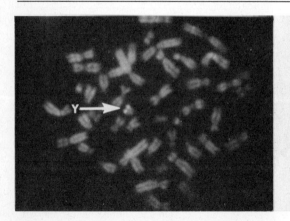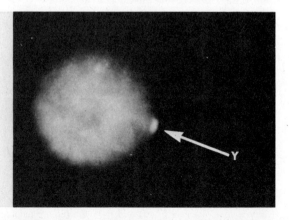

Figure 11–2. Metaphase chromosomes stained with quinacrine and examined through a fluorescence microscope. Note the bright fluorescence of the distal arms of the Y chromosome, which can also be seen in interphase cells ("Y body" at right).

Table 11–1. Nomenclature for describing the human karyotype
pertinent to designating sex chromosome abnormalities.

Paris Conference	Description	Former Nomenclature
46,XX	Normal female karyotype	XX
46,XY	Normal male karyotype	XY
47,XXY	Karyotype with 47 chromosomes including an extra Y chromosome	XXY
45,X	Monosomy X	XO
45,X/46,XY	Mosaic karyotype composed of 45,X and 46,XY cell lines	XO/XY
p	Short arm	p
q	Long arm	q
46,X,del (X) (qter → p21:)	Deletion of the short arm of the X distal to band Xp21	XXp–
46,X,del (X) (pter → q21:)	Deletion of the long arm of the X distal to band Xq21	XXq–
46,X,i(Xq)	Isochromosome of the long arm of X	XXqi
46,X,r(X)	Ring X chromosome	XXr
46,X,t(Y;7) (q11;q36)	Translocation of the distal fluorescent portion of the Y chromosome to the long arm of chromosome 7	46,XYt (Yq–7q+)

CAAAG). It bends the DNA and is thus thought to facilitate interaction between DNA-bound proteins and thus to affect the transcription of "downstream genes." One should note that almost all the mutations thus far described in 46,XY females with gonadal dysgenesis have occurred in the nucleotides of the *SRY* gene encoding the DNA binding region (the HMG box) of the SRY protein.

The number of genes involved in the testis-determining cascade is not known (Figure 11–6). Studies in 46,XY females with duplications of the distal part of Xp indicate the presence of a gene on the short arm of the X chromosome that acts in the testis determination or differentiation pathway. Likewise, studies in other patients with anomalies of sex differentiation indicate that the autosomal Wilms tumor repressor gene *WT1* (as seen in the Denys-Drash and WAGR syndromes; see below) and the gene for camptomelic dwarfism (osteochondrodysplasia) are other candidate genes for the testicular determination and differentiation cascade. Mutations in either X-linked or autosomal genes involved in testicular organogenesis or differentiation are undoubtedly responsible for the occurrence of 46,XX males and 46,XX true hermaphrodites, in whose genomes evidence for the *SRY* gene has not been found.

TESTICULAR & OVARIAN DIFFERENTIATION

Until the 12-mm stage (approximately 42 days of gestation), the embryonic gonads of males and females are indistinguishable. By 42 days, 300–1300 primordial germ cells have seeded the undifferentiated gonad from their extragonadal origin in the yolk sac dorsal endoderm. These large cells are the progenitors of oogonia and spermatogonia; lack of these cells is incompatible with further ovarian differentiation but not testicular differentiation. Under the influence of *SRY* and other genes that code for male sex determination (Figure 11–6), the gonad will begin to differentiate as a testis at 43–50 days of gestation.

Leydig cells are apparent by about 60 days, and differentiation of male external genitalia occurs by 65–77 days of gestation.

In the gonad destined to be an ovary, the lack of differentiation persists. At 77–84 days—long after differentiation of the testis in the male fetus—a significant number of germ cells enter meiotic prophase to characterize the transition of oogonia into oocytes, which marks the onset of ovarian differentiation from the undifferentiated gonads (Figure 11–7).

Differentiation of Genital Ducts (Figure 11–8)

By the seventh week of intrauterine life, the fetus is equipped with the primordia of both male and female genital ducts. The müllerian ducts, if allowed to persist, form the uterine (fallopian) tubes, the corpus and cervix of the uterus, and the upper third of the vagina. The wolffian ducts, on the other hand, have the potential for differentiating into the epididymis, vas deferens, seminal vesicles, and ejaculatory ducts of the male. In the presence of a functional testis, the müllerian ducts involute under the influence of the

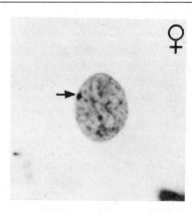

Figure 11–3. X chromatin (Barr) body in the nucleus of a buccal mucosal cell from a normal 46,XX female.

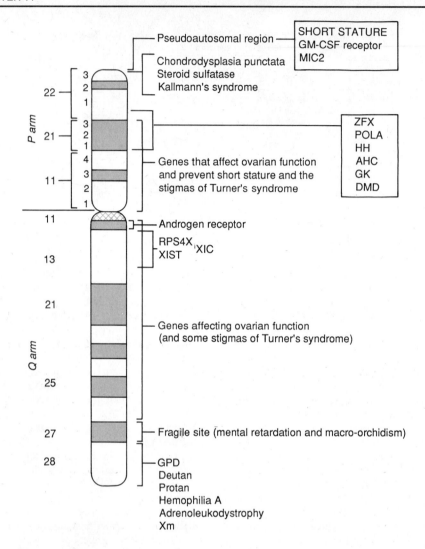

Figure 11–4. Diagrammatic representation of G-banded X chromosome. Selected X-linked genes are shown. (GM-CSF, granulocyte-macrophage colony-stimulating factor; MIC2, a cell surface antigen recognized by monoclonal antibody 12E7; ZFX, zinc finger X; POLA, RNA polymerase; HH, hypogonadotropic hypogonadism; AHC, congenital adrenal hypoplasia; GPD, glucose-6-phosphate dehydrogenase; deutan and protan, color blindness genes; Xm, X-linked serum macroglobulin; GK, glycerol kinase; DMD, Duchenne muscular dystrophy; RPS4X, ribosomal protein S4; XIST, Xi-specific transcripts; XIC, X inactivation center.) (Reproduced, with permission, from Grumbach MM, Conte FA: Disorders of sex differentiation. In: *Williams Textbook of Endocrinology*, 8th ed. Wilson JD, Foster DW (editors). Saunders, 1992.)

"anti-müllerian hormone" (AMH), a dimeric glycoprotein secreted by fetal Sertoli cells. This hormone acts "locally" to cause müllerian duct repression ipsilaterally. The differentiation of the wolffian duct is stimulated by testosterone secretion from the testis. In the presence of an ovary or in the absence of a functional fetal testis, müllerian duct differentiation occurs, and the wolffian ducts involute.

The gene for AMH encodes a 560-amino-acid protein whose carboxyl terminal domain shows marked homology with TGFβ and the B chain of porcine inhibin and activin. The gene has been localized on the short arm of chromosome 19. AMH is secreted by

human Sertoli cells until 8–10 years of age and can be used as a marker for the presence of these cells.

Differentiation of External Genitalia (Figure 11–9)

Up to the eighth week of fetal life, the external genitalia of both sexes are identical and have the capacity to differentiate into the genitalia of either sex. Female sex differentiation will occur in the presence of an ovary or streak gonads or if no gonad is present (Figure 11–10). Differentiation of the external genitalia along male lines depends on the action of testos-

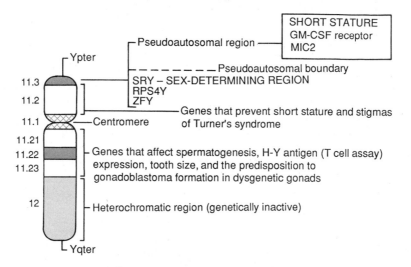

Figure 11–5. Diagrammatic representation of a G-banded Y chromosome. Y-linked genes are shown. (ZFY, zinc finger Y; SRY, sex-determining region Y; GM-CSF, granulocyte-macrophage colony-stimulating factor; MIC2, gene for a cell surface antigen recognized by monoclonal antibody 12E7; RPS4Y, ribosomal protein S4; Ypter, YP terminal; Xqter, YQ terminal.) (Reproduced, with permission, from Grumbach MM, Conte FA: Disorders of sex differentiation. In: *Williams Textbook of Endocrinology,* 8th ed. Wilson JD, Foster DW (editors). Saunders, 1992.)

terone and particularly dihydrotestosterone, the 5α-reduced metabolite of testosterone. In the male fetus, testosterone is secreted by the Leydig cells—perhaps autonomously at first, thereafter under the influence of hCG, and then by stimulation by fetal pituitary LH. Masculinization of the external genitalia and urogenital sinus of the fetus results from the action of dihydrotestosterone, which is converted from testosterone in the target cells by the enzyme 5α-reductase. Dihydrotestosterone is bound to a specific protein receptor in the nucleus of the target cell. The transformed steroid-receptor complex dimerizes and binds with high affinity to specific DNA domains, initiating

DNA-directed, RNA-mediated transcription. This results in androgen-induced proteins that lead to differentiation and growth of the cell. The gene that encodes the intracellular androgen-binding protein has been localized to the paracentromeric portion of the long arm of the X chromosome (Figure 11–4). Thus, an X-linked gene controls the androgen response of all somatic cell types by specifying the androgen receptor protein.

As in the case of the genital ducts, there is an inherent tendency for the external genitalia and urogenital sinus to develop along female lines. Differentiation of the external genitalia along male lines requires androgenic stimulation early in fetal life. The testosterone metabolite dihydrotestosterone and its specific nuclear receptor must be present to effect masculinization of the external genitalia of the fetus. Dihydrotestosterone stimulates growth of the genital tubercle, fusion of the urethral folds, and descent of the labioscrotal swellings to form the penis and scrotum. Androgens also inhibit descent and growth of the vesicovaginal septum and differentiation of the vagina. There is a critical period for action of the androgen. After about the 12th week of gestation, fusion of the labioscrotal folds will not occur even under intense androgen stimulation, though phallic growth can be induced. Impairment in the synthesis or secretion of fetal testosterone or in its conversion to dihydrotestosterone, deficient or defective androgen receptor activity, or defective production and local action of anti-müllerian hormone leads to incomplete masculinization of the male fetus. Exposure of the female fetus to abnormal amounts of androgens from either endogenous or exogenous sources, espe-

Table 11–2. Sex chromosome complement correlated with X chromatin and Y bodies in somatic interphase nuclei.[1]

Sex Chromosomes	Maximum Number in Diploid Somatic Nuclei	
	X Bodies	Y Bodies
45,XO	0	0
46,XX	1	0
46,XY	0	1
47,XXX	2	0
47,XXY	1	1
47,XYY	0	2
48,XXXX	3	0
48,XXXY	2	1
48,XXYY	1	2
49,XXXXX	4	0
49,XXXXY	3	1
49,XXXYY	2	2

[1]The maximum number of X chromatin bodies in diploid somatic nuclei is one less than the number of Xs, whereas the maximum number of Y fluorescent bodies is equivalent to the number of Ys in the chromosome constitution.

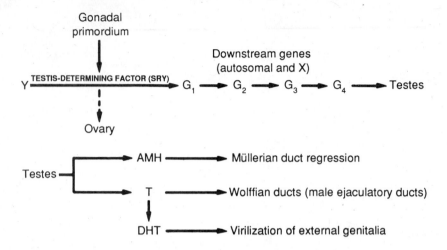

Figure 11–6. Diagrammatic representation of the cascade of genes involved in testis determination and hormones involved in male sex differentiation. TDF imposes testicular differentiation on the primordial or indifferent gonad. (AMH, antimüllerian hormone; T, testosterone; DHT, dihydrotestosterone.) (Reproduced, with permission, from Grumbach MM, Conte FA: Disorders of sex differentiation. In: *Williams Textbook of Endocrinology,* 8th ed. Wilson JD, Foster DW (editors). Saunders, 1992.)

cially before the 12th week of gestation, can result in virilization of the external genitalia.

PSYCHOSEXUAL DIFFERENTIATION

Psychosexual differentiation may be classified into four broad categories: (1) gender identity, defined as the identification of self as either male or female; (2) gender role, ie, those aspects of behavior in which males and females differ from one another in our culture at this time; (3) gender orientation, the choice of sexual partner; and (4) cognitive differences.

Studies in individuals who have been reared in a sex opposite to their chromosomal or gonadal sex, as well as of prenatally androgenized females with virilizing adrenal hyperplasia, provide strong evidence that gender identity is not determined primarily by sex chromosomes or prenatal sex steroid exposure.

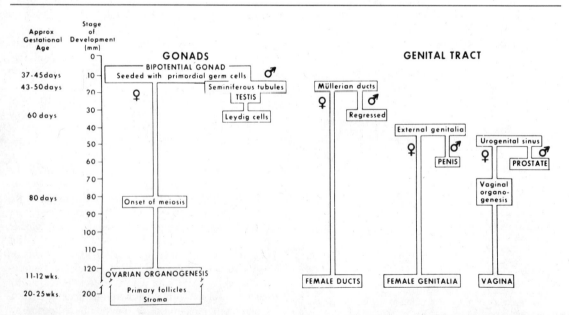

Figure 11–7. Schematic sequence of sexual differentiation in the human fetus. Note that testicular differentiation precedes all other forms of differentiation.

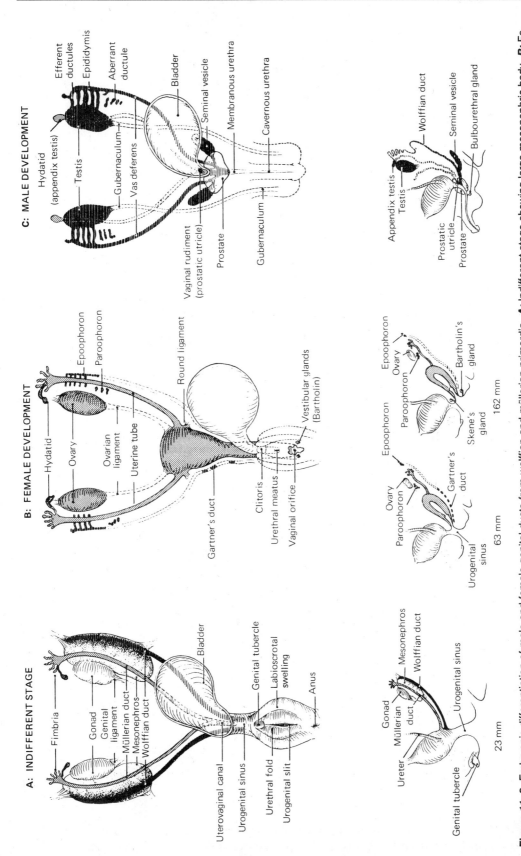

Figure 11–8. Embryonic differentiation of male and female genital ducts from wolffian and müllerian primordia. ***A:*** Indifferent stage showing large mesonephric body. ***B:*** Female ducts. Remnants of the mesonephros and wolffian ducts are now termed the epoophoron, paroophoron, and Gartner's duct. ***C:*** Male ducts before descent into the scrotum. The only müllerian remnant is the testicular appendix. The prostatic utricle (vagina masculina) is derived from the urogenital sinus. (Redrawn from Corning and Wilkins.)

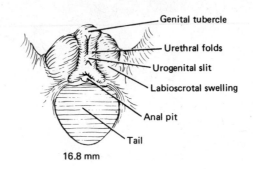

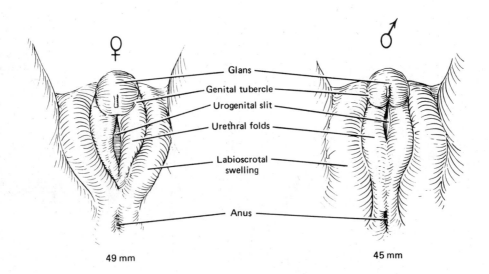

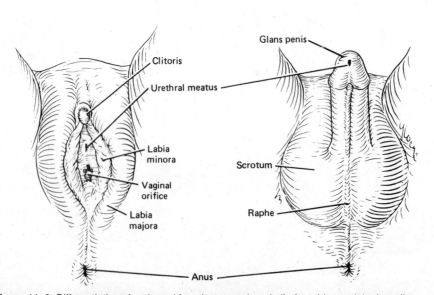

Figure 11–9. Differentiation of male and female external genitalia from bipotential primordia.

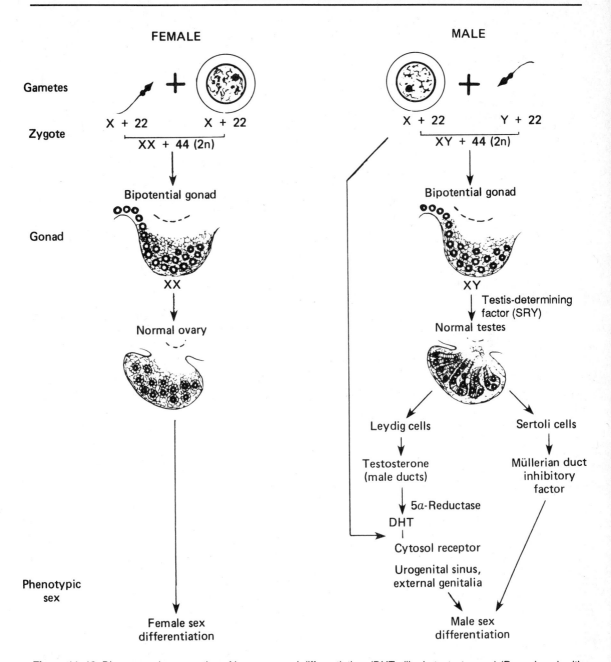

Figure 11–10. Diagrammatic summation of human sexual differentiation. (DHT, dihydrotestosterone.) (Reproduced, with permission, from Grumbach MM, Conte FA: Disorders of sex differentiation. In: *Williams Textbook of Endocrinology,* 8th ed. Wilson JD, Foster DW (editors). Saunders, 1992.)

Rather, it is imprinted postnatally by words, attitudes, and comparisons of one's body with that of others. Generally, gender identity agrees with the sex of assignment in the intersex patient, provided the child is reared *unambiguously* as a member of that sex and provided also that appropriate surgical and hormonal therapy is instituted so that the child has an unambiguous male or female phenotype. Under these circumstances, gender identity is usually established

by 18–30 months of age. If, at puberty, discordant secondary sexual characteristics are allowed to develop and persist, some intersex individuals may develop doubts about their gender identity and request a change of sex.

Thus, it appears that gender identity may be more plastic than previously thought. At puberty, sex steroids as well as socialization play a role in the function and maintenance of gender identity. How-

Table 11–3. Classification of anomalous sexual development.

I. Disorders of gonadal differentiation
  A. Seminiferous tubule dysgenesis (Klinefelter's syndrome)
  B. Syndrome of gonadal dysgenesis and its variants (Turner's syndrome)
  C. Complete and incomplete forms of XX and XY gonadal dysgenesis
  D. True hermaphroditism
II. Female pseudohermaphroditism
  A. Congenital virilizing adrenal hyperplasia
  B. P450 aromatase (placental) deficiency
  C. Androgens and synthetic progestins transferred from maternal circulation
  D. Associated with malformations of intestine and urinary tract (non-androgen-induced female pseudohermaphroditism)
  E. Other teratologic factors
III. Male pseudohermaphroditism
  A. Testicular unresponsiveness to hCG and LH (Leydig cell agenesis or hypoplasia)
  B. Inborn errors of testosterone biosynthesis
    1. Enzyme defects affecting synthesis of both corticosteroids and testosterone (variants of congenital adrenal hyperplasia)
      a. P450scc (cholesterol side chain cleavage) deficiency (congenital lipoid adrenal hyperplasia)
      b. 3β-Hydroxysteroid dehydrogenase deficiency
      c. P450c17 (17α-hydroxylase) deficiency
    2. Enzyme defects primarily affecting testosterone biosynthesis by the testes
      a. P450c17 (17,20-lyase) deficiency
      b. 17β-Hydroxysteroid oxidoreductase deficiency
  C. Defects in androgen-dependent target tissues
    1. End-organ resistance to androgenic hormones (androgen receptor and postreceptor defects)
      a. Syndrome of complete androgen resistance and its variants (testicular feminization and its variant forms)
      b. Syndrome of partial androgen resistance and its variants (Reifenstein's syndrome)
      c. Androgen resistance in infertile men
      d. Androgen resistance in fertile men
    2. Defects in testosterone metabolism by peripheral tissues
      a. 5α-Reductase deficiency (pseudovaginal perineoscrotal hypospadias)
  D. Dysgenetic male pseudohermaphroditism
    1. X chromatin-negative variants of the syndrome of gonadal dysgenesis (eg, 45,X/46,XY,47,XYp–)
    2. Incomplete forms of XY gonadal dysgenesis
    3. Associated with degenerative renal disease
    4. "Vanishing testes" (embryonic testicular regression syndrome; 46,XY agonadism; 46,XY gonadal agenesis; rudimentary testes; anorchia)
  E. Defects in synthesis, secretion, or response to AMH
    1. Female genital ducts in otherwise normal men—"herniae uteri inguinale"; persistent müllerian duct syndrome
  F. Maternal ingestion of progestogens
IV. Unclassified forms of abnormal sexual development
  A. In males
    1. Hypospadias
    2. Ambiguous external genitalia in 46,XY males with multiple congenital anomalies
  B. In females
    1. Absence or anomalous development of the vagina, uterus, and uterine tubes (Rokitansky-Küster syndrome)

ever, the weight of evidence still supports environmental factors as the principal determinant of gender identity in our culture.

ABNORMAL SEX DIFFERENTIATION

Classification of Errors in Sex Differentiation (Table 11–3)

Disorders of sexual differentiation are the result of abnormalities in complex processes that originate in genetic information on the X and Y chromosomes as well as on the autosomes. A true hermaphrodite is defined as a person who possesses both ovarian and testicular tissue. A male pseudohermaphrodite is one whose gonads are exclusively testes but whose genital ducts or external genitalia (or both) exhibit incomplete masculinization. A female pseudohermaphrodite is a person whose gonadal tissue is exclusively ovarian but whose genital development exhibits ambiguous or male appearance.

SEMINIFEROUS TUBULE DYSGENESIS: CHROMATIN-POSITIVE KLINEFELTER'S SYNDROME & ITS VARIANTS

Klinefelter's syndrome is one of the most common forms of primary hypogonadism and infertility in males. The invariable clinical features in adults are a male phenotype, firm testes less than 3 cm in length, and azoospermia. Gynecomastia is common. Affected individuals usually have a 47,XXY sex chromosome constitution and an X chromatin-positive buccal smear, though subjects with a variety of sex chromosome constitutions, including mosaicism, have been described. Virtually all of these variants have in common the presence of at least two X chromosomes and a Y chromosome, except for the rare group in which only an XX sex chromosome complement is found.

Surveys of the prevalence of 47,XXY fetuses by karyotype analysis of unselected newborn infants indicate an incidence of about 1:1000 newborn males. Prepubertally, the disorder is characterized by small testes, disproportionately long legs, personality and behavioral disorders, and a lower mean verbal IQ score when compared with that of controls but no significant difference in full-scale IQ. Severe mental retardation requiring special schooling is uncommon. Gynecomastia and other signs of androgen deficiency such as diminished facial and body hair, a small phallus, poor muscular development, and a eunuchoid body habitus occur postpubertally in affected patients. Adult males with a 47,XXY karyotype tend to be taller than average, with adult height close to the 75th percentile, mainly because of the disproportionate length of their legs. They also have an increased incidence of mild diabetes mellitus, varicose veins, chronic pulmonary disease, and carcinoma of the breast; the incidence of breast carcinoma in patients with Klinefelter's syndrome is 20 times higher than that in normal men. Patients with Klinefelter's syndrome often have a delay in the onset of adolescence. However, sexual precocity may occur rarely owing to an hCG-secreting extragonadal polyembryoma. There is an increased risk for developing malignant extragonadal germ cell tumors, including central nervous system germinomas.

The testicular lesion is progressive and gonadotropin-dependent. It is characterized in the adult by extensive seminiferous tubular hyalinization and fibrosis, absent or severely deficient spermatogenesis, and pseudoadenomatous clumping of the Leydig cells. Although hyalinization of the tubules is usually extensive, it varies considerably from patient to patient and even between testes in the same patient. Spermatogenesis is rarely found, and patients who have been reported to be fertile invariably have been 46,XY/47,XXY mosaics.

Advanced maternal age and meiotic nondisjunction have been found to play a role in the pathogenesis of the 47,XXY karyotype. Pedigree studies indicate that both X chromosomes are of maternal origin in 67% of patients.

The diagnosis of Klinefelter's syndrome is suggested by the classic phenotype and hormonal changes. It is confirmed by the finding of an X chromatin-positive buccal smear and demonstration of a 47,XXY karyotype in blood, skin, or gonads. After puberty, levels of serum and urinary gonadotropins (especially FSH) are raised. The testosterone production rate, the total and free levels of testosterone, and the metabolic clearance rates of testosterone and estradiol tend to be low, while plasma estradiol levels are normal or high. Testicular biopsy reveals the classic findings of hyalinization of the seminiferous tubules, severe deficiency of spermatogonia, and pseudoadenomatous clumping of Leydig cells.

Treatment of patients with Klinefelter's syndrome is directed toward androgen replacement, especially in patients in whom puberty is delayed or fails to progress or in those who have subnormal testosterone levels for age and developmental stage. Testosterone therapy may help to enhance secondary sexual characteristics and sexual performance, prevent osteoporosis, and improve general well-being in most patients. Testosterone therapy in adolescence should commence with 50–100 mg of testosterone enanthate in oil intramuscularly every 4 weeks and gradually increase to the adult replacement dose of 200 mg every 2 weeks. Gynecomastia is not amenable to hormone therapy but can be surgically corrected if it is severe or psychologically disturbing to the patient. Early diagnosis, support, and appropriate counseling may improve the overall prognosis. (See also Chapter 9.)

Variants of Chromatin-Positive Seminiferous Tubule Dysgenesis

A. Variants of Klinefelter's Syndrome: These include 46,XY/47,XXY mosaics as well as patients with multiple X and Y chromosomes. With increasing numbers of X chromosomes in the genome, both mental retardation and other developmental anomalies such as radioulnar synostosis become prevalent.

B. 46,XX Males: Phenotypic males with a 46,XX karyotype have been described since 1964; the incidence of 46,XX males is approximately 1:20,000 births. In general, they have a normal male phenotype, male psychosocial gender identity, and testes with histologic features similar to those observed in patients with a 47,XXY karyotype. At least 10% of patients have had hypospadias or ambiguous external genitalia. XX males have normal body proportions and a mean final height shorter than that of patients with an XXY sex chromosome constitution or normal males but taller than that of normal females. As in XXY patients, testosterone levels are low or low normal, gonadotropins are elevated, and spermatogenesis is impaired. Gynecomastia is present in approximately one-third of cases.

The presence of testes and male sexual differentiation in 46,XX individuals has been a perplexing problem. However, the paradox has been clarified by the use of recombinant DNA studies. Males with a 46,XX karyotype have been shown by genetic linkage studies and X chromosome restriction fragment length polymorphisms to possess one X chromosome from each of their parents. Approximately 90% of XX males have a Y chromosome-specific DNA segment from the distal portion of the Y short arm translocated to the distal portion of the short arm of the paternal X chromosome. This translocated segment is heterologous in length but always includes the *SRY* gene, which encodes TDF as well as the pseudoautosomal region of the Y chromosome. Thus, in 90% of XX males, an abnormal X–Y terminal exchange during paternal meiosis has resulted in two products: an X chromosome with *SRY* translocated from the Y chromosome and a Y chromosome deficient in this gene (the latter would result in a female with XY gonadal dysgenesis). Less than 10% of XX males tested have been shown to lack Y chromosome-specific DNA sequences, including the *SRY* gene and the pseudoautosomal region of the Y chromosome. These XX but Y DNA-negative males tend to have hypospadias or to have family members with true hermaphroditism. The finding of XX males who lack any evidence of Y chromosome-specific genes suggests that testicular determination and, thus, male differentiation can occur in the absence of a gene or genes from the Y chromosome. This could be a result of (1) mutation of a "downstream" autosomal gene involved in male sex determination; or (2) mutation, deletion, or aberrant inactivation of a gene sequence on the X chromosome, critical to testis determination and differentiation; or (3) circumscribed Y chromosome mosaicism (eg, occurring only in the gonads). For example, five phenotypic females have been reported with duplication of the distal portion of the X chromosome who have 46,XY gonadal dysgenesis; this observation supports the existence of a gene on the distal portion of Xp involved in testis differentiation. Further studies will be necessary to elucidate the pathogenesis of male sex determination and differentiation in those 46,XX males who lack ascertainable Y-to-X chromosome translocations.

SYNDROME OF GONADAL DYSGENESIS: TURNER'S SYNDROME & ITS VARIANTS

Turner's Syndrome: 45,X Gonadal Dysgenesis

One in 2500 newborn females has a 45,X or XO sex chromosome constitution. The cardinal features of 45,X gonadal dysgenesis are a variety of somatic anomalies, sexual infantilism at puberty secondary to gonadal dysgenesis, and short stature. Patients with a 45,X karyotype can be recognized in infancy, usually because of lymphedema of the extremities and loose skin folds over the nape of the neck. In later life, the typical patient is often recognizable by her distinctive facies, in which micrognathia, epicanthal folds, prominent low-set ears, a fish-like mouth, and ptosis are present to varying degrees. The chest is shield-like and the neck short, broad, and webbed (40% of patients). Additional anomalies associated with Turner's syndrome include coarctation of the aorta (10%), hypertension, renal abnormalities (50%), pigmented nevi, cubitus valgus, a tendency to keloid formation, puffiness of the dorsum of the hands and feet, short fourth metacarpals and metatarsals, and recurrent otitis media. Routine intravenous urography or ultrasonography is indicated for all patients to rule out a surgically correctable renal abnormality. The internal ducts as well as the external genitalia of these patients are invariably female, except in rare patients with a 45,X karyotype, in whom a Y-to-autosome or X chromosome translocation has been found.

Short stature is an invariable feature of the syndrome of gonadal dysgenesis. Mean final height in 45,X patients is 143 cm, with a range of 133–153 cm. Current data suggest that the short stature found in patients with the syndrome of gonadal dysgenesis is not due to a deficiency of growth hormone, somatomedin, sex steroids, or thyroid hormone. However, administration of high-dose biosynthetic human growth hormone results in an increase in final height.

Gonadal dysgenesis is another feature of patients with a 45,X chromosome constitution. The gonads are typically streak-like and usually contain only fibrous stroma arranged in whorls. Longitudinal studies of both basal and GnRH-evoked gonadotropin secretion in patients with gonadal dysgenesis indicate a lack of feedback inhibition of the hypothalamic-pituitary axis by the dysgenetic gonads in affected infants and children (Figure 11–11). Thus, plasma and urinary gonadotropin levels, particularly FSH levels, are high during early infancy and after 9–10 years of age. Since ovarian function is impaired, puberty does not usually ensue spontaneously; hence, sexual infantilism is a hallmark of this syndrome. Rarely, patients with a 45,X karyotype may undergo spontaneous pubertal maturation and menarche.

A variety of disorders are associated with this syndrome, including obesity, osteoporosis, diabetes mellitus, Hashimoto's thyroiditis, rheumatoid arthritis, inflammatory bowel disease, and anorexia nervosa. Because an increased prevalence of bicuspid aortic valve and aortic dilatation with aneurysm formation and rupture has been reported in patients with Turner's syndrome, a routine echocardiogram is indicated in patients with a 45,X cell line.

Phenotypic females with the following features should have a karyotype analysis: (1) short stature (> 2.5 SD below the mean value for age), (2) somatic anomalies associated with the syndrome of gonadal dysgenesis, and (3) delayed adolescence with an increased level of plasma FSH.

Therapy should be directed toward maximizing final height and inducing secondary sexual characteristics and menarche at an age commensurate with that of normal peers. The results of recent clinical trials suggest that patients treated with recombinant growth hormone (0.375 mg/kg/wk divided into seven daily doses), with or without oxandrolone (0.0625 mg/kg/d by mouth), had an increase in growth rate that was sustained and resulted in a mean 8- to 10-cm increase in height after 3–7 years of therapy. Before growth hormone therapy is started, a thorough analysis of the costs, benefits, and possible side effects must be discussed with the parents and the child. Long-term studies with low-dose estrogen therapy have not demonstrated a significant effect (positive or negative) on final height in girls with Turner's syndrome. Preliminary data indicate no synergistic effect of combined estrogen and growth hormone therapy on final height. In patients who have been treated with

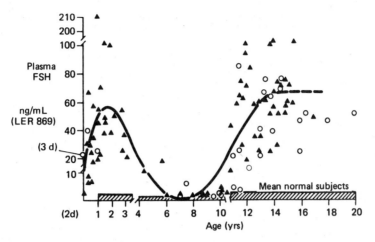

Figure 11–11. Diphasic variation in basal levels of plasma FSH (ng/mL-LER 869) in patients with a 45,X karyotype (solid triangles) and patients with structural abnormalities of the X chromosome and mosaics (open circles). Note that mean basal levels of plasma FSH in patients with gonadal dysgenesis are in the castrate range before 4 years and after 10 years of age. (Reproduced, with permission, from Conte FA, Grumbach MM, Kaplan SL: A diphasic pattern of gonadotropin secretion in patients with the syndrome of gonadal dysgenesis. J Clin Endocrinol Metab 1975;40:670.)

growth hormone and have achieved an acceptable height and in those who have refused growth hormone therapy, estrogen replacement therapy is usually initiated at 12–13 years of age. Conjugated estrogens (0.3 mg or less) or ethinyl estradiol (5 μg) are given orally for the first 21 days of the calendar month. Thereafter, the dose of estrogen is gradually increased over the next several years to 0.6–1.25 mg of conjugated estrogens or 10 μg of ethinyl estradiol daily for the first 21 days of the month. The minimum dose of estrogen necessary to maintain secondary sexual characteristics and menses and prevent osteoporosis should be administered. After the first year of estrogen therapy, médroxyprogesterone acetate, 5 mg daily, or a comparable progestin is given on the 10th–21st days of the menstrual cycle to ensure physiologic menses and to reduce the risk of endometrial carcinoma, which is associated with unopposed estrogen stimulation. (See also Chapter 10.)

X Chromatin-Positive Variants of the Syndrome of Gonadal Dysgenesis

Patients with structural abnormalities of the X chromosome (deletions and additions) and sex chromosome mosaicism with a 45,X cell line may manifest the somatic as well as the gonadal features of the syndrome of gonadal dysgenesis (Table 11–4). Evidence suggests that genes on both the long and short arms of the X chromosome control gonadal differentiation, whereas genes primarily on the short arms of the X prevent the short stature and somatic anomalies that are seen in 45,X patients (Figure 11–4). In general, 45,X/46,XX mosaicism will modify the 45,X phenotype toward normal and can even result in normal gonadal function.

X Chromatin-Negative Variants of the Syndrome of Gonadal Dysgenesis

These patients usually have mosaicism with a 45,X and a Y-bearing cell line—45,X/46,XY; 45,X/47,XXY; 45,X/46,XY/47,XYY—or perhaps a structurally abnormal Y chromosome. They range from phenotypic females with the features of Turner's syndrome through patients with ambiguous genitalia to (rarely) completely virilized males with few stigmas of Turner's syndrome. The variations in gonadal differentiation range from bilateral streaks to bilateral dysgenetic testes to apparently "normal" testes, and there may be asymmetric development, ie, a streak on one side and a dysgenetic testicle or, rarely, a normal testis on the other side—sometimes called "mixed gonadal dysgenesis." Development of the external genitalia and of the internal ducts correlates with the degree of testicular differentiation and, presumably, the capacity of the fetal testes to secrete anti-müllerian hormone and testosterone.

The risk of development of gonadal tumors is greatly increased in patients with 45,X/46,XY mosaicism, and prophylactic removal of streak gonads or dysgenetic undescended testes in this syndrome is indicated. Breast development at or after the age of puberty in these patients is commonly associated with a gonadal neoplasm, usually a gonadoblastoma. Pelvic sonography, CT, or MRI scanning may be useful in screening for neoplasms in these patients. Gonadoblastomas are calcified so that they may be visible even on a plain film of the abdomen.

The diagnosis of 45,XY/46,XY mosaicism can be established by the demonstration of both 45,X and 46,XY cells in blood, skin, or gonadal tissue. In some mosaics, a "marker" chromosome is found that is cy-

Table 11–4. Relationship of structural abnormalities of the X and Y to clinical manifestations of the syndrome of gonadal dysgenesis.

Type of Sex Chromosome Abnormality	Karyotype	Phenotype	Sexual Infantilism	Short Stature	Somatic Anomalies of Turner's Syndrome
Loss of an X or Y	45,XO	Female	+	+	+
Deletion of short arm of an X[1]	46,XXqi	Female	+ (occ. ±)	+	+
	46,XXp–	Female	+, ±, or –	+ (–)	+ (–)
Deletion of long arm of an X[1]	46,XXq–	Female	+	– (+)	– or (±)
Deletion of ends of both arms of an X	46,XXr	Female	– or +	+	+ or (±)
Deletion of short arm of Y	46,XYp–	Female	+	+	+

[1]In Xp– and Xq–, the extent and site of the deleted segment are variable.

Xqi = Isochromosome for long arm of an X; Xp– = deletion of short arm of an X; Xq– = deletion of long arm of an X; Xr = ring chromosome derived from an X.

togenetically indistinguishable as X or Y. In these cases, molecular analysis with X- and Y-specific probes is indicated to definitively determine the origin of the marker chromosome. The decision about the sex of rearing of the child should be based on the age at diagnosis and the potential for normal function of the external genitalia. Patients with 45,X/46,XY mosaicism ascertained by amniocentesis have been described who have normal male genitalia and normal testicular histologic features. Thus, the ambiguity of the genitalia often described in these patients is due to ascertainment bias. In patients assigned a female gender role, the gonads should be removed and the external genitalia repaired. Estrogen therapy should be initiated at the age of puberty, as in patients with a 45,X karyotype (see above). In affected infants who are assigned a male gender role, all gonadal tissue except that which appears histologically normal and is in the scrotum should be removed. Removal of the müllerian structures and repair of hypospadias are also indicated. At puberty, depending on the functional integrity of the retained gonads, androgen replacement therapy may be indicated in doses similar to those for patients with XY gonadal dysgenesis. In patients with retained scrotal testes, a repeat gonadal biopsy is indicated postpubertally to rule out the possibility of carcinoma in situ, a premalignant lesion (see below).

46,XX & 46,XY GONADAL DYSGENESIS

The terms XX and XY gonadal dysgenesis have been applied to 46,XX or 46,XY patients who have bilateral streak gonads, a female phenotype, and no somatic stigmas of Turner's syndrome. After the age of puberty, these patients exhibit sexual infantilism, castrate levels of plasma and urinary gonadotropins, normal or tall stature, and eunuchoid proportions.

46,XX Gonadal Dysgenesis

Familial and sporadic cases of XX gonadal dysgenesis have been reported. Pedigree analysis of familial cases is consistent with autosomal recessive

inheritance. However, in one family recently reported, four affected women had an inherited interstitial deletion of the long arm of the X chromosome involving the q21–q27 region. This region seems to contain a gene or genes "critical" to ovarian development and function. In three families, XX gonadal dysgenesis was associated with deafness of the sensorineural type. In several affected groups of siblings, a spectrum of clinical findings occurred, eg, varying degrees of ovarian function, including breast development and menses followed by secondary amenorrhea. As is not the case in Turner's syndrome, stature is normal. The diagnosis of 46,XX gonadal dysgenesis should be suspected in phenotypic females with sexual infantilism and normal müllerian structures who lack the somatic stigmas of the syndrome of gonadal dysgenesis (Turner's syndrome). Karyotype analysis reveals only 46,XX cells. As in Turner's syndrome, gonadotropin levels are high, estrogen levels are low, and treatment consists of cyclic estrogen replacement.

Sporadic cases of XX gonadal dysgenesis may represent a heterogeneous group of patients from a pathogenetic point of view. XX gonadal dysgenesis should be distinguished from ovarian failure due to infections such as mumps, antibodies to gonadotropin receptors, biologically inactive FSH, gonadotropin-insensitive ovaries, and galactosemia—as well as errors in steroid (estrogen) biosynthesis.

46,XY Gonadal Dysgenesis

46,XY gonadal dysgenesis occurs both sporadically and in familial aggregates. Patients with the complete form of this syndrome have female external genitalia, normal or tall stature, bilateral streak gonads, müllerian duct development, sexual infantilism, eunuchoid habitus, and a 46,XY karyotype. Clitoromegaly is quite common, and in familial cases a continuum of involvement ranging from the complete syndrome to ambiguity of the external genitalia has been described. The phenotypic difference between the complete form of XY gonadal dysgenesis and the incomplete form is due to the degree of differentiation of testicular tissue and the functional capacity of the fetal testis to produce testosterone and anti-müllerian hormone. Postpubertally, plasma and urinary gonadotropin levels are markedly elevated.

Analysis of familial and sporadic cases of 46,XY gonadal dysgenesis indicates that 15–20% of patients studied have a minute deletion of the short arm of the Y chromosome involving the *SRY* gene or a mutation in the HMG box of the *SRY* gene that affects DNA binding by the SRY protein. Patients with large deletions of the Y chromosome may have stigmas of Turner's syndrome. Mutations outside the HMG box region of the *SRY* gene as well as X-linked and autosomal genes may be responsible for those patients in whom no molecular abnormality has as yet been found. A mutation in the HMG box of the *SRY* gene has been described in three normal 46,XY fathers and their progeny with 46,XY gonadal dysgenesis. These three familial cohorts suggest that these mutations may affect either the quantity or the timing of *SRY* expression and in this manner result in either normal or abnormal testicular differentiation.

Therapy for patients with 46,XY gonadal dysgenesis who have female external genitalia involves prophylactic gonadectomy at diagnosis and estrogen substitution at puberty. In the incomplete form of XY gonadal dysgenesis, assignment of a male gender role may be possible. It depends upon the degree of ambiguity of the genitalia and the potential for normal function. Prophylactic gonadectomy must be considered, since fertility is unlikely and there is an increased risk of malignant transformation of the dysgenetic gonads in these patients. Biopsy of all retained gonads should be done pre- and postpubertally in order to detect early malignant changes (carcinoma in situ). In affected individuals raised as males, prosthetic testes should be implanted at the time of gonadectomy, and, at the age of puberty, androgen substitution therapy should be instituted. Testosterone enanthate in oil (or other long-acting testosterone ester) is used, beginning with 50 mg intramuscularly every 4 weeks and gradually increasing the dose over 3–4 years to a full replacement dose of 200 mg intramuscularly every 2 weeks.

TRUE HERMAPHRODITISM

In true hermaphroditism, both ovarian and testicular tissue is present in one or both gonads. Differentiation of the internal and external genitalia is highly variable. The external genitalia may simulate those of a male or female, but most often they are ambiguous. Cryptorchism and hypospadias are common. A testis or ovotestis, if present, is located in the labioscrotal folds in one-third of patients, in the inguinal canal in one-third, and in the abdomen in the remainder. In all cases, a uterus is present, though it may be hypoplastic or unicornuate. The differentiation of the genital ducts usually follows that of the ipsilateral

gonad. The ovotestis is the most common gonad found in true hermaphrodites, followed by the ovary and, least commonly, the testis. At puberty, breast development is usual in untreated patients, and menses occur in over 50% of cases. Whereas the ovary or the ovarian portion of an ovotestis may function normally, the testis or testicular portion of an ovotestis is almost always dysgenetic.

Sixty percent of true hermaphrodites have been reported to have a 46,XX karyotype, 20% 46,XY, and about 20% mosaicism or 46,XX/46,XY chimerism. 46,XX true hermaphroditism appears to be a genetically heterogeneous entity. A small percentage of 46,XX true hermaphrodites, including some in family cohorts with 46,XX males, have been reported to be *SRY*-positive. Hence, Y-to-X and Y-to-autosome translocations, hidden sex chromosome mosaicism, or chimerism can explain the pathogenesis in these patients. The majority of 46,XX true hermaphrodites studied are *SRY*-negative. A number of family cohorts have been reported in whom *SRY*-negative 46,XX males and 46,XX true hermaphrodites occur. This observation suggests a common genetic pathogenesis in these patients. Possible genetic mechanisms to explain *SRY*-negative true hermaphroditism include (1) mutation of a downstream autosomal gene or genes involved in testicular determination; (2) mutation, deletion, duplication, or anomalous inactivation of an X-linked locus involved in testes determination; or (3) circumscribed chimerism or mosaicism occurring only in the gonads.

The diagnosis of true hermaphroditism should be considered in all patients with ambiguous genitalia. The finding of a 46,XX/46,XY karyotype or a bilobate gonad compatible with an ovotestis in the inguinal region or labioscrotal folds suggests the diagnosis. If all other forms of male and female pseudohermaphroditism have been excluded, laparotomy and histologic confirmation of both ovarian and testicular tissue establish the diagnosis. The management of true hermaphroditism is contingent upon the age at diagnosis and a careful assessment of the functional capacity of the gonads, genital ducts, and external genitalia.

Gonadal Neoplasms in Dysgenetic Gonads

While gonadal tumors are rare in patients with 47,XXY Klinefelter's syndrome and 45,X gonadal dysgenesis, the prevalence of gonadal neoplasms is greatly increased in patients with certain types of dysgenetic gonads. The frequency is increased in 45,X/46,XY mosaicism and in patients with a structurally abnormal Y chromosome and in XY gonadal dysgenesis, either with a female phenotype or with ambiguous genitalia. Gonadoblastomas, dysgerminomas, seminomas, and teratomas are found most frequently. Prophylactic gonadectomy is advised in these two categories as well as in individuals with gonadal dysgenesis who manifest signs of virilization, regardless of karyotype.

The gonad should be preserved in patients who are to be raised as males only if it is a histologically normal testis that can be relocated in the scrotum. The fact that a testis is palpable in the scrotum does not preclude malignant degeneration and tumor dissemination, as seminomas tend to metastasize at an early stage before a local mass is obvious.

FEMALE PSEUDOHERMAPHRODITISM

Affected individuals have normal ovaries and müllerian derivatives associated with ambiguous external genitalia. In the absence of testes, a female fetus will be masculinized if subjected to increased circulating levels of androgens derived from a fetal or maternal source. The degree of masculinization depends upon the stage of differentiation at the time of exposure (Figure 11–12). After 12 weeks of gestation, androgens will produce only clitoral hypertrophy. Rarely, ambiguous genitalia that superficially resemble those produced by androgens are the result of teratogenic malformations.

Congenital Adrenal Hyperplasia (Figure 11–13)

There are six major types of congenital adrenal hyperplasia, all transmitted as autosomal recessive disorders. The common denominator of all six types is a defect in the synthesis of cortisol that results in an increase in ACTH and then in adrenal hyperplasia. Both males and females can be affected, but males are rarely diagnosed at birth unless they have ambiguous genitalia, are salt losers and manifest adrenal crises, are identified during newborn screening, or are at risk because they have an affected sibling. Defects of types I–III are confined to the adrenal gland

and produce virilization. Defects of types IV–VI have in common blocks in cortisol and sex steroid synthesis in both the adrenals and the gonads. The latter three types produce chiefly incomplete masculinization in the male and little or no virilization in the female (Table 11–5). Consequently, these will be discussed primarily as forms of male pseudohermaphroditism. (See also Chapters 6, 9, 10, and 12.)

P450c21 Hydroxylase Deficiency

21-Hydroxylase activity is mediated by P450c21, a microsomal cytochrome P450 enzyme. A deficiency of this enzyme results in the most common type of adrenal hyperplasia, with an overall prevalence of 1:14,000 live births in Caucasians. The locus for the gene that codes for 21-hydroxylation is on the short arm of chromosome 6, close to the locus for C4 (complement) between HLA-B and HLA-D. DNA analysis has detected two genes, designated 21-OHA and 21-OHB, in this area in tandem with the two genes for complement, C4A and C4B. 21-OHA is a nonfunctional "pseudogene," ie, it is missing critical sequences and does not code for a functional 21-hydroxylase. Patients with P450c21 (21-hydroxylase) deficiency have a mutation, deletion, or "gene conversion" (the transfer of nonfunctioning sequences from the 21-OHA gene to the 21-OHB gene) in the P450c21 B gene. Seventy-five percent of patients with P450c21 deficiency have point mutations or microgene conversions. The remainder have gene deletions and macrogene conversions. Recent work has demonstrated that classic salt-wasting 21-hydroxylase deficiency is associated with a mutation, deletion, or gene conversion that abolishes or severely reduces 21-hydroxylase activity. Most patients with 21-hydroxylase deficiency are compound heterozygotes, ie, they have a different mutation involving each of their 21-OHB allelic genes. The phenotypic spectrum observed—salt loss, simple virilization, or late onset of virilization—is a consequence of the de-

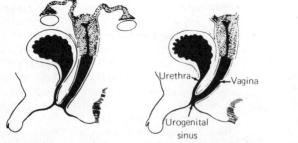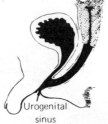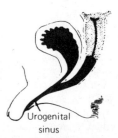

Figure 11–12. Female pseudohermaphroditism induced by prenatal exposure to androgens. Exposure after the 12th fetal week leads only to clitoral hypertrophy (diagram at left). Exposure at progressively earlier stages of differentiation (depicted from left to right in drawings) leads to retention of the urogenital sinus and labioscrotal fusion. If exposure occurs sufficiently early, the labia will fuse to form a penile urethra. (Reproduced, with permission, from Grumbach MM, Ducharme J: The effects of androgens on fetal sexual development: Androgen-induced female pseudohermaphroditism. Fertil Steril 1960;11:757.)

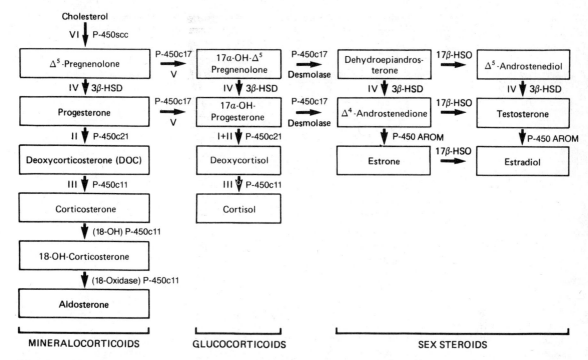

Figure 11–13. A diagrammatic representation of the steroid biosynthetic pathways in the adrenal and gonads. I–VI correspond to enzymes whose deficiency results in congenital adrenal hyperplasia. (OH, hydroxy or hydroxylase; 3β-HSD, 3β-hydroxysteroid dehydrogenase and Δ⁵-isomerase; 17β-HSO, 17β-hydroxysteroid oxidoreductase (dehydrogenase); P450scc, cholesterol side-chain cleavage, previously termed 20,22 desmolase; P450c21, 21-hydroxylase; P450c17, 17-hydroxylase; P450arom, aromatase. P450c17 also mediates 17,20-lyase activity; P450c11, 11-hydroxylase, also mediates 18-hydroxylase and 18-oxidase reactions. (See also Figures 12-4, 12-5, and 16-2.) (Modified and reproduced, with permission, from Conte FA, Grumbach MM: Pathogenesis, classification, diagnosis, and treatment of anomalies of sex. In: *Endocrinology.* DeGroot L [editor]. Grune & Stratton, 1989.)

gree of enzymatic deficiency. The latter is determined by the functionally less severe mutated allele involving the 21-OHB gene. The gene for P450c21 (21-hydroxylase) deficiency is not only closely linked to the HLA supergene complex, but certain specific HLA subtypes are found to be statistically increased in patients with 21-hydroxylase deficiency. These include Bw51 in the simple virilizing form and Bw47 in the salt-losing form.

A. Type I—P450c21 Hydroxylase Deficiency With Virilization: The defect in P450c21 (21-hydroxylase) activity results in impaired cortisol synthesis, increased ACTH levels, and increased adrenal androgen precursor and androgen secretion. Prior to 12 weeks of gestation, high fetal androgen levels lead to varying degrees of labioscrotal fusion and clitoral enlargement in the female fetus; exposure to androgen after 12 weeks induces clitoromegaly alone. In the male fetus, no structural abnormalities in the external genitalia are evident at birth, but the phallus may be enlarged. These patients produce sufficient amounts of aldosterone to prevent the signs and symptoms of mineralocorticoid deficiency. Virilization continues after birth in untreated patients. This

results in rapid growth and bone maturation as well as the physical signs of excess androgen secretion (eg, acne, seborrhea, increased muscular development, premature development of pubic or axillary hair, and phallic enlargement). True (central) precocious puberty can occur following initiation of glucocorticoid therapy in affected children with peripubertal bone ages.

Mild defects in P450c21 (21-hydroxylase) activity have been reported. Patients can be symptomatic (late-onset or nonclassic) or asymptomatic ("cryptic" form). These mild forms of P450c21 hydroxylase deficiency are HLA-linked, as is "classic" P450c21 hydroxylase deficiency; however, they occur much more frequently than the classic form of the disease. It has been postulated that "nonclassic" P450c21 hydroxylase deficiency is the most common autosomal recessive disorder, affecting one in 100 persons of all ethnic groups but having an incidence two to three times higher in Hispanics and Ashkenazi Jews. Females with late-onset P450c21 hydroxylase deficiency have normal female genitalia at birth and do not have an electrolyte abnormality. Mild virilization occurs later in childhood and adolescence, resulting

Table 11–5. Clinical manifestations of the various types of congenital adrenal hyperplasia.

Enzymatic Defect	P-450scc Cholesterol Side-Chain Cleavage		3β-Hydroxysteroid Dehydrogenase		P-450c17 (17α-Hydroxylase)		P-450c11 (11β-Hydroxylase)		P-450c21 (21α-Hydroxylase)	
Type	VI		IV		V		III		II and I	
Chromosomal	XX	XY	XX	XY	XX	XY	XX	XY	XX	XY
External genitalia	Female	Female	Female (clitori-megaly)[1]	Ambig-uous	Female	Female or am-biguous	Ambig-uous[1]	Male	Ambig-uous[1]	Male
Postnatal virilization	– (Sexual infantilism at puberty)		±	Mild to moder-ate	– (Sexual infantilism at puberty)		+		+	
Addisonian crises	+		±		–		–		+ in 80% (type II)	
Hypertension	–		–		+		+		–	

[1]Normal female in late-onset and "cryptic" forms.

in the premature development of pubic or axillary hair, slight clitoral enlargement, menstrual irregularities, acne, hirsutism, and an advanced bone age. Affected males have normal male genitalia at birth, rapid growth. and advanced skeletal maturation. Later in childhood, they exhibit premature growth of pubic or axillary hair, sexual precocity with inappropriately small testes, and increased muscular development. While tall as children, they end up as short adults due to advanced bone maturation and epiphysial fusion. Asymptomatic individuals who have the same biochemical abnormalities as patients with mild forms of P450c21 hydroxylase deficiency can be detected by hormonal testing of families in which there is at least one member with symptoms.

B. Type II—P450c21 Hydroxylase Deficiency With Virilization and Salt Loss: The salt-losing variant of P450c21 hydroxylase deficiency accounts for about 80% of patients with classic 21-hydroxylase deficiency and involves a more severe deficit of P450c21 hydroxylase, which leads to impaired secretion of both cortisol and aldosterone. This results in electrolyte and fluid losses after the fifth day of life and as a consequence hyponatremia, hyperkalemia, acidosis, dehydration, and vascular collapse. Masculinization of the external genitalia of affected females tends to be more severe than that found in patients with simple P450c21 hydroxylase deficiency. Affected males have macrogenitosomia.

The diagnosis of P450c21 hydroxylase deficiency should always be considered (1) in patients with ambiguous genitalia who have a 46,XX karyotype (and are thus female pseudohermaphrodites); (2) in apparent cryptorchid males; (3) in any infant who presents with shock, hypoglycemia, and chemical findings compatible with adrenal insufficiency; and (4) in males and females with signs of virilization prior to puberty, including premature adrenarche. In the past, the diagnosis of P450c21 hydroxylase deficiency was based on the finding of elevated levels of 17-keto-

steroids and pregnanetriol in the urine. Although still valid and useful, urinary steroid determinations have been replaced by the measurement of plasma 17-hydroxyprogesterone.

The concentration of plasma 17-hydroxyprogesterone is elevated in umbilical cord blood but rapidly decreases into the range of 100–200 ng/dL (3–6 nmol/L) by 24 hours after delivery. In premature infants and in stressed full-term newborns, the levels of 17-hydroxyprogesterone are higher than those observed in nonstressed full-term infants. In patients with P450c21 hydroxylase deficiency, the 17-hydroxyprogesterone values usually range from 3000 to 40,000 ng/dL (90–1200 nmol/L) depending on the age of the patient and the severity of P450c21 hydroxylase deficiency. Patients with mild P450c21 hydroxylase deficiency, ie, late-onset and cryptic forms, may have borderline basal 17-hydroxyprogesterone values, but they can be distinguished from heterozygotes on the basis of an elevated 17-hydroxyprogesterone response to the parenteral administration of ACTH. Measurement of plasma 17-hydroxyprogesterone levels using heel-stick capillary blood specimens blotted onto paper has been shown to be a valid screening tool for 21-hydroxylase deficiency in newborn infants.

Salt losers may be ascertained clinically or by chemical evidence of hyponatremia and hyperkalemia on a regular or low-salt diet. In these patients, aldosterone levels in both plasma and urine are low in relation to the serum sodium concentration, while plasma renin activity is elevated.

HLA typing, measurement of amniotic fluid 17-hydroxyprogesterone levels, and chorionic villus biopsy with HLA and gene analysis have been utilized in the prenatal diagnosis of affected fetuses. Data indicate that prenatal therapy with dexamethasone given to the mother early in pregnancy can lessen the genital ambiguity seen in affected newborn females.

Heterozygosity has been ascertained by HLA typing in informative pedigrees and by the use of ACTH-induced rises in plasma 17-hydroxyprogesterone levels.

C. Type III—P450c11 Hydroxylase Deficiency: (Virilization with hypertension.) Classic 11-hydroxylase deficiency occurs in about 1:100,000 births and represents 5–8% of cases of congenital adrenal hyperplasia. A defect in hydroxylation at C11 leads to the hypersecretion of 11-deoxycorticosterone and 11-deoxycortisol in addition to adrenal androgens. Marked heterogeneity in the clinical and hormonal manifestations of this defect has been described, including mild, late-onset, and even "cryptic" forms. Patients with this form of adrenal hyperplasia classically exhibit virilization secondary to increased androgen production and hypertension caused by increased 11-deoxycorticosterone secretion. The hypertension is not obligatory and may appear in late childhood or adolescence.

Two P450c11 hydroxylase genes have been localized to the long arm of chromosome 8: P450c11 and P450aldo. Similar to 21-hydroxylase, these two genes are 95% homologous. P450c11 encodes one isozyme for 11-hydroxylation expressed in the zona, fasciculata, and reticularis and is ACTH-dependent; the other, P450aldo, encodes the second isozyme, aldosterone synthetase, expressed in the zona glomerulosa, which is angiotensin-dependent. Hence, mutations, deletions, and gene duplications can produce a wide spectrum of clinical manifestations from virilization and hypertension (P450c11 deficiency) to salt wasting (aldosterone synthetase deficiency) to glucocorticoid remedial hypertension (due to fusion of the ACTH-dependent regulatory region of the 11-hydroxylase gene with the coding region of aldosterone synthetase). Since both the P450c11 and the P450aldo gene are on chromosome 8, they are not linked to HLA. ACTH stimulation tests have thus far failed to demonstrate a consistent biochemical aberration in obligate heterozygotes.

The diagnosis of P450c11β-hydroxylase deficiency can be confirmed by demonstration of elevated plasma levels of 11-deoxycortisol and 11-deoxycorticosterone and increased excretion of their metabolites in urine (mainly tetrahydro-11-deoxycortisol) either in the basal state or after the administration of ACTH.

D. Type IV—3β-Hydroxysteroid Dehydrogenase Deficiency: (Male or female pseudohermaphroditism and adrenal insufficiency.) See below.

E. Type V—P450c17 Deficiency: (Male pseudohermaphroditism, sexual infantilism, hypertension. and hypokalemic alkalosis.) See below.

F. Type VI—P450scc Side-Chain Cleavage Deficiency: (Congenital lipoid adrenal hyperplasia, male pseudohermaphroditism, sexual infantilism and adrenal insufficiency.) See below.

Treatment

Treatment of patients with adrenal hyperplasia may be divided into acute and chronic phases. In acute adrenal crises, a deficiency of both cortisol and aldosterone results in hypoglycemia, hyponatremia, hyperkalemia, hypovolemia, and shock. If the patient is hypoglycemic, an intravenous bolus of glucose, 0.25–0.5 g/kg (maximum, 25 g) should be administered. If the patient is in shock, a saline infusion of 20 mL/kg may be given over the first hour; thereafter, glucose fluid and electrolyte replacement is calculated on the basis of deficits and standard maintenance requirements. Hydrocortisone sodium succinate, 50 mg/m^2, should be given as a bolus and another 50–100 mg/m^2 added to the infusion fluid over the first 24 hours of therapy. If hyponatremia and hyperkalemia are present, 0.05–0.1 mg of fludrocortisone by mouth may be given along with the intravenous saline and hydrocortisone. Since hydrocortisone has mineralocorticoid activity, it may suffice to correct the electrolyte abnormality along with the saline. In extreme cases of hyponatremia, hyperkalemia, and acidosis, sodium bicarbonate and a cation exchange resin (eg, sodium polystyrene sulfonate) may be needed.

Once the patient is stabilized and a definitive diagnosis has been arrived at by means of appropriate steroid studies, the patient should receive maintenance doses of glucocorticoids to permit normal growth, development, and bone maturation (hydrocortisone, approximately 12–18 mg/m^2/d by mouth in three divided doses). The dose of hydrocortisone must be titrated in each patient, depending on steroid hormone levels, growth, and clinical signs of steroid overdose or virilization. Salt losers need treatment with mineralocorticoid (fludrocortisone, 0.05–0.1 mg/d by mouth) and added dietary salt. The dose of mineralocorticoid should be adjusted so that the electrolytes and blood pressure, as well as the plasma renin activity, are in the normal range. (See also Chapters 6 and 7.)

Patients with ambiguous external genitalia should have plastic repair before age 1 year. Clitoral recession or clitoroplasty is indicated, not clitoridectomy. Of major importance to the family with an affected child is the assurance that the child will grow and develop into a normal adult. In patients with the most common form of adrenal hyperplasia—21-hydroxylase deficiency—fertility in males and feminization, menstruation, and fertility in females can be expected with adequate treatment. Long-term psychologic guidance and support for the patient and family by the physician is essential.

Adrenal rests in the testes of males with P450c21 hydroxylase deficiency (especially salt losers) may enlarge under the stimulus of ACTH and be mistaken for testicular neoplasms. These adrenal rests are often bilateral and are made up of cells that appear indistinguishable from Leydig cells histologically except that they lack Reinke crystalloids. The rests are usually seen in noncompliant or undertreated patients. To prevent this complication as well as the risk of adrenal crisis, pituitary hyperplasia, and adrenal carcinoma, continuous treatment with a glucocorticoid (and, if indicated, a mineralocorticoid) is recommended even in adult males.

P450 AROMATASE DEFICIENCY

Female pseudohermaphroditism due to both placental and fetal aromatase deficiency has been described; the enzymatic deficiency leads to increased circulating fetal androgens. Mutations in the P450 aromatase gene have been found in two affected females.

MATERNAL ANDROGENS & PROGESTOGENS

Masculinization of the external genitalia of a female infant can occur if the mother is given testosterone, other androgenic steroids, or a synthetic progestational agent during the first 10 weeks of pregnancy. After the 12th week, exposure results in clitoromegaly alone. Norethindrone, ethisterone, norethynodrel, and medroxyprogesterone acetate have all been implicated in masculinization. Nonadrenal female pseudohermaphroditism can occur as a consequence of maternal ingestion of danazol, the 2,3-d-isoxazole derivative of 17α-ethinyl testosterone. In rare instances, masculinization of a female fetus is due to a maternal ovarian or adrenal tumor, congenital virilizing adrenal hyperplasia in the mother, or a luteoma of pregnancy.

The diagnosis of female pseudohermaphroditism arising from transplacental passage of androgenic steroids is based on exclusion of other forms of female pseudohermaphroditism and a history of drug exposure. Surgical correction of the genitalia, if needed, is the only therapy necessary.

Nonadrenal female pseudohermaphroditism can be associated with imperforate anus, renal anomalies, and other malformations of the lower intestine and urinary tract. Sporadic as well as familial cases have been reported.

MALE PSEUDOHERMAPHRODITISM

Male pseudohermaphrodites have gonads that are testes, but the genital ducts or external genitalia are not completely masculinized. Male pseudohermaphroditism can result from deficient testosterone secretion as a consequence of (1) defective testicular differentiation (testicular dysgenesis), (2) impaired secretion of testosterone or anti-müllerian hormone,

(3) failure of target tissue response to testosterone and dihydrotestosterone or anti-müllerian hormone, and (4) failure of conversion of testosterone to dihydrotestosterone. (See also Chapter 9.)

Testicular Unresponsiveness to hCG & LH

Male sexual differentiation is dependent upon the production of testosterone by fetal Leydig cells. Leydig cell testosterone secretion is under the influence of placental hCG during the critical period of male sexual differentiation and, thereafter, fetal pituitary LH during gestation.

The finding of normal male sexual differentiation in XY males with anencephaly, apituitarism, or congenital hypothalamic hypopituitarism suggests that, in the human, male sex differentiation occurs independently of the secretion of fetal pituitary gonadotropins.

Absence, hypoplasia, or unresponsiveness of Leydig cells to hCG-LH results in deficient testosterone production and, consequently, male pseudohermaphroditism. The extent of the genital ambiguity is a function of the degree of testosterone deficiency. A small number of patients with absent, hypoplastic, or unresponsive Leydig cells (attributed to a lack of receptor activity for hCG-LH) have been reported as well as an animal model, the "vet" rat. In most of the patients thus far reported, the defect resulted in female-appearing genitalia. Müllerian duct regression was complete. Basal gonadotropin levels as well as GnRH-evoked responses were elevated in postpubertal patients. Plasma 17-hydroxyprogesterone, androstenedione, and testosterone levels were low, and hCG elicited little or no response in testosterone or its precursors. Treatment depends on the age at diagnosis and the extent of masculinization. A female sex assignment has usually been chosen in patients with female-appearing genitalia.

Inborn Errors of Testosterone Biosynthesis

Figure 11–14 demonstrates the major pathways in testosterone biosynthesis in the gonads; each step is associated with an inherited defect that results in testosterone deficiency and, consequently, male pseudohermaphroditism (see also Chapter 12). Steps 1, 2, and 3 are enzymatic deficiencies that occur in both the adrenals and the gonads and result in defective synthesis of both corticosteroids and testosterone. Thus, they represent forms of congenital adrenal hyperplasia.

A. P450scc Deficiency, Cholesterol Side-Chain Cleavage Defect, Congenital Lipoid Adrenal Hyperplasia: (Male pseudohermaphroditism, sexual infantilism, and adrenal insufficiency.) This is a very early defect in the synthesis of all steroids and results in severe adrenal and gonadal deficiency. The P450scc gene has been isolated, cloned, and local-

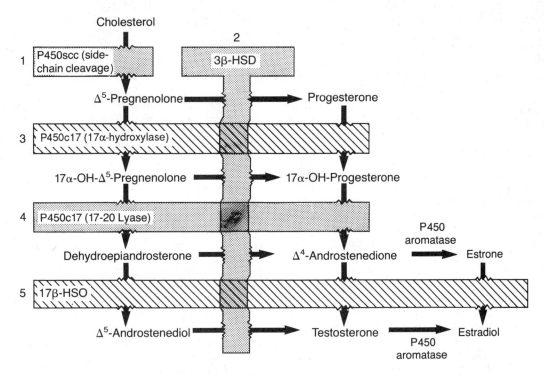

Figure 11–14. Enzymatic defects in the biosynthetic pathway for testosterone. All five of the enzymatic defects cause male pseudohermaphroditism in affected males. Although all of the blocks affect gonadal steroidogenesis, those at steps 1, 2, and 3 are associated with major abnormalities in the biosynthesis of glucocorticoids and mineralocorticoids in the adrenal. (OH, hydroxy; 3β-HSD, 3β-hydroxysteroid dehydrogenase; 17β-HSO, 17β-hydroxysteroid oxidoreductase (dehydrogenase). Chemical names for enzymes are shown with traditional names in parentheses. (Modified and reproduced, with permission, from Conte FA, Grumbach MM: Pathogenesis, classification, diagnosis, and treatment of anomalies of sex. In: *Endocrinology.* DeGroot L [editor]. Grune & Stratton, 1989.)

ized to chromosome 15. However, thus far, molecular analysis of this gene has not revealed a defect in affected patients. Affected males have female or, rarely, ambiguous external genitalia with a blind vaginal pouch and hypoplastic male genital ducts but no müllerian derivatives; the genitalia of affected females are normal. Large lipid-laden adrenals that displace the kidneys downward may be demonstrated by intravenous urography, abdominal ultrasonography, or CT scanning. Death in early infancy from adrenal insufficiency is not uncommon. The diagnosis is confirmed by the lack of or low levels of all C21, C19, and C18 steroids in plasma and urine and an absent response to ACTH stimulation. Treatment involves replacement with appropriate doses of glucocorticoids and mineralocorticoids.

B. 3β-Hydroxysteroid Dehydrogenase and Δ⁵-Isomerase Deficiency: (Male or female pseudohermaphroditism and adrenal insufficiency.) 3β-Hydroxysteroid dehydrogenase and Δ⁵-isomerase deficiency is an early defect in steroid synthesis that results in inability of the adrenals and gonads to convert 3β-hydroxy-Δ⁵ steroids to 3-keto-Δ⁴ steroids. This enzyme is encoded for by a gene on the short

arm of chromosome 1. Recent data indicate that there are two highly homologous genes encoding 3β-hydroxysteroid dehydrogenase on chromosome 1. The type I 3β-hydroxysteroid dehydrogenase gene is expressed in the placenta and peripheral tissues, while type II is expressed in the adrenals and gonads. 3β-Hydroxysteroid dehydrogenase is not a cytochrome P450 enzyme, and it requires NAD⁺ as a cofactor. Compound heterozygosity with a different point mutation in each allelic type II gene has been found in affected patients studied so far. This defect in its complete form results in a severe deficiency of aldosterone, cortisol, testosterone, and estradiol. Males with this defect are incompletely masculinized, and females have mild clitoromegaly. Salt loss and adrenal crises usually occur in early infancy in affected patients. Affected males may experience normal male puberty but often have prominent gynecomastia. Patients with a mild non-salt-losing form of 3β-hydroxysteroid dehydrogenase deficiency have been described. An affected brother and sister have been reported in whom the male had perineal hypospadias and the female had normal genitalia at birth. Both presented with premature pubarche and elevated Δ^5-17-ketosteroids in urine and blood; mineralocorticoid function was normal. "Nonclassic" (late-onset) forms of this defect usually present with premature pubarche, hirsutism, or both.

The diagnosis of 3β-hydroxysteroid dehydrogenase deficiency is based on finding elevated concentrations of Δ^5-pregnenolone, Δ^5-17α-hydroxypregnenolone, dehydroepiandrosterone (DHEA) and its sulfate, and other 3β-hydroxy-Δ^5 steroids in the plasma and urine of patients with a consistent clinical picture. The diagnosis may be facilitated by detecting abnormal levels of serum Δ^5-17α-hydroxypregnenolone and DHEA as well as abnormal ratios of Δ^5 to Δ^4 steroids after intravenous administration of 0.25 mg of synthetic ACTH. Suppression of the increased plasma and urinary 3β-hydroxy-Δ^5 steroids by the administration of dexamethasone distinguishes 3β-hydroxysteroid dehydrogenase deficiency from a virilizing adrenal tumor. Treatment of this condition is similar to that of other forms of adrenal hyperplasia (see above).

C. P450c17 Deficiency, 17-Hydroxylase Deficiency: (Male pseudohermaphroditism, sexual infantilism, hypertension, and hypokalemic alkalosis.) A defect in 17-hydroxylation in the zona fasciculata of the adrenal and in the gonads results in impaired synthesis of 17-hydroxyprogesterone and 17-hydroxypregnenolone and, consequently, cortisol and sex steroids. The secretion of large amounts of corticosterone and deoxycorticosterone (DOC) leads to hypertension, hypokalemia, and alkalosis. Increased DOC secretion with resultant hypertension produces suppression of renin and, consequently, decreased aldosterone secretion.

A single gene on chromosome 10 encodes both adrenal and testicular P450c17 hydroxylase as well as 17,20-lyase activity. This enzyme catalyzes the 17-hydroxylation of pregnenolone and progesterone to 17-hydroxypregnenolone and 17-hydroxyprogesterone as well as their scission (lyase) to C19 steroids —dehydroepiandrosterone and androstenedione—in the adrenal cortex and gonads.

The clinical manifestations result from the adrenal and gonadal defect. XX females have normal development of the internal ducts and external genitalia but manifest sexual infantilism with elevated gonadotropin concentrations at puberty. XY males have impaired testosterone synthesis by the fetal testes, which results in female or ambiguous genitalia. At adolescence, sexual infantilism and hypertension are the hallmarks of this defect.

The diagnosis of 17-hydroxylase deficiency should be suspected in XY males with female or ambiguous genitalia or XX females with sexual infantilism who also manifest hypertension associated with hypokalemic alkalosis. High levels of progesterone, Δ^5-pregnenolone, DOC, and corticosterone in plasma and increased excretion of their urinary metabolites establish the diagnosis. Plasma renin activity and al-

dosterone secretion are markedly diminished in these patients.

The following errors affect testosterone and estrogen biosynthesis in the gonads primarily:

D. P450c17 Deficiency; 17,20-lyase deficiency: The enzyme P450c17 mediates the 17-hydroxylation of pregnenolone and progesterone to 17-hydroxypregnenolone and 17-hydroxyprogesterone as well as the scission of the C17,20 bond to yield DHEA and androstenedione, respectively. Rare patients have a defect primarily in the scission of the C21 steroids to C19 steroids (DHEA and androstenedione), which results in a defect in testosterone synthesis and subsequently pseudohermaphroditism in the male and impaired sex steroid synthesis and secretion in the affected 46,XX female. Hence, affected XY individuals with 17,20-lyase deficiency have been male pseudohermaphrodites with either female or ambiguous genitalia and inguinal or intra-abdominal testes. müllerian derivatives are absent as a result of the secretion of anti-müllerian hormone by the fetal testes. At puberty, incomplete virilization without gynecomastia occurs. Affected 46,XX women with sexual infantilism and elevated serum gonadotropin levels have been reported.

Patients with 17,20-lyase deficiency have low circulating levels of testosterone, androstenedione, DHEA, and estradiol. The diagnosis can be confirmed by demonstration of an increased ratio of 17-hydroxy C21 steroids to C19 steroids (testosterone, DHEA, Δ^5-androstenediol, and androstenedione) after stimulation with ACTH or chorionic gonadotropin.

E. 17-Hydroxysteroid Oxidoreductase (Dehydrogenase) Deficiency: The last step in testosterone and estradiol biosynthesis by the gonads involves the reduction of androstenedione to testosterone and estrone to estradiol. 17-Hydroxysteroid oxidoreductase is an NADPH-dependent microsomal enzyme. Two genes are found in tandem on the long arm of chromosome 17. They are 89% homologous. As yet, it is not known whether both genes are functional. At birth, males with a deficiency of the enzyme 17-hydroxysteroid oxidoreductase have female or mildly ambiguous external genitalia resulting from testosterone deficiency during male differentiation. They have male duct development, absent müllerian structures with a blind vaginal pouch, and inguinal or intra-abdominal testes. At puberty, progressive virilization with clitoral hypertrophy occurs, often associated with the concurrent development of gynecomastia. Plasma gonadotropin, androstenedione, and estrone levels are markedly elevated, whereas testosterone and estradiol concentration are relatively low.

17-Hydroxysteroid oxidoreductase deficiency should be included in the differential diagnosis of (1) male pseudohermaphroditism in patients with absent müllerian derivatives who have no abnormality in glucocorticoid or mineralocorticoid synthesis; and (2) male pseudohermaphroditism in patients who virilize at puberty, especially if they also exhibit gynecomastia. The diagnosis of 17-hydroxysteroid oxidoreductase deficiency can be confirmed by the demonstration of inappropriately high plasma levels of estrone and androstenedione and increased ratios of plasma androstenedione to testosterone and estrone to estradiol before and after stimulation with chorionic gonadotropin.

Management of these patients, as of those with other forms of male pseudohermaphroditism, depends on the age at diagnosis and the degree of ambiguity of the external genitalia. In the patient assigned a male gender identity, plastic repair of the genitalia and testosterone replacement therapy at puberty will

be necessary. In patients reared as females (the usual case), the appropriate treatment is castration, followed by estrogen replacement therapy at puberty.

Defects in Androgen-Dependent Target Tissues

The complex mechanism of action of steroid hormones at the cellular level has recently been clarified (Figure 11–15).

Free testosterone enters the target cells and undergoes 5α reduction to dihydrotestosterone. Dihydrotestosterone enters the nucleus, where it binds to the androgen receptor and "activates" it with release of the heat shock protein. The activated androgen receptor complex dimerizes and binds to specific hormone-response elements of the DNA. It initiates transcription, translation, and protein synthesis that

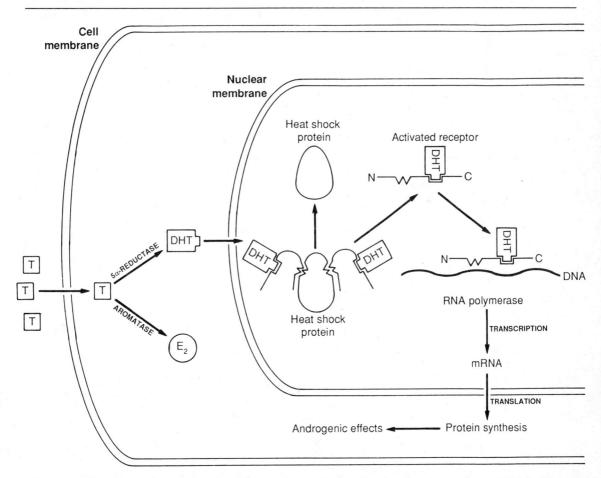

Figure 11–15. Diagrammatic representation of the putative mechanism of action of testosterone on target cells. Testosterone (T) enters the cells, where it is either 5α-reduced to dihydrotestosterone (DHT) or aromatized to estradiol. Dihydrotestosterone enters the nucleus, where it binds to the androgen receptor and "activates" it with release of the heat shock protein. The activated androgen receptor complex then binds as a dimer (not shown) to specific hormone response elements of the DNA and initiates transcription, translation, and protein synthesis, with consequent androgenic effects. (See also Figure 9–3.) (Reproduced, with permission, from Grumbach MM, Conte FA: Disorders of sex differentiation. In: *Williams Textbook of Endocrinology,* 8th ed. Wilson JD, Foster DW [editors], Saunders, 1992.)

leads to androgenic actions. A lack of androgen effect at the end organ and, consequently, male pseudohermaphroditism, may result from abnormalities in 5α-reductase activity, transformation of the steroid-receptor complex, receptor binding of dihydrotestosterone, receptor-ligand complex binding to DNA, transcription, exportation, or translation.

End-Organ Resistance to Androgenic Hormones (Androgen Receptor Defects)

A. Syndrome of Complete Androgen Resistance and Its Variants (Testicular Feminization): The syndrome of complete androgen resistance (testicular feminization) is characterized by a 46,XY karyotype, bilateral testes, absent or hypoplastic wolffian ducts, female-appearing external genitalia, a blind vaginal pouch, and absent or rudimentary müllerian derivatives. At puberty, female secondary sexual characteristics develop, but menarche does not ensue. Pubic and axillary hair is usually sparse and in one-third of patients totally absent. Some patients have a variant form of this syndrome and exhibit slight clitoral enlargement. These patients may exhibit mild virilization in addition to the development of breasts and a female habitus.

Androgen resistance during embryogenesis prevents masculinization of the external genitalia and differentiation of the wolffian ducts. Secretion of anti-müllerian hormone by the fetal Sertoli cells leads to regression of the müllerian ducts. Thus, affected patients are born with female external genitalia and a blind vaginal pouch. At puberty, androgen resistance results in augmented LH secretion with subsequent increases in testosterone and estradiol. Estradiol arises from peripheral conversion of testosterone and androstenedione as well as from direct secretion by the testes. Androgen resistance coupled with increased estradiol secretion results in the development of female secondary sexual characteristics at puberty.

The androgen receptor gene has been localized to the X chromosome between Xq11 and Xq13. The gene is composed of eight exons, A–H. Exon A encodes the amino terminal end of the androgen receptor protein and is thought to play a role in transcription. Exons B and C code for the DNA binding zinc finger of the androgen receptor protein. Exons D–H specify the carboxyl terminal portion of the androgen receptor, which is the androgen-binding domain (Figure 11–16).

Patients with complete androgen resistance have been found to be heterogeneous with respect to dihydrotestosterone binding to the androgen receptor. Receptor-negative and receptor-positive individuals with qualitative defects such as thermolability, instability, and impaired binding affinity as well as individuals with presumed normal binding (postreceptor

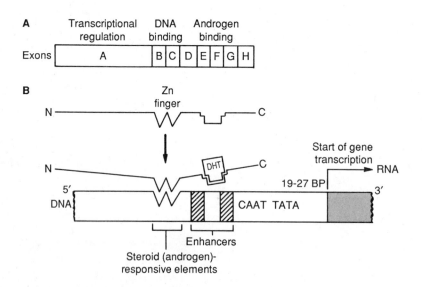

Figure 11–16. *A:* Diagrammatic representation of the androgen receptor gene divided into its eight exons. Exon A codes for the NH$_2$-terminal domain and regulates transcription. Exons B and C code for two zinc fingers. Exons D–H code for the androgen-binding domain of the receptor. ***B:*** The organization of a steroid-responsive gene. Ligand binding activates the receptor, and it binds to the steroid response elements of the gene (as a dimer; not shown). Enhancers as well as a CAAT and a TATA box are present. Gene transcription begins 19–27 base pairs downstream of the TATA box. (Reproduced, with permission, from Grumbach MM, Conte FA: Disorders of sex differentiation. In: *Williams Textbook of Endocrinology,* 8th ed. Wilson JD, Foster DW [editors]. Saunders, 1992.)

defect) have been described. Analysis of the androgen receptor gene has shed light on the pathogenesis of the heterogeneity in receptor studies found in patients with complete androgen resistance. Patients with the receptor-negative form of complete androgen resistance have primarily been found to have point mutations or substitutions in exons D–H, which code for the androgen-binding domain of the receptor. The majority of the mutations are familial in nature. Other defects such as deletions, mutations in a splice donor site, and point mutations causing premature termination codons are less common in this group of patients. A point mutation in exon C (which encodes a DNA-binding segment of the androgen receptor) is associated with normal binding of androgen to the receptor but inability of the ligand-receptor complex to bind to DNA and thus to initiate mRNA transcription. This mutation results in receptor-positive complete androgen resistance. Further studies of the androgen receptor gene will no doubt elucidate further abnormalities and shed light on the relationship between the genetic defect, the ligand-binding properties of the androgen receptor, and the phenotype.

The diagnosis of complete androgen resistance can be suspected from the clinical features. Before puberty, the presence of testis-like masses in the inguinal canal or labia in a phenotypic female suggests the diagnosis. Postpubertally, the patients present with primary amenorrhea, normal breast development, and absent or sparse pubic or axillary hair. Pelvic examination or ultrasound confirms the absence of a cervix and uterus. Characteristically, the concentrations of LH and testosterone are elevated. This latter finding is an important hormonal feature of androgen resistance. The family history, phenotype, endocrine evaluation, analysis of the androgen receptor and the androgen receptor gene, and, if necessary, the metabolic response to testosterone will help confirm the diagnosis.

Therapy of patients with complete androgen resistance involves affirmation and reinforcement of their female gender identity. Castration, either prior to or after puberty, is indicated because of the increased risk of gonadal neoplasms with age. Estrogen replacement therapy is required at the age of puberty in orchiectomized patients. In most cases, vaginal reconstructive surgery is not required.

B. Syndrome of Incomplete Androgen Resistance and Its Variants (Reifenstein's Syndrome): Patients with incomplete androgen resistance manifest a wide spectrum of phenotypes as far as masculinization is concerned. The external genitalia at birth can range from ambiguous, with a blind vaginal pouch, to hypoplastic male genitalia. Müllerian duct derivatives are absent and wolffian duct derivatives are present, but they are usually hypoplastic. At puberty, virilization is poor; pubic and axillary hair as well as gynecomastia are usually pres-

ent. The most common phenotype postpubertally is the male with perineoscrotal hypospadias and gynecomastia. Axillary and pubic hair are normal. The testes remain small and exhibit azoospermia as a consequence of germinal cell arrest. As in the case of patients with complete androgen resistance, there are elevated levels of plasma LH, testosterone, and estradiol. However, the degree of feminization in these patients despite high estradiol levels is less than that found in the syndrome of complete androgen resistance.

Androgen receptor studies in these patients have usually shown quantitative or qualitative abnormalities in androgen binding. It would be expected that mutations which lead to partial reduction of androgen action would result in incomplete virilization with a male gender identity. A mutation resulting in a two-thirds reduction in the amount of androgen receptor mRNA produced occurred in two families with Reifenstein's syndrome. As in the syndrome of complete androgen resistance, inheritance is X-linked.

Androgen Resistance in Men With Normal Male Genitalia

Partial androgen resistance has been described in a group of infertile men who have a normal male phenotype but may exhibit gynecomastia. Unlike other patients with androgen resistance, some of these patients have normal plasma LH and testosterone levels. Infertility in otherwise normal men may be the only clinical manifestation of androgen resistance. However, infertility may not always be associated with androgen resistance. Recently, a family in which five males showed signs of gynecomastia, and "undervirilization" was described. Androgen receptor studies indicated a subtle qualitative abnormality in ligand binding; plasma testosterone levels were elevated. Four of the five affected males were fertile and had fathered children. These patients represent the extreme (mildest) form of the highly variable phenotypic expression of androgen resistance.

Defects in Testosterone Metabolism by Peripheral Tissues; 5α-Reductase Deficiency (Pseudovaginal Perineoscrotal Hypospadias)

The defective conversion of testosterone to dihydrotestosterone produces a unique form of male pseudohermaphroditism (Figure 11–17). At birth, ambiguous external genitalia are manifested by a small hypospadiac phallus bound down in chordee, a bifid scrotum, and a urogenital sinus that opens onto the perineum. A blind vaginal pouch is present, opening either into the urogenital sinus or onto the urethra, immediately behind the urethral orifice. The testes are either inguinal or labial. müllerian structures are absent, and wolffian structures are well-differentiated. At puberty, affected males virilize; the

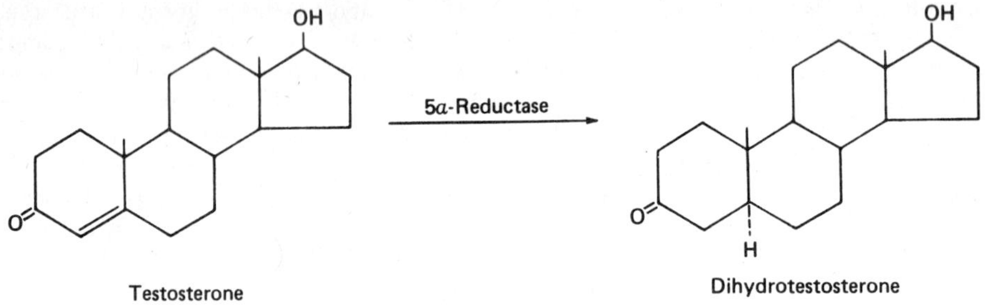

Figure 11–17. Metabolism of testosterone.

voice deepens, muscle mass increases, and the phallus enlarges. The bifid scrotum becomes rugate and pigmented. The testes enlarge and descend into the labioscrotal folds, and spermatogenesis may ensue. Gynecomastia is notably absent in these patients. Of note is the absence of acne, temporal hair recession, and hirsutism. A remarkable feature of this form of male pseudohermaphroditism has been the reported change in gender identity from female to male at puberty in this population isolate.

After the onset of puberty, patients with 5α-reductase deficiency have normal to elevated testosterone levels and slightly elevated plasma concentrations of LH. As expected, plasma dihydrotestosterone is low and the testosterone:dihydrotestosterone ratio is abnormally high. Apparently, lack of 5α reduction of testosterone to dihydrotestosterone in utero during the critical phases of male sex differentiation results in incomplete masculinization of the urogenital sinus and external genitalia, while testosterone-dependent wolffian structures are normally developed. The striking virilization that occurs at puberty in these patients is in sharp contrast to the incomplete masculinization of the external genitalia in utero and is not yet well explained.

5α-Reductase deficiency is transmitted as an autosomal recessive trait, and the enzymatic defect exhibits genetic heterogeneity. There are two classes of affected individuals: (1) those with absent enzyme activity and (2) those with a measurable but unstable enzyme. Two genes catalyze the conversion of testosterone to dihydrotestosterone. In patients with 5α-reductase deficiency, the isozyme with a pH 5.5 optimum is deficient, and it has been termed 5α-reductase type 2. This gene, which contains five exons, has been localized to chromosome 2, band p23. In the patients studied to date, point mutations in the type 2 gene have been described. A high proportion of affected patients have been compound heterozygotes.

5α-Reductase deficiency should be suspected in male pseudohermaphrodites with a blind vaginal pouch. The diagnosis can be confirmed by demonstration of an abnormally high plasma testosterone:dihydrotestosterone ratio, either under basal conditions or after hCG stimulation. Other confirmatory findings include an increased 5β:5α ratio of urinary C19 and C21 steroid metabolites, a decreased level of 5α-reductase activity in cultures of genital skin, and decreased conversion of infused labeled testosterone to dihydrotestosterone in vivo.

The early diagnosis of this condition is critical. In view of the natural history of this disorder, male gender assignment may be considered, and dihydrotestosterone (if available) or high-dose testosterone therapy should be initiated in order to augment phallic size. Repair of hypospadias should be performed as soon as possible in infancy. In patients who are diagnosed after infancy in whom gender identity is unequivocally female, prophylactic orchiectomy and estrogen substitution therapy may still be considered the treatment of choice until further experience with this biochemical entity and sex reversal in our culture is available.

Dysgenetic Male Pseudohermaphroditism (Ambiguous Genitalia Due to Dysgenetic Gonads)

Defective gonadogenesis of the testes results in ambiguous development of the genital ducts, urogenital sinus, and external genitalia. Patients with 45,X/46,XY mosaicism, structural abnormalities of the Y chromosome, and forms of XY gonadal dysgenesis manifest defective gonadogenesis and thus defective virilization. These disorders are classified under disorders of gonadal differentiation but also are included as a subgroup of male pseudohermaphroditism.

A. Ambiguous Genitalia Associated With Degenerative Renal Disease: Male pseudohermaphroditism can occur in association with degenerative renal disease and hypertension as well as with Wilms' tumor (the Denys-Drash syndrome). In this syndrome, both the kidneys and the testes are dysgenetic, and a predisposition for renal neoplasms exists. In patients with the Wilms tumor-aniridia-genital anomalies-mental retardation syndrome (WAGR), a deletion at p13 on one chromosome 11 has been described. These patients also exhibit various forms of ambiguous or hypoplastic male genitalia, including bifid scrotum, hypospadias, and cryptorchism. Recent data indicate that both the Denys-Drash and WAGR syndromes are due to mutations or deletions involving the Wilms tumor suppressor gene, WT1 on chromosome 11.

B. Vanishing Testes Syndrome: (Embryonic testicular regression syndrome; XY agonadism; rudimentary testes syndrome; congenital anorchia) Cessation of testicular function during the critical phases of male sex differentiation can lead to various clinical syndromes depending on when testicular function ceases. At one end of the clinical spectrum of these heterogeneous conditions are the XY patients in whom testicular deficiency occurred prior to 8 weeks of gestation, which results in female differentiation of the internal and external genitalia. At the other end of the spectrum are the patients with "anorchia" or "vanishing testes." These patients have perfectly normal male differentiation of their internal and external structures, but gonadal tissue is absent. The diagnosis of anorchia should be considered in all cryptorchid males. Administration of chorionic gonadotropin, 1000–2000 units intramuscularly every other day for 2 weeks (total of seven injections), is a useful test of Leydig cell function. In the presence of normal Leydig cell function, there is a rise in plasma testosterone from concentrations of less than 20 ng/dL (0.69 nmol/L) to over 200 ng/dL (6.9 nmol/L) in prepubertal males. In infants under 4 years of age and children over 10 years of age, plasma FSH levels are a sensitive index of gonadal integrity. The gonadotropin response to a 100-μg intravenous injection of GnRH can also be used to diagnose the absence of gonadal feedback on the hypothalamus and pituitary. In agonadal children, GnRH elicits a rise in LH and FSH levels that is greater than that achieved in prepubertal children with normal gonadal function. Patients with high gonadotropin levels and no testosterone response to chorionic gonadotropin are usually found to lack recognizable gonadal tissue at surgery. Recent data indicate that both anti-müllerian hormone and inhibin levels may be useful in ascertaining the absence of functioning Sertoli cells and, hence, presumed anorchia.

Defects in the Synthesis, Secretion, or Response to Anti-müllerian Hormone

A few patients have been described in whom normal male development of the external genitalia has occurred but in whom the müllerian ducts persist. The retention of müllerian structures can be ascribed (1) to failure of the Sertoli cells to synthesize a functional anti-müllerian hormone, (2) to an end-organ defect in the response of the duct to anti-müllerian hormone, or perhaps (3) to discordant timing of the release of the hormone. This condition is transmitted

as an autosomal recessive trait. The gene for anti-müllerian hormone has been cloned, mapped to chromosome 19, and mutations in the anti-müllerian hormone gene have been reported in this syndrome. Therapy involves removal of the müllerian structures.

UNCLASSIFIED FORMS OF ABNORMAL SEXUAL DEVELOPMENT IN MALES

Hypospadias

Hypospadias occurs as an isolated finding in 1–8:1000 newborn males. It is often associated with ventral contraction and bowing of the penis, called chordee. On an embryologic basis, deficient virilization of the external genitalia implies subnormal Leydig cell function in utero, end-organ resistance, or an inappropriate temporal correlation of the fetal concentration of plasma testosterone and the critical period for tissue response. Although in most patients there is little reason to suspect these mechanisms, recent reports in a small number of patients have suggested that simple hypospadias can be associated with an abnormality in the androgen receptor, the nuclear localization of the ligand-receptor complex, or an aberration in the maturation of the hypothalamic-pituitary-gonadal axis. Further studies are necessary to determine the prevalence of these abnormalities in the pathogenesis of simple hypospadias. Nonendocrine factors that affect differentiation of the primordia may be found in a variety of genetic syndromes. A study of 100 patients with hypospadias reported one patient to be a genetic female with congenital adrenal hyperplasia; five had sex chromosome abnormalities; and one had the incomplete form of XY gonadal dysgenesis. Nine affected males were the product of pregnancies in which the mother had taken progestational compounds during the first trimester. Thus, a presumed pathogenetic mechanism was found in 15% of these patients.

Microphallus

Microphallus without hypospadias can result from a heterogeneous group of disorders, but by far the most common is fetal testosterone deficiency. In the human male fetus, testosterone synthesis by the fetal Leydig cell during the critical period of male differentiation (8–12 weeks) is under the influence of placental hCG. After mid gestation, fetal pituitary LH seems to modulate fetal testosterone synthesis by the Leydig cell and, consequently, affects the growth of the differentiated penis. Thus, males with congenital hypopituitarism as well as isolated gonadotropin deficiency and "late" fetal testicular failure can present with normal male differentiation and microphallus at birth (phallus < 2 cm in length). Patients with hypothalamic hypopituitarism or pituitary aplasia may also have midline craniofacial defects, hypoglycemia, and giant cell hepatitis. After appropriate evaluation of anterior pituitary function (ie, determination of GH, ACTH, cortisol, TSH, thyroxine, and gonadotropins) and stabilization of the patient with hormone replacement, if necessary, an hCG stimulation test should be performed. Thereafter, all patients with microphallus should receive a trial of testosterone therapy before definitive gender assignment is made. Patients with fetal testosterone deficiency as a cause of microphallus—whether due to gonadotropin deficiency or to a primary testicular disorder—respond to 25–50 mg of testosterone enanthate intramuscularly monthly for 3 months with a mean increase of 2 cm in phallic length (Figure 11–18). In the rare patient in whom a trial of testosterone therapy does not result in a reasonable increase in phallic size, castration and assignment of a female gender may then be a prudent course to follow.

UNCLASSIFIED FORMS OF ABNORMAL SEXUAL DEVELOPMENT IN FEMALES

Congenital absence of the vagina occurs in 1:5000 female births. It can be associated with müllerian derivatives that vary from normal to absent. Ovarian function is usually normal. Therapy involves plastic repair of the vagina, if indicated.

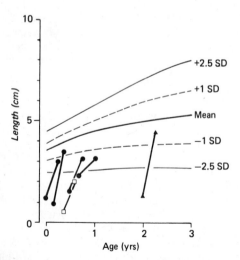

Figure 11–18. The response in phallic length to a 3-month course of testosterone in six patients with microphallus. Patients were under 2 years of age. Each patient was given 25 mg of testosterone enanthate in oil intramuscularly monthly for 3 months. Lines set off with solid triangles and open boxes indicate two patients who subsequently underwent a second course of testosterone therapy. (Reproduced, with permission, from Burstein S, Grumbach MM, Kaplan SL: Early determination of androgen-responsiveness is important in the management of microphallus. Lancet 1979;2:983.)

Müllerian agenesis may be associated with renal aplasia (an absent kidney) and cervicothoracic somite dysplasia ("MURCS").

MANAGEMENT OF PATIENTS WITH INTERSEX PROBLEMS

Choice of Sex

The goal of the physician in management of patients with ambiguous genitalia is to establish a diagnosis and to assign a sex for rearing that is most compatible with a well-adjusted life and sexual adequacy. Once the sex for rearing is assigned, the gender role is reinforced by the use of appropriate surgical, hormonal, or psychologic measures. Except in female pseudohermaphrodites, ambiguities of the genitalia are caused by lesions that almost always make the patient infertile. In recommending male sex assignment, the adequacy of the size of the phallus should be the most important consideration.

Differential Diagnosis

The steps in the diagnosis of intersexuality are delineated in Figure 11–19.

Reassignment of Sex

Reassignment of sex in infancy and childhood is always a difficult psychosocial problem for the patient, the parents, and the physicians involved. While easier in infancy than after 2 years of age, it should always be undertaken with much deliberation and with provision for long-term medical and psychiatric supervision and counseling.

Reconstructive Surgery

It is desirable to initiate plastic repair of the external genitalia prior to 6–12 months of age. In children raised as females, the clitoris should be salvaged, if possible, by clitoroplasty or clitoral recession. Reconstruction of a vagina, if necessary, can be deferred until adolescence.

Removal of the gonads in children with variant forms of gonadal dysgenesis should be performed at the time of initial repair of the external genitalia, because gonadoblastomas, seminomas, and dysgerminomas have been reported to occur during the first decade.

In a patient with complete androgen resistance, the gonads may be left in situ (provided they are not situated in the labia majora) to provide estrogen until late adolescence. The patient may then undergo prophylactic castration, having had her female identity reinforced by normal feminization at puberty.

In patients with incomplete androgen resistance reared as females or in patients with errors of testosterone biosynthesis in whom some degree of masculinization occurs at puberty, gonadectomy should be performed prior to puberty.

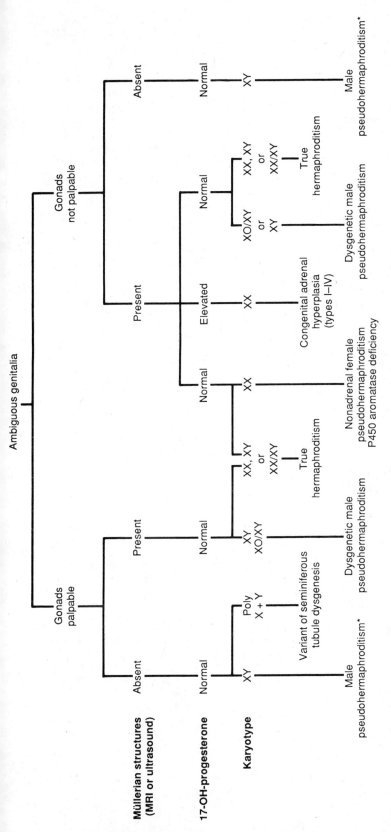

Figure 11–19. Steps in the diagnosis of intersexuality in infancy and childhood. Step 1 involves initial work-up and provisional diagnosis. Step 2 is utilized in selected cases. (Reproduced, with permission, from Grumbach MM, Conte FA: Disorders of sex differentiation. In: *Williams Textbook of Endocrinology*, 8th ed. Wilson JD, Foster DW [editors]. Saunders, 1992.)

1. History: family history, pregnancy (hormones, virilization inspection).
   Palpation of inguinal region and labioscrotal folds; rectal examination.
   Karyotype analysis.
   Initial studies: plasma 17-hydroxyprogesterone, androstenedione, dehydroepiandrosterone, testosterone, and dihydrotestosterone.
   Serum electrolytes.
   Sonogram or MRI of kidneys, ureters, and pelvic contents.
   Provisional diagnosis.

2. "Vaginogram" (urogenital sinogram): selected cases.
   Endoscopy, laparotomy, gonadal biopsy; restricted to male pseudohermaphrodites, true hermaphrodites, and selected instances of nonadrenal female pseudohermaphroditism.
   *Plasma 17-hydroxyprogesterone levels may be modestly elevated in patients with P450c11 (type III) and 3β-hydroxysteroid dehydrogenase deficiency (type IV) and are "low" in patients with P450c17 (type V) and P450scc deficiency (type V).

Labels within figure:

Müllerian structures (MRI or ultrasound)

Ambiguous genitalia

Gonads palpable — Gonads not palpable

17-OH-progesterone

Absent — Present (left branch)
Present — Elevated — Normal — Absent (right branch)

Karyotype

Normal — XY → Male pseudohermaphroditism*
Poly X + Y → Variant of seminiferous tubule dysgenesis
Normal — XY XO/XY → Dysgenetic male pseudohermaphroditism
XX, XY or XX/XY → True hermaphroditism
Normal — XX → Nonadrenal female pseudohermaphroditism P450 aromatase deficiency
Elevated — XX → Congenital adrenal hyperplasia (types I–IV)
Normal — XO/XY or XY → Dysgenetic male pseudohermaphroditism
XX, XY or XX/XY → True hermaphroditism
Normal — XY → Male pseudohermaphroditism*

Hormonal Substitution Therapy

Cyclic estrogen and progestin are used in individuals reared as females in whom a uterus is present. In males, virilization is achieved by the administration of a repository preparation of testosterone.

Psychologic Management

Sex or gender is not a single biologic feature but the sum of many morphogenetic, functional, and psychologic potentialities. The physician should not express to the parent or child any doubt as to the child's true sex. Chromosomal and gonadal sex are sec-

ondary matters; the sex of rearing is paramount. With proper surgical reconstruction, hormone substitution, and continuing psychologic support and reinforcement of the sex of rearing, the individual whose psychosexual gender is discordant with chromosomal sex need not have any psychologic catastrophes as long as the sex of rearing is accepted with conviction by the family and others during the critical early years. These individuals should reach adulthood as well-adjusted men or women capable of normal sexual interaction, though usually not of procreation.

REFERENCES

Berkovitz GD et al: Clinical and pathologic spectrum of 46,XY gonadal dysgenesis: Its relevance to the understanding of sex differentiation. Medicine 1991;70:375.

Berkovitz GD et al: The role of the sex-determining region of the Y chromosome (SRY) in the etiology of 46,XX true hermaphroditism. Hum Genet 1992;88: 411.

Conte FA, Grumbach MM: Pathogenesis, classification, diagnosis, and treatment of anomalies of sex. In: *Endocrinology*, 2nd ed. DeGroot L (editor). Saunders, 1988.

Donahue PK et al: Clinical management of intersex abnormalities. Curr Probl Surg 1992;28:515.

Griffen JE, Wilson JD: The androgen resistance syndromes: 5α Reductase deficiency, testicular feminization and related syndromes. In: *The Metabolic Basis of Inherited Disease*, 6th ed. Scriver CR et al (editors). McGraw-Hill, 1989.

Grumbach MM, Conte FA: Disorders of sex differentiation. In: *Williams Textbook of Endocrinology*, 8th Ed. Wilson JD, Foster DW (editors). Saunders, 1992.

Harada N et al: Biochemical and molecular genetic analyses on placental aromatase (P450arom) deficiency. J Biol Chem 1992;267:4781.

Harly VR et al: DNA binding activity of recombinant SRY from normal males and XY females. Science 1992;255:453.

Hawkins JR et al: Mutational analysis of SRY: Nonsense and missense mutations in XY sex reversal. Hum Genet 1992;88:471.

Josso N et al: An enzyme linked immunoassay for anti-müllerian hormone: A new tool for the evaluation of testicular function in infants and children. J Clin Endocrinol Metab 1990;70:23.

Knebelmann B et al: Anti-Müllerian hormone Bruxelles: A nonsense mutation associated with the persistent Müllerian duct syndrome. Proc Natl Acad Sci USA 1991;88:3767.

Koopman P et al: Male development of chromosomally female mice transgenic for SRY. Nature 1991;351: 117.

Lustig RH, et al. Ontogeny of gonadotropin secretion in congenital anorchia: Sexual dimorphism versus syndrome of gonadal dysgenesis and diagnostic considerations. J Urol 1987;138:587.

McPhaul MJ et al: Genetic basis of endocrine disease 3: The spectrum of mutations in the androgen receptor gene that causes androgen resistance. J Clin Endocrinol Metab 1993;76:17.

McPhaul MJ et al: Mutations in the ligand binding domain of the androgen receptor gene cluster in two regions of the gene. J Clin Invest 1992;90:2097.

Moore CCD, Grumbach MM: Sex determination and gonadogenesis: A transcription cascade of sex chromosome and autosomal genes. Semin Perinatol 1992; 16:266.

Morel Y, Miller W: Clinical and molecular genetics of congenital adrenal hyperplasia due to 21-hydroxylase deficiency. Adv Genet 1991;20:1.

New MI et al: The adrenal hyperplasias. In: *The Metabolic Basis of Inherited Disease*, 6th ed. Scriver CR et al (editors). McGraw-Hill, 1989.

Pelletier J et al: Germline mutations in the Wilms tumor suppressor gene are associated with abnormal urogenital development in Denys-Drash syndrome. Cell 1991; 67:437.

Petit C et al: An abnormal terminal X–Y interchange accounts for most but not all cases of human XX maleness. Cell 1987;49:595.

Rheaume E et al: Congenital adrenal hyperplasia due to point mutations in the type II 3β-hydroxysteroid dehydrogenase gene. Nature Genetics 1992;1:239.

Speiser PW et al: Disease expression and molecular genotype in congenital adrenal hyperplasia due to 21-hydroxylase deficiency. J Clin Invest 1992;90:584.

Thigpen AE et al: Molecular genetics of steroid 5α-reductase deficiency. J Clin Invest 1992;90:799.

Van Niekerk WA: *True Hermaphroditism*. Harper & Row, 1974.

Wilson JD et al: Syndromes of androgen resistance. Biol Reprod 1992;46:168.

Puberty

12

Dennis M. Styne, MD

Puberty is one stage in the continuing process of growth and development that begins during gestation and continues until the end of reproductive life. After an interval of childhood quiescence, hypothalamic-pituitary-gonadal activity intensifies in the peripubertal period, leading to increased secretion of gonadal sex steroids that cause secondary sexual development, the pubertal growth spurt, and fertility. Historical records show that the age at onset of certain stages of puberty in boys and girls in Western countries has steadily declined over the last several hundred years; this is probably due to improvements in socioeconomic conditions, nutrition, and general health during that period. However, this trend ceased during the last five decades in the "developed world," suggesting the attainment of optimal conditions to allow puberty to begin at a genetically determined age.

Many factors can alter age at onset of puberty. Moderate obesity may be associated with an earlier onset of puberty, while severe, morbid obesity may delay puberty. Chronic illness and malnutrition often delay puberty. There is a significant concordance of age at menarche between mother-daughter pairs and within ethnic populations, indicating the influence of genetic factors.

Physical Changes Associated With Puberty

Descriptive standards proposed by Tanner for assessing pubertal development in males and females are in wide use. They focus attention on specific details of the examination and make it possible to objectively record subtle progression of secondary sexual development that may otherwise be overlooked.

A. Female Changes: The first sign of puberty in the female, as noted in longitudinal studies, is an increase in growth velocity that heralds the beginning of the pubertal growth spurt; girls are not usually examined frequently enough to demonstrate this change in clinical practice, so breast development is the first sign of puberty noted by most examiners. Breast development (Figure 12–1) is stimulated chiefly by ovarian estrogen secretion, though other hormones also play a part. The size and shape of the breasts may be determined by genetic and nutritional factors, but the characteristics of the stages in Figure 12–1 are the same in all females. Standards are now avail-

---

ACRONYMS USED IN THIS CHAPTER

AASH	Adrenal androgen-stimulating hormone
ACTH	Adrenocorticotropic hormone
cAMP	Cyclic adenosine monophosphate
DHEA	Dehydroepiandrosterone
DHEAS	Dehydroepiandrosterone sulfate
FSH	Follicle-stimulating hormone
GH	Growth hormone
GnRH	Gonadotropin-releasing hormone
hCG	Human chorionic gonadotropin
hGH	Human growth hormone
LH	Luteinizing hormone
PRL	Prolactin
RIA	Radioimmunoassay
SHBG	Sex hormone-binding globulin
TSH	Thyroid-stimulating hormone (thyrotropin)

---

able for the change in nipple plateau diameter during puberty: Nipple diameter changes little from stages B1 to B3 (approximately 3–4 mm); but it enlarges substantially in subsequent stages (approximately 7.4 mm at stage B4 to 10 mm at stage B5), presumably as a result of increased estrogen secretion at the time of menarche. Other features reflecting estrogen action include enlargement of the labia minora and majora, dulling of the vaginal mucosa, and production of a clear or slightly whitish vaginal secretion prior to menarche. Pubic hair development (Figure 12–2) is determined primarily by adrenal and ovarian androgen secretion. Breast development and growth of pubic hair usually proceed at similar rates, but because discrepancies in rates of advancement are possible, it is best to stage breast development separately from pubic hair progression.

Uterine size and shape change with pubertal development; with prolonged estrogen stimulation, the fundus/cervix ratio increases, leading to a bulbous form, and the uterus elongates from less than 3 cm to 5 cm. Ovaries enlarge with puberty from a volume of less than 1 mL to 2–10 mL. Clinicians can use ultrasonography to determine the developmental stage of the uterus and ovaries by comparing the results with established standards.

B. Male Changes: The first sign of normal puberty in boys is usually an increase in the size of the

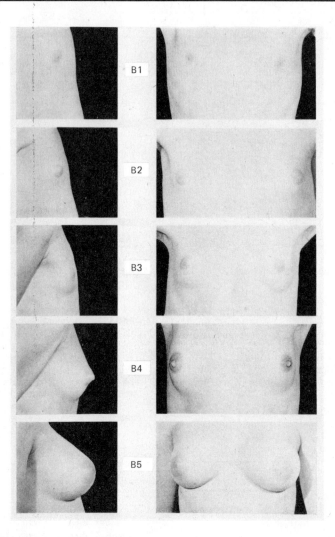

Figure 12–1. Stages of breast development, according to Marshall and Tanner. (Photographs from van Wieringen JC et al, 1971; with permission.) *Stage B1:* Preadolescent; elevation of papilla only. *Stage B2:* Breast bud stage; elevation of breast and papilla as a small mound, and enlargement of areolar diameter. *Stage B3:* Further enlargement of breast and areola, with no separation of their contours. *Stage B4:* Projection of areola and papilla to form a secondary mound above the level of the breast. *Stage B5:* Mature stage; projection of papilla only, owing to recession of the areola to the general contour of the breast. (Reproduced, with permission, from Marshall WA, Tanner JM: Variations in the pattern of pubertal changes in girls. Arch Dis Child 1969;44:291.)

testes to over 2.5 cm in the longest diameter, excluding the epididymis. Most of the increase in testicular size is due to seminiferous tubular development secondary to stimulation by FSH, but a smaller component is due to Leydig cell stimulation by LH. Pubic hair development is caused by adrenal and testicular androgens and is classified separately from genital development, as noted in Figure 12–3. The appearance of spermatozoa in early morning urinary specimens (spermarche) occurs at a mean chronologic age of 13.4 years or a similar bone age in gonadal stage 3–4 and pubic hair stage 2–4; if puberty starts earlier or later, the age of spermarche changes accordingly.

Thus, boys are reproductively mature prior to physical maturity and certainly prior to psychologic maturity!

C. Age at Onset: Although data are sparse, the limits of onset of normal secondary sexual development in 98.8% of North American children (ie, mean ± 2.5 SD) are accepted as 8–13 years for girls and 9–14 years for boys. A graphic representation of the stages of pubertal development for British children is shown in Figure 12–4; North American and British boys develop at about the same ages, but 6 months should be subtracted from these figures to correct for North American girls. Black boys develop comparably to white boys, but black girls develop earlier than white girls. (Black girls have a mean age of men-

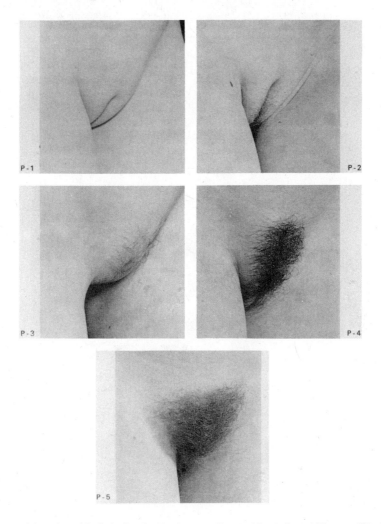

Figure 12–2. Stages of female pubic hair development, according to Marshall and Tanner. (Photographs from van Wieringen JC et al, 1971; with permission.) **Stage P1:** Preadolescent; the vellus over the pubes is no further developed than that over the anterior abdominal wall, ie, no pubic hair. **Stage P2:** Sparse growth of long, slightly pigmented, downy hair, straight or only slightly curled, appearing chiefly along the labia. This stage is difficult to see on photographs. **Stage P3:** Hair is considerably darker, coarser, and curlier. The hair spreads sparsely over the junction of the pubes. **Stage P4:** Hair is now adult in type, but the area covered by it is still considerably smaller than in most adults. There is no spread to the medial surface of the thighs. **Stage P5:** Hair is adult in quantity and type, distributed as an inverse triangle of the classic feminine pattern. Spread is to the medial surface of the thighs but not up the linea alba or elsewhere above the base of the inverse triangle. (Reproduced, with permission, from Marshall WA, Tanner JM: Variations in the pattern of pubertal changes in girls. Arch Dis Child 1969;44:291.)

arche 0.3 years younger than white girls.) Late onset of pubertal development may indicate hypothalamic, pituitary, or gonadal failure. The time from onset of puberty to complete adult development is also of importance; delays in reaching subsequent stages may indicate hypogonadism. Girls complete secondary sexual development in 1.5–6 years, with a mean of 4.2 years; and boys in 2–4.5 years, with a mean of 3.5 years.

D. Growth Spurt: The striking increase in growth velocity in puberty (pubertal growth spurt) is under complex endocrine control. GH and sex steroids appear to be important in this process; when either or both are deficient, the growth spurt is decreased or absent. Sex steroids indirectly stimulate IGF-1 production by increasing the secretion of GH and directly by stimulating IGF-1 production in cartilage. Sex steroids stimulate maturation of the chondrocytes and osteoblasts, ultimately leading to epiphysial fusion. Hypothyroidism interferes with the pubertal growth spurt.

It is essential to realize that a pubertal growth spurt

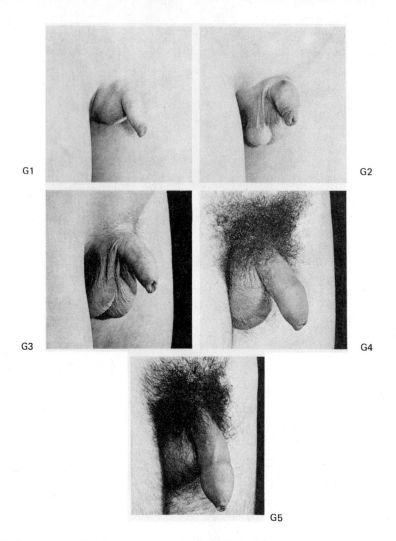

Figure 12–3. Stages of male genital development and pubic hair development, according to Marshall and Tanner. (Photographs from van Wieringen JC et al, 1971; with permission.) **Genital:** *Stage G1:* Preadolescent. Testes, scrotum, and penis are about the same size and proportion as in early childhood. *Stage G2:* The scrotum and testes have enlarged, and there is a change in the texture and some reddening of the scrotal skin. *Stage G3:* Growth of the penis has occurred, at first mainly in length but with some increase in breadth; further growth of testes and scrotum. *Stage G4:* Penis further enlarged in length and girth with development of glans. Testes and scrotum further enlarged. The scrotal skin has further darkened. *Stage G5:* Genitalia adult in size and shape. No further enlargement takes place after stage G5 is reached. **Pubic hair:** *Stage P1:* Preadolescent. The vellus over the pubes is no further developed than that over the abdominal wall, ie, no pubic hair. *Stage P2:* Sparse growth of long, slightly pigmented, downy hair, straight or only slightly curled, appearing chiefly at the base of the penis. *Stage P3:* Hair is considerably darker, coarser, and curlier and spreads sparsely over the junction of the pubes. *Stage P4:* Hair is now adult in type, but the area it covers is still considerably smaller than in most adults. There is no spread to the medial surface of the thighs. *Stage P5:* Hair is adult in quantity and type, distributed as an inverse triangle. Spread is to the medial surface of the thighs but not up the linea alba or elsewhere above the base of the inverse triangle. Most men will have further spread of pubic hair. (Modified and reproduced, with permission, from Marshall WA, Tanner JM: Variations in the pattern of pubertal changes in boys. Arch Dis Child 1970;45:13.)

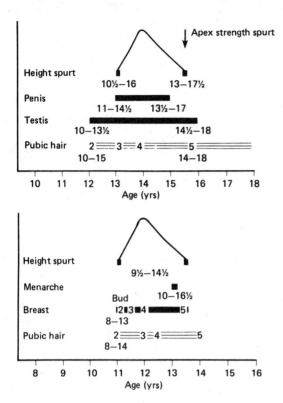

Figure 12–4. Sequence of secondary sexual development in British males *(top)* and females *(bottom)*. The range of ages is indicated. (Reproduced, with permission, from Marshall WA, Tanner JM: Variations in the pattern of pubertal changes in boys. Arch Dis Child 1970;45:13.)

in a young patient with precocious puberty may increase growth rate sufficiently to mask the presence of coexisting GH deficiency; This situation may occur, for example, in a child with a brain tumor treated with radiation that decreases GH secretion. In girls, the pubertal growth spurt begins in early puberty and is mostly completed by menarche. In boys, the pubertal growth spurt occurs toward the end of puberty, at an average age 2 years older than the growth spurt in girls. Total height attained during the growth spurt in girls is about 25 cm; in boys, it is about 28 cm. The mean adult height differential of 12 cm between men and women is due in part to heights already attained before onset of the pubertal growth spurt and in part to the height gained during the spurt.

E. Changes in Body Composition: Changes in body composition are also prominent during pubertal development. Prepubertal boys and girls start with equal lean body mass, skeletal mass, and body fat, but at maturity men have approximately 1 1/2 times the lean body mass, skeletal mass, and muscle mass of women, while women have twice as much body fat as men.

F. Other Changes of Puberty: Other changes that are characteristic of puberty are mediated either directly or indirectly by the change in sex steroids. Bone density increases during pubertal development. Seborrheic dermatitis may appear at this age. The mouth flora changes, and periodontal disease, rare in childhood, may appear at this stage. The amplitude of growth hormone secretion increases in puberty, as does production of IGF-1; peak IGF-1 levels are reached about 1 year after peak growth velocity, and IGF-1 levels remain above normal adult levels for up to 4 years thereafter. Insulin resistance intensifies in adolescents with insulin-dependent diabetes mellitus; this may be partly related to the increased GH levels.

Endocrine Changes From Fetal Life to Puberty

Pituitary gonadotropin secretion is controlled by the hypothalamus, which releases pulses of gonadotropin-releasing hormone (GnRH) into the pituitary-portal system to reach the anterior pituitary gland. Control of GnRH secretion is exerted by a "hypothalamic pulse generator" in the arcuate nucleus that is sensitive to feedback control from sex steroids and inhibin, a protein product that varies the frequency and amplitude of gonadotropin secretion during development in both sexes and during the progression of the menstrual cycle in females (see Chapter 2). Individual GnRH neurons have an intrinsic pulsatility that appears to be the basis of the pattern of GnRH secretion.

In males, luteinizing hormone (LH) stimulates the Leydig cells to secrete testosterone, while follicle-stimulating hormone (FSH) stimulates the Sertoli cells to produce inhibin, which in turn feeds back and inhibits FSH. Inhibin is also released in a pulsatile pattern, but concentrations do not change with pubertal progression. In females, FSH stimulates the granulosa cells to produce estrogen and the follicles to secrete inhibin, while LH appears to play a minor role until menarche, when it triggers ovulation and later stimulates the theca cells to secrete androgens (see Chapters 9 and 10).

A. Fetal Life: The concept of the continuum of development between the fetus and the adult is well illustrated by the changes that occur in the hypothalamic-pituitary-gonadal axis. Gonadotropins are demonstrable in fetal pituitary glands and serum during the first trimester. The pituitary content of gonadotropins rises to a plateau at mid gestation. Serum concentrations of LH and FSH peak at mid gestation and then gradually decrease until term. During the first half of gestation, hypothalamic GnRH content also increases, and the hypophysial-portal circulation achieves anatomic maturity. These data are compatible with a theory of early unrestrained GnRH secretion stimulating pituitary gonadotropin secretion, followed by the appearance of factors that inhibit GnRH release and decrease gonadotropin secretion after mid gestation. Since the male fetus has measurable serum testosterone concentrations but lower serum gonadotropin concentrations than the female fetus, negative feedback inhibition of gonadotropin secretion by testosterone appears operative after mid gestation.

B. Changes at Birth: At term, plasma gonadotropin concentrations are suppressed, but with postnatal clearance of high circulating estrogen concentrations, negative inhibition is reduced and postnatal peaks of LH and FSH are measurable several months after birth. Plasma testosterone concentrations may be increased to midpubertal levels several months after birth in males. While episodic peaks of plasma gonadotropins may occur until 2 years of age, serum gonadotropin concentrations are low during later years in normal childhood.

C. Mid-Childhood Nadir of Gonadotropin Secretion: Patients with gonadal failure—such as those with the syndrome of gonadal dysgenesis (Turner's syndrome)—demonstrate an exaggeration of the normal pattern of gonadotropin secretion, with exceedingly high concentrations of LH and FSH during the first several years of life (see Chapter 11). Such patients show that negative feedback inhibition is active during childhood; without sex steroid or inhibin secretion to exert inhibition, gonadotropin values are greatly elevated. During mid childhood, normal individuals and patients with primary hypogonadism have lower gonadotropin levels than they do in the neonatal period, but the range of gonadotropin concentrations in hypogonadal patients during mid childhood is still higher than that found in healthy children of the same age. The decrease in gonadotropin concentrations in hypogonadal children during mid childhood is incompletely understood but has been attributed to an increase in the central nervous system inhibition of gonadotropin secretion during these years.

D. Peripubertal Gonadotropin Increase: During the peripubertal period of endocrine change prior to secondary sexual development, gonadotropin secretion becomes less sensitive to negative feedback inhibition. Before this time, a small dose of exogenous sex steroids virtually eliminates gonadotropin secretion, while afterward a far larger dose is required to suppress FSH and LH. In prepuberty or early puberty, naltrexone, an opiate receptor antagonist, can completely suppress gonadotropin secretion as a consequence of its weak opioid effects, while after mid puberty the anti-opioid effects predominate and gonadotropin secretion increases, demonstrating decrease in sensitivity to opioids with pubertal development. In the peripubertal period, endogenous GnRH secretion increases in amplitude and frequency during the early hours of sleep and testosterone levels rise several hours later in boys (Figure 12–5). As puberty progresses in both sexes, the peaks of LH and FSH occur more often during waking hours, and, finally, in late puberty, the peaks occur at all times, eliminating the diurnal variation. Thus,

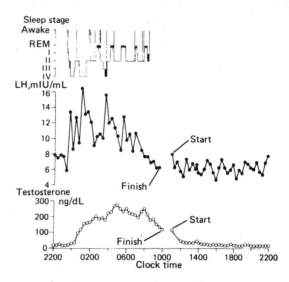

Figure 12–5. Plasma LH and testosterone measured during a 24-hour period in a 14-year-old boy in pubertal stage 2. Samples collected at night are displayed with electroencephalographic sleep stages. (Reproduced, with permission, from Boyar RM et al: Simultaneous augmented secretion of luteinizing hormone and testosterone during sleep. J Clin Invest 1974;54:609.)

daytime samples of plasma for determination of gonadotropin concentrations are of less value during early puberty because such sampling misses these nighttime peaks.

Most studies on gonadotropin secretion measure gonadotropin concentrations by radioimmunoassay (RIA). However, the biologic activity of LH may change because of changes in the glycosylation and tertiary structure of gonadotropin molecules; this change may not be reflected in the RIA. Studies comparing immunoassayable LH (I-LH) to bioassayable LH (B-LH) suggest that the ratio of B-LH:I-LH increases with the onset of puberty and that this ratio may explain the profound endocrine changes of puberty better than the rather small changes in I-LH secretion. Recently, highly sensitive "sandwich" assays (IRMA) for gonadotropins became available. They promise to diagnose the state of pubertal development by the use of basal samples without the necessity for GnRH testing.

E. Sex Steroid Secretion: Sex steroid secretion is correlated with the development of gonadotropin secretion. During the postnatal period of episodic gonadotropin secretion, plasma concentrations of gonadal steroids are occasionally elevated. This indicates the potential for secretory activity in the neonatal gonad. Later, when gonadotropin secretion decreases in mid childhood, gonadal activity decreases, but testes can still be stimulated by LH or hCG and ovaries by FSH with resulting secretion of

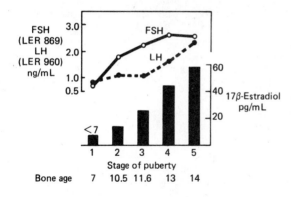

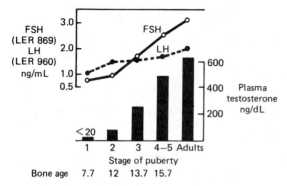

Figure 12–6. Mean plasma LH, FSH, and estradiol (girls) or testosterone (boys) correlated with stage of puberty and bone age. LER 869 and LER 960 are the reference standards for FSH and LH, respectively. The values reported here in ng/mL would be reported as mIU/mL in most laboratories. The conversion factors are as follows: for FSH (LER 869), 1 ng = 3 mIU; for LH (LER 960), 1 ng = 7.8 mIU. (Reproduced, with permission, from Grumbach MM: Onset of puberty. In: *Puberty.* Berenberg SR [editor]. H.E. Stenfert Kroese. Copyright © 1975 by Martinus Nijhoff.)

gonadal steroids. With the onset of puberty, plasma gonadal steroid concentrations progressively increase (Figure 12–6). While sex steroids are secreted in a diurnal rhythm in early puberty, because they are bound to sex hormone-binding globulin, the half-life of sex steroids is longer than that of gonadotropins. Thus, random daytime measurements of sex steroids are more helpful in determining pubertal status than random daytime samples for gonadotropins.

Most (97–99%) of the circulating estradiol and testosterone is associated with sex hormone-binding globulin (SHBG). The free hormone is the active fraction, but SHBG modulates the activity of the total testosterone and estradiol. Prepubertal boys and girls have equal concentrations of SHBG, but because testosterone decreases and estrogen increases SHBG, adult males have only half the concentration of SHBG than that of adult females. Thus, SHBG am-

plifies androgen effect in men; while adult men have 20 times the amount of plasma testosterone that adult women have, men have 40 times the amount of free testosterone (see Chapter 9).

F. GnRH Stimulation: The use of intravenous GnRH has further clarified the pattern of pubertal development (Figure 12–7). When GnRH is administered to children under 2 years of age, pituitary secretion of LH and FSH increases markedly. During the period of low basal gonadotropin secretion (age 2 to age 9 or 10 years), exogenous GnRH has less effect on LH release. By the peripubertal period, 100 μg of intravenous GnRH induces a rise in LH concentrations of more than 15.6 mIU/mL in boys and girls, and this response continues until adulthood. There is no significant change in the magnitude of FSH secretion after GnRH with the onset of puberty, though females at all ages release more FSH than males.

Gonadotropins are released in secretory spurts in response to endogenous GnRH, which itself is secreted episodically about every 90–120 minutes in response to a central nervous system "pulse generator." Individual GnRH-containing neurons secrete GnRH in a pulsatile manner with an intrinsic rhythm. GnRH administered to patients in episodic boluses mimics the natural secretory episodes. A prepubertal subject without significant gonadotropin peaks will demonstrate the normal pubertal pattern of episodic secretion of gonadotropins after only a few days of exogenously administered GnRH boluses. Hypogonadotropic patients, who in the basal state do not have great secretory episodes of gonadotropin release, may be converted to a pattern of normal adult episodic gonadotropin secretion and become fertile by this method of pulsatile GnRH administration. Varying the timing of pulsatile GnRH administration can regulate the ratio of FSH to LH; the frequency of endogenous hypothalamic GnRH release shifts during the menstrual cycle and puberty to naturally change the ratio. Increasing the frequency of GnRH pulses increases the LH:FSH ratio; an increased ratio is characteristic of midcycle and peripubertal dynamics. If GnRH is administered continuously rather than in pulses or if long-acting superactive analogues of GnRH are given, a brief period of increased gonadotropin secretion is followed by LH and FSH suppression. This phenomenon is responsible for the therapeutic effects of GnRH analogues in conditions such as central precocious puberty (see Chapter 10).

Menarche

The last stage in hypothalamic-pituitary development is the onset of positive feedback, leading to ovulation and menarche. After mid puberty, estrogen can stimulate gonadotropin release. The frequency of pulsatile GnRH release increases during the normal menstrual cycle and raises the ratio of LH to FSH secretion. This stimulates the ovary to produce estro-

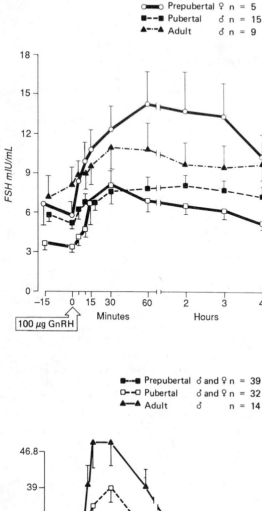

□——□ Prepubertal ♂ n = 13
○——○ Prepubertal ♀ n = 5
■––■ Pubertal ♂ n = 15
▲––▲ Adult ♂ n = 9

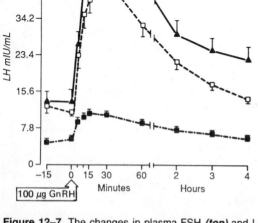

■––■ Prepubertal ♂ and ♀ n = 39
□––□ Pubertal ♂ and ♀ n = 32
▲—▲ Adult ♂ n = 14

Figure 12–7. The changes in plasma FSH *(top)* and LH *(bottom)* after GnRH was administered in prepubertal, pubertal, and adult subjects. (Modified and reproduced, with permission, from Grumbach MM et al: *Control of the Onset of Puberty.* Grumbach MM, Grave GD, Mayer FE [editors]. Wiley, 1974.)

gen and leads to the midcycle LH surge that causes ovulation. Even if the midcycle surge of gonadotropins is present, ovulation may not occur during the first menstrual cycles; 90% of all menstrual cycles are anovulatory in the first year after menarche, and it is not until 4–5 years after menarche that the percentage of anovulatory cycles decreases to less than 20%. However, even the first cycles after menarche may be ovulatory, and *girls may become pregnant prior to physical maturity.* In the USA, the mean age at menarche is 12.8 years ± 1.2 years (mean ± 1 SD). Menarche is closely correlated with a skeletal age of 13 years (see Chapter 3).

Adrenarche

While the hypothalamic-pituitary axis has been well characterized in recent years, our understanding of the mechanism of control of adrenal androgen secretion is still somewhat rudimentary. The adrenal cortex secretes the weak androgens dehydroepiandrosterone (DHEA), its sulfate, dehydroepiandrosterone sulfate (DHEAS), and androstenedione in increasing amounts at an average age of 6–7 years in girls and 7–8 years in boys (Table 12–1). A continued rise in adrenal androgen secretion persists until late puberty. Thus, adrenarche (the secretion of adrenal androgens) occurs years before gonadarche (the secretion of gonadal sex steroids). The observation that patients with Addison's disease, who do not secrete adrenal androgens, and patients with premature adrenarche, who secrete increased amounts of adrenal androgens at an early age, usually enter gonadarche at a normal age suggests that age at adrenarche does not significantly influence age at gonadarche. Furthermore, patients treated with a GnRH agonist to suppress gonadotropin secretion progress through adrenarche despite their suppressed gonadarche. Measurements of urinary 17-ketosteroids reflect principally adrenal androgen secretion and not secretion of testosterone or its metabolites. Thus, urinary 17-ketosteroid levels rise considerably at adrenarche but less so at gonadarche.

Miscellaneous Metabolic Changes

The onset of puberty is associated with many changes in laboratory values that are either directly or indirectly caused by the rise of sex steroid concentrations. Thus, in boys, hematocrit rises and HDL concentrations fall as a consequence of increasing testosterone. The latter effect causes older boys and men to have a higher risk of arteriosclerotic coronary artery disease. In both boys and girls, alkaline phosphatase rises during the pubertal growth spurt. Serum IGF-1 concentrations rise with the growth spurt, but IGF-1 is more closely correlated with sex steroid concentration than with growth rate. IGF-1 levels peak 1 year after peak growth velocity is reached and remain elevated for 4 years thereafter even though growth rate is decreasing.

Table 12–1. Mean serum concentrations of DHEAS during childhood.[1]

	Boys		Girls	
	(µg/dL)	(µmol/L)	(µg/dL)	(µmol/L)
Chronologic age (years)				
1–6	15.4 ± 6.8	0.53 ± 0.23	24.7 ± 11.1	0.86 ± 0.38
6–8	18.8 ± 4.1	0.65 ± 0.14	30.4 ± 7.6	1.05 ± 0.26
8–10	58.6 ± 10.1	2.03 ± 0.35	117.3 ± 41.7	4.06 ± 1.44
10–12	126.4 ± 28.0	4.38 ± 0.97	112.7 ± 16.4	3.90 ± 0.57
12–14	133.4 ± 22.2	4.62 ± 0.77	168.9 ± 19.3	5.85 ± 0.67
14–16	264.3 ± 19.4	9.15 ± 0.67	253.5 ± 41.3	8.78 ± 1.43
16–20	264.1 ± 61.8	9.14 ± 2.14	232.5 ± 49.8	8.05 ± 1.72
Bone age (years)				
1–6	16.6 ± 6.1	0.57 ± 0.21	2.5 ± 2.5	0.09 ± 0.09
6–8	36.3 ± 6.7	1.25 ± 0.23	27.2 ± 9.6	0.94 ± 0.33
8–10	57.4 ± 8.5	1.98 ± 0.29	. . .	. . .
10–12	125.0 ± 22.7	4.33 ± 0.79	112.9 ± 27.6	3.91 ± 0.96
12–14	214.9 ± 30.1	7.44 ± 1.04	159.7 ± 26.3	5.53 ± 0.91
14–16	403.4 ± 99.4	14.00 ± 3.44	261.0 ± 45.0	9.04 ± 1.56
16–20	. . .	. . .	145.3 ± 32.2	5.03 ± 1.12

[1]Modified and reproduced, with permission, from Reiter EO, Fuldauer LG, Root AW: *J Pediatr* 1977;**90**:766.

DELAYED PUBERTY OR ABSENT PUBERTY (Sexual Infantilism)

Any girl of 13 or boy of 14 years of age with no signs of pubertal development falls more than 2.5 SD below the mean and is considered to have delayed puberty (Table 12–2). By this definition, 0.6% of the healthy population are classified with constitutional delay in growth and adolescence. These patients need reassurance rather than treatment and will ultimately progress through the normal stages of puberty, albeit later than their peers. The examining physician must decide which patients are constitutionally delayed and which truly have organic disease. In some cases this is a difficult decision.

Constitutional Delay in Growth & Adolescence

A patient with delayed onset of secondary sexual development who has a history of always being shorter than age-matched peers but who consistently maintains a normal growth velocity for bone age and whose skeletal development is delayed more than 2 SD from the mean is likely to have constitutional delay in puberty (Figure 12–8). There is often a family history of a similar pattern of development in a parent or sibling. The subject is usually thin. These patients are at the older end of the distribution curve of age at onset of puberty. In many cases, even if they show no physical signs of puberty at the time of examination, the initial elevation of gonadal sex steroids has already begun, or their plasma LH response to intravenous GnRH is pubertal (a rise in LH of > 15.6 mIU/mL). These results suggest that secondary sexual development will commence within 6 months. However, in some cases, observation for endocrine or physical signs of puberty must continue

for a period of months or years before the diagnosis is made. Generally, signs of puberty will appear after the patient reaches a skeletal age of 11 years (girls) or 12 years (boys). Patients with constitutional delay in adolescence will almost always manifest secondary sexual development by 18 years of chronologic age, though there is one reported case of spontaneous puberty occurring at 25 years of age. (This patient may have had Kallmann's syndrome; see below and Chapter 2.) Adrenarche is characteristically delayed—along with gonadarche—in constitutional delayed puberty.

Table 12–2. Classification of delayed puberty.

Constitutional delay in growth and adolescence
Hypogonadotropic hypogonadism
    Central nervous system disorders
        Tumors
        Other acquired disorders
        Congenital disorders
    Isolated gonadotropin deficiency
    Multiple pituitary hormonal deficiencies
    Miscellaneous disorders
        Prader-Willi syndrome
        Laurence-Moon, Bardet-Biedl syndrome
        Chronic disease
        Weight loss
        Anorexia nervosa
        Increased physical activity in female athletes
        Hypothyroidism
Hypergonadotropic hypogonadism
    Males
        Klinefelter's syndrome
        Other forms of primary testicular failure
        Anorchia or cryptorchism
    Females
        Turner's syndrome
        Other forms of primary ovarian failure
    Pseudo-Turner's syndrome
    XX and XY gonadal dysgenesis

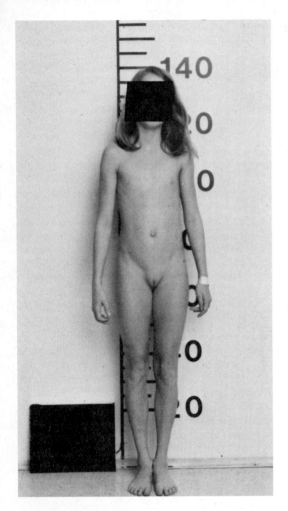 

Figure 12–8. Girl 13 4/12 years old with constitutional delay in growth and puberty. History revealed a normal growth rate but short stature at all ages. Physical examination revealed a height of 138 cm (–4.5 SD) and a weight of 28.6 kg (–3 SD). The patient had early stage 2 breast development, with 1 cm of glandular tissue on the right breast and 2 cm on the left breast. The vaginal mucosa was dulled, and there was no pubic hair. Karyotype was 46,XX. Bone age was 10 years. After administration of GnRH, LH rose from 14.8 to 37.4 mIU/mL (from 1.9 to 4.8 ng/mL) and FSH from 11.7 to 20.1 mIU/mL (from 3.9 to 6.7 ng/mL). Estradiol was 40 pg/mL. She has since spontaneously progressed through pubertal development. (Reproduced, with permission, from Styne DM, Kaplan SL: Pediatr Clin North Am 1979;26:123.)

Hypogonadotropic Hypogonadism

The absent or decreased ability of the hypothalamus to secrete GnRH or of the pituitary to secrete LH and FSH leads to hypogonadotropic hypogonadism. This classification denotes an irreversible condition requiring replacement therapy. If the pituitary deficiency is limited to gonadotropins, patients are usually close to normal height for age—in contrast to the shorter patients with constitutional delay. Bone age is usually not delayed in childhood but does not progress normally after the patient reaches the age at which sex steroid secretion ordinarily increases. If GH deficiency accompanies gonadotropin deficiency, severe short stature will result.

A. Central Nervous System Disorders:

1. Tumors– A tumor involving the hypothalamus or pituitary gland can interfere with hypothalamic-pituitary-gonadal function as well as the control of GH, ACTH, TSH, PRL, and vasopressin secretion. Thus, delayed puberty may be a manifestation of a central nervous system tumor accompanied by any or all of the following: GH deficiency, secondary hypothyroidism, secondary adrenal insufficiency, hyperprolactinemia, and diabetes insipidus. The combination of anterior and posterior pituitary deficiencies acquired after birth indicates the likelihood of a hypothalamic-pituitary tumor.

Craniopharyngioma is the most common type of

hypothalamic-pituitary tumor leading to delay or absence of pubertal development. This neoplasm originates in Rathke's pouch but may develop into a suprasellar tumor. The peak age incidence of craniopharyngioma is between 6 and 14 years. Presenting symptoms may include headache, visual deficiency, growth failure, polyuria, and polydipsia; presenting signs may include visual defects, optic atrophy or papilledema. Clinical manifestations may reflect gonadotropin, thyroid, and GH deficiency. Laboratory evaluation may reveal any type of anterior or posterior pituitary deficiencies. Bone age is often retarded at the time of presentation.

Calcification in the suprasellar region is the hallmark of craniopharyngiomas; 80% of cases will have calcifications on lateral skull x-ray, and a higher percentage will show this on CT scan. The tumor often presents a cystic appearance on CT or MRI scan and at the time of surgery may contain dark, cholesterol-laden fluid. The rate of growth of craniopharyngiomas is quite variable—some are indolent and some are quite aggressive. Small intrasellar tumors may be resected by transsphenoidal surgery; larger ones may require partial resection and radiation therapy (see Chapter 2).

Extrasellar tumors that involve the hypothalamus and produce sexual infantilism include germinomas, gliomas (sometimes with neurofibromatosis), and astrocytomas (see Chapter 2). Intrasellar tumors such as chromophobe adenomas are quite rare in children. Hyperprolactinemia—with or without a diagnosed microadenoma or galactorrhea—may delay the onset or progression of puberty; with therapy to decrease prolactin concentrations, puberty progresses.

2. Other acquired central nervous system disorders– Other acquired central nervous system disorders may lead to hypothalamic-pituitary dysfunction. Granulomatous diseases such as Hand-Schüller-Christian disease or histiocytosis X, when involving the hypothalamus, most frequently lead to diabetes insipidus, but any other hypothalamic defect may also occur. Tuberculous or sarcoid granulomas, other postinfectious inflammatory lesions, vascular lesions, and trauma more rarely cause hypogonadotropic hypogonadism.

3. Developmental defects– Developmental defects of the central nervous system may cause hypogonadotropic hypogonadism or other types of hypothalamic dysfunction. Optic dysplasia is associated with small, hypoplastic optic disks and, in some patients, absence of the septum pellucidum on pneumoencephalography, CT scanning, or MRI; associated hypothalamic deficiencies are often present. Optic hypoplasia or dysplasia must be differentiated from optic atrophy; optic atrophy implies an acquired condition and may indicate a hypothalamic-pituitary tumor. Both anterior and posterior pituitary deficiencies may occur with congenital midline defects. Early onset of such a combination suggests a congenital defect, while late onset more strongly indicates a neoplasm. Cleft palate or other midline anomalies may also be associated with hypothalamic dysfunction.

4. Radiation therapy– Central nervous system radiation therapy involving the hypothalamic-pituitary area can lead to hypogonadotropic hypogonadism with onset at 6–18 months (or sometimes longer) after treatment. Growth hormone secretion is more frequently affected than gonadotropin secretion.

B. Isolated Hormonal Deficiency: Patients who have isolated deficiency of gonadotropins but normal GH secretion tend to be of normal height for age but will lack a pubertal growth spurt. They have eunuchoid proportions of increased span for height and decreased US:LS (upper to lower segment) ratios. Their skeletal development will be delayed for chronologic age during the teenage years.

Kallmann's syndrome is the most common form of isolated gonadotropin deficiency (Figure 12–9). Gonadotropin deficiency in these patients is associated with hypoplasia or aplasia of the olfactory lobes and hyposmia or anosmia; remarkably, they may not notice that they have no sense of smell, although olfactory testing will reveal it. GnRH-containing neurons fail to migrate from the olfactory placode (where they originate) to the medial basal hypothalamus in Kallmann's syndrome. This is a familial syndrome of variable manifestations in which anosmia may occur with or without hypogonadism in a given member of a kindred. Gene deletions in the region of Xp22.3 can lead to association of Kallmann's syndrome and X-linked ichthyosis due to steroid sulfatase deficiency, mental retardation, and chondroplasia punctata. Associated abnormalities in Kallmann's syndrome may affect the kidneys and bones, and patients may have undescended testes, gynecomastia, and obesity. Ultimate height is normal, though patients are delayed in reaching adult height and so are shorter than peers until the late teenage years.

Other cases of hypogonadotropic hypogonadism may occur sporadically or via an autosomal recessive pattern without anosmia. X-linked congenital adrenal hypoplasia is associated with hypogonadotropic hypogonadism; glycerol kinase deficiency and muscular dystrophy have been linked to this syndrome. Some hypogonadal patients lack only LH secretion and have spermatogenesis without testosterone production (fertile eunuch syndrome); others lack only FSH.

C. Idiopathic Hypopituitary Dwarfism: Patients with congenital GH deficiency have early onset of growth failure (Figure 12–10); this feature distinguishes them from patients with GH deficiency due to hypothalamic tumors, who usually have late onset of growth failure. Even without associated gonadotropin deficiency, untreated GH-deficient patients often have delayed onset of puberty associated with their delayed bone ages. With appropriate hGH ther-

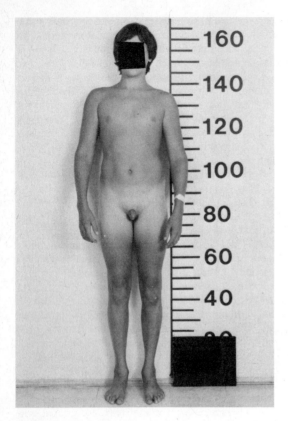 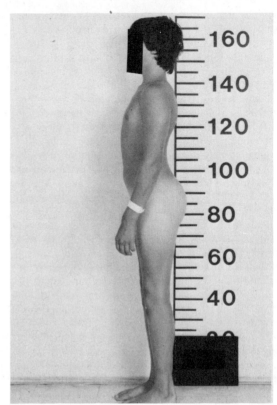

Figure 12–9. Boy 15 10/12 years old with Kallmann's syndrome. His testes were originally undescended, but they descended into the scrotum after human chorionic gonadotropin treatment was given. His height was 163.9 cm (–1.5 SD), and the US:LS ratio was 0.86 (eunuchoid). The penis was 6.3 × 1.8 cm. Each testis was 1 × 2 cm. Plasma LH was not detectable and rose to 5.5 mIU/mL (0.7 ng/mL) after administration of 100 µg of GnRH; FSH rose from 3.6–7.2 mIU/mL (1.2–2.4 ng/mL). Testosterone did not change from 17 ng/dL. He had no ability to smell standard odors. (Reproduced, with permission, from Styne DM, Grumbach MM: *Reproductive Endocrinology*. Yen SSC, Jaffe RB [editors]. Saunders, 1978.)

apy, however, onset of puberty occurs at a normal age. Patients who have combined GH and gonadotropin deficiency do not undergo puberty even when bone age reaches the pubertal stage. Idiopathic hypopituitarism is usually sporadic but may follow an autosomal recessive or X-linked inheritance pattern. Birth injury or breech delivery is a common feature of the neonatal history of patients with idiopathic hypopituitarism.

The syndrome of microphallus (due to congenital gonadotropin deficiency) and neonatal hypoglycemic seizures (due to congenital ACTH deficiency, GH deficiency, or both) must be diagnosed and treated early to avoid mental retardation. Patients with this syndrome will not undergo spontaneous pubertal development. Testosterone in low doses (testosterone enanthate, 25 mg intramuscularly every month for three doses) can increase the size of the penis in infants diagnosed with congenital hypopituitarism without significantly advancing the bone age. Males with isolated GH deficiency can also have microphallus; the penis will enlarge to some degree with hGH

therapy in these patients. It is important to note that microphallus due to hypopituitarism is medically treatable, and sex reversal usually need not be considered (see Chapter 11).

D. Miscellaneous Disorders:

1. Prader-Willi syndrome– Prader-Willi syndrome occurs sporadically and is associated with fetal and infantile hypotonia, short stature; poor feeding in infancy but insatiable hunger later, leading to massive obesity; characteristic facies with almond shaped eyes, small hands and feet after infancy, mental retardation, and emotional instability in patients of either sex; delayed menarche in females; and micropenis and cryptorchidism in males. Osteoporosis is common in these patients during the teenage years, and sex steroid replacement, when indicated, may help. Behavioral modification may improve the usual pattern of rampant weight gain. About 50% of patients have deletion or translocation of chromosome 15, and the affected chromosome is usually the paternally derived one.

2. Laurence-Moon, Bardet-Biedl syndrome–

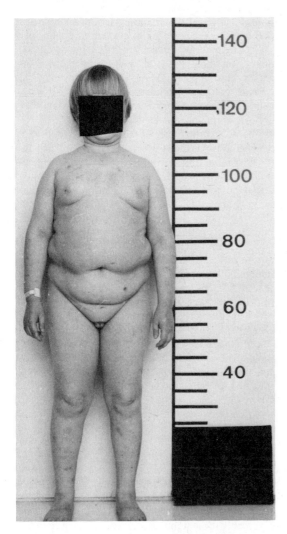

Figure 12–10. Twenty-year-old male with congenital deficiency of GH, GnRH, TSH, and ACTH. Height was 8 SD below the mean, and the phallus was 2 × 1 cm. Bone age was 10 years, and the sella turcica was small on lateral skull x-ray. LH was 1.5 mIU/mL (0.2 ng/mL) and rose only to 7.5 mIU/mL (0.6 ng/mL) after administration of 100 μg of GnRH. Testosterone was less than 10 ng/dL and did not rise after administration of GnRH. (Reproduced, with permission, from Styne DM, Grumbach MM: *Reproductive Endocrinology.* Yen SSC, Jaffe RB [editors]. Saunders, 1978.)

This autosomal recessive condition is characterized by obesity, short stature, mental retardation, and retinitis pigmentosa. Hypogonadotropic hypogonadism and primary hypogonadism have variously been reported in affected patients. Recently, the distinction between Laurence-Moon and Bardet-Biedl syndromes was emphasized, with the latter demonstrating polydactyly and obesity while the former was characterized by paraplegia.

3. Chronic disease and malnutrition– A delay in sexual maturation may be due to chronic disease or malnutrition. For example, children with intractable asthma have delayed pubertal development leading to short stature during the teenage years, though in general they ultimately reach an appropriate height. Children with other chronic diseases may not fare so well in long-term follow-up. Weight loss to less than 80% of ideal weight caused by disease or voluntary dieting may result in gonadotropin deficiency; weight gain toward the ideal usually restores gonadotropin function.

4. Anorexia nervosa– Anorexia nervosa involves weight loss associated with significant psychologic disorder. Patients are usually girls who have a disturbed body image, avoid food, and often induce regurgitation after ingestion. Weight loss may be so severe as to cause a fatal complication such as immune dysfunction, fluid and electrolyte imbalance, or circulatory collapse. Primary or secondary amenorrhea is a classic finding in these patients and has been correlated with the degree of weight loss, though there is evidence that patients with anorexia nervosa may cease to menstruate before their substantial weight loss. Other endocrine abnormalities in anorexia nervosa include elevated growth hormone, decreased IGF-1, decreased triiodothyronine, decreased 1,25-dihydroxyvitamin D, and elevated 24,25-hydroxyvitamin D levels. Weight gain to the normal range for height, however, does not ensure immediate resumption of menses. There appears to be an increased incidence of anorexia nervosa in ballet dancers or ballet students; the incidence of scoliosis and mitral valve insufficiency is also increased in these patients. Functional amenorrhea may also occur in women of normal weight, some of whom demonstrate evidence of psychologic stress. Decreased LH response to GnRH administration, impaired monthly cycles of gonadotropin secretion, and retention of a diurnal rhythm of gonadotropin secretion are found in anorexia nervosa patients, patterns which indicate a reversion to an earlier pubertal state

5. Increased physical activity– Girls who regularly participate in strenuous athletics, ballet dancing, etc, may have delayed thelarche, delayed menarche, and irregular or absent menstrual periods; this effect is not always related to less than ideal weight. One such athletic amenorrheic patient resumed menses while she was temporarily bedridden, which serves as evidence that increased physical activity and not decreased weight was at the root of her problem.

6. Hypothyroidism– Hypothyroidism can delay all aspects of growth and maturation, including puberty and menarche. Galactorrhea may occur in severe primary hypothyroidism. With thyroxine therapy, catch-up growth and resumed pubertal development and menses will occur. Conversely, severe hypothyroidism may be associated with precocious puberty and galactorrhea in some patients (Van Wyk-Grumbach syndrome).

Hypergonadotropic Hypogonadism

Primary gonadal failure is heralded by elevated gonadotropin concentration due to the absence of negative feedback effects of gonadal sex steroids. The most common causes of hypergonadotropic hypogonadism are associated with karyotypic and somatic abnormalities, but isolated gonadal failure can also present with delayed puberty without other physical findings.

A. Syndrome of Seminiferous Tubule Dysgenesis (Klinefelter's Syndrome): (See Chapters 9 and 11.) The most common form of primary testicular failure is Klinefelter's syndrome (47,XXY karyotype), with an incidence of 1:1000 males. Before puberty, patients have decreased US:LS ratios, small testes, and an increased incidence of mental retardation and personality disorders. Onset of puberty is not usually delayed, because Leydig cell function is characteristically less affected than seminiferous tubule function. Gonadotropin levels rise after the onset of puberty; the testes become firm and are rarely larger than 3.5 cm in diameter. After the onset of puberty, there are histologic changes of seminiferous tubule hyalinization and fibrosis, adenomatous changes of the Leydig cells, and impaired spermatogenesis. Gynecomastia is common, and variable degrees of male secondary sexual development are found.

Other forms of male hypergonadotropic hypogonadism are found with 46,XX/47,XXY, 48,XXYY, 48,XXXY, and 49,XXXXY karyotypes. Phenotypic males have been described with 46,XX karyotypes and some physical features of Klinefelter's syndrome.

B. Other Forms of Primary Testicular Failure: Patients surviving treatment for malignant diseases form a growing category of patients with testicular failure. Chemotherapy—primarily with alkylating agents—or radiation therapy directed to the gonads may lead to gonadal failure; injury is more likely if the treatment is given during puberty than if it occurs in the prepubertal period. Theoretically, the use of GnRH agonists to revert the pubertal state to prepuberty may prevent testicular damage during such treatment for malignancy.

The "Sertoli cell only" syndrome (germinal cell aplasia) is a congenital form of testicular failure manifested by azoospermia and elevated FSH concentrations but generally normal secondary sexual characteristics, normal testosterone concentrations, and no other anomalies. Patients with Down's syndrome may have elevated LH and FSH levels even in the presence of normal testosterone levels, suggesting some element of primary gonadal failure.

C. Cryptorchism or Anorchia: Phenotypic males with a 46,XY karyotype but no palpable testes have either cryptorchism or anorchia. Cryptorchid males should produce a rise in testosterone levels > 2 ng/mL 72 hours after intramuscular administration of 2000 units of chorionic gonadotropin, and the testes may descend during 2 weeks of treatment with 2000 units given three times a week. Patients with increased plasma testosterone levels in response to chorionic gonadotropin administration but no testicular descent have cryptorchism; their testes should be surgically brought into the scrotum to decrease the likelihood of further testicular damage due to the elevated intra-abdominal temperature or undetected tumor formation. Cryptorchid testes may have congenital abnormalities and may not have normal function even if brought into the scrotum early in life. Furthermore, the descended testis in a unilaterally cryptorchid boy may itself show abnormal histologic features; such patients have a 69% incidence of decreased sperm counts and can be infertile even with early treatment of cryptorchism. In addition, patients undergoing orchiopexy may sustain subtle damage to the vas deferens, leading to the later production of antibodies to sperm that may result in infertility.

It is important to determine if any testicular tissue is present in a boy with no palpable testes, since unnoticed malignant degeneration of the tissue is a possibility. The diagnosis of anorchia may be pursued by ultrasound or MRI, laparotomy or laparoscopic examination, or by endocrine evaluation. The presence of normal basal gonadotropin levels in a prepubertal boy without palpable testes suggests the presence of testicular tissue even if the testosterone response to hCG is low, while the presence of elevated gonadotropin levels without any testosterone response to hCG suggests anorchia. Except for absent testes, patients with anorchia have normal infantile male genital development, including wolffian duct formation and müllerian duct regression. The testes were presumably present in these patients early in fetal life during sexual differentiation but degenerated after the 13th week of gestation for unknown reasons ("vanishing testes syndrome").

D. Syndrome of Gonadal Dysgenesis (Turner's Syndrome): (See Chapters 10 and 11.) 45,X gonadal dysgenesis is associated with short stature, female phenotype with sexual infantilism, and a chromatin-negative buccal smear. Patients have "streak" gonads consisting of fibrous tissue without germ cells. Other classic but variable phenotypic features include micrognathia, "fish" mouth (downturned corners), ptosis, low-set or deformed ears, a broad shield-like chest with the appearance of widely space nipples, hypoplastic areolae, a short neck with low hairline and webbing (pterygium colli), short fourth metacarpals, cubitus valgus, structural anomalies of the kidney, extensive nevi, hypoplastic nails, and cardiovascular anomalies of the left side of the heart (most commonly coarctation of the aorta). The medical history of patients with gonadal dysgenesis will often reveal small size at birth, lymphedema of the extremities most prominent in the newborn period, and loose posterior cervical skin folds. (The terms Bonnevie-Ullrich syndrome and infant Turner's syndrome have been applied to this neonatal appearance.) Affected patients often have a history of frequent otitis media with conductive hearing loss. Intelligence is normal but there is often impaired spatial orientation. Patients have no pubertal growth spurt and reach a mean final height of 143 cm. Short stature is a classic feature of Turner's syndrome but not of other forms of hypergonadotropic hypogonadism that occur without karyotypic abnormalities. GH function is usually normal in Turner's syndrome, and the cause of short stature is not known. However, preliminary studies suggest that hGH treatment may improve growth rate in affected girls (see Chapter 11). Pubic hair may appear late and is usually sparse in distribution owing to the absence of any ovarian secretions; thus, adrenarche progresses in Turner's syndrome even in the absence of gonadarche.

Serum gonadotropin concentrations in Turner's syndrome are extremely high between birth and age 4 years. They decrease toward the normal range in prepubertal patients and then rise again to castrate levels after age 10 years. (See Chapter 11.)

Sex chromatin-positive variants of gonadal dysgenesis include 45,X/46,XX, 45,X/47,XXX, and 45,X/46,XX/47,XXX mosaicism with chromatin-positive buccal smears. Patients with these karyotypes may resemble patients with the classic syndrome of gonadal dysgenesis, or they may have fewer manifestations and normal or nearly normal female phenotypes. Streak gonad formation is not invariable; some patients have had secondary sexual development, and menarche and (rarely) even pregnancy have been reported. A few patients with Turner's syndrome have benefited from in vitro fertilization techniques. After exogenous hormonal preparation, a fertilized ovum (possibly her sister's ovum fertilized by the patient's male partner, or an extra fertilized ovum from another couple undergoing in vitro fertilization) can be introduced into the patient's uterus.

Sex chromatin-negative variants of the syndrome of gonadal dysgenesis have karyotypes with 45,X/46,XY mosaicism. Physical features vary; some patients have the features of classic Turner's syndrome, while others may have ambiguous genitalia or even the features of phenotypic males. Gonads are dysgenetic but vary from streak gonads to functioning testes. These patients are at risk for gonadoblastoma formation. Since gonadoblastomas may secrete androgens or estrogens, patients with gonadoblastoma may virilize or feminize as though they had functioning gonads, confusing the clinical picture. Gonadoblastomas may demonstrate calcification on abdominal x-ray. Malignant germ cell tumors may arise in dysgenetic testes, and orchiectomy is generally indicated. In some mosaic patients with one intact X chromosome and one chromosomal fragment, it is difficult to determine whether the fragment is derived from an X chromosome or a Y chromosome; present research into appropriate markers for the chromosome or for the presence of testis-determining factor will probably in future allow diagnosis of patients at risk for such complications. At present, the use of Y chromosome-specific DNA probes may identify such patients at risk.

E. Other Forms of Primary Ovarian Failure: Ovaries appear to be more resistant to damage from the chemotherapy used in the treatment of malignant disease than are testes. Nonetheless, ovarian failure can occur with medical therapy. Damage is common if the ovaries are not "tacked" out of the path of the beam in abdominal radiation therapy. Premature menopause has also been described in otherwise healthy girls owing to the presence of antiovarian antibodies. Patients with Addison's disease may have autoimmune oophoritis as well as adrenal failure. A sex steroid biosynthetic defect due to 17α-hydroxylase deficiency will be manifested as sexual infantilism and primary amenorrhea in a phenotypic female (regardless of genotype) with hypokalemia and hypertension. The patient may have ovaries or testes.

F. Pseudo-Turner's Syndrome (Noonan's Syndrome, Ullrich's Syndrome, Male Turner's Syndrome): Pseudo-Turner's syndrome is associated with manifestations of Turner's syndrome such as webbed neck, ptosis, short stature, cubitus valgus, and lymphedema, but other clinical findings such as a normal karyotype, triangular-shaped facies, pectus excavatum, right-sided heart disease, and an increased incidence of mental retardation should differentiate these patients from those with Turner's syndrome. Males may have undescended testes and variable degrees of germinal cell and Leydig cell dysfunction. Pseudo-Turner's syndrome follows an autosomal dominant pattern of inheritance with incomplete penetrance.

G. Familial and Sporadic Forms of 46,XX or 46,XY Gonadal Dysgenesis: These forms of gonadal dysgenesis are characterized by structurally normal chromosomes and streak gonads or partially functioning gonads. If there is some gonadal function, 46,XY gonadal dysgenesis may present with ambiguous genitalia or virilization at puberty. If no gonadal function is present, patients appear as phenotypic sexually infantile females. Patients with 46,XY gonadal dysgenesis and dysgenetic testes should undergo gonadectomy to eliminate the possibility of malignant germ cell tumor formation.

H. Primary Amenorrhea Associated With Normal Secondary Sexual Development: If a structural anomaly of the uterus or vagina interferes with the onset of menses but the endocrine milieu remains normal, the patient presents with primary amenorrhea in the presence of normal breast and pubic hair development. A transverse vaginal septum will seal the uterine cavity from the vaginal orifice, leading to the retention of menstrual flow—as may an imperforate hymen. The Rokitansky-Küster-Hauser syndrome combines congenital absence of the vagina with abnormal development of the uterus, ranging from a rudimentary bicornuate uterus that may not open into the vaginal canal to a virtually normal uterus; surgical repair may be possible in patients whose anatomic abnormalities tend toward normal, and fertility has been reported. Associated abnormalities include major urinary tract anomalies and spinal or other skeletal disorders. The rarest anatomic abnormality in this group is absence of the uterine cervix in the presence of a functional uterus.

Male pseudohermaphroditism is an alternative cause of primary amenorrhea if a patient has achieved thelarche. The syndrome of complete androgen resistance leads to female genitalia and phenotype without axillary or pubic hair development in the presence of pubertal breast development (syndrome of testicular feminization; see Chapter 11).

Differential Diagnosis of Delayed Puberty (Table 12–3)

Patients who do not begin secondary sexual development by age 13 (girls) or age 14 (boys) and patients who do not progress through development on a timely basis (girls should menstruate within 5 years after breast budding; boys should reach stage 5 pubertal development 4 1/2 years after onset) should be evaluated for hypogonadism. The yield of diagnosable conditions is quite low in children younger than these ages, but many patients and families will request evaluation well before these limits.

If the diagnosis is not obvious on the basis of physical or historical features, the differential diagnostic process begins with determination of whether plasma gonadotropins are (1) elevated owing to primary gonadal failure or (2) decreased owing to secondary or tertiary hypogonadism or constitutional delayed puberty. If plasma gonadotropins are low, the differential diagnosis rests between hypogonadotropic hypogonadism and constitutionally delayed puberty. A patient with constitutional delay may

have a characteristic history of short stature for age with normal growth velocity for bone age and a family history of delayed but spontaneous puberty. The patient's mother may have had late onset of menses, or the father may have begun to shave late or grow well after high school graduation. Not all patients with constitutional delay are classic, and gonadotropin-deficient patients may have some features similar to those of constitutional delay in adolescence. Determination of the rise in LH after administration of GnRH is helpful in differential diagnosis; secondary sexual development usually follows within 6 months after conversion to a pubertal LH response to GnRH. Frequent nighttime sampling (every 20 minutes through an indwelling catheter) to determine the amplitude of peaks of LH secretion during sleep is an alternative to GnRH testing but quite cumbersome. Unfortunately, the results of GnRH infusions or nighttime sampling are not always straightforward. Patients may have pubertal responses to exogenous GnRH but not spontaneously secrete adequate gonadotropins to allow secondary sexual development. In females with amenorrhea, the frequency and amplitude of gonadotropin secretion may not change to allow monthly menstrual cycles. The retention of a diurnal rhythm of gonadotropin secretion (normal in early puberty) into late puberty interferes with pubertal progression. Other methods of differential diagnosis between constitutional delay and hypogonadotropic hypogonadism have been proposed but are complex or are not definitive.

Clinical observation for signs of pubertal development and laboratory evaluation for the onset of rising levels of sex steroids may have to continue until the patient is 18 years of age before the diagnosis is definite. In most cases, if spontaneous pubertal development is not noted by 18 years of age, the diagnosis is gonadotropin deficiency. Of course, the presence of neurologic impairment or other endocrine deficiency should immediately lead to investigation for central nervous system tumor or congenital defect in a patient with delayed puberty. CT or MRI scanning may be helpful in this situation.

Table 12–3. Differential diagnosis of delayed puberty.

	Serum Gonadotropins	Serum Gonadal Steroids	Miscellaneous
Constitutional delay in growth and adolescence	Prepubertal (low)	Low	Patient usually has short stature for chronologic age but appropriate height and growth rate for bone age. Adrenarche and gonadarche are delayed.
Hypogonadotropic hypogonadism	Prepubertal (low)	Low	Patient may have anosmia (Kallmann's syndrome) or other associated pituitary hormone deficiencies. If gonadotropin deficiency is isolated, patient usually has normal height and growth rate. Adrenarche may be normal in spite of absent gonadarche (serum DHEA sulfate may be pubertal).
Hypergonadotropic hypogonadism	Elevated	Low	Patient may have abnormal karyotype and stigmas of Turner's or Klinefelter's syndrome.

Treatment of Delayed Puberty

A. Constitutional Delay in Growth and Adolescence:

1. Psychologic support– Patients with constitutional delay in growth and adolescence should be counseled that normal pubertal development will occur spontaneously. Peer pressure and teasing can be oppressive. Severe depression must be treated appropriately, since short patients with pubertal delay have become suicidal. In some cases it helps to excuse the patient from physical education class, as the lack of development is most apparent in the locker room.

2. Sex steroids– Teenagers who are so embarrassed about short stature and lack of secondary sexual development as to have significant psychologic problems may require special help if they have passed the ages of 13 years for girls or 14 years for boys. The following treatment can be given: (1) for girls, a 3-month course of conjugated estrogen (0.3 mg) or ethinyl estradiol (5–10 μg) given orally each day; or (2) for boys, a 3-month course of testosterone enanthate (100 mg) given intramuscularly once every 28 days for three doses. This treatment will elicit noticeable secondary sexual development and a slight increase in stature. The low doses recommended have not significantly changed final height. Such low-dose sex steroid treatment may actually promote spontaneous pubertal development after it has been discontinued. The short course of therapy may also improve patients' psychologic outlook and allow them to await spontaneous pubertal development with greater ease. Continuous gonadal steroid replacement in these patients is not indicated, as it will advance bone age and lead to epiphysial fusion and a decrease in ultimate stature; however, after a 3- to 6-month break to observe spontaneous development, another course of therapy may be offered.

B. Permanent Hypogonadism: Once a patient has been diagnosed as having delayed puberty due to permanent hypogonadism, either primary or secondary, replacement therapy must be considered.

Males with hypogonadism may be treated with testosterone enanthate intramuscularly every month, gradually increasing the dosage from 100 mg to 300 mg every 28 days. Frequent erections or priapism may occur if the higher dose is used initially. Oral halogenated testosterone or methylated testosterone is not recommended because of the risk of hepatocellular carcinoma or cholestatic jaundice.

Testosterone therapy may not cause adequate pubic hair development, but patients with secondary or tertiary hypogonadism may benefit from hCG administration with increased pubic hair growth resulting from endogenous androgen secretion in addition to the exogenous testosterone.

Therapy with oxandrolone has been suggested as a method of increasing secondary sexual development and increasing growth without advancing skeletal development; such claims have not been sufficiently well documented to justify a preference for oxandrolone therapy over low-dose testosterone. Furthermore, testosterone, which can be aromatized, increases the generally low endogenous growth hormone secretion in constitutional delayed puberty to normal, while oxandrolone, which cannot be aromatized, does not increase growth hormone secretion (see Chapter 9).

Females may be treated with ethinyl estradiol (increasing from 5 μg/d to 10–20 μg/d depending upon clinical results) or conjugated estrogens (0.3 or 0.625 mg/d) on days 1–21. Ten milligrams of medroxyprogesterone acetate are then added on days 12–21 after physical signs of estrogen effect are noted and breakthrough bleeding occurs (and always within 6 months after initiating estrogen). Neither hormone is administered from day 22 to the end of the month to allow regular withdrawal bleeding (see Chapter 10).

C. Coexisting GH Deficiency: The treatment of patients with coexisting GH deficiency requires consideration of their bone age and amount of growth left before epiphysial fusion; if they have not yet received adequate treatment with growth hormone, sex steroid therapy may be kept in the lower range or even delayed to optimize final adult height. The goal is to allow appropriate pubertal changes to support psychologic development and to allow the synergistic effects of combined sex steroids and GH without fusing the epiphyses prematurely.

Constitutional delayed puberty may be associated with decreased growth hormone secretion in 24-hour profiles of spontaneous secretion or in stimulated testing. Growth hormone secretion increases when pubertal gonadal steroid secretion rises, so decreased GH secretion in this condition should be considered temporary. Growth hormone therapy is not proved to increase final height in patients with constitutional delay in puberty and normal height predictions; some studies have shown an increased growth rate in the first year of such therapy with a decreasing growth rate thereafter. Nonetheless, true growth hormone-deficient patients may have delayed puberty due to the growth hormone deficiency or to coexisting gonadotropin deficiency. Therefore, deciding whether a pubertal patient has temporary or a permanent GH deficiency can be difficult; previous growth rate and bone age progression may indicate a long history characteristic of constitutional delay in adolescence, while a recent decrease in growth rate may suggest the onset of a brain tumor and hypopituitarism.

D. The Syndrome of Gonadal Dysgenesis: In the past, patients with the syndrome of gonadal dysgenesis were frequently not given estrogen replacement until after age 13 years, for fear of compromising final height. It has now been demonstrated that low-dose estrogen therapy (5–10 μg of ethinyl estradiol orally) can be administered to allow feminization and improve psychologic status at 12–13 years of age without decreasing final height in these patients. Low-dose estrogen will increase growth velocity, while high-dose estrogen suppresses it; even if growth velocity is increased, however, final height is reportedly not increased with estrogen. Treatment of Turner's syndrome with GH may be more successful in increasing adult stature (see Chapter 11).

PRECOCIOUS PUBERTY (Sexual Precocity)

The appearance of secondary sexual development before the age of 8 years in girls and 9 years in boys is greater than 2.5 SD below the mean age of onset of puberty and constitutes precocious sexual development (Table 12–4). When the cause is premature activation of the hypothalamic-pituitary axis, the diagnosis is complete (true) precocious puberty; if ectopic gonadotropin secretion occurs in boys or autonomous sex steroid secretion occurs in either sex, the diagnosis is incomplete precocious puberty. In all forms of sexual precocity, there is an increase in growth velocity, somatic development, and skeletal maturation. When unchecked, this rapid epiphysial development may lead to tall stature during the early phases of the disorder but to short final stature because of early epiphysial fusion. Plasma IGF-1 values may be elevated for age but more appropriate for pubertal stage in the untreated state.

Complete (True) Precocious Puberty (Figure 12–11)

A. Constitutional Complete (True) Precocious Puberty: Children who demonstrate isosexual precocity at an age more than 2.5 SD below the mean may simply represent the lower reaches of the distri-

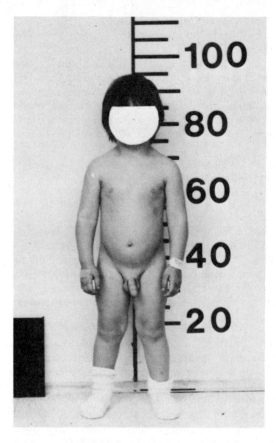

Figure 12–11. Boy 2 5/12 years of age with idiopathic true precocious puberty. By 10 months of age, he had pubic hair and phallic and testicular enlargement. At 1 year of age, his height was 4 SD above the mean; the phallus was 10 × 3.5 cm; each testis was 2.5 × 1.5 cm. Plasma LH was 14.8 mIU/mL and rose to 65.5 mIU/mL after administration of 100 μg of GnRH. Plasma testosterone was 416 ng/dL. At the time of the photograph, he had been treated with medroxyprogesterone acetate for 1 1/2 years, with reduction of his rapid growth rate and decreased gonadotropin and testosterone secretion. His height was 95.2 cm (> 2 SD above mean height for his age); plasma testosterone was 7 ng/dL, and after 100 μg of GnRH, plasma LH rose from 7 mIU/mL (0.9 ng/mL) to 11 mIU/mL (2.3 ng/mL). (Reproduced, with permission, from Styne, DM, Grumbach MM: *Reproductive Endocrinology.* Yen SSC, Jaffe RB [editors]. Saunders, 1978.)

Table 12–4. Classification of precocious puberty.

Complete (true) precocious puberty
Constitutional
Idiopathic
Central nervous system disorders
Following androgen exposure
Incomplete precocious puberty
Males
Gonadotropin-secreting tumors
Excessive androgen production
Premature Leydig and germinal cell maturation
Females
Ovarian cysts
Estrogen-secreting neoplasms
Males and females
Severe hypothyroidism
McCune-Albright syndrome
Sexual precocity due to gonadotropin or sex steroid exposure
Variation in pubertal development
Premature thelarche
Premature menarche
Premature pubarche
Adolescent gynecomastia

bution curve of age of onset of puberty; often there is a familial tendency toward early puberty. True precocious puberty is rarely reported to be due to an autosomal dominant or (in males) X-linked autosomal dominant trait.

B. Idiopathic Complete (True) Precocious Puberty: Affected children with no familial tendency toward early development and no organic disease may be considered to have idiopathic precocious puberty. Electroencephalographic abnormalities or other evidence of neurologic dysfunction may be

found in these patients. Pubertal development may follow the normal course in these patients or may wax and wane. Gonadotropin and sex steroid concentrations and response to GnRH are similar to those found in normal pubertal subjects. In idiopathic true precocious puberty, as in all forms of true isosexual precocity, testicular enlargement in boys should be the first sign; in girls, either breast development or pubic hair appearance may be first. Girls present with idiopathic precocious puberty more commonly than boys.

C. Central Nervous System Disorders:

1. Tumors– Central nervous system tumor as a cause of precocious puberty is more common in boys than in girls. Optic gliomas or hypothalamic gliomas (isolated or with neurofibromatosis), astrocytomas, ependymomas, and other central nervous system tumors may cause precocious puberty by interfering with neural pathways and thus inhibiting GnRH secretion. Remarkably, craniopharyngiomas, which are known to cause delayed puberty, can also trigger precocious pubertal development. Hamartomas of the tuber cinereum have been reported to contain GnRH and neurosecretory cells such as are found in the median eminence; they may cause precocious puberty by secreting GnRH. With improved methods of imaging the central nervous system, hamartomas, with their characteristic radiographic appearance, are now being more frequently diagnosed in patients who were previously thought to have idiopathic precocious puberty. These tumors do not grow and so pose no increasing threat to the patients; surgical removal is not indicated, as hamartomas respond readily to GnRH agonist therapy. Surgery is a dangerous alternative to GnRH therapy owing to the location of the hamartoma. Radiation therapy is indicated in radiosensitive tumors such as germinomas and craniopharyngiomas, where complete surgical extirpation is impossible.

Tumors or other abnormalities of the central nervous system may cause growth hormone deficiency in association with precocious puberty. Such patients will grow much faster than isolated growth hormone-deficient patients but slower than children with classic precocious puberty. Often the growth hormone deficiency will be unmasked after successful treatment of precocious puberty. This combination must be considered during the diagnostic process.

2. Other causes of true precocious puberty– Infectious or granulomatous conditions such as encephalitis, brain abscess, postinfectious (or postsurgical or congenital) suprasellar cysts, sarcoidosis, and tuberculous granulomas of the hypothalamus have been reported to cause true precocious puberty. Suprasellar cysts and hydrocephalus are conditions that cause precocious puberty and are particularly amenable to surgical correction. Brain trauma may be followed by either precocious or delayed puberty. Radiation therapy for acute lymphoblastic leukemia is characteristically associated with hormonal deficiency, but cases have been reported of precocious puberty occurring after such therapy. Epilepsy and mental retardation have also been associated with precocious puberty in the absence of anatomic lesions of the central nervous system.

D. Virilizing Syndromes: Patients with long-untreated virilizing adrenal hyperplasia who have advanced bone ages may manifest precocious puberty after the adrenal hyperplasia is controlled with glucocorticoid suppression. Children with virilizing tumors or those given long-term androgen therapy may follow the same pattern when the androgen source is removed. Advanced maturation of the hypothalamic-pituitary-gonadal axis appears to occur with any condition causing excessive androgen secretion and advanced skeletal age.

Incomplete Precocious Puberty

A. Males: Male patients may manifest premature sexual development in the absence of hypothalamic-pituitary maturation from either of two causes: (1) ectopic or autonomous endogenous secretion of hCG or LH or iatrogenic exogenous administration of chorionic gonadotropin, which can stimulate Leydig cell production of testosterone; or (2) autonomous endogenous secretion of androgens from the testes or adrenal glands or from iatrogenic exogenous administration of androgens. (In females, secretion of hCG will not by itself cause secondary sexual development.)

1. Gonadotropin-secreting tumors– These include hepatomas or hepatoblastomas of the liver as well as teratomas or choriocarcinoma of the mediastinum, gonads, retroperitoneum, or pineal gland and germinomas of the central nervous system.

2. Autonomous androgen secretion– Secretion of androgens can occur because of inborn errors of adrenal enzyme function, as in 21-hydroxylase or 11β-hydroxylase deficiency, virilizing adrenal carcinomas, interstitial cell tumors of the testes, or premature Leydig and germinal cell maturation. Newly recognized forms of late-onset congenital adrenal hyperplasia, generally of the 21-hydroxylase deficiency form, may occur years after birth with no congenital or neonatal manifestations of virilization. Adrenal rest tissue may be found in the testes as a vestige of the embryonic common origin of these two organs; in states of ACTH excess, primarily congenital adrenal hyperplasia, adrenal rests can enlarge and secrete adrenal androgens (see Chapter 11).

In all forms of incomplete male isosexual precocity, FSH is not elevated, and since the seminiferous tubules are not stimulated, the testes do not enlarge as much as in complete sexual precocity. If incomplete sexual precocity is due to a testicular tumor, the testes may be large, asymmetric, and irregular in contour. Symmetric bilateral moderate enlargement of the testes suggests gonadotropin-independent premature maturation of Leydig and germinal cells, which is a sex-limited dominant condition. The testes are somewhat smaller in this condition than in true precocious puberty but are still over 2.5 cm in diameter. In boys with premature Leydig and germinal cell maturation, plasma testosterone levels are in the pubertal range but plasma gonadotropin levels and the LH response to exogenous GnRH are in the prepubertal range because autonomous testosterone secretion suppresses endogenous GnRH release. The differential diagnosis rests between testosterone-secreting tumor of the adrenal, testosterone-secreting Leydig cell neoplasm, and premature Leydig and germinal cell maturation.

B. Females: Female patients with incomplete isosexual precocity have a source of excessive estrogens. In all cases of autonomous endogenous estrogen secretion or exogenous administration, serum LH and FSH levels should be low.

1. Follicular cysts– If follicular cysts are large enough, they can secrete sufficient estrogen to cause breast development and even vaginal withdrawal bleeding; some girls have recurrent cysts that lead to several episodes of vaginal bleeding. Patients with cysts may have levels of serum estrogen high enough to mimic a tumor. Larger follicular cysts can twist on their pedicles and become infarcted, causing symptoms of acute abdomen in addition to the precocious estrogen effects.

2. Granulosa or theca cell tumors– These tumors of the ovaries secrete estrogen and are palpable in 80% of cases. Gonadoblastomas found in streak gonads, lipoid tumors, cystadenomas, and ovarian carcinomas are rare ovarian sources of estrogens or androgens.

3. Adrenal rest tissue– Adrenal rest tissue has long been known to cause testicular enlargement and androgen secretion in boys, particularly with the increased ACTH secretion of congenital adrenal hyperplasia. Recently, however, a girl with an ovarian adrenal rest was reported to have hypertension, precocious puberty, Cushing's syndrome, and ovarian enlargement.

4. Exogenous estrogen administration– Ingestion of estrogen-containing substances or even cutaneous absorption of estrogen can cause feminization in children. Epidemics of gynecomastia and precocious thelarche in Puerto Rico and Italy have variously been attributed to ingestion of estrogen-contaminated food, estrogens in the environment, or undetermined causes. One outbreak of gynecomastia in boys and precocious thelarche in girls in Bahrain was traced to a cow given continuous estrogen treatment by its owner to ensure uninterrupted milk production.

5. Virilization in girls– Excess androgen effect can be caused by premature adrenarche or more significant pathologic conditions such as congenital or late-onset adrenal hyperplasia or adrenal or ovarian

tumors. Adrenal hyperplasia can be diagnosed on the basis of elevated 17-hydroxyprogesterone concentrations. Both adrenal and ovarian tumors generally secrete testosterone, while adrenal tumors secrete DHEA as well. The source of the tumor may be difficult to differentiate if it produces only testosterone; MRI or CT scanning may be inadequate to diagnose the tumor's organ of origin, and selective venous sampling may be needed.

C.Males and Females:

1. McCune-Albright syndrome– McCune-Albright syndrome is classically manifested as a triad of irregular café au lait spots, fibrous dysplasia of long bones with cysts, and precocious puberty. However, cases have been reported that also included hyperthyroidism, adrenal nodules with Cushing's syndrome, acromegaly, hyperprolactinemia, hyperparathyroidism, hypophosphatemic hyperphosphaturic rickets, or autonomous endogenous functioning ovarian cysts in girls. Precocious puberty may be complete or incomplete; longitudinal study suggests that some patients start with incomplete precocious puberty and progress to complete precocious puberty. Long-term follow-up of McCune-Albright patients reveals a high incidence of pathologic fractures and orthopedic deformities due to the bone cysts, as well as hearing impairment due to the thickening of the temporal area of the skull. The disorder appears to be caused be a mutation of the Arg_{201} of exon 8 of the G protein alpha subunit that stimulates cAMP formation; this leads to decreased G protein and increased adenylyl cyclase activity. This defect originates in somatic rather than germ cells.

2. Hypothyroidism– Severe untreated hypothyroidism can be associated with sexual precocity and galactorrhea (Van Wyk-Grumbach syndrome); treatment with thyroxine will correct hypothyroidism, halt precocious puberty and galactorrhea, and lower PRL levels. The cause of this syndrome is postulated to be increased gonadotropin secretion associated with the massive increase in TSH secretion.

Variations in Pubertal Development

A. Premature Thelarche: The term "premature thelarche" denotes unilateral or bilateral breast enlargement without other signs of androgen or estrogen secretion of puberty. Patients are usually under 3 years of age; the breast enlargement may regress within months or remain until actual pubertal development occurs at a normal age. Nipple development and vaginal mucosal signs of estrogen effect are usually absent. Premature thelarche may be caused by brief episodes of estrogen secretion from ovarian cysts. Plasma estrogen levels are usually low in this disorder, perhaps because blood samples are drawn after the initiating secretory event.

B. Premature Menarche: In rare cases, girls may begin to menstruate at an early age without showing other signs of estrogen effect. An unproved theory suggests that they may be manifesting increased uterine sensitivity to estrogen. In most subjects, menses stop within 1–6 years, and normal pubertal progression occurs thereafter.

C. Premature Adrenarche: The term "premature adrenarche" denotes the early appearance of pubic or axillary hair without other signs of virilization or puberty. This nonprogressive disorder is compatible with a normal age of onset of other signs of puberty. It is more common in girls than in boys and usually is found in children over 6 years of age. Plasma and urinary DHEAS are elevated to stage 2 pubertal levels, which are higher than normally found in this age group. Bone and height ages may be slightly advanced for chronologic age. Patients may have abnormal electroencephalographic tracings without other signs of neurologic dysfunction. The presenting symptoms of late-onset adrenal hyperplasia may be similar to those of premature adrenarche, and the diagnosis may require ACTH stimulation testing.

D. Adolescent Gynecomastia: Seventy-five percent of boys will have unilateral or bilateral gynecomastia, usually beginning in stage 2 or 3 of puberty and regressing about 2 years later. Plasma estrogen and testosterone concentrations are normal, but the estradiol/testosterone ratio may be elevated, and SHBG concentrations may be high. Reassurance is usually all that is required, but some severely affected patients with extremely prominent breast development will require reduction mammoplasty if psychologic distress is extreme. Some pathologic conditions such as Klinefelter's and Reifenstein's syndromes and the syndrome of incomplete androgen resistance are also associated with gynecomastia; these disorders should be clearly differentiated from the gynecomastia of normal puberty in males.

Differential Diagnosis of Precocious Puberty

The history and physical examination should be directed toward one of the diagnostic possibilities discussed above. Gonadotropin and sex steroid concentrations are determined in order to distinguish gonadotropin-mediated secondary sexual development (gonadotropin and sex steroid levels elevated) from autonomous endogenous secretion or exogenous administration of gonadal steroids (gonadotropin levels suppressed and sex steroid levels elevated).

New commercial immunoassays are said to more clearly indicate the onset of gonadotropin secretion with only a basal unstimulated sample. In the past, a GnRH test was required to confirm an increase in LH secretion at puberty because of the overlap of pubertal and prepubertal values of LH in the basal state. It is not yet clear that these new assays will replace the GnRH test in the diagnosis of disorders of puberty.

If plasma LH (or hCG) levels are quite high in a boy or a pregnancy screening test is positive, the likely diagnosis is an extrapituitary hCG-secreting tumor. If no abdominal source of hCG is found, CT scan or MRI of the head with particular attention to the hypothalamic-pituitary area is indicated to evaluate the possibility of a germinoma of the pineal gland.

If plasma sex steroid levels are very high and gonadotropin levels are low, an autonomous source of gonadal steroid secretion must be assumed. If plasma gonadotropin and sex steroid levels are in the pubertal range, the most likely diagnosis is complete precocious puberty. In such patients, the GnRH test will usually result in a rise in LH levels compatible with normal puberty and will thus confirm the diagnosis (Table 12–5).

The onset of true or complete precocious puberty may indicate the presence of a hypothalamic tumor. Boys more often than girls have central nervous system tumors associated with complete precocious puberty. Skull x-rays are not usually helpful, but CT or MRI scanning is indicated in children with true precocious puberty. The present generation of CT and MRI scanners can make thin cuts through the hypothalamic-pituitary area with good resolution; small hypothalamic hamartomas are now being diagnosed more frequently.

Treatment of Precocious Puberty

A. Complete Precocious Puberty: In the past, medical treatment of true precocious puberty was most commonly accomplished with medroxyprogesterone acetate or cyproterone acetate, progestational agents that reduce gonadotropin secretion by negative feedback.

New primary treatment for precocious puberty due to a central nervous system lesion has now been established. Chronic use of highly potent and long-acting analogues of GnRH has been shown to downregulate GnRH receptors and reduce pituitary gland response to GnRH, thereby causing decreased secretion of gonadotropin and sex steroids and rapidly stopping the progression of signs of sexual precocity in numerous children studied at many centers. This suppressive effect is reversed after therapy is discontinued. Treatment of idiopathic precocious puberty and precocious puberty caused by hamartomas of the tuber cinereum, neoplasms of the central nervous system, or long-term androgen exposure has been successful. The FDA has presently approved histrelin, a GnRH agonist administered on a daily basis and lueprolide acetate, a long acting GnRH for use in precocious puberty, but other agents are used in clinical studies.

The GnRH agonists are given daily subcutaneously or by intranasal insufflation; the successful use of these agents in microcapsules that are injected every 3 weeks or in depot preparations has made treatment even easier. Numerous agents with varying potencies are used. Because of the differing potencies,

Table 12–5. Differential diagnosis of precocious puberty.

	Serum Gonadotropin Concentrations	LH Response to GnRH	Serum Sex Steroid Concentrations	Gonadal Size	Miscellaneous
Complete (true) pre-cocious puberty	Pubertal.	Pubertal pattern.	Pubertal values.	Normal pubertal enlargement of testes in males.	CT or MRI scan of head to rule out a central nervous system tumor.
Incomplete pre-cocious puberty **Males** Gonadotropin-secreting tumor	High hCG or LH (positive pregnancy test).	High basal LH that does not rise with GnRH.	High or pubertal values.	Slight to moderate enlargement of testes.	Hepatic tumor must be considered. CT or MRI scan of head if go-nadotropin-secret-ing central nervous system tumor suspected.
Leydig cell tumor	Prepubertal (low).	Prepubertal or suppressed pattern.	Extremely high testosterone.	Irregular asymmetric enlargement of testes.	
Gonadotropin-independent sexual precocity with premature Leydig and germinal cell maturation	Prepubertal (low).	Prepubertal or suppressed pattern.	Pubertal or higher values.	Testes larger than 2.5 cm but smaller than expected for stage of pubertal development.	Often found in sex-limited dominant patterns.
Females Granulosa cell tumor (follicular cysts may be similar to presentation)	Prepubertal (low).	Prepubertal or suppressed pattern.	Extremely high estradiol.	Ovarian enlargement on physical, CT, or sonographic examination.	Granulosa cell tumor is usually palpable on rectal examination.
Follicular cyst	Prepubertal (low).	Prepubertal pattern of LH. FSH secretion may rise above normal range.	Estradiol may be normally low or quite high, depending upon the stage of cyst formation or regression.	Cysts may be visible on sonogram.	Withdrawal bleeding may occur when estrogen levels decrease. Cysts may recur.

it is possible that patients may only be partially treated, and therefore their response to GnRH may be only partially suppressed. Such a patient may appear to have arrested pubertal development while actually secreting low but significant levels of sex steroids, so that bone age is advancing while the growth rate is suppressed. Side effects have generally been limited to allergic skin reactions and elevation of immunoglobulins directed to the agent. However, at least one child manifested a significant anaphylactic reaction to an injection.

GnRH agonists are the preferred treatment for true precocious puberty. Without therapy, final height in patients with central precocious puberty approaches 152 cm in girls and 155–164 cm in boys. With correct dosage and early initiation of therapy, final height may be preserved in patients with central precocious puberty. Growth velocity decreases within 6 months after the start of therapy, and rapid bone age

advancement decreases to a rate below the increase in chronologic age. The first patients treated with GnRH agonists have recently reached final height, and the girls have a mean height of 157 cm and the boys a mean height of 164 cm. This is a definite improvement over the untreated state, and as earlier diagnosis is made in children with central precocious puberty and earlier therapy is offered, better results are expected in the future. Mild central precocious puberty may not require GnRH therapy. Patients without significant elevation of estrogen or IGF-1 who have slowly progressing variants may maintain an appropriate final height without therapy.

3. Psychologic support– Psychologic support is important for patients with sexual precocity. The somatic changes or menses will frighten some children and may make them the object of ridicule. These patients do not experience social maturation to match their physical development, though their peers, teachers, and relatives will tend to treat them as if they were older because of their large size. Thus, supportive counseling must be offered to both patient and family. Evidence indicates that children with precocious puberty are more often sexually abused, so appropriate precautions are necessary.

B. Incomplete Precocious Puberty: Treatment of the disorders discussed above under incomplete precocious puberty is directed toward the underlying tumor or abnormality rather than toward the signs of precocious puberty. If the primary cause is controlled, signs of sexual development will be halted in progression or may even regress.

Males with familial Leydig cell maturation will not initially respond to GnRH agonist therapy, but some have improved with medroxyprogesterone acetate. Boys were successfully treated with ketoconazole, which can block 17–20 lyase and therefore decrease testosterone production. After initial control with ketoconazole, the boys developed true precocious puberty, because prolonged exposure to andro-

gens matured their hypothalamic-pituitary axis; treatment with GnRH agonist then effectively halted this pubertal progression. Males with McCune-Albright syndrome have had their incomplete precocious puberty controlled with testolactone. Girls with recurrent estrogen-secreting ovarian cyst formation may have a decreased incidence of cysts with medroxyprogesterone acetate therapy, and GnRH agonist may be effective in such cases. Surgical removal of such ovarian cysts is unnecessary with such medical therapy available.

Precocious thelarche or adrenarche requires no treatment, as both are self-limited benign conditions. No therapy has been reported for premature menarche and none may be indicated, though GnRH agonists or medroxyprogesterone acetate would seem to be possibilities. Severe cases of adolescent gynecomastia have been treated successfully by testolactone and dihydrotestosterone heptanoate, suggesting that less surgery will be necessary for such cases in the future.

REFERENCES

General

Grumbach MM, Styne DM: Puberty: ontogeny, neuroendocrinology, physiology, and disorders. In: *Williams' Textbook of Endocrinology,* 8th ed. Wilson JD, Foster DW (editors). Saunders, 1992.

Styne DM: Puberty. In: *Pediatric Endocrinology for the House Officer.* Williams & Wilkins, 1988.

Styne DM, Grumbach MM: Puberty in the male and female: Its physiology and disorders. In: *Reproductive Endocrinology,* 3rd ed. Yen SSC, Jaffe RB (editors). Saunders, 1992.

Wilkins L: *The Diagnosis and Treatment of Endocrine Disorders in Childhood and Adolescence,* 2nd ed. Thomas, 1965.

Physical Changes Associated With Puberty

Attie KM et al: The pubertal growth spurt in eight patients with true precocious puberty and growth hormone deficiency: Evidence for a direct role of sex steroids. J Clin Endocrinol Metab 1990;71:975.

Bayley N, Pinneau SF: Tables for predicting adult height from skeletal age: Revised for use with the Greulich-Pyle standards. J Pediatr 1952;40:423.

Greulich WW, Pyle SI: *Radiographic Atlas of Skeletal Development of the Hand and Wrist,* 2nd ed. Stanford Univ Press, 1959.

Harlan WR, Harlan EA, Grillo GP: Secondary sex characteristics of girls 12 to 17 years of age: The U.S. Health Examination Survey. J Pediatr 1980;96:1074.

Harlan WR et al: Secondary sex characteristics of boys 12 to 17 years of age: The U.S. Health Examination Survey. J Pediatr 1979;95:293.

Marshall JC, Kelch RP: Low dose pulsatile gonadotropin-releasing hormone in anorexia nervosa: A model of human pubertal development. J Clin Endocrinol Metab 1979;49:712.

Marshall WA, Tanner JM: Variations in the pattern of pubertal changes in boys. Arch Dis Child 1970;45:13.

Marshall WA, Tanner JM: Variations in the pattern of pubertal changes in girls. Arch Dis Child 1969;44:291.

Nielsen CT et al: Onset of the release of spermatozoa (spermarche) in boys in relation to age, testicular growth, pubic hair, and height. J Clin Endocrinol Metab 1986;62:532.

Rohn RD: Nipple (papilla) development in puberty: Longitudinal observations in girls. Pediatrics 1987;79:745.

Tanner JM et al: The adolescent growth spurt of boys and girls of the Harpenden Growth Study. Ann Hum Biol 1976;3:109.

Van Wieringen JC et al: *Growth Diagrams 1965 Netherlands: Second National Survey on 0–24 Year Olds.* Groningen, Netherlands Institute for Preventive Medicine TNO Leiden, Wolters-Noordhoff Publishing, 1971.

Endocrine Changes From Fetal Life to Puberty

Boyar RM et al: Simultaneous augmented secretion of luteinizing hormone and testosterone during sleep. J Clin Invest 1974;54:609.

Hale PM et al: Increased luteinizing hormone pulse frequency during sleep in early to midpubertal boys: Effects of testosterone infusion. J Clin Endocrinol Metab 1988;66:785.

Harris DA et al: Somatomedin-C in normal puberty and in true precocious puberty before and after treatment with a potent LRF agonist: Evidence for an effect of estrogen and testosterone on somatomedin-C concentrations. J Clin Endocrinol Metab 1985;61:152.

Kirkland RT et al: Decrease in plasma high-density lipoprotein cholesterol levels at puberty in boys with delayed adolescence: Correlation with plasma testosterone levels. JAMA 1987;257:502.

Link K et al: The effect of androgens on the pulsatile release and the twenty-four-hour mean concentration of growth hormone in peripubertal males. J Clin Endocrinol Metab 1986;62:159.

Reiter EO et al: Responsivity of pituitary gonadotropes to luteinizing hormone-releasing factors in idiopathic precocious puberty, precocious thelarche, and precocious adrenarche. Pediatr 1975;9:111.

Sklar CA et al: Human chorionic gonadotropin-secreting pineal tumor: Relation to pathogenesis and sex limitation of sexual precocity. J Clin Endocrinol Metab 1981;53:656.

Reiter EO, Fuldauer VG, Root AW: Secretion of the adrenal androgen, dehydroepiandrosterone sulfate, during normal infancy, childhood, and adolescence, in sick infants and in children with endocrinologic abnormalities. J Pediatr 1977;90:766.

Sklar CA, Kaplan SL, Grumbach MM: Evidence for dissociation between adrenarche and gonadarche: Studies in patients with idiopathic precocious puberty, gonadal dysgenesis, isolated gonadotropin deficiency, and constitutionally delayed growth and adolescence. J Clin Endocrinol Metab 1980;51:548.

Delayed Puberty & Sexual Infantilism

Connors MH, Styne DM: Familial functional anorchism: A review of etiology and management. J Urol 1985; 133:1049.

Frisch RE, Wyshak G, Vincent L: Delayed menarche and amenorrhea in ballet dancers. N Engl J Med 1980; 303:17.

Grumbach MM, Conte FA: Disorders of sexual differentiation. In: *Williams' Textbook of Endocrinology,* 8th ed. Wilson JD, Foster DW (editors). Saunders, 1992.

Jarow JP et al: Elevation of serum gonadotropins establishes the diagnosis of anorchism in prepubertal boys with bilateral cryptorchidism. J Urol 1986;136:227.

Kaplan SL, Grumbach MM, Hoyt WF: A syndrome of hypopituitary dwarfism, hypoplasia of optic nerves, and malformation of prosencephalon: Report of 6 patients. Pediatr Res 1970;4:480.

Pugliese MT et al: Fears of obesity: A cause of short stature and delayed puberty. N Engl J Med 1983; 309:513.

Rivkees SA, Crawford JD: The relationship of gonadal activity and chemotherapy-induced gonadal damage. JAMA 1988;259:2123.

Rosenfeld RG, Northcraft GB, Hintz RL: A prospective, randomized study of testosterone treatment of constitutional delay of growth and development in male adolescents. Pediatrics 1982;69:681.

Santoro N, Filicori M, Crowley WF Jr: Hypogonadotropic disorders in men and women: Diagnosis and therapy with pulsatile gonadotropin-releasing hormone. Endocr Rev 1986;7:11.

Sklar CA et al: Hormonal and metabolic abnormalities associated with central nervous system germinoma in children and adolescents and the effect of therapy: Report of 10 patients. J Clin Endocrinol Metab 1981;52:9.

Thomsett MJ et al: Endocrine and neurologic outcome in childhood craniopharyngioma: Review of effect of treatment in 42 patients. J Pediatr 1980;97:728.

Van Dop C et al: Isolated gonadotropin deficiency in boys: Clinical characteristics and growth. J Pediatr 1987;111:684.

Wilson DM et al: Effects of testosterone therapy for pubertal delay. Am J Dis Child 1988;142:96.

Sexual Precocity

Boepple PA et al: Use of a potent, long-acting agonist of gonadotropin-releasing hormone in the treatment of precocious puberty. Endocr Rev 1986;7:24.

Eberle AJ, Sparrow JT, Keenan BS: Treatment of persistent pubertal gynecomastia with dihydrotestosterone heptanoate. J Pediatr 1986;109:144.

Egli CA et al: Pituitary gonadotropin-independent male-limited autosomal dominant sexual precocity in nine generations: Familial testotoxicosis. J Pediatr 1985; 106:33.

Feuillan PP et al: Treatment of precocious puberty in the McCune-Albright syndrome with the aromatase inhibitor testolactone. N Engl J Med 1986;315:1115.

Herman-Giddens ME, Sandler AD, Friedman NE: Sexual precocity in girls: An association with sexual abuse? Am J Dis Child 1988;142:431.

Holland FJ: Gonadotropin-independent precocious puberty. Endocrinol Metab Clin North Am 1991;20:191.

Judge DM et al: Hypothalamic hamartoma: A source of luteinizing hormone-releasing factor in precocious puberty. N Engl J Med 1977;296:7.

Kreiter M et al: Preserving adult height potential in girls with idiopathic true precocious puberty. J Pediatr 1990 117:364.

Lee PA, Van Dop C, Migeon CJ: McCune-Albright syndrome: Long-term follow-up. JAMA 1986;256:2980.

Manasco PK et al: Six-year results of luteinizing hormone releasing hormone (LHRH) agonist treatment in children with LHRH-dependent precocious puberty. J Pediatr 1989;115:105.

Mills JL et al: Premature thelarche: Natural history and etiologic investigation. Am J Dis Child 1981;135:743.

Pescovitz OH et al: The NIH experience with precocious puberty: Diagnostic subgroups and response to short-term luteinizing hormone-releasing hormone analogue therapy. J Pediatr 1986;108:47.

Reiter EU et al: Male-limited familial precocious puberty in three generations. N Engl J Med 1984;311:515.

Rosenthal SM, Grumbach MM, Kaplan SL: Gonadotropin-independent familial sexual precocity with premature Leydig and germinal cell maturation (familial testotoxicosis): Effects of a potent luteinizing hormone-releasing factor agonist and medroxyprogesterone acetate therapy in four cases. J Clin Endocrinol Metab 1983;57:571.

Styne DM: Puberty and its disorders in boys. Endocrinol Metab Clin North Am 1991;20:43.

Styne DW et al: Treatment of true precocious puberty with a potent luteinizing hormone-releasing factor agonist: Effect on growth, sexual maturation, pelvic sonography, and the hypothalamic-pituitary-gonadal axis. J Clin Endocrinol Metab 1985;61:142.

Van Wyk JJ, Grumbach MM: Syndrome of precocious menstruation and galactorrhea in juvenile hypothyroidism: An example of hormonal overlap in pituitary feedback. J Pediatr 1960;57:416.

Wheeler MD, Styne DM: Diagnosis and management of precocious puberty. Pediatr Clin North Am 1990; 37:1255.

Wheeler MD, Styne DM: The treatment of precocious puberty. Endocrinol Metab Clin North Am 1991;29:183.

The Endocrinology of Pregnancy

13

Mary C. Martin, MD, Robert N. Taylor, MD, PhD, & John L. Kitzmiller, MD

Throughout pregnancy, the fetal-placental unit secretes protein and steroid hormones into the mother's bloodstream, and these apparently or actually alter the function of every endocrine gland in her body. Both clinically and in the laboratory, pregnancy can mimic hyperthyroidism, Cushing's disease, pituitary adenoma, diabetes mellitus, and polycystic ovary syndrome.

The endocrine changes associated with pregnancy are adaptive, allowing the mother to nurture the developing fetus. Although maternal reserves are usually adequate, occasionally, as in the case of gestational diabetes or hypertensive disease of pregnancy, a woman may develop overt signs of disease as a direct result of pregnancy.

Aside from creating a satisfactory maternal environment for fetal development, the placenta serves as an endocrine gland as well as a respiratory, alimentary, and excretory organ. Measurements of fetal-placental products in the maternal serum provide one means of assessing the health of the developing fetus. This chapter will consider the changes in maternal endocrine function in pregnancy and during parturition as well as fetal endocrine development. The chapter concludes with a discussion of some endocrine disorders complicating pregnancy.

CONCEPTION & IMPLANTATION

Fertilization

In fertile women, ovulation occurs approximately 12–16 days after the onset of the previous menses. The ovum must be fertilized within 24–48 hours if conception is to result. For about 48 hours around ovulation, cervical mucus is copious, nonviscous, and slightly alkaline and forms a gel matrix that acts as a filter and conduit for sperm. Following intercourse, sperm that are to survive penetrate the cervical mucus within minutes and can remain viable there until the mucus character changes, approximately 24 hours following ovulation. Sperm begin appearing in the outer third of the uterine tube (the ampulla) 5–10 minutes after coitus and continue to migrate to this location from the cervix for about 24–48 hours. Of the 200×10^6 sperm that are deposited in the vaginal fornices, only approximately 200 reach the distal uterine tube. Fertilization normally occurs in the ampulla.

ACRONYMS USED IN THIS CHAPTER	
ACTH	Adrenocorticotropic hormone
cAMP	Cyclic adenosine monophosphate
CBG	Corticosteroid-binding globulin
CST	Contraction stress test
DHEA	Dehydroepiandrosterone
DOC	Deoxycorticosterone
EGF	Epidermal growth factor
FGF	Fibroblast growth factor
FSH	Follicle-stimulating hormone
GnRH	Gonadotropin-releasing hormone
hCG	Human chorionic gonadotropin
hCGnRH	Human chorionic gonadotropin-releasing hormone
hCS	Human chorionic somatomammotropin
hGH	Human growth hormone
hPL	Human placental lactogen
hPRL	Human prolactin
IGFs	Insulin-like growth factors
LATS	Long-acting thyroid stimulator
LH	Luteinizing hormone
L/S	Lecithin/sphingomyelin (ratio)
NST	Nonstress test
PDGF	Platelet-derived growth factor
SHBG	Sex hormone-binding globulin
TBG	Thyroid hormone-binding globulin
TRH	Thyrotropin-releasing hormone
TSH	Thyroid-stimulating hormone (thyrotropin)
TSI	Thyroid-stimulating immunoglobulin

Implantation

Implantation in the uterus does not occur until 6 or 7 days later, when the conceptus is a blastocyst. In most pregnancies, the dates of ovulation and implantation are not known. Weeks of gestation ("gestational age") are by convention calculated from the first day of the last menstrual period. Within 24 hours after implantation, or at about 3 weeks of gestation, human chorionic gonadotropin (hCG) is detectable in maternal serum. Under the influence of increasing hCG production, the corpus luteum continues to secrete steroid hormones in increasing quantities. Without effective implantation and subsequent hCG production, the corpus luteum survives for only about 14 days following ovulation.

Symptoms of Pregnancy

Breast tenderness, fatigue, nausea, absence of menstruation, softening of the uterus, and a sustained elevation of basal body temperature are all attributable to hormone production by the corpus luteum and developing placenta.

Ovarian Hormones of Pregnancy

The hormones produced by the corpus luteum include progesterone, 17-hydroxyprogesterone, and estradiol. The indispensability of the corpus luteum in early pregnancy has been demonstrated by ablation studies, in which luteectomy or oophorectomy before 42 days of gestation results in precipitous decreases in levels of serum progesterone and estradiol, followed by abortion. Exogenous progesterone will prevent abortion, proving that progesterone alone is required for maintenance of early pregnancy. After about the seventh gestational week, the corpus luteum can be removed without subsequent abortion, owing to increasing progesterone production by the placenta.

Because the placenta does not produce appreciable amounts of 17-hydroxyprogesterone, this steroid provides a marker of corpus luteum function. As shown in Figure 13–1, the serum concentrations of estrogens and total progesterone exhibit a steady increase, but the concentration of 17-hydroxyprogesterone rises and then declines to low levels that persist for the duration of the pregnancy. The decline of corpus luteum function occurs despite the continued production of hCG; in fact, corpus luteum production of 17-hydroxyprogesterone declines while hCG is still rising to maximal levels.

Another marker of corpus luteum function is the polypeptide hormone relaxin, a protein with a molecular mass of about 6000. It is similar in its tertiary structure to insulin. Relaxin becomes detectable at about the same time as hCG begins to rise, and it maintains a maximum maternal serum concentration of about 1 ng/mL during the first trimester. The serum concentration then falls approximately 20% and is constant for the remainder of the pregnancy.

Pharmacologically, relaxin ripens the cervix, softens the pubic symphysis, and acts synergistically with progesterone to inhibit uterine contractions. A major physiologic role for relaxin in human gestation has not been established. Luteectomy after 7 weeks of gestation does not interfere with gestation in spite of undetectable relaxin levels. Extraluteal production of relaxin by the decidua and placenta has been demonstrated, however.

FETAL-PLACENTAL-DECIDUAL UNIT

The function of the placenta is to establish effective communication between the mother and the developing fetus while maintaining the immune and genetic integrity of both individuals. Initially, the placenta functions autonomously. By the end of the first trimester, however, the fetal endocrine system is sufficiently developed to influence placental function and to provide some hormone precursors to the placenta. From this time, it is useful to consider the conceptus as the fetal-placental unit.

The fetal-placental unit will be considered in three separate but related categories: as sources of secretion of protein and steroid hormones into the maternal circulation; as participants in the control of fetal endocrine function, growth, and development; and as selective barriers governing the interaction between fetal and maternal systems.

Within 7 days after fertilization, implantation begins. The trophoblast invades the endometrium, and two layers of developing placenta can be demonstrated. The mature syncytiotrophoblast adjacent to the endometrium is derived from the precursor cytotrophoblast. The syncytiotrophoblast is the major source of hormone production, containing the cellular machinery needed for synthesis, packaging, and secretion of both steroid and polypeptide hormones. It is in direct contact with the maternal circulation and the decidua.

The decidua is the endometrium of pregnancy. Recent investigation has shown that the decidual cells are capable of synthesizing a variety of polypeptide hormones, including prolactin (PRL), relaxin, and a variety of paracrine factors. The importance of the role of the decidua as an endocrine organ has not been established, but its role as a source of prostaglandins during labor is certain (see Endocrine Control of Parturition, below).

POLYPEPTIDE HORMONES

Human Chorionic Gonadotropin

The first marker of trophoblast differentiation and the first measurable product of the placenta is chorionic gonadotropin (hCG). hCG is a glycoprotein consisting of about 237 amino acids. It is quite similar in structure to the pituitary glycoproteins in that it consists of two chains: an alpha chain, which is species-specific; and a beta chain, which determines receptor interaction and ultimate biologic effect. The alpha chain is almost identical in sequence to the alpha chains of the hormonal glycoproteins TSH, FSH, and LH. The beta chain has significant sequence homology with LH but is not identical; of the 145 amino acids in β-hCG, 97 (67%) are identical to those of β-LH. In addition, the placental hormone has a carboxyl terminal segment of 30 amino acids not found in the pituitary LH molecule. Carbohydrate constitutes approximately 30% by weight of each subunit. Sialic acid alone accounts for 10% of the weight of the molecule and confers a high degree of resistance to degradation.

SYSTEM	HORMONE	PATTERN	AVERAGE PEAK CONCENTRATION (TIME)
Placenta and corpus luteum	Progesterone	Rises to term.	190 ng/mL (552 nmol/L) (term)
	17-Hydroxy-progester-one	Peaks at 5 weeks, then declines.	6 ng/mL (19 nmol/L) (5 weeks)
Adrenal	Cortisol	Increases to 3 times prepregnancy values at term.	300 ng/mL (0.83 μmol/L) (term)
	Aldosterone	Plateaus at 34 weeks with small rise near term.	100 ng/mL (277 nmol/L)
	DOC	Increases to 10 times prepregnancy value at term.	1200 pg/mL (3.48 nmol/L) (term)
Thyroid	Total T₄	Increases during first trimester, then plateaus.	150 ng/mL (193 pmol/L)
	Free T₄	Unchanged.	30 pg/mL (38.6 pmol/L)
	Total T₃	Increases during first trimester, then plateaus.	2 ng/mL (3.1 nmol/L)
	Free T₃	Unchanged.	4 pg/mL (5.1 pmol/L)

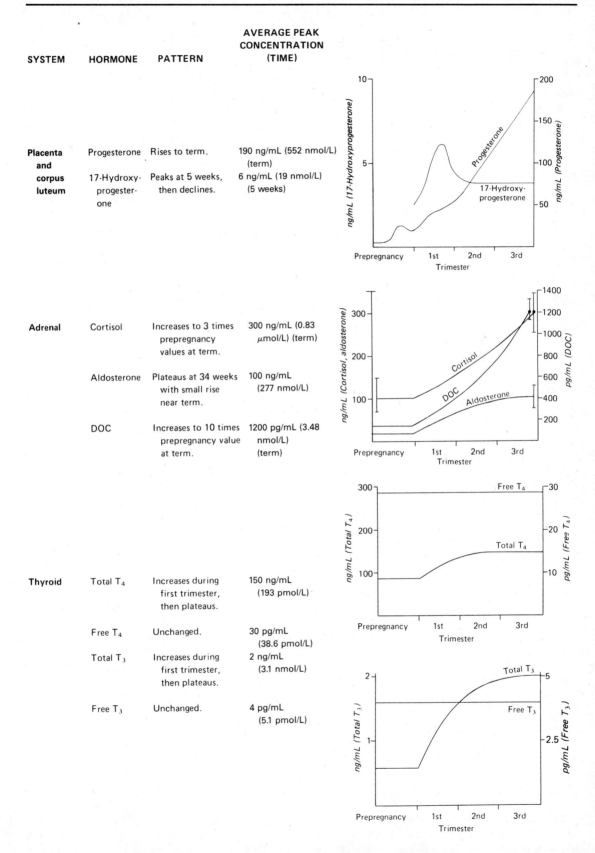

Figure 13–1. Maternal serum hormone changes during pregnancy.

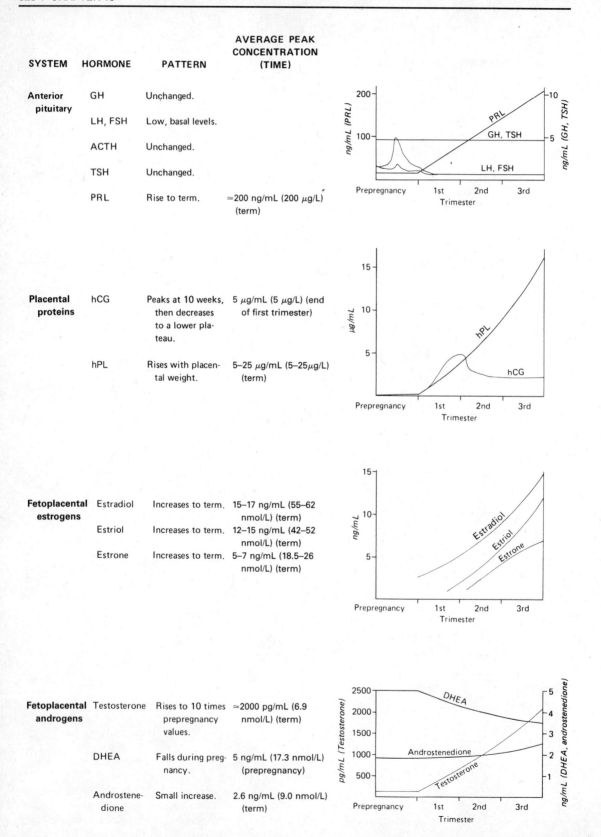

SYSTEM	HORMONE	PATTERN	AVERAGE PEAK CONCENTRATION (TIME)
Anterior pituitary	GH	Unchanged.	
	LH, FSH	Low, basal levels.	
	ACTH	Unchanged.	
	TSH	Unchanged.	
	PRL	Rise to term.	≈200 ng/mL (200 μg/L) (term)
Placental proteins	hCG	Peaks at 10 weeks, then decreases to a lower plateau.	5 μg/mL (5 μg/L) (end of first trimester)
	hPL	Rises with placental weight.	5–25 μg/mL (5–25μg/L) (term)
Fetoplacental estrogens	Estradiol	Increases to term.	15–17 ng/mL (55–62 nmol/L) (term)
	Estriol	Increases to term.	12–15 ng/mL (42–52 nmol/L) (term)
	Estrone	Increases to term.	5–7 ng/mL (18.5–26 nmol/L) (term)
Fetoplacental androgens	Testosterone	Rises to 10 times prepregnancy values.	≈2000 pg/mL (6.9 nmol/L) (term)
	DHEA	Falls during pregnancy.	5 ng/mL (17.3 nmol/L) (prepregnancy)
	Androstenedione	Small increase.	2.6 ng/mL (9.0 nmol/L) (term)

Figure 13–1 (cont'd). Maternal serum hormone changes during pregnancy.

In the early weeks of pregnancy, the concentration of hCG doubles every 1.7–2 days, and serial measurements provide a sensitive index of early trophoblast function. Maternal plasma hCG peaks at about 100,000 mIU/mL during the tenth gestational week and then declines gradually to about 10,000 mIU/mL in the third trimester.

These characteristics of hCG all contribute to the possibility of diagnosing pregnancy several days before any symptoms occur or a menstrual period has been missed. Without the long plasma half-life of hCG (approximately 24 hours), the tiny mass of cells comprising the blastocyst could not produce sufficient hormone to be detected in the peripheral circulation within 24 hours of implantation. The unique β-carboxyl terminal segment of hCG has been isolated, and antibodies to this sequence have been raised. The beta subunit assay for hCG that uses this antibody does not cross-react significantly with any of the pituitary glycoproteins. As little as 5 mIU/mL (1 ng/mL) of hCG in plasma can be detected without interference from the higher levels of LH, FSH, and TSH.

Like its pituitary counterpart LH, hCG is luteotropic, and the corpus luteum has high-affinity receptor for hCG. The stimulation of increased amounts of progesterone production by corpus luteum cells is driven by increasing concentrations of hCG. Steroid synthesis can be demonstrated in vitro and is mediated by the cAMP system. hCG has been shown to enhance placental conversion of maternal low-density lipid cholesterol to pregnenolone and progesterone.

The concentration of hCG in the fetal circulation is less than 1% of that found in the maternal compartment. However, there is evidence that fetal hCG is an important regulator of the development of the fetal adrenal and gonad during the first trimester.

hCG is also produced by trophoblastic neoplasms such as hydatidiform mole and choriocarcinoma, and the concentration of hCG or its beta subunit is used as a tumor marker, for diagnosis, and for monitoring the success or failure of chemotherapy in these disorders. Women with very high hCG levels due to trophoblastic disease may become clinically hyperthyroid and revert to euthyroidism as hCG is reduced during chemotherapy.

Human Placental Lactogen

A second placental polypeptide hormone, also with homology to a pituitary protein, is termed placental lactogen (hPL) or chorionic somatomammotropin (hCS). hPL is detectable in the early trophoblast, but detectable serum concentrations are not reached until 4–5 gestational weeks. hPL is a protein of about 190 amino acids whose primary, secondary, and tertiary structures are similar to those of growth hormone (GH). The two molecules cross-react in immunoassays and in some receptor and bioassay systems. However, hPL has only some of the biologic activities of GH. Like GH, hPL is diabetogenic, but it has minimal growth-promoting activity as measured by standard GH bioassays. hPL also shares many structural features with prolactin (PRL).

The physiologic role of hPL during pregnancy remains controversial, and normal pregnancy without detectable hPL production has been reported. Although not clearly shown to be a mammotropic agent, hPL contributes to altered glucose metabolism and mobilization of free fatty acids; causes of hyperinsulinemic response to glucose loads; and contributes to the peripheral insulin resistance characteristic of pregnancy. Factors that regulate the synthesis or release of hPL from the syncytiotrophoblast have not been fully determined, but prolonged fasting and insulin-induced hypoglycemia raise hPL concentrations. hPL production is roughly proportionate to placental mass. Actual production rates may reach as much as 1–1.5 g/d. The disappearance curve shows multiple components but yields a serum half-life of 15–30 minutes. Serum hPL concentration had been proposed as an indicator of the continued health of the placenta, but the range of normal values is wide, and serial determinations are necessary. hPL determinations have largely been replaced by biophysical profiles, which are more sensitive indicators of fetal jeopardy.

Other Chorionic Peptide Hormones & Growth Factors

Other chorionic peptides have been identified, but their functions have not yet been defined. One of these proteins is a glycoprotein with partial sequence and functional homology to TSH. Its existence as a separate entity from hCG has been debated in the literature, with some reports suggesting that chorionic TSH is a protein with a molecular weight of about 28,000, structurally different from hCG, with weak thyrotropic activity. Similarly, ACTH-like, lipotropin-like, and endorphin-like peptides have been isolated from placenta, but they have low biologic potency and undetermined physiologic roles. A chorionic FSH-like protein has also been isolated from placenta but has not yet been detected in plasma. Good evidence now exists that the cytotrophoblast produces a human chorionic gonadotropin-releasing hormone (hCGnRH) that is biologically and immunologically indistinguishable from the hypothalamic GnRH. The release of hCG from the syncytiotrophoblast may be under the direct control of this factor, in a fashion analogous to the hypothalamic control of anterior pituitary secretion of gonadotropins. Preliminary evidence is also available for similar paracrine control of syncytiotrophoblastic release of TSH, somatostatin, and corticotropin by analogous cytotrophoblastic releasing hormones. Activin, inhibin, corticotropin-releasing factor, and multiple peptide growth factors, including fibroblast growth factor

(FGF), epidermal growth factor (EGF), platelet-derived growth factor (PDGF), and the insulin-like growth factors (IGFs)—and many of their cognate receptors—have all been isolated from placental tissue.

STEROID HORMONES

In contrast to the impressive synthetic capability exhibited in the production of placental proteins, the placenta does not appear to have the capability to synthesize steroids de novo. All steroids produced by the placenta are derived from maternal or fetal precursor steroids.

No tissue, however, even remotely approaches the syncytiotrophoblast in its capacity to efficiently interconvert steroids. This activity is demonstrable even in the early blastocyst, and by the seventh gestational week, when the corpus luteum has undergone relative senescence, the placenta becomes the dominant source of steroid hormones.

Progesterone

The placenta relies on maternal cholesterol as its substrate for progesterone production. Fetal death has no immediate influence on progesterone production, suggesting that the fetus is a negligible source of substrate. Enzymes in the placenta cleave the cholesterol side chain, yielding pregnenolone, which in turn is partially isomerized to progesterone; 250–350 mg of progesterone is produced daily by the third trimester, and most enters the maternal circulation. The maternal plasma concentration of progesterone rises progressively throughout pregnancy and appears to be independent of factors that normally regulate steroid synthesis and secretion. Whereas exogenous hCG increases progesterone production in pregnancy, hypophysectomy has no effect. Administration of ACTH or cortisol does not influence progesterone concentrations, nor does adrenalectomy or oophorectomy do so after 7 weeks.

Progesterone is necessary for establishment and maintenance of pregnancy. Insufficient corpus luteum production of progesterone may contribute to failure of implantation, and luteal phase deficiency is implicated in some cases of infertility and recurrent pregnancy loss. Furthermore, progesterone contributes to maintaining a relatively quiescent state of the myometrium. In some animals, such as the rabbit or sheep, labor is heralded by a decrease in progesterone concentration, and the administration of progesterone in these species can delay labor indefinitely. Progesterone also may act as an immunosuppressive agent in some systems and inhibits T cell-mediated tissue rejection. Thus, high local concentrations of progesterone may contribute to immunologic tolerance by the uterus of invading embryonic trophoblast tissue.

Estrogens

Estrogen production by the placenta also depends on circulating precursors, but in this case both fetal and maternal steroids are important sources. Most of the estrogens are derived from fetal androgens, primarily dehydroepiandrosterone sulfate (DHEA sulfate). Fetal DHEA sulfate, produced mainly by the fetal adrenal, is converted by placental sulfatase to the free dehydroepiandrosterone (DHEA) and then, through enzymatic pathways common to steroid-producing tissues, to androstenedione and testosterone. These androgens are finally aromatized by the placenta to estrone and estradiol, respectively.

The greater part of fetal DHEA sulfate is metabolized to produce a third estrogen: estriol. While serum estrone and estradiol concentrations are increased during pregnancy about 50-fold over their maximal prepregnancy values, estriol increases approximately 1000-fold. The key step in estriol synthesis is 16α-hydroxylation of the steroid molecule (see Figure 10–4). The substrate for the reaction is primarily fetal DHEA sulfate, and the vast majority of the production of the 16α-hydroxy-DHEA sulfate occurs in the fetal adrenal and liver, not in maternal or placental tissues. The final steps of desulfation and aromatization to estriol occur in the placenta. Maternal serum or urinary estriol measurements, unlike measurements of progesterone or hPL, reflect fetal as well as placental function. Normal estriol production, therefore, reflects the integrity of fetal circulation and metabolism as well as adequacy of the placenta. Rising serum or urinary estriol concentrations are the best available biochemical indicator of fetal well-being. When estriol is assayed daily, a significant drop (> 50%) may be a sensitive early indicator of fetal jeopardy.

There are some circumstances in which altered estriol production does not signal fetal compromise but is instead the result of congenital derangements or iatrogenic intervention. Maternal estriol remains low in pregnancies with placental sulfatase deficiency and in cases of fetal anencephaly. In the first case, DHEA sulfate cannot be hydrolyzed; in the second, little fetal DHEA is produced because fetal adrenal stimulation by ACTH is lacking. Maternal administration of glucocorticoids inhibits fetal ACTH and lowers maternal estriol. Administration of DHEA to the mother during a healthy pregnancy increases estriol production. Antibiotic therapy can reduce estriol levels by interfering with bacterial glucuronidases and maternal reabsorption of estriol from the gut. Estetrol, an estrogen with a fourth hydroxyl at the 15 position, is unique to pregnancy.

MATERNAL ADAPTATION TO PREGNANCY

As a successful "parasite," the fetal-placental unit manipulates the maternal "host" for its own gain but normally avoids imposing excessive stress that would jeopardize the "host" and thus the "parasite" itself. The prodigious production of polypeptide and steroid hormones by the fetal-placental unit directly or indirectly results in physiologic adaptations of virtually every maternal organ system. These alterations are summarized in Figure 13–2. Most of the commonly measured maternal endocrine function tests are radically changed. In some cases, true physiologic alteration has occurred; in others, the changes are due to increased production of specific serum binding proteins by the liver or to decreased serum levels of albumin. Additionally, some hormonal changes are mediated by altered clearance rates owing to increased glomerular filtration, decreased hepatic excretion of metabolites, or metabolic clearance of steroid and protein hormones by the placenta. The changes in endocrine function tests are summarized in Table 13–1. Failure to recognize normal pregnancy-induced alterations in endocrine function tests can lead to unnecessary diagnostic tests and therapy that may be seriously detrimental to mother and fetus.

Maternal Pituitary Gland

The mother's anterior pituitary gland hormones have little influence on pregnancy after implantation has occurred. The gland itself enlarges by about one-third, with the major component of this increase being hyperplasia of the lactotrophs in response to the high plasma estrogens. PRL, the product of the lactotrophs, is the only anterior pituitary hormone that rises progressively during pregnancy, with contributions from both the anterior pituitary and the decidua. In spite of the high serum concentrations, pulsatile release of PRL and nocturnal and food-induced increases persist. Hence, the normal neuroendocrine regulatory mechanisms appear to be intact. Pituitary ACTH and TSH secretion remain unchanged. Serum FSH and LH fall to the lower limits of detectability and are unresponsive to GnRH stimulation. GH concentrations are not significantly different from nonpregnant levels, but pituitary response to provocative testing is markedly altered. GH response to hypoglycemia and arginine infusion is enhanced in early pregnancy but thereafter becomes depressed. Established pregnancy can continue in the face of hypophysectomy, and in women hypophysectomized prior to pregnancy, induction of ovulation and normal pregnancy can be achieved with appropriate replacement therapy. In cases of primary pituitary hyperfunction, the fetus is not affected.

Maternal Thyroid Gland

The thyroid becomes palpably enlarged during the first trimester, and a bruit may be present. Thyroid iodide clearance and ^{131}I uptake (which are clinically contraindicated in pregnancy) have been shown to be increased. These changes are due in large part to the increased renal clearance of iodide, which causes a relative iodine deficiency. While total serum thyroxine is elevated as a result of increased thyroid hormone-binding globulin (TBG), free thyroxine and triiodothyronine are normal (Figure 13–1).

Maternal Parathyroid Gland

The net calcium requirement imposed by fetal skeletal development is estimated to be about 30 g by term. This is met by hyperplasia of the parathyroid glands and elevated serum levels of parathyroid hormone. The maternal serum calcium concentration declines to a nadir at 28–32 weeks, largely owing to the hypoalbuminemia of pregnancy. Ionized calcium is maintained at normal concentrations throughout pregnancy.

Maternal Pancreas

The nutritional demands of the fetus require alteration of maternal metabolic homeostatic control, which results in both structural and functional changes in the maternal pancreas. The size of pancreatic islets increases, and insulin-secreting β cells undergo hyperplasia. Basal levels of insulin are lower or unchanged in early pregnancy but increase during the second trimester. Thereafter, pregnancy is a hyperinsulinemic state, with resistance to the peripheral metabolic effects of insulin. The increased concentration of insulin has been shown to be a result of increased secretion rather than decreased metabolic clearance. The measured half-life for insulin is unchanged in pregnant women. The effects of pregnancy on the pancreas can be mimicked by appropriate treatment with estrogen, progesterone, hPL, and corticosteroids.

Pancreatic production of glucagon remains responsive to usual stimuli and is suppressed by glucose loading, although the degree of responsiveness has not been well evaluated.

The major role of insulin and glucagon is the intracellular transport of nutrients, specifically glucose, amino acids, and fatty acids. These concentrations are regulated during pregnancy for fetal as well as maternal needs, and the pre- and postfeeding levels cause pancreatic responses that act to support the fetal economy. Insulin is not transported across the placenta but rather exerts its effects on transportable metabolites. During pregnancy, peak insulin secretion in response to meals is accelerated, and glucose tolerance curves are characteristically altered. Fasting glucose levels are maintained at low normal levels. Excess carbohydrate is converted to fat, and fat is readily mobilized during decreased caloric intake.

Amino acid metabolism is also altered during pregnancy at the expense of maternal needs. Because alanine, the key amino acid for gluconeogenesis, is preferentially transported to the fetus, maternal hypoglycemia leads to lipolysis.

The normal result of pregnancy, then is to reduce

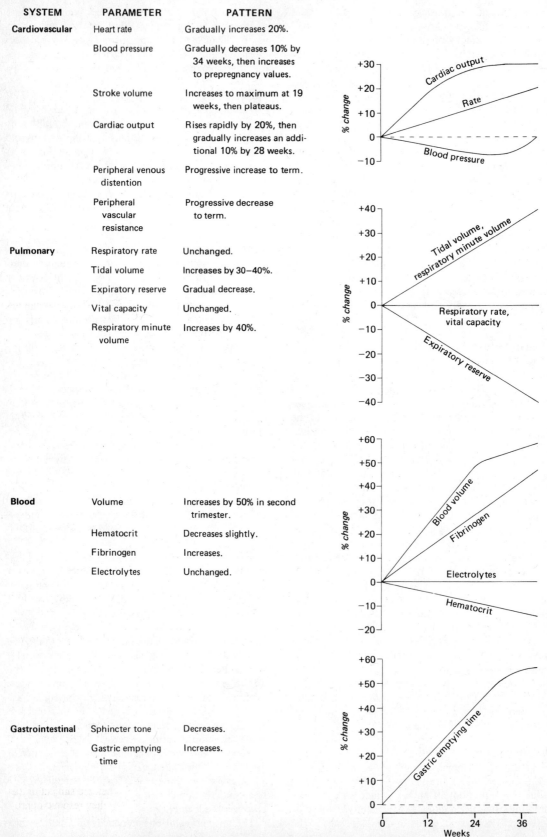

SYSTEM	PARAMETER	PATTERN
Cardiovascular	Heart rate	Gradually increases 20%.
	Blood pressure	Gradually decreases 10% by 34 weeks, then increases to prepregnancy values.
	Stroke volume	Increases to maximum at 19 weeks, then plateaus.
	Cardiac output	Rises rapidly by 20%, then gradually increases an additional 10% by 28 weeks.
	Peripheral venous distention	Progressive increase to term.
	Peripheral vascular resistance	Progressive decrease to term.
Pulmonary	Respiratory rate	Unchanged.
	Tidal volume	Increases by 30–40%.
	Expiratory reserve	Gradual decrease.
	Vital capacity	Unchanged.
	Respiratory minute volume	Increases by 40%.
Blood	Volume	Increases by 50% in second trimester.
	Hematocrit	Decreases slightly.
	Fibrinogen	Increases.
	Electrolytes	Unchanged.
Gastrointestinal	Sphincter tone	Decreases.
	Gastric emptying time	Increases.

Figure 13–2. Maternal physiologic changes during pregnancy.

SYSTEM	PARAMETER	PATTERN
Renal	Renal flow	Increases 25–50%.
	Glomerular filtra-tion rate	Increases early, then plateaus.
Weight	Uterine weight	Increases from about 60–70 g to about 900–1200 g.
	Body weight	Average 11-kg (25-lb) increase.

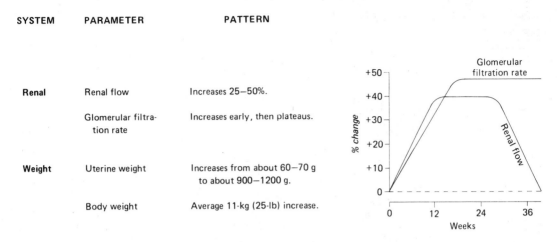

Figure 13–2 (cont'd). Maternal physiologic changes during pregnancy.

glucose levels modestly but to reserve glucose for fetal needs while maternal energy requirements are met increasingly by the peripheral metabolism of fatty acids. These changes in energy metabolism are beneficial to the fetus and innocuous to the mother with an adequate diet. Even modest fasting, however, causes ketosis, which is potentially injurious to the fetus.

Maternal Adrenal Cortex

A. Glucocorticoids: Plasma cortisol concentrations increase to three times nonpregnant levels by the third trimester. Most of the increase can be accounted for by a doubling of corticosteroid-binding globulin (CBG). The increased estrogen levels of pregnancy account for the increase in CBG, which, in turn, is sufficient to account for decreased catabolism of cortisol by the liver. The result is a doubling of the half-life of plasma cortisol. The actual production of cortisol by the zona fasciculata also is increased in pregnancy. The net effect of these changes is an increase in plasma free cortisol, which is approximately doubled by late pregnancy. Whether this increase is mediated through ACTH or by other mechanisms is not known. In spite of cortisol concentrations approaching those found in Cushing's syndrome, diurnal variation in plasma cortisol is maintained. The elevated free cortisol probably contributes to the insulin resistance of pregnancy and possibly to the appearance of striae, but most signs of hypercortisolism do not occur in pregnancy. It is possible that high progesterone levels act as a glucocorticoid antagonist and prevent some cortisol effects.

B. Mineralocorticoids and the Renin-Angiotensin System: Serum aldosterone is markedly elevated in pregnancy. The increase is due to an eight- to tenfold increased production of aldosterone by the zona glomerulosa and not to increased binding or decreased clearance. The peak in aldosterone pro-

duction is reached by mid pregnancy and is maintained until delivery. Renin substrate is increased owing to the influence of estrogen on hepatic synthesis, and renin also is increased.

The increases in both renin and renin substrate inevitably lead to increases in renin activity and angiotensin. In spite of these dramatic changes, normal pregnant women show few signs of hyperaldosteronism. There is no tendency to hypokalemia or hypernatremia, and blood pressure at mid pregnancy—when changes in the aldosterone-renin-angiotensin system are maximal—tends to be lower than in the nonpregnant state. It has been suggested that edema of late pregnancy may be due to these changes, but hyperaldosteronism in nonpregnant women leads to hypertension, not edema.

Although the quantitative aspects of this apparent paradox are not fully understood, a qualitative explanation is possible. Progesterone is an effective competitive inhibitor of mineralocorticoids in the distal renal tubules. Exogenous progesterone (but not synthetic progestins) is natriuretic and potassium-sparing in intact humans, whereas it has no effect in adrenalectomized subjects not receiving mineralocorticoids. Progesterone also blunts the response of the kidney to exogenous aldosterone—thus, the increases in renin and aldosterone may simply be an appropriate response to the high gestational levels of progesterone. The concomitant increase in angiotensin II as a result of increased plasma renin activity apparently does not normally result in hypertension, because of diminished sensitivity of the maternal vascular system to angiotensin. Even during the first trimester, exogenous angiotensin provokes less of a rise in blood pressure than in the nonpregnant state.

It is clear that the high levels of renin, angiotensin, and aldosterone in pregnant women are subject to the usual feedback controls, because they respond appropriately to changes in posture, dietary sodium, and

Table 13–1. Effect of pregnancy on endocrine function tests.

	Test	Result
Pituitary FSH, LH	GnRH stimulation	Unresponsive from third gestational week until puerperium.
GH	Insulin tolerance test	Response increases during the first half of pregnancy and then is blunted until the puerperium.
	Arginine stimulation	Hyperstimulation during the first and second trimesters, then suppression
TSH	TRH stimulation	Response unchanged.
Pancreas Insulin	Glucose tolerance	Peak glucose increases, and glucose concentration remains elevated longer.
	Glucose challenge	Insulin concentration increases to higher peak levels.
	Arginine infusion	Insulin response is blunted in mid to late pregnancy.
Adrenal Cortisol	ACTH infusion	Exaggerated cortisol and 17-hydroxycorticosterone responses.
	Metyrapone	Diminished response.
Mineralo- corti- coids	ACTH infusion	No DOC response.
	Dexamethasone suppression	No DOC response.

water loading and restriction in qualitatively the same way as they do in nonpregnant women. Finally, in patients with preeclampsia, the most common form of pregnancy-related hypertension, serum renin, aldosterone, and angiotensin levels are lower than in normal pregnancy, thus ruling out any primary role for the renin-angiotensin system in this disorder. Production of the mineralocorticoid 11-deoxycorticosterone (DOC) rises throughout pregnancy, and plasma levels six to ten times normal are achieved by term. In contrast to the nonpregnant state, DOC production in pregnancy is unaffected by ACTH or glucocorticoid administration. The source of DOC appears to be conversion of progesterone to DOC in peripheral tissue. DOC is not elevated in hypertensive disorders of pregnancy.

C. Androgens: In normal pregnancy, the maternal production of androgens is slightly increased. The most important determinant of plasma levels of specific androgens, however, appears to be whether or not the androgen binds to sex hormone-binding globulin (SHBG). Testosterone, which binds avidly to SHBG, increases to the normal male range by the end of the first trimester, but free testosterone levels are actually lower than in the nonpregnant state. De-

hydroepiandrosterone sulfate (DHEA sulfate) does not bind significantly to SHBG, and plasma concentrations of DHEA sulfate actually decrease during pregnancy. The desulfation of DHEA sulfate by the placenta and the conversion of DHEA sulfate to estrogens by the fetal-placental unit also are important factors in its increased metabolic clearance.

FETAL ENDOCRINOLOGY

Because of the inaccessibility of the fetus, much of our information about fetal endocrinology is derived indirectly. Most early studies of fetal endocrinology relied upon observations of infants with congenital disorders or inferences from ablation studies or acute experiments in mammals. The development of effective cell culture methods and sensitive radiolabeled assay systems and the ability to achieve stable preparations of chronically catheterized monkey fetuses have increased our understanding of the dynamics of intrauterine endocrine events.

Study of the fetal endocrine system is further complicated by the multiplicity of sources of the various hormones. The fetus is exposed to maternal and placental hormones as well as to those it produces itself. Amniotic fluid contains a variety of hormones of mixed fetal and maternal origin, and these hormones are of uncertain importance. Study of the isolated fetus, even if possible, would thus be of little physiologic relevance.

A final pitfall in the study of fetal endocrine systems relates to the process of development itself. Inferences from the behavior of adult endocrine systems are not transferable to the fetus, because target organs, receptors, modulators, and regulators develop at different times. Thus, the role of a particular hormone in the fetal economy at any one point in gestation may bear little or no relationship to its role in postnatal life.

Dating of events in fetal development is usually given in "fetal weeks," which begin at the time of ovulation and fertilization. Thus, fetal age is always 2 weeks less than gestational age.

Fetal Anterior Pituitary Hormones

The characteristic anterior pituitary cell types are discernible as early as 8–10 fetal weeks, and all of the hormones of the adult anterior pituitary are extractable from the fetal adenohypophysis by 12 weeks. Similarly, the hypothalamic hormones thyrotropin-releasing hormone (TRH), gonadotropin-releasing hormone (GnRH), and somatostatin are present by 8–10 weeks. The direct circulatory connection between hypothalamus and pituitary develops later, with capillary invasion initially visible at about 16 weeks.

The role of the fetal pituitary in organogenesis of various target organs during the first trimester appears to be negligible. None of the pituitary hormones are released into the fetal circulation in large quantities until after 20 fetal weeks. Even growth hormone (GH) appears not to be influential, and in fact total absence of GH is consistent with normal development at birth. Development of the gonads and adrenals during the first trimester appears to be directed by hCG rather than by fetal pituitary hormones.

During the second trimester, there is a marked increase in secretion of all of the anterior pituitary hormones, which coincides with maturation of the hypophysial portal system. Observations include a marked rise in production of GH and an increase in fetal serum TSH, with a concomitant increase in fetal thyroidal iodine uptake. Gonadotropin production also increases, with the female achieving higher FSH levels in both pituitary and serum than does the male. The fetal gonadotropins do not direct the events of early gonadal development but are essential for normal development of the differentiated gonads and external genitalia. ACTH rises significantly during the second trimester and assumes an increasing role in directing the maturation of the differentiated adrenal, as shown by the anencephalic fetus, in which the fetal zone of the adrenal undergoes atrophy after 20 weeks. Fetal PRL secretion also increases after the 20th fetal week, but the functional significance of this hormone, if any, is unknown.

During the third trimester, maturation of feedback systems modulating hypothalamic release signals causes serum concentrations of all of the pituitary hormones except PRL to decline.

Fetal Posterior Pituitary Hormones

Vasopressin and oxytocin are demonstrable by 12–18 weeks in the fetal posterior pituitary gland and correlate with the development of their sites of production, the supraoptic and paraventricular nuclei. The hormone content of the gland increases toward term, with no evidence of feedback control.

During labor, umbilical artery oxytocin is higher than umbilical vein oxytocin. It has been suggested that the fetal posterior pituitary may contribute to the onset or maintenance of labor.

Fetal Thyroid Gland

The thyroid gland develops in the absence of detectable TSH. By 12 weeks the thyroid is capable of iodine-concentrating activity and thyroid hormone synthesis.

During the second trimester, TRH, TSH, and free T_4 all begin to rise. The maturation of feedback mechanisms is suggested by the subsequent plateau of TSH at about 20 fetal weeks. Fetal T_3 and reverse T_3 do not become detectable until the third trimester. The hormone produced in largest amount throughout fetal life is T_4, with the metabolically active T_3 and its inactive derivative, reverse T_3, rising in parallel to T_4 during the third trimester. At birth, conversion of T_4 to T_3 becomes demonstrable.

The development of thyroid hormones occurs independently of maternal systems, and very little placental transfer of thyroid hormone occurs in physiologic concentrations. This prevents maternal thyroid disorders from affecting the fetal compartment but also prevents effective therapy for fetal hypothyroidism through maternal supplementation. Goitrogenic agents such as propylthiouracil are transferred across the placenta and may induce fetal hypothyroidism and goiter.

The function of the fetal thyroid hormones appears crucial to somatic growth and for successful neonatal adaptation.

Fetal Parathyroid Gland

The fetal parathyroid is capable of synthesizing parathyroid hormone by the end of the first trimester. However, the placenta actively transports calcium into the fetal compartment, and the fetus remains relatively hypercalcemic throughout gestation. This contributes to a suppression of parathyroid hormone, and fetal serum levels in umbilical cord have been reported to be low or undetectable. Fetal serum calcitonin levels are elevated, enhancing bone accretion. Fetal vitamin D levels reflect maternal levels but do not appear to be significant in fetal calcium metabolism.

Fetal Adrenal Cortex

The fetal adrenal differs anatomically and functionally from the adult gland. The cortex is identifiable as early as 4 weeks of fetal age, and by the seventh week, steroidogenic activity can be detected in the inner zone layers.

By 20 weeks, the adrenal cortex has increased to a mass that is considerably larger than its relative postnatal size. During gestation, it occupies as much as 0.5% of total body volume, and most of this tissue is composed of a unique fetal zone that subsequently regresses or is transformed into the definitive (adult) zone during the early neonatal period. The inner fetal zone is responsible for the majority of steroids produced during fetal life and comprises 80% of the mass of the adrenal. During the second trimester, the inner fetal zone continues to grow, while the outer zone remains relatively undifferentiated. At about 25 weeks, the definitive (adult) zone develops more rapidly, ultimately assuming the principal role in steroid synthesis during the early postnatal weeks. This transfer of function is accompanied by involution of the fetal zone, which is completed during the first months of neonatal life.

Fetal Gonads

The testis is a detectable structure by about 6 fetal weeks. The interstitial or Leydig cells, which synthesize fetal testosterone, are functional at this same stage. The maximal production of testosterone coincides with the maximal production of hCG by the placenta; binding of hCG to fetal testes with stimulation of testosterone release has been demonstrated. Other fetal testicular products of importance are the reduced testosterone metabolite dihydrotestosterone and müllerian-inhibiting substance. Dihydrotestosterone is responsible for development of the external genital structures, whereas müllerian-inhibiting substance prevents development of female internal structures.

Little is known about fetal ovarian function. By 7–8 weeks of intrauterine life, the ovaries become recognizable, but their importance in fetal physiology has not been established, and the significance of the steroids produced by the ovaries remains unclear.

ENDOCRINE CONTROL OF PARTURITION

During the last few weeks of normal pregnancy, two processes herald approaching labor. Uterine contractions, usually painless, become increasingly frequent, and the lower uterine segment and cervix become softer and thinner, a process known as effacement, or "ripening." Although false alarms are not uncommon, the onset of true labor is usually fairly abrupt, with the establishment of regular contractions every 2–5 minutes, leading to delivery in less than 24 hours. There is a huge literature describing the physiologic and biochemical events that occur during human labor, but the key inciting event has eluded detection. For sheep, it is the fetus that controls the onset of labor. The initial measurable event is an increase in fetal plasma cortisol, which, in turn, alters placental steroid production, resulting in a drop in progesterone. Cortisol reliably induces labor in sheep, but in humans, glucocorticoids do not induce labor and there is no clear drop in plasma progesterone prior to labor. Furthermore, exogenous progesterone does not prevent labor in humans.

The difficulty in identifying a *single* initiating event in human labor suggests that there is more than one. Approaching the matter in a different way, one could ask: What are the factors responsible for maintenance of pregnancy, and how can they fail?

Sex Steroids

Progesterone is essential for maintenance of early pregnancy, and withdrawal of progesterone leads to termination of pregnancy. Progesterone causes hyperpolarization of the myometrium, decreasing the amplitude of action potentials and preventing effective contractions. In various experimental systems, progesterone decreases alpha-adrenergic receptors, stimulates cAMP production, and inhibits oxytocin receptor synthesis. Progesterone also inhibits estrogen receptor synthesis, promotes the storage of prostaglandin precursors in the decidua and fetal membranes, and stabilizes the lysosomes containing prostaglandin-synthesizing enzymes. Estrogen opposes progesterone in these actions and may have an independent role in ripening the uterine cervix and promoting uterine contractility. Thus, the estrogen: progesterone ratio may be an important parameter. In a small series of patients, an increase in the estrogen:progesterone ratio has been shown to precede labor. Thus, for some individuals, a drop in progesterone or an increase in estrogen may initiate labor. The cause of the change in steroids may be placental maturation or a signal from the fetus, but there are not data to support either thesis. It has been shown that an increase in the estrogen:progesterone ratio increases the number of oxytocin receptors and myometrial gap junctions; this finding may explain the coordinate, effective contractions that characterize true labor as opposed to the nonpainful, ineffective contractions of false labor.

Oxytocin

Oxytocin infusion is commonly used to induce or augment labor. Both maternal and fetal oxytocin levels increase spontaneously during labor, but neither has been convincingly shown to increase prior to labor. Data in animals suggest that oxytocin's role in initiation of labor is due to increased sensitivity of the uterus to oxytocin rather than increased plasma concentrations of the hormone. Even women with diabetes insipidus are able to deliver without oxytocin augmentation; thus a maternal source of the hormone is not indispensable.

Prostaglandins

Prostaglandin $F_{2\alpha}$ administered intra-amniotically or intravenously is an effective abortifacient as early as 14 weeks of gestation. Prostaglandin E_2 administered by vagina will induce labor in most women in the third trimester. The amnion and chorion contain high concentrations of arachidonic acid, and the decidua contains active prostaglandin synthetase. Prostaglandins are almost certainly involved in maintenance of labor once it is established. They also probably are important in initiating labor in some circumstances, such as in amnionitis or when the membranes are "stripped" by the physician. They probably are part of the "final common pathway" of labor.

Prostaglandin synthetase inhibitors abolish premature labor, but their clinical usefulness has been restricted by their simultaneous effect of closing the ductus arteriosus, which can lead to fetal pulmonary hypertension.

Catecholamines

Catecholamines with α_2-adrenergic activity cause uterine contractions, whereas β_2-adrenergics inhibit labor. Progesterone increases the ratio of beta receptors to alpha receptors in myometrium, thus favoring continued gestation. There is no evidence that changes in catecholamines or their receptors initiate labor, but it is likely that such changes help sustain labor once initiated. The beta-adrenergic drug ritodrine has proved to be a valuable agent in the management of premature labor. Alpha-adrenergic agents have not been useful in inducing labor, because of their cardiovascular side effects.

ENDOCRINOLOGY OF THE PUERPERIUM

Extirpation of any active endocrine organ leads to compensatory changes in other organs and systems. Delivery of the infant and placenta causes both immediate and long-term adjustment to loss of the pregnancy hormones. The sudden withdrawal of fetal-placental hormones at delivery permits determination of their serum half-lives and some evaluation of their function during pregnancy.

Physiologic & Anatomic Changes

Some of the physiologic and anatomic adjustments that take place after delivery are hormone-dependent, whereas others are themselves responsible for hormonal changes. For example, major readjustments of the cardiovascular system occur in response to the normal blood losses associated with delivery and to loss of the low-resistance placental shunt. By the third postpartum day, blood volume is estimated to decline to about 84% of predelivery values. These cardiovascular changes influence renal and liver clearance of hormones.

Reproductive Tract Changes

The uterus decreases progressively in size at the rate of about 500 g/wk and continues to be palpable abdominally until about 2 weeks postpartum, when it reoccupies its position entirely within the pelvis. Nonpregnant size and weight (60–70 g) are reached by 6 weeks. The reversal of myometrial hypertrophy occurs with a decrease in size of individual myometrial cells rather than by reduction in number. Uterine discharge also changes progressively during this period, with the mixture of fresh blood and decidua becoming a serous transudate and then ceasing in 3–6 weeks.

The endometrium, which is sloughed at the time of delivery, regenerates rapidly; by the seventh day, there is restoration of surface epithelium, except at the placental site. By the second week after delivery, the endometrium resembles normal proliferative-phase endometrium, except for the characteristic hyalinized decidual areas. The earliest documented appearance of a secretory endometrium occurred on day 44 in one series of daily biopsies. These rapid regenerative changes do not apply to the area of pla-

cental implantation, which requires much longer for restoration and retains pathognomonic histologic evidence of placentation indefinitely.

The cervix and vagina also recover rapidly from the effects of pregnancy, labor, and delivery. The cervix regains tone over the first week; by 6 weeks postpartum, it usually exhibits complete healing of trauma sustained at the time of delivery. Histologically, involution may continue beyond 6 weeks, with stromal edema, leukocytic infiltration, and glandular hyperplasia still apparent. Similarly, the vagina regains muscular tone following delivery, and rugae appear as early as 3 weeks. However, in women who nurse, the vaginal mucosa may remain atrophic for months, sometimes resulting in dyspareunia and a watery discharge.

Endocrine Changes

A. Steroids: With expulsion of the placenta, the steroid levels decline precipitously, their half-lives being measured in minutes or hours. As a consequence of continued low-level production by the corpus luteum, progesterone does not reach basal prenatal levels as rapidly as does estradiol. Plasma progesterone falls to luteal-phase levels within 24 hours after delivery but to follicular-phase levels only after several days. Removal of the corpus luteum results in a fall to follicular levels within 24 hours. Estradiol reaches follicular-phase levels within 1–3 days after delivery.

B. Pituitary Hormones: The pituitary gland, which enlarges during pregnancy owing primarily to an increase in lactotrophs, does not diminish in size until after lactation ceases. Secretion of FSH and LH continues to be suppressed during the early weeks of the puerperium, and stimulus with bolus doses of GnRH results in subnormal release of LH and FSH. Over the ensuing weeks, responsiveness to GnRH gradually returns to normal, and most women exhibit follicular-phase serum levels of LH and FSH by the third or fourth postpartum week.

C. Prolactin: Serum prolactin (PRL), which rises throughout pregnancy, falls with the onset of labor and then exhibits variable patterns of secretion depending upon whether breast feeding occurs. Delivery is associated with a surge in PRL, which is followed by a rapid fall in serum concentrations over 7–14 days in the nonlactating mother.

In nonlactating women, the return of normal cyclic function and ovulation may be expected as soon as the second postpartum month, with the initial ovulation occurring at an average of 9–10 weeks postpartum. In lactating women, PRL usually causes a persistence of anovulation. Surges of PRL are believed to act on the hypothalamus to inhibit GnRH secretion. Administration of exogenous GnRH during this time induces normal pituitary responsiveness, and occasional ovulation may occur spontaneously even during lactation. The average time for ovulation in women who have lactated for at least 3 months is about 17 weeks. The percentage of nonlactating women who have resumed menstruation increases linearly up to 12 weeks, by which time 70% will have restored menses. In contrast, the linear increase for lactating women exhibits a much shallower slope, and 70% of lactating women will have menstruated by about 36 weeks.

Lactation

Development of the breast alveolar lobules occurs throughout pregnancy. This period of mammogenesis requires the concerted participation of estrogen, progesterone, PRL, GH, and glucocorticoids. hPL may also play a role but is not indispensable. Milk secretion in the puerperium is associated with further enlargement of the lobules, followed by synthesis of milk constituents such as lactose and casein.

Lactation requires PRL, insulin, and adrenal steroids. It does not occur until unconjugated estrogens fall to nonpregnant levels at about 36–48 hours postpartum.

PRL is essential to milk production. Its action involves induced synthesis of large numbers of PRL receptors; these appear to be autoregulated by PRL, since PRL increases receptor levels in cell culture and since bromocriptine, a PRL inhibitor, causes a decrease in both PRL and its receptors. In the absence of PRL, milk secretion does not take place; but even in the presence of high levels of PRL during the third trimester, milk secretion does not take place until after delivery, owing to the blocking effect of high levels of estrogen.

Galactopoiesis, or the process of continued milk secretion, is also dependent upon the function and integration of several hormones. Evidence from GH-deficient dwarfs and hypothyroid patients suggests that GH and thyroid hormone are not required.

Milk secretion requires the additional stimulus of emptying of the breast. A neural arc must be activated for continued milk secretion. Milk ejection occurs in response to a surge of oxytocin, which induces a contractile response in the smooth muscle surrounding the gland ductules. Oxytocin release is occasioned by stimuli of a visual, psychologic, or physical nature that prepare the mother for suckling.

ENDOCRINE DISORDERS & PREGNANCY

PREGNANCY & PITUITARY ADENOMAS

In women of reproductive age, small tumors of the anterior pituitary are not uncommon (see also Chapter 2). While most are nonfunctional and asymptomatic, the most common symptom of pituitary microadenomas is amenorrhea, frequently accompanied by galactorrhea. In the past, few affected women became pregnant, but now most can be made to ovulate and to conceive with the aid of clomiphene citrate, menotropins and hCG, or bromocriptine. Before ovulation is induced in any patient, serum PRL should be determined. If it is elevated, the sella turcica should be evaluated by magnetic resonance imaging (MRI) or by high-resolution CT scanning with contrast. About 10% of women with secondary amenorrhea will be found to have adenomas, while 20–50% of women with amenorrhea and galactorrhea will have detectable tumors.

The effect of pregnancy on pituitary adenomas depends on the size of the adenoma. Among 215 women with microadenomas (< 10 mm in diameter), fewer than 1% developed progressive visual field defects, 5% developed headaches, and none experienced more serious neurologic sequelae. Of 60 patients who had macroadenomas and became pregnant, 20% developed abnormal changes in their visual fields or other neurologic signs, usually in the first half of their pregnancies. Many of these required therapy. Monitoring of patients with known PRL-secreting adenomas during pregnancy is primarily based on clinical examination. The normal gestational increase in PRL may obscure the increase attributable to the adenoma, and radiographic procedures are undesirable in pregnancy.

Visual disturbances are usually experienced as "clumsiness" and are objectively found to be due to visual field changes. The most frequent finding is bitemporal hemianopia, but in advanced cases the defect can progress to concentric contraction of fields and enlargement of the blind spot.

Since the pituitary normally increases in size during pregnancy, headaches are common and bitemporal hemianopia not uncommon in patients with adenomas. These changes almost always revert to normal after delivery, so that aggressive therapy for known pituitary adenomas is not indicated except in cases of rapidly progressive visual loss.

Management

Management of the pregnant woman with a small adenoma includes early ophthalmologic consultation for formal visual field mapping and repeat examinations once a month or every other month throughout pregnancy.

If visual field disturbances are minimal, pregnancy may be allowed to proceed to term. If symptoms become progressively more severe and the fetus is mature, labor should be induced. If symptoms are severe and the fetus is immature, management may consist of transsphenoidal resection of the adenoma or medical treatment with bromocriptine. While bromocriptine inhibits both fetal and maternal pituitary PRL secretion, it does not affect decidual PRL secretion. At present, bromocriptine appears not to be teratogenic, and no adverse fetal effects have been reported. It should, of course, be used with caution in pregnancy, but in most cases it is probably preferable to surgery. Radiation therapy should not be used in pregnancy.

Management of PRL-secreting tumors in women who want to become pregnant is controversial. Surgical resection by surgeons with experience in transsphenoidal procedures results in reduction of PRL levels and resumption of normal ovulation in 60–80% of women with microadenomas and 30–50% of women with macroadenomas. The incidence of recurrence is at least 10–15% and will probably increase with further follow-up. Bromocriptine is usually well tolerated and is successful in achieving normal menstrual cycles and lowering PRL levels in 40–80% of patients. Bromocriptine also causes a marked decrease in tumor size, but the original size of the tumor is usually regained within days or weeks after discontinuing therapy. In the case of large tumors, combined medical and surgical management may often be appropriate. Radiation therapy has an important role in arresting growth of tumors that are resistant to other management, particularly large tumors that involve the cavernous sinuses and tumors that secrete both GH and PRL (see Chapter 2).

Prognosis & Follow-Up

There appears to be no increase in obstetric complications associated with pituitary adenomas, and no fetal jeopardy. The rate of prematurity increases in women with tumors requiring therapy, but this is probably due to aggressive intervention rather than to spontaneous premature labor.

The postpartum period is characterized by rapid relief of even severe symptoms, with less than 1% of untreated tumors developing permanent sequelae. In some cases, tumors improve following pregnancy, with normalization or lowering of PRL relative to prepregnancy values. Management should include radiography and assessment of PRL levels 4–6 weeks after delivery. There are no contraindications to breast-feeding.

PREGNANCY & BREAST CANCER

Breast cancer complicates one in 1500–5000 pregnancies. Only one-sixth of breast cancers occur in women of reproductive age, but of these, one in seven is diagnosed during pregnancy or the puerperium. Pregnancy and breast cancer have long been considered such an ominous combination that only one in 20 young women who have had breast cancer have later become pregnant. It now appears, however, that pregnancy has little effect on growth of breast cancer, though it presents problems of detection and management of the cancer (see Chapter 19).

Influence of Pregnancy on Breast Cancer

Pregnancy is not an etiologic factor in breast cancer. Indeed, there is good evidence that pregnancy at an early age actually reduces the risk of developing mammary cancer, and multiple pregnancies may also make the disease less likely. Moreover, contemporary concepts of the rate of tumor growth suggest that a tumor becomes clinically evident only 8–10 years after its inception. Thus, a tumor cannot arise and be discovered during the same pregnancy. In view of the increased glandular proliferation and blood flow and marked increase in lymph flow that occur during pregnancy, it could be argued that pregnancy accelerates the appearance of previously subclinical diseases, but this has not been demonstrated.

Probably the most important influence of pregnancy on breast cancer is the delay it may cause in making the diagnosis and starting therapy. In some series, the interval between initial symptoms and treatment was 6–7 months longer than in the absence of pregnancy. The increased density of the breasts in pregnancy makes small masses less apparent; and even when masses are found, both the patient and the physician are apt to attribute them to expected physiologic changes in pregnancy. Larger tumors may be misdiagnosed as galactoceles, and inflammatory carcinoma in the puerperium is liable to be misdiagnosed as mastitis.

At the time of diagnosis, 60% of pregnancy-associated breast cancers have metastasized to regional lymph nodes, and an additional 20% have distant metastases. Stage for stage, however, salvage rates following appropriate therapy are comparable to those achieved in nonpregnant patients. Termination of pregnancy, either by abortion or by early delivery, does not influence maternal survival.

Pregnancy After Treatment for Cancer

Pregnancy following definitive treatment of breast cancer has no adverse effect on survival. Indeed, women who become pregnant following stage I or II breast cancer have a somewhat better 5-year survival rate than matched controls who did not become pregnant but who survived at least as long as their match before becoming pregnant.

Women who have had breast cancer are frequently advised to avoid pregnancy for 5 years. Because most fertile women with breast cancer are in their mid 30s, such a plan virtually precludes pregnancy. Because pregnancy is not known to influence the rate of cancer recurrence, the only reasons for proscribing pregnancy are to avoid the possibility that management of a recurrence will be complicated by the pregnancy or to avoid the problem of producing motherless children. For a couple strongly desiring pregnancy, these risks may become acceptable in a much shorter time than 5 years, especially if the original lesion was small and the spread of disease minimal.

Estrogen and Cancer

Determinations of soluble estrogen and progesterone receptors are frequently used in breast cancer to predict whether the tumor is likely to respond to endocrine therapy. There is also evidence that the presence of estrogen receptor-positive tumors is correlated with a lower risk of early recurrence. In the pregnant patient, however, high progesterone levels inhibit estrogen and progesterone receptor synthesis, and high levels of both hormones cause their receptors to become tightly associated with the nuclear fraction. Thus, when soluble receptors are quantified, all breast cancers arising in pregnancy appear to be receptor-negative, making such measurements in pregnancy at best worthless and at worst dangerously misleading. The introduction of immunohistochemical assays, which allow identification of occupied nuclear receptors, may lead to a more reliable assessment.

Early Diagnosis

It is clear that early diagnosis of breast cancer in pregnancy gives the best chance of improved survival. Self-examination should be encouraged in spite of the anxiety it will cause, and thorough breast examinations should be performed periodically throughout pregnancy, not just at the initial examination. Even mildly suspicious lesions should be investigated if they persist for 1–2 weeks; waiting for a lesion to grow before further investigation is not acceptable practice. If a woman has discovered a small mass, her assessment should be accepted even if the physician cannot feel the mass by the usual techniques. Small lesions that would otherwise be missed can often be felt if soap and water are used for lubrication. Cytologic examination of fine-needle aspirates is probably the best technique for investigating discrete lesions. If any question persists, ultrasonography or low-dose mammography should be employed. Unless one is very experienced with evaluating early breast carcinomas, consultation with a surgical oncologist is always in order.

Treatment of Breast Cancer in Pregnancy

Once the diagnosis of cancer is made, the patient must be treated surgically without delay. In view of the large percentage of patients with positive nodes, the procedure should be one that provides adequate sampling of the axillary nodes, such as modified radical mastectomy. Simple mastectomy with axillary irradiation should be avoided. Therapeutic abortion is not routinely indicated. If, on the basis of surgical staging, adjuvant therapy is considered advisable, the decision must be made either to terminate the pregnancy by abortion or early delivery or to postpone

therapy. Since delay in treatment is the principal known reason for the poorer prognosis of breast cancer in pregnancy, delivery should be accomplished as soon as there is a substantial probability of good fetal outcome—usually at 32–34 weeks. Many of the drugs used in cytotoxic therapy of breast carcinoma are contraindicated in pregnancy. Radiation can be given with appropriate shielding, but the dose to the fetus will not be negligible.

HYPERTENSIVE DISORDERS OF PREGNANCY

Hypertension associated with pregnancy is generally categorized as chronic, in which elevated blood pressures antedate the pregnancy or are clinically recognized prior to the 20th week, or gestational, when the onset is beyond 20 weeks of gestation. If the latter is complicated by proteinuria and generalized edema, the triad is referred to as preeclampsia. When seizures accompany this syndrome, the condition is termed eclampsia. The incidence of preeclampsia is about 7%. Women at highest risk include primigravidas under 18 years old, multiparous women over 35 years old, black women, and women with twin gestations, diabetes, hydramnios, or prepregnancy hypertension. As many as half of women with prepregnancy hypertension develop exacerbations of hypertension in the third trimester.

Course of Hypertension in Pregnancy

In normal pregnancies, as well as those complicated by mild essential hypertension, diastolic blood pressure decreases 10–15 mm Hg in the second trimester. Hypertensive patients first seen at that time may be mistakenly identified as having preeclampsia when the blood pressure again increases in the third trimester. Clinically, preeclampsia usually appears after the 32nd week of gestation and, most frequently, during labor. In severe cases, especially those complicated by essential hypertension, acute rises in blood pressure may occur as early as 26 weeks. If hypertension appears in the first or early second trimester, it is associated either with gestational trophoblastic disease or an underlying disorder such as an acute flare-up of lupus nephritis. Occasionally, the onset of hypertension is recognized during the 24 hours following delivery.

In normal pregnancies, all of the components of the renin-angiotensin-aldosterone system are markedly elevated. In pregnancies complicated by chronic hypertension or preeclampsia, these components are slightly reduced toward normal nonpregnant levels, suggesting an appropriate feedback response. The most consistent finding in women with preeclampsia is the increased sensitivity to vasopressor agents compared to women with normal pregnancy. In pregnancies destined to be complicated by preeclampsia, an *increase* in arteriolar response to angiotensin that becomes statistically significant by 18–22 weeks of gestation–long before changes in blood pressure are detectable. The cause of this increase in vascular sensitivity to angiotensin is not known. Considerable evidence suggests that endothelial cell dysfunction may explain many of the pathophysiologic features of preeclampsia.

Symptoms & Signs

Signs of preeclampsia include a rise in diastolic pressure by 15 mm Hg or more over first trimester values, and proteinuria exceeding 500 mg daily. Symptoms include headaches, visual disturbances, and epigastric pain. Eclampsia may occur even with mild elevation of blood pressure and is associated with a maternal mortality rate as high as 10%. Deaths occur most frequently from cerebral hemorrhage, renal failure, disseminated intravascular coagulopathy, acute pulmonary edema, or hepatic failure. The fetal perinatal mortality rate is in excess of 30%, and the risk of perinatal morbidity due to hypoxia is even higher.

Treatment of Preeclampsia

The only definitive therapy for preeclampsia is delivery. If a modest increase in blood pressure first occurs in association with proteinuria at 32–36 weeks of gestation, bed rest, preferably in the left lateral decubitus position, is frequently effective in temporarily inducing diuresis and controlling progression of the disease, thus gaining time for the developing fetus. If labor occurs or induction of labor is attempted, parenteral magnesium sulfate should be used to prevent seizures and should be continued for 24 hours following delivery. Moderate hypertension need not be treated with antihypertensive agents; however, diastolic blood pressure above 120 mm Hg must be controlled to reduce the risk of intracranial hemorrhage. The agent of choice is hydralazine, 5 mg intravenously at 15- to 20-minute intervals, until the diastolic pressure is approximately 100 mm Hg. If hydralazine is unsuccessful, diazoxide or nitroprusside may be used, but these agents are rarely required. Recent trials indicate that low-dose aspirin can prevent the development of preeclampsia in high-risk situations. Reduction of the thromboxane:prostacyclin ratio at the platelet:endothelial cell interface appears to be the protective mechanism.

Treatment of Chronic Hypertension

Women with chronic hypertension who become pregnant require special management. Roberts's recommendations are probably the best:

(1) Diastolic pressures under 100 mm Hg should not be treated. However, if a woman is receiving antihypertensive therapy when first seen in pregnancy, therapy should be continued. If she is taking propranol, consideration may be given to switching to a more specific β_1-antagonist such as metoprolol or atenolol. The rare patient who has been taking ganglionic blockers should receive another form of therapy instead. Owing to a transient decrease in blood volume and placental perfusion associated with thiazide diuretics, use of these agents should usually not be initiated during pregnancy; however, if a woman is already receiving such therapy, it may be continued.

(2) Diastolic pressures above 100 mm Hg discovered during pregnancy call for antihypertensive management. Initial therapy should be with methyldopa, 250 mg orally at bedtime. This may be increased 1 g twice daily as required. If unacceptable drowsiness lasting more than 2–3 days occurs, the dosage may be reduced, and hydralazine, beginning at 10 mg orally twice daily and increasing up to 100 mg twice daily, may be added. If hydralazine is not tolerated, prazosin may be gradually added to the methyldopa therapy.

(3) Accelerated hypertension at any stage of gestation should be managed with bed rest and, if necessary, intravenous hydralazine. Unless diastolic pressure can be reduced to 110 mm Hg promptly, delivery should be performed regardless of gestational age.

Prognosis

The prognosis for hypertensive cardiovascular disease in later life in women with pregnancy-related hypertension depends on the type of disorder. Preeclampsia in the young primigravida is not associated with an increased risk of hypertension in later pregnancies or in later life. By contrast, transient hypertension (late-gestation hypertension without proteinuria) is associated with an increased risk of chronic hypertension in later life.

HYPERTHYROIDISM IN PREGNANCY

Pregnancy mimics hyperthyroidism. There is thyroid enlargement, increased cardiac output, and peripheral vasodilation. Owing to the increase in thyroid hormone-binding globulin (TBG), total serum thyroxine is in the range expected for hyperthyroidism. Free thyroxine, the free thyroxine index, and TSH levels, however, remain in the normal range (see Chapter 4).

True hyperthyroidism complicates one or two per 1000 pregnancies. The most common form of hyperthyroidism during pregnancy is Graves' disease. Hyperthyroidism is associated with an increased risk of premature delivery (11–25%) and may modestly increase the risk of early abortion. In Graves' disease, thyroid-stimulating immunoglobulin (TSI), a 7S immune gamma globulin, crosses the placenta and may cause fetal goiter and transient neonatal hyperthyroidism, but these effects rarely jeopardize the fetus.

Treatment

The treatment of maternal hyperthyroidism is complicated by pregnancy. Radioiodides are strictly contraindicated. Iodide therapy can lead to huge fetal goiter and is contraindicated except as acute therapy to prevent thyroid storm before thyroid surgery. All antithyroid drugs cross the placenta and may cause fetal hypothyroidism and goiter or cretinism in the newborn. However, propylthiouracil in doses of 300 mg/d or less has been shown to be reasonably safe, although even at low doses about 10% of newborns will have a detectable goiter. Propranolol has been used to control maternal cardiovascular symptoms but may result in fetal bradycardia, growth retardation, premature labor, and neonatal respiratory depression. Partial or total thyroidectomy, especially in the second trimester, is a reasonably safe procedure except for the risk of premature labor.

A. Propylthiouracil: A reasonable plan of management is to begin therapy with propylthiouracil in doses high enough to bring the free T_4 index into the mildly hyperthyroid range and then to taper the dose gradually. Giving thyroxine along with propylthiouracil in the hope that it will cross the placenta in sufficient quantities to prevent fetal hypothyroidism is not effective and serves only to increase the amount of propylthiouracil required. If the maintenance dose of propylthiouracil is above 300 mg/d, serious consideration should be given to partial thyroidectomy.

B. Propranolol: Propranolol may be used transiently to ameliorate cardiovascular symptoms while control is being achieved.

Management of Newborn

Newborns should be observed carefully. In infants of mothers given propylthiouracil, even equivocal evidence of hypothyroidism is an indication for thyroxine replacement therapy. Neonatal Graves' disease, which may present as late as 2 weeks after delivery, requires intensive therapy (see Chapter 4).

HYPOTHYROIDISM IN PREGNANCY

Hypothyroidism is uncommon in pregnancy, since most women with the untreated disorder are oligoovulatory. As a practical matter, women taking thyroid medication at the time of conception should be maintained on the same or a slightly larger dose throughout pregnancy, whether or not the obstetrician believes thyroid replacement was originally indicated. Physiologic doses of thyroid are innocuous, but maternal hypothyroidism may be hazardous to the developing fetus. The correlation between maternal and fetal thyroid status is poor, and hypothyroid mothers frequently deliver euthyroid infants. The strongest correlation between maternal and newborn hypothyroidism occurs in areas where endemic goiter due to iodide deficiency is common. In these regions, dietary iodide supplementation in addition to thyroid hormone treatment of the mother may be of the greatest importance in preventing cretinism.

DIABETES M542ELLITUS & PREGNANCY

Hormone & Fuel Balance During Normal Pregnancy

Pregnancy produces major changes in the homeostasis of all metabolic fuels and in this way affects the management of diabetes. Plasma concentrations of glucose in the **postabsorptive state** decline as pregnancy advances, because of increasing placental uptake of glucose and a probable limitation on hepatic glucose output. Therefore, fasting hypoglycemia is more common during pregnancy. Gluconeogenesis could be limited by a relative lack of the major substrate alanine. The plasma concentration of alanine has been shown in some studies to be lower during pregnancy, probably as a result of placental uptake and a restraint on proteolysis. Although fat deposition is accentuated in early pregnancy, lipolysis is enhanced by human placental lactogen (hPL) later in gestation, and more glycerol and free fatty acids are released in the postabsorptive state. Ketogenesis is thus accentuated in the postabsorptive state during pregnancy, probably secondary to increased provision of substrate free fatty acids and hormonal effects on the maternal liver cells.

The balance of metabolic fuels is also different in the **fed state** during pregnancy. Despite hyperinsulinism in normal pregnancy, the disposal of glucose is impaired, producing somewhat higher maternal blood levels. The contra-insulin effects of gestation have been related to hPL, progesterone, and cortisol. The disappearance in plasma of administered insulin is not greater during pregnancy, despite the presence of placental insulin receptors and degrading enzymes. Glucagon is well suppressed by glucose during pregnancy, and secretory responses of glucagon to amino acids are not increased above nonpregnant levels. After meals, more glucose is converted to triglyceride in pregnant compared with nonpregnant animals, which would tend to conserve calories and enhance fat deposition. Insulin resistance during pregnancy apparently does not extend to the lipogenic and antilipolytic effects of the hormone.

Overview of Diabetes During Pregnancy

Diabetic pregnant women have been classified on the basis of duration and severity of diabetes (Table 13–2). A classification system (White) was originally

Table 13–2. Classification of diabetes during pregnancy (Priscilla White).

Class	Characteristics	Implications
Gestational diabetes	Abnormal glucose tolerance during pregnancy; postprandial hyperglycemia during pregnancy.	Diagnosis before 30 weeks' gestation important to prevent macrosomia. Treat with diet adequate in calories to prevent maternal weight loss. Goal is postprandial blood glucose <130 mg/dL (7.2 mmol/L) at 1 hour or <105 mg/dL (5.8 mmol/L) at 2 hours. If insulin is necessary, manage as in classes B, C, and D.
A	Chemical diabetes diagnosed before pregnancy; managed by diet alone; any age at onset.	Management as for gestational diabetes.
B	Insulin treatment or oral hypoglycemic agent used before pregnancy; onset at age 20 or older; duration <10 years.	Some endogenous insulin secretion may persist. Fetal and neonatal risks same as in classes C and D, as is management; can be type I or II.
C	Onset at age 10–20, or duration 10–20 years.	Insulin-deficient diabetes of juvenile onset; type I.
D	Onset before age 10, or duration >20 years, or chronic hypertension (not preeclampsia), or background retinopathy (tiny hemorrhages).	Fetal macrosomia or intrauterine growth retardation possible. Retinal microaneurysms, dot hemorrhages, and exudates may progress during pregnancy, then regress after delivery.
F	Diabetic nephropathy with proteinuria.	Anemia and hypertension common; proteinuria increases in third trimester, declines after delivery. Fetal intrauterine growth retardation common; perinatal survival about 90% under optimal conditions; bed rest necessary.
H	Coronary artery disease.	Serious maternal risk.
R	Proliferative retinopathy.	Neovascularization, with risk of vitreous hemorrhage or retinal detachment; laser photocoagulation useful; abortion usually not necessary. With active process of neovascularization, prevent bearing-down efforts.

used for prognosis of perinatal outcome and to determine obstetric management. Because the perinatal mortality rate has declined dramatically for many reasons in women in all classes, the system is now used mainly to describe and compare populations of diabetic pregnant women. However, certain characteristics of patients are still pertinent. The risk of complications is minimal if gestational diabetes is well controlled by diet alone, and these patients may be otherwise managed as normal pregnant women. Class B patients, whose insulin dependence is of recent onset, will probably have residual islet B cell function, and control of hyperglycemia may be easier than in class C or D patients. Finally, the most complicated and difficult pregnancies occur in women with renal, retinal, or cardiovascular disease.

The hormonal and metabolic effects of pregnancy are associated with increased risks of both hypoglycemic reactions and ketoacidosis. Increasing amounts of insulin are usually required to control hyperglycemia throughout gestation.

If diabetes is poorly controlled in the first weeks of pregnancy, the risks of spontaneous abortion and congenital malformation of the infant are increased. Later in pregnancy, polyhydramnios is also common in women with poorly controlled diabetes and may lead to preterm delivery. Fetal distress may develop in the third trimester if diabetic control has been inadequate. Careful fetal monitoring must be used to prevent stillbirth. The high incidence of fetal macrosomia (birth weight > 90th percentile for gestational age) increases the potential for traumatic vaginal delivery; primary cesarean deliveries are more common in these cases. Fetal intrauterine growth retardation may occur in diabetic women with vascular disease.

Other neonatal risks include respiratory distress syndrome, hypoglycemia, hyperbilirubinemia, hypocalcemia, and poor feeding; however, these problems are limited to the first days of life, and childhood development is usually normal. Despite these possible complications, diabetic women now have a 97–98% chance of delivering a healthy child if they adhere to a program of careful management and surveillance.

In the following sections, the convention used for designating the number of weeks of gestation is the number of weeks from the last menstrual period.

Gestational Diabetes

The hormonal and metabolic changes of pregnancy result in the diagnosis of glucose intolerance during the second half of gestation in 2–3% of pregnant women. Criteria for diagnosis are given in Table 13–3. Gestational diabetes may result from inadequate insulin response to carbohydrate load, from excessive resistance to the action of insulin, or from both. Once the diagnosis has been made, the patient should be placed on a diabetic diet modified for pregnancy: 25–35 kcal/kg ideal weight, 40–55% carbohy-

Table 13–3. Diagnosis of gestational diabetes.

Screening with glucose loading test:

Indications: (1) Screen all gravidas or (2) screen all gravidas who are overweight[1] or over 25 years of age (misses 10% of cases) plus all gravidas with glycosuria, a family history of diabetes in parents, sibling, aunts, or uncles), or a history of still-birth or macrosomic infants (misses 40% of cases).

Procedure: Give 50 g of glucose by mouth at 24–26 weeks of gestation.[2] Measure plasma glucose 1 hour later. If value exceeds 130 mg/dL (7.2 mmol/L), give the oral glucose tolerance test.

Oral glucose tolerance test:

Procedure: Give 100 g of glucose by mouth. Normal values for venous plasma glucose are as follows:

	NDDG[3]	C and C,S[4]
Fasting	105 mg/dl (5.8 mmol/L)	95 mg/dL (5.3 mmol/L)
1	190 mg/dL (10.5 mmol/L)	180 mg/dL (10.0 mmol/L)
2	165 mg/dL (9.2 mmol/L)	155 mg/dL (8.6 mmol/L)
3	145 mg/dL (8.0 mmol/L)	140 mg/dL (7.7 mmol/L)

[1] Overweight = height under 165 cm with weight over 68 kg (< 5 ft 5 in, > 150 lb) in first trimester; height over 156 cm with weight over 81 kg (> 5 ft 5 in, > 180 lb) in first trimester.
[2] Screen at 12–14 weeks for women at high risk of gestational diabetes; if negative, repeat at 24–26 weeks. If glucose loading test is done fasting, threshold of 140 mg/dl (7.7 mmol/L) is used.
[3] National Diabetes Data Group's modification of O'Sullivan's original criteria.
[4] O'Sullivan's criteria adapted for current methodology of measurement by Carpenter and Coustan, experimentally validated by Sacks.

drate, 20% protein, and 25–40% fat. Calories are distributed over three meals and three snacks (Table 13–4). The goal of therapy is not weight reduction but prevention of both fasting and postprandial hyperglycemia. If 1-hour or 2-hour postprandial glucose values are consistently greater (respectively) than 130 or 105 mg/dL (7.2 or 5.8 mmol/L), therapy is begun with human insulin, and the patient is managed as if insulin-dependent.

The risk of developing overt diabetes later in life is influenced by body weight and the need for insulin treatment in pregnancy. Follow-up studies indicate that 5–15% of nonobese gestational diabetics will need treatment in 5–20 years, compared to 35–50% of gestational diabetic women with a body weight greater than 120% of ideal. This suggests the possibility of preventive benefits of achieving weight loss after pregnancy and lactation. All patients with gesta-

tional diabetes mellitus should undergo a 75-g 2-hour glucose tolerance test at 6–10 weeks after delivery to guide future medical management. Diagnostic criteria for the nonpregnant state are presented in Table 13–5.

Insulin Management

The goal of insulin therapy during pregnancy is to prevent both fasting and postprandial hyperglycemia and to avoid debilitating hypoglycemic reactions. Maternal hyperglycemia is associated with fetal macrosomia and delayed lung maturation. Most experts believe that one should aim for fasting plasma glucose levels below 105 mg/dL (5.8 mmol/L) and postprandial levels below 140 mg/dL (7.8 mmol/L). Self-monitoring of capillary blood glucose at home with glucose oxidase strips and portable reflectance colorimeters has proved a reliable means of helping patients monitor the course of therapy. Since glycosylated hemoglobin correlates with mean daily capillary blood glucose over a few weeks during pregnancy, sequential measurement will provide another indicator of long-term control. Yet because insulin dosage must be frequently adjusted up or down during the metabolically dynamic state of pregnancy, capillary blood glucose must be measured several times each day to assist in the "fine-tuning" of insulin management.

Most pregnant insulin-dependent patients will require at least two injections of about a 1:2 mixture of regular and intermediate insulin each day in order to prevent fasting and postprandial hyperglycemia. The usual practice is to give two-thirds of the insulin before breakfast and one-third before supper (Table 13–6). More stringent regimens of administering regular subcutaneous insulin three times a day before meals and NPH at bedtime, or continuously with a

Table 13–4. Management of diet for patients with gestational diabetes.

(1) Assess present pattern of food consumption.
(2) Balance calories with optimal weight gain.
   (a) Caloric intake: 25–35 kcal/kg ideal weight.
   (b) Weight gain: 0.45 kg (1 lb) per month during the first trimester; 0.2–0.35 kg (0.5–0.75 lb) per week during the second and third trimesters.
(3) Distribute calories and carbohydrates over 3 meals and 3 snacks; evening snack to include complex carbohydrate and at least one meat exchange.
(4) Use food exchanges to assess the amount of carbohydrate, protein, and fat:
   (a) Carbohydrate: 40–55% of calories or ≥150 g/d.
   (b) Protein: 20% of calories or ≥74 g/d.
   (c) Fat: 25–40% of calories.
(5) Emphasize high-fiber, complex carbohydrate foods.
(6) Identify individual glycemic responses to certain foods.
(7) Tailor eating plans to personal needs.

Table 13–5. National Diabetes Data Group diagnostic criteria for diabetes mellitus in nonpregnant women.[1]

Diagnosis	Fasting	Two Hours
Normal	<115 mg/dL (<6.4 mmol/L)	<140 mg/dL (< 7.8 mmol/L)
Impaired glucose tolerance	>115 mg/dL and <140 mg/dL	>140 mg/dL and <200 mg/dL
Diabetes	≥140 mg/dL (≥ 7.8 mmol/L)	≥200 mg/dL (≥11.1 mmol/L)

[1] Test consists of giving 75 g glucose load and then measuring venous plasma glucose.
[2] The National Diabetes Data Group also requires one intervening value ≥200 mg/dL between fasting and 2 hours for the diagnosis of diabetes after pregnancy.

portable insulin pump, may be necessary to achieve normoglycemia in some patients.

Hypoglycemic reactions are more frequent and sometimes more severe in early pregnancy. Therefore, patients must keep glucagon on hand, and a member of the household must be instructed in the technique of injection. Hypoglycemic reactions have not been associated with fetal death or congenital anomalies.

Fetal Development & Growth

Major congenital anomalies are those which may severely affect the life of the individual or require major surgery for correction. The incidence of major congenital anomalies in infants of diabetic mothers is 6–12%, compared with 2% in infants of a nondiabetic population. While perinatal deaths due to stillbirth and respiratory distress syndrome have declined in pregnancies complicated by diabetes, the proportion of fetal and neonatal deaths ascribed to congenital anomalies has risen to 50–80%. The types of anomalies most common in infants of diabetic mothers and their presumed time of occurrence during embryonic development are listed in Table 13–7. It is apparent that any intervention to reduce the incidence of major congenital anomalies must be applied very early in pregnancy. The additional finding that the excess risk of anomalies is associated with the group of diabetic women with elevated glycosylated hemoglobin early in pregnancy suggests that poor diabetic control is related to the risk of major congenital anomalies in infants of diabetic mothers. Protocols of intensive diabetic management instituted prior to conception and continued through early pregnancy have resulted in significant reduction in the frequency of anomalies. This means that primary care physicians treating diabetic women of reproductive age must evaluate them for the possibility of becoming pregnant and inform them of the risks related to the level of hyperglycemia.

Ultrasonography in the first half of pregnancy may detect neural tube defects (anencephaly, meningomyelocele) that occur with a higher than normal incidence in infants of diabetic mothers. The physician should also screen all insulin-dependent pregnant women for elevated serum alpha-fetoprotein levels at 14–16 weeks of gestation to detect other cases of neural tube defects. Later in pregnancy, sophisticated ultrasonographic examinations may detect congenital heart defects or other anomalies.

The initial ultrasonographic examination at 18–20 weeks confirms the dating of gestation, and subsequent examinations at 26 and 36 weeks measure fetal growth. Many of these infants are large for dates, ie, macrosomic infants with increased fat stores, increased length, and increased abdomen-to-head or thorax-to-head ratios. The hypothesis that fetal macrosomia results from the causal chain of maternal

Table 13–6. Illustration of use of self-monitoring blood glucose to determine insulin dosage during pregnancy.

Self-Monitored Capillary Blood Glucose		Insulin Doses
Fasting blood glucose	148 mg/dL (8.2 mmol/L)	14 units regular, 28 units intermediate
1 h after breakfast	206 mg/dL (11.4 mmol/L)	
1 h after lunch	152 mg/dL (8.4 mmol/L)	
1 h after supper	198 mg/dL (11.0 mmol/L)	9 units regular, 10 units intermediate
2–4 AM	142 mg/dL (7.9 mmol/L)	

Suggested changes based on pattern of blood glucose values over 2–3 days: slight increases in presupper intermediate insulin to control fasting blood glucose next day, in morning regular insulin to control postbreakfast glucose, and in presupper regular insulin to control postsupper hyperglycemia. Dose of morning intermediate insulin is adequate to control early afternoon blood glucose. When dose of presupper intermediate insulin is increased, patient should test to detect and prevent nocturnal hypoglycemia. One-hour postprandial testing is advised to detect the probable peaks of glycemic excursions. Patient should also test when symptoms of hypoglycemia appear.

Table 13–7. Congenital malformations in infants of diabetic mothers.[1]

	Ratio of Incidences Diabetic vs Control Group	Latest Gestational Age for Occurrence (Weeks After Menstruation)
Caudal regression	252	5
Anencephaly	3	6
Spina bifida, hydro-cephalus, or other central nervous system defects	2	6
Cardiac anomalies	4	
Transposition of great vessels		7
Ventricular septal defect		8
Atrial septal defect		8
Anal/rectal atresia	3	8
Renal anomalies	5	
Agenesis	6	7
Cystic kidney	4	7
Ureter duplex	23	7
Situs inversus	84	6

[1]Modified and reproduced, with permission, from Kucera J: Rate and type of congenital anomalies among offspring of diabetic women. *J Reprod Med* 1971;**7**:61; and Mills JL, Baker L, Goldman AS: Malformations in infants of diabetic mothers occur before the seventh gestational week: Implications for treatment. *Diabetes* 1979;**28**:292.

hyperglycemia → fetal hyperglycemia → fetal hyperinsulinemia → fetal macrosomia has long been debated. Macrosomic infants of diabetic mothers have significantly higher concentrations of C peptide in their cord sera or amniotic fluid (representing endogenous insulin secretion) than do infants of diabetic mothers with birth weights appropriate for gestational age. The determinants of fetal hyperinsulinemia throughout pregnancy may not be simply maternal hyperglycemia, however. Other metabolic substrates that cross the placenta and are insulinogenic (eg, branched-chain amino acids) may play a role in fetal macrosomia, and transplacental lipids could contribute to fat deposition.

The degree of maternal glycemia is related to birth weights of infants of diabetic mothers, as adjusted for gestational age. This suggests that prevention of maternal hyperglycemia throughout pregnancy may reduce the incidence of macrosomia. The glycemic threshold for fetal macrosomia seems to be *postprandial* peak values above 130—140 mg/dL. On the other hand, average peak postprandial blood sugar levels below 110 mg/dL are associated with insuffi-

cient fetal growth and small-for-dates infants, which may also induce complications in the neonatal period. The metabolic and nutritional determinants of birth weights of infants of diabetic mothers other than maternal glucose are under study.

Polyhydramnios is an excess volume of amniotic fluid (> 1000 mL, often > 3000 mL). It may cause severe discomfort or premature labor and is most often associated with fetal macrosomia. The excess volume of amniotic fluid was not related to the concentration of glucose or other solutes in amniotic fluid or to excess fetal urine output as measured by change in bladder size by means of ultrasonography. Additional possible factors in causation of polyhydramnios in diabetic pregnancies include fetal swallowing, decidual and amniotic fluid PRL, and as yet unknown determinants of the complicated multicompartmental intrauterine transfer of water. However, diuretics do little to mobilize excessive amniotic fluid. Polyhydramnios is rare in women with well-controlled diabetes.

In contrast to fetal macrosomia, the fetus of a woman with diabetes of long duration and vascular disease may suffer intrauterine growth retardation. This problem is apparently related to inadequate uteroplacental perfusion. All body diameters may be below normal on ultrasonographic measurements; oligohydramnios is common; and after 30 weeks of gestation, maternal plasma or urinary estriol levels are usually below the 95% confidence limits for stage of gestation.

Obstetric Management

Not long ago the incidence of apparently sudden intrauterine fetal demise in the third trimester of diabetic pregnancies was at least 5%. Since the risk increased as pregnancies approached term, preterm delivery was instituted but the incidence of neonatal deaths from respiratory distress syndrome increased. Curiously, the cause of stillbirth was usually not obvious. The risk was greater with poor diabetic control, and the incidence of fetal death exceeded 50% with ketoacidosis. Some instances of fetal demise were associated with preeclampsia, which is a common complication of diabetic pregnancy. Fetal death was also associated with pyelonephritis, which is now largely prevented by screening for and treating asymptomatic bacteriuria. Other than these known risk factors, one can speculate that fetal distress was related to (1) a combination of relative fetal hypoxia and hyperglycemia or (2) fetal myocardial dysfunction.

Advances during the past decade have led to techniques for detecting fetal distress and preventing stillbirth. The infrequency of fetal movement as noted in fetal activity determinations (< 4/h) may indicate fetal jeopardy. More quantitative studies of fetal activity patterns using ultrasonography are now available.

Maternal estriol assays were also used for fetal evaluation, based on the knowledge that placental production of estriol is dependent on precursors from the fetal adrenals. It has been demonstrated that the maternal 24-hour urine estriol level correlates with the mass of the fetal-placental unit and that a 40% or greater drop in maternal plasma or urinary estriol level usually precedes fetal demise in pregnancies complicated by diabetes. However, estriol monitoring was somewhat nonspecific and has been replaced by biophysical assessment at most centers.

The primary mode of fetal assessment is antepartum fetal heart rate monitoring. The presence of fetal heart rate accelerations and good long-range variability on the nonstress test (NST) and the absence of late decelerations (lower rate persists after the contraction subsides) on the contraction stress test (CST) almost always suggest that the fetus is well oxygenated and has a low risk of dying within several days. However, the predictive value of normal test results is only valid for a short duration in diabetic women with unstable metabolic control or hypertension. Generally, the NST and CST are sensitive screening tests, and abnormal results in these tests of fetal heart monitoring will overestimate the diagnosis of fetal distress. Therefore, some authorities require that additional evidence of fetal distress (by biophysical ultrasonographic assessment) be obtained before intervention in preterm pregnancies can be recommended.

Insulin-dependent diabetic patients were usually admitted to the hospital at 36 weeks' gestation or earlier for fetal monitoring and careful control of diabetes. However, normotensive women achieving very good control (fasting blood glucose about 100 mg/dL, 1-hour postprandial blood glucose < 140 mg/dL) with self-monitoring of blood glucose levels have no excess risk of fetal distress and do not require antepartum admission to the hospital.

Unless maternal or fetal complications arise, the goal for the termination of pregnancy should be 38 weeks or even later, in order to reduce neonatal morbidity from preterm deliveries. On the other hand, the obstetrician may wish to induce labor before 38 weeks if there is concern about increasing fetal weight. Before the delivery decision is made, fetal pulmonary maturity should be determined. The standard test for pulmonary maturity is the lecithin/sphingomyelin (L/S) ratio, in which a value greater than 2 indicates a low risk for respiratory distress syndrome. However, in pregnancies complicated by diabetes, many authors have reported a false-positive rate of 6–12% with L/S values between 2 and 3. The reason for the discrepancy may be related to low surfactant apoprotein production due to fetal hyperinsulinemia. The lowest risk for respiratory distress syndrome is attained by delaying delivery (if possible) until the L/S ratio becomes abnormally high (> 3.5). The false-negative rate for L/S ratios of 1.5–2.0 is at least

50% in nondiabetic pregnancies (ie, delivery occurs within 72 hours, but respiratory distress syndrome does not develop). Other amniotic fluid assays (eg, measurement of phosphatidylglycerol) can be used to evaluate the risk for respiratory distress syndrome. If phosphatidylglycerol is present in the amniotic fluid, the risk is low even if the L/S ratio is below 3.5.

Once fetal lung maturity is likely, the route of delivery must be selected based on the usual obstetric indications. If the fetus seems large (> 4200 g) on clinical and ultrasonographic or CT pelvimetric examination, cesarean section probably should be performed because of the possibility of shoulder dystocia and permanent deformity from birth trauma. Otherwise, induction of labor is reasonable, because maternal and peripartum risks are fewer following vaginal delivery. Once labor is under way, continuous fetal heart rate monitoring (with scalp pH backup measurements) must be performed. Maternal blood glucose levels > 150 mg/dL are associated with intrapartum fetal distress problems.

Insulin Management for Labor & Delivery

The diabetic parturient may be unusually sensitive to insulin during active labor and delivery, and insulin shock is possible if delivery occurs sooner than anticipated. Protocols for continuous low-dose intravenous insulin administration during labor or prior to cesarean delivery are now used to achieve stringent control of blood glucose in order to reduce the incidence of intrapartum fetal distress and neonatal metabolic problems (Table 13–8). A cord blood glucose level at delivery correlates positively with the higher maternal levels, and there does not seem to be an upper limit on placental transfer of glucose. During labor, maternal plasma glucose can usually be kept below 100 mg/dL (5.6 mmol/L) with 1–2 units of regular insulin and 7.5 g of dextrose given intravenously every hour. If cesarean section is necessary, insulin management is similar, and infants do equally well with general, spinal, or epidural anesthesia. Nonetheless, the anesthesiologist should be cautioned against the administration of copious glucose-containing intravenous solutions.

Neonatal Morbidity

Planning for the care of infants of diabetic mothers should begin prior to delivery, with participation by the neonatologist in decisions about timing and management of delivery. The pediatrician must be in attendance to know of antenatal problems, to assess the need for resuscitation, and to determine major congenital anomalies.

Infants of diabetic mothers have an increased risk of respiratory distress syndrome compared with infants of matched nondiabetic mothers. Possible reasons include abnormal production of pulmonary surfactant or connective tissue changes leading to

Table 13–8. Intrapartum insulin infusion.

Capillary Glucose (mg/dL)	Insulin Rate (units/h)
<70	0.0
71–90	0.5
91–110	1.0
111–130	2.0
131–150	3.0
151–170	4.0
171–190	5.0
>190	Call MD

[1] With blood glucose < 130 mg/dL, infusion should be 5% dextrose in lactated Ringer's solution at a rate of 125 mL/h; if blood glucose ≥ 130 mg/dL, use lactated Ringer's without dextrose until blood glucose declines.

decreased pulmonary compliance. However, in recent years, the incidence of respiratory distress syndrome has declined from 24% to 5%, probably related to use of the L/S ratio and delivery of most infants at term (see above). The diagnosis of respiratory distress syndrome is based on clinical signs (grunting, retraction, respiratory rate > 60/min), typical findings on chest x-ray (diffuse reticulogranular pattern and air bronchogram), and an increased oxygen requirement (to maintain the PaO_2 at 50–70 mm Hg) for more than 48 hours with no other identified cause of respiratory difficulty (heart disease, infection). Survival of infants with respiratory distress

syndrome has dramatically improved as a result of advances in ventilation therapy.

Hypoglycemia is common in the first 48 hours after delivery and is defined as blood glucose below 30 mg/dL (1.7 mmol/L) regardless of gestational age. The symptomatic infant may be lethargic rather than jittery, and hypoglycemia may be associated with apnea, tachypnea, cyanosis, or seizures. Hypoglycemia has been related to elevated fetal insulin levels during and after delivery. Nevertheless, infants of diabetic mothers may also have deficient catecholamine and glucagon secretion, and the hypoglycemia may be related to diminished hepatic glucose production and oxidation of free fatty acids. The neonatologist attempts to prevent hypoglycemia in "well" infants with early feedings of 10% dextrose in water by bottle or gavage by 1 hour of age. If this is not successful, treatment with intravenous dextrose solutions is indicated. Rigid control of diabetes to prevent fetal hyperglycemia may reduce the incidence of neonatal hypoglycemia. There are usually no long-term sequelae of episodes of neonatal hypoglycemia.

Other frequent problems in infants of diabetic mothers include hypocalcemia (< 7 mg/dL [1.75 mmol/ L]), hyperbilirubinemia (> 15 mg/dL [256 μmol/L]), polycythemia (central hematocrit > 70%), and poor feeding. Further investigation is necessary to determine the cause of these problems. Better control of the maternal diabetic state in the future should reduce their incidence.

REFERENCES

General

Burrow GN, Ferris TF (editors): *Medical Complications During Pregnancy,* 3rd ed. Saunders, 1988.
Chez RA (editor): Fetal and placental endocrinology. Clin Obstet Gynecol 1980;23:719.
Goebelsmann U: Protein and steroid hormones in pregnancy. J Reprod Med 1979;23:166.
Jaffe RB: Endocrine-metabolic alterations induced by pregnancy. In: *Reproductive Endocrinology: Physiology, Pathophysiology, and Clinical Management,* 3rd ed. Yen SSC, Jaffe RB (editors). Saunders, 1991.
Milne JA (editor): The physiologic response to pregnancy in health and disease. Proceedings of a symposium arranged by the Department of Obstetrics and Gynaecology, University of Cambridge, Sept 15–16, 1978. Postgrad Med J 1979;55:293.
O'Leary P et al: Longitudinal assessment of changes in reproductive hormones during normal pregnancy. Clin Chem 1991;37:667.
Tulchinsky D, Ryan KJ (editors): *Maternal-Fetal Endocrinology. Saunders,* 1980.

Chorionic Proteins & Pregnancy Tests

Derman R, Edelman DA, Berger GS: Current status of immunologic pregnancy tests. Int J Gynaecol Obstet 1979;17:190.

Fisher DA: Maternal-fetal thyroid function in pregnancy. Clin Perinatol 1983;10:615.
Healy DL, Hodgen GD: The endocrinology of human endometrium. Obstet Gynecol Surv 1983;38:509.
Horne CHW, Nisbet AD: Pregnancy proteins: A review. Invest Cell Pathol 1979;2:217.
Hsueh AJW, Jones PBC: Gonadotropin-releasing hormone: Extrapituitary actions and paracrine control mechanisms. Annu Rev Physiol 1983;45:83.
Petraglia F: Placental neurohormones secretion and physiological implications. Mol Cell Endocrinol 1991;78:C109.
Siler-Khodr TM: Hypothalamic-like releasing hormones of the placenta. Clin Perinatol 1983;10:533.
Weiss G: Relaxin. Annu Rev Physiol 1984;46:43.

Steroid Hormones

Bammann BL, Coulam CB, Jiang NS: Total and free testosterone during pregnancy. Am J Obstet Gynecol 1980;137:293.
Buster JE: Gestational changes in steroid hormone biosynthesis, secretion, metabolism, and action. Clin Perinatol 1983;10:527.
Conley AJ, Mason JI: Placental steroid hormones. Ballieres Clin Endocrinol Metab 1990;Jun 4:249.
Donaldson A et al: Changes in concentrations of cortisol,

dehydroepiandrosterone sulfate and progesterone in fetal and maternal serum during pregnancy. Clin Endocrinol 1991;35(4):447.

Laatikainen T et al: Fetal and maternal serum levels of steroid sulfates, unconjugated steroids and prolactin at term pregnancy and in early spontaneous labor. J Clin Endocrinol Metab 1980;50:489.

Lind T: Clinical chemistry of pregnancy. Adv Clin Chem 1980;21:1.

Parker CR et al: Hormone production during pregnancy in the primigravid patient. 2. Plasma levels of desoxycorticosterone throughout pregnancy of normal women and women who developed pregnancy-induced hypertension. Am J Obstet 1980;138:626.

Partsch CJ et al: The steroid hormone milieu of the undisturbed human fetus and mother at 16–20 weeks gestation. J Clin Endocrinol Metab 1991;73(5):969.

Siiteri PK et al: Progesterone and maintenance of pregnancy: Is progesterone nature's immunosuppressant? Ann NY Acad Sci 1977;286:384.

Fetal Endocrinology

Hercz P et al: Quantitative comparison of serum steroid and peptide hormone concentrations in male and female fetuses in the maternal-fetoplacental system during the 28th–40th weeks of pregnancy. Eur J Obstet Gynecol Reprod Biol 1989;30(3): 201.

Jaffe RB: Fetoplacental endocrine and metabolic physiology. Clin Perinatol 1983;10:669.

Serón-Ferré M, Jaffe RB: The fetal adrenal gland. Annu Rev Physiol 1981;43:141.

Parturition

Challis JRG: Endocrinology of late pregnancy and parturition. In: *Reproductive Physiology, III, International Review of Physiology*. Vol 22. Greep RO (editor). University Park Press, 1980.

Fuchs AR: Hormonal control of myometrial function during pregnancy and parturition. Acta Endocrinol [Suppl] 1978;89:1.

Garfield RE et al: Hormonal control of GAP junction formation in sheep myometrium during parturition. Biol Reprod 1979;21:999.

Liggins GC et al: Control of parturition in man. Biol Reprod 1977;16:39.

Ryan KJ: New concepts in hormonal control of parturition. Biol Reprod 1977;16:88.

Steer PJ: The endocrinology of parturition in the human. Bailliere's Clin Endocrinol Metab 1990;4:333.

Thorburn G, Challis JRG: Endocrine control of parturition. Physiol Rev 1979;59:863.

Puerperium & Lactation

Duchesne C, Leke R: Bromocriptine mesylate for prevention of postpartum lactation. Obstet Gynecol 1981;57:464.

Harrison RG: Suppression of lactation. Semin Perinatol 1979;3:287.

Monheit AG, Cousins L, Resnick R: The puerperium, anatomic and physiologic readjustments. Clin Obstet Gynecol 1980;23:973.

Tucker HA: Endocrinology of lactation. Semin Perinatol 1979;3:199.

Vance ML, Evans WS, Thorner MO: Bromocriptine. Ann Intern Med 1984;100:78.

Vorherr H: Hormonal and biochemical changes of pituitary and breast during pregnancy. Semin Perinatol 1979;3:193.

Pituitary Adenomas

Barbieri RL, Ryan KJ: Bromocriptine: Endocrine pharmacology and therapeutic applications. Fertil Steril 1983;39:727.

Johnston DG et al: Hyperprolactinemia: Long-term effects of bromocriptine. Am J Med 1983;75:868.

Marshall JR: Pregnancy in patients with prolactin-producing pituitary tumors. Clin Obstet Gynecol 1980; 23:453.

Breast Cancer & Pregnancy

Bottles K, Taylor RN: Diagnosis of breast masses in pregnancy and lactating women by aspiration cytology. Obstet Gynecol 1985;66(3 Suppl):76S.

Donegan WL: Breast cancer and pregnancy. Obstet Gynecol 1977;50:244.

Saunders CM, Baum M: Breast cancer and pregnancy: A review. J R Soc Med 1993;86(3):162.

Hypertensive Disorders

Carr BR, Gant NF: The endocrinology of pregnancy-induced hypertension. Clin Perinatol 1983;10:737.

Chesley LC: The control of hypertension in pregnancy. Obstet Gynecol Annu 1981;10:67.

de Groot CJM, Taylor RN: New insights into the etiology of pre-eclampsia. 1993;25:243.

Roberts JM: Pregnancy-related hypertension. Pages 703–752 in: Maternal-Fetal Medicine: Principles and Practice. Creasy RK, Resnick R (editors). Saunders, 1984.

Rodgers GM, Taylor RN, Roberts JM: Preeclampsia is associated with a serum factor cytotoxic to human endothelial cells. Am J Obstet Gynecol 1988;159:908.

Sullivan JM: The hypertensive diseases of pregnancy and their management. Adv Intern Med 1982;27:407.

Symonds EM: The renin-angiotensin system in pregnancy. Obstet Gynecol Annu 1981;10:45.

Wilson M et al: Blood pressure, the renin-aldosterone system and sex steroids throughout normal pregnancy. Am J Med 1980;68:97.

Worley AJ et al: Vascular responsiveness to pressor agents during human pregnancy. J Reprod Med 1979;23:115.

Hyperthyroidism in Pregnancy

Burrow GN: Hyperthyroidism during pregnancy. N Engl J Med 1978;298:150.

Cheron RG et al: Neonatal thyroid function after propylthiouracil therapy for maternal Graves' disease. N Engl J Med 1981;304:525.

Glinoer D et al: Regulation of maternal thyroid during pregnancy. J Clin Endocrinol Metab 1990;71(2):276.

Diabetes Mellitus & Pregnancy

Algert A, Shragg P, Hollingsworth DR: Moderate caloric restriction in obese women with gestational diabetes. Obstet Gynecol 1985;65:487.

Bochner CJ et al: Early third trimester ultrasound screening in gestational diabetes to determine the risk of macrosomia and labor dystocia at term. Am J Obstet Gynecol 1987;157:703.

Carpenter MW, Coustan DR: Criteria for screening tests

of gestational diabetes. Am J Obstet Gynecol 1982;144:768.

Cheney C, Shragg P, Hollingsworth D: Demonstration of heterogeneity in gestational diabetes by a 400 kcal breakfast meal tolerance test. Obstet Gynecol 1985;65:17.

Cousins L: Pregnancy complications among diabetic women. Obstet Gynecol Surv 1987;42:140.

Coustan DR et al: Should the fifty-gram, one-hour plasma glucose screening test be administered in the fasting or fed state? Am J Obstet Gynecol 1986;154:1031.

Coustan DR et al: Maternal age and screening for gestational diabetes: A population-based study. Obstet Gynecol 1989;73:557.

Fuhrmann K et al: Prevention of congenital malformations in infants of insulin-dependent diabetic mothers. Diabetes Care 1983;6:219.

Gabbe SG et al: Management and outcome of pregnancy in diabetes mellitus, classes B to R. Am J Obstet Gynecol 1977;129:723.

Jovanovic L, Peterson CM: Optimal insulin delivery for the pregnant diabetic patient. Diabetes Care 1982;5 (Suppl 1):24.

Kitzmiller JL et al: Diabetic pregnancy and perinatal morbidity. Am J Obstet Gynecol 1978;131.

Kitzmiller JL et al: Diabetic nephropathy and perinatal outcome. Am J Obstet Gynecol 1981;141.

Kitzmiller JL et al: Measurement of fetal shoulder width with computed tomography in diabetic women. Obstet Gynecol 1987;70:941.

Kitzmiller JL et al: Preconception care of diabetes glycemic control prevents congenital anomalies. JAMA 1991;265:731.

Klein BEK, Moss SE, Klein R.: Effect of pregnancy on progression of diabetic retinopathy. Diabetes Care 1990;13:34.

Landon MB et al: Neonatal morbidity in pregnancy complicated by diabetes mellitus: Predictive value of maternal glycemic profiles. Am J Obstet Gynecol 1987; ß156:1089.

Langer O et al: Gestational diabetes: Insulin requirements in pregnancy. Am J Obstet Gynecol 1987; 157:669.

Magee MS et al: Influence of diagnostic criteria on the incidence of gestational diabetes and perinatal morbidity. JAMA 1993;269:609.

Miller E et al: Elevated maternal hemoglobin A_{1c} in early pregnancy and major congenital anomalies in infants of diabetic mothers. N Engl J Med 1981;304:1331.

Mills JL, Baker L, Goldman AS: Malformations in infants of diabetic mothers occur before the seventh gestational week: Implications for treatment. Diabetes 1979;28:292.

Miadovnik M et al: Elevated maternal glycohemoglobin in early pregnancy and spontaneous abortion among insulin-dependent diabetic women. Am J Obstet Gynecol 1985;153:439.

Moloney IBM, Drury MI: The effect of pregnancy on the natural course of diabetic retinopathy. Am J Ophthalmol 1982;93:745.

Mueller-Heubach E et al: Lecithin/sphingomyelin ratio in amniotic fluid and its value for the prediction of neonatal respiratory distress syndrome in pregnant diabetic women. Am J Obstet Gynecol 1978;130.

Norton M, Kitzmiller JL, Buchanan T: The endocrine pancreas and maternal metabolism. In: *Maternal-Fetal Endocrinology,* 2nd ed. Tulchinsky DT, Ryan KJ (editors). Saunders, 1980.

O'Sullivan JB et al: Medical treatment of the gestational diabetic. Obstet Gynecol 1974;43:817.

O'Sullivan JB: Body weight and subsequent diabetes mellitus. JAMA 1982;248:949.

Reece EA, Coustan DR (editors): *Diabetes Mellitus in Pregnancy,* Churchill Livingstone, 1988.

Sacks DA et al: Do the current standards for glucose tolerance testing in pregnancy represent a valid conversion of O'Sullivan's original criteria? Am J Obstet Gynecol 1989;161:638.

White P: Diabetes mellitus in pregnancy. Clin Perinatol 1974;1:331.

Regulatory Peptides of the Gut

14

Sean J. Mulvihill, MD, & Haile T. Debas, MD

The origins of gastrointestinal endocrinology can be traced to experiments performed by William Bayliss and Ernest Starling at University College in London in 1902. They showed that acidification of the duodenum or denervated jejunum stimulated exocrine pancreatic secretion in anesthetized dogs. Furthermore, intravenous injection of an extract of jejunal—but not ileal—mucosa similarly stimulated pancreatic secretion. They postulated the presence of a chemical messenger, which they termed secretin, within the duodenal and jejunal mucosa. Starling later went on to define chemical messengers as substances "carried from the organ where they are produced to the organ where they affect by means of the bloodstream." He called these messengers "hormones," a word suggested by William Hardy. Thus began the physiologic era of gastrointestinal endocrinology, in which hormones such as gastrin, secretin, and cholecystokinin were discovered through their physiologic actions. Only later were these substances isolated and characterized.

Since the early 1970s, in what could be termed the "biochemical era" of gastrointestinal endocrinology, about 30 new peptides have been described through biochemical purification of extracts of gastrointestinal mucosa. The discovery that many of these peptides are located in the central nervous system and in enteric neurons—in addition to being found in specialized endocrine cells of the gastrointestinal tract—has led to the concept of a brain-gut axis (see below). Recently, recombinant DNA technology has been used to identify gastrointestinal peptides in the absence of physiologic or biochemical information, initiating a "molecular era." The presence of calcitonin gene-related peptide (CGRP) in many neural tissues, including those of the gut, was identified in this manner after an examination of the calcitonin gene suggested the presence of a second peptide sequence.

The physiologic importance of many of the newly discovered peptides is unclear. Unlike the hormonal components of other systems, in which specific kinds of endocrine cells are concentrated into distinct organs, those of the gut are widely dispersed. Furthermore, disease states attributable to disorders of gut endocrine cells are rare, and there are no known deficiency states. In other endocrine organs, such as the thyroid and adrenal, disorders of function have pro-

ACRONYMS USED IN THIS CHAPTER	
ACTH	Adrenocorticotropic hormone
APUD	Amine precursor uptake and decarboxylation
CCK	Cholecystokinin
CGRP	Calcitonin gene-related peptide
CRH	Corticotropin-releasing hormone
DNA	Deoxyribonucleic acid
ECL	Enterochromaffin-like
ENS	Enteric nervous system
GH	Growth hormone
GIP	Glucose-dependent insulin-releasing peptide (gastric inhibitory peptide)
GRH	Growth hormone-releasing hormone
GRP	Gastrin-releasing peptide
5-HIAA	5-Hydroxyindoleacetic acid
MEN	Multiple endocrine neoplasia
MSH	Melanocyte-stimulating hormone
NPY	Neuropeptide Y
NSE	Neuronal-specific enolase
PHI	Peptide histidine isoleucine
PHM	Peptide histidine methionine
PP	Pancreatic polypeptide
PRL	Prolactin
PTH	Parathyroid hormone
PYY	Peptide YY
TRH	Thyrotropin-releasing hormone
VIP	Vasoactive intestinal polypeptide

vided natural models for physiologic study, but this is uncommon in the gastrointestinal tract.

Modes of Gut Peptide Delivery (Table 14–1)

Gastrointestinal peptides are delivered to their sites of action in three main ways: Some circulate in the bloodstream in order to reach the target cell (**endocrine delivery**); some are released into the interstitial fluid and affect nearby cells (**paracrine delivery**); and still others, within neurons, act as neurotransmitters or neuromodulators (**neurocrine delivery**) (Figure 14–1; see also Chapter 2). Some peptides have more than one mode of delivery. For example, somatostatin has an endocrine function, is present in neurons, and also exercises paracrine actions in the gastric body and antrum. Because of their various modes of delivery, it may be preferable to re-

Table 14–1. Gastrointestinal hormones.

	Mode of Delivery			
	Endo-crine	Neuro-crine	Para-crine	Major action
Gastrin	+	+	–	Gastric acid and pepsin secretion.
CCK	+	(+)	–	Pancreatic amylase secretion.
Secretin	+	–	–	Pancreatic bicarbonate secretion.
GIP	+	–	–	Enhances glucose-mediated insulin release. Inhibits gastric acid secretion.
VIP	–	+	(+)	Smooth muscle relaxation. Stimulates pancreatic bicarbonate secretion.
Motilin	+	–	–	Initiates interdigestive intestinal motility.
Somatostatin	+	+	+	Numerous inhibitory effects.
PP	+	–	(+)	Inhibits pancreatic bicarbonate and protein secretion.
Enkephalins	–	+	(+)	Opiate-like actions.
Substance P	–	+	(+)	Smooth muscle contractions
GRP[1]	–	+	(+)	Stimulates release of gastrin and CCK.
Neurotensin	+	+	(+)	Smooth muscle contraction.
Enteroglucagon	(+)	(+)	(+)	Physiologic actions unknown.
PYY	+	–	(+)	Inhibits pancreatic bicarbonate and protein secretion.
NPY	–	+	–	Inhibits pancreatic bicarbonate and protein secretion.
CGRP	–	+	–	Stimulates acid secretion and somatostatin release.

[1] GRP is probably the mammalian form of bombesin and is responsible for bombesin-like immunoreactivity (BLI).

fer to these substances as regulatory peptides rather than as hormones.

To prove that a substance has a possible endocrine function in the gastrointestinal tract, two criteria must be met: (1) blood levels of the substance must rise after a meal, and (2) infusion of the substance at a rate that reproduces postprandial blood levels must elicit a physiologic response from the target organ. Only a handful of peptides meet these criteria in the gastrointestinal tract: gastrin, for stimulation of gastric acid and pepsin secretion; secretin, for stim-ulation of pancreatic bicarbonate secretion; chole-cystokinin (CCK), for stimulation of gallbladder contraction and pancreatic enzyme secretion; so-matostatin, for inhibition of gastric acid secretion; and gastric inhibitory polypeptide (GIP), for stimula-tion of insulin release. Most gut peptides serve as neurocrine or paracrine agents. It has been difficult to prove that these agents have important regulatory ac-tivities on digestive processes, because there is no way to measure the concentrations of these locally acting agents at their presumed sites of action.

LUMEN

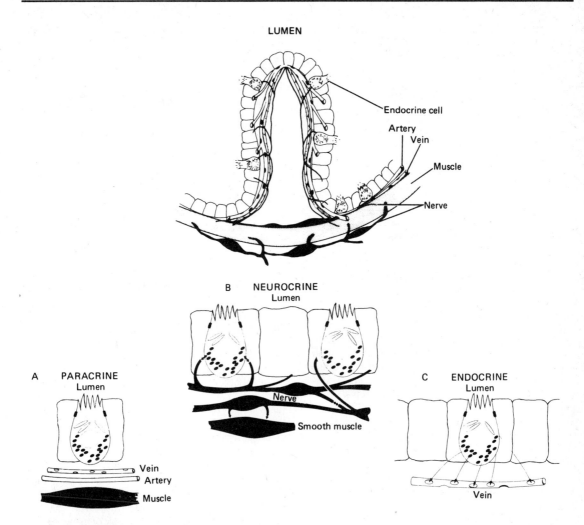

Figure 14–1. Schematic representation of the wall of the small intestine. Note the close proximity of endocrine cells and nerves to mucosal cells, blood vessels, and smooth muscle. Anatomically, local release of hormone by endocrine cells or nerves could affect secretion and absorption (mucosal cells), motility (muscle), and blood flow (blood vessels). *A:* Paracrine delivery—release of a messenger locally to affect adjacent cells. *B:* Neurocrine delivery—release of messenger by nerves to affect mucosal cells, other endocrine cells, or smooth muscle of both small intestine and blood vessels. *C:* Endocrine delivery—release of messenger into the blood to act as a circulating hormone.

Cellular Mechanisms of Action

The actions of most gastrointestinal peptide hormones are mediated by membrane-bound receptors. It is now possible to clone receptor complementary DNAs (cDNAs) for some gut peptides, allowing identification of primary structural information. These receptors are proteins whose synthesis is subject to regulation, often by the hormone itself. In the best-studied examples, such as gastrin, CCK, and somatostatin, receptor concentrations are down-regulated by high plasma levels of the hormone. This may be due to alterations in synthesis, function, or degradation of the receptor. Hormone-receptor affinity can be quantified by measurement of binding in the presence of varying concentrations of the hor-

mone. There is some evidence, particularly in the case of CCK, that there may be two classes of receptor—one with low affinity and high capacity and one with high affinity and low capacity.

Binding to the cell membrane receptors activates one of two major intracellular pathways and stimulates cell function. These pathways have been termed second messengers (see Chapter 1). The effects of some hormones (eg, gastrin, CCK, and the neurotransmitter acetylcholine) are due to the release of intracellular calcium from stores in rough endoplasmic reticulum. Other peptides, such as secretin, vasoactive intestinal polypeptide (VIP), glucagon, and the paracrine substance histamine, activate adenylyl cyclase, the enzyme responsible for catalyzing the con-

Table 14–2. Gastrointestinal peptide families.

Family	Peptides
Gastrin	Gastrin CCK
Secretin	Secretin VIP PHI PHM Glucagon GIP
PP	PP PYY NPY
Tachykinin	Substance P Neuromedins Neurokinins
Others	Motilin Neurotensin Somatostatin GRP Galanin

version of ATP to cyclic AMP (cAMP). These two second messenger systems, intracellular calcium and cAMP, are distinct in their early steps but may cause similar changes in intracellular processes. For example, in the parietal cell, histamine, acting through the generation of intracellular cAMP, and acetylcholine, acting through the release of intracellular calcium, both stimulate the H+-K+ ATPase in canalicular membranes, resulting in the secretion of H+ into the extracellular space.

Structure of Gastrointestinal Peptide Hormones

Most gut regulatory substances are polypeptides. Notable exceptions include histamine and serotonin. Many exhibit structural homology, which allows them to be grouped into families (Table 14–2). Most of these peptides are probably synthesized as precursor molecules, with posttranslational processing to their active forms. The amino acid sequence for most gut peptides is now known, and in many instances the gene sequence has also been determined.

Distribution of Gut Peptides

Gut peptides are located both in specialized endocrine cells and in neurons widely dispersed throughout the gastrointestinal tract. The endocrine cells are distinguished by a clear cytoplasm and prominent basal acidophilic granules. Most gut endocrine cells are triangular, with a broad base and narrow apex, usually with a brush border facing the intestinal lumen (Figure 14–2). In enteric neurons, gut peptides probably act as neurotransmitters, or neurocrine agents. The bodies of enteric neurons are located within the gut wall, usually in the submucosal or myenteric plexus, from which their pathways extend to cells of the mucosa, smooth muscle,

blood vessels, and other endocrine cells. It is estimated that the gut contains between 80 million and 100 million neurons. This **enteric nervous system** (ENS) is best thought of as a third division of the autonomic nervous sytem. Table 14–3 summarizes the distribution of gut peptides in their respective cells.

Brain-Gut Axis

Many of the peptides originally isolated from the gut are also found in the brain, and vice versa (Table 14–4). This observation led to the concept of a brain-gut axis. In the central nervous system, gut peptides are thought to be important in the regulation of bodily functions such as satiety (CCK) and thermoregulation (bombesin). Furthermore, neurons of the central nervous system interact with those of the enteric nervous system to influence digestive processes. Many of these neurons are peptidergic. This interaction occurs via both afferent and efferent pathways and involves vagal and spinal neurons. Neurons of the enteric nervous system exert local control over digestive processes, including absorption, secretion, motility, immune function, and blood flow. It is likely that the pathophysiology of some poorly understood conditions, such as the irritable bowel syndrome, are the result of abnormalities of regulation of gut function by the enteric nervous system and central nervous system.

APUD Concept

The cytochemical and ultrastructural characteristics of gastrointestinal endocrine cells were described by Pearse in 1966. These cells are similar in their ability to produce peptide hormones and biogenic amines (epinephrine, norepinephrine, dopamine, and serotonin) and to actively absorb amine precursors and convert them to amines. It was speculated that the uptake of 5-hydroxytryptophan and conversion of 5-hydroxytryptamine (serotonin) was linked to the production of peptide hormones. Most of the cells possessing these characteristics are found in the gut or central nervous system (hypothalamus, pituitary axis, and pineal gland), but they are also present in the thyroid (calcitonin cell), parathyroid, and placenta. Pearse referred to them as APUD cells from their characteristic amine handling (**amine precursor uptake and decarboxylation**). It was postulated that APUD cells originated from the primitive neural crest. It has now been shown that these cells actually have their origins from gut endoderm. Regardless of their origin, it is clear that the endocrine cells of the gut are remarkably similar to other cells of the hypothalamic-pituitary axis and to neurons within the gut wall.

GASTRIN

In 1905, Edkins discovered a potent gastric acid secretagogue in extracts of antral mucosa and named

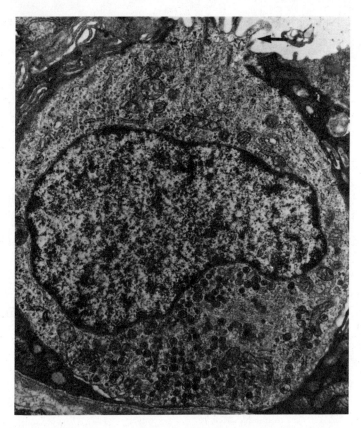

Figure 14–2. Typical endocrine cell of the gut. The arrow points to the brush border, which is at the cell apex and is open to the lumen of the gut. Granules at the cell base contain a peptide messenger, which in this cell is gastrin (G cell). (Reproduced, with permission, from Lechago J: Endocrine cells of the gastrointestinal tract and their pathology. Pathol Annu 1978;13:329.)

it "gastrin." Initially, it was not possible to exclude the possibility that the extract contained histamine, another secretagogue. The existence of gastrin was firmly established in the early 1960s, when Gregory et al isolated the peptide, identified its amino acid sequence, and synthesized the hormone.

Biochemistry & Distribution

Gastrin exists in three known biologically active forms of 14, 17, and 34 amino acids (Figure 14–3). They are also known as "mini gastrin," "little gastrin," and "big gastrin," respectively. The biologically active portion of the gastrin molecule is the 14-amino-acid carboxyl terminal residue. This sequence is identical in all three forms. Gastrin is secreted in an inactive form with a glycine extension at the carboxyl terminus. Conversion into the active form requires the presence of a deaminizing enzyme.

Both the human and porcine genes that encode for gastrin have been characterized. In the pig, a precursor cDNA to gastrin corresponds to an mRNA sequence of 312 nucleotides, which codes for a preprogastrin of 104 amino acids. The corresponding

human mRNA codes for a preprogastrin of 101 amino acids. The entire human gene, which includes two introns, is 4100 base pairs long.

Ninety percent of gastrointestinal gastrin is found in G cells of the gastric antrum. G17 accounts for most of the gastrin at this site. Most of the remainder of gastrointestinal tract gastrin is in the duodenum. Although immunoreactive gastrin is present in fetal pancreas, expression of gastrin is lost at term. This embryologic finding, however, may explain the presence of gastrinomas in the pancreas. Gastrin has been identified in the central nervous system.

Measurement & Release

Measurement of serum concentration of gastrin is widely available by radioimmunoassay. Fasting levels average between 21 and 105 pg/mL (10 and 50 pmol/L) and increase by 42–84 pg/mL (20–40 pmol/L) 30–60 minutes postprandially. The main stimulants for gastrin release are partially digested proteins, peptides, and amino acids, while carbohydrates and fats are ineffective. Minor stimulants of gastrin release include calcium, beer, wine, and cof-

Table 14–3. Distribution of gastrointestinal hormones.[1]

	Endocrine Cell[2]	Localization	Localized in Gut Nerves
Gastrin	G	Gastric antrum, duodenum	No
CCK	I	Duodenum, jejunum	Yes
Secretin	S	Duodenum, jejunum	No
GIP	K	Small bowel	No
VIP	D_1	Pancreas	Yes
Motilin	EC_2	Small bowel	No
Substance P	EC_1	Entire gastrointestinal tract	Yes
Neurotensin	N	Ileum	No
Somatostatin	D	Stomach, duodenum, pancreas	Yes
Enkephalins	. . .	Stomach, duodenum, gallbladder	Yes
GRP	. . .	Stomach, duodenum	Yes
PP	D_2F	Pancreas	No
Enteroglucagon	A	Pancreas	No
	L	Small intestine	
PYY	. . .	Small intestine, colon	No
CGRP	. . .	Entire gastrointestinal tract	Yes
NPY	. . .	Small intestine	Yes

[1]Note that several peptides are found both in nerves and in endocrine cells. VIP has been found only in nerves and is probably not present in endocrine cells.
[2]Endocrine cells identified with a specific hormone are identified by a letter. EC = enterochromaffin cell. The cells containing enkephalins and PYY have yet to be named.

Table 14–4. Peptides found in the brain and gut (brain-gut axis).

Originally Found in Brain	Originally Found in Gut
Substance P	CCK
Thyrotropin-releasing hormone (TRH)	Gastrin
Somatostatin	Secretin
Enkephalins	VIP
CGRP	Glucagon
Corticotropin-releasing hormone (CRH)	PHI
	PP
	PYY
	NPY
	Bombesin
	GRP
	Neurotensin
	Insulin

tion indirectly by release of histamine from enterochromaffin-like (ECL) cells in the gastric mucosa and directly by activation of specific cell-surface gastrin receptors. This receptor has recently been cloned. The relative contributions of the direct and indirect effects of gastrin on the parietal cell are controversial. Nonetheless, it is clear that histamine H_2 receptor antagonists nearly completely inhibit gastrin-stimulated acid secretion in vivo. The trophic effects of gastrin have been observed in vitro and in vivo and appear to involve polyamine synthesis. Prolonged hypergastrinemia is associated with enterochromaffin-like cell hyperplasia in rodents.

Other gastric effects of gastrin include stimulation of mucosal blood flow and pepsin release. It is not known whether these effects are directly due to gastrin or secondary to increased acid secretion. Several other actions have been ascribed to gastrin, such as contraction of the lower esophageal sphincter and gallbladder, but they are not seen at physiologic concentrations.

fee. Gastrin release is inhibited by antral acidification. Substantial inhibition occurs at pH 2.5, and release is abolished at pH 1.0.

Vagal stimulation by electrical current, insulin hypoglycemia, or injection of 2-deoxyglucose stimulates gastrin release. This pathway appears to be mediated by neurons of the enteric nervous system using GRP as a neurotransmitter. The observation that cholinergic blockade with atropine enhances meal-stimulated gastrin release suggests the presence of a vagal inhibitory mechanism. This pathway appears to due to paracrine release of somatostatin from antral D cells.

Actions

The main actions of gastrin that occur at physiologic levels are stimulation of gastric acid secretion and parietal cell growth. Gastrin evokes acid secre-

The gastrin-cholecystokinin family

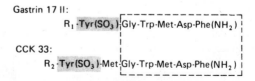

Gastrin 17 II:

$R_1 \cdot Tyr(SO_3) \cdot$ Gly-Trp-Met-Asp-Phe(NH_2)

CCK 33:

$R_2 \cdot Tyr(SO_3) \cdot$ Met-Gly-Trp-Met-Asp-Phe(NH_2)

Figure 14–3. Gastrin and cholecystokinin possess identical carboxyl terminal pentapeptides. However, the tyrosine is seven amino acids from the carboxyl end of CCK and must be sulfated for maximal potency. The tyrosine is six positions from the carboxyl end in gastrin and need not be sulfated for maximal potency. R_1 and R_2 represent the amino terminal sequences for gastrin and CCK.

CHOLECYSTOKININ

In 1928, Ivy and Oldberg observed that instillation of fat into the small intestine caused the gallbladder to contract. They postulated a hormonal mechanism and named the mediator "cholecystokinin" (CCK). In the early 1940s, Harper and Raper discovered a substance in extracts of duodenal mucosa that stimulated the secretion of enzyme-rich juice by the pancreas and called the substance "pancreozymin." In 1964, Jorpes et al found that increasing purification of a single extract from porcine small intestine proportionately increased its potency for both gallbladder contraction and pancreatic enzyme secretion, indicating that the two actions were properties of a single hormone. In 1971, Mutt and Jorpes reported the amino acid sequence of what we now know as CCK.

Biochemistry & Distribution

CCK exists in several molecular forms containing 58, 39, 33, and 8 amino acids (Figure 14–3). The carboxyl terminal octapeptide sequences are identical for all molecular forms. Like gastrin, CCK is probably synthesized as a precursor, with CCK39 and CCK33 representing progressive steps in the creation of CCK8. All of the biologic activity of CCK is contained in this terminal octapeptide. The human gene for CCK consists of a sequence of 345 base pairs that codes for a preprocholecystokinin of 115 amino acids. Sulfation of the tyrosine moiety in position 7 from the carboxyl terminus is necessary for full biologic potency.

CCK is located in the duodenum and proximal jejunum within the mucosal I cell (Table 14–3). It is also found in the central nervous system, in neurons of the myenteric plexus of the intestine, and in nerves supplying the urinary bladder and uterus. CCK8 is the major molecular form in the brain. CCK33 appears to be the major circulating form.

Measurement & Release

Development of a radioimmunoassay for CCK has been difficult, because antibodies directed at the carboxyl terminus tend to cross-react with gastrin, while those directed at the amino terminus tend to miss small molecular weight forms, such as CCK8. An in vitro bioassay using dispersed pancreatic acini has been developed. Fasting CCK levels vary from nil to 78 pg/mL (nil to 20 pmol/L), and postprandial levels rise to 78–392 pg/mL (20–100 pmol/L), depending on the assay used. The half-life of CCK in blood is short (2.5–7 minutes).

Release of CCK is stimulated by digested intraduodenal protein and fat.The aromatic amino acids phenylalanine and tryptophan are particularly potent stimulants. Fatty acids require dispersion into micelles and chain lengths of nine or more carbon atoms to be effective. The mechanism of stimulation of CCK release appears to involve a low-molecular-weight trypsin-sensitive peptide that has been termed CCK-releasing factor. A second stimulatory factor (monitor peptide) appears to be present in pancreatic juice.

CCK release is inhibited by somatostatin. The presence of increasing concentrations of bile acids in the intestine progressively inhibits the CCK-like effects of luminal stimuli but has no effect on the gallbladder response to intravenous CCK. This suggests that bile acids block the release of endogenous CCK and that this constitutes a mechanism which allows the gallbladder to relax again in the late stages after a meal.

Actions

The two major actions of CCK are stimulation of gallbladder contraction and pancreatic enzyme secretion. CCK also has potent trophic effects on pancreatic acini both in vitro and in vivo. CCK causes relaxation of the sphincter of Oddi via an indirect neural mechanism. Paradoxically, at higher doses, CCK has a direct stimulatory effect on contraction of sphincter smooth muscle. CCK delays gastric emptying and, at pharmacologic doses, increases small intestinal and colonic motility. Finally, CCK induces satiety in several species, including humans. This effect appears to CCK-A receptors on vagal afferent neurons. The presence of CCK in gut neurons as well as endocrine cells suggests that CCK acts in a neurocrine manner in addition to its endocrine function.

SECRETIN

Secretin is the prototypical gastrointestinal hormone. Bayliss and Starling in 1902 demonstrated that jejunal acidification or intravenous injection of extracts of jejunal mucosa stimulated secretion of water and bicarbonate from the pancreas. Secretin was purified by Jorpes and Mutt in 1961, and its amino acid sequence was identified in 1966.

Biochemistry & Distribution

Unlike most other hormones, secretin has been identified in only one form. It is a basic 27-amino-acid polypeptide containing four arginine residues and one histidine residue. Secretin shows structural similarities to glucagon, GIP, VIP, peptide histidine isoleucine (PHI), and peptide histidine methionine (PHM). These peptides are known as the secretin-glucagon family (Table 14–2). The entire molecule of secretin is necessary for biologic activity. Secretin is found in S cells in the duodenum and proximal jejunum and in the central nervous system. The DNA encoding the secretin receptor has recently been cloned.

Measurement & Release

Measurement of secretin has been difficult because the molecule is highly unstable and lacks a tyrosine residue for iodination. The latter problem has been solved by iodination under conditions that label histidine or by using a synthetic secretin analogue in which tyrosine has been substituted for one of the other amino acids. The most sensitive immunoassays for secretin have reported fasting serum values of 3–15 pg/mL (1–5 pmol/L), but it has not been possible to measure changes after a meal.

The only known stimulus for secretin release is duodenal acidification, which causes an increase in serum levels within minutes. The threshold for secretin release is a duodenal pH of less than 4.5. Infusion of bile salt into the duodenum also causes a small increase in serum levels of secretin. Other substances such as fats, alcohols, glucose, and amino acids do not release secretin if the pH of the duodenum is kept constant. Neither vagotomy nor atropine alters the secretin response to intraduodenal acid. Vagotomy may indirectly affect secretin release by elevating duodenal pH. The half-life of secretin in blood is 3–7.5 minutes.

Actions

The main action of secretin is stimulation of pancreatic bicarbonate and water secretion. Infusion of secretin intravenously to mimic physiologic levels produces a corresponding increase in pancreatic water and bicarbonate secretion. Therefore, it is probably correct to conclude that secretin has physiologic effects. CCK markedly potentiates the effect of secretin on pancreatic secretion. Although pharmacologic doses of secretin inhibits meal-stimulated gastrin release and gastric acid secretion, these effects are not seen at physiologic levels of secretin.

Clinical Uses

Secretin is used clinically to evaluate pancreatic function, to obtain specimens of pancreatic juice for cytologic study, and as a provocative agent for the release of gastrin from gastrinomas. When used for clinical tests, secretin is measured in clinical units (4000 clinical units [CU] = 1 mg).

To evaluate **pancreatic function,** a Dreiling tube is placed in the duodenum to aspirate pancreatic secretions, and secretin (1 CU/kg body weight) is injected intravenously. Duodenal juice is collected, and volume and bicarbonate concentration are measured. A maximal bicarbonate concentration of less than 90 meq/L and a flow of less than 2 mL/kg body weight over 80 minutes are diagnostic of impaired pancreatic function. Secretin may also be used to stimulate secretion of pancreatic juice for examination for malignant cells. The juice may be collected through a duodenal tube or by direct endoscopic cannulation of the pancreatic duct. A description of the use of secretin in the diagnosis of gastrinoma appears in the section on gastrinoma (see below).

SOMATOSTATIN

Somatostatin was first isolated from the hypothalamus, where it was found to inhibit the release of GH. Somatostatin was subsequently found in large amounts in both the brain and the gut. It is the preeminent inhibitory peptide of the gastrointestinal tract.

Biochemistry & Distribution

Somatostatin is a cyclic peptide with two naturally occurring forms of 14 and 28 amino acids (Figure 15–7). An 8-amino-acid analogue has been synthesized (octreotide) which preserves the biologic activity of somatostatin and has a longer serum half-life. Somatostatin is widely distributed in both the central nervous system and the gastrointestinal tract. In the gastrointestinal tract, somatostatin is most prominent in endocrine cells within the mucosa of the gastric antrum, in the D cells of the pancreatic islets, and in neurons of the myenteric plexus.

The gene sequence for somatostatin has been deduced, and it codes for a 116-amino-acid preprosomatostatin molecule. Posttranslational processing occurs at both the amino- and carboxyl terminal regions. The sequence of the tetradecapeptide somatostatin is strongly conserved among species. Expression of somatostatin mRNA in the foregut occurs early in gestation and precedes morphologic differentiation of the D cell.

Measurement & Release

The main stimulant for somatostatin release is ingestion of a meal. In the antrum, somatostatin release is reciprocally linked with gastrin release. Cholinergic stimulation increases gastrin release and suppresses somatostatin release. Conversely, antral acidification inhibits gastrin release and stimulates somatostatin release. This reciprocal regulation of release of gastrin and somatostatin is also seen at the level of mRNA expression. Somatostatin itself inhibits its release from the D cell, an example of autocrine regulation.

Actions

Somatostatin has broad inhibitory activity in the gut. It inhibits the release and action of numerous gut peptides, including gastrin, CCK, secretin, VIP, motilin, GIP, insulin, and glucagon. It has potent inhibitory effects on gut secretion, including gastric acid, pancreatic enzymes and bicarbonate, and intestinal fluid and electrolytes. Somatostatin at higher doses inhibits gut motility and gallbladder contraction. At lower doses, however, somatostatin initiates the migratory motor complex and increases the rate of gastric emptying. Somatostatin inhibits mesenteric blood flow and reduces portal pressures, even in patients with portal hypertension, but it has no significant systemic hemodynamic effects. Finally, somatostatin has antitrophic effects in both normal tissues, particularly the pancreas, and some neoplastic tissues.

Somatostatin is unique among gut peptides in that evidence is available to support delivery to the target cell by endocrine, paracrine, neurocrine, and autocrine routes. Postprandial elevations in plasma somatostatin, for example, are sufficient to inhibit gastric and pancreatic exocrine secretion. The evidence for a paracrine function for somatostatin is indirect and is based on the morphology of somatostatin-containing D cells and their proximity to target cells in sites such as the gastric antrum and the pancreatic islet. The presence of somatostatin in neurons in the gut wall and the inhibitory action of somatostatin on myenteric plexus acetylcholine release and intestinal motility support its role as a neurotransmitter. Finally, recent evidence supports the autocrine regulation of somatostatin release in the D cell.

Clinical Uses

Octreotide has found a clinical role in the management of patients with metastatic gut endocrine tumors, secretory diarrhea, enterocutaneous fistula, and a variety of unusual conditions such as the postgastrectomy dumping syndrome.

BOMBESIN & GASTRIN-RELEASING PEPTIDE

Bombesin, a peptide found in the skin, brain, and gut of frogs, shares biologic activity with mammalian gastrin-releasing peptide (GRP). The ten carboxyl terminal amino acid sequences of GRP and bombesin are nearly identical, accounting for their similar physiologic actions.

Biochemistry & Distribution

Frog bombesin, a 14-amino-acid polypeptide, belongs to a group of homologous amphibian peptides (litorin, ranatensin, and alytensin). Bombesin has not been identified in mammals. GRP is a 27-amino-acid polypeptide isolated from mammalian gut and brain. The human GRP gene has been cloned from a patient with carcinoid tumor metastatic to the lungs. It encodes a precursor molecule of 148 amino acids, termed preproGRP, which undergoes posttranslational processing to the active 27-amino-acid form. Recently, the GRP gene has been identified in frog gut extracts, and sequence analysis reveals that it codes for a precursor peptide distinct from that encoded by the frog bombesin gene. GRP is found throughout the gut and in the brain in neurons. It is most concentrated in the antral and duodenal mucosa. The receptor for GRP has been cloned and its amino acid sequence determined. GRP receptors are found on gastric G cells, gut smooth muscle cells, and pancreatic acinar cells.

Measurement & Release

Little or no change in plasma GRP concentrations occurs postprandially. In anesthetized pigs, marked release of GRP occurs in the venous outflow of the stomach in response to electrical vagal stimulation. The neuronal origin, mechanism of release, and low plasma levels of GRP support its function as a neurotransmitter. Gene expression of antral—but not fundic—GRP is increased by fasting and acid inhibition.

Actions

The main physiologic action of GRP is stimulation of gastrin release from antral G cells. Paradoxically, in the gastric fundus, GRP-containing neurons appear to inhibit parietal cell acid secretion indirectly via the release of somatostatin. At pharmacologic doses, GRP stimulates pancreatic exocrine secretion via a mechanism independent of CCK. Additionally, GRP stimulates smooth muscle contraction in the gallbladder, duodenum, and stomach. GRP has mitogenic effects in vitro and is a potent autocrine stimulant of growth of certain tumors, including small-cell lung cancer. In the brain, it may play a role in thermoregulation and pain perception.

CALCITONIN GENE-RELATED PEPTIDE

Biochemistry & Distribution

CGRP is a 37-amino-acid peptide produced by alternative processing of the calcitonin gene. Two CGRP-encoding genes and four highly homologous CGRPs have been described. CGRP is widely distributed in neurons of the central, peripheral, and enteric nervous systems. It is found throughout the gut, especially in sensory neurons. CGRP is commonly colocalized with substance P.

Measurement & Release

CGRP immunoreactivity may be measured in plasma, but it probably functions as a neurotransmitter. It is released by electrical stimulation and by specific sensory neuron stimulation with agents such as capsaicin.

Actions

CGRP probably plays an important role in the gut as a sensory neurotransmitter. Actions ascribed to CGRP in the gastrointestinal tract include inhibition of gastric and pancreatic secretion and smooth muscle contraction. Furthermore, CGRP stimulates somatostatin and acetylcholine release and increases mucosal blood flow. CGRP may have important effects in gastric mucosal cytoprotection.

GASTRIC INHIBITORY POLYPEPTIDE

Biochemistry & Distribution

GIP is a 42-amino-acid polypeptide with a structure similar to those of secretin, glucagon, and VIP. It has been found in serum in larger molecular forms that may represent precursors of the 42-amino-acid hormone. GIP is mainly localized in mucosal K cells in the duodenum, jejunum, and ileum. GIP may also be found in glucagon-containing pancreatic islet A cells.

Measurement & Release

Basal levels of GIP are in the range of 250 pg/mL (50 pmol/L). GIP release is stimulated by ingestion of food, with a peak of approximately 1000 pg/mL (200 pmol/L) occurring 60 minutes postprandially. The most potent stimuli for release of GIP are intraluminal glucose and triglyceride. Release of GIP may also be modulated by adrenergic stimulation, calcium, and glucagon. The half-life of GIP in plasma is about 20 minutes.

Actions

Originally, GIP was identified by its inhibitory effect on acid secretion. The main physiologic action of GIP, however, is to increase the insulin response to glucose in the presence of elevated blood glucose levels. This has prompted some to suggest that GIP be renamed **glucose-dependent insulin-releasing polypeptide.** GIP may function as an "incretin," enhancing insulin release and glucose disposal during intestinal absorption of glucose when compared to intravenous administration of glucose. GIP also inhibits gastrin release and gastric acid secretion, but it is unlikely that these effects occur at physiologic levels of the hormone. The amino terminal portion of the molecule is essential for the effect on insulin, and the carboxyl terminal portion is essential for the gastric effect. GIP in physiologic doses causes secretion of fluid and electrolytes by the ileal mucosa, but the importance of this is not known.

VASOACTIVE INTESTINAL POLYPEPTIDE

Biochemistry & Distribution

Vasoactive intestinal polypeptide (VIP) was first isolated in 1970 by Said and Mutt from porcine small intestine. VIP is colocalized on a gene with peptide histidine isoleucine (PHI). VIP is a basic 28-amino-acid peptide with strong homology to PHI, PHM, secretin, glucagon, GIP, and GRP. In addition, it has a close structural relationship to helospectin and helo-

dermin, which occur in the venom of Gila monsters. This suggests that, as a highly conserved molecule, it has important biologic activity.

VIP is distributed in a wide range of neurons in the gut, the central nervous system, and the urogenital tract. It is not present in gut endocrine cells except in lower vertebrates. It probably functions as a neurocrine agent, and its presence in neurons with processes extending to mucosal cells, smooth muscle, and blood vessels suggests that VIP affects local secretion, motility, and blood flow.

Measurement & Release

Fasting serum levels of VIP are low (> 23 pg/mL [> 7 pmol/L]) and do not increase significantly postprandially. VIP concentrations in venous effluent from the gut increase with electrical stimulation, esophageal distention, and mechanical stimulation of intestinal mucosa. The half-life of VIP in blood is about 1 minute in humans.

Actions

The most important physiologic actions of VIP are probably relaxation of the lower esophageal sphincter, receptive relaxation of the gastric fundus, and relaxation of the anal sphincter. Additionally, VIP increases gut blood flow and is responsible for penile erection. When infused intravenously, VIP inhibits pentagastrin and histamine-stimulated gastric acid and pepsin secretion. It stimulates lipolysis, glycogenolysis, and secretion by the small intestine and pancreas. The action of VIP is mediated by stimulatory G proteins and activation of adenylyl cyclase.

GALANIN

Biochemistry & Distribution

Galanin is a recently characterized 29-amino-acid peptide found in both the central nervous system and the gastrointestinal tract. It does not have structural similarity to any other gut peptides. In the gut, galanin is found in neurons of the myenteric and submucosal plexuses. It is commonly colocalized with VIP. An mRNA encoding a 123-amino-acid precursor molecule has been described.

Measurement & Release

Antibodies for estimation of galanin concentration by radioimmunoassay are available. Circulating levels are low. Galanin is released by neural stimulation, and increased concentrations are seen in venous drainage from the intestine and pancreas.

Actions

The physiologic role of galanin is unclear. Reported actions include inhibition of postprandial release of neurohumoral substances such as insulin, neurotensin, somatostatin, and pancreatic polypeptide. Additionally, galanin inhibits intestinal motility. This effect may be indirect, via inhibition of release of the excitatory neurotransmitters acetylcholine and substance P. Minor effects include inhibition of acid and pancreatic secretion.

SUBSTANCE P

Substance P was discovered by Von Euler and Gaddum in 1931 and was the first peptide found in both brain and gut. Little further research was done on substance P until 1970, when Chang and Leeman isolated and purified it from the brain.

Biochemistry & Distribution

Substance P is an 11-amino-acid polypeptide of the tachykinin family (Table 14–2). The gene encoding substance P has been cloned and sequenced. Distinct mRNA sequences have been identified coding for substance P and another tachykinin known as **substance K** (also called neurokinin-α or neuromedin-L). Substance P is distributed throughout the body in tissues of neural crest origin. In the gut, substance P is localized in neurons. It appears especially important as a neurotransmitter substance in small-diameter, unmyelinated sensory C fibers and in motor neurons of the myenteric plexus. Substance P is up-regulated in some inflammatory conditions in the intestine.

Measurement & Release

Substance P is released from enteric neurons in response to electrical stimulation, serotonin, and CCK. This release is inhibited by somatostatin. The normal serum concentration of substance P is about 91 pg/mL (70 pmol/L), most of which is of enteric origin. Substance P is not released into the blood except in disease states (eg, carcinoid syndrome and dumping syndrome).

Actions

The major gastrointestinal actions of substance P are stimulation of smooth muscle contraction and epithelial secretion. Paradoxically, in the circulatory system, substance P causes marked vasodilation, though this is probably due to release of secondary mediators. Substance P has marked stimulatory effects on the gut immune response. Receptors for substance P are up-regulated in colon from patients with inflammatory bowel disease. It is postulated that substance P has a pathophysiologic role in these and similar conditions.

ENKEPHALINS

The enkephalins are neuropeptides closely related to other central nervous system opiate peptides, the α-, β-, and γ-endorphins. The endorphins and enkephalins bind to opiate receptors found in the brain and gut.

Biochemistry & Distribution

Each of the two enkephalins in the gastrointestinal tract, met-enkephalin and leu-enkaphalin, contains five amino acids and differs only at the terminal –COOH residue, which is either methionine or leucine. Three distinct genes have been identified that code for opiate peptides. The pro-opiomelanocortin gene gives rise to ACTH, MSH, and α-endorphin. Its expression in the enteric nervous system is poorly understood. A second gene codes for precursor molecules of met-enkephalin and leu-enkephalin. There is direct evidence of synthesis of these peptides within myenteric neurons in the gut. A third gene codes for precursor molecules of dynorphin, α-neoendorphin, and leu-enkephalin. Enkephalins are widely distributed in neurons throughout the gastrointestinal tract.

Measurement & Release

Enkephalins are rapidly destroyed in blood, which makes it unlikely that they act as circulating hormones. The normal stimulus for the release of enkephalins is unclear. It is likely that they function as neurocrine or paracrine agents within the gut wall. Specific and nonspecific degrading enzymes have been found in the interstitial fluid and lymphatic channels of the gut.

Actions

The main actions of enkephalins in the gastrointestinal tract are inhibition of gut motility, stimulation of sphincter tone, and inhibition of mucosal secretion. Opioid receptors have been identified on smooth muscle cells isolated from the circular muscle layer of the gut but appear to be absent on cells from the longitudinal layer. In vitro, enkephalins cause dose-dependent contraction of smooth muscle cells and inhibit acetylcholine release from myenteric plexus neurons.

NEUROTENSIN

Neurotensin was discovered accidentally during isolation of substance P from the hypothalamus when a fraction of the extract was found to produce vasodilation and hypotension. The term "neurotensin" derives from its neurologic origin and its hypotensive properties.

Biochemistry & Distribution

Neurotensin is a 13-amino-acid polypeptide found extensively in nerve cells in the central nervous system. In the gut, it is located in the N cells of the ileum and is almost absent from nerve fibers. The carboxy terminal segment of the molecule is responsible for the biologic activity of neurotensin.

Measurement & Release

Neurotensin in serum can be measured by radioimmunoassay; however, amino terminal antisera tend to overestimate the amount of biologically active circulating peptide. The main stimulant for the release of neurotensin is intraluminal fat. An exaggerated postprandial release of neurotensin has been reported to occur in patients with dumping syndrome.

Actions

The physiologic actions of neurotensin are not known. Reported gastrointestinal actions include stimulation of pancreatic and bicarbonate secretion, stimulation of colonic motility, and inhibition of gastric and small intestinal motility. Additionally, neurotensin has trophic effects on gastric, small bowel, and colonic mucosa. Central nervous system neurotensin may participate in gastric mucosal cytoprotection. Neurotensin binds to mast cells, and since many of its effects are histamine-like (ie, hypotension, hypoglycemia, increased vascular permeability, smooth muscle contraction), neurotensin may act by releasing histamine.

MOTILIN

Biochemistry & Distribution

Motilin is a 22-amino-acid polypeptide found in endocrine cells in the mucosa of the duodenum, proximal jejunum, antrum, and fundus. Some immunoassays have purportedly shown localization of motilin within enterochromaffin cells, though this finding has been disputed. Motilin-like immunoreactivity has been identified in the brain, especially the pituitary and pineal glands. The entire molecule appears neccessary for full biologic activity.

Measurement & Release

Motilin is released into the blood in cyclic fashion in the fasting state. Its release corresponds to phase III of the cyclic migratory motor complex. The mechanism of regulation of motilin release is unclear. Both cholinergic and noncholinergic regulation has been suggested from animal studies. Serum motilin concentrations do not rise postprandially.

Actions

Motilin was first identified by its ability to stimulate gastric motility. Its main action appears to be induction of myoelectric complexes in the antroduodenal region which propagate distally. This action is mimicked by the macrolide antibiotic erythromycin. In vitro, motilin causes contraction of duodenal, ileal, colonic, and gallbladder smooth muscle. Motilin may participate in the control of gallbladder emptying,

particularly in the fasting state. Other pharmacologic properties include stimulation of pepsin and of pancreatic and chloride secretion.

PANCREATIC POLYPEPTIDE FAMILY

Biochemistry & Distribution

The pancreatic polypeptide family consists of three peptides: pancreatic polypeptide (PP), peptide YY (PYY), and neuropeptide Y (NPY). All three are 36-amino-acid peptides with strong structural similarities. PP and PYY are localized in endocrine cells of the gut, mainly in the pancreas and colon, respectively. NPY is found both in the brain and in enteric neurons. NPY is commonly colocalized with norepinephrine. Both the PP and NPY genes have been characterized.

Measurement & Release

Both PP and PYY appear to have endocrine function and are released postprandially. NPY appears to function as a neuropeptide. Basal plasma PP concentrations in humans average 50.4 pg/mL (12 pmol/L) and increase somewhat with age. PP release is strongly stimulated by protein and by cholinergic stimulation. Release of PYY is stimulated by intestinal fat.

Actions

The major physiologic action of PP is inhibition of pancreatic bicarbonate and protein secretion. Minor effects include relaxation of the gallbladder. PYY inhibits gastric motility and acid secretion and, in dogs, pancreatic secretion. The mechanism of PYY action on motility probably involves inhibition of cholinergic neurotransmission and activation of inhibitory G proteins. NPY is a potent vasoconstrictor and inhibits acetylcholine release.

ENTEROGLUCAGON

Biochemistry & Distribution

The best-known form of glucagon is a 29-amino-acid peptide found mainly in the pancreatic A cells. A number of other larger forms exist in the gut, including glicentin and enteroglucagon. All are coded for by the same gene sequence and share amino terminal homology. Forms of glucagon have been found in the intestinal mucosa, stomach, salivary glands, and brain.

Measurement & Release

Measurement of serum levels of enteroglucagon is imprecise, owing to the presence of multiple molecular forms and cross-reactivity of antibody assays with pancreatic glucagon. Ileal fat perfusion appears to be the most important stimulant of enteroglucagon release.

Actions

The intestinal forms of glucagon are much less potent than pancreatic glucagon in the regulation of hepatic glucose production. It has been postulated that enteroglucagon is an important trophic factor for small intestinal mucosa.

HORMONAL ABNORMALITIES IN DISEASES OF THE GASTROINTESTINAL TRACT

Although gastrointestinal peptide hormones are clearly important in the regulation of digestion, their role in disease states of the gut is less clear. A variety of tumors have been identified that secrete large quantities of gut hormones and produce definable clinical syndromes. These so-called neuroendocrine tumors of the gut have provided important clues to the physiologic actions of peptides. It is strongly suspected that abnormalities of regulation by the enteric nervous system underly several motility disorders of the gut. More recently, evidence has been obtained supporting the concept that abnormalities of gut regulatory peptides play important roles in the pathogenesis of inflammatory bowel disease.

DUODENAL ULCER

Although patients with duodenal ulcer secrete more acid than do subjects without duodenal ulcer, fasting serum gastrin levels and the number of antral G cells are normal. Meal-stimulated gastrin release, however, is greater than normal in these patients, and inhibition of gastrin release by antral acidification is diminished. Acid secretion is greater than normal at any given dose of gastrin in ulcer patients—ie, the parietal cells have a heightened sensitivity to stimulation. It thus appears that two abnormalities—increased gastrin response to a meal and increased sensitivity of the parietal cells to stimulation by gastrin—may contribute to the pathophysiology of duodenal ulcer.

Evaluation of Hypergastrinemia

Seven causes of basal hypergastrinemia have been described. In the evaluation of a patient with recurrent duodenal ulcer, one should measure gastrin levels, and if hypergastrinemia is present, these conditions should be considered.

A. Gastrinoma: Patients with gastrinoma have unregulated secretion of large amounts of gastrin by a tumor. The result is excessive acid secretion and severe ulcer disease. Evaluation and treatment are discussed in some detail later in this chapter.

B. Hypercalcemia: Patients with hypercalcemia may secrete increased amounts of gastrin and gastric acid. In patients with hyperparathyroidism, removal of a parathyroid adenoma with return of the serum calcium level to normal usually also allows the serum gastrin and gastric acid secretion to become normal. However, the relationship between hypercalcemia and duodenal ulcer disease is not close, and in general, if severe duodenal ulcer disease is present in a patient with hyperparathyroidism, the cause is more likely to be gastrinoma (as part of multiple endocrine neoplasia [MEN] syndrome type I) than a direct effect of hypercalcemia (see Chapter 21).

C. Massive Small Bowel Resection: Following massive small bowel resection, patients often have acid hypersecretion and hypergastrinemia. The pathophysiology of the hypergastrinemia is unclear, but the disorder may be due to loss of an enterogastrone (a hormone from the intestine that inhibits gastrin release and gastric acid secretion). The increased acid secretion that follows enterectomy usually subsides within a few months, so that treatment with H_2 blocking agents is usually sufficient.

D. Renal Failure: Renal failure may be accompanied by hypergastrinemia and gastric hyperacidity, probably because of decreased catabolism of the large molecular forms of gastrin by the diseased kidneys. Treatment consists of antacids and H_2 blocking agents.

E. Gastric Outlet Obstruction: Hypergastrinemia in association with gastric outlet obstruction is probably caused by antral distention. Tube decompression of the stomach usually results in a return of gastrin levels to normal.

F. Antral G-Cell Hyperplasia: Rare patients have hypergastrinemia from hyperactivity of the G cells, a condition referred to as antral G cell hyperplasia. Treatment consists of H_2 blocking agents or antrectomy.

G. Retained Antrum Syndrome: If, in the course of a distal gastrectomy, antral tissue adjacent to the pylorus is left intact and recontruction of gastrointestinal continuity is made by a Billroth II gastrojejunostomy, hypergastrinemia may occur as a result of lack of acid inhibition of G cell secretion. This syndrome is rare now that the factors regulating gastrin secretion are widely known.

MOTILITY DISORDERS OF THE GASTROINTESTINAL TRACT

Achalasia is characterized by abnormal or absent peristalsis in the body of the esophagus, a high resting lower esophageal pressure, and absence of relaxation of the sphincter with swallowing. Immunochemical staining of the sphincter reveals decreased or absent VIPergic neurons in the myenteric plexus. In view of the known relaxant effects of VIP on the lower esophageal sphincter, it is likely that achalasia represents an acquired disorder of sphincteric VIPergic innervation.

Hirschsprung's disease is due to congenital absence of neural ganglia in the distal colon. The affected colon is contracted and aperistaltic. The proximal colon dilates as a consequence of chronic partial obstruction. The concentration of VIP as well as the number of nerves containing VIP are greatly decreased in the contracted colonic segment. This absence of the relaxing effects of VIP probably results in the tonic contracted state.

Chronic intestinal pseudoobstruction. This is a poorly characterized disorder of intestinal motility which clinically simulates obstruction in the absence of any mechanical cause. Abnormalities of myenteric ganglia and intestinal nerve fibers have been described, but the defects are not uniform among patients. It is likely, however, that abnormalities of enteric neurons are responsible for the motility defect.

Irritable bowel syndrome. Evidence is accumulating that patients with irritable bowel syndrome have heightened sensitivity of gut afferent neurons. Rectal balloon distention, for example, results in more pain in patients with irritable bowel syndrome than in controls. It is possible that this heightened sensitivity to luminal stimuli initiates reflex arcs, resulting in the diarrhea and gut hypermotility characteristic of irritable bowel syndrome.

Other motility disorders suspected of being due to abnormalities of regulation by gut peptides include biliary dyskinesia, gastric dysrhythmias, and Chagas' disease.

INFLAMMATORY BOWEL DISEASE

Recently, it has been noted that gut peptides have effects on immune function and conversely that immune regulators affect gut function. Rectal concentrations of VIP are increased in patients with Crohn's disease. Receptors for other gut peptides, such as substance P, are up-regulated. These findings have led to the concept that gut regulatory peptides may play a role in the pathophysiology of inflammatory conditions such as Crohn's disease and ulcerative colitis.

NEUROENDOCRINE TUMORS OF THE GUT

Most neuroendocrine tumors of the gut are found in the pancreas, but a few occur in the wall of the duodenum or the retroperitoneum. They are also known by the general term "apudomas." These tumors probably arise from pleuripotential stem cells (nesidioblasts) present in pancreatic ducts. Most gut endocrine tumors secrete more than one peptide, but they are named after the one responsible for the clinical manifestations.

The diagnosis of a neuroendocrine tumor of the gut is first suspected by the clinical history and physical examination. Biochemical confirmation of the diagnosis is made by measurement of the hormonal marker in the blood or urine. Radiologic staging of the tumor with CT scan or MRI of the abdomen is used to identify hepatic metastases or (rarely) the primary tumor. The primary tumors are usually small, and efforts at preoperative localization have been disappointing. It now appears that exploration of the pancreas and complementary use of intraoperative sonography are the most efficient approach to localization. In general, tumor excision is the preferred treatment. When resection is not possible, palliation of the hormonal syndrome can generally be achieved with the somatostatin analogue octreotide. In selected cases, systemic chemotherapy, hepatic chemoembolization, or hepatic resection of metastases is valuable.

MULTIPLE ENDOCRINE NEOPLASIA SYNDROMES

Wermer's syndrome is an autosomal dominant inherited condition in which two or more endocrine glands become hyperplastic or undergo tumor formation. Wermer's syndrome is also called multiple endocrine neoplasia (MEN) type I. In MEN type I, the pancreas, pituitary, and parathyroid glands are most often involved, and the most common pancreatic tumors are gastrinoma, insulinoma, and VIPoma. MEN type IIa, also known as **Sipple's syndrome,** consists of medullary carcinoma of the thyroid, pheochromocytoma, and hyperparathyroidism (see Chapter 21). The tumors are always multiple and diffuse in both MEN type I and MEN type IIa. Screening of afflicted families through the use of specific DNA probes linked to MEN appears feasible.

ZOLLINGER-ELLISON SYNDROME

Zollinger-Ellison syndrome is characterized by virulent peptic ulceration associated with gastric acid hypersecretion and a gastrin-producing tumor (gastrinoma). Gastrinomas occur commonly in the pancreas and duodenum and rarely in the antrum. The tumors may be as small as 2–3 mm and are often difficult to find. When associated with MEN type I, they are nearly always multiple. Gastrinomas should be viewed as malignant tumors. Even though the histologic appearance may be benign, 50% of patients present with lymph node or liver metastases.

Most patients with gastrinoma present with symptoms of peptic ulcer disease recalcitrant to histamine

H_2 receptor antagonist therapy. Hemorrhage, perforation, and obstruction are common complications. Patients with multiple duodenal ulcers, jejunal ulcers, or recurrent ulcers following previous acid-reductive surgery should be suspected of having gastrinoma. About 5% of patients with gastrinoma have only diarrhea as their presenting symptom.

Diagnosis

The diagnosis of gastrinoma is generally suspected from the history and confirmed by measurement of serum gastrin levels. In gastrinoma, hypergastrimemia is associated with acid hypersecretion. Other conditions in which acid secretion is reduced, including pernicious anemia, atrophic gastritis, gastric ulcer, and the postvagotomy state, may be associated with hypergastrinemia; however, they may be differentiated from gastrinoma by history, endoscopy, and acid secretory studies.

A. Measurement of Serum Gastrin: Normal fasting gastrin concentrations are less than 200 pg/mL (95 pmol/L). In gastrinoma, levels usually exceed 500 pg/mL (238 pmol/L). Patients with borderline gastrin values (200–500 pg/mL [95–238 pmol/L]) whose acid secretion is in the range associated with ordinary duodenal ulcer disease should have a secretin provocative test. After administration of secretin, 2 units/kg as a bolus, a rise in the gastrin level of 150 pg/mL within 15 minutes is diagnostic. The secretin stimulation test is useful to differentiate gastrinoma from hypergastrinemia due to gastric outlet obstruction, retained antrum after Billroth II gastrojejunostomy, and antral gastrin cell hyperplasia (Table 14–5). Calcium given intravenously has also been used for this purpose, but secretin is both safer and more reliable. Postprandially, the serum gastrin levels do not change appreciably in patients with gastrinoma, whereas in normal subjects they double within 30 minutes.

B. Acid Secretory Studies: Marked basal acid hypersecretion (> 15 meq H^+/h) occurs in most patients with Zollinger-Ellison syndrome who have an intact stomach. In a patient with a previous gastrectomy, a basal acid output of 5 meq/h or more would be highly suggestive. Since the parietal cells are already under near-maximal stimulation from hypergastrinemia, there is little increase in acid secretion following an injection of betazole or pentagastrin, and the ratio of basal to maximal acid output (BAO/MAO) characteristically exceeds 0.6.

C. Localization Studies: Efforts to localize gastrinomas preoperatively have been disappointing. Computed tomography of the abdomen should be performed to exclude the presence of liver metastases. Selective angiography and transhepatic portal vein blood sampling can sometimes demonstrate the pancreatic tumor, but misleading results are common. Careful exploration by an experienced surgeon, intraoperative endoscopy with duodenal transillumination, and intraoperative ultrasonography of the pancreas is currently the most efficient localization strategy. Recent studies suggest that over 90% of gastrinomas can be identified intraoperatively with these methods.

Treatment

In the absence of known liver metastases or MEN type I, virtually all patients with gastrinoma should be explored with the intent of curative excision of the tumor. This approach results in 5-year survival rates over 90% for completely resected patients. Tumor recurrence is reported in about half of patients in long-term follow-up studies. Total gastrectomy, formerly a mainstay of therapy, is reserved now only for noncompliant patients with unresectable tumors.

Inhibition of acid secretion for palliation in unresectable patients is best achieved with omeprazole, which acts to inhibit the parietal cell H^+-K^+ ATPase. Omeprazole has proved to be superior to histamine H_2 receptor antagonists such as cimetidine, ranitidine, and famotidine. The goal of medical therapy is reduction of basal acid output to less than 10 mmol/h. A long-acting somatostatin analogue (octreotide) inhibits gastrin release, gastric acid secretion, and diarrhea in patients with gastrinoma. It may have occasional application in patients refractory to histamine H_2 receptor antagonists or omeprazole.

VIPOMA

VIPoma (also known as pancreatic cholera or the Verner-Morrison syndrome) is characterized by profuse watery diarrhea, marked fecal loss of potassium and bicarbonate, hypokalemia, and low or absent gastric acid secretion. Severe metabolic acidosis may be present. Many patients are hypercalcemic, perhaps from secretion by the tumor of a PTH-like substance. Abnormal glucose tolerance may result from hypokalemia and altered sensitivity to insulin. The syn-

Table 14–5. Hormones that may affect acid secretion or duodenal pH.

Action	Stimulation	Inhibition
Acid secretion	Gastrin CCK	VIP GIP Somatostatin Secretin
Gastrin release	Bombesin GRP	Secretin Somatostatin VIP GIP Glucagon
Pancreatic bicarbonate secretion	CCK Secretin VIP	PP Somatostatin
Delay of gastric emptying of acid into duodenum	CCK	

drome is due to intestinal secretion of fluid and electrolytes in response to elevated circulating levels of VIP, usually from an islet cell tumor of the pancreas.

Diagnosis

The diagnosis is suspected by the clinical presentation of severe watery secretory diarrhea and hypokalemia. The diarrhea persists with fasting—unlike that due to malabsorption. Other causes of diarrhea such as infection and surreptitious laxative use should be excluded. The diagnosis is confirmed by measurement of fasting VIP serum levels by radioimmunoassay.

Localization of the tumor is begun with computed tomography, which occasionally identifies the primary tumor in the pancreas or retroperitoneum and may reveal liver metastases. As with gastrinomas, occult tumors are best approached with thorough intraoperative exploration aided by intraoperative sonography.

Treatment

The optimal treatment for VIPoma is surgical resection, which is possible in about 50% of patients. In the absence of a visible tumor, some patients have been cured by distal or subtotal pancreatectomy. The pathologic finding in these patients has been pancreatic islet cell hyperplasia. Palliative therapy includes cytotoxic chemotherapy (usually streptozocin plus fluorouracil), indomethacin, and a somatostatin analogue.

GLUCAGONOMA

Glucagonoma syndrome is characterized by a migratory necrolytic dermatitis (usually involving the legs and perineum), weight loss, stomatitis, hypoaminoacidemia, anemia, and mild diabetes mellitus. Visual scotomas and changes in visual acuity have been reported in some cases. The age range is 20–70 years, and the condition is more common in women. The diagnosis is usually suspected from the distinctive skin lesion; in fact, the presence of a prominent rash in a patient with diabetes mellitus should be enough to raise suspicions. Confirmation of the diagnosis depends on demonstration of elevated serum glucagon levels. It may be possible to demonstrate the tumor by arteriography or CT scanning.

Glucagonomas arise from A_2 cells in the pancreatic islets. About 25% are benign and confined to the pancreas. The remainder have metastasized by the time of diagnosis, most often to the liver, lymph nodes, adrenal glands, or vertebrae. A few cases have been the result of islet cell hyperplasia.

Surgical removal of the primary lesion and metastases is indicated if technically feasible. Even if it is not possible to remove all of the tumor deposits, considerable palliation may result from subtotal removal. Streptozocin, dacarbazine, and somatostatin analogues are effective palliative agents for unresectable lesions. The clinical course generally parallels changes in serum levels of glucagon in response to therapy.

CARCINOID TUMORS & CARCINOID SYNDROME

Carcinoids are the most common of the gut endocrine tumors. They arise throughout the gut from the gastroesophageal junction to the anus, and a few are found in extraintestinal sites such as the bronchus and ovary. Their malignant potential depends both on size and on location. For example, fewer than 10% of the appendiceal or rectal carcinoids—but 30% of ileal and 60% of colonic carcinoids—are malignant. Carcinoids have been categorized as foregut (bronchus and stomach), midgut (small intestine and colon), or hindgut (rectum) tumors. Hindgut carcinoids synthesize no specific by-products, and they do not stain with silver salts (ie, they are argentaffin- and argyrophil-negative). Foregut carcinoids secrete 5-hydroxytryptophan and are argentaffin-negative and argyrophil-positive. Midgut tumors secrete 5-hydroxytryptamine (serotonin) and are both argentaffin- and argyrophil-positive.

Carcinoid syndrome is caused by the systemic release of substances from carcinoid tumors. The syndrome is also occasionally caused by other tumors, such as oat cell carcinoma and medullary carcinoma of the thyroid. Because the humoral substances liberated by carcinoids are metabolized by the liver, the presence of the syndrome implies either a primary lesion draining into the systemic circulation or hepatic metastasis from a gastrointestinal lesion. The distribution of primary tumors in the carcinoid syndrome is as follows: ileum (45%), bronchus (30%), ovary (10%), stomach (5%), and other sites rarely. Fortunately, only 1% of patients with a gastrointestinal carcinoid manifest the carcinoid syndrome.

Clinical Features

The most common symptoms of the carcinoid syndrome are flushing of the head and neck and diarrhea. The flushing attacks last a few minutes and may be accompanied by hypotension. The attacks may be provoked by emotional stress, ingestion of particular foods, and straining at stool. Diarrhea is often severe and may be debilitating. It appears that the diarrhea is due to serotonin, whereas the flushing is due to release of tachykinins from the tumor. About 35% of patients develop endocardial fibrosis of the tricuspid and pulmonary valves. Retroperitoneal fibrosis, arthritis, and bronchial asthma also occur but less frequently.

Diagnosis

The diagnosis of carcinoid syndrome is biochemically confirmed by the measurement of elevated levels of a metabolite of serotonin, 5-hydroxyindoleacetic acid (5-HIAA), in the urine. Measurements of serotonin, histamine, prostaglandin, and bradykinin levels in blood are less reliable. Staging of the tumor consists of a chest radiograph and CT scan of the abdomen. Radionucleide scanning using radiolabeled octreotide has promise, in early series, of high sensitivity in identifying occult primary and metastatic deposits. Small bowel contrast studies and arteriography help to localize primary gastrointestinal carcinoid tumors. In selected patients, echocardiography should be performed to assess valvular fibrosis.

Treatment

Where feasible, localized carcinoid tumors should be resected. In the most common situation, small tumors of the appendix may be treated with appendectomy alone. Tumors involving the cecum at the base of the appendix or those greater than 2 cm in size should be treated with right hemicolectomy to encompass regional lymph node drainage. Patients with carcinoid syndrome occasionally require operation for resection of ileal primary tumors causing obstruction. Selected patients benefit from hepatic resection for tumor debulking.

Palliation of the symptoms of carcinoid syndrome is best achieved with the long-acting analogue of somatostatin, octreotide. This is successful in about 80% of patients. Octreotide is useful also for management of life-threatening carcinoid crisis. Other agents, such as methysergide, cyproheptadine, and diphenoxylate with atropine (Lomotil), have been largely been replaced by octreotide for symptomatic management of these patients.

Cytotoxic chemotherapy should be considered for patients with rapidly progressive tumors, for those with urinary excretion of 5-HIAA greater than 150 mg/d, and for those with carcinoid-induced valvular heart disease. The most widely used regimen consists of streptozocin plus fluorouracil. Other agents with potential antitumor activity include doxorubicin and alpha-interferon. Hepatic artery chemoembolization has produced long-lasting palliation in a few patients.

Prognosis

The 5-year survival rate for patients with metastases is 20%. However, the cure rate for surgical resection of localized disease is good. If only regional nodes are involved, the 5-year survival rate is 65%; if the tumor is locally invasive without lymph node involvement, the 5-year survival rate is 95%. The 5-year survival rates associated with different tumor sites are 99% for appendix, 87% for lung, 50% for small intestine and colon, and 83% for rectum and rectosigmoid.

MISCELLANEOUS TUMORS

Other islet cell tumors have been reported that produce pancreatic polypeptide, somatostatin, neurotensin, vasopressin, a GH-releasing factor, ACTH, and MSH. Of these, the pancreatic polypeptide-secreting tumors (PPomas) have been the most common. Since PP produces few (if any) symptoms, the clinical manifestations in patients with PPomas have been chiefly due to direct effects of the tumor (eg, abdominal pain, weight loss). The tumor is malignant in 50% of cases. Treatment consists of tumor resection.

Somatostatinomas are rare tumors characterized by diabetes mellitus (usually mild), diarrhea and malabsorption, and dilation of the gallbladder (usually with cholelithiasis). High levels of calcitonin and IgM have been present in the serum in some patients. The syndrome results from secretion of somatostatin by an islet cell tumor of the pancreas, which in most cases is malignant and accompanied by hepatic metastases. The diagnosis may be made by recognizing the clinical syndrome and measuring increased concentrations of somatostatin in the serum. In most cases, however, the somatostatin syndrome has been unsuspected until histologic evidence of metastatic islet cell carcinoma has been obtained. Surgery is indicated if the disease is localized. More often, chemotherapy or chemoembolization is the only treatment possible.

REFERENCES

General

Debas HT, Mulvihill SJ: Neuroendocrine design of the gut. Am J Surg 1991;161:243.

Guillemin R. The language of polypeptides and the wisdom of the body. Physiologist 1985;28:391.

Le Douarin NM: On the origin of pancreatic endocrine cells. Cell 1988;53:169.

Miller LJ: A Historical perspective of gastrointestinal endocrinology: The new age of molecular receptorology. Gastroenterology 1992;102:2168.

Tache Y, Garrick TG, Raybould H: Central nervous system action of peptides to influence gastrointestinal motor function. Gastroenterology 1990;98:517.

Gastrin

Kopin AS et al: Expression cloning and characterization of the canine parietal cell gastrin receptor. Proc Natl Acad Sci USA 1992;89:3605.

Kovacs TOG et al: Gastrin is a major mediator of the gastric phase of acid secretion in dogs: Proof by monoclonal antibody neutralization. Gastroenterology 1989;97:1406.

Mulholland MW, Debas HT: Physiology and pathophysiology of gastrin: A review. Surgery 1988;103:135.

Sugano K, Aponte GW, Yamada T: Identification and characterization of glycine-extended posttranslational processing intermediates of progastrin in porcine stomach. J Biol Chem 1985;260:11724.

Waldum HL, Sandvik AK, Brenna E, Petersen H: Gastrin-histamine sequence in the regulation of gastric acid secretion. Gut 1991;32:698.

Wiborg O et al: Structure of a human gastrin gene. Proc Natl Acad Sci USA 1984;81:1067.

Cholecystokinin

Deschenes RJ et al: Cloning and sequence analysis of a cDNA encoding rat preprocholecystokinin. Proc Natl Acad Sci USA 1984;81:726.

Drewe J et al: Role of circulating cholecystokinin in control of fat-induced inhibition of food intake in humans. Gastroenterology 1992;102:1654.

Hokfelt T et al: Distribution patterns of CCK and CCK mRNA in some neuronal and non-neuronal tissues. Neuropeptides 1991;19(Suppl):31.

Liddle RA et al: Cholecystokinin cells purified by fluorescence-activating cell sorting respond to monitor peptide with an increase in intracellular calcium. Proc Natl Acad Sci USA 1992;89:5147.

Lu L, Louie D, Owyang C: A cholecystokinin releasing peptide mediates feedback regulation of pancreatic secretion. Am J Physiol 1989;256:G430.

Soudah HC et al: Cholecystokinin at physiological levels evokes pancreatic enzyme secretion via a cholinergic pathway. Am J Physiol 1992;263:G102.

Secretin

Gyr K et al: Plasma secretin and pancreatic response to various stimulants including a meal. Am J Physiol 1984;246:G535.

Hacki WH: Secretin. Clin Gastroenterol 1980;9:609.

Ishihara T et al: Molecular cloning and expression of a cDNA encoding the secretin receptor. EMBO J 1991;10:1635.

Kleibeuker J et al: Role of endogenous secretin on acid-induced inhibition of human gastrin function. J Clin Invest 1984;73:526.

Mutt V, Jorpes J, Magnusson S: Structure of porcine secretin: The amino acid sequence. Eur J Biochem 1970;15:513.

Somatostatin

Gittes GK, Rutter WJ: Onset of cell-specific gene expression in the developing mouse pancreas. Proc Natl Acad Sci USA 1992;89:1128.

Pinski J et al: Biological activity and receptor binding characteristics to various human tumors of acetylated somatostatin analogs. Proc Soc Exp Biol Med 1992;200:49.

Reichlin S: Somatostatin. (Two parts.) N Engl J Med 1983;309:1495, 1556.

Shen LP, Rutter WJ: Sequence of the human somatostatin I gene. Science 1984;224:168.

Toro MJ et al: Mechanism of action of somatostatin. Horm Res 1988;29:59.

Yamada Y et al: Cloning and functional characterization of a family of human and mouse somatostatin receptors expressed in brain, gastrointestinal tract, and kidney. Proc Natl Acad Sci USA 1992;89:251.

Bombesin & Gastrin-Releasing Peptide

Dimaline R et al: Functional control of gastrin releasing peptide (GRP) mRNA in rat stomach. FEBS Lett 1992;301:291.

Hajri A et al: Gastrin-releasing peptide: in vivo and in vitro growth effects on an acinar pancreatic carcinoma. Cancer Res 1992;52:3726.

Hildebrand P et al: Human gastrin-releasing peptide: Biologic potency in humans. Regul Pept 1991;36:423.

Nagalla SR et al: Gastrin-releasing peptide (GRP) is not mammalian bombesin: Identification and molecular cloning of a true amphibian GRP distinct from amphibian bombesin in Bombina orientalis. J Biol Chem 1992;267:6916.

Schubert ML et al: Regulation of acid secretion by bombesin/GRP neurons of the gastric fundus. Am J Physiol 1991;260:G156.

Spindel ER et al: Cloning and characterization of cDNAs encoding human gastrin-releasing peptide. Proc Natl Acad Sci USA 1984;81:5699.

Spindel ER et al: Cloning and functional characterization of a complementary DNA encoding the murine fibroblast bombesin/gastrin-releasing peptide receptor. Mol Endocrinol 1990;4:1956.

Terashima H, Debas HT, Bunnett NW: Effects of cholecystokinin and gastrin antagonists on pancreatic exocrine secretion stimulated by gastrin-releasing peptide. Pancreas 1992;7:212.

Calcitonin Gene-Related Peptide

DeGiorgio R et al: Tissue distribution and innervation pattern of peptide immunoreactivities in the rat pancreas. Peptides 1992;13:91.

Helton WS et al: Inhibition of gastric and pancreatic secretion in dogs by CGRP: Role of somatostatin. Am J Physiol 1989;256:G715.

Morris HR et al: Isolation and characterization of human calcitonin gene-related peptide. Nature 1984;308:746.

Gastric Inhibitory Polypeptide

Brown JC: Gastric inhibitory polypeptide. Monogr Endocrinol 1982;24:1.

Cataland S: Physiology of GIP in man. In: Gut Hormones, 2nd ed. Bloom SR (editor). Churchill Livingstone, 1981.

Lacroix A et al: Gastric inhibitory polypeptide-dependent cortisol hypersecretion: A new cause of Cushing's syndrome. New Engl J Med 1992;327:974.

Sarson D, Hayter R, Blood S: The pharmacokinetics of porcine glucose-dependent insulinotropic polypeptide (GIP) in man. Eur J Clin Invest 1982;12:457.

Vasoactive Intestinal Polypeptide

Biancani P, Walsh J, Behar J: Vasoactive intestinal polypeptide: A neurotransmitter for esophageal sphincter relaxation. J Clin Invest 1984;73:963.

Fahrenkrug J: Vasoactive intestinal polypeptide: Functional aspects. Br Med Bull 1982;38:265.

Itoh N et al: Human preprovasoactive intestinal polypeptide contains a novel PHI-27-like peptide, PHM-27. Nature 1983;304:547.

Krejs G et al: Effect of VIP infusion in water and ion

transport in the human jejunum. Gastroenterology 1980;78:722.

Said SI: Vasoactive intestinal polypeptide (VIP): Current status. Peptides 1984;5:145.

Sreedharan SP, Robichon A, Peterson KE, Goetzl EJ: Cloning and expression of the human vasoactive intestinal peptide receptor. Proc Natl Acad Sci USA 1991;88:4986.

Galanin

Kaplan LM et al: Tissue-specific expression of the rat galanin gene. Proc Natl Acad Sci USA 1988;85:1065.

Rattan S: Role of galanin in the gut. Gastroenterology 1991;100:1762.

Substance P

Nawa H et al: Nucleotide sequences of cloned cDNAs for two types of bovine brain substance P precursor. Nature 1983;306:32.

Rothstein RD, Johnson E, Ouyang A: Distribution and density of substance P receptors in the feline gastrointestinal tract using autoradiography. Gastroenterology 1991;100:1576.

Reynolds J, Ouyang A, Cohen S: A lower esophageal sphincter reflex involving substance P. Am J Physiol 1984;246:G346.

Swain MG et al: Increased levels of substance P in the myenteric plexus of *Trichinella*-infected rats. Gastroenterology 1992;102:1913.

Enkephalins

Ambinder RF, Schuster MM: Endorphins: New gut peptides with a familiar face. Gastroenterology 1979;77: 1132.

Nakanishi S et al: Nucleotide sequence of cloned cDNA for bovine corticotropin-—lipotropin precursor. Nature 1979;278:423.

Polak J et al: Enkephalin-like immunoreactivity in the human gastrointestinal tract. Lancet 1972;1:972.

Neurotensin

Evers BM et al: Neurotensin stimulates growth of colonic mucosa in young and aged rats. Gastroenterology 1992;103:86-91.

Miller RJ: Neurotensin as a gastrointestinal hormone. Med Biol 1981;59:65.

Xing L et al: Mesolimbic dopamine mediates gastric mucosal protection by central neurotensin. Am J Physiol 1991;260:G34.

Motilin

Fox JE: Motilin: An update. Life Sci 1984;35:695.

Kondo Y et al: Erythromycin and its derivatives with motilin-like biological activities inhibit the specific binding of ^{125}I-motilin to duodenal muscle. Biochem Biophys Res Commun 1988;150:877.

Peeters TG et al: Erythromycin is a motilin receptor agonist. Am J Physiol 1989;257:G470.

Poitros P et al: Motilin-independent ectopic fronts of the interdigestive myoelectric complex in dogs. Am J Physiol 1980;239:215.

Pancreatic Polypeptide Family

Adrian TE et al: Human distribution and release of a putative new gut hormone, peptide YY. Gastroenterology 1985;89:1070.

Takeuchi T, Yamada T: Isolation of a cDNA clone encoding pancreatic polypeptide. Proc Natl Acad Sci USA 1985;82:1536.

Tatemoto K: Isolation and characterization of peptide YY (PYY), a candidate gut hormone that inhibits pancreatic exocrine secretion. Proc Natl Acad Sci USA 1982;79:2514.

Wiley JW, Lu Y, Owyang C: Mechanism of action of peptide YY to inhibit gastric motility. Gastroenterology 1991;100:865.

Enteroglucagon

Holst JJ: Gut glucagon, enteroglucagon, gut glucagonlike immunoreactivity, glicentin: Current status. Gastroenterology 1983;84:1602.

Lund PK et al: Pancreatic preproglucagon cDNA contains two glucagon-related coding sequences arranged in tandem. Proc Natl Acad Sci USA 1982;79:345.

Hormonal Abnormalities in Diseases of the Gastrointestinal Tract

Debas HT: Clinical significance of gastrointestinal hormones. Adv Surg 1987;21:157.

Eysselein VE: Regulation of gastric acid secretion by gastrin in duodenal ulcer patients and healthy subjects. Gastroenterology 1992;102:1142.

Geracioti TD Jr, Liddle RA: Impaired cholecystokinin secretion in bulimia nervosa. New Engl J Med 1988;319:683.

Mayer EA, Raybould HE: Role of visceral afferent mechanisms in functional bowel disorders. Gastroenterology 1990;99:1688.

Mulvihill S et al: The use of somatostatin and its analogs in the treatment of surgical disorders. Surgery 1986; 100:467.

Multiple Endocrine Neoplasia Syndromes

Larsson C et al: Predictive testing for multiple endocrine neoplasia type I using DNA polymorphisms. J Clin Invest 1992;89:1344.

Shepherd JJ: The natural history of multiple endocrine neoplasia type I: Highly uncommon or highly unrecognized? Arch Surg 1991;126: 935.

Zollinger-Ellison Syndrome

Andersen DK: Current diagnosis and management of Zollinger-Ellison syndrome. Ann Surg 1989;210:685.

Jaffe BM: Current issues in the management of Zollinger-Ellison syndrome. Surgery 1992;111:241.

Maton PN et al: Medical management of patients with Zollinger-Ellison syndrome who have had previous gastric surgery: A prospective study. Gastroenterology 1988;94:294.

Norton JA et al: Curative resection in Zollinger-Ellison syndrome: Results of a 10-year prospective study. Ann Surg 1992;215:8.

VIPoma

Kane M, O'Dorisio T, Krejs G: Production of secretory diarrhea by intravenous infusion of vasoactive intestinal polypeptide. N Engl J Med 1983;309:1482.

Krejs GJ: VIPoma syndrome. Am J Med 1987;82(Suppl 5B):37.

Mekhjian HS, O'Dorisio TM: VIPoma syndrome. Semin Oncol 1987;14:282.

Rood RP et al: Pancreatic cholera syndrome due to a vasoactive intestinal polypeptide-producing tumor: Further insights into the pathophysiology. Gastroenterology 1988;94:813.

Yamaguchi K et al: The WDHA syndrome: Clinical and laboratory data on 28 Japanese cases. Peptides 1984; 5:415.

Glucagonoma

Bloom SR, Polak JM: Glucagonoma syndrome. Am J Med 1987;82(Suppl 5B):25.

Edney JA, Hofmann S, Thompson JS, Kessinger A: Glucagonoma syndrome is an underdiagnosed clinical entity. Am J Surg 1990;160:625.

Leichter SB: Clinical and metabolic aspects of glucagonoma. Medicine 1980;59:100.

Stacpoole PW: The glucagonoma syndrome: Clinical features, diagnosis, and treatment. Endocr Rev 1981; 76:125.

Carcinoid Tumors & Carcinoid Syndrome

Codd JE, Drozda J, Merjavy J: Palliation of carcinoid heart disease. Arch Surg 1987;122:1076.

Hodgson HJ: Controlling the carcinoid syndrome. Br Med J 1988;297:1213.

Kvols LK et al: Treatment of the malignant carcinoid syndrome: Evaluation of a long-acting somatostatin analogue. N Engl J Med 1986;315:663.

Lamberts SWJ et al: Somatostatin-receptor imaging in the localization of endocrine tumors. N Engl J Med 1990;323:1246.

Maton PN: The carcinoid syndrome. JAMA 1988;260: 1602.

Moertel CG et al: Streptozocin-doxorubicin, streptozocin-fluorouracil, or chlorozotocin in the treatment of advanced islet-cell carcinoma. N Engl J Med 1992;326:519.

Norheim I et al: Malignant carcinoid tumors: An analysis of 103 patients with regard to tumor localization, hormone production, and survival. Ann Surg 1986;206: 115.

Miscellaneous Tumors

Krejs GJ et al: Somatostatinoma syndrome: Biochemical, morphologic and clinical features. N Engl J Med 1979;301:285.

Sawady J, Katzin WE, Mendelsohn G, Aron DC: Somatostatin-producing neuroendocrine tumor of the ampulla (ampullary somatostatinoma): evidence of prosomatostatin production. Am J Clin Pathol 1992; 97:411.

Strodel WE et al: Pancreatic polypeptide-producing tumors: Silent lesions of the pancreas? Arch Surg 1984;119:508.

Vinik AI et al: Somatostatinomas, PPomas, neurotensinomas. Semin Oncol 1987;14:263.

Pancreatic Hormones & Diabetes Mellitus

15

John H. Karam, MD, & Peter H. Forsham, MD

I. THE ENDOCRINE PANCREAS

The pancreas is made up of two functionally different organs: the **exocrine pancreas,** the major digestive gland of the body; and the **endocrine pancreas,** the source of insulin, glucagon, somatostatin, and pancreatic polypeptide. Whereas the major role of the products of the exocrine pancreas (the digestive enzymes) is the processing of ingested foodstuffs so that they become available for absorption, the hormones of the endocrine pancreas modulate every other aspect of cellular nutrition from rate of adsorption of foodstuffs to cellular storage or metabolism of nutrients. Dysfunction of the endocrine pancreas or abnormal responses to its hormones by target tissues result in serious disturbances in nutrient homeostasis, including the important clinical syndromes grouped under the name of **diabetes mellitus.**

ANATOMY & HISTOLOGY

The endocrine pancreas consists of 0.7–1 million small endocrine glands—the islets of Langerhans—scattered within the glandular substance of the exocrine pancreas. The islet volume comprises 1–1.5% of the total mass of the pancreas and weighs about 1–2 g in adult humans.

At least four cell types—A, B, D, and F—have been identified in the islets (Table 15–1). These cell types are not distributed uniformly throughout the pancreas. The F cell, which secretes pancreatic polypeptide (PP), has been found primarily in islets in the posterior portion (posterior lobe) of the head, a discrete lobe of the pancreas separated from the anterior portion by a fascial partition. This lobe originates in the primordial ventral bud as opposed to the dorsal bud. The posterior lobe receives its blood supply from the superior mesenteric artery; the remainder of the pancreas derives most of its blood flow from the celiac artery.

Islets in the posterior lobe area consist of 80–85% F cells, 15–20% B cells, and less than 0.5% gluca-

ACRONYMS USED IN THIS CHAPTER

ADA	American Diabetes Association
ADH	Antidiuretic hormone (vasopressin)
ATP	Adenosine triphosphate
cAMP	Cyclic adenosine monophosphate
CBMW	Capillary basement membrane width
CCK	Cholecystokinin
DCCT	Diabetes control and complications trial
DNA	Deoxyribonucleic acid
FDA	Food and Drug Administration
GH	Growth hormone
GI	Glycemic index
GIP	Gastric inhibitory polypeptide
GLP-1	Glucagon-like peptide 1
GLP-2	Glucagon-like peptide 2
HDL	High-density lipoprotein(s)
HLA	Human leukocyte antigen
IDDM	Insulin-dependent diabetes mellitus
MODY	Maturity-onset diabetes of the young
NIDDM	Non-insulin-dependent diabetes mellitus
NPH	Neutral protamine Hagedorn
PP	Pancreatic polypeptide
RNA	Ribonucleic acid
UGDP	University Group Diabetes Program
VLDL	Very low density lipoprotein(s)

gon-producing A cells. The pancreatic polypeptide cell volume varies with age and sex—the volume tends to be larger in men and in older persons. In contrast to the posterior lobe, the PP-poor islets located in the tail, body, and *anterior* portion of the head of the pancreas, arising from the embryonic dorsal bud, contain predominantly insulin-secreting B cells (70–80% of the islet cells), with approximately 20% of the cells being glucagon-secreting A cells and about 3–5% D cells that produce somatostatin. A typical islet from this part of the pancreas is depicted in Figure 15–1.

Islet Vascularization

The islets are richly vascularized, receiving five to ten times the blood flow of a comparable portion of exocrine pancreatic tissues. The direction of the blood flow within the islet has been postulated to play a role in carrying insulin secreted from the central region of an islet to its peripheral zone where the insulin modulates and decreases glucagon release

Table 15–1. Cell types in pancreatic islets of Langerhans.

Cell types	Approximate Percentage of Islet Volume		Secretory Products
	Dorsally Derived (Anterior Head, Body, Tail)	**Ventrally Derived (Posterior Portion of Head)**	
A cell (α)	10%	<0.5%	Glucagon, proglucagon, glucagon-like peptides (GLP-1 and GLP-2)
B cell (β)	70–80%	15–20%	Insulin, C peptides, proinsulin, amylin, γ-aminobutyric acid (GABA)
D cell (δ)	3–5%	<1%	Somatostatin
F cell (PP cell)	<2%	80–85%	Pancreatic polypeptide

from A cells which are mainly located in the periphery of islets.

HORMONES OF THE ENDOCRINE PANCREAS

1. INSULIN

Biosynthesis

The human insulin gene is located on the short arm of chromosome 11. A precursor molecule, **preproinsulin,** a long-chain peptide of MW 11,500, is produced by DNA/RNA-directed synthesis in the rough endoplasmic reticulum of pancreatic B cells (Figure 15–2). It is cleaved by microsomal enzymes to **proinsulin** (MW about 9000) almost immediately after synthesis. Proinsulin (Figure 15–3) is transported to the Golgi apparatus, where packaging into clathrin-coated secretory granules takes place. Maturation of the secretory granule is associated with loss of the clathrin coating and conversion of proinsulin into **insulin** and a smaller connecting peptide, or **C peptide,** by proteolytic cleavage at two sites along the peptide chain. Normal mature (uncoated) secretory granules contain insulin and C peptide in equimolar amounts and only small quantities of proinsulin, a small portion of which consists of partially cleaved intermediates.

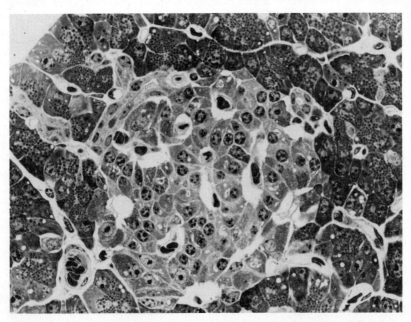

Figure 15–1. Photomicrograph of a section of the pancreas. In the islet of Langerhans, A cells appear mainly in the periphery as large cells with dark cytoplasm. Some D cells are also present in the periphery, while the central core is composed chiefly of B cells. (Reproduced, with permission, from Junqueira LC, Carneiro J, Long JA: *Basic Histology,* 7th ed. Appleton & Lange, 1992.)

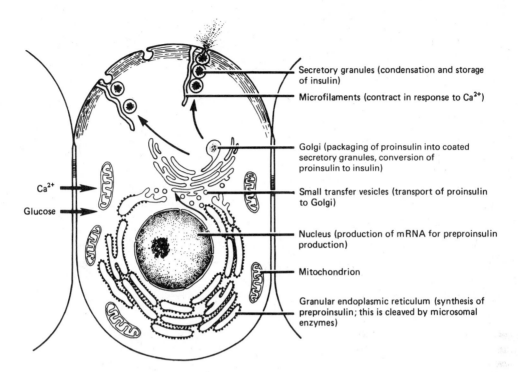

Figure 15–2. Structural components of the pancreatic B cell involved in glucose-induced biosynthesis and release. Schematic representation of secretory granular alignment on microfilament "tracks" that contract in response to calcium. (Based on data presented by Orci L: A portrait of the pancreatic B cell. Diabetologia 1974;10:163.) (Modified and reproduced, with permission, from Junqueira LC, Carneiro J, Long JA: *Basic Histology,* 5th ed. Lange, 1986)

Biochemistry

Proinsulin (Figure 15–3) consists of a single chain of 86 amino acids, which includes the A and B chains of the insulin molecule plus a connecting segment of 35 amino acids. Converting enzymes (probably trypsin-like and carboxypeptidase-B-like proteases) cleave off two pairs of dibasic amino acids (three arginines and one lysine) from the proinsulin molecule as shown in Figure 15–3. The result is a 51-amino-acid insulin molecule and a 31-amino-acid residue, the C peptide.

A small amount of proinsulin produced by the pancreas escapes cleavage and is secreted intact into the bloodstream, along with insulin and C peptide. Most anti-insulin sera used in the standard immunoassay for insulin cross-react with proinsulin; about 3–5% of immunoreactive insulin extracted from human pancreas is actually proinsulin. Because proinsulin is not removed by the liver, it has a half-life three to four times that of insulin. This allows proinsulin to accumulate in the blood, where it accounts for 12–20% of the circulating immunoreactive "insulin" in the basal state in humans. Human proinsulin has about 7–8% of the biologic activity of insulin. The kidney is the principal site of proinsulin degradation.

Of the two major split proinsulin products, the one split at arginine 32–33 is the major proinsulin-like molecule present in plasma, far exceeding the barely detectable 65–66 split product. In control subjects, concentrations of proinsulin and 32–33 split proinsulin after an overnight fast averaged 2.3 and 2.2 pmol/L, respectively, with corresponding postprandial rises to 10 and 20 pmol/L.

C peptide, the 31-amino-acid residue (MW 3000) formed during cleavage of insulin from proinsulin, has no known biologic activity. It is released from the B cells in equimolar amounts with insulin. It is not removed by the liver but is degraded or excreted chiefly by the kidney. It has a half-life three to four times that of insulin. In the basal state after an overnight fast, the average concentration of C peptide may be as high as 1000 pmol/L.

Insulin is a protein consisting of 51 amino acids contained within two peptide chains: an A chain, with 21 amino acids; and a B chain, with 30 amino acids. The chains are connected by two disulfide bridges as shown in Figure 15–3. In addition, there is an intrachain disulfide bridge that links positions 6 and 11 in the A chain. The molecular weight of human insulin is 5808.

Human insulin differs only slightly in amino acid composition from the two mammalian insulins, which are also used at present for therapeutic insulin

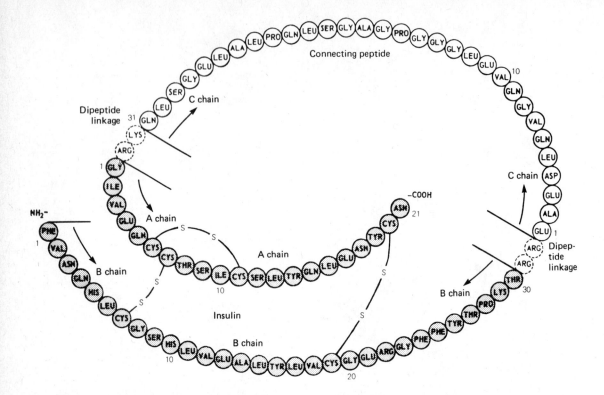

Figure 15–3. Structure of human proinsulin C peptides and insulin molecules connected at two sites by dipeptide links.

replacement. Pork insulin differs from human by only one amino acid—alanine instead of threonine at the carboxyl terminus of the B chain (position B 30). Beef insulin differs by three amino acids—alanine instead of threonine at A 8 as well as the B 30 position and valine instead of isoleucine at A 10.

Endogenous insulin has a circulatory half-life of 3–5 minutes. It is catabolized chiefly by insulinases in liver, kidney, and placenta. Approximately 50% of insulin is removed in a single pass through the liver.

Secretion

The human pancreas secretes about 40–50 units of insulin per day in normal adults. The basal concentration of insulin in the blood of fasting humans averages 10 μU/mL (0.4 ng/mL, or 69 pmol/L). In normal control subjects, insulin seldom rises above 100 μU/mL (690 pmol/L) after standard meals. There is an increase in peripheral insulin concentration beginning 8–10 minutes after ingestion of food and reaching peak concentration in peripheral blood by 30–45 minutes. This is followed by a rapid decline in postprandial plasma glucose concentration, which returns to baseline values by 90–120 minutes (Figure 15–4).

Basal insulin secretion, which occurs in the absence of exogenous stimuli, is the quantity of insulin secreted in the fasting state. Although it is known that plasma glucose levels below 80–100 mg/dL

(4.4–5.6 mmol/L) do not stimulate insulin release, it has also been demonstrated that the presence of glucose is necessary (in in vitro systems) for most other known regulators of insulin secretion to be effective.

Stimulated insulin secretion is that which occurs in response to exogenous stimuli. In vivo, this is the response of the B cell to ingested meals. Glucose is

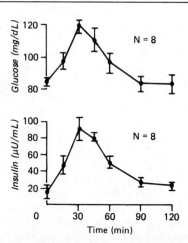

Figure 15–4. Plasma glucose and insulin response to a standard 530-kcal breakfast in normal subjects.

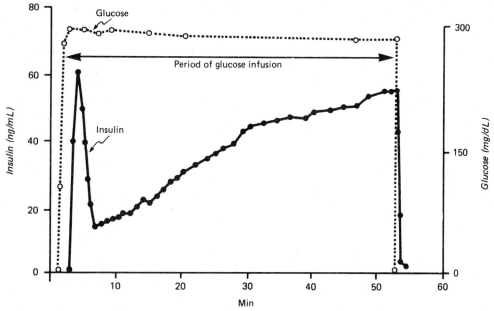

Figure 15–5. Multiphasic response of the in vitro perfused pancreas during constant stimulation with glucose. (Modified from Grodsky GM et al: Further studies on the dynamic aspects of insulin release in vitro with evidence for a two-compartmental storage system. Acta Diabetol Lat 1969;6[Suppl 1]:554.)

the most potent stimulant of insulin release. The perfused rat pancreas has demonstrated a biphasic release of insulin in response to glucose (Figure 15–5). When the glucose concentration in the system is increased suddenly, an initial short-lived burst of insulin release occurs (the **early phase**); if the glucose concentration is held at this level, the insulin release gradually falls off and then begins to rise again to a steady level (the **late phase**). However, sustained levels of high glucose stimulation (≥ 4 hours in vitro or > 24 hours in vivo) results in a reversible desensitization of the B cell response to glucose but not to other stimuli.

Currently, the mechanism of action of glucose-stimulated insulin release is not well understood. Glucose is known to enter the pancreatic B cell by passive diffusion, which is facilitated by a specific membrane protein term glucose transporter-2. By virtue of its relatively low affinity for glucose, this protein more effectively facilitates transport of glucose during the hyperglycemia after meals than at the lower levels of blood glucose during an overnight fast. There is a body of data suggesting that *metabolism* of glucose is essential in stimulating insulin release. Indeed, agents such as 2-deoxyglucose that inhibit the metabolism of glucose interfere with release of insulin.

Insulin release has been shown to require calcium. It has been proposed that mature insulin-containing granules in the B cell attach linearly to microtubules that contract after exposure to high intracellular calcium, thereby ejecting the granules (Figure 15–2).

The following effects of glucose on calcium ion movement have been demonstrated: (1) Calcium uptake is increased by glucose stimulation of the B cell. (2) Calcium efflux from the cell is retarded by some action of glucose. (3) Mobilization of calcium from mitochondrial compartments occurs secondary to cAMP induction by glucose.

cAMP is another important modulator of insulin release. As mentioned above, glucose has been shown to directly induce cAMP formation. Furthermore, many nonglucose stimuli to insulin release are known to increase intracellular cAMP. Elevations of cAMP, however, will not stimulate insulin release in the absence of glucose.

Other factors involved in the regulation of insulin secretion are summarized in Table 15–2. These factors can be divided into three categories: **direct stimulants,** which are known to stimulate insulin release directly; **amplifiers,** which appear to potentiate the response of the B cell to glucose; and **inhibitors.** The action of the amplifier substances, many of which are gastrointestinal hormones stimulated by ingestion of meals, explains the observation that insulin response to an ingested meal is greater than the response of intravenously administered substrates.

Insulin Receptors & Insulin Action

Insulin action begins with binding of insulin to a receptor on the surface of the target cell membrane. Many cells of the body appear to have specific cell surface insulin receptors. In fat, liver, and muscle cells, binding of insulin to these receptors is associ-

Table 15–2. Regulation of insulin release in humans.

Stimulants of insulin release
  Glucose, mannose
  Leucine
  Vagal stimulation
  Sulfonylureas
Amplifiers of glucose-induced insulin release
  1. Enteric hormones:
     Glucagon-like peptide I (7–37)
     Gastrin inhibitory peptide
     Cholecystokinin
     Secretin, gastrin
  2. Neural amplifiers: beta-adrenergic stimulation
  3. Amino acids: arginine
Inhibitors of insulin release
  Neural: alpha-adrenergic effect of catecholamines
  Humoral: somatostatin
  Drugs: diazoxide, phenytoin, vinblastine, colchicine

ated with the biologic response of these tissues to the hormone. These receptors bind insulin rapidly, with high specificity and with an affinity high enough to bind picomolar amounts.

It has recently been demonstrated that insulin receptors are membrane glycoproteins composed of two subunits, a larger alpha subunit (MW 130,000), which extends extracellularly and is involved in binding the insulin molecule, and a smaller beta subunit (MW 90,000), which is predominantly cytoplasmic and contains a kinase that becomes activated during insulin binding and results in autophosphorylation of the beta subunit itself. After insulin is bound to its receptor, a number of insulin-receptor complexes are internalized. However, it remains controversial whether these internalized complexes contribute to further action of insulin or whether they limit continued insulin action by exposing insulin to intracellular scavenger lysosomes.

Two models for insulin action have been proposed. One involves a cascade of phosphorylations emanating from the activated kinase region that induces an intracellular compartment of proteins, including the glucose transporter-4 (see below), transferrin, the low-density lipoprotein receptor, and the insulin-like growth factor II (IGF-II) receptor, to move to the cell surface. When these proteins, which are sequestered intracellularly during the postabsorptive period, move to the cell surface during feeding they facilitate transport of nutrients into insulin target tissues and can promote growth by giving circulating IGF-II access to a cell surface receptor. Within this model, genetic defects distal to the insulin receptor could result in "postreceptor" insulin resistance. Possible defects include abnormalities in the enzymes responsible for phosphorylation of the glucose transporter protein, mutation of the glucose transporter itself, or abnormalities in its processing. Moreover, abnormalities in phosphatase enzymes might account for a delay in the normal restoration of the insulin receptor to its surface membrane locus, resulting in resistance to the further action of insulin. A second model invokes the hydrolysis of a membrane glycolipid by insulin-stimulated phospholipase C activity. Potential "second messengers" such as inositol monophosphate, glucosamine, or diacylglycerol may mediate the intracellular response to insulin, with diacylglycerol promoting intracellular phosphorylations by activating protein kinase C (see Chapter 1).

Abnormalities of insulin receptors—in concentration, affinity, or both—will affect insulin action. **"Down-regulation"** is a phenomenon in which the number of insulin receptors is decreased in response to chronically elevated circulating insulin levels, probably by increased intracellular degradation. When insulin levels are low, on the other hand, receptor binding is up-regulated. Conditions associated with high insulin levels and lowered insulin binding to the receptor include obesity, high intake of carbohydrates, and (perhaps) chronic exogenous overinsulinization. Conditions associated with low insulin levels and increased insulin binding include exercise and fasting. The presence of excess amounts of cortisol decreases insulin binding to the receptor, although it is not clear if this is a direct effect of the hormone itself or one that is mediated through accompanying increases in the insulin level.

Metabolic Effects of Insulin

The major function of insulin is to promote **storage of ingested nutrients.** Although insulin directly or indirectly affects the function of almost every tissue in the body, the discussion here will be limited to a brief overview of the effects of insulin on the three major tissues specialized for energy storage: liver, muscle, and adipose tissue. In addition, the **paracrine effects** of insulin will be discussed briefly. The section on hormonal control of nutrient metabolism (see below) presents a detailed discussion of the effects of insulin and glucagon on the regulation of intermediary metabolism.

A. Paracrine Effects: The effects of the products of endocrine cells on surrounding cells are termed "paracrine" effects, in contrast to actions that take place at sites distant from the secreting cells, which are termed "endocrine" effects. Paracrine effects of the B and D cells on the close-lying A cells (Figure 15–1) are of considerable importance in the endocrine pancreas. The first target cells reached by insulin are the pancreatic A cells at the periphery of the pancreatic islets. In the presence of insulin, A cell secretion of glucagon is reduced. In addition, somatostatin, which is released from D cells in response to most of the same stimuli that provoke insulin release, also acts to inhibit glucagon secretion.

Because glucose stimulates only B and D cells (whose products then inhibit A cells) whereas amino acids stimulate glucagon as well as insulin, the type and amounts of islet hormones released during a meal depend on the ratio of ingested carbohydrate to protein. The higher the carbohydrate content of a meal, the less glucagon will be released by any amino acids absorbed. In contrast, a predominantly protein meal will result in relatively greater glucagon secretion, because amino acids are less effective at stimulating insulin release in the absence of concurrent hyperglycemia but are potent stimulators of A cells.

B. Endocrine Effects: (Table 15–3.)

1. Liver– The first major organ reached by insulin via the bloodstream is the liver. Insulin exerts its action on the liver in two major ways:

a. Insulin promotes anabolism– Insulin promotes glycogen synthesis and storage at the same time it inhibits glycogen breakdown. These effects are mediated by changes in the activity of enzymes in the glycogen synthesis pathway (see below). The liver has a maximum storage capacity of 100–110 g of glycogen, or approximately 440 kcal of energy.

Insulin increases both protein and triglyceride synthesis and VLDL formation by the liver. It also inhibits gluconeogenesis and promotes glycolysis through its effects on enzymes of the glycolytic pathway.

b. Insulin inhibits catabolism– Insulin acts to reverse the catabolic events of the postabsorptive state by inhibiting hepatic glycogenolysis, ketogenesis, and gluconeogenesis.

2. Muscle– Insulin promotes protein synthesis in muscle by increasing amino acid transport as well as by stimulating ribosomal protein synthesis. In addition, insulin promotes glycogen synthesis to replace glycogen stores expended by muscle activity. This is accomplished by increasing glucose transport into the muscle cell, enhancing the activity of glycogen synthetase, and inhibiting the activity of glycogen phosphorylase. Approximately 500–600 g of glycogen are stored in the muscle tissue of a 70-kg man, but because of the lack of glucose 6-phosphatase in this tissue, it cannot be used as a source of blood glucose. except by indirectly supplying the liver with lactate for conversion to glucose.

3. Adipose tissue– Fat, in the form of triglyceride, is the most efficient means of storing energy. It provides 9 kcal per gram of stored substrate, as opposed to the 4 kcal/g generally provided by protein or carbohydrate. In the typical 70-kg man, the energy content of adipose tissue is about 100,000 kcal.

Insulin acts to promote triglyceride storage in adipocytes by a number of mechanisms: (1) It induces the production of lipoprotein lipase (this is the lipase that is bound to endothelial cells in adipose tissue and other vascular beds), which leads to hydrolysis of triglycerides from circulating lipoproteins; (2) By increasing glucose transport into fat cells, insulin increases the availability of α-glycerol phosphate, a substance used in the esterification of free fatty acids into triglycerides; (3) Insulin inhibits intracellular lipolysis of stored triglyceride by inhibiting intracellular lipase (also called "hormone-sensitive lipase").

Glucose Transporter Proteins

Glucose oxidation is a major source of energy for many cells of the body and is especially essential for brain function. Since cell membranes are impermeable to hydrophilic molecules such as glucose, all cells require carrier proteins to transport glucose across the lipid bilayers into the cytosol. While the intestine and kidney have an energy dependent Na^+-glucose cotransporter, all other cells have non-energy-dependent transporters that facilitate diffusion of glucose from a higher concentration to a lower concentration across cell membranes. At least five "facilitative glucose transporters" have been described, and these have different affinities for glucose. They have been termed GLUT 1, GLUT 2, GLUT 3, GLUT 4, and GLUT 5, with the numbers designating the order of their identification (Table 15–4).

GLUT 1 is present in all human tissues. It appears to mediate basal glucose uptake, since it has a very high affinity for glucose and therefore is able to transport glucose at relatively low concentrations as found in the basal state. For this reason, it is an important component of the brain vascular system (blood-brain barrier) to ensure adequate transport of plasma glucose into the central nervous system. GLUT 3, which is also found in all tissues, is the major glucose transporter on the neuronal surface. It also has a very high affinity for glucose and is responsible for transferring glucose from the cerebrospinal fluid into neuronal cells.

In contrast, GLUT 2 has a very low affinity for glucose and seems to act as a transporter only when plasma glucose levels are relatively high, such as

Table 15–3. Endocrine effects of insulin.

Effects on liver
  Anabolic effects:
    Promotes glycogenesis
    Increases synthesis of triglycerides, cholesterol, and VLDL.
    Increases protein synthesis
  Anticatabolic effects:
    Inhibits glycogenolysis.
    Inhibits ketogenesis.
    Inhibits gluconeogenesis.
Effects on muscle
  Promotes protein synthesis:
    Increases amino acid transport.
    Stimulates ribosomal protein synthesis.
  Promotes glycogen synthesis:
    Increases glucose transport.
    Enhances activity of glycogen synthetase.
    Inhibits activity of glycogen phosphorylase.
Effects on fat
  Promotes triglyceride storage:
    Induces lipoprotein lipase, making fatty acids available for absorption into fat cells.
    Increases glucose transport into fat cells, thus increasing availability of α-glycerol phosphate for triglyceride synthesis.
    Inhibits intracellular lipolysis.

Table 15–4. Human glucose transporters.

Name	Major Sites of Expression	Affinity for Glucose[1]	Chromosomal Location of Gene
1	Brain vasculature, red blood cells, all tissues	High (Km = 1 mmol/L)	1
2	Liver, pancreatic B cell; serosal surfaces of gut and kidney	Low (Km 15–20 mmol/L)	3
3	Brain neurons; also found in all tissues	High (Km < 1 mmol/L)	12
4	Muscle, fat cells	Medium (Km = 2.5–5 mM)	17
5	Jejunum, liver, spermatozoa	Medium (Km = 6 mmol/L)	1

[1] Km represents the level of blood glucose at which the transporter has reached one-half of its maximum capacity to transport glucose. It is inversely proportionate to the affinity.

postprandially. It is the major transporter of glucose in the pancreatic B cell and hepatic cells, so that diffusion of glucose into these cells is facilitated only when hyperglycemia exists. This prevents hepatic uptake of glucose or inappropriate insulin discharge during the basal state or during fasting.

GLUT 4 is found in two major insulin target tissues: skeletal muscle and adipose tissue. It appears to be sequestered mainly within an intracellular compartment of these cells and thus is not able to function as a glucose transporter until a signal from insulin results in translocation of GLUT 4 to the cell membrane, where it facilitates glucose entry into these storage tissues after a meal.

GLUT 5 is expressed on the brush border of human small intestine cells, and its biochemical properties suggest that it is mainly a fructose transporter. Since a large fraction of calories is derived from fructose, this relatively high-affinity transporter is responsible for its absorption as well as its uptake by liver cells and spermatozoa, where it is also highly expressed.

Islet Amyloid Polypeptide (IAPP), or Amylin

IAPP, or amylin, is a recently identified peptide made up of 37 amino acids which is stored with insulin in the pancreatic B cell, but only in a low ratio of one molecule of amylin to 100 of insulin. It is cosecreted with insulin in response to glucose and other B cell stimulators. Amylin's function has not been determined, but it appears to produce amyloid deposits in pancreatic islets of most patients with type II diabetes of long duration. These amyloid deposits are insoluble fibrillar proteins (containing mainly amylin as well as its precursor peptide) which encroach upon and may even occur within pancreatic B cells. There have been reports of amylin producing insulin resistance when administered to animals in

supraphysiologic doses, but evidence currently available does not support this activity in humans. Islets of nondiabetic elderly persons often contain some amyloid deposits indistinguishable from those in diabetics but to a much lesser extent. This observation—as well as the failure to detect mutations of amylin in type II diabetes—suggests that the extensive deposition of amyloid in islets of patients with type II diabetes is a consequence of their disordered islet function rather than a direct genetic effect that produces an abnormal amylin molecule.

2. GLUCAGON

Biochemistry

Pancreatic glucagon, whose gene is located on human chromosome 2, is a single-chain polypeptide consisting of 29 amino acids with a molecular weight of 3485 (Figure 15–6). It is synthesized in the A cells on the islets of Langerhans and derived from a large

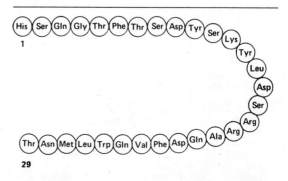

Figure 15–6. Amino acid sequence of glucagon polypeptide. (Reproduced, with permission, from Katzung BG [editor]: *Basic & Clinical Pharmacology*, 4th ed. Appleton & Lange, 1989.)

160-amino-acid precursor molecule that is five to six times larger than glucagon. Within this proglucagon molecule are several other peptides connected in tandem: glicentin-related peptide, glucagon, glucagon-like peptide 1 (GLP-1), and glucagon-like peptide 2 (GLP-2). The combination of glicentin-related peptide with glucagon consists of 69 amino acids and comprises the hormone glicentin, which is predominantly secreted from the intestine and not the pancreas. Both GLP-1 and GLP-2 increase after meals. An endogenous natural derivative of GLP-1, with the first six of its 37 amino acids absent (GLP-1 [7–37]), is an extremely potent stimulator of pancreatic B cells. It is several times more potent than glucagon itself as an insulinotropic secretagogue, whereas intact GLP-1 (1–37) and GLP-2 do not stimulate insulin secretion. In healthy humans, the average fasting plasma immunoreactive glucagon level is 75 pg/mL (25 pmol/L). Only 30–40% of this is actually pancreatic glucagon, the remainder being a heterogeneous composite of higher-molecular-weight molecules with glucagon immunoreactivity such as proglucagon, glicentin, GLP-1, and GLP-2. The circulation half-life of pancreatic glucagon is 3–6 minutes. Glucagon is mainly removed by the liver and kidney.

Secretion

Glucagon secretion is inhibited by glucose—in contrast to the effect of glucose on insulin secretion. There are conflicting data about whether the effect of glucose is a direct one on the A cell or whether it is mediated via release of insulin or somatostatin, both of which are known to inhibit the A cell directly (see above).

In addition, since γ-aminobutyric acid (GABA) is released by B cells and its receptors have recently been detected on A cells, GABA may participate in the inhibition of A cells during B cell stimulation.

Many amino acids stimulate glucagon release, although there are differences in their ability to do so. Some, such as arginine, release both glucagon and insulin; others (eg, alanine) stimulate primarily glucagon release. Leucine, a good stimulant for insulin release, does not stimulate glucagon. Other substances that promote glucagon release are catecholamines, the gastrointestinal hormones (cholecystokinin [CCK], gastrin, and gastric inhibitory polypeptide [GIP]), and glucocorticoids. Both sympathetic and parasympathetic (vagal) stimulation promote glucagon release; this is especially important in augmenting the response of the A cell to hypoglycemia. High levels of circulating fatty acid are associated with suppression of glucagon secretion.

Action of Glucagon

In contrast to insulin, which promotes energy storage in a variety of tissues, glucagon is a humoral mechanism for making energy available to the tissues between meals, when ingested food is not available for absorption. Glucagon stimulates the breakdown of stored glycogen, maintains hepatic output of glucose from amino acid precursors (gluconeogenesis), and promotes hepatic output of ketone bodies from fatty acid precursors (ketogenesis). The liver, because of its geographic proximity to the pancreas, represents the major target organ for glucagon, with portal vein glucagon concentrations reaching as high as 300–500 pg/mL (100–166 pmol/L). Binding of glucagon to its receptor on hepatocytes results in activation of adenylyl cyclase and generation of cAMP, which both promotes glycogenolysis and stimulates gluconeogenesis. Uptake of alanine by liver cells is facilitated by glucagon, and fatty acids are directed away from reesterification to triglycerides and toward ketogenic pathways (see below). It is unclear whether physiologic levels of glucagon affect tissues other than the liver.

The ratio of insulin to glucagon affects key target tissues by mediating phosphorylation or dephosphorylation (either or both) of key enzymes affecting nutrient metabolism. In addition, this ratio increases or decreases actual quantities of certain enzymes, thereby controlling the flux of these nutrients into or out of storage.

3. SOMATOSTATIN

The gene for somatostatin is on the long arm of chromosome 3. It codes for a 116-amino-acid peptide, preprosomatostatin, from whose carboxyl terminus is cleaved the hormone somatostatin, a 14-amino-acid cyclic polypeptide with a molecular weight of 1640 (Figure 15–7). It is present in D cells at the periphery of the human islet (Figure 15–1). It was first identified in the hypothalamus and owes its name to its ability to inhibit release of growth hormone (pituitary somatotropin). Since that time, somatostatin has been identified in a number of tissues, including many areas of the brain, the gastrointestinal tract, and the pancreas. In the central nervous system and the pancreas, somatostatin-14 predominates, but approximately 5–10% of the somatostatin-like immunoreactivity is due to a 28-amino-acid peptide, somatostatin-28 (prosomatostatin). This consists of an N-terminal region of 14 amino acids and a carboxyl terminal segment containing somatostatin-14. In small intestine, the larger molecule is more prevalent, with 70–75% of the hormone having 28 amino acids and only 25–30% being somatostatin-14. Unlike most prohormones, the larger peptide somatostatin-28 is ten times more potent than somatostatin-14 in inhibiting growth hormone and insulin.

Almost every known stimulator of release of insulin from pancreatic B cells also promotes somatostatin release from D cells. This includes glucose, arginine, gastrointestinal hormones, and tolbutamide. The importance of circulating somatostatin is un-

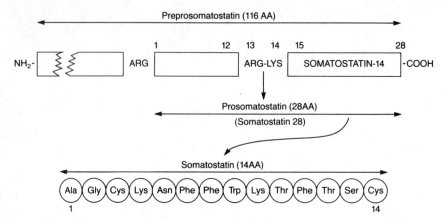

Figure 15–7. Amino acid sequence of somatostatin and its cleavage from dibasic amino acid residue in prosomatostatin and preprosomatostatin.

clear, since a major role of this peptide may be as a paracrine regulator of the pancreatic islet and the tissues of the gastrointestinal tract (see Chapter 14). Physiologic levels of somatostatin in humans seldom exceed 80 pg/mL (49 pmol/L). The metabolic clearance of exogenously infused somatostatin in humans is extremely rapid; the half-life of the hormone is less than 3 minutes.

Somatostatin acts in several ways to restrain the movement of nutrients from the intestinal tract into the circulation. It prolongs gastric emptying time, decreases gastric acid and gastrin production, diminishes pancreatic exocrine secretion, decreases splanchnic blood flow, and retards xylose absorption. Neutralization of circulating somatostatin with antisomatostatin serum is associated with enhanced nutrient absorption in dogs. This implies that at least some of the effects of somatostatin are truly endocrine, as opposed to the paracrine effects discussed earlier.

4. PANCREATIC POLYPEPTIDE

Pancreatic polypeptide (PP) is found in F cells located chiefly in islets in the posterior portion of the head of the pancreas. PP is a 36-amino-acid peptide with a molecular weight of 4200. Little is known about its biosynthesis. Circulating levels of the peptide increase in response to a mixed meal; however, intravenous infusion of glucose or triglyceride does not produce such a rise, and intravenous amino acids cause only a small increase. Vagotomy abolishes the response to an ingested meal.

In healthy subjects, basal levels of PP average 24 ± 4 pmol/L and may become elevated owing to a variety of factors including old age, alcohol abuse, diarrhea, chronic renal failure, hypoglycemia, or inflammatory disorders. Values above 300 pmol/L are found in most patients with pancreatic endocrine tumors such as glucagonoma or VIPoma and in all patients with tumors of the pancreatic F cell. As many as 20% of patients with insulinoma and one-third of those with gastrinomas also have pancreatic polypeptide plasma concentrations of greater than 300 pmol/L.

The physiologic action of PP is unknown. It is discussed further in Chapter 14.

II. DIABETES MELLITUS

Clinical diabetes mellitus is a syndrome of disordered metabolism with inappropriate hyperglycemia due either to an absolute deficiency of insulin secretion or a reduction in the biologic effectiveness of insulin (or both).

CLASSIFICATION

Traditionally, diabetes has been classified according to the patient's age at onset of symptoms (juvenile-onset versus adult-onset). In 1979, the NIH Diabetes Data Group recommended that diabetes mellitus be classified into one of two major types according to dependence on exogenous insulin. Most patients with diabetes fall into one of two major categories: **insulin-dependent** (type I) or **non-insulin-dependent** (type II) diabetes mellitus (Table 15–5).

Table 15–5. Clinical classification of diabetes mellitus.[1]

Terminology and Estimated Prevalence	Ketosis	Islet Cell Antibodies	HLA Association	Treatment
INSULIN-DEPENDENT DIABETES (IDDM; type I) (10–20% of all diabetics)	Marked	Usually present at onset	Yes	1. Insulin 2. Diet
NON-INSULIN-DEPENDENT DIABETES (NIDDM; type II) (80–90% of all diabetics) Nonobese (15% of NIDDM patients)	Absent	Absent	No	1. Eucaloric diet alone or, 2. Diet plus sulfonylurea or insulin
Obese (85% of NIDDM patients)	Absent	Absent	No	1. Weight reduction 2. Hypocaloric diet plus sulfonylureas or insulin for symptomatic control only

SECONDARY DIABETES: Diabetes mellitus and impaired glucose tolerance secondary to or associated with other conditions, eg, pancreatic disease, drug toxicity, endocrine disorders, genetic disease, insulin receptor abnormalities with acanthosis nigricans.

Treatment varies according to the specific condition. In general, removal or correction of offending agent if possible, diet, and insulin are the foundations of treatment. See text for details.

[1] Gestational diabetes is discussed in Chapter 13.

The above "therapeutic" classification is far from satisfactory. The term "type II" implies a single type of disorder even though patients who are not dependent on insulin therapy to sustain life represent a variety of heterogeneous disorders, including all diabetic conditions that are not type I diabetes. Furthermore, many patients whose diabetes is not "insulin-dependent" may be managed with insulin therapy by their physicians yet are still identified as being "non-insulin-dependent." Likewise, occasional young adults with a classic onset of diabetic ketoacidosis associated with islet cell antibodies may enter remissions during which insulin therapy is discontinued, rendering them "non-insulin-dependent" despite an evident pathogenetic mechanism characteristic of patients with IDDM. These inadequacies of the current "therapeutic" classifications have led to semantic confusion about whether type II patients can become type I patients and vice versa.

With the establishment of an autoimmune pathogenesis for clinical type I diabetes and immunoassays to detect islet cell antibodies, the classification of diabetes should be based on etiologic rather than therapeutic criteria.

One possibility would be "immune-dependent diabetes mellitus" as one type, with all the other types being termed "non-immune-dependent diabetes mellitus," so that we can retain the acronyms IDDM and NIDDM.

TYPE I: INSULIN-DEPENDENT (IMMUNE-DEPENDENT) DIABETES MELLITUS (IDDM)

Type I is a severe form of diabetes mellitus and is associated with ketosis in the untreated state. About 10–20% of diabetics in North America and Europe are of the insulin-dependent type. It is most common in young individuals but occurs occasionally in nonobese adults. It is a catabolic disorder in which circulating insulin is virtually absent, plasma glucagon is elevated, and the pancreatic B cells fail to respond to all known insulinogenic stimuli. In the absence of insulin, the three main target tissues of insulin (liver, muscle, and fat) not only fail to appropriately take up absorbed nutrients but continue to deliver glucose, amino acids, and fatty acids into the bloodstream from their respective storage depots. Furthermore, alterations in fat metabolism lead to the production and accumulation of ketones. This inappropriate persistence of the fasted state postprandially can be reversed by the administration of insulin.

Genetics of Type I Diabetes

Studies in monozygotic twins suggest that genetic influences are less marked in type I diabetes than in type II diabetes. Only 40% of identical twins of type I diabetic patients will develop the disease. This also suggests that an environmental factor is required for

induction of diabetes in these cases. In contrast, the identical twin of a type II diabetic will usually develop diabetes within a year of onset of the disease in the sibling.

Type I diabetes is believed to result from an infectious or toxic environmental insult to the pancreatic B cells in genetically predisposed persons whose aggressive immune system destroys pancreatic B cells while overcoming the invasive agent. Environmental factors that have been associated with altered pancreatic islet cell function include viruses (mumps, rubella, coxsackievirus B4), toxic chemical agents such as vacor (a nitrophenylurea rat poison), and other destructive cytotoxins such as hydrogen cyanide from spoiled tapioca or cassava root.

Type I diabetes is strongly associated with an increased frequency of certain HLA antigens. Genes coding for these antigens are on the short arm of chromosome 6. They consist of the class I genes, termed A, B, and C, whose protein biosynthesis products are found on the surfaces of all body cells except red blood cells and sperm; and class II genes, located closer to the centromere of chromosome 6. These latter genes code for the class II antigens expressed on the surfaces of macrophages and B lymphocytes. These antigens are glycoproteins that allow the immune system to distinguish other body cells from foreign invaders such as viruses, bacteria, or fungi. The predominant HLA antigens associated with type I diabetes vary in different racial groups. Thus, HLA-B8, -B15, -B18, -Cw3, -DR3, and -DR4 occur with increased frequency on leukocytes of Caucasian diabetics, whereas of the above, only HLA-DR3 and -DR4 appear to be correlated with type I diabetes in Asians, Africans, and Latin-Americans. Either HLA-DR3 or -DR4 occurs in about 95% of Caucasian type I diabetics, compared with 45–50% of Caucasian controls. It has been shown that HLA-DQ genes are even more specific markers of susceptibility to type I diabetes, since a particular variety (HLA-DQw3.2) is invariably found in the HLA-DR4 patients with type I diabetes while a "protective" gene (HLA-DQw3.1), which has an aspartic acid encoded in region 57 of the HLA-DQ beta chain, is prevalent in the HLA-DR4 controls. Moreover, HLA-DR2, which is generally protective against type I diabetes, seems to be so by virtue of its linkage to HLA-DQ genes which express antigens containing aspartic acid at position 57 of their beta chains.

It remains a mystery why people with certain HLA types are predisposed to development of type I diabetes. The concept of an autoimmune destruction of pancreatic B cells with selective loss of immune tolerance is supported by evidence that immune suppression therapy interrupts progression to insulin deficiency in a number of newly diagnosed IDDM patients. Moreover, extensive infiltration with both helper and cytotoxic T lymphocytes is present in the islets of children who just developed IDDM, and their serum contains autoantibodies against structural and secretory proteins of the pancreatic B cells before the onset of IDDM and for some time after diagnosis.

On the strength of the above evidence, a theory for autoimmune B cell destruction has been proposed based on molecular mimicry, wherein the immune system mistakenly targets B cell proteins that share homologies with certain viral peptides. The efficiency of presenting certain proteins depends on the composition of the class II antigens on the surface of the antigen-presenting cells (macrophages). Maximum susceptibility to IDDM was found when a certain HLA-DQ gene was present that expressed on the macrophage surface both a "nonaspartic" amino acid at position 57 on the DQ beta chain and an arginine at position 52 on the DQ alpha chain. Structural analysis of the DQ protein suggested that this configuration facilitated presentation of certain antigens to the immune system, whereas either an aspartic acid in the DQ beta chain at the 57 position or a "nonarginine" at the DQ alpha chain at the 52 position interfered with efficient presentation of certain peptides such as those found during the processing of coxsackie B4 viruses.

Circulating islet cell autoantibodies, virtually absent in nondiabetics, have been detected in as many as 85% of type I diabetics tested in the first few weeks after onset of diabetes. Moreover, when sensitive immunoassays are used, up to 60% of these patients also have detectable antibodies to insulin prior to receiving insulin therapy, and these are especially prevalent with an onset of disease in childhood. The high prevalence of these islet cell and insulin autoantibodies in type I diabetes, as well as in certain of their siblings who later develop overt diabetes, supports the concept that autoimmune mechanisms may contribute significantly to progressive B cell destruction.

It has recently been documented that most islet cell antibodies are directed against glutamic acid decarboxylase (GAD), an enzyme localized within pancreatic B cells. This enzyme has isoforms with molecular weights of 65,000 and 67,000 which are also found in central nervous system "inhibitory" neurons that secrete γ-aminobutyric acid. Evidence that a rare neurologic condition, "stiff man syndrome," was associated with an autoimmune destruction of neurons containing GAD—and that these patients' sera also had islet cell antibodies—led to the discovery that antibodies to GAD made up the bulk of antibodies previously described in IDDM as being against a 64-kDa antigen in pancreatic B cells. The concept of "molecular mimicry" is supported by the recent finding that part of the protein component of the coxsackie B4 virus contains a sequence of 24 amino acids with considerable homology to GAD.

Manifestations of stiff man syndrome have not been reported in patients with IDDM even though their islet cell antibodies contain a major component that reacts in vitro with GAD-containing neurons. The blood-brain barrier may have some protective effect against neuronal damage of a degree that might cause stiff man syndrome in IDDM. However, investigations are in progress to see if autoimmunity to GAD plays a role in some severe forms of peripheral neuropathy.

Another candidate for the molecular mimicry hypothesis is bovine serum albumin, which has a region of homology with a B cell surface protein, p69. Children who were exclusively breast-fed as infants had a statistically lower incidence of IDDM than those who received cow's milk. Moreover, 142 Finnish children with newly diagnosed IDDM had high titers of antibodies against bovine serum albumin, in contrast to much lower levels in a control population of children. It is postulated that immature gut enzymes in infants permit absorption of peptide fragments of bovine serum albumin that induce immune responses which attack B cell protein p69.

A genetic link to chromosome 11 has been identified in type I diabetes. Population studies of a polymorphic DNA locus flanking the 5' region of the insulin gene on chromosome 11 revealed a slight, but statistically significant linkage between IDDM and this genetic locus in a Caucasian population of type I diabetics. This polymorphic locus does not seem either to encode a protein or to affect insulin gene expression, but it may represent a marker for a linked gene relating to B cell replication such as IGF-2, which is contiguous with the insulin gene on chromosome 11, or to some other linked gene whose function influences susceptibility to type I diabetes.

Immunosuppression in the Treatment of Recent-Onset Type I Diabetes

Since the destruction of B cells in type I diabetes is a progressive, immune-mediated process, several clinical trials with immunosuppressive therapy at the onset of type I diabetes are in progress. Unfortunately, their outcomes have so far been disappointing. Although some reduction or elimination of insulin requirement has been observed, most subjects manifest continued carbohydrate intolerance while being exposed to considerable risk from the adverse effects of immunosuppressive drugs. Cyclosporine, as a result of its substantial nephrotoxicity and nonspecific immunosuppression, is not recommended for the treatment of patients with newly diagnosed IDDM.

More specific strategies for immunosuppression, such as the use of monoclonal antibodies against particular T cell products, may reduce the hazards of long-term immunotherapy.

Some nonimmunosuppressive therapeutic modalities under investigation include probucol, which tends to quench free radicals that have been implicated as a means of T lymphocyte cytotoxicity, and nicotinamide, an inhibitor of poly(ADP-ribose) synthetase, an enzyme whose repair of DNA injury tends to deplete the cell of its vital supply of NAD. Furthermore, since feeding insulin to a strain of mice prone to developing autoimmune diabetes has been reported to delay the expected incidence of diabetes, human trials with oral insulin have been instituted in children considered to be at high risk for IDDM.

TYPE II: NON-INSULIN-DEPENDENT (NON-IMMUNE-DEPENDENT) DIABETES MELLITUS (NIDDM)

Type II diabetes, which comprises a heterogeneous group of the milder forms of diabetes, occurs predominantly in adults but may occasionally have its onset in childhood.

Type II diabetes is defined mainly in negative terms. It is a nonketotic form of diabetes which is not linked to HLA markers on the sixth chromosome and is not associated with islet cell autoantibodies. The patients are not dependent on exogenous insulin therapy to sustain life—thus the name, non-insulin-dependent diabetes mellitus. An element of tissue insensitivity to insulin has been noted in most NIDDM patients. Possible mechanisms for this are shown in Table 15–6.

Syndrome X (Insulin Resistance Syndrome)

Several investigators speculate that type II diabetes may represent only one facet of a syndrome caused by insulin resistance. They have noted that the well-established association of **hyperglycemia, hyperinsulinemia, dyslipidemia,** and **hypertension,** which leads to coronary artery disease and stroke, may result from a genetic defect producing insulin resistance, particularly when obesity aggravates the degree of insulin resistance. They propose that impaired action of insulin predisposes to hyperglycemia, which in turn induces hyperinsulinemia. If this

hyperinsulinemia is of insufficient magnitude to correct the hyperglycemia, type II diabetes will be manifested. They feel that this excessive insulin level increases sodium retention by renal tubules, thereby contributing to or causing hypertension; an increased VLDL production in the liver, leading to hypertriglyceridemia (and consequently a low HDL-cholesterol level), has also been attributed to hyperinsulinism. Moreover, they propose that high insulin levels can stimulate endothelial and vascular smooth muscle cell proliferation—by virtue of the hormone's action on growth factor receptors—to initiate atherosclerosis.

While there is full agreement on an association of the above disorders, the mechanism of their interrelationship remains speculative and open to experimental investigation. Controversy persists about whether or not hypertension is caused by hyperinsulinism, since these two manifestations, which often coexist in whites, are not highly associated in American blacks or Pima Indians. Moreover, patients with hyperinsulinism due to an insulinoma are generally normotensive, and there is no reduction of blood pressure after surgical removal of the insulinoma restores normal insulin levels. Australian epidemiologists prefer to group these disorders together as a syndrome, without necessarily implying that hyperinsulinism is etiologically responsible for the other components. They suggest the acronym CHAOS to signify *c*oronary artery disease, *h*ypertension, *a*dult-onset diabetes, *o*besity, and *s*troke. The main value of grouping these disorders as a syndrome, regardless of its nomenclature, is to remind physicians that the therapeutic goals are not only to correct hyperglycemia but also to manage the elevated blood pressure and hyperlipidemia that result in considerable cardiovascular morbidity as well as cardiovascular deaths in these patients. It also raises awareness that indiscriminate therapeutic use of high doses of exogenous insulin may conceivably have adverse effects on a patient's risk profile for cardiovascular disease if the hypothesis behind the insulin resistance syndrome is substantiated. Finally, it reminds physicians that when choosing antihypertensive agents or lipid-lowering drugs to manage one of the components of this syndrome, their possible untoward effects on other components of the syndrome should be carefully considered. For example, physicians aware of this syndrome are less likely to prescribe antihypertensive drugs that raise lipids (diuretics, beta-blockers) or that raise blood sugar (diuretics). Likewise, they will refrain from prescribing drugs that correct hyperlipidemia but increase insulin resistance with aggravation of hyperglycemia (niacin).

Table 15–6. Factors reducing response to insulin.

Prereceptor inhibitors: Insulin antibodies
Receptor inhibitors:
  Insulin receptor autoantibodies
  "Down-regulation" of receptors by hyperinsulinism:
    Primary hyperinsulinism (B cell adenoma)
    Hyperinsulinism, secondary to a postreceptor defect (obesity, Cushing's syndrome, acromegaly, pregnancy) or prolonged hyperglycemia (diabetes mellitus, post-glucose tolerance test)
Postreceptor influences:
  Poor responsiveness of principal target organs: obesity, hepatic disease, muscle inactivity
  Hormonal excess: glucocorticoids, growth hormone, oral contraceptive agents, progesterone, human chorionic somatomammotropin, catecholamines, thyroxine

Subgroups of Type II Diabetes

Type II diabetics can be distributed on the basis of body weight into obese or nonobese subtypes. Currently, it is impossible to identify diagnostic characteristics that allow further clear-cut separation into more specific subtypes. Circulating insulin levels are presently considered too variable to be of use in classification.

Among this "non-type I" group are a wide assortment of heterogeneous disorders. These include rare instances in which a defective insulin gene produces a biologically inadequate abnormal insulin or a proinsulin that is not transformed to insulin in the B cell. Receptor blocks to insulin action have been demonstrated in some cases. In most patients with type II diabetes, the cause of the disorder is presently undefined although both a defect in insulin secretion and a defect in insulin action at the postreceptor level are generally present.

Obese NIDDM

Up to 85% of type II diabetics are obese. These patients have an insensitivity to endogenous insulin that is positively correlated with the presence of an abdominal distribution of fat, producing an abnormally high waist to hip ratio. In addition, distended adipocytes and overnourished liver and muscle cells may also resist the deposition of additional glycogen and triglycerides in their storage depots. Hyperplasia of pancreatic B cells is often present and probably accounts for the normal or exaggerated insulin responses to glucose and other stimuli seen in the milder forms of this disease. In more severe cases, secondary (but potentially reversible) failure of pancreatic B cell secretion may result after exposure to prolonged fasting hyperglycemia. This phenomenon has been called "desensitization." It is selective for glucose, and the B cell recovers sensitivity to glucose stimulation once the sustained hyperglycemia is corrected by any form of therapy, including diet therapy, sulfonylureas, and insulin.

A major cause of the observed resistance to insulin in target tissues of obese patients is believed to be a postreceptor defect in insulin action. This is associated with overdistended storage depots and a reduced ability to clear nutrients from the circulation after meals. Consequent hyperinsulinism can further enhance insulin resistance by down-regulation of insulin receptors. Furthermore, when hyperglycemia becomes sustained, a specific glucose transporter protein in insulin target tissue (GLUT 4) also becomes down-regulated after continuous activation. This contributes to further defects in postreceptor insulin action, thereby aggravating the hyperglycemia.

When overfeeding is corrected so that storage depots become less saturated, the cycle is interrupted. Insulin sensitivity improves and is further normalized by a reduction in both the hyperinsulinism and the hyperglycemia.

Nonobese NIDDM

Approximately 15% of patients with NIDDM are nonobese diabetics. In most of these patients, impaired insulin action at the postreceptor level and an absent or delayed early phase of insulin release in response to glucose can be demonstrated. However, other insulinogenic stimuli, such as acute infusion of amino acids, intravenous tolbutamide, or intramuscular glucagon, often remain effective in eliciting acute insulin release.

The hyperglycemia in patients with nonobese NIDDM often responds to dietary therapy or to oral hypoglycemic agents. Occasionally, insulin therapy is required to achieve satisfactory glycemic control even though it is not needed to prevent ketoacidosis.

While most nonobese NIDDM patients cannot be subclassified, several discrete subtypes are suggested in a small proportion of patients on the basis of genetic characteristics:

A. NIDDM Occurring in Late Childhood or Young Adulthood:

1. Autosomal dominant nonobese NIDDM– A specific subclass of nonobese NIDDM includes patients with "maturity-onset diabetes of the young" (MODY, or Mason type). These patients have mild hyperglycemia with onset in late childhood or young adulthood. Their strong family history of a mild form of diabetes occurring in one parent and in one-half of the parent's offspring suggests an autosomal dominant transmission. Among 32 families in France with this syndrome, 18 were found to have mutations of the glucokinase gene on chromosome 7. Sixteen different mutations were identified in these 18 families, and they include 10 mutations resulting in an amino acid substitution, three that resulted in a truncated protein, and three that affected RNA processing of glucokinase. A reduction in glucokinase activity within the pancreatic B cell is critical in determining the threshold of plasma glucose at which the B bell secretes insulin. In those families with mutations of glucokinase, mild hyperglycemia began during childhood, while in the 14 French families without detectable glucokinase mutations, hyperglycemia was not observed until after puberty.

In a large kindred in Michigan consisting of more than 285 individuals over five generations, 40 subjects with MODY were found to have an as yet unidentified genetic defect traced to the long arm of chromosome 20, where it is tightly linked to the adenosine deaminase gene.

2. Type II diabetes of early onset– A high familial prevalence of type II diabetes has been noted in patients whose age at onset of mild diabetes is 25–40 years. Epidemiologic studies suggest that this familial prevalence is due to inheritance of diabetogenic genes from both parents (homozygous state). When only one parent passes on the diabetogenic gene (heterozygous state), its later expression as clinical diabetes may require additional genetic or environmental factors (eg, aging, obesity). Thus, two heterozygous parents may or may not each develop diabetes after age 40 years, but as many as 75% of their offspring are at high risk of developing diabetes, with as many as 25% of them becoming diabetic before age 40 years.

B. Mutant Insulins: Despite awareness of this disorder over the past 12 years, only eight families have been identified as having abnormal circulating forms of insulin. In three of these families, there is impaired cleavage of the proinsulin molecule; in the other five families, abnormalities of the insulin molecule itself have been reported (Table 15–7).

Analysis of the insulin gene, circulating insulin, and clinical features of family members in these cases indicates that individuals with mutant insulin are heterozygous for this defect, with both a normal and an abnormal insulin molecule being equally expressed. However, because the abnormal insulin binds to receptors poorly, it has very low biologic activity and accumulates in the blood to exceed the concentration of the normal insulin. This decreased removal rate of mutant insulin results in hyperinsulinemia after overnight fasting and a subnormal molar ratio of C peptide to immunoreactive insulin. Diabetes mellitus may or may not be present in association with mutant insulin, depending on the concentration and bioactivity of circulating normal and abnormal insulins and on the insulin responsiveness of peripheral tissues. Since there is no obvious resistance to insulin in any of these cases, it appears that abnormal insulin does not interfere with binding of normal insulin to receptors; therefore, a feature of this syndrome is the normal response to exogenously administered insulin.

1. Abnormalities of the proinsulin molecule– A partially cleaved intermediate of proinsulin comprising up to 90% of circulating insulin immunoreactivity has been described in two families, one from Japan and one from Boston. Both families seem to have similar defects, with the arginine in position 65 being replaced by histidine and thereby interfering with cleavage of the C peptide from the A chain of insulin. However, mild diabetes mellitus was present only in the three affected members of the family from Japan; it was not present in 17 affected members of the large kindred in Boston, despite a similar mutation of the insulin gene.

In a third family, hyperproinsulinemia was reported in five members. Although one of the five members (a 12-year-old girl) had borderline glucose intolerance, the other four had normal blood glucose levels. In this family, a mutation in the insulin gene coding for histidine at B 10 results in substitution of an aspartic acid, inducing a conformational change that prevents conversion of proinsulin to insulin.

2. Abnormalities of the insulin molecule– Genetic defects in insulin synthesis have resulted in substitutions of leucine for phenylalanine at position B 25 ("insulin Chicago") and serine for phenylalanine at position B 24 ("insulin Los Angeles"). (See Figure 15–3.) The observation that there was loss of a normal restriction endonuclease cleavage site in the area of the insulin gene coding for B 24 and B 25 phenylalanine was used in conjunction with results of high-performance liquid chromatographic analysis of circulating insulin to establish the nature of the mutant insulin in affected family members. Glucose tolerance ranged from normal to overtly diabetic in affected individuals, who were generally nonobese and had subnormal molar ratios of C peptide to immunoreactive insulin.

In Japan, a mutant insulin with a substitution of leucine for the normal valine at A 3 was initially described in Wakayama but was subsequently identified in the adjacent Osaka region in two other families who had no documented relationship.

With improved screening techniques becoming available such as the polymerase chain reaction, more cases of mutation of the insulin gene will undoubtedly be detected. However, from present experience it is unlikely that patients with this defect will make up more than a very small fraction of the NIDDM population.

"NIDDM" Diabetics Who May Be Type I Diabetics in Remission

The current classification of diabetes mellitus has been widely accepted throughout the world, but its deficiencies are apparent in many cases. A subgroup that has been difficult to place in the current "therapeutic" classification is made up of those type I diabetics who remain in temporary remission for up to 2 years. A history of ketoacidosis with the finding of islet cell autoantibodies at the onset of the diabetes— and an HLA pattern that includes HLA-B8, -B15, -DR3, or -DR4—would indicate that these patients have type I diabetes from an etiologic standpoint even though they may be temporarily not "insulin-dependent."

Moreover, it is possible that a number of adult-onset diabetic patients, particularly when not obese, may represent an early stage of type I diabetes due to autoimmune destruction of enough pancreatic B cells to make them hyperglycemic but not necessarily insulin-dependent. In one study, as many as 16% of a group of adult-onset diabetics in a British clinic population who were classified as NIDDM were found to be positive for islet cell antibodies. With the avail-

Table 15–7. Mutant insulins and proinsulins.

	Amino Acid Substitution
Insulin Chicago (USA)	B 25 (Phe → Leu)
Insulin Los Angeles (USA)	B 24 (Phe → Ser)
Insulin Wakayama (Japan) I, II, III (three families)	A 3 (Val → Leu)
Proinsulin Tokyo (Japan)	Arg 65 (Arg → His)
Proinsulin Boston (USA)	Arg 65 (Arg → ?)
Proinsulin Providence (USA)	B 10 (His → Asp)

ability of more convenient radioimmunoassays for islet cell antibodies, such as those for antibodies against glutamic acid decarboxylase, it will be possible to screen many more populations of adult diabetics. This will be particularly useful in ethnic groups who are prone to autoimmune disease and in whom IDDM is prevalent. This might permit earlier identification of those patients with immune-induced partial B cell destruction who may thus be more likely to fail sulfonylureas and to require insulin therapy.

SECONDARY DIABETES

As noted in Table 15–5, there is a diverse group of disorders characterized by the association of diabetes with another condition. Only a few of the many types of secondary diabetes will be discussed here.

Pancreatic Disease

Surgical removal of the pancreas, pancreatic disease due to chronic alcoholism, and other forms of pancreatitis are associated with many of the clinical characteristics of insulin-dependent diabetes mellitus, because the primary abnormality is insulin deficiency. There is, however, a greater tendency to develop insulin-induced hypoglycemia, probably because of the concomitant lack of the counterregulatory hormone glucagon. At least two-thirds of the pancreas must be destroyed to develop the clinical syndrome. It is usually associated with exocrine pancreatic insufficiency as well.

Drug Toxicity

Many drugs are associated with carbohydrate intolerance or frank diabetes mellitus. Some act by interfering with insulin release from the B cells (thiazides, phenytoin), some by inducing insulin resistance (glucocorticoids, oral contraceptive pills), and some by causing B cell destruction (pentamidine).

While calcium channel blockers as well as clonidine are potent inhibitors of glucose-induced insulin release from in vitro preparations of pancreatic B cells, the inhibitory concentrations required are quite high and are not generally achieved during standard antihypertensive therapy with these agents in humans.

Endocrine Disorders

Excess production of certain hormones—growth hormone (acromegaly), glucocorticoids (Cushing's syndrome or disease), catecholamines (pheochromocytoma), glucagon (glucagonoma), or pancreatic somatostatin (somatostatinoma)—can produce the syndrome of NIDDM by a number of mechanisms. In all but the last instance (somatostatinoma), peripheral responsiveness to insulin is impaired. In addition, excess of catecholamines or somatostatin decreases insulin release from B cells.

Insulin-Resistant Diabetes With Acanthosis Nigricans

Patients with the rare syndrome of extreme insulin resistance associated with acanthosis nigricans can be divided into two groups on the basis of clinical and laboratory manifestations. **Group A** consists of younger women with androgenic features (hirsutism, amenorrhea, polycystic ovaries) in whom insulin receptors are deficient in number. With development of newer molecular biology methods using polymerase chain reaction analysis, as many as 25 different mutations of the insulin receptor have been characterized. When patients with type A insulin resistance have two mutant alleles, they tend to be more insulin-resistant than when only one mutant allele is present. **Group B** consists of older people, mostly women, in whom immunologic disease is suspected. They have a high erythrocyte sedimentation rate, DNA autoantibodies, and a circulating immunoglobulin that binds to insulin receptors, thereby reducing their affinity for insulin.

In both of the above groups, carbohydrate tolerance may at times be normal, and in most cases ketoacidosis does not develop despite severe insulin resistance and diabetes. Occasionally, spontaneous remission of insulin resistance and diabetes occurs, particularly in the group A patients. In neither of the above groups is insulin therapy very effective. Acanthosis nigricans seems to be a consequence of very high circulating levels of insulin binding to insulin-like growth factor receptors on epidermal and melanin-containing cutaneous cells.

Other Forms of Secondary Diabetes

Other rare diseases associated with insulin receptor or postreceptor abnormalities include leprechaunism, ataxia-telangiectasia, Prader-Willi syndrome, and certain forms of myotonic dystrophy.

CLINICAL FEATURES OF DIABETES MELLITUS

The principal clinical features of the two major types of diabetes mellitus are listed for comparison in Table 15–8.

TYPE I DIABETES (IDDM)

IDDM patients present with a characteristic symptom complex, as outlined below. An absolute deficiency of insulin results in excessive accumulation of circulating glucose and fatty acids, with consequent

Table 15–8. Clinical features of diabetes at diagnosis.

	Diabetes Type I (IDDM)	Diabetes Type II (NIDDM)
Polyuria and thirst	++	+
Weakness or fatigue	++	+
Polyphagia with weight loss	++	–
Recurrent blurred vision	+	++
Vulvovaginitis or pruritus	+	++
Peripheral neuropathy	+	++
Nocturnal enuresis	++	–
Often asymptomatic	–	++

hyperosmolality and hyperketonemia. The severity of the insulin deficiency and the acuteness with which the catabolic state develops determine the intensity of the osmotic and ketotic excess.

Clinical Features

A. Symptoms: Increased urination is a consequence of osmotic diuresis secondary to sustained hyperglycemia. This results in a loss of glucose as well as free water and electrolytes in the urine. Nocturnal enuresis due to polyuria may signal the onset of diabetes in very young children. Thirst is a consequence of the hyperosmolar state, as is blurred vision, which often develops as the lenses and retinas are exposed to hyperosmolar fluids.

Weight loss despite normal or increased appetite is a common feature of IDDM when it develops subacutely over a period of weeks. The weight loss is initially due to depletion of water, glycogen, and triglyceride stores. Chronic weight loss due to reduced muscle mass occurs as amino acids are diverted to form glucose and ketone bodies.

Lowered plasma volume produces dizziness and weakness due to postural hypotension when sitting or standing. Total body potassium loss and the general catabolism of muscle protein contribute to the weakness.

Paresthesias may be present at the time of diagnosis of type I diabetes, particularly when the onset is subacute. They reflect a temporary dysfunction of peripheral sensory nerves and usually clear as insulin replacement restores glycemic levels closer to normal; thus, their presence suggests neurotoxicity from sustained hyperglycemia.

When insulin deficiency is severe and of acute onset, the above symptoms progress in an accelerated manner. Ketoacidosis exacerbates the dehydration and hyperosmolality by producing anorexia, nausea, and vomiting, thus interfering with oral fluid replacement. As plasma osmolality exceeds 330 mosm/L (normal, 285–295 mosm/L), impaired consciousness ensues. With progression of acidosis to a pH of 7.1 or less, deep breathing with a rapid ventilatory rate (Kussmaul respiration) occurs as the body attempts to eliminate carbonic acid. With worsening acidosis (to pH 7.0 or less), the cardiovascular system may be unable to maintain compensatory vasoconstriction; severe circulatory collapse may result.

B. Signs: The patient's level of consciousness can vary depending on the degree of hyperosmolality. When insulin deficiency develops relatively slowly and sufficient water intake is maintained to permit renal excretion of glucose and appropriate dilution of extracellular sodium chloride concentration, patients remain relatively alert and physical findings may be minimal. When vomiting occurs in response to worsening ketoacidosis, dehydration progresses and compensatory mechanisms become inadequate to keep plasma osmolality below 330 mosm/L. Under these circumstances, stupor or even coma may occur. Evidence of dehydration in a stuporous patient, with rapid deep breathing and the fruity breath odor of acetone, suggests the diagnosis of diabetic ketoacidosis.

Postural hypotension indicates a depleted plasma volume; hypotension in the recumbent position is a serious prognostic sign. Loss of subcutaneous fat and muscle wasting are features of more slowly developing insulin deficiency. In occasional patients with slow, insidious onset of insulin deficiency, subcutaneous fat may be considerably depleted. An enlarged liver, eruptive xanthomas on the flexor surface of the limbs and on the buttocks, and lipemia retinalis indicate that chronic insulin deficiency has resulted in chylomicronemia, with circulating triglycerides elevated usually to over 2000 mg/dL (see Chapter 17).

TYPE II DIABETES (NIDDM)

NIDDM patients also present with characteristic signs and symptoms. The presence of obesity or a strongly positive family history of mild diabetes also suggests a high risk for the development of type II diabetes.

Clinical Features

A. Symptoms: The classic symptoms of polyuria, thirst, recurrent blurred vision, paresthesias, and fatigue are manifestations of hyperglycemia and osmotic diuresis and are therefore common to both forms of diabetes. However, many patients with type II diabetes have an insidious onset of hyperglycemia and may be relatively asymptomatic initially. This is particularly true in obese patients, whose diabetes may be detected only after glycosuria or hyperglycemia is noted during routine laboratory studies. Chronic skin infections are common. Generalized pruritus and symptoms of vaginitis are frequently the initial complaints of women with NIDDM. Diabetes should be suspected in women with chronic candidal vulvovaginitis as well as in those who have delivered large infants (> 9 lb, or 4.1 kg) or have had polyhydramnios, preeclampsia, or unexplained fetal losses. Occasionally, a man with previously undiagnosed diabetes may present with impotence.

B. Signs: Nonobese patients with this mild form of diabetes often have no characteristic physical findings at the time of diagnosis. Obese diabetics may have any variety of fat distribution; however, diabetes seems to be more often associated in both men and women with localization of fat deposits on the upper part of the body (particularly the abdomen, chest, neck, and face) and relatively less fat on the appendages, which may be quite muscular. This centripetal fat distribution has been termed "android" and is characterized by a high waist to hip ratio. It differs from the more centrifugal "gynecoid" form of obesity, in which fat is localized more in the hips and thighs and less in the upper parts of the trunk. Refined radiographic techniques of assessing abdominal fat distribution with CT scans has documented that a "visceral" obesity, due to accumulation of fat in the omental and mesenteric regions, correlates with insulin resistance, whereas fat predominantly in subcutaneous tissues of the abdomen has little, if any, association with insulin insensitivity. Mild hypertension may be present in obese diabetics, particularly when the "android" form of obesity is predominant. In women, candidal vaginitis with a reddened, inflamed vulvar area and a profuse whitish discharge may herald the presence of diabetes.

LABORATORY FINDINGS IN DIABETES MELLITUS

Tests of urine glucose and ketone bodies as well as whole blood or plasma glucose measured in samples obtained under basal conditions and after glucose administration are very important in evaluation of the diabetic patient. Tests for glycosylated hemoglobin have proved useful in both initial evaluation and in assessment of the effectiveness of therapeutic management. In certain circumstances, measurements of insulin or C peptide levels and levels of other hormones involved in carbohydrate homeostasis (eg, glucagon, GH) may be useful. In view of the increased risk of atherosclerosis in diabetics, determination of serum cholesterol (including its beneficial HDL fraction) and triglycerides may be helpful. From these three measurements, an estimate of LDL-cholesterol can be made. (See Chapter 17.)

URINALYSIS

Glycosuria

Several problems are associated with using urine glucose as an index of blood glucose, regardless of the method employed. First of all, the glucose concentration in bladder urine reflects the blood glucose at the time the urine was formed. Therefore, the first voided specimen in the morning contains glucose that was excreted throughout the night and does not reflect the morning blood glucose at all. Some improvement in the correlation of urine glucose to blood glucose can be obtained if the patient "double voids"—that is, empties the bladder completely, discards that sample, and then urinates again about one-half hour later, testing only the second specimen for glucose content. However, difficulty in completely emptying the bladder (large residual volumes), problems in understanding the instructions, and the inconvenience impair the usefulness of this test. Self-monitoring of blood glucose has replaced urine glucose testing in most patients with IDDM and in many patients with NIDDM (particularly those receiving insulin therapy).

Several commercial products are available for determining the presence and amount of glucose in urine. The older and more cumbersome bedside assessment of glycosuria with Clinitest tablets has generally been replaced by the dipstick method, which is rapid, convenient, and glucose-specific. This method consists of paper strips (Clinistix, Diastix, Tes-Tape) impregnated with enzymes (glucose oxidase and hydrogen peroxidase) and a chromogenic dye that is colorless in the reduced state. Enzymatic generation of hydrogen peroxide oxidizes the dye to produce colors whose intensity depends on the glucose concentration. These dipsticks are sensitive to as little as 0.1% glucose (100 mg/dL) but do not react with the smaller amounts of glucose normally present in urine. The strips are subject to deterioration if exposed to air, moisture, and extreme heat and must be kept in tightly closed containers except when in use. False-negative results may be obtained in the presence of alkaptonuria and when certain substances such as salicylic acid or ascorbic acid are ingested in excess. All of these false-negative results occur because of the interference of strong reducing agents with oxidation of the chromogen.

Differential Diagnosis of Glycosuria

Although glycosuria reflects hyperglycemia in over 90% of patients, two major classes of nondiabetic glycosuria must be considered:

A. Nondiabetic Glycosuria Due to Glucose: This occurs when glucose appears in the urine despite a normal amount of glucose in the blood. Disorders associated with abnormalities in renal glucose handling include Fanconi's~syndrome (an autosomal dominant genetic disorder), dysfunction of the proximal renal tubule, chronic renal failure, and a benign familial disorder of the renal tubule manifest only by a defect in renal glucose reabsorption (occurs predominantly in males).

In addition, glycosuria is relatively common in

pregnancy as a consequence of the increased load of glucose presented to the tubules by the elevated glomerular filtration rate during pregnancy. As many as 50% of pregnant women normally have demonstrable sugar in the urine, especially after the first trimester. This sugar is almost always glucose except during the late weeks of pregnancy, when lactose may be present (see below).

B. Nondiabetic Glycosuria Due to Sugars Other Than Glucose: Occasionally, a sugar other than glucose is excreted in the urine. Lactosuria during the late stages of pregnancy and the period of lactation is the most common example. Much rarer are other conditions in which inborn errors of metabolism allow fructose, galactose, or a pentose (1-xylose) to be excreted in the urine. Testing the urine with glucose-specific strips will help differentiate true glucosuria from other glycosurias.

Ketonuria

In the absence of adequate insulin, three major "ketone bodies" are formed and excreted into the urine: β-hydroxybutyric acid, acetoacetic acid, and acetone (see also Serum Ketone Determinations, below). Commercial products are available to test for the presence of ketones in the urine. Acetest tablets, Ketostix, and Keto-Diastix utilize a nitroprusside reaction that measures only acetone and acetoacetate. Therefore, these tests can be misleading if β-hydroxybutyric acid is the predominant metabolite present. Ketostix and Keto-Diastix have short shelf-lives once the containers are opened and thus may give false-negative results.

Other conditions besides diabetic ketoacidosis may cause ketone bodies to appear in the urine; these include starvation, high-fat diets, alcoholic ketoacidosis, fever, and other conditions in which metabolic requirements are increased.

Proteinuria

Proteinuria as noted on a routine dipstick examination of the urine is often the first sign of renal complications of diabetes. If proteinuria is detected, a 24-hour urine collection should be analyzed to quantify the degree of proteinuria (normal individuals excrete < 30 mg of protein per day) and the rate of urinary creatinine excretion; at the same time, serum creatinine levels should be determined so that the creatinine clearance (an estimate of the glomerular filtration rate) can be calculated. In some cases, heavy proteinuria (3–5 g/d) develops later, along with other features of the nephrotic syndrome such as edema, hypoalbuminemia, and hypercholesterolemia.

Microalbuminuria

Urinary albumin can now be detected in microgram concentrations using a radioimmunoassay method that is more sensitive than the dipstick method, whose minimal detection limit is 0.3–0.5%.

Conventional 24-hour urine collections, in addition to being inconvenient for patients, also show wide variability of albumin excretion, since several factors such as sustained upright posture, dietary protein, and exercise tend to increase albumin excretion rates. For these reasons, many clinics prefer to screen patients with a timed *overnight* urine collection beginning at bedtime, when the urine is discarded and the time recorded. The collection is ended at the time the bladder is emptied the next morning, and this urine, as well as any other urine voided overnight, is assayed for albumin. Normal subjects excrete less than 15 µg/min during overnight urine collections; values between 20 and 200 µg/min or higher represent abnormal microalbuminuria, which may be an early predictor of the development of diabetic nephropathy.

BLOOD GLUCOSE TESTING

Normal Values

The normal fasting *whole blood* glucose varies from 60 to 110 mg/dL (3.3–6.1 mmol/L). Plasma or serum levels are 10–15% higher because structural components of blood cells are absent, so that more glucose is present per unit volume. Thus, the normal range of fasting plasma or serum glucose is 70–120 mg/dL (3.9–6.7 mmol/L). Plasma or serum glucose measurements are more frequently used clinically because they are independent of the hematocrit, more closely approach the glucose level in the interstitial tissue spaces, and lend themselves to automated analytic procedures. Whole blood glucose determinations are used in spot testing of glucose in emergency situations and also in the procedures for self-monitoring of capillary blood glucose, a technique that has become widely accepted in the management of diabetes mellitus (see below).

The accepted normal range of blood or plasma glucose requires a correction for age of 1 mg/dL (0.056 mmol/L) per year of age past 60. Thus, fasting plasma glucose in elderly nondiabetics will range from 80 to 150 mg/dL (4.4–8.3 mmol/L).

Venous Blood Samples

Samples should be collected in tubes containing sodium fluoride, which prevents glycolysis in the blood sample that would artifactually lower the measured glucose level. If such tubes are not available, samples must be centrifuged within 30 minutes of collection and the plasma or serum stored at 4 °C.

The laboratory methods regularly used for determining plasma glucose utilize enzymatic methods (such as glucose oxidase or hexokinase), colorimetric methods (such as *o*-toluidine), or automated methods. The automated methods utilize reduction of copper or iron compounds by reducing sugars in dialyzed serum. They are convenient but are not specific for glucose, since they react with other reducing substances (which are elevated in azotemia or with high ascorbic acid intake).

Capillary Blood Samples

There are several paper strip (glucose oxidase) methods for measuring capillary whole blood glucose. All have been adapted for use with portable, battery-operated reflectance meters that give a digital readout. One test strip kit, Chemstrip bG, provides a color chart for visual comparison and estimation of the blood glucose range. More conventional reflectance meters (eg, Glucometer, Glucoscan, Glucochek, Diascan, or AccuChek) require exact timing by the operator as well as careful removal of all traces of blood from the strip prior to reading the color. Second-generation devices (eg, One Touch II, ExacTech) have eliminated these two potential sources of technical error by providing automatic timing and allowing colorimeter quantitation without removal of the blood. To monitor their own blood glucose levels, patients must prick their fingers with a small lancet (eg, Monolet), which can be facilitated by a small plastic trigger device (eg, Autolet, Penlet). With proper instruction in technique, patients can obtain accurate and reliable measurements of their own blood glucose levels, which are indispensable to the proper long-term management of their diabetes. These methods are also of great value to health care professionals in the bedside management of seriously ill hospitalized diabetic patients.

Third-generation devices are presently in the developmental stage. They represent a noninvasive method relying on infrared absorption spectra which allow quantitation of glycemia flowing through capillary beds of the finger or earlobe. Present pilot models are relatively large and expensive, but they appear to be accurate and have the great advantage of eliminating painful finger sticks. Developmental goals are directed toward smaller, less expensive devices with which patients can perform self-monitoring of blood glucose.

SERUM KETONE DETERMINATIONS

As noted above in the section on ketonuria, there are three major ketone bodies: β-hydroxybutyrate (often the most prevalent in diabetic ketoacidosis), acetoacetate, and acetone. The same testing materials used for determining urine ketones may be used to measure serum (or plasma) ketones. However, whereas urine readily penetrates "intact" Acetest tablets, more viscous fluids such as serum or plasma do not have access to the bulk of the tablet unless it is first crushed. When a few drops of serum are placed on a crushed Acetest tablet, the appearance of a purple color indicates the presence of ketones. A strongly positive reaction in undiluted serum corre-

lates with a serum ketone concentration of at least 4 mmol/L. It must be kept in mind that Acetest tablets (as well as Ketostix and Keto-Diastix) utilize the nitroprusside reaction, which measures only acetoacetate and acetone. Specific enzymatic techniques are available to quantitate each of the ketone acids, but these techniques are cumbersome and not necessary in most clinical situations.

GLYCOSYLATED HEMOGLOBIN ASSAYS

Glycohemoglobin is produced by a ketoamine reaction between glucose and the N-terminal amino acid of both beta chains of the hemoglobin molecule. The major form of glycohemoglobin is hemoglobin A_{1c}, which normally comprises only 4–6% of total hemoglobin. The remaining glycohemoglobins (2–4% of total hemoglobin) contain phosphorylated glucose or fructose and are termed hemoglobin A_{1a} and A_{1b}, respectively. The hemoglobin A_{1c} fraction is abnormally elevated in diabetics with chronic hyperglycemia and appears to correlate positively with metabolic control. Specific assays for hemoglobin A_{1c} are technically less convenient than assays for total glycohemoglobin and offer little advantage for clinical purposes. Therefore, most laboratories measure the sum of these three glycohemoglobins and report it simply as hemoglobin A_1 or "glycohemoglobin."

The glycosylation of hemoglobin is dependent on the concentration of blood glucose. The reaction is not reversible, so that the half-life of glycosylated hemoglobin relates to the life span of red cells (which normally circulate for up to 120 days). Thus, glycohemoglobin generally reflects the state of glycemia over the preceding 8–12 weeks, thus providing a method of assessing chronic diabetic control. A glycosylated hemoglobin close to the normal range (5–8%) would reflect good control during the preceding 2–3 months, whereas a glycosylated hemoglobin in the range of 12–15% would reflect poor control during the same period.

Conditions Interfering With Glycohemoglobin Measurements (Table 15–9)

The most common laboratory error in measuring glycohemoglobins occurs when chromatographic methods measure an acutely generated intermediary aldimine in blood (prehemoglobin A_{1c}), which fluctuates directly with the prevailing blood glucose level. This artifact can falsely elevate glycohemoglobin by as much as 1–2% during an episode of acute hyperglycemia. It can be eliminated either by washing the red blood cells with saline prior to assay or by dialyzing the hemolysate prior to chromatography. Other substances that falsely elevate "glycohemoglobin" are carbamoylated hemoglobin and hemoglo-

Table 15–9. Factors interfering with chromatographic measurement of glycohemoglobins.

Substances causing falsely high values:
  Prehemoglobin A_{1c} (reversible aldimine intermediate)
  Carbamoylated hemoglobin (uremia)
  Hemoglobin F
Conditions causing falsely low values:
  Hemoglobinopathies (hemoglobins C, D, and S)
  Reduced life span of erythrocytes:
    Hemorrhage of therapeutic phlebotomies
    Hemolytic disorders

---

bin F; the former is seen in association with uremia, and the latter circulates in some adults with genetic or hematologic disorders. In these cases, more intricate methodology such as thiobarbituric acid colorimetry or isoelectric focusing is required to distinguish hemoglobin A_{1c} from the interfering substance.

Hemoglobinopathies such as those associated with hemoglobin C, D, and S will cause falsely low values, since their glycosylated products elute only partially from chromatographic columns. In addition, these hemoglobinopathies are often associated with hemolytic anemias that shorten the life span of red blood cells, thereby further lowering glycohemoglobin measurements. Falsely low values are also seen in patients with chronic or acute blood loss from hemorrhage or phlebotomies and in diabetic patients with hemochromatosis; under these conditions, measurements of glycohemoglobin are not valid for assessment of diabetic therapy.

Glycohemoglobin assays suffer from the lack of universally available reference standards. However, in a reliable laboratory where reversible aldimines (prehemoglobin A_{1c}) are routinely removed prior to chromatography, they are useful in assessing the effectiveness of diabetic therapy and particularly helpful in evaluating the reliability of a patient's self-monitoring records of urine or blood glucose values. A glycosylated hemoglobin test has been evaluated for diagnostic screening purposes, and while the test is generally too insensitive to rule out impaired glucose tolerance, a value above the normal range is generally a specific indicator of diabetes mellitus.

When abnormal hemoglobins or hemolytic states affect the interpretation of glycohemoglobin results or when a narrower time frame is required, eg, when ascertaining glycemic control at the time of conception in a diabetic woman who has recently become pregnant, serum fructosamine assays offer some advantage. Serum fructosamine is formed by nonenzymatic glycosylation of serum proteins (predominantly albumin). Since serum albumin has a much shorter half-life than hemoglobin, serum fructosamine generally reflects the state of glycemic control for only the preceding 2 weeks. In most circumstances, however, glycohemoglobin assays remain the preferred method for assessing long-term glycemic control in diabetic patients.

CAPILLARY MORPHOMETRY

The basement membrane of capillaries from skeletal muscle tissue of the quadriceps area is abnormally thickened in adults with overt spontaneous diabetes (fasting hyperglycemia of 140 mg/dL [7.8 mmol/L] or more). Capillary morphometry appears to be less discriminatory in diabetic children, being normal in as many as 60% of those below age 18. Evidence of the reversibility of capillary basement membrane thickening after near-normalization of glycemia with intensive therapy suggests that this thickening in diabetes is a consequence of long-term hyperglycemia, although the rapidity and severity of its progression may vary according to an individual's genetic predisposition.

DIAGNOSIS OF DIABETES MELLITUS

SIMPLE DIAGNOSTIC TEST BY FASTING PLASMA GLUCOSE

A fasting plasma glucose value above 140 mg/dL (7.8 mmol/L) on more than one occasion establishes the diagnosis of diabetes mellitus. The sample for fasting plasma glucose is best drawn in the morning after an overnight fast.

ORAL GLUCOSE TOLERANCE TEST

An oral glucose tolerance test is only rarely indicated, since the criteria for a positive test are still poor, being based on a nonhospitalized group of active young people who are not really comparable to any bedridden, ill, or aging population. In the past, oral glucose tolerance testing led to the overdiagnosis of diabetes. The much more rigid criteria currently recommended (see interpretation, below) should alleviate this tendency for overdiagnosis and improve the utility of the test.

If the fasting plasma glucose is between 120 and 140 mg/dL, an oral glucose tolerance test may be considered, especially in men with impotence or women who have delivered infants above 9 lb (4.1 kg) birth weight or have had recurrent vaginal yeast infections.

Preparation for Test

In order to optimize insulin secretion and effectiveness, especially when patients have been on a low-carbohydrate diet, a minimum of 150–200 g of carbohydrate per day should be included in the diet for 3 days preceding the test. The patient should eat nothing after midnight prior to the test day.

Testing Procedure

Adults are given 75 g of glucose in 300 mL of water; children are given 1.75 g of glucose per kilogram of ideal body weight. The glucose load is consumed within 5 minutes. Blood samples for plasma glucose are obtained at 0, 30, 60, 90, and 120 minutes after ingestion of glucose.

Interpretation

An oral glucose tolerance test is normal if the fasting venous plasma glucose value is less than 115 mg/dL (6.4 mmol/L), the 2-hour value falls below 140 mg/dL (7.8 mmol/L), and the value in none of the samples exceeds 200 mg/dL (11.1 mmol/L). A 2-hour value of greater than 200 mg/dL (11.1 mmol/L) in addition to one other value greater than 200 mg/dL (11.1 mmol/L) is diagnostic of diabetes mellitus. The diagnosis of "impaired glucose tolerance" is reserved for values between the upper limits of normal and those values diagnostic for diabetes. False-positive results may occur in patients who are malnourished at test time, bedridden, or afflicted with an infection or severe emotional stress. Diuretics, oral contraceptives, glucocorticoids, excess thyroxine, phenytoin, nicotinic acid and some of the psychotropic drugs may also cause false-positive results.

INSULIN LEVELS

To measure insulin levels during the glucose tolerance test, serum or plasma must be separated within 30 minutes after collection of the specimen and frozen prior to assay. Normal immunoreactive insulin levels range from 5–20 μU/mL in the fasting state, reach 50–130 μU/mL at 1 hour, and usually return to levels below 30 μU/mL by 2 hours. Insulin levels are rarely of clinical usefulness during glucose tolerance testing for the following reasons: When fasting glucose levels exceed 120 mg/dL (6.7 mmol/L), B cells generally have reduced responsiveness to further degrees of hyperglycemia regardless of the type of diabetes. When fasting glucose levels are below 120 mg/dL (6.7 mmol/L), late hyperinsulinism may occur as a result of insulin resistance in type II diabetes; however, it also may occur even in mild forms or in the early phases of type I diabetes when sluggish early insulin release results in late hyperglycemia that may stimulate excessive insulin secretion at 2 hours.

INTRAVENOUS GLUCOSE TOLERANCE TEST

The intravenous glucose tolerance test is performed by giving a rapid infusion of glucose followed by serial plasma glucose measurements to determine the disappearance rate of glucose per minute.

The disappearance rate reflects the patient's ability to dispose of a glucose load. Perhaps its most widespread present use is to screen siblings at risk for type I diabetes to determine if autoimmune destruction of B cells has reduced peak early insulin responses (at 1–5 minutes after the glucose bolus) to levels below the normal lower limit of 40 μU/mL. It has also been used to evaluate glucose tolerance in patients with gastrointestinal abnormalities (such as malabsorption). Caution should be used in clinical interpretation of the results, because the test bypasses normal glucose absorption and associated changes in gastrointestinal hormones that are important in carbohydrate metabolism. Furthermore, the test is relatively insensitive, and adequate criteria for diagnosis of diabetes have not been established for the various age groups.

Preparation for Test

Preparation is the same as for the oral glucose tolerance test (see above).

Testing Procedure

Intravenous access is established and the patient is given a bolus of 50 g of glucose per 1.7 m^2 body surface area (or 0.5 g/kg of ideal body weight) as a 25% or 50% solution over 2–3 minutes. Timing begins with injection. Samples for plasma glucose determination are obtained from an indwelling needle in the opposite arm at 0, 10, 15, 20, and 30 minutes. The plasma glucose values are plotted on semilogarithmic paper against time. K, a rate constant that reflects the rate of fall of blood glucose in percent per minute, is calculated by determining the time necessary for the glucose concentration to fall by one-half ($t_{1/2}$) and using the following equation:

$$K \text{ (glucose)} = (0.693 - t_{1/2}) \times 100$$

The average K value for a nondiabetic patient is approximately 1.72% per minute; this value declines with age but remains above 1. 3% per minute. Diabetic patients almost always have a K value of less than 1% per minute.

TREATMENT OF DIABETES MELLITUS

Rational therapy of diabetes requires the application of principles derived from current knowledge concerning both the nature of the particular type of diabetes and the mechanism of action, efficacy, and safety of the available treatment regimens: diet, oral hypoglycemic drugs, and insulin.

A fundamental controversy regarding whether microangiopathy is related exclusively to the existence and duration of hyperglycemia or whether it reflects a separate genetic disorder has recently been resolved by the findings of the Diabetes Control and Complications trial which confirmed the beneficial effects of intensive therapy to achieve improved glycemic control in IDDM (NEJM Aug. 1993, In Press, also see below).

The Diabetes Control and Complications Trial (DCCT):

In June 1993, a longterm randomized prospective study involving 1441 IDDM patients in 29 medical centers reported that "near" normalization of blood glucose resulted in a delay in the onset and a major slowing of the progression of established microvascular and neuropathic complications of diabetes during an up to 10 year follow-up.

The patients were divided into two equal study groups. Approximately one half of the total group had no detectable diabetic complications (prevention trial) while mild background retinopathy was present in the other half (intervention trial). Some patients in the latter group had slightly elevated microalbuminuria, and mild neuropathy, but no one with serious diabetic complications was enrolled in the trial. Multiple insulin injections (66%) or insulin pumps (34%) were used in the intensively treated group who were trained to modify their therapy depending on frequent glucose monitoring. The conventionally treated group used no more than two insulin injections, and clinical well-being was the goal with no attempt to modify management based on glycated hemoglobin or their glucose results. Patients were between the ages of 13 and 39 years with an average age of 27 years; half the subjects were women.

In the intensively treated subjects, a mean glycated hemoglobin of 7.2% (normal <6%) and a blood glucose of 155 mg/dL was achieved using intensive therapy, while in the conventionally treated group, glycated hemoglobin averaged 8.9% with an average blood glucose of 225 mg/dL. Over the study period, which averaged 7 years, there was an approximate 60% reduction in risk between the two groups in regard to diabetic retinopathy, nephropathy, and neuropathy.

Intensively treated patients had a three-fold greater risk of serious hypoglycemia as well as a greater tendency toward weight gain. However, there were no deaths from hypoglycemia in any subjects in the DCCT study and no evidence of post-hypoglycemic neurological damage was detected.

The general consensus of the American Diabetes Association is that intensive insulin therapy associated with comprehensive self-management training should become standard therapy in most IDDM patients after the age of puberty. Exceptions include those with advanced renal disease and the elderly since, in these groups, the detrimental risks of hypoglycemia outweigh the benefits of tight glycemic control. In children under the age of 7 years, the extreme susceptibility of the developing brain to damage from hypoglycemia contraindicates attempts at tight glycemic control, particularly since diabetic complications do not seem to occur until some years after the onset of puberty.

While patients with NIDDM were not studied in the DCCT, there is no reason to believe that the effects of better control of blood glucose levels would not also apply to NIDDM. The eye, kidney, and nerve abnormalities are quite similar in both types of diabetes and it is likely that similar underlying mechanisms apply. However, because weight gain may be greater in obese NIDDM on intensive insulin therapy, and because of an increased prevalence of macrovascular disease in older patients with NIDDM (in whom hypoglycemia may be more hazardous) the American Diabetes Association feels that common sense and clinical judgment on an individual basis should determine whether tight glycemic control is appropriate in NIDDM.

With the above caveats and exceptions, the recommendations of the Executive Committee of the American Diabetes Association are to try to restore known metabolic derangements to normal in an attempt to retard (if not prevent) the progression of microvascular disease. One should aim at simulating a normal physiologic status by administering insulin in such a manner as to provide a continuous low basal level of circulating insulin and produce an eight- to tenfold rise in plasma insulin concentration with the average meal. Care should be taken to avoid administration of excessive insulin that might induce hypoglycemia. To achieve these goals, the patient, in cooperation with the physician, must make adjustments in diet, exercise, and, if indicated, hypoglycemic agents, based on appropriate self-monitoring of their blood glucose.

AVAILABLE TREATMENT REGIMENS

1. DIET

A proper diet remains a fundamental element of therapy in all patients with diabetes. However, in over half of cases, diabetics fail to follow their diet. The reasons include unnecessary complexity of dietary instructions and poor understanding of the goals of dietary control by the patient and physician.

Exchange lists for meal planning can be obtained from the American Diabetes Association (ADA; 1660 Duke Street, Alexandria, Virginia 22314) and its affiliate associations or from the American Dietetic Association (430 North Michigan Avenue, Chicago 60611). The ADA diet stresses caloric restriction as the major method of achieving or maintaining ideal weight and recommends no more than 300 mg of cholesterol per day with a fat intake of

35% or less of total calories. Furthermore, it is recommended that saturated fat be reduced to only one-third of this amount by substitution of unsaturated fats for saturated fats and by substitution of poultry, veal, and fish for red meats as the major protein source. Previous recommendations of polyunsaturated fat supplements as part of a prudent diabetic diet have been revised because of their potential hazards. Polyunsaturated fatty acids appear to promote oxidation of LDL and lower HDL-cholesterol, both of which may contribute to atherogenesis; also, they may promote carcinogenesis. Therefore, polyunsaturated fats should comprise no more than 6–8% of total calories and, wherever possible, monounsaturated fats such as olive oil or rapeseed oil (canola oil) should be substituted to comprise 15–17% of total calories since they do not induce cholesterol formation. Likewise, of the saturated fatty acids, stearic acid is the least cholesterologenic, since it is rapidly converted to oleic acid—in contrast to palmitic acid (found in animal fat as well as coconut oil), which is a major substrate for cholesterol formation. Complex carbohydrates may be consumed liberally (as much as 50% of total calories) as long as refined and simple sugars are limited. In obese NIDDM patients, who tend to have elevated triglycerides with low HDL when taking high-carbohydrate diets, it has been suggested that one should replace some of the dietary carbohydrate with noncholesterologenic monounsaturated oils (olive oil, rapeseed oil). This maneuver is also indicated for IDDM patients being maintained on intensive insulin regimens in whom near-normoglycemic control is less achievable with carbohydrate content of the diet of 50% or more.

Prescribing the Diet

A. Type I Diabetes (IDDM): In type I diabetes, total calories are calculated to maintain ideal body weight. In the typical patient, insulin is administered at least twice a day, often as a mixture of a short-acting and an intermediate-acting insulin. Meals should be adjusted accordingly in an effort to match food intake with insulin action. Breakfast should be eaten within 1/2 –1 hour after the morning insulin dose (especially if short-acting insulin is administered at this time). A carbohydrate snack should be eaten 3 hours later and lunch no later than 5 hours after the morning insulin dose. A midafternoon carbohydrate snack is given 7–8 hours after the morning insulin. Dinner should follow the second injection by 1/2–1 1/2 hours, depending on whether a short-acting insulin is administered at this time. A bedtime snack containing protein as well as carbohydrate should be given 3 hours after the evening insulin in order to provide a slow influx of carbohydrate from metabolized protein during most of the night. When multiple insulin injections are prescribed, greater flexibility with regard to timing of meals is possible.

B. Type II Diabetes (NIDDM): In type II dia-

betes, patients are often at least mildly obese. Treatment requires a vigorous program to achieve weight reduction. A fall in fasting blood sugar may follow caloric restriction prior to any significant weight loss. Weight reduction is an elusive goal that can be achieved and maintained only by close supervision of the obese patient and a supervised exercise program. The total amount of calories prescribed must take into account the patient's ideal body weight, lifestyle, and activity level. A diet consisting of no more than 600 kcal daily may be appropriate for a sedentary patient who is overweight, but a mildly active person can lose weight on a diet of up to 1400 kcal.

Special Considerations in Dietary Control

A. Dietary Fiber: Plant components such as cellulose, gum, and pectin are indigestible by humans and are termed dietary "fiber." **Insoluble fibers** such as cellulose or hemicellulose, as found in bran, tend to increase intestinal transit time and may have beneficial effects on colonic function. In contrast, **soluble fibers** such as gums and pectins, as found in beans, oatmeal, or apple skin, tend to decrease gastric and intestinal transit so that glucose absorption is slower and hyperglycemia is diminished. Although the ADA diet does not require insoluble fiber supplements such as added bran, it recommends foods such as oatmeal, cereals, and beans with relatively high soluble fiber content as stable components of the diet in diabetics. High soluble fiber content in the diet may also have a favorable effect on blood cholesterol levels.

B. Glycemic Index: Quantitation of the relative glycemic contribution of different carbohydrate foods has formed the basis of a "glycemic index" (GI), in which the area of blood glucose (plotted on a graph) generated over a 3-hour period following ingestion of a test food containing 50 g of carbohydrate is compared with the area plotted after giving a similar quantity of reference food such as glucose or white bread:

$$GI = \frac{\text{Blood glucose area of test food}}{\text{Blood glucose area of reference food}} \times 100$$

White bread is preferred to glucose as a reference standard because it is more palatable and has less tendency to slow gastric emptying by high tonicity, as happens when glucose solution is used.

Differences in GI were noted in normal subjects and diabetics when various foods were compared. In comparison to white bread, which was assigned an index of 100, the mean GI for other foods was as follows: baked potato, 135; table sugar (sucrose), 86; spaghetti, 66; kidney beans, 54; ice cream, 52; and lentils, 43. Some investigators have questioned whether the GI for a food ingested alone is meaningful, since the GI may become altered considerably by the presence of fats and protein when the food is consumed in a mixed meal.

Further studies of the reproducibility of the GI in the same person and the relation of a particular food's GI to its insulinotropic action on pancreatic B cells are needed before the utility of the GI in prescribing diabetic diets can be appropriately assessed. At present, however, it appears that small amounts of sucrose—particularly when taken with high-fiber substances such as cereals or whole-grain breads—may have no greater glycemic effects than comparable portions of starch from potatoes, rice, or bread.

C. Sweeteners: The nonnutritive sweetener **saccharin** is widely used as a sugar substitute (Sweet N'Low) and continues to be available in certain foods and beverages despite recent warnings by the FDA about its potential long-term bladder carcinogenicity. A committee of the National Academy of Sciences recommended restrictions in the use of saccharin in children and pregnant women. The panel felt that physicians might be best suited to determine on an individual basis its comparative benefit versus risk for patients with diabetes or obesity.

Aspartame (NutraSweet) may prove to be the safest sweetener for use in diabetics; it consists of two major amino acids, aspartic acid and phenylalanine, which combine to produce a nutritive sweetener 180 times as sweet as sucrose. A major limitation is its heat lability, which precludes its use in baking or cooking.

Other sweeteners such as sorbitol and fructose have recently gained popularity. Except for acute diarrhea induced by ingestion of large amounts of sorbitol-containing foods, their relative risk has yet to be established. **Fructose** represents a "natural" sugar substance that is a highly effective sweetener which induces only slight increases in plasma glucose levels and does not require insulin for its utilization.

D. Starch Blockers: The FDA has decided that enzymatic antagonists of amylase and sucrase (alpha-glucosidase inhibitors) can no longer be classified as "foods" but must be classified as drugs. At present, clinical trials are in progress to ascertain the efficacy and safety of these substances in reducing postprandial hyperglycemia in diabetes. They have not proved effective as an adjunct to weight reduction in the management of obesity.

2. ORAL HYPOGLYCEMIC DRUGS (Sulfonylureas & Biguanides)

There are two major types of oral hypoglycemic drugs: the sulfonylureas and the biguanides. The modes of action of the two types are quite different. In 1977, the United States Department of Health, Education, and Welfare recommended discontinuing general use of phenformin, the only biguanide available in the USA. It was considered to be a health hazard because of its reported association with the development of lactic acidosis. Recently, clinical trials with another biguanide, metformin, have been initiated. This agent is said to be less likely to produce lactic acidosis.

Sulfonylureas

Currently, the sulfonylureas are the only oral hypoglycemic drugs approved for use in the USA. This group of drugs contains a sulfonic acid-urea nucleus that can be modified by chemical substitutions to produce agents that have similar qualitative actions but differ widely in potency. The proposed mechanisms of action of the sulfonylureas include (1) augmentation of insulin release from pancreatic B cells and (2) potentiation of insulin's action on its target cells.

A. Mechanism of Action: Specific receptors on the surface of pancreatic B cells bind sulfonylureas in the rank order of their insulinotropic potency (glyburide with the greatest affinity and tolbutamide with the least). It has been shown that activation of these receptors closes potassium channels, resulting in depolarization of the B cell. This depolarized state permits calcium to enter the cell and actively promote insulin release (Figure 15–8). Controversy persists, however, about whether this well-documented insulinotropic action during acute administration is sufficient to explain adequately the hypoglycemic effect of sulfonylureas during chronic therapy. Additional extrapancreatic effects of sulfonylureas, such as their potentiation of the peripheral effects of insulin at the receptor or postreceptor level, have been invoked to account for their continued effectiveness during long-term treatment despite a lack of demonstrable increase in insulin secretion. However, several clinical trials have failed to demonstrate any therapeutic benefit on long-term glycemic control when sulfonylureas are added to insulin therapy in the patient with IDDM. These observations suggest that in vitro evidence for a potentiation by sulfonylureas of the peripheral effects of insulin may have little clinical relevance.

B. Indications: Sulfonylureas are not indicated in ketosis-prone type I diabetic patients, since these drugs require functioning pancreatic B cells to produce their effect on blood glucose. Moreover, clinical trials show no benefit from the use of sulfonylureas as an adjunct to insulin replacement in type I diabetic patients. The sulfonylureas seem most appropriate for use in the nonobese patient with mild maturity-onset diabetes whose hyperglycemia has not responded to diet therapy. In obese patients with mild diabetes and slight to moderate peripheral insensitivity to levels of circulating insulin, the primary emphasis should be on weight reduction. When hyperglycemia in obese diabetics has been more severe, with consequent impairment of pancreatic B cell function, sulfonylureas may improve glycemic con-

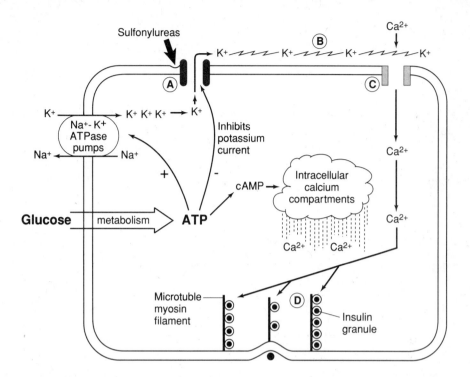

Figure 15–8. Proposed mechanism for sulfonylurea stimulation of insulin release by the pancreatic B cell. Energy-dependent pumps maintain a high intracellular concentration of potassium (K+). In the resting B cell, K+ diffuses from the cell through non-energy-dependent potassium channels (A). This current of potassium ions generates an electrical potential that polarizes the resting cell membrane (B) and closes a voltage-gated calcium channel (C), thereby preventing extracellular calcium from entering the cell. When sulfonylureas bind to a specific receptor on the potassium channel (or when glucose metabolism generates ATP), the potassium channel closes. This depolarizes the cell, allowing calcium to enter and cause microtubules to contract (D), moving insulin granules to the cell surface for emeiocytosis. (Modified and reproduced, with permission, from Karam JH: Type II diabetes and syndrome X. Endocrinol Metab Clin North Am 1992;21:339.)

trol until concurrent measures such as diet, exercise, and weight reduction can sustain the improvement without the need for oral drugs.

C. Sulfonylureas Currently Available in the USA: (Table 15–10.)

1. Tolbutamide (Orinase)– Tolbutamide is supplied in tablets of 250 and 500 mg. It is rapidly oxidized in the liver to an inactive form. Because its duration of effect is short (6–10 hours), it is usually administered in divided doses (eg, 500 mg before each meal and at bedtime). The usual daily dose is 1.5–3 g; some patients, however, require only 250–500 mg daily. Acute toxic reactions are rare, with skin rashes occurring most commonly. Because of its short duration of action, which is independent of renal function, tolbutamide is probably the safest agent to use in elderly patients in whom hypoglycemia would be a particularly serious risk. Prolonged hypoglycemia has been reported rarely, mainly in patients receiving certain drugs (eg, warfarin, phenylbutazone, or sulfonamides) that compete with sulfonylureas for hepatic oxidation, resulting in maintenance of high levels of unmetabolized active sulfonylureas in the circulation.

2. Chlorpropamide (Diabinese)– This drug is supplied in tablets of 100 and 250 mg. It has a half-life of 32 hours and a duration of action of up to 60 hours. It is slowly metabolized by the liver, with approximately 20–30% excreted unchanged in the urine. Since the metabolites retain hypoglycemic activity, elimination of the biologic effect is almost completely dependent on renal excretion, so that its use is contraindicated in patients with renal insufficiency. The average maintenance dose is 250 mg daily (range, 100–500 mg), given as a single dose in the morning. Chlorpropamide is a potent agent that is occasionally effective in controlling hyperglycemia in NIDDM despite the failure of maximum therapeutic doses of other less potent sulfonylureas such as tolbutamide, tolazamide, and acetohexamide. A potential hazard in the use of this drug is development of prolonged hypoglycemia, which occurs more commonly with the use of chlorpropamide than with the shorter-acting oral hypoglycemic agents. Elderly pa-

Table 15–10. Sulfonylureas.[1]

	Chemical Structure	Daily Dose	Duration of Action (hours)
Tolbutamide (Orinase)	H_3C—⟨⟩—SO_2—NH—C(=O)—NH—$(CH_2)_3$—CH_3	1500–3000 mg in divided doses	6–12
Tolazamide (Tolinase)	H_3C—⟨⟩—SO_2—NH—C(=O)—NH—N⟨⟩	200–1000 mg as single dose or in divided doses	12–24
Acetohexamide (Dymelor)	H_3C—C(=O)—⟨⟩—SO_2—NH—C(=O)—NH—⟨⟩	250–1500 mg as single dose or in divided doses	12–24
Chlorpropamide (Diabinese)	Cl—⟨⟩—SO_2—NH—C(=O)—NH—$(CH_2)_2$—CH_3	100–500 as single dose	Up to 60
Glyburide (glibenclamide; DiaBeta, Micronase)	Cl, OCH_3—⟨⟩—C(=O)—NH—$(CH_2)_2$—⟨⟩—SO_2—NH—C(=O)—NH—⟨⟩	2.5–20 mg	10–24
Glipizide (glydiazinamide; Glucotrol)	H_3C—pyrazine—C(=O)—NH—$(CH_2)_2$—⟨⟩—SO_2—NH—C(=O)—NH—⟨⟩	2.5–40 mg	3–8

[1] Modified slightly and reproduced, with permission, from Katzung BG (editor): *Basic & Clinical Pharmacology*, 2nd ed. Lange, 1984.

tients, especially those with reduced renal function, are at greatest risk for development of hypoglycemia with chlorpropamide, and the drug should probably not be used in patients over 65 years of age. Doses in excess of 500 mg/d increase the risk of jaundice, which does not occur with the usual dose of 250 mg or less. About 15% of patients taking chlorpropamide develop a facial flush when they drink alcohol, and occasionally they may develop a full-blown disulfiram-like reaction, with nausea, vomiting, weakness, and even syncope. There appears to be a genetic predisposition to the development of this reaction.

Other side effects of chlorpropamide include water retention and the development of hyponatremia, effects that are mediated through an ADH mechanism. The hyponatremia is generally a benign condition with sodium values between 125 and 130 meq/L, but occasional cases of symptomatic hyponatremia with sodium concentrations below 125 meq/L have been reported, particularly when concomitant diuretic therapy is being used. Chlorpropamide stimulates ADH secretion and also potentiates its action at the renal tubule. Its antidiuretic effect is somewhat unusual, since three other sulfonylureas (acetohexamide, tolazamide, and glyburide) appear to facilitate water excretion in humans. Hematologic toxicity (transient leukopenia, thrombocytopenia) occurs in less than 1% of patients.

3. Tolazamide (Tolinase)– Tolazamide is supplied in tablets of 100, 250, and 500 mg. The average daily dose is 200–1000 mg, given in one or two doses. It is comparable to chlorpropamide in potency

but is devoid of disulfiram-like or water-retaining effects. Tolazamide is more slowly absorbed than the other sulfonylureas, with effects on blood glucose not appearing for several hours. Its duration of action may last up to 20 hours, with maximal hypoglycemic effect occurring between the fourth and 14th hours. Tolazamide is metabolized to several compounds that retain hypoglycemic effects. If more than 500 mg/d is required, the dose should be divided and given twice daily. Doses larger than 1000 mg/d do not improve the degree of glycemic control.

4. Acetohexamide (Dymelor)– This agent is supplied in tablets of 250 and 500 mg. Its duration of action is about 10–16 hours (intermediate in duration of action between tolbutamide and chlorpropamide). The usual daily dose is 250–1500 mg given in one or two doses. Liver metabolism is rapid, but an active metabolite is produced and excreted by the kidney.

5. Second-generation sulfonylureas– In April, 1984, the FDA approved two potent sulfonylurea compounds, glyburide and glipizide. These agents have similar chemical structures, with cyclic carbon rings at each end of the sulfonylurea nucleus; this causes them to be highly potent (100-fold more potent than tolbutamide). The drugs should be used with caution in patients with cardiovascular disease as well as in elderly patients, in whom hypoglycemia would be especially dangerous. Neither glyburide nor glipizide should be prescribed to patients with hepatic or renal impairment, since a reduced clearance of these drugs from the blood would greatly increase the risk of hypoglycemia.

Diabetic patients who have not responded to tolbutamide or even tolazamide often—but not always—respond to the more potent first-generation sulfonylurea, chlorpropamide, or to either of the second-generation sulfonylureas. Unfortunately, substantial glycemic benefit has not always resulted when a maximum therapeutic dose of chlorpropamide has been replaced with that of a second-generation drug.

a. Glyburide (glibenclamide)– Glyburide is supplied in tablets containing 1.25, 2.5, and 5 mg. The usual starting dose is 2.5 mg/d, and the average maintenance dose is 5–10 mg/d given as a single morning dose. If patients are going to respond to glyburide, they generally do so at doses of 10 mg/d or less, given once daily. If they fail to respond to 10 mg/d, it is uncommon for an increase in dosage to result in improved glycemic control. Maintenance doses higher than 20 mg/d are not recommended. Glyburide is metabolized in the liver into products with such low hypoglycemic activity that they are considered clinically unimportant unless renal excretion is compromised. Although assays specific for the unmetabolized compound suggest a plasma half-life of only 1–2 hours, the biologic effects of glyburide clearly persist for 24 hours after a single morning dose in diabetic patients.

A recently marketed 3-mg Press Tab formulation of "micronized" glyburide which is easy to divide in half with slight pressure if necessary is currently available. However, there is some question as to its bioequivalency as compared with nonmicronized formulations, so that the FDA recommends careful monitoring to retitrate dosage when switching from standard glyburide doses or from other sulfonylurea drugs.

Glyburide does not cause water retention, as chlorpropamide does, and even slightly enhances free water clearance. Glyburide has few adverse effects other than its potential for causing hypoglycemia. It is particularly hazardous in patients over 65 years of age, in whom serious, protracted, and even fatal hypoglycemia can occur even with relatively small daily doses. Drugs with a shorter half-life, eg, tolbutamide or possibly glipizide, are preferable in the treatment of type II diabetes in the elderly patient.

b. Glipizide (glydiazinamide)– Glipizide is supplied in tablets containing 5 and 10 mg. For maximum effect in reducing postprandial hyperglycemia, this agent should be ingested 30 minutes before breakfast, since rapid absorption is delayed when the drug is taken with food. The recommended starting dose is 5 mg/d, with up to 15 mg/d given as a single daily dose. When higher daily doses are required, they should be divided and given before meals. The maximum recommended dose is 40 mg/d.

At least 90% of glipizide is metabolized in the liver to inactive products, and only a small fraction is excreted unchanged in the urine. Glipizide therapy is contraindicated in patients who have hepatic or renal impairment and who would therefore be at high risk for hypoglycemia, but because of its lower potency and shorter half-life, it is preferable to glyburide in elderly patients.

Biguanides

Unlike sulfonylureas, the biguanides (Table 15–11) do not require functioning pancreatic B cells for reduction of hyperglycemia. Use of **phenformin** was discontinued in the USA because of its association with the development of lactic acidosis in patients with coexisting liver or kidney disease. Also of note was lack of documentation of any long-term efficacy of this drug in treating diabetes. Biguanides continue to be used in many countries throughout the world. **Metformin,** a biguanide reported to be less likely to produce lactic acidosis, has generally replaced phenformin in the treatment of diabetics.

Metformin (1,1-dimethylbiguanide hydrochloride) was introduced in France in 1957 as an oral agent for therapy of type II diabetes, either alone or in conjunction with sulfonylureas. It is awaiting FDA approval in the USA pending the outcome of multicenter clinical trials.

Table 15–11. Biguanides.

Biguanide $H_2N-C(=NH)-N(H)-C(=NH)-R$	R	Daily Dose	Duration of Action (hours)
Phenformin (DBI, Meltrol-50)[1]	$-NH-(CH_2)_2-\bigcirc$	0.025–0.15 g as single dose or in divided doses	4–6 / 8–14[2]
Buformin[1]	$-NH-(CH_2)_3-CH_3$	0.05–0.3 g in divided doses	10–12
Metformin[1]	$-N-(CH_3)_2$	1–3 g in divided doses	10–12

[1] In clinical use outside USA.
[2] Timed-disintegration capsules.

The exact mechanism of action of metformin remains unclear. It reduces both the fasting level of blood glucose and the degree of postprandial hyperglycemia in patients with type II diabetes but has no effect on fasting blood glucose in normal subjects. Metformin does not stimulate insulin action, particularly in reducing hepatic gluconeogenesis. Other proposed mechanisms include a slowing down of gastrointestinal absorption of glucose and increased glucose uptake by skeletal muscle, which have been reported in some but not all clinical studies.

Metformin has a half-life of 1 1/2 –3 hours, is not bound to plasma proteins, and is not metabolized in humans, being excreted unchanged by the kidneys.

Metformin may be used as an adjunct to diet for the control of hyperglycemia and its associated symptomatology in patients with type II diabetes, particularly those who are obese or are not responding optimally to maximal doses of sulfonylureas. A side benefit of metformin therapy is its tendency to improve hyperglycemia and hypertriglyceridemia in obese diabetics without the weight gain associated with insulin or sulfonylurea therapy. For this reason—and because of its ability to correct hyperglycemia while having an insulin-sparing action—metformin has particular potential in treating patients with the insulin resistance syndrome (syndrome X). Metformin is not indicated for patients with type I diabetes and is contraindicated in diabetics with renal or hepatic insufficiency, alcoholism, or a propensity to develop hypoxia (eg, disease associated with cardiorespiratory insufficiency).

Metformin is dispensed as 500 mg or 850 mg tablets, and the dosage range is from 500 mg to a maximum of 2.5 g daily, with the lowest possible effective dose being recommended. It is important that metformin be taken in divided doses—and with meals—to reduce minor gastrointestinal upsets. A common schedule would be one 500 mg tablet four times a day with meals or one 850 mg tablet twice daily at breakfast and dinner.

The most frequent side effects of metformin are gastrointestinal symptoms (anorexia, nausea, vomiting, abdominal discomfort, diarrhea), which occur in up to 20% of patients. These effects are dose-related, tend to occur at onset of therapy, and often are transient. However, in 3–5% of patients, therapy may have to be discontinued because of persistent diarrheal discomfort.

Hypoglycemia does not occur with therapeutic doses of metformin, which permits its description as a "euglycemic" or "antihyperglycemic" drug rather than an oral hypoglycemic agent. Dermatologic or hematologic toxicity is rare.

Lactic acidosis (see below) has been reported as a side effect but is uncommon with metformin in contrast to phenformin, and almost all reported cases have involved subjects with associated risk factors that should have contraindicated its use (renal, hepatic, or cardiorespiratory insufficiency, alcoholism, advanced age).

Efficacy & Safety of Oral Hypoglycemic Agents

The University Group Diabetes Program (UGDP) reported that the number of deaths due to cardiovascular disease in diabetic patients treated with tolbutamide or phenformin was excessive when compared to either insulin-treated patients or to patients receiving placebos. Controversy persists about the validity of the conclusions reached by the UGDP because of the heterogeneity of the population studied, its preponderance of obese subjects, and certain features of the experimental design, such as the use of a fixed dose of oral drug and lack of control for cigarette smoking. At present, a warning label outlining their cardiovascular risk is inserted in each packet of sulfonylureas dispensed. However, the American Diabetes Association has withdrawn its original support for the UGDP conclusions.

3. INSULIN

Insulin is indicated for type I diabetics as well as for those type II diabetics whose hyperglycemia does not respond to diet therapy and oral hypoglycemic drugs.

Insulin replacement in patients with type I diabetes has been less than optimal because it is not possible to completely reproduce the normal physiologic pattern of insulin secretion into the portal vein. The problem of achieving optimal insulin delivery remains unsolved with the present state of technology. Subcutaneous injections do not reproduce the physiologic patterns of insulin secretion; however, with the help of appropriate modifications of diet and exercise and careful monitoring of capillary blood glucose levels at home, it is possible to achieve acceptable control of blood glucose by using multiple injections of mixtures of short- and intermediate-acting insulins. In some patients, a portable insulin infusion pump or a single injection of a long-acting insulin may be required for optimal control.

With the development of highly purified human insulin preparations, immunogenicity has been markedly reduced, thereby decreasing the incidence of therapeutic complications such as insulin allergy, immune insulin resistance, and localized lipoatrophy at the injection site.

Characteristics of Currently Available Insulin Preparations

Commercial insulin preparations differ with regard to the animal species from which they are obtained; their purity, concentration, and solubility; and their time of onset and duration of biologic action (Tables 15–12 and 15–13; Figure 15–9). In 1992, approxi-

Table 15–12. Summary of bioavailability characteristics of the insulins.

	Insulin Type	Onset	Peak Action	Duration
Short-acting	Regular, Actrapid, Velosulin	15–30 minutes	1–3 hours	5–7 hours
	Semilente, Semitard	30–60 minutes	4–6 hours	12–16 hours
Intermediate-acting	Lente, Lentard, Monotard, NPH, Insulatard, Protaphane	2–4 hours	8–10 hours	18–24 hours
Long-acting	Ultralente, Ultratard	4–5 hours	8–14 hours	25–36 hours

Table 15–13. Insulin preparations available in the USA.[1]

Preparation	Special Source	Concentration
SHORT-ACTING INSULINS		
Standard[2]		
Regular (Novo Nordisk)	Pork	U100
Regular Iletin I (Lilly)	Beef and pork	U100
Semilente (Novo Nordisk)	Beef	U100
Semilente Iletin I (Lilly)	Beef and pork	U100
"Purified"[3]		
Regular (Novo Nordisk)[4]	Pork or human	U100
Regular Humulin (Lilly)	Human	U100
Regular Iletin II (Lilly)	Pork or beef	U100, U500[5]
Semilente (Novo Nordisk)	Pork	U100
Velosulin (Novo Nordisk)	Pork or human	U100
Humulin BR (Lilly)[6]	Human	U100
INTERMEDIATE-ACTING INSULINS		
Standard[2]		
Isophane NPH (Novo Nordisk)	Beef	U100
Lente (Novo Nordisk)	Beef	U100
Lente Iletin I (Lilly)	Beef and pork	U100
NPH Iletin I (Lilly)	Beef and pork	U100
"Purified"[3]		
Insulatard NPH (Novo Nordisk)[4]	Pork or human	U100
Lente Humulin (Lilly)	Human	U100
Lente Iletin II (Lilly)	Pork or beef	U100
Lente (Novo Nordisk)[4]	Pork or human	U100
NPH Humulin (Lilly)	Human	U100
NPH Iletin II (Lilly)	Pork or beef	U100
NPH (Novo Nordisk)	Pork or human	U100
PREMIXED INSULINS		
(70% NPH, 30% REGULAR)		
Mixtard (Novo Nordisk)	Pork or human	U100
Novolin 70/30 (Novo Nordisk)	Human	U100
Humulin 70/30 (Lilly)	Human	U100
LONG-ACTING INSULINS		
Standard[2]		
Ultralente (Novo Nordisk)	Beef	U100
Ultralente Iletin I (Lilly)	Beef and pork	U100
"Purified"[3]		
Ultralente (Novo Nordisk)	Beef	U100
Ultralente Humulin (Lilly)	Human	U100

[1] These agents are all available without prescription. Wholesale prices for all preparations are similar.
[2] Greater than 10 but less than 25 ppm proinsulin.
[3] Less than 10 ppm proinsulin.
[4] Novo Nordisk human insulins are termed Novolin R, L, and N.
[5] U500 available only as pork insulin.
[6] Humulin BR (Buffered Regular) is recommended for use only in pumps. Its phosphate buffer precludes its being mixed with lente insulin.

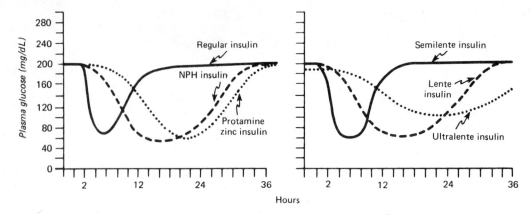

Figure 15–9. Extent and duration of action of various types of insulin (in a fasting diabetic). (Reproduced, with permission, from Katzung BG [editor]: *Basic & Clinical Pharmacology,* 2nd ed. Lange, 1984.)

mately 40 different formations of insulin were available in the USA.

A. Species of Insulin: Because the supply of human or pork insulin is too limited to satisfy the demand for insulin in the USA, most commercial insulins are composed of beef insulin or mixtures of beef and pork insulin. Beef insulin, which differs by three amino acids from human insulin, is more antigenic than pork insulin, which differs from human insulin by just one amino acid. The standard preparation of Iletin I (Lilly) is a mixture of 70% beef and 30% pork insulin, whereas the highly purified Iletin II insulins are available as either beef or pork insulin. Human insulin is now produced by recombinant DNA techniques. Human insulin prepared by the recombinant DNA method in *E coli* is available for clinical use as Humulin (Lilly) and dispensed as either Regular (R), NPH (N), or Lente (L). Human insulin formerly prepared by enzymatic conversion of pork insulin but now exclusively made by recombinant DNA methods using yeast is marketed as Novolin by Novo Nordisk and as Velosulin-Human by Nordisk. Novolin-R is a rapid-acting soluble form of human insulin. Novolin-L is a zinc suspension with an intermediate duration of action similar to that of Novolin-N, which is an isophane suspension of human insulin with protamine. Since human insulin tends to be slightly more hydrophilic than beef insulin, an ultralente formulation of human insulin with the required degree of insolubility has only recently been introduced, but questions persist as to whether it has the same slow and sustained release as beef ultralente.

B. Purity of Insulin: (Table 15–13.) Improvements in purification techniques with Sephadex gel columns have reduced or eliminated contamination with proteins having molecular weights greater than that of insulin (eg, proinsulin). Although these contaminants were biologically inactive, they were capable of inducing anti-insulin antibodies. The degree of purification in which proinsulin contamination is greater than 10 ppm but less than 25 ppm justifies their present labeling as "new improved single peak insulin." When the proinsulin content is reduced to less than 10 ppm, manufacturers are entitled by FDA regulations to label the insulin **"purified."** These "purified" insulins are generally available as a monospecies of pork or beef or human insulin (Table 15–13); however, a monocomponent beef and pork mixture is also available (Lentard, Novo Nordisk).

The more highly purified insulins currently in use preserve their potency quite well; therefore, refrigeration while in use is not necessary. During travel, reserve supplies of insulin can be readily transported for weeks without significant loss of potency provided they are protected from extremes of heat or cold.

Concentrations of Insulin

At present, insulins in the USA are available only in a concentration of 100 units/mL (U100); all are dispensed in 10-mL vials. To accommodate children and the occasional adult who may require small quantities of insulin, "low-dose" (0.5-mL and 0.3-mL) disposable insulin syringes have been introduced so that U100 insulin can now be measured accurately in doses as low as 1 or 2 units. This has eliminated the need for lower concentrations of insulin and has resulted in the phasing out of all U40 insulins in the United States. For use in rare cases of severe insulin resistance in which large quantities of insulin are required, a limited supply of U500 (500 units/mL) regular insulin is available from Lilly (pork, Iletin II).

Bioavailability Characteristics

Three principal types of insulin are available: (1) short-acting insulin, with rapid onset of action; (2)

intermediate-acting; and (3) long-acting, with slow onset of action (Table 15–12). Short-acting (unmodified) insulin is a crystalline zinc insulin with a neutral pH in soluble form; it is dispensed as a clear solution. All other commercial insulins have been specifically modified to obtain more prolonged action. They are dispensed as opaque suspensions at neutral pH with either protamine (derived from fish sperm) in phosphate buffer (NPH) or varying concentrations of zinc in acetate buffer (ultralente, semilente, and lente insulins), rendering the insulin insoluble.

As noted above, conventional insulin therapy relies on combinations of short-acting and either intermediate-acting or long-acting insulin. The characteristics of these various insulins are discussed below and summarized in Table 15–12. It is important to recognize that values given for time of onset of action, peak effect, and duration of action are only approximate ones and that there is great variability in these parameters from patient to patient and even in a given patient depending on the size of the dose, the site of injection, the degree of exercise, the avidity of circulating anti-insulin antibodies, and other less well defined variables.

A. Short-Acting Insulins:

1. Regular insulin– Regular insulins (Regular Iletin I or II, or Humulin [Lilly], Insulin Injection Actrapid or Novolin-R [Novo Nordisk], Velosulin [Nordisk]) are short-acting, soluble crystalline zinc insulins whose hypoglycemic effect appears within 15 minutes after subcutaneous injection, peaks at 1–3 hours, and lasts for about 5–7 hours when usual quantities, eg, 5–15 units, are administered. Regular insulin is the only type that can be administered intravenously or used in continuous subcutaneous infusion pumps. It is particularly useful in the treatment of diabetic ketoacidosis and when the insulin requirement is changing rapidly, such as after surgery or during acute infections.

Regular insulin produced by Novo Nordisk and Lilly is dispensed without a buffer, but when it is used in reservoirs or infusion pumps, stability is improved when regular insulin is buffered with disodium phosphate, as in Velosulin (Nordisk). A special formation of Humulin Buffered Regular (Lilly) is designated for use only in infusion pumps.

2. Semilente insulin– Semilente (Lilly) and Semitard (Novo Nordisk) insulins are an amorphous (or microcrystalline) form of insulin and zinc in acetate buffer. The onset of action is 30–60 minutes, peak action is reached at 6 hours, and the duration of action is 12–16 hours. Most physicians prefer to prescribe regular insulin rather than the semilente series, because of the more prompt onset of action of regular insulin when injected before meals.

B. Intermediate-Acting Insulins:

1. Lente insulin– This is a mixture of 30% semilente with 70% ultralente insulin (Lente Iletin I and II and Humulin-L [Lilly], Lente Insulin [beef], Mono-

tard [pork], Lentard [beef-pork], and Novolin-L [Novo Nordisk]). Its onset of action is delayed to 2–4 hours, and its peak response is generally reached in about 8–10 hours. Because its duration of action is often less than 24 hours (with a range of 18–24 hours), most patients require at least two injections daily to maintain a sustained insulin effect. The supernatant of the lente suspension contains an excess of zinc ions, which may precipitate regular insulin if it is added to lente.

2. NPH (neutral protamine Hagedorn, or isophane) insulin– (NPH Iletin I and II or Humulin-N [Lilly], NPH Insulin Protaphane and Novolin-N [Novo Nordisk], Insulatard NPH [pork or human] [Nordisk].) NPH is an intermediate-acting insulin in which the onset of action is delayed by combining two parts of soluble crystalline zinc insulin with one part protamine zinc insulin. The mixture is reported to have equivalent concentrations of protamine and insulin, so that neither is in excess ("isophane"). The peak action and duration of action of NPH insulin are similar to those of lente insulin, however, in contrast to lente insulin, regular insulin retains its solubility and independent rapid action when mixed with NPH.

Flocculation of suspended particles may occasionally "frost" the sides of a bottle of NPH insulin or "clump" within bottles from which multiple small doses are withdrawn over a prolonged period. These bottles generally have been kept at room temperature and subjected to recurrent agitation. Patients should be vigilant for early signs of frosting or clumping of the NPH insulin, because it indicates a pronounced loss of potency. Several cases of diabetic ketoacidosis have been reported in IDDM patients who had been inadvertently injecting this denatured insulin.

C. Long-Acting Insulin: Ultralente insulin—Iletin I Ultralente (Lilly), Ultratard (Novo Nordisk)—is a long-acting crystalline suspension of insulin whose onset of action is quite delayed, with peak effects at 8–14 hours and a duration of action of up to 36 hours. Beef insulin is less soluble than pork insulin, producing larger crystals and thus assuring a prolonged action. Beef insulin has thus been preferred in producing the ultralente insulins. Ultratard (Novo Nordisk) is a pure beef insulin, whereas Ultralente Iletin I is 70% beef and 30% pork. Recently, a human insulin formulation (Humulin-U, [Lilly]) whose pharmacokinetics are similar to those of beef insulin (except for a slightly shorter duration of action (24–28 hours rather than 28–36 hours) has been developed. Ultralente is increasingly used in association with multiple preprandial injections of regular insulin in an attempt to establish optimal control in IDDM patients. Its very slow onset of action and prolonged duration have led to its use in providing a basal level of insulin comparable to that achieved by basal endogenous secretion or by the overnight infusion rate programmed into insulin pumps.

D. Premixed Insulins: As a convenience to patients, particularly those with impaired visual acuity or hand coordination, premixed insulin preparations with fixed ratios of 70% NPH insulin and 30% regular insulin are available. These include Mixtard pork or human insulin (Nordisk), Novolin 70:30 (Novo Nordisk) and Humulin 70:30.

E. Insulin Analogues: Among the many variables affecting the absorptive kinetics of insulin, an important one seems to be the property of insulin molecules of aggregating in hexameric form when formulated at pharmacologic concentrations. This causes lag periods of up to 30 minutes before insulin absorption is initiated from a subcutaneous depot site and results in a prolonged profile of absorption because the U100 injected regular insulin must be diluted more than 1000-fold by tissue fluids before it becomes monomeric and more readily absorbable into the circulation. The Novo Research Institute is currently developing insulin analogues such as one with two amino acid substitutions (Asp^{B9}, Glu^{B27}) that has the property of remaining monomeric even at therapeutic concentrations. This analogue and others are undergoing clinical trials at present with encouraging preliminary results as regards a favorable profile of rapid absorption after subcutaneous injection, excellent biologic activity in vivo, and relatively low immunogenicity.

Methods of Insulin Administration

A. Insulin Syringes and Needles: Disposable plastic syringes with needles attached are available in 1-mL, 0.5-mL, and 0.3-mL sizes. Their finely honed 27- or 28-gauge attached needles have greatly reduced the pain of injections. They are light, not susceptible to damage, and convenient when traveling. Moreover, their clear markings and tight plungers allow accurate measurement of insulin dosage. In cases where very low insulin doses are prescribed, specially calibrated 0.3-mL and 0.5-mL disposable syringes facilitate accurate measurement of U100 insulin in doses up to 50 units. These "low-dose" syringes have become increasingly popular because it is now recommended that diabetics not take more than 50 units of insulin in a single injection except in the rare instance of extreme insulin resistance. Several reports indicate that "disposable" syringes may be reused until blunting of the needle occurs (usually after three to five injections). Wiping the needle with a clean alcohol swab, reapplying the needle guard, and refrigeration after use appear to maintain adequate sterility to avoid infection. A concern, however, arises from a report that flecks of silicone may become suspended in insulin bottles into which disposable syringes have been repeatedly inserted; the silicone flecks seem to reduce the activity of the insulin.

B. Mixing Insulin: Since intermediate insulin requires several hours to reach adequate therapeutic levels, supplements of regular insulin are generally added preprandially in IDDM patients. Several studies have shown that using insulin mixtures containing increased proportions of lente to regular insulins retards the rapid action of admixed regular insulin. The excess zinc in lente insulin binds the soluble insulin and partially blunts its action, particularly when a relatively small proportion of regular insulin is mixed with lente (eg, one part regular to 1.5 or more parts lente). NPH preparations do not delay absorption of admixed regular insulin. They are therefore preferable to lente when mixtures of intermediate and regular insulins are prescribed. For convenience, regular and NPH insulin may be mixed together in the same syringe and injected subcutaneously in split dosage before breakfast and supper.

When mixing insulin, it is necessary to inject into both bottles a quantity of air equivalent to the volume of insulin being withdrawn. Traditionally, regular insulin is withdrawn first, and the longer-action insulin is then added to the syringe. Care must be taken to avoid contaminating either insulin bottle with insulin of the different type. The injection is preferably given immediately after loading the syringe, and no attempt should be made to mix the insulins in the syringe.

C. Sites for Injection: Any part of the body covered by loose skin can be used as an injection site, including the abdomen, thighs, upper arms, flanks, and upper outer quadrants of the buttocks. In general, regular insulin is absorbed more rapidly from upper regions of the body such as the deltoid area or the abdomen rather than from the thighs or buttocks. Exercise appears to facilitate insulin absorption when the injection site is adjacent to the exercising muscle. Rotation of sites continues to be recommended to avoid delayed absorption when fibrosis or lipohypertrophy occurs owing to repeated use of a single site. However, considerable variability of absorption rates from different sites, particularly with exercise, may contribute to the instability of glycemic control in certain IDDM patients if injection sites are rotated indiscriminately over different areas of the body. Consequently, diabetologists recommend limiting injection sites to a single region of the body and rotating sites within that region. It is possible that some of the stability of glycemic control achieved by infusion pumps may be related to the constancy of the site of infusion from day to day. For most patients the abdomen is the recommended site for injection, since it provides a considerable area in which to rotate sites and there may be less variability of absorption with exercise than when the thigh or deltoid areas are used.

D. Insulin Delivery Systems: Efforts to administer insulin by **"closed loop"** systems (glucose-controlled insulin infusion systems [Biostator]) have been successful in acute situations such as diabetic ketoacidosis or during surgery. However, chronic use is precluded by the bulkiness of the computerized pump and by the need for continuous aspiration of blood for the external glucose sensor that activates the appropriate insulin or glucose infusion.

Several small portable **"open loop" devices** for the delivery of insulin are on the market. These devices contain an insulin reservoir and a pump programmed to deliver regular insulin subcutaneously; they do not contain a glucose sensor. With improved methods for self-monitoring of *blood* glucose at home (see below), these pump systems have become very useful for managing some diabetic patients. However, there have been reports of numerous acute complications, such as infection at the catheter site and ketoacidosis due to kinking of the tube attached to the insulin reservoir. At present, conventional methods of insulin administration, with multiple subcutaneous injections of mixtures of a rapid and either an intermediate-acting or long-acting insulin, can provide glycemic control almost as effectively as the open loop systems in most patients with IDDM who self-monitor their blood glucose levels accurately and regularly. However, occasional patients continue to have extreme lability of blood glucose control and frequent hyperglycemia after overnight fasting despite meticulous compliance with a regimen of multiple subcutaneous injections of insulin. In these cases, switching over to the appropriate use of continuous subcutaneous insulin infusion pumps has achieved improved glycemic control. Currently, the results of clinical trials have been encouraging regarding the usefulness of implantable insulin pumps that deliver insulin intraperitoneally under control of a programmed radio signal activated by the subject in response to information obtained from periodic self-monitoring of capillary blood glucose concentrations.

To facilitate treatment of patients who are adhering to a regimen of multiple preprandial injections of regular insulin that supplement a single injection of long-acting insulin delivered by a conventional syringe, portable **pen injectors** have been introduced. These pen-sized devices (Novo-Pen, Insuject) contain cartridges of U100 regular human insulin and retractable needles and eliminate the need to carry an insulin bottle and syringes during the day.

Intranasally administered soluble insulin is rapidly absorbed when given along with a detergent substance to facilitate adsorption. Preliminary clinical trials have demonstrated its efficacy in reducing postprandial hyperglycemia in insulin-dependent diabetics. Further studies are in progress to assess its usefulness as an insulin delivery system in treating diabetic patients.

Pancreatic islet cells have been successfully transplanted in genetically similar strains of rodents with experimental diabetes; however, this approach has not yet been successful in humans because of difficulties in preparing and maintaining viable islets and because of immunologic rejection of the tissue. Similarly, **whole pancreas transplants** have gener-

ally proved unsatisfactory in treating the insulin-dependent (type I) patient because of the present hazards of prolonged antirejection therapy.

STEPS IN THE MANAGEMENT OF THE DIABETIC PATIENT

Diagnostic Examination

A. History and Physical Examination: A complete history is taken and physical examination is performed for diagnostic purposes and to rule out the presence of coexisting or complicating disease. Nutritional status should be noted, particularly if catabolic features such as progressive weight loss are present despite a normal or increased food intake. The family history should include not only the incidence but also the age at onset of diabetes in other members of the family, and it should be noted whether affected family members were obese and whether they required insulin. Other factors that increase cardiovascular risk, such as a smoking history, presence of hypertension or hyperlipidemia, or oral contraceptive pill use should be documented.

A careful physical examination should include baseline height and weight, pulse rate, and blood pressure. If obesity is present, it should be characterized as to its distribution and a waist to hip ratio should be recorded. All peripheral arterial pulses should be examined, noting whether bruits or other signs of atherosclerotic disease are present. Neurologic and ophthalmologic examinations should be performed, with emphasis on investigation of abnormalities that may be related to diabetes, such as neovascularization of the retina or stocking/glove sensory loss in the extremities.

B. Laboratory Diagnosis: (See also Laboratory Findings in Diabetes Mellitus, above.) Laboratory diagnosis should include documentation of the presence of fasting hyperglycemia (plasma glucose > 140 mg/dL [7.7 mmol/L]) or postprandial (post-glucose tolerance test) values consistently above 200 mg/dL (11.1 mmol/L). An attempt should be made to characterize the diabetes as IDDM or NIDDM, based on the clinical features present and on whether or not ketonuria accompanies the glycosuria. With current emphasis on home blood glucose monitoring, laborious attempts to document the renal threshold for glucose are no longer necessary in the initial evaluation of diabetic patients, particularly since "double-voided" urine specimens are difficult to obtain and since acceptable control of glycemia now allows only rare episodes of glycosuria.

Other baseline laboratory measurements that should be made part of the record include either glycohemoglobin or hemoglobin A_{1c}, total and HDL cholesterol, plasma triglycerides, electrocardiogram, chest x-ray, complete blood count, complete urinalysis, and renal function studies (serum creatinine, blood urea nitrogen, and, if possible, creatinine clearance).

Patient Education

Education is the most important task of the physician who provides care to diabetic patients. It must be remembered that education is necessary not only for newly diagnosed diabetic patients and their families but also for patients with diabetes of any duration who may never have been properly educated about their disorder or who may not be aware of advances in diabetes management. The "teaching curriculum" should include explanations of the nature of diabetes, its potential acute and chronic complications, and information on how these complications can be prevented or at least recognized and treated early. The importance of self-monitoring of blood glucose should be emphasized, particularly in all insulin-requiring diabetic patients, and instructions on proper testing and on recording of data should be provided. Patients should be taught to use algorithms to adjust the timing and quantity of their insulin dose, food, and exercise in response to their recorded blood glucose values, so that optimal blood glucose control is achieved. Patients must be helped to accept the fact that they have diabetes; until this difficult adjustment has been made efforts to cope with the disorder are likely to be futile. Counseling should be directed at avoidance of extremes such as compulsive rigidity or self-destructive neglect. All patients should be made aware of community agencies (Diabetes Association chapters, etc.) that serve as resources for continuing education.

A. Diet Instruction: All diabetic patients should receive individual instruction on diet, as described earlier in this chapter. Unrestricted diets are not advised for insulin requiring diabetics. Until new methods of insulin replacement are available to provide more normal patterns of insulin delivery in response to metabolic demands, multiple small feedings restricted in simple sugars will continue to be recommended.

B. Insulin: Give the patient an understanding of the actions of the various insulins and the methods of administration of insulin. Since infections, particularly pyogenic ones with fever and toxemia, provoke a marked increase in insulin requirements, patients must be taught how to appropriately administer supplemental regular insulin as needed to correct hyperglycemia during infections. Patients and their families or friends should also be taught to recognize signs and symptoms of hypoglycemia and how to institute appropriate therapy for hypoglycemic reactions (see Acute Complications of Diabetes Mellitus, below).

C. Oral Hypoglycemic Agents: Information must be provided on the principles of hypoglycemic therapy (including information about time of onset, peak action, and duration of action of any pharmaco-

logic agent being used). Patients should be made aware of the maximum recommended dose of the sulfonylureas that they are taking and should learn to inquire about possible drug interactions whenever any new medications are added to their regimens.

D. Effect of Exercise: Exercise increases the effectiveness of insulin, and regular daily moderate exercise is an excellent means of improving utilization of fats and carbohydrates in diabetic patients. A judicious balance of the size and frequency of meals with moderate regular exercise can often stabilize the insulin dosage in diabetics who tend to slip out of control easily. Strenuous exercise, however, can precipitate hypoglycemia in an unprepared patient, and diabetics must therefore be taught to reduce their insulin dosage or take supplemental carbohydrate in anticipation of strenuous activity. Injection of insulin into a site farthest away from the muscles most involved in exercise may help meliorate exercise-induced hypoglycemia, since insulin injected to exercising muscle is much more rapidly mobilized. With more knowledge regarding the relationship between caloric intake and expenditure and insulin requirements, the patient can become liberated from much of the regimentation imposed by the disorder.

E. Good Hygiene: All diabetic patients must receive adequate instruction on personal hygiene, especially with regard to care of the feet, skin, and teeth.

F. Infections: Infections with fever and severe illness provoke the release of high levels of insulin antagonists that will bring about a marked increase in insulin requirements. It is essential to limit the period of infection, since infection raises the blood glucose level and this, in turn, can impair the general defense mechanisms that the body uses against bacterial and even viral organisms. Thus, the early and sufficient use of bactericidal antibiotics is imperative. Type I diabetics must be taught how to supplement the regimen with regular insulin if persistent glycosuria and ketonuria occur—especially if associated with infection. Patients must understand that insulin therapy should never be withheld in the presence of gastric upset and vomiting if glycosuria with ketonuria is present. When food intake is limited by nausea or vomiting, the patient should take ginger ale, apple juice, or grape juice in small sips and should notify the physician in case supplemental intravenous fluids might be required.

G. Self-Monitoring: Patients in whom labile diabetes is difficult to control should receive instructions on techniques for self-monitoring of blood glucose (see below). They should be encouraged to keep careful records of their glucose measurements and instructed on appropriate measures to correct for emerging patterns of hyperglycemia as well as to prevent recurrent episodes of hypoglycemia. Self-monitoring instructs patients on the glycemic effects of specific foods and exercise and alleviates the likelihood of unexpected episodes of severe hypogly-

Table 15–14. Advantages and disadvantages of various insulin regimens in treatment of type I diabetes.

Regimen	Advantages	Disadvantages
Single injection of NPH or Lente	Convenience only	Poor hyperglycemic control or nocturnal hypoglycemia. Requires frequent feedings to avoid hypoglycemia if acceptable control attempted. Inflexible feeding schedules. Variability of absorption of large doses predisposes to hypoglycemia, which is common. Because of these disadvantages, this regimen is not recommended.
Conventional split dose of mixture (regular and NPH twice daily)	Relatively convenient. Controls postprandial glycemia at breakfast and dinner.	Prebreakfast hyperglycemia is common. Increased risk of nocturnal hypoglycemia in attempt to control prebreakfast hyperglycemia. Variability of absorption due to relatively large NPH doses to last overnight.
Three injections (mixture of regular and NPH in the morning; regular at dinner; NPH at bedtime)	Controls postprandial glycemia at breakfast and dinner. Can prevent prebreakfast hyperglycemia with less risk of nocturnal hypoglycemia. Less variability of absorption of NPH, since lower doses are injected to last overnight.	Less convenient. Lunch schedule is relatively inflexible as to time and quantity to avoid hypoglycemia from morning NPH. Dinner schedule cannot be delayed without extra feedings.
Four injections (regular before meals and NPH, Lente, or Ultralente at bedtime) or subcutaneous infusion of regular insulin with pump	Controls postprandial glycemia. Allows flexibility of meal schedules and quantity. Less variability of absorption of small doses of insulins given more frequently. Tight glycemic control is possible with least risk of hypoglycemia.	Relatively inconvenient. Pumps are expensive and are generally less convenient than multiple injections and add risk of skin infections and pump failures.

cemia. Moreover, when combined with an appropriate algorithm for therapy so that patients can respond appropriately to the various effects of glycemia, self-monitoring allows for greater flexibility in life-style and enables patients to be more fully in control of their diabetes.

H. Identification Bracelet: All patients receiving hypoglycemic therapy should wear a Medic-Alert bracelet or necklace that clearly states that insulin or an oral sulfonylurea drug is being taken. A card in the wallet or purse is less useful, since legal problems may arise if a victim's person and belongings are searched without permission. (Information on how to obtain a Medic-Alert identification device can be obtained from the Medic-Alert Foundation, PO Box 1009, Turlock, CA 95380.)

I. Restrictions on Occupation: Certain occupations potentially hazardous to the diabetic patient or others will continue to be prohibited (eg, piloting airplanes, operating cranes).

Avoidance of Stress & Emotional Turmoil

Prevention of psychologic turmoil is of great importance in the control of diabetes, particularly when the disease is difficult to stabilize. One reason blood glucose control in diabetics may be particularly sensitive to emotional upset is that their pancreatic A cells are hyperresponsive to physiologic levels of epinephrine, producing excessive levels of glucagon with consequent hyperglycemia.

Specific Therapy

Treatment must be individualized depending on the specific needs of each patient. Certain general principles of management pertaining to each type of diabetes are outlined below.

A. Type I Diabetes (IDDM): IDDM patients require replacement therapy with exogenous insulin. This should be instituted under conditions of an individualized diabetic diet with multiple feedings and normal daily activities so that an appropriate dosage regimen can be developed.

At the onset of diabetes, many type I patients recover some pancreatic B cell function and may temporarily need only low doses of exogenous insulin to supplement their own endogenous insulin secretion. This is known as the "honeymoon period." Within 8 weeks to 2 years, however, most of these patients show either absent or negligible pancreatic B cell function. At this point, these patients may be instructed to take a "conventional" regimen of two injections of insulin mixtures (a short-acting combined with intermediate-acting NPH insulin). Alternatively, if more flexibility with meal intervals and exercise is desired, multiple preprandial small injections of regular insulin may be prescribed along with a bedtime injection of long-acting or intermediate-acting insulin. (See Table 15–14 for advantages and disadvantages of various insulin regimens.) Self-monitoring of blood glucose levels is the recommended means of determining the adjustment of insulin dosage and the modulation of food intake and exercise in type I diabetes.

1. Conventional insulin therapy (split doses of insulin mixtures)– A conventional insulin regimen in a 70-kg patient taking 2200 kcal divided into six feedings might be 10 units of regular and 10 units of NPH insulin in the morning and 8 units of regular and 8 units of NPH insulin in the evening. The morning blood glucose level gives a measure of the effectiveness of NPH insulin administered the previous evening; the noon level reflects the effects of the morning regular insulin; and the 5 PM and 9 PM levels represent the effects of the morning NPH and the evening regular insulins, respectively. A properly educated patient should be taught to adjust insulin dosage by observing the pattern of recorded self-monitored blood glucose levels and correlating it with the approximate duration of action and the time of peak effect after injection of the various insulin preparations (Table 15–12). Adjustments should be made gradually, preferably not more often than every 2 or 3 days if possible.

Certain caveats should be kept in mind regarding insulin treatment. Considerable variations in absorption and bioavailability exist, even when the same dose is injected in the same region on different days in the same individual. Such variation often can be minimized by injecting smaller quantities of insulin at each dose and consequently using multiple doses. Also, a given insulin dose may undergo considerable differences in pharmacokinetics in different individuals, either because of insulin antibodies that bind insulin with different avidity, or for other as yet unknown reasons.

2. Intensive multiple-dose insulin therapy– While split doses of insulin mixtures daily have improved the quality of glycemic control as compared to single injections of intermediate insulin in type I diabetics, blood glucose values throughout the day are often not optimal, and nocturnal hypoglycemia may result from attempts to achieve prebreakfast euglycemia. In cases in which conventional split doses of insulin mixtures cannot maintain near-normalization of blood glucose without hypoglycemia (particularly at night), multiple injections of insulin may be required. An increasingly popular regimen consists of reducing or omitting the evening dose of intermediate insulin and adding a portion of it at bedtime. For example, 10 units of regular insulin mixed with 10 units of NPH insulin might be prescribed in the morning, 8–10 units of regular insulin before the evening meal, and 6 units of NPH at bedtime.

To further reduce variation in absorption kinetics, which is aggravated when ratios of insulin in mixtures are altered on different days, a multiple injection regimen that avoids mixing insulin has been devised. The patient administers small doses of regular insulin more frequently (eg, four times a day) and one injection of a long-acting insulin at bedtime (eg, ultralente insulin). Both of these multiple-dose regimens give greater flexibility regarding meal patterns and content than conventional therapy with split doses of insulin mixtures and are helpful in reducing the frequency and severity of hypoglycemia in patients attempting near-normalization of blood glucose.

3. Intensive insulin therapy using insulin pumps–Several types of portable battery-operated "open loop" devices have been marketed to deliver insulin continuously (see Methods of Insulin Administration, above). These generally infuse insulin through a needle or catheter implanted subcutaneously in the abdomen. A basal infusion rate of regular insulin is provided over a 24-hour period, and this is augmented by a bolus of regular insulin prior to meals. In addition, since insulin requirements appear to increase slightly in the early dawn period in the majority of patients with type I diabetes, most pumps also have adjustable basal rates that can be programmed to rise automatically at 6 AM. Unbuffered regular insulins such as Humulin-R, Iletin I and II, or Novolin-R have been associated with frequent blockage of pump tubing due to precipitation of the insulin. Accordingly, only insulin buffered with phosphate such as Velosulin or the specially issued Humulin Buffered Regular (for pump use only) have been recommended for use in insulin infusion pumps.

The use of pumps requires knowledgeable and compliant patients who can be depended on to monitor their blood glucose levels as often as four times daily. The indwelling needle or catheter should be changed every 48 hours to reduce the risk of infection, and patients should be alert for symptoms of sudden deterioration of glycemic control, due to pump blockage, pump failure, or leakage of insulin from the tubing. The selection of dosage is usually based on providing 40–50% of the estimated daily dose of insulin as the basal infusion rate and the remaining amount divided as intermittent boluses given prior to meals to control postprandial metabolism. For example, in a 70-kg patient requiring 40–45 units of insulin a day, 20 units of regular insulin would be administered as a basal infusion of 0.8 unit/h, with the remaining units administered as follows: 7–8 units before breakfast, 5–6 units before lunch, 6–8 units before supper, and 0–2 units prior to a bedtime snack. The results of blood glucose monitoring as well as the extent of physical activity and dietary intake will all contribute to fine-tuning the proper dosage of insulin administered at various meals and basally.

4. Selection of patients for intensive insulin therapy–Patient selection is difficult, and exact criteria are controversial. Patients should be highly motivated and willing to monitor their blood glucose levels several times daily and record the results. They should not have impaired adrenergic responses to hypoglycemia, as is often seen with autonomic neuropathy, since this reduces their awareness of being hypoglycemic and increases the risk of severe hypoglycemic episodes. Finally, if nonproliferative ("background") or proliferative retinopathy is present, intensive insulin therapy should be initiated slowly and with careful attention to possible progression of retinal disease (see Ophthalmologic Complications, below).

5. Self-monitoring of blood glucose levels– Glycemic self-monitoring should be considered a *means* of achieving near-normal blood glucose control rather than being an *end in itself.* This implies that diabetic patients must be educated to make appropriate behavioral adjustments in their diet, activity, timing of insulin injections, etc, based on their preprandial capillary blood glucose measurements, in order to achieve the desired level of blood glucose control. Knowledge of the level of blood glucose has been particularly helpful at bedtime in ascertaining the need for supplementary feedings to avoid nocturnal hypoglycemia. Unfortunately, a 1992 NIH report revealed that despite current nationwide efforts toward patient education, no more than 38% of adults with IDDM in the United States monitored their own blood glucose.

Self-monitoring of blood glucose levels is helpful in managing diabetes in all patients on insulin therapy, and especially in the following groups: patients with brittle diabetes; patients who are attempting ideal glycemic control, such as during pregnancy; and patients with impaired or absent early warning of hypoglycemic episodes. Self-monitoring is useful in educating patients about the glycemic effects of specific foods in their diet and reduces the likelihood of unexpected episodes of severe hypoglycemia in insulin-treated diabetics.

There are three essential elements to self-monitoring of blood glucose: (1) obtaining the blood specimen, (2) applying the specimen to enzyme-impregnated strips capable of discriminating the glucose level, and (3) reading the glucose level from the test strip. Each of these will be discussed briefly.

The patient may obtain a capillary blood sample from the fingertip by means of a lancet designed for this purpose. The patient should be taught how to clean the site and how to rapidly pierce the skin to obtain a drop of blood. Automatic spring-loaded devices such as the Autolet or Penlet are useful in simplifying the finger-pricking technique and ensuring an adequate blood sample.

The drop of blood is then applied to the appropriate area of an enzyme-impregnated strip such as the Dextrostix, Chemstrip bG, or Glucostix. It is important to follow the instructions for each type of strip. The strips vary with respect to the area necessary to cover with the blood drop, washing technique, and timing of the procedure.

Chemstrip bG results can be visually interpreted by comparing the colors obtained on the strip with the color chart supplied by the manufacturer. For patients who have difficulty with color discrimination or who prefer more exact results, devices with automated digital readouts are available to quantitate the color changes (Glucometer, Glucoscan, AccuChek bG, Diascan, One Touch II, or ExacTech). These devices vary in cost, ease of use, portability, and strip compatibility.

Newer meters such as One Touch II, and particularly ExacTech, are more compact and have the distinct advantage of automatically timing the entire reaction as well as obviating the need to wipe off the strip, thereby reducing the potential for technical error. The physician should learn the advantages and disadvantages of these devices and help the patient make an appropriate choice.

Initially, blood glucose levels should be checked at least four times a day in patients with type I diabetes. Generally, these measurements are taken before each meal and at bedtime. In an adult with IDDM receiving multiple daily injections of insulin, a standard premeal dose of regular insulin should be prescribed (eg, 4–7 units) along with an algorithm for raising or lowering this dose appropriately by 1 or more units depending on the level of the premeal capillary blood glucose. This insulin dose adjustment is given in conjunction with other measures to modulate glycemic responses to the meal—such as altering the time interval after injecting the insulin or modifying the quantities or the order of ingestion of foodstuffs. Patients should be urged to review their recorded patterns of glycemic measurements over a 2- to 3-day period in relation to insulin dose, food intake, and exercise and to make *prospective* changes in their program when appropriate to correct for deficiencies in the therapeutic regimen. Once glycemic levels are brought into an acceptable range, the patient should continue to check blood glucose levels at least twice daily. In addition, patients should be taught to check their blood glucose level whenever they develop symptoms that could represent a hypoglycemic episode. All blood glucose levels and their timing and corresponding insulin doses should be recorded in an organized fashion and brought with the patient for physician review during regularly scheduled checkups; such personal blood glucose logs are commercially available.

6. Management of early morning hyperglycemia in IDDM patients–

a. Etiology and diagnosis– One of the more difficult therapeutic problems in managing patients with IDDM is determining the proper adjustment of insulin dose when the early morning blood glucose level is high before breakfast. Prebreakfast hyperglycemia is sometimes due to the **Somogyi effect,** in which nocturnal hypoglycemia evokes a surge of counterregulatory hormones to produce high blood glucose levels by 7 AM. If this is the case, lowering the evening dose of intermediate insulin is indicated. However, a more common cause of prebreakfast hyperglycemia is the **waning of circulating insulin levels,** which requires use of more (rather than less) intermediate insulin in the evening. These two phenomena are not mutually exclusive and can occur together to produce a greater magnitude of hyperglycemia in affected patients with IDDM. A third phenomenon—the **"dawn phenomenon"**—has been reported to occur in as many as 75% of IDDM patients and in the majority of NIDDM patients and normal subjects as well. It is characterized by a reduced tissue sensitivity to insulin between 5 AM and 8 AM (dawn), and apparently is evoked by spikes of growth hormone released hours before, at onset of sleep. When the "dawn phenomenon" occurs alone, it may produce only mild hyperglycemia in the early morning; however, when it is associated with either or both of the other phenomena, it can further aggravate the hyperglycemia (Table 15–15). Diagnosis of the cause of prebreakfast hyperglycemia can be facilitated by asking the patient to self-monitor blood glucose levels at 3 AM in addition to monitoring at the usual times, bedtime and 7 AM. When this was done, the Somogyi effect was found to be much less prevalent and of lower magnitude as a cause of prebreakfast hyperglycemia than had been previously suspected. In insulin-treated patients, serum levels of free immunoreactive insulin (particularly in the basal or low ranges) are difficult to quantitate accurately because of technical interference. In specialized research laboratories, however, these levels have been measured in hospitalized patients with prebreakfast hyperglycemia (Table 15–15).

b. Treatment– When a particular pattern emerges from monitoring blood glucose levels at 10 PM, 3 AM, and 7 AM, appropriate therapeutic measures can be taken. Prebreakfast hyperglycemia due to the Somogyi effect can be treated by either reducing the dose of intermediate insulin, giving a portion of it at bedtime, or supplying more food at bedtime. When the "dawn phenomenon" alone is present, shifting a portion of the intermediate insulin from dinnertime to bedtime often suffices; or when insulin pumps are used, the basal infusion rate can be stepped up appro-

priately (eg, from 0.8 unit/h to 1 unit/h) from 6 AM until breakfast. Finally, in cases in which the circulating insulin level is waning, either increasing the evening insulin dose or, preferably, shifting it from dinnertime to bedtime (or both) may be efficacious.

B. Type II Diabetes (NIDDM): The principles of therapy are less well defined in this heterogeneous group of diabetic patients than is the case with type I diabetes. Therapeutic recommendations are based upon the relative contributions of B cell insufficiency and insulin insensitivity in individual patients. With prolonged duration of NIDDM, deposits of amyloid accumulate in islets and encroach on pancreatic B cells, resulting in progressive diminution of insulin-secretory capacity.

1. The obese patient– The most common type of diabetic patient is the obese diabetic with insulin insensitivity. Characteristically, obese patients compensate for their insulin resistance with increased basal levels of circulating insulin and are capable of responding to a glucose load with hypersecretion of insulin. However, as hyperglycemia progresses, the insulin response to a glucose load decreases. This refractoriness of the B cell may be partially reversed with therapeutic correction of the hyperglycemia and seems to be selectively related to the hyperglycemic stimulation, since other B cell-stimulating agents such as sulfonylureas, arginine, and glucagon still provoke rapid insulin release.

a. Weight reduction– One of the primary modes of therapy in the obese type II diabetic patient is weight reduction. Normalization of glycemia can be achieved by reducing adipose stores, with consequent restoration of tissue sensitivity to insulin. A combination of caloric restriction, increased exercise, modification of behavior, and consistent reinforcement of good eating habits is required if a weight reduction program is to be successful. Knowledge of the symptoms of diabetes and an understanding of the risks and complications of diabetes often increase the patient's motivation for weight reduction. Even so, significant weight loss is seldom achieved in the morbidly obese patient; there is a variable effectiveness

Table 15–15. Typical patterns of overnight blood glucose levels and serum free immunoreactive insulin levels in prebreakfast hyperglycemia due to various causes in patients with IDDM.

	Blood Glucose Levels (mg/dL)			Serum Free Immunoreactive Insulin Levels (μU/mL)		
	10 PM	3 AM	7 AM	10 PM	3 AM	7 AM
Somogyi effect	90	40	200	High	Slightly high	Normal
"Dawn phenomenon"	110	110	150	Normal	Normal	Normal
Waning of circulating insulin levels plus "dawn phenomenon"	110	190	220	Normal	Low	Low
Waning of circulating insulin levels plus "dawn phenomenon" plus Somogyi effect	110	40	380	High	Normal	Low

in moderately obese patients depending on the enthusiasm of the therapist and the motivation of the patient.

b. Hypoglycemic agents– Hypoglycemic agents, including insulin as well as the oral hypoglycemic drugs are generally *not* indicated for long-term use in the obese patient with mild diabetes. A weight reduction program can be disrupted by real or imagined hypoglycemic reactions when insulin therapy is used, and weight gain is quite common in the insulin-treated obese diabetic patient. It is also possible that administration of insulin to an obese patient who already has excessive circulating levels may maintain insulin insensitivity through down-regulation of receptor sites and by interference with catabolic mechanisms during caloric deprivation. The obese diabetic who has been previously treated with conventional beef-pork insulin, often in high doses and in an interrupted fashion, may occasionally develop immune insulin resistance (see below). This not only increases the requirements for exogenous insulin but may further impair the effectiveness of endogenous insulin because of cross-reacting antibodies; on occasion, this can even precipitate ketoacidosis. Fortunately, this complication is presently much less common due to greater use of less immunogenic human insulins.

Oral sulfonylureas, therefore, are more appropriate than insulin for *symptomatic* moderately severe diabetes in an obese patient. If sulfonylurea therapy (combined with a weight reduction regimen) is inadequate to control symptoms of hyperglycemia (eg, nocturia, blurred vision, or candidal vulvovaginitis), insulin therapy may be necessary, directed at elimination of symptoms rather than restoration of euglycemia. Use of a sulfonylurea agent or insulin to supplement a weight reduction program should be for a limited period (weeks or months) to ameliorate hyperglycemic symptoms until sufficient weight reduction has occurred to keep the patient symptom-free.

2. The nonobese patient– In the nonobese NIDDM diabetic with moderately severe hyperglycemia, pancreatic B cells are refractory to glucose stimulation. Peripheral insulin resistance is also detectable but is considerably less intense than in obese diabetics who have a comparable degree of hyperglycemia; it is also of less therapeutic import, since insulin-treated nonobese patients do not generally need an excessive dosage of insulin.

a. Diet– If hyperglycemia is mild (fasting blood glucose levels of < 200 mg/dL [11.1 mmol/L]), normal metabolic control can occasionally be restored by a diet devoid of simple sugars and with calories calculated to maintain ideal body weight. Restriction of saturated fats and cholesterol is also strongly advised. The standard ADA diet with its recommended exchange list should be prescribed for these nonobese NIDDM patients.

b. Oral hypoglycemic agents– When diet therapy alone is not sufficient to correct hyperglycemia, a trial of sulfonylurea drugs is indicated to supplement the dietary regimen. The controversies raised by the UGDP (see Efficacy and Safety of Oral Hypoglycemic Agents, above) apply mainly to obese patients with relatively mild diabetes (who represented the great majority of patients in that study), and there are few data on which to base an assessment of the risk-benefit ratio of sulfonylureas in nonobese patients with fasting hyperglycemia above 140 mg/dL (7.8 mmol/L). Therefore, once their efficacy is demonstrated in these patients and since there is no evidence suggesting harm to them, it seems reasonable to continue the use of sulfonylureas as long as they remain effective in controlling hyperglycemia. The degree of control to aim for remains arbitrary at present; however, data from the United Kingdom and from studies of Pima Indians suggest that maintaining postprandial plasma glucose levels below 200 mg/dL (11.1 mmol/L) seems to spare NIDDM patients from increased risk of severe retinopathy or vascular complications. Once the dosage of sulfonylurea reaches the upper recommended limit in a compliant patient without maintaining plasma glucose below 200 mg/dL (11.1 mmol/L) throughout the day, insulin therapy is indicated.

c. Insulin– When sulfonylureas fail and NIDDM patients require insulin to control their hyperglycemia, various insulin regimens may be effective. Although reliance on a single morning injection of insulin is not recommended in type I diabetes, there are some NIDDM patients with enough residual insulin secretion to get by satisfactorily on a single daily injection of 20–25 units of NPH or lente insulin before breakfast. If hyperglycemia persists on this regimen—or if hypoglycemia occurs before lunch or dinner—a number of alternatives are available. The most popular insulin regimen under these circumstances is to use a split dose of a fixed 70:30 mixture of NPH:regular insulin, which can be started as 15–20 units before breakfast and 10–15 units before dinner, and this can be adjusted appropriately depending on target blood glucoses at 7 AM and 5 PM. If more than 50 units per day does not achieve satisfactory glycemic control, these patients may benefit from more intensive multiple-injection regimens as described for IDDM. Many nonobese patients with mild insulinopenia can have their glycohemoglobin levels brought into the normal range with relatively small doses of insulin and without provoking nocturnal hypoglycemia. Patients with more severe insulinopenia may require split doses of insulin.

d. Therapeutic combinations of sulfonylureas with insulin– Both nonobese and obese NIDDM patients usually show a modest glycemic improvement with a regimen combining sulfonylurea drugs and insulin, but this improvement can generally be achieved with insulin therapy alone. At present, there is no overall consensus regarding how these agents should be combined. One proposed regimen adds a bedtime intermediate-acting insulin to reduce excessive nocturnal hepatic glucose output in NIDDM patients who are responding poorly on maximal doses of sulfonylureas; more commonly, however, diabetologists recommend stopping the sulfonylureas in these circumstances and changing over to insulin therapy alone. Only in the case of NIDDM patients requiring excessive amounts of insulin (> 100 units/d) is it considered a reasonable option to add sulfonylureas to improve glycemic control rather than prescribing inordinately higher insulin doses.

In IDDM patients, the absence of glycemic improvement or reduction in insulin dose when sulfonylureas are added to the insulin regimen suggests that the predominant effect of sulfonylureas is their insulinotropic action, and that any effect on potentiation of insulin action is limited to in vitro systems and of little clinical importance. In NIDDM patients, observations of an improvement in insulin action during sulfonylurea therapy need not be a direct "extrapancreatic" effect but could be explained by improved endogenous insulin release, since other means of reducing hyperglycemia (eg, diet therapy or insulin administration) have been equally effective in decreasing insulin resistance.

Immunopathology of Insulin Therapy

At least five molecular classes of insulin antibodies are produced during the course of insulin therapy: IgA, IgD, IgE, IgG, and IgM. Even though the use of highly purified pork and human insulins has considerably reduced the immunogenicity of insulin, many diabetics continue to be treated with mixed beef-pork insulins (Table 15–13). These beef-containing insulins usually induce antibodies to insulin after about 2–3 weeks of therapy.

A. Insulin Allergy: Insulin allergy, a hypersensitivity reaction of the immediate type, is a rare condition in which local or systemic urticaria occurs immediately after insulin injection. This reaction is due to histamine release from tissue mast cells sensitized by adherence of IgE antibodies to their surface. In severe cases, anaphylaxis can occur. The appearance of a subcutaneous nodule at the site of insulin injection, occurring several hours after the injection and lasting for up to 24 hours, has been attributed to an IgG-mediated complement-binding Arthus reaction. Because sensitivity was often due to noninsulin protein contaminants, the highly purified insulins have markedly reduced the incidence of insulin allergy, especially of the local variety. When allergy to beef insulin is present, a species change (eg, to pure pork insulin or to human insulin) may correct the problem, although in rare cases allergic reactions persist even to injected human insulin.. Antihistamines, corticosteroids, and even desensitization may be required, especially for systemic hypersensitivity in an insulin-dependent pa-

tient. A commercial kit containing various dilutions of pure beef or pure pork insulin for allergy testing and insulin desensitization is available from the Eli Lilly Company, although requests for its use have greatly diminished, as more human insulins are being prescribed from the outset of insulin therapy.

B. Immune Insulin Resistance: Except for some patients initially treated with highly purified pork or human insulin, all patients who receive insulin develop a low titer of circulating IgG antibodies to insulin, and this neutralizes to a small extent the rapid action of insulin. In some diabetic patients with a history of intermittent exposure to insulin therapy—and especially those with some degree of tissue insensitivity to insulin (such as obese NIDDM patients)—a high titer of circulating IgG antibodies to insulin develops. This results in extremely high insulin requirements, often to more than 200 units/d. This frequently is a self-limited condition and may clear spontaneously after several months. However, in cases where the circulating antibody is specifically more reactive to beef insulin, switching to a less antigenic highly purified pork insulin or human insulin may make possible a dramatic reduction in insulin dosage or at least may shorten the duration of immune resistance. In NIDDM patients, whose excessive circulating insulin antibodies do not completely neutralize endogenous (human) insulin, the foreign insulin can be discontinued and the patient maintained on oral sulfonylureas combined with diet therapy. Owing to the usual effectiveness of human insulin in treating this syndrome, immunosuppressive therapy with high doses of glucocorticoids is no longer required.

C. Lipodystrophy at Injection Sites: Rarely, a disfiguring atrophy of subcutaneous fatty tissue occurs at the site of insulin injection. Although the cause of this complication is obscure, it seems to represent a form of immune reaction, particularly since it occurs predominantly in females and is associated with lymphocyte infiltration in the lipoatrophic area. This complication has become even less common since the development of highly purified insulin preparations of neutral pH. Injection of highly purified preparations of insulin directly into the atrophic area often results in restoration of normal contours.

Lipohypertrophy, on the other hand, is not a consequence of immune responses; rather, it seems to be due to the pharmacologic effects of depositing insulin in the same location repeatedly. It can occur with purified insulins and is best treated with localized liposuction of the hypertrophic areas by an experienced plastic surgeon. It is prevented by rotation of injection sites.

ACUTE COMPLICATIONS OF DIABETES MELLITUS

HYPOGLYCEMIA

Hypoglycemic reactions (see below and Chapter 16) are the most common complications that occur in insulin-treated diabetic patients. They may also occur in patients taking oral sulfonylureas, especially older patients or those with impaired liver or kidney function treated with long-acting and highly potent agents such as chlorpropamide or glyburide. Hypoglycemia may result from delay in taking a meal or from unusual physical exertion without supplemental calories or a decrease in insulin dose.

Clinical Features

Signs and symptoms of hypoglycemia may be divided into those resulting from neuroglycopenia (insufficient glucose for normal central nervous system function leading to confusion and coma) and those resulting from stimulation of the autonomic nervous system. There is great variation in the pattern of hypoglycemic signs and symptoms from patient to patient; however, individual patients tend to experience the same pattern from episode to episode. In older diabetics, in patients with frequent hypoglycemic episodes, and in those with diabetic autonomic neuropathy, autonomic responses may be blunted or absent, so that hypoglycemia may be manifested only by signs and symptoms of neuroglycopenia. The gradual onset of hypoglycemia with intermediate-acting or long-acting insulin also makes recognition more difficult in older patients.

A. Neuroglycopenia: Signs and symptoms of neuroglycopenia include mental confusion with impaired abstract and, later, concrete thought processes; this may be followed by bizarre antagonistic behavior. Stupor, coma, and even death may occur with profound hypoglycemia. Full recovery of central nervous system function does not always occur if treatment is delayed.

B. Autonomic Hyperactivity: Signs and symptoms of autonomic hyperactivity can be both adrenergic (tachycardia, palpitations, sweating, tremulousness) and parasympathetic (nausea, hunger). Except for sweating, most of the sympathetic symptoms of hypoglycemia are blunted in patients receiving beta-blocking agents for angina or hypertension. Though not absolutely contraindicated, these drugs must be used with great caution in insulin-requiring diabetics.

C. Counterregulatory Responses to Hypoglycemia: (See Table 15–16.)

1. Normal counterregulation– When plasma glucose is acutely lowered in normal subjects by intravenous insulin, a rapid surge of both glucagon and epinephrine acts to counterregulate the hypoglycemia. Plasma glucagon is considered the first line of defense against acute hypoglycemia, while the role of epinephrine and the sympathetic system is to provide a backup system. The latter helps to restore euglycemia and serves as an alarm system to warn the subject of the urgent need for carbohydrate intake in case the counterregulatory response is inadequate to prevent the potentially disastrous consequences of life-threatening neuroglycopenia.

2. Defective counterregulation in diabetes– For unexplained reasons, patients with type I diabetes uniformly lose their ability to secrete glucagon in response to acute insulin-induced hypoglycemia within a few years after developing diabetes. After that time, they are solely dependent upon triggered autonomic adrenergic responses to counteract an impending hypoglycemic crisis as well as for early warning. It is well documented that with advanced age these autonomic responses may be blunted considerably, and in diabetic patients with clinical autonomic neuropathy as a complication of diabetes they may be absent. In these circumstances, reduced awareness of hypoglycemia can lead to potentially life-threatening sequelae from neuroglycopenic convulsions or coma.

3. "Iatrogenic" autonomic failure– Cryer has proposed that frequent and recurrent hypoglycemic episodes such as may be encountered in patients receiving intensive insulin therapy to achieve normoglycemia may result in failure of the sympathetic

Table 15–16. Counterregulatory responses to hypoglycemia.

Normal Counterregulation	Defective Counterregulation in Type I Diabetes[1]
Glucagon rises rapidly to 3–5 times baseline after insulin-induced hypoglycemia, provoking hepatic glycogenolysis.	Glucagon response to insulin-induced hypoglycemia is lost after onset of type I diabetes.
Adrenergic discharge (1) raises hepatic glucose output by glycogenolysis and (2) provides warning to subject of impending hypoglycemic crisis.	Blunted or absent adrenergic response may occur as a result of— (1) Neural damage with (a) advanced age or (b) autonomic neuropathy (2) Neural dysfunction (iatrogenic) from (a) frequent hypoglycemia or (b) human insulin therapy (?)

[1] Type II diabetics are less well characterized for their defective counterregulation as regards glucagon loss but appear to have the same frequency and causes of adrenergic loss as type I diabetics.

nervous system to respond to hypoglycemia. While the mechanism for this failure is not yet established, adaptation of the central nervous system to recurrent hypoglycemic episodes seems to alter the threshold for recognizing hypoglycemia so that much lower plasma glucose levels are needed to trigger an autonomic response—and by the time this occurs, cognition may already be impaired in some cases with onset of neuroglycopenia. That this adaptation and autonomic failure are a consequence of chronic hypoglycemia and not diabetes is evidenced by reports of two well-studied patients with insulinomas who had chronic recurrent episodes of hypoglycemia of which they often were unaware. These were patients who had loss of epinephrine responses and symptoms during acute insulin-induced hypoglycemia and whose symptoms and adrenergic responses during repeat testing returned to normal after euglycemia had been restored following resection of the insulinomas. This documented reversibility of the syndrome of hypoglycemia unawareness due to chronic hypoglycemia has exciting implications for therapy of those diabetic patients whose unawareness may be iatrogenic as a result of recurrent hypoglycemia during attempts at normalization of blood glucose during intensive insulin therapy.

4. Human insulin and hypoglycemic awareness– In 1987, a preliminary report contended that hypoglycemia unawareness became more prevalent in diabetics transferred from beef-pork to human insulin. Although occasional studies gave support to this claim, most investigators failed to find evidence for a detrimental effect of human insulin on recognition of hypoglycemia. There is some evidence that many of the anecdotal reports of loss of hypoglycemic awareness after changing from animal to human insulin may be a consequence of an increased number of hypoglycemic episodes. The latter may occur on switching from animal to human insulin if the switch is made at equivalent or nearly equivalent dosages without taking the precaution of using a lower human insulin dose to compensate for the reduced neutralization of the injected insulin by preexisting anti-beef or anti-pork insulin antibodies. Another possible cause of more frequent hypoglycemic episodes is the inclination of patients and their physicians to attempt tighter glycemic control when switching from animal to human insulin as part of a general upgrading of diabetes care. As evidenced by the results of the Diabetes Control and Complications Trial (DCCT), the risk of frequent hypoglycemic episodes is greatly increased when "normalization" of the blood glucose is attempted with present suboptimal methods of insulin delivery, and this was independent of the species of insulin used in the DCCT. Although the controversy has not been completely resolved, most authorities do not recommend restricting the use of human insulin on the basis of the present evidence.

D. Management of Hypoglycemic Unawareness: (See Table 15–17.) Many insulin-treated diabetics have nocturnal episodes of hypoglycemia of which they are often unaware. These may be detected only with screening by capillary blood testing at least once a week at 2–3 AM. If such episodes do occur, appropriate reduction of evening insulin doses or an increase in the amount of food taken as a snack at bedtime should be advised.

When hypoglycemic unawareness occurs while the patient is awake, two patterns of presentation have been described. In some cases, patients appear perfectly alert with no obvious neuroglycopenia or adrenergic symptoms when a scheduled preprandial capillary blood glucose measurement indicates a level below 40 or 50 mg/dL (2.2 or 2.7 mmol/L). This suggests some degree of adaptation with probable provision of increased glucose transporter-1 proteins among brain capillaries to provide minimum requirements of glucose to the brain despite the hypoglycemia. These patients are at increased risk, however, of developing severe neuroglycopenia if hypoglycemia progresses.

In the second pattern of presentation, patients exhibit neuroglycopenia and progress to require assistance for recovery without having had any awareness of the impending crisis. This form of unawareness is life-threatening and requires immediate measures to prevent recurrences.

When either of these patterns of hypoglycemic unawareness presents while the patient is awake, careful evaluation for autonomic neuropathy with reduced or absent adrenergic responses is indicated. Evidence for this condition consists of orthostatic hypotension or a fixed heart rate measured during a

Table 15–17. Hypoglycemic "unawareness" in insulin-dependent diabetes mellitus.

I. Sleeping patient (nocturnal hypoglycemia)
II. Hypoglycemia with unawareness while awake—
  A. Manifestations:
    1. Without detectable neuroglycopenia:
      a. Adaptation to chronic hypoglycemia (increased brain glucose transporter I)
    2. With neuroglycopenia:
      a. Maladaptation to hypoglycemia
  B. Mechanisms:
    1. Defective autonomic response:
      a. Due to diabetic autonomic neuropathy
      b. Iatrogenic
        i. Frequent hypoglycemia
        ii. Human insulin therapy (?)
  C. Management:
    1. Identify patients at risk and reevaluate glycemic goals
    2. Advise frequent self-monitoring of blood glucose
    3. Learn to detect subtle symptoms of neuroglycopenia
    4. Avoid recurrent hypoglycemia
    5. Frequent snacks should be prescribed
    6. Multiple small doses of insulin may be needed
    7. Injectable glucagon made available to family

change in position, during respiration, or after a Valsalva maneuver.

If autonomic neuropathy is detected, glycemic target goals should be appropriately raised by lowering the daily insulin dosage and ensuring that it is administered in multiple small doses, which have a more predictable pharmacokinetic pattern than do larger depot injections. To further lower the risk of severe hypoglycemic episodes, the frequency of self-monitoring of blood glucose should be increased to provide awareness of glycemic status at regular intervals.

In patients without obvious autonomic neuropathy who have lost awareness to hypoglycemia, special efforts should be made to avoid hypoglycemia for weeks or months in order to reverse central nervous system adaptation to recurrent hypoglycemia. This can be done by increasing the frequency of self-monitoring of blood glucose, raising the mean blood glucose level to be targeted, eating frequent small snacks, and reducing the size of insulin doses at any one injection.

Treatment

All of the manifestations of hypoglycemia are rapidly relieved by glucose administration. Because of the danger of insulin reactions, diabetic patients should carry packets of table sugar or a candy roll at all times for use at the onset of hypoglycemic symptoms. Tablets containing 3 g of glucose are available. The educated patient soon learns to take the amount of glucose needed to correct symptoms without ingesting excessive quantities of orange juice or candy, which can provoke very high glycemic levels. Family members or friends of the patient should be provided with a glucagon emergency kit (Lilly), which contains a syringe, diluent, and a 1-mg ampule of glucagon that can be injected intramuscularly if the patient is found unconscious; these kits are available by prescription. Detailed instructions in the use of glucagon are an essential part of the diabetic education program.

A. The Conscious Patient: Patients with symptoms of hypoglycemia who are conscious and able to swallow should eat or drink orange juice, glucose tablets, or any sugar-containing beverage or food except pure fructose (which does not cross the blood-brain barrier).

B. The Unconscious Patient: In general, oral feeding is contraindicated in stuporous or unconscious patients. If trained personnel are not available to administer intravenous glucose, the treatment of choice is for a family member or friend to administer 1 mg of glucagon intramuscularly (see above), which will usually restore the patient to consciousness within 10–15 minutes; the patient should then be given an oral form of sugar to ingest. If glucagon is not available, small amounts of honey, syrup, or glucose gel can be rubbed into the buccal mucosa. Rectal administration of syrup or honey (30 mL per 500 mL of warm water) has also been used effectively.

COMA

Coma is a *medical emergency* calling for immediate evaluation to determine its cause so that proper therapy can be started. There are several causes of coma that result directly from diabetes mellitus or its treatment. When evaluating a comatose diabetic patient, these must be considered *in addition* to the myriad causes included in the differential diagnosis of coma (cerebrovascular accidents, head trauma, intoxication with alcohol or other drugs, etc).

Etiologic Classification of Diabetic Coma

The causes of coma resulting directly from diabetes mellitus or its treatment include the following:

A. Hyperglycemic Coma: Hyperglycemic coma may be associated with either severe insulin deficiency (diabetic ketoacidosis) or with mild to moderate insulin deficiency (hyperglycemic, hyperosmolar, nonketotic coma).

B. Hypoglycemic Coma: This results from excessive doses of insulin or oral hypoglycemic agents (see above).

C. Lactic Acidosis: Lactic acidosis in diabetics is particularly apt to occur in association with severe tissue anoxia, sepsis, or cardiovascular collapse.

Emergency Management of Coma

The standard approach to *any comatose patient* is outlined below. Prompt action is required.

(1) Establish an airway.

(2) Establish intravenous access. About 30 mL of blood should be drawn and sent for complete blood count, serum electrolyte determinations, renal function and liver function tests, and blood glucose measurements.

(3) Administer 50 mL of 50% dextrose in water to all comatose patients, unless bedside monitoring of blood glucose shows marked hyperglycemia. This will rapidly reverse hypoglycemic coma and will not significantly alter the ultimate course of the mildly hyperglycemic patient. Since hypoglycemic blood left on an enzyme-impregnated glucose oxidase strip for longer than 1 minute (which can occur in the hectic atmosphere of an emergency situation) will give falsely elevated values, it is probably best not to withhold administration of intravenous dextrose to undiagnosed comatose patients in the absence of marked hyperglycemia (240 mg/dL or more).

(4) Administer 1 ampule (0.4 mg) of naloxone intravenously and 100 mg of thiamine intravenously.

Diagnosis of Coma

After emergency measures have been instituted, a careful history (from family, friends, paramedics, etc), physical examination, and laboratory evaluation are required to resolve the differential diagnosis. Patients in deep coma from a hyperosmolar nonketotic state or from hypoglycemia are generally flaccid and have quiet breathing—in contrast to patients with acidosis, whose respirations are rapid and deep if the pH of arterial blood has dropped to 7.1 or below. When hypoglycemia is a cause of the coma, hypothermia is usually present and the state of hydration is usually normal. Although the clinical laboratory remains the final arbiter in confirming the diagnosis, a rapid *estimation* of blood glucose and ketones can be obtained by the use of enzyme-impregnated glucose oxidase strips and crushed Acetest tablets (see Laboratory Findings in Diabetes Mellitus, above). Table 15–18 is a summary of some laboratory abnormalities found in diabetic patients with coma attributable to diabetes or its treatment. The individual clinical syndromes are discussed in detail on the following pages.

1. DIABETIC KETOACIDOSIS

This acute complication of diabetes mellitus may be the first manifestation of previously undiagnosed diabetes, or it may be the result of failure of a known diabetic to take adequate exogenous insulin. In either case, precipitating factors, such as infection, should be searched for and treated appropriately. Poor compliance, either for psychological reasons or because of inadequate patient education, is probably the most common cause of diabetic ketoacidosis, particularly when episodes are recurrent. In adolescents with type I diabetes, recurrent episodes of severe ketoacidosis often indicate the need for counseling to alter this behavior.

Diabetic ketoacidosis has been found to be one of the more common serious complications of insulin pump therapy, occurring in approximately one per 80 patient months of treatment. Many patients who monitor capillary blood glucose regularly ignore urine ketone measurements, which would signal the possibility of insulin leakage or pump failure before serious illness develops.

Pathogenesis

Acute insulin deficiency results in rapid mobilization of energy from stores in muscle and fat depots, leading to an increased flux of amino acids to the liver for conversion to glucose and of fatty acids for conversion to ketones (acetoacetate, β-hydroxybutyrate, and acetone). In addition to this increased availability of precursor, there is a direct effect of the low insulin:glucagon ratio on the liver that promotes increased production of ketones. In response to both the acute insulin deficiency and the metabolic stress of ketosis, the levels of insulin-antagonistic hormones (corticosteroids, catecholamines, glucagon, and GH) are consistently elevated. Furthermore, in the absence of insulin, peripheral utilization of glucose and ketones is reduced. The combination of increased production and decreased utilization leads to an accumulation of these substances in blood, with plasma glucose levels reaching 500 mg/dL (27.8 mmol/L) or more and plasma ketones reaching levels of 8–15 mmol/L or more.

The hyperglycemia causes osmotic diuresis leading to depletion of intravascular volume. As this progresses, impaired renal blood flow reduces the kidney's ability to excrete glucose, and hyperosmolality is worsened. Severe hyperosmolality (> 330 mosm/kg) correlates closely with central nervous system depression and coma.

In a similar manner, impaired renal excretion of hydrogen ions aggravates the metabolic acidosis that occurs as a result of the accumulation of the ketone acids, β-hydroxybutyrate and acetoacetate. The accumulation of ketones may cause vomiting, which exacerbates the intravascular volume depletion. In addition, prolonged acidosis can compromise cardiac output and reduce vascular tone. The result may be severe cardiovascular collapse with generation of lactic acid, which then adds to the already existent metabolic acidosis.

Table 15–18. Summary of some laboratory abnormalities in patients with coma directly attributable to diabetes or its treatment.

	Urine		Plasma			
	Glucose	Acetone	Glucose	Bicarbonate	Acetone	Osmolality
Diabetic ketoacidosis	++ to ++++	++++	High	Low	++++	+++
Hyperglycemic nonketotic coma	++ to ++++	0 or +[1]	High	Normal or slightly low[2]	0	++++
Hypoglycemia	0[3]	0 or +	Low	Normal	0	Normal
Lactic acidosis	0 to +	0 or +	Normal, low, or high	Low	0 or +	Normal

[1] A small degree of ketonuria may be present if the patient is severely stressed or has not been eating because of illness.
[2] A patient may be acidotic if there is severe volume depletion with cardiovascular collapse or if sepsis is present.
[3] Leftover urine in bladder might still contain sugar from earlier hyperglycemia.

Clinical Features

A. Symptoms and Signs: As opposed to the acute onset of hypoglycemic coma, the appearance of diabetic ketoacidosis is usually preceded by a day or more of polyuria and polydipsia associated with marked fatigue, nausea, and vomiting. Eventually, mental stupor ensues and can progress to frank coma. On physical examination, evidence of dehydration in a stuporous patient with rapid and deep respirations and the "fruity" breath odor of acetone would strongly suggest the diagnosis. Postural hypotension with tachycardia indicates profound dehydration and salt depletion.

B. Laboratory Findings: Four-plus glycosuria, strong ketonuria, hyperglycemia, ketonemia, low arterial blood pH, and low plasma bicarbonate (5–15 meq/L) are typical laboratory findings in diabetic ketoacidosis. Serum potassium is usually normal or slightly elevated (5–8 meq/L) despite total body potassium depletion, because of the shift of potassium from the intracellular to extracellular spaces that occurs in systemic acidosis. The average total body potassium deficit resulting from osmotic diuresis, acidosis, and gastrointestinal losses is about 5–10 meq/kg body weight. Similarly, serum phosphate is elevated (6–7 mg/dL), but total body phosphate is generally depleted. Serum sodium may be slightly reduced (to about 125–130 meq/L) because of expansion of plasma volume by glucose. (For every 100 mg/dL of plasma glucose above normal, serum sodium decreases by 1.6 meq/L.) Serum osmolality can be directly measured by standard tests of freezing-point depression or can be estimated by calculating the molarity of sodium, chloride, and glucose in the serum. A convenient formula for estimating serum osmolality is as follows (physiologic values in humans are generally between 280–300 mosm/L):

$$\text{mosm/L} = 2\,[Na^+] + \frac{\text{glucose (mg/dL)}}{18} + \frac{\text{BUN (mg/dL)}}{2.8}$$

These calculated estimates are usually 10–20 mosm/L lower than values recorded by standard cryoscopic techniques. Blood urea nitrogen and serum creatinine are invariably elevated because of dehydration. In the presence of keto acids, values from multichannel chemical analysis of serum creatinine may be falsely elevated and therefore quite unreliable. However, most laboratories can correct for these interfering chromogens by using a more specific method if asked to do so.

In about 90% of cases, serum amylase is elevated. However, this often represents salivary as well as pancreatic amylase and correlates poorly with symptoms of pancreatitis, such as pain and vomiting. Therefore, in patients with diabetic ketoacidosis, an elevated serum amylase does not justify a diagnosis of acute pancreatitis; serum lipase may be useful if the diagnosis of pancreatitis is being seriously considered.

C. Data Recording on a Flow Sheet: The need for frequent evaluation of the patient's status cannot be overemphasized. Patients with moderately severe diabetic ketoacidosis (pH < 7.2) are best managed in an intensive care unit. Essential baseline blood chemistries include glucose, ketones, electrolytes, arterial blood gases, blood urea nitrogen, and serum creatinine. Typically, the patient with moderately severe diabetic ketoacidosis will have a plasma glucose of 350–900 mg/dL (19.4–50 mmol/L), the presence of serum ketones at a dilution of 1:8 or greater, slight hyponatremia of 130 meq/L, hyperkalemia of 5–8 meq/L, hyperphosphatemia of 6–7 mg/dL, and an elevated blood urea nitrogen and creatinine. Acidosis may be severe (pH ranging from 6.9 to 7.2 and bicarbonate ranging from 5 to 15 meq/L); P_{CO_2} is low (15–20 mm Hg) from hyperventilation.

A comprehensive flow sheet that includes vital signs, serial laboratory data, and therapeutic interventions should be meticulously maintained by the physician responsible for the patient's care. Plasma glucose should be recorded hourly and electrolytes and pH at least every 2–3 hours during the initial treatment period. Insulin therapy is greatly facilitated when plasma glucose results are available within a few minutes of sampling. This can be achieved by the use of reflectance colorimeters designed for bedside glucose measurements of capillary blood glucose. With trained personnel, these devices are also sufficiently accurate for use in this situation (see Blood Glucose Testing, above). Fluid intake and output as well as details of insulin therapy and the administration of other medications should also be carefully recorded on the flow sheet.

Treatment

A. Immediate Resuscitation and Emergency Measures: If the patient is stuporous or comatose, immediately institute the emergency measures outlined in the section on coma (see above). Once the diagnosis of diabetic ketoacidosis is established, a rapid intravenous bolus of 0.3 unit of regular insulin per kilogram of body weight should be given. This will inhibit both gluconeogenesis and ketogenesis while promoting utilization of glucose and keto acids. Administration of at least 2 L of normal saline (in an adult patient) in the first 2–3 hours is recommended initially to help restore plasma volume and stabilize blood pressure while acutely reducing the hyperosmolar state. In addition, by improving renal plasma flow, fluid replacement also restores the renal capacity to excrete hydrogen ions, thereby ameliorating the acidosis as well. If arterial blood pH is 7.0 or less, intravenous bicarbonate may be administered (details of administration are outlined below). Gastric intubation is recommended in the comatose patient to prevent vomiting and aspiration that may occur as a result of gastric atony, a common complication of diabetic ketoacidosis. An indwelling bladder catheter is required in all comatose patients but should be avoided, if possible, in a fully cooperative diabetic patient because of the risk of bladder infection. In patients with preexisting cardiac or renal failure or those in severe cardiovascular collapse, a central venous pressure catheter or a Swan-Ganz catheter should be inserted to evaluate the degree of hypovolemia and to monitor subsequent fluid administration.

B. Specific Measures: Each case must be managed individually depending on the specific abnormalities present and subsequent response to initial therapy.

1. Insulin– Only regular insulin, and preferably human insulin, should be used in the management of diabetic ketoacidosis. As noted above, a "loading" dose of 0.3 unit/kg body weight of regular insulin is given initially as an intravenous bolus followed by 0.1 unit/kg/h, either continuously infused or injected intramuscularly. Doses of insulin as low as 0.1 unit/kg, given hourly either by slow intravenous drip or intramuscularly, are as effective in most cases as the much higher doses previously recommended, and they appear to be safer. When a continuous infusion of insulin is used, 25 units of regular human insulin should be placed in 250 mL of physiologic saline and the first 50 mL of solution flushed through to saturate the tubing before connecting it to the intravenous line. An I-Vac or Harvard pump provides a reliable infusion rate. The insulin dose should be "piggybacked" into the fluid line so the rate of fluid replacement can be changed without altering the insulin delivery rate. For optimal effects, continuous low-dose insulin infusions should always be preceded by a rapid intravenous loading dose of regular insulin, 0.3 unit/kg, to prime the tissue insulin receptors. If the plasma glucose level fails to fall at least 10% in the first hour, a repeat loading dose is recommended. Insulin therapy is greatly facilitated when plasma glucose can be measured within a few minutes of sampling. Rarely, a patient with insulin resistance is encountered; this requires doubling the insulin dose every 2–4 hours if hyperglycemia does not improve after the first two doses of insulin.

Insulin therapy, either as a continuous infusion or as injections given every 1–2 hours, should be continued until arterial pH has normalized.

2. Fluid replacement– In most adult patients, the fluid deficit is 4–5 L. Initially, normal saline is preferred for restoration of plasma volume and, as noted above, should be infused rapidly to provide 1 L/h over the first 1–2 hours. After the first 2 L of fluid have been given, the fluid should be changed to 0.45% saline solution given at a rate of 300–400 mL/h; this is because water loss exceeds sodium loss in uncontrolled diabetes with osmotic diuresis. When blood glucose falls to approximately 250 mg/dL, the fluids should be changed to a 5% glucose solution to maintain plasma glucose in the range of 250–300 mg/dL. This will prevent the development of hypoglycemia and reduce the likelihood of cerebral edema, which could result from too rapid decline of blood glucose. Intensive insulin therapy should be continued until the ketoacidosis is corrected.

3. Sodium bicarbonate– The use of sodium bicarbonate in management of diabetic ketoacidosis has been questioned by some because of the following potential consequences: (1) development of hypokalemia from rapid shift of potassium into cells if the acidosis is overcorrected; (2) tissue anoxia from reduced dissociation of oxygen from hemoglobin when acidosis is rapidly reversed (leftward shift of the oxygen dissociation curve); and (3) cerebral acidosis resulting from lowering of cerebrospinal fluid pH. It must be emphasized, however, that these considerations are less important when severe acidosis exists. It is therefore recommended that bicarbonate be administered to diabetic patients in ketoacidosis if the arterial blood pH is 7.0 or less or if hypotension, arrhythmia, or coma is present along with an arterial blood pH of less than 7.1 with careful monitoring to prevent overcorrection.

One to two ampules of sodium bicarbonate (one ampule contains 44 meq/50 mL) should be added to 1 L of 0.45% saline. (*Note:* Addition of sodium bicarbonate to 0.9% saline would produce a markedly hypertonic solution that could aggravate the hyperosmolar state already present.) This should be administered rapidly (over the first hour). It can be repeated until the arterial pH reaches 7.1 *but should not be given if pH is 7.1 or greater*. As noted earlier, serious consideration should be given to placement of a central venous or Swan-Ganz catheter when administering fluids to severely ill patients with cardiovascular compromise.

4. Potassium– Total body potassium loss from polyuria and vomiting may be as high as 200 meq. However, because of shifts of potassium from cells into the extracellular space as a consequence of acidosis, serum potassium is usually normal to slightly elevated prior to institution of treatment. As the acidosis is corrected, potassium flows back into the cells, and hypokalemia can develop if potassium replacement is not instituted. If the patient is not uremic and has an adequate urine output, potassium chloride in doses of 10–30 meq/h should be infused during the second and third hours after beginning therapy as soon as the acidosis starts to resolve. Replacement should be started sooner if the initial serum potassium is inappropriately normal or low. Cooperative patients with only mild ketoacidosis may receive part or all of their potassium replacement orally.

An ECG can be of help in monitoring the patient's potassium status: high peaked T waves are a sign of hyperkalemia, and flattened T waves with U waves are a sign of hypokalemia.

5. Phosphate– Because severe hypophosphatemia also develops during insulin therapy of diabetic ketoacidosis, some of the potassium can be replaced as the phosphate salt. Correction of hypophosphatemia helps to restore the buffering capacity of the plasma, thereby facilitating renal excretion of hydrogen. It also corrects the impaired oxygen dissociation from hemoglobin by regenerating 2,3-diphosphoglycerate. However, three randomized studies in which phosphate was replaced in only half of a group of patients with diabetic ketoacidosis did not show any apparent clinical benefit from phosphate administration. Moreover, attempts to use the phosphate salt of potassium as the sole means of replacing potassium have led to a number of reported cases of severe hypocalcemia with tetany. To minimize the risk of inducing tetany from too rapid replacement of phosphate, the average deficit of 40–50 mmol of phosphate should be replaced intravenously at a rate *no greater than 3–4 mmol/h* in a 60- to 70-kg person. A stock solution (Abbott) provides a mixture of 1.12 g KH_2PO_4 and 1.18 g K_2HPO_4 in a 5-mL single-dose vial (this equals 22 mmol of potassium and 15 mmol of phosphate). One-half of this vial (2.5 mL) should be added to 1 L of either 0.45% saline or 5% dextrose in water. Two liters of this solution, infused at a rate of 400 mL/h, will correct the phosphate deficit at the optimal rate of 3 mmol/h while providing 4.4 meq of potassium per hour. (Additional potassium should be administered as potassium chloride to provide a total of 10–30 meq of potassium per hour, as noted above.) If the serum phosphate remains below 2.5 mg/dL after this infusion, a repeat 5-hour infusion can be given.

It remains controversial whether phosphate replacement is beneficial. Several clinics prohibit its use in the routine treatment of diabetic ketoacidosis, since the risk of inducing hypocalcemia is thought to outweigh its potential benefits. However, potential hazards of phosphate replacement can be greatly reduced by administering phosphate at a rate no greater than 3–4 mmol/h. To prevent errors of overreplacement, phosphate should be administered separately rather than included as a component of potassium replacement.

6. Hyperchloremic acidosis during therapy– Because of the considerable loss of keto acids in the urine during the initial phase of therapy, substrate for subsequent regeneration of bicarbonate is lost and correction of the total bicarbonate deficit is hampered. A portion of the bicarbonate deficit is replaced with chloride ions infused in large amounts as saline to correct the dehydration. In most patients, as the ketoacidosis clears during insulin replacement, a hyperchloremic, low-bicarbonate pattern emerges with a normal anion gap. This is a relatively benign condition that reverses itself over the subsequent 12–24 hours once intravenous saline is no longer being administered.

Prognosis

Insulin and fluid and electrolyte replacement combined with careful monitoring of patients' clinical and laboratory responses to therapy have dramatically reduced the morbidity and mortality rates of diabetic ketoacidosis. However, this complication still represents a potential threat to survival, especially in older people with cardiovascular disease. Even in specialized centers, the mortality rate may approach 5–10%. Therefore, physicians treating diabetic ketoacidosis must not be lured into adopting "cookbook" approaches that lessen their attentiveness to changes in the patient's condition. Signs to be watched for include failure of improvement in mental status after a period of treatment, continued hypotension with minimal urine flow, or prolonged ileus (which may suggest bowel infarction). Laboratory abnormalities to be watched include failure of blood glucose to fall by 80–100 mg/dL during the first hour of therapy, failure to increase serum bicarbonate or arterial pH appropriately, serum potassium above 6 or below 2.8 meq/L, and electrocardiographic evidence of cardiac arrhythmias. Any of these signs call for a careful search for the cause of the abnormality and prompt specific therapy.

Disposition

After recovery and stabilization, patients should receive intensive detailed instructions about how to avoid this potentially disastrous complication of diabetes mellitus. They should be taught to recognize the early symptoms and signs of ketoacidosis.

Urine ketones should be measured in patients with signs of infection or in those using an insulin pump when capillary blood glucose is unexpectedly and persistently high. When heavy ketonuria and glycosuria persist on several successive examinations, supplemental regular insulin should be administered and liquid foods such as lightly salted tomato juice and broth should be ingested to replenish fluids and electrolytes. Patients should be instructed to contact the physician if ketonuria persists, and especially if vomiting develops or if appropriate adjustment of the infusion rate on an insulin pump does not correct the hyperglycemia and ketonuria. In adolescents, recurrent episodes of severe diabetic ketoacidosis often indicate poor compliance with the insulin regimen, and these patients should receive intensive family counseling.

2. HYPERGLYCEMIC, HYPEROSMOLAR, NONKETOTIC STATE

This form of hyperglycemic coma is characterized by severe hyperglycemia, hyperosmolality, and dehydration in the absence of significant ketosis. It occurs in middle-aged or elderly patients with non-insulin-dependent diabetes which is often mild or occult. Lethargy and confusion develop as serum osmolality exceeds 300 mosm/L, and coma can occur if osmolality exceeds 330 mosm/L. Underlying renal insufficiency or congestive heart failure is common, and the presence of either worsens the prognosis. A precipitating event such as pneumonia, cerebrovascular accident, myocardial infarction, burns, or recent operation can often be identified. Certain drugs, such as phenytoin, diazoxide, glucocorticoids, and thiazide diuretics, have been implicated in its development, as have procedures associated with glucose loading, eg, peritoneal dialysis.

Pathogenesis

A partial or relative insulin deficiency may initiate the syndrome by reducing glucose utilization by muscle, fat, and the liver while at the same time inducing hyperglucagonemia and increasing hepatic glucose output. The result is hyperglycemia that leads to glycosuria and osmotic diuresis with obligatory water loss. The presence of even small amounts of insulin is believed to prevent the development of ketosis by inhibiting lipolysis in the adipose stores. Therefore even though a low insulin:glucagon ratio promotes ketogenesis in the liver, the limited availability of precursor free fatty acids from the periphery restricts the rate at which ketones are formed. If a patient is unable to maintain adequate fluid intake because of an associated acute or chronic illness or has suffered excessive fluid loss (eg, from burns or therapy with diuretics), marked dehydration results. As plasma volume contracts, renal insufficiency develops; this, then, limits renal glucose excretion and contributes markedly to the rise in serum glucose and osmolality. As serum osmolality exceeds 320–330 mosm/L, water is drawn out of cerebral neurons, resulting in mental obtundation and coma.

Clinical Features

A. Symptoms and Signs: The onset of the hyperglycemic, hyperosmolar, nonketotic state may be insidious, preceded for days or weeks by symptoms of weakness, polyuria, and polydipsia. A history of reduced fluid intake is common, whether due to inappropriate absence of thirst, gastrointestinal upset, or, in the case of elderly or bedridden patients, lack of access to water. A history of ingestion of large quantities of glucose-containing fluids, such as soft drinks or orange juice, can occasionally be obtained; these patients are usually less hyperosmolar than those in whom fluid intake was restricted. The absence of toxic features of ketoacidosis may retard recognition of the syndrome and thus delay institution of therapy until dehydration is profound. Because of this delay in diagnosis, the hyperglycemia, hyperosmolality, and dehydration in hyperglycemic, hyperosmolar, nonketotic coma is often more severe than in diabetic ketoacidosis.

Physical examination will reveal the presence of profound dehydration (orthostatic fall in blood pressure and rise in pulse, supine tachycardia or even frank shock, dry mucous membranes, decreased skin turgor). The patient may be lethargic, confused, or comatose. Kussmaul respirations are absent unless the precipitating event for the hyperosmolar state has also led to the development of metabolic acidosis (eg, sepsis or myocardial infarction with shock).

B. Laboratory Findings: Severe hyperglycemia is present, with blood glucose values ranging from 800 to as high as 2400 mg/dL (44.4–133.2 mmol/L). In mild cases, where dehydration is less severe, dilutional hyponatremia as well as urinary sodium losses may reduce serum sodium to about 120–125 meq/L*—this protects, to some extent, against extreme hyperosmolality. Once dehydration progresses further, however, serum sodium can exceed 140 meq/L, producing serum osmolalities of 330–440 mosm/L (normal, 280–295 mosm/L). Ketosis is usually absent or mild; however, a small degree of ketonuria may be present if the patient has not been eating because of illness. Acidosis is not a part of the hyperglycemic, hyperosmolar state, but it may be present (usually lactic acidosis) because of other acute underlying conditions (sepsis, acute renal failure, myocardial infarction, etc). (See Lactic Acidosis, below.)

Treatment

There are some differences in fluid, insulin, and electrolyte replacement in this disorder, as compared to diabetic ketoacidosis. However, in common with the treatment of ketoacidotic patients, careful monitoring of the patient's clinical and laboratory response to therapy is essential.

A. Fluid Replacement: Fluid replacement is of paramount importance in treating nonketotic hyperglycemic coma. If circulatory collapse is present, fluid therapy should be initiated with isotonic saline. In all other cases, initial replacement with hypotonic (usually 0.45%) saline is preferable, because these patients are hyperosmolar with considerable loss of body water and excess solute in the vascular compartment. As much as 4–6 L of fluid may be required in the first 8–10 hours. Careful monitoring of fluid quantity and type, urine output, blood pressure, and pulse is essential. Placement of a central venous pressure or Swan-Ganz catheter should be strongly considered to guide replacement of fluid, especially if the patient is elderly or has underlying renal or cardiac disease. Because insulin therapy will decrease plasma glucose and therefore serum osmolality, a change to isotonic saline may be necessary at some

---

*See p 617 for formula used in correcting hyponatremia due to hyperglycemia.
A convenient method for estimating serum osmolality is provided on p 617.

time during treatment in order to maintain an adequate blood pressure and a urine output of at least 50 mL/h. Once blood glucose reaches 250 mg/dL, 5% dextrose in 0.45% or 0.9% saline solution should be substituted for the sugar-free fluids. When consciousness returns, oral fluids should be encouraged.

B. Electrolyte Replacement: Hyperkalemia is less marked and much less potassium is lost in the urine during the osmotic diuresis of hyperglycemic, hyperosmolar, nonketotic coma than in diabetic ketoacidosis. There is, therefore, less severe total potassium depletion, and less potassium replacement is needed to restore potassium stores to normal. However, because the initial serum potassium usually is not elevated and because it declines rapidly as insulin therapy allows glucose and potassium to enter cells, it is recommended that potassium replacement be initiated earlier than in ketotic patients: 10 meq of potassium chloride can be added to the *initial* liter of fluid administered if the initial serum potassium is not elevated and if the patient is making urine. When serum phosphate falls below 1 mg/dL during insulin therapy, phosphate replacement can be given intravenously with the same precautions as those outlined for ketoacidotic patients (see above). If the patient is awake and cooperative, part or all of the potassium and phosphate replacement can be given orally.

C. Insulin Therapy: In general, less insulin is required to reduce the hyperglycemia of nonketotic patients than is the case for patients in diabetic ketoacidosis. In fact, fluid replacement alone can decrease glucose levels considerably. An initial dose of 15 units of regular insulin given intravenously and 15 units given intramuscularly is usually quite effective in lowering blood glucose. In most cases, subsequent doses need not be greater than 10–25 units every 4 hours. (Insulin should be given intramuscularly or intravenously until the patient has stabilized; it may then be given subcutaneously.) Some patients—especially those who are severely ill because of other underlying diseases—may require continuous intravenous administration of insulin (in a manner similar to that described for ketoacidosis) with careful monitoring, preferably in an intensive care setting.

D. Search for the Precipitating Event: The physician must initiate a careful search for the event that precipitated the episode of hyperglycemic, hyperosmolar, nonketotic coma if it is not obvious after the initial history and physical examination. Chest x-rays and cultures of blood, urine, and other body fluids should be obtained to look for occult sources of sepsis; empiric antibiotic coverage should be considered in the seriously ill patient. Cardiac enzymes and serial ECGs can be ordered to look for evidence of "silent" myocardial infarction.

Prognosis

The overall mortality rate of hyperglycemic, hyperosmolar, nonketotic coma is over ten times that of diabetic ketoacidosis, chiefly because of its higher incidence in older patients, who may have compromised cardiovascular systems or associated major illnesses. (When patients are matched for age, the prognoses of these two forms of hyperosmolar coma are reasonably comparable.)

Disposition

After the patient is stabilized, the appropriate form of long-term management of the diabetes must be determined. This must include patient education on how to recognize situations (gastrointestinal upset, infection) that will predispose to recurrence of hyperglycemic, hyperosmolar, nonketotic coma as well as detailed information on how to prevent the escalating dehydration (small sips of sugar-free liquids, increase in usual hypoglycemic therapy, or early contact with the physician) that culminates in hyperosmolar coma. For a detailed discussion of therapeutic alternatives for type II diabetic patients, see Steps in the Management of the Diabetic Patient (above).

3. HYPOGLYCEMIC COMA

Hypoglycemia is a common complication of insulin replacement therapy in diabetic patients. In most cases, it is detected and treated by patients or their families before coma results. However, it remains the most frequent cause of coma in the insulin-treated diabetic patient. In addition, it can occur in any patient taking oral sulfonylurea drugs, particularly if the patient is elderly, has renal or liver disease, or is taking certain other medications that alter metabolism of the sulfonylureas (eg, phenylbutazone, sulfonamides, or warfarin). It occurs more frequently with the use of long-acting sulfonylureas than when shorter-acting agents are used.

Clinical Findings & Treatment

The clinical findings and emergency treatment of hypoglycemia are discussed above (see pp 612–614).

Prognosis

Many patients who arrive at emergency rooms in hypoglycemic coma appear to recover fully; however, profound hypoglycemia or delays in therapy can result in permanent neurologic deficit or even death. Furthermore, repeated episodes of hypoglycemia may have a cumulative adverse effect on intellectual functioning.

Disposition

The physician should carefully review with the patient the events leading up to the hypoglycemic episode. Associated use of other medications, as well as alcohol or narcotics, should be noted. Careful attention should be paid to diet, exercise pattern, insulin or sulfonylurea dosage, and general compliance with the prescribed diabetes treatment regimen. Any factors thought to have contributed to the development of the episode should be identified and recommendations made in order to prevent recurrences of this potentially disastrous complication of diabetes therapy.

If the patient is hypoglycemic from use of a long-acting oral hypoglycemic agent (eg, chlorpropamide or glyburide) or from high doses of a long-acting insulin, admission to hospital for treatment with continuous intravenous glucose and careful monitoring of blood glucose is indicated.

4. LACTIC ACIDOSIS

When severely ill diabetic patients present with profound acidosis but relatively low or undetectable levels of keto acids in plasma, the presence of excessive plasma lactate (> 6 mmol/L) should be considered, especially if other causes of acidosis such as uremia are not present.

Pathogenesis

Lactic acid is the end product of anaerobic metabolism of glucose. Normally, the principal sources of this acid are the erythrocytes (which lack the enzymes for aerobic oxidation), skeletal muscle, skin, and brain. The chief pathway for removal of lactic acid is by hepatic (and to some degree renal) uptake for conversion first to pyruvate and eventually back to glucose, a process that requires oxygen. Lactic acidosis occurs when excess lactic acid accumulates in the blood. This can be the result of overproduction (tissue hypoxia), deficient removal (hepatic failure), or both (circulatory collapse). Patients with lactic acidosis are usually severely ill, with problems such as myocardial infarction with shock, sepsis, hemorrhage, severe anemia, carbon monoxide poisoning, severe pulmonary disease, severe liver disease, or cyanide poisoning. Phenformin, an oral hypoglycemic agent no longer available in the USA, has been reported to cause lactic acidosis, especially in patients with altered lactate or phenformin metabolism. In addition, lactic acidosis has been reported after the use of salicylates, sodium nitroprusside, intravenous fructose, sorbitol, ethanol, and other substances.

Clinical Features

A. Symptoms and Signs: The main clinical features of lactic acidosis are marked hyperventilation and mental confusion, which may progress to stupor or coma. When lactic acidosis is secondary to tissue hypoxia or vascular collapse, the clinical presentation is variable, being that of the prevailing catastrophic illness. In the rare instance of idiopathic or spontaneous lactic acidosis, the onset is rapid (usually over a few hours), the cardiopulmonary status is stable, and mentation may be relatively normal.

B. Laboratory Findings: Plasma glucose can be low, normal, or high in diabetic patients with lactic acidosis, but usually it is moderately elevated. Plasma bicarbonate and arterial pH are quite low. An anion gap will be present (calculated by subtracting the sum of the plasma bicarbonate and chloride from the plasma sodium; normal is 12–16 meq/L). Ketones are usually absent from plasma, but small amounts may be present in urine if the patient has not been eating recently. Other causes of "anion gap" metabolic acidosis should be excluded—eg, uremia, diabetic or alcoholic ketoacidosis, and salicylate, methanol, ethylene glycol, or paraldehyde intoxication. In the absence of azotemia, hyperphosphatemia may be a clue to the presence of lactic acidosis.

The diagnosis is confirmed by demonstrating, in a sample of blood that is promptly chilled and separated, a plasma lactate concentration of 6 mmol/L or higher (normal is about 1 mmol/L). Failure to rapidly chill the sample and separate the plasma can lead to falsely high plasma lactate values as a result of continued glycolysis by the red blood cells. Frozen plasma remains stable for subsequent assay.

Treatment

The cornerstone of therapy is aggressive treatment of the precipitating cause. An adequate airway and good oxygenation should be ensured. If hypotension is present, fluids and, if appropriate, pressor agents must be given to restore tissue perfusion. Appropriate cultures and empiric antibiotic coverage should be instituted in any seriously ill patient with lactic acidosis in whom the cause is not immediately apparent. Alkalinization with intravenous sodium bicarbonate to keep the pH above 7.2 has been recommended in the emergency treatment of severe lactic acidosis. However, there is no evidence that the mortality rate is favorably affected by administering bicarbonate and the matter is at present controversial, particularly because of the hazards associated with bicarbonate therapy. Dichloroacetate, an anion that facilitates pyruvate removal by activating pyruvate dehydrogenase, reverses certain types of lactic acidosis in animals but has not proved useful in treating lactic acidosis in humans.

CHRONIC COMPLICATIONS OF DIABETES MELLITUS (Table 15–19)

In most patients with diabetes, a number of pathologic changes occur at variable intervals during the course of the disease. These changes involve the vascular system for the most part; however, they also occur in the nerves, the skin, and the lens.

In addition to the above complications, diabetic patients have an increased incidence of certain types of infections and may handle their infections less well than the general population.

Classifications of Diabetic Vascular Disease

Diabetic vascular disease is conveniently divided into two main categories: microvascular disease and macrovascular disease.

A. Microvascular Disease: Disease of the smallest blood vessels, the capillary and the precapillary arterioles, is manifested mainly by thickening of the capillary basement membrane. Microvascular disease involving the retina leads to diabetic retinopathy, and disease involving the kidney causes diabetic nephropathy. Small vessel disease may also involve the heart, and cardiomegaly with heart failure has been described in diabetic patients with patent coronary arteries.

B. Macrovascular Disease: Large vessel disease in diabetes is essentially an accelerated form of atherosclerosis. It accounts for the increased incidence of myocardial infarction, stroke, and peripheral gangrene in diabetic patients. Just as in the case of atherosclerosis in the general population, the exact cause of accelerated atherosclerosis in the diabetic population remains unclear. Abnormalities in vessel walls, platelets and other components of the clotting system, red blood cells, and lipid metabolism have all been postulated to play a role. In addition, there is evidence that coexistent risk factors such as cigarette smoking and hypertension may be important in determining the course of the disease.

Prevalence of Chronic Complications by Type of Diabetes

Although all of the known complications of diabetes can be found in both types of the disease, some are more common in one type than in the other. Renal failure due to severe microvascular nephropathy is the major cause of death in patients with type I diabetes, whereas macrovascular disease is the leading cause in type II. Although blindness occurs in both types, it occurs more commonly as a result of severe

Table 15–19. Chronic complications of diabetes mellitus.

Eyes
  Diabetic retinopathy
    Nonproliferative (background)
    Proliferative
  Cataracts
    Subcapsular (snowflake)
    Nuclear (senile)

Kidneys
  Intracapillary glomerulosclerosis
    Diffuse
    Nodular
  Infection
    Pyelonephritis
    Perinephric abscess
    Renal papillary necrosis
  Renal tubular necrosis
    Following dye studies (urograms, arteriograms)

Nervous system
  Peripheral neuropathy
    Distal, symmetric sensory loss
    Motor neuropathy
      Foot drop, wrist drop
      Mononeuropathy multiplex (diabetic amyotrophy)
  Cranial neuropathy
    Cranial nerves III, IV, VI, VII
  Autonomic neuropathy
    Postural hypotension
    Resting tachycardia
    Loss of sweating
    Gastrointestinal neuropathy
      Gastroparesis
      Diabetic diarrhea
    Urinary bladder atony
    Impotence (may also be secondary to pelvic vascular disease)

Skin
  Diabetic dermopathy (shin spots)
  Necrobiosis lipoidica diabeticorum
  Candidiasis
  Foot and leg ulcers
    Neurotropic
    Ischemic

Cardiovascular system
  Heart disease
    Myocardial infarction
    Cardiomyopathy
  Gangrene of the feet
    Ischemic ulcers
    Osteomyelitis

Bones and joints
  Diabetic cheirarthropathy
  Dupuytren's contracture
  Charcot joint

Unusual infections
  Necrotizing fasciitis
  Necrotizing myositis
  Mucor meningitis
  Emphysematous cholecystitis
  Malignant otitis externa

proliferative retinopathy, vitreous hemorrhages, and retinal detachment in type I disease, whereas macular edema and ischemia or cataracts are the usual cause in type II. Similarly, although diabetic neuropathy is common in both type I and type II diabetes, severe autonomic neuropathy with gastroparesis, diabetic diarrhea, resting tachycardia, and postural hypotension is much more common in type I.

Relationship of Glycemic Control to Development of Chronic Complications

The cause of chronic microvascular complications in diabetic patients has now been resolved. A compelling argument for its being a consequence of impaired metabolic control was initially made by observations in Korean patients who ingested a B cell-toxic rodenticide, vacor, during a suicide attempt and developed persistent diabetes. As many as 44% of these patients developed retinopathy during a 6- to 7-year follow-up of their acquired diabetes, while 28% had clinical proteinuria and more than half showed significant thickening of their quadriceps capillary basement membrane width.

However, in patients with idiopathic diabetes mellitus, the most compelling argument that chronic diabetic complications relate to poor glycemic control is based on the findings of the Diabetes Control and Complications trial. This study in 1441 IDDM patients over a 7–10 year period conclusively demonstrated that near normalization of blood glucose with intensive therapy was able to substantially prevent or delay the development of diabetic retinopathy, nephropathy, and neuropathy. (See DCCT, above.)

Genetic Factors in Susceptibility to Development of Chronic Complications of Diabetes

Although no genetic susceptibility genes have been identified as yet, three unrelated observations indicate that roughly 40% of people may be unusually susceptible to the ravages of hyperglycemia or other metabolic sequelae of an inadequate insulin effect.

(1) In one retrospective study of 164 juvenile-onset diabetics with a median age at onset of 9 years, 40% were incapacitated or dead from end-stage renal disease with proliferative retinopathy after a 25-year follow-up, while the remaining subjects were either mildly affected (40%) or had no clinically detected microvascular disease (20%). This study was completed long before the availability of glycemic self-monitoring methodology, so it is unlikely that any of these patients were near optimal glycemic control.

(2) Data from renal transplantation indicate that only about 40% of normal kidneys developed evidence of moderate to severe diabetic nephropathy within 6–14 years of being transplanted into diabetic subjects with end-stage renal failure, whereas as many as 60% were only minimally affected.

(3) Among children under 21 years of age with type I diabetes, 40% had thickening of the capillary basement membrane width (CBMW) of the quadriceps muscle, while 60% had vessels within the normal range. This finding was unrelated to the severity or duration of diabetes and is in contrast to results in diabetic adults 21 years of age or older, in whom virtually 100% have thickened CBMWs.

These three observations support the hypothesis that while approximately 60% of people suffer only minimal consequences from hyperglycemia and other metabolic hazards of insulin insufficiency, 40% or so suffer severe, potentially catastrophic microvascular complications if the disease is poorly controlled. The genetic mechanisms for this increased susceptibility are as yet unknown but could relate to overproduction or reduced removal of accelerated glycosylation end products in particular tissues. If further studies indicate that the presence of early thickening of the CBMW—found in 40% of children—represents a marker of this susceptibility gene and a predictor of severe microvascular disease, it could justify more intensive insulin therapy in that group to achieve near-normalization of blood glucose. The remaining 60% of less susceptible individuals might then be spared the inconveniences of strict glycemic control as well as the risks of hypoglycemia inherent in present methods of intensive insulin therapy.

SPECIFIC CHRONIC COMPLICATIONS OF DIABETES MELLITUS (Table 15–19)

1. OPHTHALMOLOGIC COMPLICATIONS

Diabetic Retinopathy

For early detection of diabetic retinopathy, adolescent or adult patients who have had type I diabetes for more than 5 years and *all* non-IDDM patients should be referred to an ophthalmologist for examination and follow-up. When hypertension is present in a patient with diabetes, it should be treated vigorously, since hypertension is associated with an increased incidence and accelerated progression of diabetic retinopathy.

A. Pathogenesis and Clinical Features: Two main categories of diabetic retinopathy exist: nonproliferative and proliferative.

Nonproliferative ("background") retinopathy represents the earliest stage of retinal involvement by diabetes and is characterized by such changes as microaneurysms, dot hemorrhages, exudates, and retinal edema. During this stage, the retinal capillaries leak proteins, lipids, or red cells into the retina. When this process occurs in the macula, the area of greatest concentration of visual cells, there will be interference with visual acuity; this is the most common cause of visual impairment in type II diabetes and occurs in about 6% of these patients over time.

Proliferative retinopathy involves the growth of new capillaries and fibrous tissue within the retina and into the vitreous chamber. It is a consequence of small vessel occlusion, which causes retinal hypoxia; this in turn stimulates new vessel growth. Proliferative retinopathy can occur in both types of diabetes but is more common in type I, developing about 7–10 years after onset of symptoms. Prior to proliferation of new capillaries, a preproliferative phase often occurs in which arteriolar ischemia is manifested as cotton-wool spots (small infarcted areas of retina). Vision is usually normal until vitreous hemorrhage or retinal detachment occurs. Proliferative retinopathy is a leading cause of blindness in the USA, particularly since it increases the risk of retinal detachment. After 10 years of diabetes, half of all patients have at least some degree of retinopathy, and this proportion increases to more than 80% after 15 years of diabetes.

B. Treatment: Once maculopathy or proliferative changes are detected, panretinal xenon or argon laser photocoagulation therapy is indicated. Destroying retinal tissue with photocoagulation means that surviving tissue receives a greater share of the available oxygen supply, thereby abolishing hypoxic stimulation of new vessel growth. Results of a large-scale clinical trial (the Diabetic Retinopathy Study) have verified the effectiveness of photocoagulation, particularly when recent vitreous hemorrhages have occurred or when extensive new vessels are located near the optic disk.

The best results with photocoagulation are achieved if proliferative retinopathy is detected early. This is best done by obtaining a baseline fluorescein angiogram within 5–10 years after onset of type I diabetes and then repeating this study at intervals of 1–5 years, depending on the severity of the retinal involvement found. Prepubertal children do not develop diabetic retinopathy regardless of the duration of their diabetes. They need not be scheduled for routine ophthalmologic examination until several years after the onset of puberty.

Pituitary ablation, which has been associated with delay in progression of severe retinopathy in the past, is rarely used today because photocoagulation therapy is just as effective and avoids the risks associated with destruction of the pituitary. Occasional cases of rapidly progressive ("florid") proliferative retinopathy in type I adolescent diabetics have been reported in which photocoagulation was less effective than pituitary ablation in preventing blindness.

Cataracts

Two types of cataracts occur in diabetic patients: subcapsular and senile. **Subcapsular cataract** occurs predominantly in type I diabetics, may come on fairly rapidly, and has a significant correlation with the hyperglycemia of uncontrolled diabetes. This type of cataract has a flocculent or "snowflake" appearance and develops just below the lens capsule.

Senile cataract represents a sclerotic change of the lens nucleus. It is by far the most common type of cataract found in either diabetic or nondiabetic adults and tends to occur at a younger age in diabetic patients, particularly when glycemic control is poor.

Two separate abnormalities found in diabetic patients, both of which are related to elevated blood glucose levels, may contribute to the formation of cataracts: (1) glycosylation of the lens protein and (2) an excess of sorbitol, which is formed from the increased quantities of glucose found in the insulin-independent lens. Accumulation of sorbitol leads to osmotic changes in the lens that ultimately result in fibrosis and cataract formation.

2. RENAL COMPLICATIONS

Diabetic Nephropathy

A. Pathogenesis and Clinical Findings: About 4000 cases of end-stage renal disease due to diabetic nephropathy occur annually among diabetic patients in the USA. This represents about one-fourth of all patients being treated for renal failure. Thickening of capillary basement membranes and of the mesangium of renal glomeruli produces varying degrees of glomerulosclerosis and renal insufficiency. Diffuse glomerulosclerosis is more common than nodular intercapillary glomerulosclerosis (Kimmelstiel-Wilson lesions); both produce heavy proteinuria.

1. Microalbuminuria– New methods of detecting small amounts of urinary albumin have permitted detection of microgram concentrations—in contrast to the less sensitive dipstick strips, whose minimal detection limit is 0.3–0.5%. Conventional 24-hour urine collections, in addition to being inconvenient for patients, also show wide variability of albumin excretion, since several factors such as sustained erect posture, dietary protein, and exercise tend to increase albumin excretion rates. For these reasons, most laboratories prefer to screen patients with a timed overnight urine collection beginning at bedtime, when the urine is discarded and the time noted. Normal subjects excrete less than 15 μg/min during overnight urine collections; values of 20 μg/min or higher are considered to represent abnormal microalbuminuria. Subsequent renal failure can be predicted by urinary albumin excretion rates exceeding 30 μg/min. Increased microalbuminuria correlates with increased levels of blood pressure, and this may explain why increased proteinuria in diabetic patients is associated with an increase in cardiovascular deaths even in the absence of renal failure. Careful glycemic control as well as a low-protein diet (0.6 g/kg/d) may reduce both the hyperfiltration and the elevated microalbuminuria in patients in the early stages of diabetes and those with incipient diabetic nephropathy.

Antihypertensive therapy also decreases microalbuminuria, and clinical trials with inhibitors of angiotensin I converting enzyme (eg, enalapril, 20 mg/d) show a reduction of microalbuminuria in diabetic patients even in the absence of hypertension.

2. Progressive diabetic nephropathy– Progressive diabetic nephropathy consists of proteinuria of varying severity, occasionally leading to nephrotic syndrome with hypoalbuminemia, edema, and an increase in circulating betalipoproteins as well as progressive azotemia. In contrast to all other renal disorders, the proteinuria associated with diabetic nephropathy does not diminish with progressive renal failure (patients continue to excrete 10–11 g daily as creatinine clearance diminishes). As renal failure progresses, there is an elevation in the renal threshold at which glycosuria appears.

Hypertension develops with progressive renal involvement, and coronary and cerebral atherosclerosis seems to be accelerated. Once diabetic nephropathy has progressed to the stage of hypertension, proteinuria, or early renal failure, glycemic control is not beneficial in influencing its course. In this circumstance, antihypertensive medications, including ACE inhibitors, and restriction of dietary protein to 0.6 g/kg body weight per day are recommended.

When the serum creatinine reaches 3 mg/dL, consultation with a nephrologist or a diabetologist experienced in the treatment of diabetic nephropathy is recommended. When the serum creatinine reaches 4 mg/dL, consultation with personnel at a center where renal transplantation is performed is indicated.

B. Treatment: Hemodialysis has been of limited success in the treatment of renal failure due to diabetic nephropathy, primarily because of progression of large-vessel disease with resultant death and disability from stroke and myocardial infarction. Growing experience with chronic ambulatory peritoneal dialysis suggests that it may be a more convenient method of providing adequate dialysis with a lower incidence of complications.

Renal transplantation, especially from related donors, is often successful. For patients with compatible donors and no contraindications (such as severe cardiovascular disease), it is the treatment of choice.

Necrotizing Papillitis

This unusual complication of pyelonephritis occurs primarily in diabetic patients. It is characterized by fever, flank pain, pyuria, and sloughing of renal papillae in the urine. It is treated by intravenous administration of appropriate antibiotics.

Renal Decompensation After Radiographic Dyes

The use of radiographic contrast agents in diabetic patients with reduced creatinine clearance has been associated with the development of acute renal failure. Diabetic patients with normal renal function do not appear to be at increased risk for contrast nephropathy. If a contrast study is considered essential, patients with a serum creatinine of 1.5–2.5 mg/dL should be adequately hydrated before the procedure to produce a gentle diuresis of about 75 mL or so per hour. Other nephrotoxic agents such as nonsteroidal anti-inflammatory agents should be avoided. Although it was once believed that newer nonionic contrast agents were less likely to cause acute renal failure in diabetic patients, more recent prospective trials show no difference between these agents and conventional and much less costly ionic radiographic dyes. After the procedure, serum creatinine should be followed closely. Radiographic contrast material should not be given to a patient with a serum creatinine greater than 3 mg/dL unless the potential benefit outweighs the high risk of acute renal failure.

3. NEUROLOGIC COMPLICATIONS (Diabetic Neuropathy)

Peripheral and autonomic neuropathy are the two most common complications of both types of diabetes. Their pathogenesis is poorly understood. Some lesions, such as the acute cranial nerve palsies and diabetic amyotrophy, have been attributed to ischemic infarction of the involved peripheral nerve. The much more common symmetric sensory and motor peripheral neuropathies and autonomic neuropathy are felt to be due to metabolic or osmotic toxicity somehow related to hyperglycemia.

Unfortunately, there is no consistently effective treatment for any of the neuropathies. It remains to be demonstrated definitively whether normalization of blood glucose levels can prevent development and progression of this devastating complication.

Peripheral Sensory Neuropathy

A. Pathogenesis and Clinical Features: Sensory loss is commonly preceded by months or years of paresthesias such as tingling, itching, and increasing pain. The pains can vary from mild paresthesias to severe shooting pains and may be more severe at night. Discomfort of the lower extremities can be incapacitating at times. Radicular pains in the chest and the abdominal area may be extremely difficult to distinguish from pain due to an intrathoracic or intra-abdominal source. Eventually, patients develop numbness, and tactile sensations decrease. The sensory loss is generally bilateral, symmetric, and associated with dulled perception of vibration, pain, and temperature, particularly in the lower extremities, but also evident in the hands. Sensory nerve conduction is delayed in peripheral nerves, and ankle jerks may be absent. Highly sensitive neurothesiometer devices are being utilized to characterize the threshold levels for pain and touch, so that signs of sensory defects can be detected earlier and patients with higher risk for neuropathic foot ulcers can be identified. Because all of these sensory disturbances are made worse by pressure applied to the involved nerves, symptoms may appear first in nerves that are entrapped, such as the median nerve in carpal tunnel syndrome or the nerves around the ankle.

Characteristic syndromes that develop in diabetic patients with sensory neuropathy and are related to their failure to perceive trauma include osteopathy of the distal hand and foot, deformity of the knee or ankle (so-called Charcot joint), and neuropathic ulceration of the foot.

B. Treatment: Amitriptyline (50–75 mg at bedtime) has produced remarkable improvement in the lower extremity pain in some patients with sensory neuropathy. Dramatic relief has often occurred within 48–72 hours. This rapid response is in contrast to the 2 or 3 weeks required for an antidepressive effect. Patients often attribute benefit to their having a full night's sleep after amitriptyline in contrast to many prior sleepless nights occasioned by neuropathic pain. Mild to moderate morning drowsiness is a side effect that generally improves with time or can be lessened by giving the medication several hours before bedtime. This drug should be discontinued if there is no improvement after 4–5 days. Desipramine in doses of 25–150 mg per day has been reported to have the same efficacy for neuropathic leg pains as amitriptyline. Other drugs have been used, including carbamazepine and phenytoin, but these are of questionable benefit for leg pain. Capsaicin, a topical irritant, has relieved local nerve pain in some studies; it is dispensed as a cream to be rubbed into the skin over the painful region.

It is essential that diabetic patients with peripheral neuropathy receive detailed instructions in foot care. Special custom-made shoes are usually required to redistribute weight evenly over an insensitive foot, particularly when it has been deformed by surgery, by asymptomatic fractures, or by a Charcot joint.

Motor Neuropathy

Symmetric motor neuropathy occurs much less frequently than sensory neuropathy and is associated with delayed motor nerve conduction and muscle weakness and atrophy. Its pathogenesis is presumed to be similar to that of sensory loss. Mononeuropathy develops when there is vascular occlusion of a specific nerve trunk; if more than one nerve trunk is involved, the syndrome of **mononeuritis multiplex** occurs. Motor neuropathy is manifested by an abrupt onset of weakness in a distribution that reflects the nerve involved (eg, peroneal nerve involvement produces foot drop). A surprising number of these motor neuropathies improve after 6–8 weeks. Reversible **cranial nerve palsies** can occur and may present as lid ptosis (cranial nerve III), lateral deviation of the eye (IV), inability to move the eye laterally (VI), or facial paralysis (Bell's palsy) (VII). Acute pain and weakness of thigh muscles bilaterally can occur with progressive wasting and weight loss. This has been termed **diabetic amyotrophy** and is more common in elderly men. Again, the prognosis is good, with recovery of motor function over several months in many cases. In more severe cases with extensive atrophy of limb musculature, this disorder has been termed "malignant cachexia" and mimics the end stages of advanced neoplasia, particularly when depression produces anorexia and weight loss. With this more severe manifestation of diabetic amyotrophy, recovery of muscle function may only be partial.

Autonomic Neuropathy

Neuropathy of the autonomic nervous system is common in patients with diabetes of long duration and can be a very disconcerting clinical problem. It can affect many diverse visceral functions. With autonomic neuropathy, there may be postural hypotension, resting fixed tachycardia, decreased cardiovascular responses to the Valsalva maneuver, gastroparesis, alternating bouts of diarrhea (often nocturnal) and constipation, difficulty in emptying the bladder, and impotence.

Impotence due to neuropathy differs from the psychogenic variety in that the latter may be intermittent (erections occur under special circumstances), whereas diabetic impotence is usually persistent. To distinguish neuropathic or psychogenic impotence from the impotence caused by aortoiliac occlusive disease or vasculopathy, papaverine is injected into the corpus cavernosum. If the blood supply is competent, a penile erection will occur. Urinary incontinence, with large volumes of residual urine, and retrograde ejaculation can also result from pelvic neuropathy.

Gastroparesis should be a diagnostic consideration in insulin-dependent diabetic patients who develop unexpected fluctuations and variability in their blood glucose levels after meals. Radiographic studies of the stomach and radioisotopic examination of gastric emptying after liquid and solid meals are of diagnostic value in these patients. Involvement of the gastrointestinal system may be manifested by nausea, vomiting, and postprandial fullness (from gastric atony); symptoms of reflux or dysphagia (from esophageal involvement); constipation and recurrent diarrhea, especially at night (from involvement of the small bowel and colon); and fecal incontinence (from anal sphincter dysfunction). Gallbladder function is altered, and this enhances stone formation.

Therapy is difficult and must be directed specifically at each abnormality. Use of Jobst fitted stockings, tilting the head of the bed, and arising slowly from the supine position are useful in minimizing symptoms of **orthostatic hypotension.** Some patients may require the addition of a mineralocorticoid such as fludrocortisone acetate (0.1–0.2 mg twice daily). Metoclopramide has been of some help in treating diabetic gastroparesis over the short term, but its effectiveness seems to diminish over time. It is a dopamine antagonist with central antiemetic effects as well as cholinergic action to facilitate gastric emptying. It can be given intravenously (10–20 mg) or orally (20 mg of liquid metoclopramide) before breakfast and supper. Drowsiness is its major adverse effect. Bethanechol has also been used for gastroparesis (as well as for an atonic urinary bladder) because of its anticholinergic effects.

Diabetic diarrhea is occasionally aggravated by bacterial overgrowth from stasis in the small intestine, and a trial of broad-spectrum antibiotics may give relief. If this does not help, symptomatic relief can sometimes be achieved with antidiarrheal agents such as diphenoxylate with atropine or loperamide. Clonidine has been reported to lessen diabetic diarrhea, but its tendency to lower blood pressure in those patients who already have some degree of orthostatic hypotension often limits its usefulness. Metamucil and other bulk-providing agents may relieve either the diarrhea or the constipation phases, which often alternate. Beta-lactulose is useful in managing severe constipation. Bethanechol has occasionally improved emptying of the **atonic urinary bladder.** When **impotence** is due to neuropathy, it is usually permanent, and a penile prosthesis should be considered as a therapeutic option in appropriate cases (see Chapter 9).

Aldose reductase inhibitors have been generally disappointing, with only marginal therapeutic results in either autonomic or peripheral diabetic neuropathy and a relatively high incidence of toxic side effects such as skin rash and neutropenia.

4. CARDIOVASCULAR COMPLICATIONS

Heart Disease

Microangiopathy has recently been recognized to occur in the heart and may explain the existence of congestive cardiomyopathies found in diabetic patients without demonstrable coronary artery disease. Much more commonly, however, heart failure in the diabetic is a consequence of coronary atherosclerosis. Myocardial infarction is three to five times more common in diabetic patients than in age-matched controls and is the leading cause of death in patients with type II diabetes. A loss of the protection against myocardial infarction usually present in women during the age of childbearing is particularly evident in diabetic women. The exact reason for the increased incidence of atherosclerosis in diabetics is not clear. It may be a consequence of hyperlipidemia; abnormalities of platelet adhesiveness or coagulation factors (or both); or hypertension.

Peripheral Vascular Disease

Atherosclerosis is markedly accelerated in the larger arteries. It is often diffuse, with localized enhancement in certain areas of turbulent blood flow, such as at the bifurcation of the aorta or other large vessels. Clinical manifestations of peripheral vascular disease include ischemia of the lower extremities, impotence, and intestinal angina.

The incidence of **gangrene of the feet** in diabetics is 30 times that in age-matched controls. The factors responsible for its development, in addition to peripheral vascular disease, are small vessel disease, peripheral neuropathy with loss of both pain sensation and neurogenic inflammatory responses and secondary infection. In two-thirds of patients with ischemic gangrene, pedal pulses are not palpable. In the remaining one-third who have palpable pulses, reduced blood flow through these vessels can be demonstrated by plethysmographic or Doppler ultrasound examination. Prevention of foot injury is imperative; agents that reduce peripheral blood flow such as tobacco and propranolol should be avoided. Control of other risk factors such as hypertension is essential. Patients should be advised to seek immediate medical care if a diabetic foot ulcer develops. Improvement in peripheral blood flow with endarterectomy and bypass operations is possible in certain patients.

5. SKIN CHANGES

Diabetic dermopathy is characterized by atrophic brown spots on the skin, usually in the pretibial area ("shin spots"). These changes may be a consequence of increased glycosylation of tissue proteins or vasculopathy. Eruptive xanthomas may develop in some poorly controlled diabetics who have marked hypertriglyceridemia. A rare skin complication, necrobiosis lipoidica diabeticorum, occurs predominantly on the shins and is characterized by marked thinning of the skin which allows the subcutaneous vessels to be seen as though through tissue paper. An element of vascular occlusion is generally present.

6. BONE & JOINT COMPLICATIONS

Bone and joint complications are generally attributed to metabolic or vascular sequelae of diabetes of long standing.

Juvenile Diabetic "Cheirarthropathy"

This is a syndrome of chronic progressive stiffness of the hand secondary to contracture and tightening of the skin over the joints. It is characterized by inability to flatten the palms against a flat surface. It usually occurs within 5–6 years after onset of type I diabetes. It is believed to be due to glycosylation of collagen and perhaps other proteins in connective tissue.

Dupuytren's Contracture

This consists of nodular thickening of the palmar fascia of the hand, producing a claw-like deformity. Although not specific to diabetes, when it occurs in a diabetic patient it may be the result of ischemic necrosis and secondary scarring of connective tissue as a consequence of diabetic microangiopathy.

Bone Demineralization

Bone demineralization has been reported to occur with increased frequency in diabetic patients. Bone density, as measured by photon absorption in the forearms, is 10–20% below normal in diabetics as compared to appropriately matched controls. Diabetes mellitus, however, does not seem to be associated with clinically important osteopenia, since there is no increase in the occurrence of skeletal fractures.

Joint Abnormalities

Bursitis, particularly of the shoulders and hips, occurs more frequently than expected in patients with diabetes. Gout also has a higher than expected incidence, especially in obese diabetics.

7. INFECTION

Certain types of infection, such as bacteriuria, candidal esophagitis, and candidal vaginitis, occur more frequently in diabetic patients than in nondiabetic matched controls. There are also several unusual infections that occur almost exclusively in diabetics (eg, emphysematous cholecystitis, mucormycosis, malignant otitis externa and necrotizing papillitis). As noted above, atherosclerosis with peripheral vascular disease is very common in the diabetic population, and the resultant ischemia undoubtedly plays a role in the frequent lower extremity infections seen in these patients.

SURGERY IN THE DIABETIC PATIENT

Surgery represents a stress situation during which most of the insulin antagonists (catecholamines, GH, corticosteroids) are mobilized. In the diabetic patient, this can lead to a worsening of hyperglycemia and perhaps even ketoacidosis. The aim of medical management of diabetics during the perioperative period is to minimize these stress-induced changes. Recom-

mendations for management depend both on the patient's usual diabetic regimen and on the type of surgery (major or minor) to be done.

DIABETICS REGULATED BY DIET ALONE

No special precautions must be taken unless diabetic control is markedly disturbed by the procedure. If this occurs, small amounts of regular insulin twice a day will establish euglycemia in a patient whose food intake is adequate. Human insulin is recommended, since it sensitizes the patient least—ie, anaphylactic complications are very rare, and patients are less likely to be sensitized to the future use of insulin.

DIABETICS TAKING ORAL HYPOGLYCEMIC AGENTS

When oral medications are allowed, these agents should be administered in the usual doses in the perioperative period. Carbohydrates should be supplied orally or by intravenous infusion of dextrose in water, with careful monitoring of blood glucose levels to avoid hypoglycemia or extremes of hyperglycemia. As in the case of diet-controlled diabetes, human insulin can be substituted if symptomatic hyperglycemia or ketosis develops.

DIABETICS TAKING INSULIN

Patients taking insulin represent the only serious challenge to management of diabetes when surgery is necessary. However, with careful attention to changes in the clinical or laboratory picture, most diabetic patients can be managed successfully.

Minor Surgery

For minor surgery requiring only local or spinal anesthesia or intravenous administration of a very transient anesthetic, half of the usual dose of insulin should be given in the morning. The patient should be placed early on the operating room schedule. A constant drip of 5% dextrose in water (at a rate of approximately 5 g of glucose per hour) should be infused, and blood glucose levels should be checked at regular intervals.

Major Surgery

The night before major surgery, a 9 PM bedtime snack is given. Thereafter, the patient should receive nothing by mouth. On the morning of surgery, the usual morning subcutaneous insulin dose is omitted; instead, 10 units of regular insulin is added to 1 L of 5% dextrose in half-normal saline, and this is infused intravenously at a rate of 100–180 mL/h. This will

Table 15–20. Guidelines for perioperative diabetes management with an insulin pump.[1]

- Insulin: Regular (human) 25 units in 250 mL of normal saline (1 unit/10 mL).
- Intravenous infusions of insulin: Flush 50 mL through line before connecting to patient. Piggyback insulin line to the perioperative maintenance fluid line.
- Perioperative maintenance fluid: Fluids must contain 5% dextrose (rate 100 mL/h).
- Blood glucose: Monitor hourly intraoperatively.[2]

Blood Glucose	Insulin	
(mg/dL)	(units/h)	(mL/h)
< 80	0.0	0.0
81–100	0.5	5.0
101–140	1.0	10
141–180	1.5	15
181–220	2.0	20
221–260	2.5	25
261–300	3.0	30
301–340	4.0	40
> 341	5.0	50

- Blood glucose <80 mg/dL: Stop insulin and administer intravenous bolus of 50% dextrose in water (25 mL). One blood glucose >80 mg/dL, restart insulin infusion. It may be necessary to modify the algorithm.
- Decreased insulin needs: Patients treated with diet or oral agents or <50 units insulin per day, endocrinologic deficiencies.
- Increased insulin needs: Obesity, sepsis, steroid therapy, renal transplant, coronary artery bypass.

[1] Reproduced, with permission, from Gavin LA: Perioperative management of the diabetic patient. Endocrinol Metab Clin North Am 1992;21:457.
[2] Blood glucose value ÷ 100 gives a reasonable estimate of infusion dosage (units/h).

give the patient 1–1.8 units of insulin per hour, which, except in the most severe cases, will generally keep the blood glucose within the range of 100–250 mg/dL (5.5–13.9 mmol/L). The infusion may be continued for several days if necessary. Plasma glucose or blood glucose should be determined every 2–4 hours to be sure metabolic control is adequate. If it is not, adjustments in the ratio of insulin to dextrose in the intravenous solution can be made.

An alternative method which is gaining in popularity consists of separate infusions of insulin and glucose delivered by pumps to permit independent adjustments of each infusion rate depending on hourly variation of blood glucose values. Table 15–20 provides guidelines for management with an insulin drip, and the algorithms are designed to achieve glycemic control in the range of 120–180 mg/dL blood glucose.

After surgery, when the patient has resumed an adequate oral intake, intravenous administration of insulin and dextrose can be stopped. Two hours after discontinuing the intravenous insulin, subcutaneous administration of insulin can be resumed. Insulin needs may vary in the first several days after surgery because of continuing postoperative stresses and because of variable caloric intake. In this situation, multiple doses of regular insulin guided by blood glucose determinations can keep the patient in acceptable metabolic control.

PROGNOSIS FOR PATIENTS WITH DIABETES MELLITUS

The period between 10 and 20 years after the onset of diabetes seems to be a critical one. If the patient survives this period without fulminating microvascular complications, there is a strong likelihood that reasonably good health will continue. Currently, the prospect for retarding the progression of diabetic eye complications is good because of benefits derived from laser photocoagulation. Education as to proper foot care has been immensely valuable in reducing morbidity from diabetic foot problems. Management of hypertension, dyslipidemia, and cessation of cigarette smoking have been of great benefit in preventing or reducing the progression of retinopathy, nephropathy, and atherosclerosis. Newer methods for delivering purified insulins and for self-monitoring blood glucose have improved the overall outlook for patients with diabetes mellitus. However, present methods of insulin delivery remain quite primitive and need much improvement before physiologic insulin secretion is reproduced. Hypoglycemia remains a serious risk in all regimens of intensive insulin therapy attempting normalization of blood glucose. It is clear that the diabetic patient's intelligence, motivation, and awareness of potential complications of the disease are major factors contributing to a successful outcome. In addition, appropriate education of diabetic patients to provide the knowledge, the guidelines, and the tools to help them take charge of their own day-to-day diabetes management is essential to improve the long-term prognosis.

REFERENCES

The Endocrine Pancreas

Atria TE et al: Secretion of pancreatic polypeptide in patients with pancreatic endocrine tumors. N Engl J Med 1986;315:287.

Bell GI et al: Molecular biology of mammalian glucose transporters. Diabetes Care 1990;13:198.

Bloom SR, Polak JM: Somatostatin. Br Med J 1987; 295:288.

Burant CF et al: Fructose transporter in human spermatozoa and small intestine is GLUT 5. J Biol Chem 1992;267:14523.

Ebert R, Creutzfeldt W: Gastrointestinal peptides and insulin secretion. Diabetes Metab Rev 1987;3:1.

Fehmann H-C, Goke R, Goke B: Glucagon-like peptide-1 (7–37)/(7–36) amide is a new incretin. Mol Cell Endocrinol 1992;85:C39.

Galloway JA et al: Biosynthetic human proinsulin: Review of chemistry, in vitro and in vivo receptor binding, animal and human pharmacology studies, and clinical trial experience. Diabetes Care 1992;15:666.

Gepts W, In't-Veld PA: Islet morphologic changes. Diabetes Metab Rev 1987;3:859.

Goldfine ID, Pilch P: Insulin secretion and action and diabetes mellitus. J Cell Biochem 1992;48:1.

Howell SL: The mechanism of insulin secretion. Diabetologia 1984;26:319.

McCullough AJ et al: Effect of graded intraduodenal glucose infusions on the release and physiological actions of gastric inhibitory polypeptide. J Clin Endocrinol Metab 1983;56:234.

Orskov C et al: Pancreatic and intestinal processing of proglucagon in man. Diabetologia 1987;30:874.

Philippe J: Structure and pancreatic expression of the insulin and glucagon genes. Endocr Rev 1991;12:252.

Pipeleers DG et al: Interplay of nutrients and hormones in the regulation of glucagon release. Endocrinology 1985;117:817.

Pipeleers G: The biosociology of pancreatic B cells. Diabetologia 1987;30:277.

Reichlin S: Somatostatin. (Two parts.) N Engl J Med 1983;309:1495, 1556.

Steiner DF et al: Is islet amyloid polypeptide a significant factor in pathogenesis or pathophysiology of diabetes? Diabetes 1991;40:305.

Swenne I: Pancreatic beta-cell growth and diabetes mellitus. Diabetologia 1992;35:193.

Westermark P et al: Islet amyloid polypeptide A novel controversy in diabetes research. Diabetologia 1992; 35:297.

Diagnosis, Classification, & Pathophysiology of Diabetes Mellitus

Bell GI, Horita S, Karam JH: A polymorphic locus near the human insulin gene is associated with insulin-dependent diabetes mellitus. Diabetes 1984;33:176.

Bell GI: Molecular defects in diabetes mellitus. Diabetes 1991;40:413.

Bennett PH: The diagnosis of diabetes: New international classification and diagnostic criteria. Annu Rev Med 1983;34:295.

Bjorntorp P: Metabolic implications of body fat distribution. Diabetes Care 1991;14:1132.

Caro JF: Insulin resistance in obese and nonobese man. J Clin Endocrinol Metab 1991;73:691.

Cavan D, Bain S, Barnett A: The genetics of type I (insulin dependent) diabetes mellitus. J Med Genetics 1992;29:441.

Clare-Salzer MJ, Tobin AJ, Kaufman DL: Glutamate decarboxylase: An autoantigen in IDDM. Diabetes Care 1992;15:132.

DeFronzo RA, Ferrannini E: Insulin resistance: A multifaceted syndrome responsible for NIDDM, obesity, hypertension, dyslipidemia, and atherosclerotic cardiovascular disease. Diabetes Care 1991;14:173.

Flier JS: Syndromes of insulin resistance: From patient to gene and back again. Diabetes 1992;41:1207.

Froguel P et al: Familial hyperglycemia due to mutations in glucokinase. N Engl J Med 1993;328:697.

Fujioka S et al: Contribution of intra-abdominal fat accumulation to the impairment of glucose and lipid metabolism in human obesity. Metabolism 1987;36: 54.

Garrow JS: Treatment of obesity. Lancet 1992;340:409.

Kahn BB: Facilitative glucose transporters: Regulatory mechanisms and dysregulation in diabetes. J Clin Invest 1992;89:1367.

Karam JH: Type II diabetes and syndrome X: Pathogenesis and glycemic management. Endocrinol Metab Clin North Am 1992;21:329.

Karjalainen J et al: A bovine albumin peptide as a possible trigger of insulin-dependent diabetes mellitus. N Engl J Med 1992;327:302.

Leahy JL, Bonner-Weir S, Weir GC: Beta cells dysfunction induced by chronic hyperglycemia: Current ideas on mechanism of impaired glucose-induced insulin secretion. Diabetes Care 1992;15:442.

Moller DE, Flier JS: Insulin resistance: Mechanisms, syndromes, and implications. N Engl J Med 1991; 325:938.

Muir A, Schatz DA, Maclaren NK: The pathogenesis, prediction, and prevention of insulin-dependent diabetes mellitus. Endocrinol Metab Clin North Am 1992;21:199.

O'Rahilly S, Moller DE: Mutant insulin receptors in syndromes of insulin resistance. Clin Endocrinol 1992; 36:121.

Palmer JP: Predicting IDDM: Use of humoral immune markers. Diabetes Reviews 1993;1:104.

Permutt MA, Chiu KC, Tanizawa Y: Glucokinase and NIDDM: A candidate gene that paid off. Diabetes 1992;41:1367.

Porte D Jr: Beta cells in type II diabetes mellitus. Diabetes 1991;40:166.

Ravussin E, Swinburn BA: Pathophysiology of obesity. Lancet 1992;340:404.

Reaven GM: Role of insulin resistance in human disease. Diabetes 1988;37:1595.

Rossini AA et al: Immunopathogenesis of diabetes mellitus. Diabetes Reviews 1993;1:43.

Schade DS et al: The etiology of incapacitating, brittle diabetes. Diabetes Care 1985;8:12.

Sobey WJ et al: Sensitive and specific two-site immunoradiometric assays for human insulin, proinsulin, 65–66 split and 32–33 split proinsulins. Biochem J 1989;260:535.

Solimena M et al: Autoantibodies to GABA-ergic neurons and pancreatic beta cells in stiff-man syndrome. N Engl J Med 1990;332:1555.

Taylor SI et al: Molecular genetics of insulin resistant diabetes mellitus. J Clin Endocrinol Metab 1991;73:1158.

Todd JA, Bell JI, McDevitt HO: HLA-DQβ gene contributes to susceptibility and resistance to insulin-dependent diabetes mellitus. Nature 1987;329:599.

Trucco M: To be or not to be Asp 57, that is the question. Diabetes Care 1992;15:705.

Velho G et al: Primary pancreatic beta-cell secretory defect caused by mutations in glucokinase gene in kindreds of maturity onset diabetes of the young. Lancet 1992;340:444.

Treatment of Diabetes Mellitus

Alberti KG, Gries FA: Management of non-insulin-dependent diabetes mellitus in Europe: A concensus view. Diabetic Med 1988;5:275.

Anderson JW, Akanji AO: Dietary fiber: An overview. Diabetes Care 1991;14:1126.

Arauz-Pacheco C, Raskin P: Management of hypertension in diabetes. Endocrinol Metab Clin North Am 1992;21:371.

Bailey CJ: Biguanides and NIDDM. Diabetes Care 1992;15:755.

Bettmann MA: Radiographic contrast agents: A perspective. (Editorial.) N Engl J Med 1987;317:891.

Binder C et al: Insulin pharmacokinetics. Diabetes Care 1984;7: 188.

Bolli GB et al: Glucose counterregulation and waning of insulin in the Somogyi phenomenon (posthypoglycemic hyperglycemia). N Engl J Med 1984;311:1214.

Boyd AE III: Sulfonylurea receptors, ion channels, and fruit flies. Diabetes 1988;37:847.

Brange J et al: Monomeric insulins and their experimental and clinical implications. Diabetes Care 1990;13:923.

Bressler R, Johnson D: New pharmacological approaches to therapy of NIDDM. Diabetes Care 1992;15:792.

Brink SJ, Stewart C: Insulin pump treatment in insulin-dependent diabetes mellitus: Children, adolescents, and young adults. JAMA 1986;255:617.

Capsaicin Study Group: Effect of treatment with capsaicin on daily activities of patients with painful diabetic neuropathy. Diabetes Care 1992;15:159.

Clarke WL et al: Multifactorial origin of hypoglycemic symptom unawareness in IDDM. Diabetes 1991;40: 680.

Cryer PE: Iatrogenic hypoglycemia as a cause of hypoglycemia-associated autonomic failure in IDDM: A vicious cycle. Diabetes 1992;41:255.

Davis MR, Shamoon H: Deficient counterregulatory hormone responses during hypoglycemia in a patient with insulinoma. J Clin Endocrinol Metab 1991;72:788.

DCCT Research Group: Epidemiology of severe hypoglycemia in the diabetes control and complications trial. Am J Med 1991;90:450.

Dunn FL: Management of hyperlipidemia in diabetes mellitus. Endocrinol Metab Clin North Am 1992;21: 395.

Garvey WT et al: The effect of insulin treatment on insulin secretion and insulin action in type II diabetes mellitus. Diabetes 1985;34:222.

Gavin LA: Perioperative management of the diabetic patient. Endocrinol Metab Clin North Am 1992;21:457.

Genuth S: Management of the adult onset diabetic with sulfonylurea drug failure. Endocrinol Metab Clin North Am 1992;21:351.

Groop LC et al: Morning or bedtime insulin combined with sulfonylurea in treatment of NIDDM. Diabetes Care 1992;15:831.

Groop LC: Sulfonylureas in NIDDM. Diabetes Care 1992;15:737.

Heine RJ et al: Absorption kinetics and action profiles of mixtures of short- and intermediate-acting insulins. Diabetologia 1984;27:558.

Kang S et al: Subcutaneous insulin absorption explained by insulin's physicochemical properties. Diabetes Care 1991;14:942.

Karam JH, Root RK: Therapeutic dilemmas in type 2 diabetes mellitus: Improving and maintaining beta cell and insulin sensitivity. West J Med 1988;148:685.

Karam JH: Type II diabetes and syndrome X: Pathogenesis and glycemic management. Endocrinol Metab Clin North Am 1992;21:329.

The Kroc Collaborative Study Group: Blood glucose control and the evolution of diabetic retinopathy and albuminuria: A multicenter trial. N Engl J Med 1984;311:365.

Lebovitz HE (editor): *Therapy for Diabetes Mellitus and Related Disorders.* American Diabetes Association, 1991.

Lebovitz HE (editor): *Physician's Guide to Non-Insulin-Dependent (Type II) Diabetes: Diagnosis and Treatment,* 2nd ed. American Diabetes Association, 1988.

Little RR et al: Relationship of glycosylated hemoglobin to oral glucose tolerance: Implications for diabetes screening. Diabetes 1988;37:60.

Max MB et al: Effects of desipramine, amitriptyline, and fluoxetine on pain in diabetic neuropathy. N Engl J Med 1992;326:1250.

Mecklenburg RS et al: Long-term metabolic control with insulin pump therapy: Report of experience with 127 patients. N Engl J Med 1985;313:465.

Melander A: Clinical pharmacology of sulfonylureas. Metabolism 1987;36(2 Suppl 1):12.

Mulhauser I et al: Hypoglycemic symptoms and frequency of severe hypoglycemia in patients treated with human and animal insulin preparations. Diabetes Care 1991;14:745.

Nathan DM et al: The clinical information value of the glycosylated hemoglobin assay. N Engl J Med 1984; 310:341.

Nathan DM: The rationale for glucose control in diabetes mellitus. Endocrinol Metab Clin North Am 1992; 21:221.

Nolte MS: Insulin therapy in insulin-dependent (type I) diabetes mellitus. Endocrinol Metab Clin North Am 1992;21:281.

Patrick AW, Williams G: The Liverpool symposium on human insulin and hypoglycemia. Diabetic Med 1992; 9:579.

Perriello G, De Feo P, Bolli GB: The dawn phenomenon: Nocturnal blood glucose homeostasis in insulin-dependent diabetes mellitus. Diabetic Med 1988;5:13.

Raskin P et al: The effect of diabetic control on the width of skeletal-muscle capillary basement membrane in patients with type I diabetes mellitus. N Engl J Med 1983;309: 1546.

Robertson RP: Pancreas transplantation in humans with diabetes mellitus. Diabetes 1991;40;1085.

Santiago JV: Intensive management of insulin-dependent diabetes: Risks, benefits, and unanswered questions. J Clin Endocrinol Metab 1992;75:977.

Tamborlane WV, Amiel SA: Hypoglycemia in the treated diabetic patient: A risk of intensive insulin therapy. Endocrinol Metab Clin North Am 1992;21: 313.

Tordjman KM et al: Failure of nocturnal hypoglycemia to cause fasting hyperglycemia in patients with insulin-dependent diabetes mellitus. N Engl J Med 1987;317:1552.

Vinik AI, Wing RR: The good, the bad, and the ugly in diabetic diets. Endocrinol Metab Clin North Am 1992;21:237.

Watkins PJ: Clinical observations and experiments in diabetic neuropathy. Diabetologia 1992;35:2.

Yki-Jarvinen H et al: Clinical benefits and mechanisms of a sustained response to intermittent insulin therapy in type 2 diabetic patients with secondary drug failure. Am J Med 1988;84: 185.

Acute Complications of Diabetes Mellitus

Adrogue HJ et al: Plasma acid-base patterns in diabetic ketoacidosis. N Engl J Med 1982;307: 1603.

Bending JJ, Pickup JC, Keen H: Frequency of diabetic ketoacidosis and hypoglycemic coma during treatment with continuous subcutaneous insulin infusion. Am J Med 1985;79:685.

Brown, RH et al: Caveat on fluid replacement in hyperglycemic hyperosmolar nonketotic coma. Diabetes Care 1978;1:305.

Casparie AF, Elving LD: Severe hypoglycemia in diabetic patients: Frequency, causes, prevention. Diabetes Care 1985;8:141.

Cefalu WT: Diabetic ketoacidosis. Crit Care Clin 1991; 7:89.

Clements RS, Vourganti B: Fatal diabetic ketoacidosis: Major causes and approaches to their prevention. Diabetes Care 1978;1:314.

Cohen RD, Woods HF: Lactic acidosis revisited. Diabetes 1983;32:181.

Fisher JN, Kitabchi AE: A randomized study of phosphate therapy in the treatment of diabetic ketoacidosis. J Clin Endocrinol Metab 1983;57:177.

Flexner CW et al: Repeated hospitalization for diabetic ketoacidosis: The game of "Sartoris." Am J Med 1984;76:691.

Henderson G. The psychosocial treatment of recurrent diabetic ketoacidosis: An interdisciplinary team approach. Diabetes Educator 1991;17:119.

Krane EJ et al: Subclinical brain swelling in children during treatment of diabetic ketoacidosis. N Engl J Med 1985;312:1147.

Kreisberg RA: Pathogenesis and management of lactic acidosis. Annu Rev Med 1984,35: 181.

Morris LR, Murphy MB, Kitabchi AE: Bicarbonate therapy in severe diabetic ketoacidosis. Ann Intern Med 1986;105:836.

Narins RG, Cohen JJ: Bicarbonate therapy for organic acidosis: The case for its continued use. Ann Intern Med 1987;106;615.

Rumbak MJ, Kitabchi AE: Diabetic ketoacidosis: Etiology, pathophysiology, and treatment. Compr Ther 1991;17:46.

Salzman R et al: Intranasal aerosolized insulin: Mixed-meal studies and long-term use in type I diabetes. N Engl J Med 1985;312: 1078.

Siperstein MD: Diabetic ketoacidosis and hyperosmolar coma. Endocrinol Metab Clin North Am 1992;21: 415.

Stacpoole PW: Lactic acidosis: The case against bicarbonate therapy. Ann Intern Med 1986;105:276.

Wachtel TJ, Silliman RA, Lamberton P: P~disposing factors for the diabetic hyperosmolar state. (Letter.) Arch Intern Med 1988:148:747.

Wrenn KD et al: The syndrome of alcoholic ketoacidosis. Am J Med 1991;91:119.

Chronic Complications of Diabetes Mellitus

Ai E: Current management of diabetic retinopathy. West J Med 1992;157:67.

Brownlee M: Glycation products and the pathogenesis of diabetic complications. Diabetes Care 1992;15:1835.

Cogan DG et al: Aldose reductase and complications of diabetes. Ann Intern Med 1984;101:82.

Davis MD: Diabetic retinopathy. Diabetes Care 1992;15: 1844.

Deckert T et al: Microalbuminuria: Implications for micro- and macrovascular disease. Diabetes Care 1992; 15:1181.

Donahue RP, Orchard TJ: Diabetes mellitus and macrovascular complications: An epidemiological perspective. Diabetes Care 1992;15;1141.

Feingold KR et al: Muscle capillary basement membrane width in patients with vacor-induced diabetes mellitus. J Clin Invest 1986;78:102.

Hostetter TH: Diabetic nephropathy: Metabolic versus hemodynamic considerations. Diabetes Care 1992;15: 1205.

Klein R, Klein BEK, Moss SE: Epidemiology of proliferative diabetic retinopathy. Diabetes Care 1992;15: 1875.

Knowles HC Jr: Long-term juvenile diabetes treated with unmeasured diet. Trans Assoc Am Physicians 1971; 84:95.

LoGerfo FW, Coffman D: Vascular and microvascular disease of the foot in diabetes: Implications for foot care. N Engl J Med 1984;311: 1615.

Markell MS, Friedman EA: Diabetic nephropathy: Management of the end stage patient. Diabetes Care 1992; 15:1226.

Mauer SM et al: Long-term study of normal kidneys

transplanted into patients with type I diabetes. Diabetes 1989;38:516.

McCulloch DK et al: The prevalence of diabetic impotence. Diabetologia 1980;18:279.

Mogensen CE: Management of diabetic renal involvement and disease. Lancet 1988;1:867.

Parkhouse N, Le Quesne PM: Impaired neurogenic vascular response in patients with diabetes and neuropathic foot lesions. N Engl J Med 1988;318:1306.

Ramsay RC et al: Progression of diabetic retinopathy af-

ter pancreas transplantation for insulin-dependent diabetes mellitus. N Engl J Med 1988;318:208.

Raskin P et al: Capillary basement membrane width in diabetic children. Am J Med 1975;58:365.

Rosenbloom AL et al: Limited joint mobility in childhood diabetes: Family studies. Diabetes Care 1983; 6:370.

Vinik AI et al: Diabetic neuropathies. Diabetes Care 1992;15:1926.

Ward JD: The diabetic leg. Diabetologia 1982;22:141.

Hypoglycemic Disorders

16

John H. Karam, MD, & Clinton W. Young, MD

Circulating plasma glucose concentrations are kept within a relatively narrow range by a complex system of interrelated neural, humoral, and cellular controls. Under the usual metabolic conditions, the central nervous system is wholly dependent on plasma glucose and counteracts declining blood glucose concentrations with a carefully programmed response. This is often associated with a sensation of hunger; and, as the brain receives insufficient glucose to meet its metabolic needs (neuroglycopenia), an autonomic response is triggered to mobilize storage depots of glycogen and fat. Hepatic glycogen reserves directly supply the central nervous system with glucose, which is carried across the blood-brain barrier by a specific glucose transport system, while the mobilization of fatty acids from triglyceride depots provides energy for the large mass of skeletal and cardiac muscle, renal cortex, liver, and other tissues that utilize fatty acids as their basic fuel, thus sparing glucose for use by the tissues of the central nervous system.

PATHOPHYSIOLOGY OF THE COUNTERREGULATORY RESPONSE TO NEUROGLYCOPENIA

The plasma concentration of glucose that will signal the need by the central nervous system to mobilize energy reserves depends on a number of factors, such as the status of blood flow to the brain, the integrity of cerebral tissue, the prevailing arterial level of plasma glucose, the rapidity with which plasma glucose concentration falls, and the availability of alternative metabolic fuels. In most healthy people, hypoglycemic symptoms occur at plasma glucose levels below 45 mg/dL (2.5 mmol/L) (blood glucose < 40 mg/dL [2.2 mmol/L]). However, in elderly people with compromised cerebral blood supply, neuroglycopenic manifestations may be provoked at slightly higher plasma glucose levels. Patients with chronic hyperglycemia, eg, those with poorly controlled insulin-dependent diabetes mellitus, may experience symptoms of neuroglycopenia at considerably higher plasma glucose concentrations than persons without diabetes. This has been attributed to a "down-regulated" glucose transport system across the blood-brain barrier. Conversely, in patients exposed to chronic hypoglycemia—eg, those with an insulin-secreting tumor or those with diabetes who are receiving excessively "tight" glycemic control with an insulin pump—"up-regulation" of the glucose transporters may explain the greater tolerance of hypoglycemia without manifesting symptoms of neuroglycopenia (Figure 16–1).

Restoring and maintaining an adequate supply of glucose for cerebral function proceeds by a series of neurogenic events that act directly to raise the plasma glucose concentration and to stimulate hormonal responses that augment the adrenergic mobilization of energy stores (Table 16–1).

Hormonal Response to Hypoglycemia

A. Insulin: Endogenous insulin secretion is lowered both by reduced glucose stimulation to the pancreatic B cell and by sympathetic nervous system inhibition from a combination of alpha-adrenergic neural effects and increased circulating catecholamine levels. This reactive insulinopenia facilitates the mobilization of energy from existing energy stores (glycogenolysis and lipolysis), increases hepatic enzymes involved in gluconeogenesis and ketogenesis, and at the same time prevents muscle tissue from consuming the blood glucose being released from the liver (see Chapter 15).

B. Catecholamines: Circulating catecholamines—and norepinephrine produced at sympathetic nerve endings—provide muscle tissue with alternative sources of fuel by activating beta-adrenergic receptors, resulting in mobilization of muscle glycogen, and by providing increased plasma free fatty acids from lipolysis of adipocyte triglyceride.

C. Glucagon: Plasma glucagon is released by the beta-adrenergic effects of both sympathetic innervation and circulating catecholamines on pancreatic A cells as well as by the direct stimulation of A cells by the low plasma glucose concentration itself. This glucagon release increases hepatic output of glucose by direct glycogenolysis as well as by facilitating the activity of gluconeogenic enzymes. As shown in Figure 16–2, plasma glucagon appears to be the key counterregulatory hormone affecting recovery from acute hypoglycemia in humans, with the adrenergic-

CHRONIC HYPERGLYCEMIA

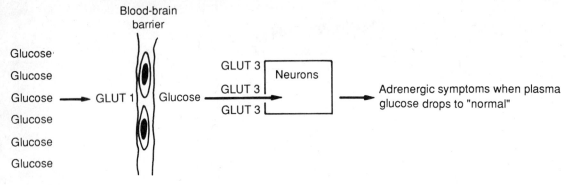

NORMAL GLUCOSE LEVELS

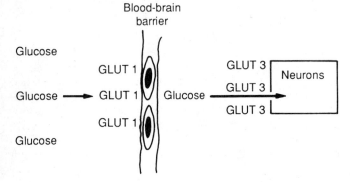

FREQUENT HYPOGLYCEMIA

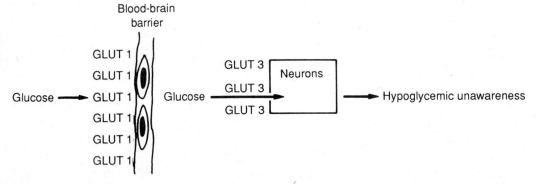

Figure 16–1. Glycemic regulation of glucose transporters. The center panel depicts the normal component of the high-affinity glucose transporter 1 (GLUT 1) on the vascular cells of the central nervous system during euglycemia. An appropriate amount of glucose diffuses across the blood-brain barrier and is then transported into the neurons by another high-affinity glucose transporter, GLUT 3. The upper and lower panels, respectively, show adaptation by either down-regulation of GLUT 1 in the face of chronic hyperglycemia (upper panel) or up-regulation of GLUT 1 in the presence of chronic hypoglycemia. (GLUT 1, glucose transporter 1; GLUT 3, glucose transporter 3.)

Table 16–1. Sympathetic nervous system response to hypoglycemia.

Alpha-Adrenergic Effects
Inhibition of endogenous insulin release.
Increase in cerebral blood flow (peripheral vasoconstriction).
Beta-Adrenergic Effects
Hepatic and muscle glycogenolysis.
Stimulation of plasma glucagon release.
Lipolysis to raise plasma free fatty acids.
Impairment of glucose uptake by muscle tissue.
Increase in cerebral blood flow (increase in cardiac output).
Adrenomedullary Discharge of Catecholamines
Augmentation of all of the above alpha- and beta-adrenergic effects.

catecholamine response representing a major backup system.

D. Corticotropin and Hydrocortisone: Pituitary ACTH is released in association with the sympathetic nervous system stimulation by neuroglycopenia. This results in elevation of plasma cortisol levels, which in turn permissively facilitates lipolysis and actively promotes protein catabolism and conversion of amino acids to glucose by the liver.

E. Growth Hormone: Pituitary growth hormone is also released in response to falling plasma glucose levels. Its role in counteracting hypoglycemia is less well defined, but it is known to antagonize the action of insulin on glucose utilization in muscle cells and to directly activate lipolysis by adipocytes.

Maintenance of Euglycemia in the Postabsorptive State

Glucose absorption from the gastrointestinal tract ceases by 5–8 hours after a meal. During the "postabsorptive state" immediately following, glucose must be produced endogenously from previously stored nutrients to meet the requirements of the central nervous system. The liver is the central organ involved in this process, producing the 125 mg of glucose per minute required by the brain as well as an additional 25 mg/min for other glucose-dependent tissues—predominantly blood cell elements. This is initially provided by the breakdown of stored hepatic glycogen. However, because these reserves are limited to 80–100 g, they begin to be depleted several hours into the postabsorptive state. Thereafter, hepatic glucose production is augmented by gluconeogenesis—the formation of glucose from amino acids, lactate, and glycerol. These substrates are delivered to the liver from peripheral stores: Muscle and other structural tissues supply amino acids, mainly alanine; blood cell elements supply lactate, the end product of glycolytic metabolism; and adipose tissue supplies glycerol from lipolysis of triglyceride. In addition, oxidation of the free fatty acids released from adipose cells during lipolysis supplies the energy required for gluconeogenesis and provides ketone bodies, acetoacetate, and β-hydroxybutyrate, which can serve as alternative metabolic fuels for the central nervous system during periods of prolonged fasting.

Hormonal changes that begin early in the postabsorptive state regulate the enzymatic steps necessary for hepatic glycogenolysis and gluconeogenesis and ensure the delivery of the necessary substrate (Table 16–2). An appropriate fall in circulating insulin levels with a corresponding rise in glucagon is most important; elevations in the counterregulatory hormones cortisol and growth hormone contribute but are less critical.

In summary, numerous endocrine and metabolic events interact to provide a continuous source of fuel for proper functioning of the central nervous system. Malfunction of any of these mechanisms can lead to symptomatic hypoglycemia.

CLASSIFICATION OF HYPOGLYCEMIC DISORDERS

Symptomatic Hypoglycemia

A clinical classification of the more common causes of symptomatic hypoglycemia in adults is presented in Table 16–3. (The inborn errors of metabolism that produce hypoglycemia in infants and children are mentioned but will not be discussed in detail in this chapter.) This classification is useful in directing diagnostic considerations.

Symptomatic **fasting hypoglycemia** is a serious and potentially life-threatening problem warranting thorough evaluation. Conditions that produce inappropriate fasting hyperinsulinism are the most common cause of fasting hypoglycemia in otherwise healthy adults. These include insulin-secreting pancreatic B cell tumors and iatrogenic or surreptitious administration of insulin or sulfonylureas. In patients with illnesses that produce symptomatic fasting hypoglycemia despite appropriately suppressed insulin levels, the clinical picture is dominated by the signs and symptoms of the primary disease, with hypoglycemia often only a late or associated manifestation. This is in contrast to patients with inappropriate hyperinsulinism, who usually appear healthy between hypoglycemic episodes.

Symptoms of **nonfasting hypoglycemia** in adults, although distressing to the patient, do not imply serious illness or warrant extensive evaluation. Overstimulation of the B cells postprandially as a result of accelerated glucose absorption after rapid gastric emptying may result in too rapid disposal of glucose, with resulting symptoms of sympathetic nervous system hyperactivity. Other than in patients who have had gastric surgery, this diagnosis may be difficult to establish.

Asymptomatic Hypoglycemia

Hypoglycemia may be seen during prolonged fasting, strenuous exercise, or pregnancy, or may occur

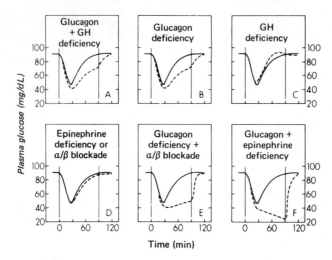

Figure 16–2. Solid lines show changes in plasma glucose that occur in normal subjects in response to insulin administration. Note the rapid recovery of glucose levels mediated by intact counterregulatory mechanisms. The dashed lines show the response to insulin-induced hypoglycemia in patients with deficiencies of the counterregulatory mechanisms induced as follows: **A:** Somatostatin infusion (inhibits both glucagon and growth hormone [GH] release). **B:** Somatostatin infusion plus GH infusion (now with functional isolated glucagon deficiency). **C:** Somatostatin infusion plus glucagon infusion (isolated GH deficiency). Note return of glucose response to normal, implying that glucagon is the main counterregulatory hormone. **D:** Bilateral adrenalectomy, leading to epinephrine deficiency, or infusion of phentolamine plus propranolol (alpha and beta blockers, respectively). Note that such deficiencies cause no major abnormality in response to induced hypoglycemia when glucagon is present. **E and F:** Sympathetic modulation (by phentolamine plus propranolol in **E** and by bilateral adrenalectomy in **F**), which seriously impairs the ability to respond to hypoglycemia in the patient made glucagon-deficient by somatostatin infusion. (Reproduced, with permission, from Cryer PE: Glucose counterregulation in man. Diabetes 1981:30:261.)

as a laboratory artifact. In normal men, plasma glucose does not fall below 55 mg/dL (3 mmol/L) during a 72-hour fast. However, for reasons that are not clear, normal women may experience a fall to levels as low as 30 mg/dL (1.7 mmol/L) despite a marked suppression of circulating insulin to less than 6 μU/mL. They remain asymptomatic in spite of this degree of hypoglycemia, presumably because ketogenesis is able to satisfy the energy needs of the central nervous system. Basal plasma glucose declines progressively during normal pregnancy, and hypoglycemic levels may be reached during prolonged

fasting. This may be a consequence of a continuous fetal consumption of glucose and diminished availability of the gluconeogenic substrate alanine. The cause of these diminished alanine levels in pregnancy is unclear. The greatly increased glucose consumption by skeletal muscle that occurs during prolonged strenuous exercise may lead to hypoglycemia despite increases in hepatic glucose production. Whether the hypoglycemia in this circumstance contributes to fatigue or other symptoms in distance runners is unknown.

In vitro consumption of glucose by blood cell elements may give rise to laboratory values in the hypoglycemic range. This is most commonly seen when an insufficient amount of the metabolic inhibitor sodium fluoride is added to specimens containing increased numbers of leukocytes (as in leukemia and leukemoid reactions).

Table 16–2. Hormonal changes to maintain euglycemia in the postabsorptive state.

Decreased Insulin Secretion
Increases hepatic glycogenolysis.
Increases lipolysis.
Increases hepatic gluconeogenesis.
Decreases muscle uptake of glucose.

Increased Glucagon Secretion
Increases hepatic glycogenolysis.
Facilitates hepatic gluconeogenesis.

Increased Cortisol Secretion
Facilitates lipolysis.
Increases protein catabolism.
Augments hepatic gluconeogenesis.

CLINICAL PRESENTATION OF HYPOGLYCEMIA

Regardless of the cause, hypoglycemia presents certain common features characterized by Whipple's triad: (1) symptoms and signs of hypoglycemia, (2)

Table 16–3. Common causes of symptomatic hypoglycemia.

Fasting
  A. With Hyperinsulinism:
    Insulin reaction.
    Sulfonylurea overdose.
    Surreptitious insulin or sulfonylurea administration.
    Autoimmune hypoglycemia (idiopathic insulin antibodies, insulin receptor autoantibodies).
    Pentamidine-induced hypoglycemia.
    Pancreatic B cell tumors.
  B. Without Hyperinsulinism:
    Severe hepatic dysfunction.
    Chronic renal insufficiency.
    Inanition, ketotic hypoglycemia of childhood.
    Hypocortisolism.
    Alcohol use.
    Nonpancreatic tumors.
    Inborn errors of carbohydrate metabolism (glycogen storage disease, gluconeogenic enzyme deficiencies).
Nonfasting
  Alimentary.
  Functional.
  Occult diabetes.
  Ethanol.
  Leucine sensitivity.
  Hereditary fructose intolerance.
  Galactosemia.
  Newborn infant of diabetic mother.

an associated plasma glucose level of 45 mg/dL (2.5 mmol/L) or less, and (3) reversibility of symptoms upon administration of glucose.

The symptoms and signs of hypoglycemia are the consequences of neuroglycopenia. They vary depending on the degree of hypoglycemia, the age of the patient, and the rapidity of the decline. In diabetic patients treated with insulin, a precipitous fall in plasma glucose from hyperglycemia toward euglycemia may produce neuroglycopenic symptoms.

A. Acute Hypoglycemia: A rapid fall in plasma glucose (> 1 mg/dL/min [> 0.06 mmol/L/min]) to low levels often accompanies conditions associated with arterial hyperinsulinism—a condition that leads to increased peripheral glucose uptake and decreased hepatic glucose output. In diabetics, excessive absorption of exogenous insulin either from overtreatment or from rapid mobilization from an injection site during exercise may be responsible. In nondiabetics, reactive hypersecretion of insulin may be the cause, as in postgastrectomy patients with rapid gastric emptying time. The symptoms include anxiety, tremulousness, and feelings of unnaturalness or detachment. These are usually accompanied by palpitations, tachycardia, sweating, and hunger and can progress to neurologic sequelae of ataxia, coma, or convulsions. These warning symptoms of hypoglycemia occur even in the absence of adrenal glands and therefore are due to neurogenic responses to hypoglycemia. The autonomic response has probably evolved as more of an alarm than a counterregulatory mechanism, since glucagon is generally sufficient to

provide necessary counterregulation to hypoglycemia. In IDDM, however, the adrenergic system becomes of greater importance since the glucagon response to hypoglycemia is lost in most patients (see Chapter 15).

B. Subacute and Chronic Hypoglycemia: A relatively slow fall in plasma glucose accompanies conditions caused primarily by a reduction in hepatic glucose output in response to hyperinsulinism (predominantly within the portal vein [insulinoma]), to the inappropriately sustained effects of long-acting insulin preparations on the liver in the postabsorptive state, or to metabolic derangements of liver functions (eg, alcohol hypoglycemia). Symptoms due to hypoglycemia in patients with these conditions may be less apparent, particularly because symptoms of sympathetic overactivity are usually absent. These patients develop progressive confusion, inappropriate behavior, lethargy, and drowsiness. If the patient does not eat, seizures or coma may develop—though this is not inevitable, and spontaneous recovery can occur. Because these patients are seldom aware of their degree of functional impairment, a history should be obtained from relatives or friends who have observed the episode. Except for hypothermia (often seen during hypoglycemic coma), there are no identifying characteristics on physical examination. Hypoglycemia will often be misdiagnosed as a seizure disorder, transient ischemic attack, or personality disorder.

Documentation of Low Plasma Glucose Values

With the specific laboratory methods now available, it has been arbitrarily decided that fasting hypoglycemia is present when plasma glucose is 45 mg/dL (2.5 mmol/L) or less after an overnight fast (corresponding to a blood glucose level of 40 mg/dL [2.2 mmol/L] or less). In the fasting state, there is no substantial difference between arterial, venous, or capillary blood samples (in contrast to nonfasting hyperglycemia, in which arteriovenous glucose differences may be considerable because of arterial hyperinsulinism and consequent increases in glucose uptake across capillary beds).

The development of glucose oxidase-hydrogen peroxidase paper strips has been of great value for rapid estimation of blood glucose levels, particularly for insulin-treated diabetics undergoing home monitoring. In emergency room or hospital settings, the paper strips are helpful in the differential diagnosis of coma, particularly when used with a reflectance meter, but a sample should also be sent to the laboratory for definitive diagnosis. Although therapeutic decisions to administer glucose can be based on the paper strip results alone in an emergency situation, variability due to exposure to air or aging makes them less dependable as the sole laboratory indicator for a definitive diagnosis of hypoglycemia.

Reversibility of Clinical Manifestations of Hypoglycemia With Treatment

Because prolonged hypoglycemia may cause permanent brain damage and death, prompt recognition and treatment are mandatory. (It is prudent to consider the possibility of hypoglycemic coma in most unconscious patients.)

The goal of therapy is to restore normal levels of plasma glucose as rapidly as possible. If the patient is conscious and able to swallow, glucose-containing foods such as candy, orange juice with added sugar, and cookies should be quickly ingested. Fructose, found in many nutrient low-calorie sweeteners for diabetics, should not be used, because although it can be metabolized by neurons, it lacks a transport system and therefore does not cross the blood-brain barrier.

If the patient is unconscious, rapid restoration of plasma glucose must be accomplished by giving 20–50 mL of 50% dextrose intravenously over 1–3 minutes (the treatment of choice) or, when intravenous glucose is not available, 1 mg of glucagon intramuscularly or intravenously. Families or friends of insulin-treated diabetics should be instructed in the administration of glucagon intramuscularly for emergency treatment at home. Attempts to feed the patient or to apply glucose-containing jelly to the oral mucosa should be avoided because of the danger of aspiration.

When consciousness is restored, oral feedings should be started immediately. Periodic blood glucose surveillance after a hypoglycemic episode may be needed for 12–24 hours to ensure maintenance of euglycemia. Prevention of recurrent hypoglycemic attacks depends upon proper diagnosis and management of the specific underlying disorder.

SPECIFIC HYPOGLYCEMIC DISORDERS

SYMPTOMATIC FASTING HYPOGLYCEMIA WITH HYPERINSULINISM

1. INSULIN REACTION

It is not surprising that insulin-treated diabetics make up the bulk of the patient population with symptomatic hypoglycemia. Present methods of insulin delivery rely upon subcutaneous depots of mixtures of soluble and insoluble insulin whose absorption varies with the site of injection and the degree of exercise in surrounding muscles. Variations in physical and emotional stresses can alter the response of patients to insulin, as can the cyclic hormonal changes relating to menstruation. A deficient glucagon response to hypoglycemia in diabetes compounds the problem, as does the lack of awareness of hypoglycemic symptoms in older patients, in those with neuropathy, and in those with recurrent hypoglycemic episodes, who adapt to lower levels of blood glucose without triggering their autonomic alarm system. (See Figure 16–1 and Chapter 15 for further discussion of hypoglycemic unawareness.)

Once the patient's acute hypoglycemic episode is managed, the physician should carefully examine possible correctable factors that may have contributed to the insulin reaction.

Inadequate Food Intake

An insufficient quantity of food or a missed meal is one of the commonest causes of hypoglycemia in insulin-treated diabetics. Until improved insulin delivery systems are available, patients attempting to achieve satisfactory glycemic control should self-monitor their blood glucose levels and eat three regular meals as well as small midmorning, midafternoon, and bedtime snacks, particularly when they are receiving two or more injections of insulin mixtures daily.

Exercise

The insulin-treated diabetic is especially prone to exercise-induced hypoglycemia. In nondiabetics, the enhancement of skeletal muscle glucose uptake (a 20- to 30-fold increase over basal uptake) is compensated for by enhanced hepatic glucose production. This is mediated primarily by a fall in circulating insulin levels consequent to an exercise-induced catecholamine discharge, which inhibits B cell secretion. Such regulation is impossible in the insulin-treated diabetic, whose subcutaneous depot not only continues to release insulin during exercise but also shows an accelerated absorption rate when the injection site is in close proximity to the muscles being exercised. When this occurs, increased levels of circulating insulin compromise the hepatic output of glucose. To prevent hypoglycemia, insulin-treated diabetics must be advised to avoid injections into areas adjacent to muscles most involved in the particular exercise and either to eat supplementary carbohydrate before exercising or to reduce their insulin dose appropriately.

Impaired Glucose Counterregulation in Diabetics

Most patients with insulin-dependent diabetes have a deficient glucagon response to hypoglycemia. They are thus solely dependent on an adrenergic autonomic response to recover from hypoglycemia and particularly to provide them with symptoms they recognize as a warning of impending hypoglycemia and as a signal to ingest sugar or fruit juice. Some patients, especially those with long-standing diabetes or autonomic neuropathy, lack both a glucagon and an epinephrine response and are virtually defenseless against insulin-induced hypoglycemia. Insulin infusion tests can be used to identify these alterations in glucose counterregulation; however, at present these tests are cumbersome, and their ability to accurately predict which patients will suffer frequent severe and prolonged hypoglycemic episodes is yet to be established. Easier and more reliable methods of identifying such patients are needed. The ability of a patient to spontaneously recover from hypoglycemia may determine whether or not aggressive attempts to maintain euglycemia are associated with undue risk.

Some patients who originally had a normal counterregulatory response to hypoglycemia (except for glucagon) lose this protective response when insulin therapy is intensified to achieve tight control. The mechanisms for this reduction of hormonal response are unknown but may be related to "up-regulated" mechanisms of glucose transport across the blood-brain barrier induced by relatively low circulating blood glucose levels.

Inadvertent or Deliberate Insulin Overdosage in Diabetics

Excessive insulin may be administered inadvertently by patients with poor vision or inadequate instruction or understanding of dosage and injection technique. The widespread use of highly concentrated U100 insulin enhances the likelihood of overdosage with relatively small excesses of administered insulin.

Deliberate overdosage may occur in certain maladjusted patients, particularly adolescents, who wish to gain special attention from their families or escape tensions at school or work.

Miscellaneous Causes of Hypoglycemia in Insulin-Treated Diabetics

A. Stress: Physical stresses—such as intercurrent illnesses, infection, and surgery—or psychic stresses often require an increased insulin dosage to control hyperglycemia. Reduction to prestress doses is necessary to avoid subsequent hypoglycemia when the stresses have abated.

B. Hypocortisolism: In patients with insulin-dependent diabetes who have otherwise unexplained hypoglycemic attacks, reduced insulin requirements may indicate unusual causes (eg, Addison's disease).

C. Diabetic Gastroparesis: Unexplained episodes of postprandial hypoglycemia in insulin-dependent diabetics may be due to delayed gastric emptying consequent to autonomic neuropathy. This diagnosis can be established by appropriate radiologic studies of gastric motility using liquid or solid test meals containing radioisotopic markers.

D. Pregnancy: Pregnancy, with high fetal glucose consumption, decreases insulin requirements in the first trimester.

E. Renal Insufficiency: Renal insufficiency, through impairment of insulin degradation while hepatic gluconeogenesis and food intake are often reduced, also requires a reduction in insulin dosage.

F. Drugs: Numerous pharmacologic agents may potentiate the effects of insulin and predispose to hypoglycemia. Common offenders include ethanol, salicylates, and beta-adrenergic blocking drugs. Beta blockade inhibits fatty acid and gluconeogenic substrate release and reduces plasma glucagon levels; furthermore, the symptomatic response is altered, because tachycardia is blocked while hazardous elevations of blood pressure may result during hypoglycemia in response to the unopposed alpha-adrenergic stimulation from circulating catecholamines and neurogenic sympathetic discharge. However, symptoms of sweating, hunger, and uneasiness are not masked by beta-blocking drugs and remain indicators of hypoglycemia in the aware patient.

2. SULFONYLUREA OVERDOSE

Any of the sulfonylureas may produce hypoglycemia. Chlorpropamide, with its prolonged half-life (35 hours), is a common offender. Older patients—especially those with impaired hepatic or renal function—are particularly susceptible to sulfonylurea-induced hypoglycemia: Liver dysfunction prolongs the hypoglycemic activity of tolbutamide, acetohexamide, and tolazamide, as well as that of the second-generation compounds glyburide and glipizide; renal insufficiency perpetuates the blood glucose-lowering effects of many sulfonylureas, especially chlorpropamide and glyburide. Elderly patients with gradually decreasing creatinine clearance seem to be more at risk for prolonged and severe hypoglycemia when treated with chlorpropamide or glyburide and less so when treated with shorter-acting agents such as tolbutamide or glipizide. In the presence of other pharmacologic agents such as warfarin, phenylbutazone, or certain sulfonamides, the hypoglycemic effects of sulfonylureas may be markedly prolonged.

3. SURREPTITIOUS INSULIN OR SULFONYLUREA ADMINISTRATION (Factitious Hypoglycemia)

Factitious hypoglycemia should be suspected in any patient with access to insulin or sulfonylurea drugs. It is most commonly seen in health professionals and diabetic patients or their relatives. The reasons for self-induced hypoglycemia vary, with many patients having severe psychiatric disturbances or a need for attention.

When insulin is used to induce hypoglycemia, an elevated serum insulin level often raises suspicion of an insulin-producing pancreatic B cell tumor. It may be difficult to prove that the insulin is of exogenous origin. The triad of hypoglycemia, high immunoreactive insulin levels, and suppressed plasma C peptide immunoreactivity* is pathognomonic of exogenous insulin administration. Technical difficulties in measuring immunoreactive insulin, caused by the inappropriate presence of circulating antibodies (usually seen only in insulin-treated individuals), will generally support the diagnosis of factitious hypoglycemia. However, the absence of detectable insulin antibodies does not rule out the possibility of exogenous insulin administration, especially with the advent of human insulins with low immunogenicity in humans.

When sulfonylurea abuse is suspected, plasma or urine should be screened for its presence.

Treatment of factitious hypoglycemia involves psychiatric therapy and social counseling.

4. AUTOIMMUNE HYPOGLYCEMIA

In recent years, a rare autoimmune disorder has been reported in which patients have circulating insulin antibodies and the paradoxic feature of hypoglycemia. While some of these patients may be surreptitiously administering insulin, in an increasing number of case reports it has not been possible to document exogenous insulin as the inducer of insulin antibodies. Hypoglycemia generally occurs 3–4 hours after a meal and is attributed to a dissociation of insulin-antibody immune complexes, releasing free insulin. This autoimmune hypoglycemia due to accumulation of high titers of antibodies capable of reacting with endogenous insulin has been most commonly reported in methimazole-treated patients with Graves' disease from Japan but also in patients with lymphoma, multiple myeloma, or lupus syndromes in which paraproteins or antibodies cross-react with insulin.

Hypoglycemia due to insulin receptor autoantibodies is also an extremely rare syndrome, reported in only six patients. All of these patients have also had episodes of insulin-resistant diabetes and acanthosis nigricans. Their hypoglycemia is attributed to an agonistic action of the antibody on the insulin receptor. Balance between the antagonistic and agonistic effects of the antibody determines whether insulin-resistant diabetes or hypoglycemia occurs. Hypoglycemia was found to respond to glucocorticoid therapy but not to plasmapheresis or immunosuppression.

5. PENTAMIDINE-INDUCED HYPOGLYCEMIA

With the increasing use of pentamidine for treatment of *Pneumocystis carinii* infection in patients with AIDS, more reports of pentamidine-induced hypoglycemia are appearing. The cause of acute hypoglycemia appears to be the drug's lytic effect on B cells, which produces acute hyperinsulinemia in about 10–20% of patients receiving the drug. Physicians treating patients with pentamidine should be aware of the potential complication of acute hypoglycemia, which may be followed later by occasionally persistent insulinopenia and hyperglycemia.

Intravenous glucose should be administered during pentamidine administration and for the period immediately following to prevent or ameliorate hypoglycemic symptoms. Following a complete course of therapy with pentamidine, fasting blood glucose or a subsequent glycohemoglobin should be monitored to assess the extent of pancreatic B cell recovery or residual damage.

6. PANCREATIC B CELL TUMORS

Spontaneous fasting hypoglycemia in an otherwise healthy adult is most commonly due to insulinoma, an insulin-secreting tumor of the islets of Langerhans. Eighty percent of these tumors are single and benign; 10% are malignant (if metastases are identified); and the remainder are multiple, with scattered micro- or macroadenomas interspersed within normal islet tissue. (As with some other endocrine tumors, histologic differentiation between benign and malignant cells is difficult, and close follow-up is necessary to ensure the absence of metastases.) Diffuse B cell hyperplasia has rarely been documented as a cause of hypoglycemia in adults.

These adenomas may be familial and have been found in conjunction with tumors of the parathyroid glands and the pituitary (multiple endocrine neoplasia type I). (See Chapter 21.) Ninety-nine percent of them are located within the pancreas and less than 1% in ectopic pancreatic tissue.

These tumors may appear at any age, though they are most common in the fourth to sixth decades. There is no sex predilection.

Clinical Findings

The signs and symptoms are chiefly those of subacute neuroglycopenia rather than adrenergic discharge. The typical picture is that of recurrent central nervous system dysfunction at times of exercise or fasting. The preponderance of neurologic symptoms

---

*C peptide, a major portion of the connecting chain of amino acids in proinsulin, remains intact during the conversion of proinsulin to insulin (see Chapter 15).

rather than those commonly associated with hypoglycemia (adrenergic symptoms) often leads to delayed diagnosis following prolonged psychiatric care or treatment for seizure disorders or transient ischemic attacks. Some patients learn to relieve or prevent their symptoms by taking frequent feedings. Obesity may be the result; however, obesity is seen in less than 30% of patients with insulin-secreting tumors.

Diagnosis of Insulinoma

B cell tumors do not reduce secretion in the presence of hypoglycemia, and a serum insulin level of 10 μU/mL or more with concomitant plasma glucose values below 45 mg/dL (2.5 mmol/L) suggests an insulinoma. Other causes of hyperinsulinemic hypoglycemia must be considered, however, such as surreptitious administration of insulin or sulfonylureas.

A. Insulin Assay: Because the insulin radioimmunoassay is crucial in diagnosing insulin-secreting tumors, it is important to be aware of certain limitations in its use. It detects not only human but also beef and pork insulins, and a high level may therefore indicate either endogenous or exogenous insulin. (C peptide measurements are necessary to make this distinction.) In addition, the assay is of no value in patients who have ever taken insulin, as virtually all will have developed low-titer insulin antibodies that will interfere. Falsely low or elevated values will result depending on the method used. Proper collection of samples is also important: If they are not frozen immediately, falsely low values will result, because the insulin molecule will undergo proteolytic digestion.

B. Suppression Tests: Failure of endogenous insulin secretion to be suppressed in the presence of hypoglycemia is the hallmark of an insulin-secreting tumor. The most reliable suppression test is the prolonged supervised fast in hospitalized subjects, and this remains the preferred diagnostic maneuver in the workup of suspected insulinomas.

In normal men, the blood glucose value will not fall below 55 mg/dL (3.1 mmol/L) during a 72-hour fast, while insulin levels fall below 10 μU/mL; in some normal women, however, plasma glucose may fall below 30 mg/dL (1.7 mmol/L) (lower limits have not been established), while serum insulin levels also fall appropriately. (These women remain asymptomatic despite this degree of hypoglycemia, presumably because ketogenesis is able to provide sufficient fuel for the central nervous system.) Calculation of ratios of insulin (in μU/mL) to plasma glucose (in mg/dL) is useful diagnostically. Nonobese normal subjects maintain a ratio of less than 0.25; obese subjects may have an elevated ratio, but hypoglycemia does not occur with fasting. Virtually all patients with insulin-secreting islet cell tumors will have an abnormally high insulin:glucose ratio at some time during a 72-hour fast. The majority of these will experience progressive and symptomatic fasting hypo-

glycemia with associated elevated insulin levels within 24–36 hours and no evidence of ketonuria. However, an occasional patient will not demonstrate hypoglycemia until 72 hours have elapsed. Brisk exercise during the fast may help precipitate hypoglycemia. Once symptoms of hypoglycemia occur, plasma glucose should be obtained and the fast immediately terminated if plasma glucose is below 45 mg/dL (2.5 mmol/L).

C. Stimulation Tests: A variety of stimulation tests with intravenous tolbutamide, glucagon, or calcium have been devised to demonstrate exaggerated and prolonged insulin secretion. However, because insulin-secreting tumors have a wide range of granule content and degrees of differentiation, they are variably responsive to these secretagogues. Thus, absence of an excessive insulin secretory response during any of these stimulation tests does not rule out the presence of an insulinoma. In addition, the tests may be extremely hazardous to patients with responsive tumors by inducing prolonged and refractory hypoglycemia. (None of these secretagogues should be given to a patient when hypoglycemia is present.) The following stimulation tests should be reserved for the difficult case in which results of a prolonged fast are equivocal. They can also be useful for screening when the index of suspicion for an insulin-secreting tumor is low.

1. Tolbutamide stimulation test– One gram of sodium tolbutamide dissolved in 20 mL of distilled water is infused intravenously over 2 minutes. Serum insulin is measured every 5 minutes for 15 minutes; a level exceeding 195 μU/mL during this time suggests an insulin-secreting tumor. However, this response is seen in only 60% or less of patients with insulinomas, and false-positive results may occur (eg, with obesity or hepatic disease). Continuation of the test beyond 15 minutes will uncover additional patients with insulinomas by demonstrating prolonged elevations of insulin; however, hazardous hypoglycemia may result.

2. Glucagon stimulation test– One milligram of glucagon is given intravenously, and serum insulin levels are measured every 5 minutes for 15 minutes. A level exceeding 135 μU/mL suggests an insulin-secreting tumor. However, only about half of patients with insulinomas will demonstrate this hyperinsulinism, and false-positive results may occur. When an exaggerated increase in serum insulin occurs, the hyperglycemic effect of glucagon may be subnormal, and profound hypoglycemia may subsequently develop by 60 minutes.

D. Oral Glucose Tolerance Test: The oral glucose tolerance test is of no value in the diagnosis of insulin-secreting tumors. A common misconception is that patients with insulinomas will have flat glucose tolerance curves, because the tumor will discharge insulin in response to oral glucose. In fact, most insulinomas respond poorly, and curves typical of diabetes are more common. In those rare tumors that do release insulin in response to glucose, a flat curve may result; however, this also can be seen in normal subjects.

E. Euglycemic Clamp: Continuous blood glucose monitoring with feedback-controlled dextrose infusion by an artificial pancreas has been used to demonstrate excessive dextrose requirements to maintain fasting euglycemia in insulinoma patients. This test remains experimental; however, it has the advantage of avoiding hypoglycemia during a supervised fast.

F. Proinsulin Measurements: In contrast to normal subjects, whose proinsulin concentration is less than 20% of the total immunoreactive insulin, patients with insulinoma have elevated levels of proinsulin that represent 30–90% of total immunoreactive insulin. Sensitive new assays for human proinsulin that incorporate specific monoclonal antibodies offer considerable potential in the evaluation of patients with suspected insulinoma.

G. Glycohemoglobin Measurements: Low glycohemoglobin values have been reported in occasional cases of insulinoma, reflecting the presence of chronic hypoglycemia. However, the diagnostic usefulness of glycohemoglobin measurements is limited by the relatively low sensitivity of this test as well as poor accuracy at the lower range of normal in many of the assays. In addition, it is nonspecific for hypoglycemia, with low levels being found in certain hemoglobinopathies and hemolytic states.

H. Tumor Localization Studies:

1. Imaging studies– The diagnosis of an insulin-secreting tumor is dependent on biochemical testing. Since most tumors are too small (80% are < 2 cm) to localize by either ultrasonography, CT scanning, or MRI, a negative result will not be conclusive.

Arteriography is often used for preoperative localization of small tumors. The results are improved if catheterization of small arterial branches and subbranches of the celiac artery (selective and subselective arteriography) is combined with calcium injections, which stimulate insulin release from neoplastic tissue but not from normal islets. Simultaneous measurement of hepatic venous insulin (from a catheter inserted into the hepatic vein) during each selective calcium injection has been reported to help localize small tumors not visible with selective arteriography alone. However, even with these advances, arteriography is seldom helpful enough to outweigh its disadvantages, and it remains a painful and relatively imprecise procedure that exposes insulinoma patients to the risk of hypoglycemia and the discomfort of several hours of invasive and expensive radiography. In most cases, a tumor mass large enough to "blush" on arteriography is large enough for an experienced surgeon to identify by direct visualization or palpation. In addition, false-positive and false-negative results are so common that reliance on operative local-

ization by an experienced surgeon has preempted the use of arteriography in a growing number of medical centers.

Small tumors within the pancreas that are not palpable at laparotomy have been localized using intraoperative ultrasound in which a transducer is wrapped in a sterile rubber glove and passed over the exposed pancreatic surface. This is at present probably the most effective method of localizing insulinomas.

2. Transhepatic portal vein sampling– Demonstration of insulin gradients or "step-ups" in insulin concentration in the pancreatic venous effluent can be effective in localizing small insulin-secreting tumors. The procedure entails percutaneous transhepatic portal vein catheterization under local anesthesia with subsequent cannulation of the splenic vein. Samples for insulin assay are obtained along the splenic and portal venous systems in an attempt to show a gradient of 300 μU/mL or more of insulin concentration that would evidence a tumor. Results may be equivocal, however, because of the high rate of blood flow in these venous systems and the consequent dilution of insulin values. In addition, this uncomfortable procedure is not without complications; bile leakage, intraperitoneal hemorrhage, and infection have been reported. This procedure is most helpful when multiple insulinomas are suspected, as in patients with coexisting pituitary or parathyroid tumors who develop hypoglycemia. Since diazoxide would interfere with this test, it should be discontinued for at least 48–72 hours before sampling. An infusion of dextrose may be required, therefore, and patients should be closely monitored during the procedure to avoid hypoglycemia (as well as hyperglycemia, which could affect insulin gradients). Venous sampling is indicated for cases in which hypoglycemia does not respond to diazoxide (see below), so that surgical removal of the insulinoma is therefore mandated. In this instance, only an angiographer with extensive experience in the technique should perform the procedure.

Treatment of Insulinoma

The treatment of choice for insulin-secreting tumors is surgical resection. A flow diagram for the approach to these patients is shown in Figure 16–3.

A. Surgical Treatment: Tumor resection should be performed only by surgeons with extensive experience with removal of islet cell tumors, since these tumors may be small and difficult to recognize. An 85% success rate has been reported without localization procedures if surgeons have prior experience with insulinomas.

1. Preoperative management–

a. Trial of diazoxide– Oral diazoxide, a potent inhibitor of insulin secretion, will maintain euglycemia in most patients with insulin-secreting tumors. Doses of 300–400 mg/d (divided) will usually suf-

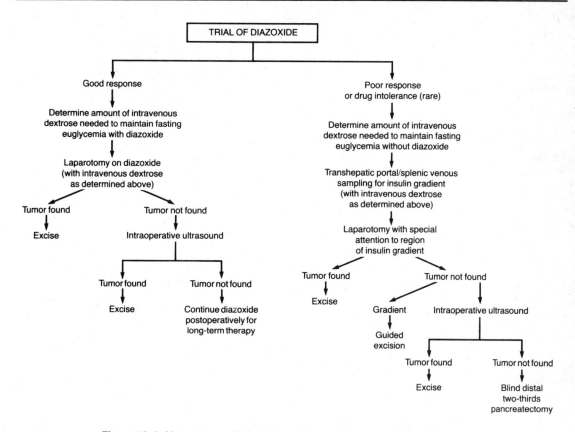

Figure 16–3. Management of the patient with a confirmed diagnosis of insulinoma.

fice, but an occasional patient will require up to 800 mg/d. Side effects include edema due to sodium retention (which generally necessitates concomitant thiazide administration), gastric irritation, and mild hirsutism.

b. Selection of patients– Patients who remain euglycemic on diazoxide may be operated on by an experienced surgeon, without attempts at preoperative tumor localization. However, intraoperative ultrasound should be available on call in case an insulinoma is not palpated after exposure and mobilization of the pancreas. Patients who do not respond to diazoxide or cannot tolerate its side effects are candidates for venous sampling studies in an attempt to localize the tumor preoperatively, since failure to successfully remove the tumor has a poorer prognosis in patients in whom diazoxide therapy is not effective.

2. Treatment during surgery–

a. Glucose need during surgery– To estimate glucose needs during surgery, 5% or 10% dextrose should be infused a day or so before surgery to determine the approximate rate of glucose administration needed to maintain euglycemia. This amount can then be prescribed on the day of surgery; counterregulatory stress responses during surgery should ensure that additional glucose will probably not be required.

However, plasma glucose should be monitored frequently to regulate glucose replacement during surgery, especially during manipulation of the pancreas.

b. Diazoxide– Diazoxide should be administered preoperatively as well as on the day of surgery in patients who are responsive to it, since the drug greatly reduces the need for glucose supplements and the risk of hypoglycemia during surgery while not masking the glycemic rise indicative of surgical cure.

3. Postoperative hyperglycemia– Postoperatively, several days of hyperglycemia may ensue. This is due to a combination of factors, including edema and inflammation of the pancreas after surgery, high levels of counterregulatory hormones induced by the procedure, chronic down-regulation of insulin receptors by the previously high circulating insulin levels from the tumor, and perhaps suppression of normal pancreatic B cells by long-standing hypoglycemia. Small subcutaneous doses of regular insulin may be prescribed every 4–6 hours if plasma glucose exceeds 300 mg/dL (16.7 mmol/L), but in most cases pancreatic insulin secretion recovers after 48–72 hours, and very little insulin replacement is required.

4. Failure to find the tumor at operation– In approximately 10% of patients with biochemically demonstrated autonomous insulin secretion, no tumor can be found at exploratory laparotomy. The tumor will most likely be in the head of the pancreas, as this is the most difficult area for the surgeon to mobilize and explore; therefore, blind distal two-thirds pancreatectomy is seldom successful. If intraoperative ultrasound does not identify a tumor, it is best to let the prior response to diazoxide therapy dictate the proper procedure (Figure 16–3). If the patient has responded to diazoxide, this can be continued indefinitely. If the patient has not responded or is intolerant of diazoxide therapy, and if preoperative venous sampling has not been helpful in localizing a tumor, then—and only then—a blind distal two-thirds pancreatectomy should be performed. This procedure has a success rate of only 25%.

B. Medical Treatment: Diazoxide therapy is the treatment of choice in patients with inoperable functioning islet cell carcinomas and in those who are poor candidates for operation. Many patients have been maintained on long-term (> 10 years) diazoxide therapy without apparent ill effects. Hydrochlorothiazide, 25–50 mg daily, should also be prescribed to counteract the edema and hyperkalemia secondary to diazoxide therapy as well as to potentiate its hyperglycemic effect. Frequent carbohydrate feedings (every 2–3 hours) can also be helpful in maintaining euglycemia, though obesity may become a problem.

When patients are unable to tolerate diazoxide because of side effects such as gastrointestinal upset, hirsutism, or edema, a calcium channel blocker such as verapamil (80 mg given orally every 8 hours) may be tried in view of its inhibitory effect on insulin release from insulinoma cells in vitro.

A potent long-acting synthetic octapeptide analogue of somatostatin (octreotide) has been used to inhibit release of hormones from a number of endocrine tumors, including inoperable insulinomas. When hypoglycemia persists after attempted surgical removal of the insulinoma and if diazoxide or verapamil is poorly tolerated or ineffective, a trial of 50 μg of octreotide injected subcutaneously twice daily may control the hypoglycemic episodes in conjunction with multiple small carbohydrate feedings.

Streptozocin has proved beneficial in patients with islet cell carcinomas, and effective cytotoxic doses have been achieved without the undue renal toxicity that characterized early experience. Benign tumors appear to respond poorly, if at all.

SYMPTOMATIC FASTING HYPOGLYCEMIA WITHOUT HYPERINSULINISM

1. DISORDERS ASSOCIATED WITH LOW HEPATIC GLUCOSE OUTPUT

Reduced hepatic gluconeogenesis can result from a direct loss of hepatic tissue (acute yellow atrophy from fulminating viral or toxic damage); from disorders reducing amino acid supply to hepatic parenchyma (severe muscle wasting and inanition from anorexia nervosa, chronic starvation, uremia, and glucocorticoid deficit from adrenocortical deficiency); or from inborn errors of carbohydrate metabolism affecting glycogenolytic or gluconeogenic enzymes.

2. ETHANOL HYPOGLYCEMIA

Ethanol impairs hepatic gluconeogenesis but has no effect on hepatic glycogenolysis. In the patient who is imbibing ethanol but not eating, fasting hypoglycemia may occur after hepatic glycogen stores have been depleted (within 8–12 hours of a fast). No correlation exists between the blood ethanol levels and the degree of hypoglycemia, which may occur while blood ethanol levels are declining. It should be noted that ethanol-induced fasting hypoglycemia may occur at ethanol levels as low as 45 mg/dL (10 mmol/L)—considerably below most states' legal standards (80 mg/dL [17.4 mmol/L]) for being "under the influence." Most patients present with neuroglycopenic symptoms, which may be difficult to differentiate from the neurotoxic effects of the alcohol. These symptoms in a patient whose breath smells of alcohol may be mistaken for alcoholic stupor. Intravenous dextrose should be administered promptly to all such stuporous or comatose patients. Because hepatic glycogen stores have been depleted by the time hypoglycemia occurs, parenteral glucagon will not be effective. Adequate food intake during alcohol ingestion will prevent this type of hypoglycemia.

3. NONPANCREATIC TUMORS

A variety of nonpancreatic tumors have been found to cause fasting hypoglycemia. Most are large and mesenchymal in origin, retroperitoneal fibrosarcoma being the classic prototype. However, hepatocellular carcinomas, adrenocortical carcinomas, hypernephromas, gastrointestinal tumors, lymphomas and leukemias, and a variety of other tumors have also been reported.

Laboratory diagnosis depends upon fasting hypoglycemia associated with serum insulin levels below 8 μU/mL. The mechanisms by which these tumors produce hypoglycemia are not entirely clear. None have been unequivocally shown to secrete insulin; thus, true ectopic hyperinsulinemia probably does not exist. Up to 50% of these tumors have been reported to secrete low-molecular-weight peptides with insulin-like activity. These peptides include human insulin-like growth factors of various molecular weights. Whether further refinement in the assays for these peptides will allow the demonstration of NSILA in all cases of nonpancreatic tumors that are associated with hypoglycemia remains to be seen. Messenger RNA for IGF-2 has been found in high levels in some extrapancreatic tumor tissues. Hypoglycemia in these cases was attributed to a high-molecular-weight form of IGF-2 that was disproportionately present in higher concentration despite normal *total* blood levels of IGF-2 in these patients. Treatment is aimed toward the primary tumor, with supportive therapy using frequent feedings. Diazoxide is ineffective in reversing the hypoglycemia caused by these tumors.

NONFASTING HYPOGLYCEMIA
(Reactive Hypoglycemia)

Reactive hypoglycemia may be classified as early (within 2–3 hours after a meal) or late (3–5 hours). Early (alimentary) hypoglycemia occurs when there is a rapid discharge of ingested carbohydrate into the small bowel followed by rapid glucose absorption and hyperinsulinism. It may be seen after gastrointestinal surgery and is notably associated with the "dumping syndrome" after gastrectomy; occasionally, it is functional and may result from overactivity of the parasympathetic nervous system mediated via the vagus nerve. Late hypoglycemia (occult diabetes) is caused by a delay in early insulin release, which then results in exaggeration of initial hyperglycemia during a glucose tolerance test. As a consequence, an exaggerated insulin response produces late hypoglycemia. Early or late hypoglycemia may also occur as a consequence of ethanol's potentiation of the insulin-secretory response to glucose, as when sugar-containing soft drinks are used as mixers to dilute alcohol in beverages (gin and tonic, rum and cola).

1. POSTGASTRECTOMY ALIMENTARY HYPOGLYCEMIA

Reactive hypoglycemia after gastrectomy is a consequence of hyperinsulinism. This results from rapid gastric emptying of ingested food, which produces overstimulation of vagal reflexes and overproduction of beta-cytotropic gastrointestinal hormones, causing arterial hyperinsulinism and consequent acute hypoglycemia. The symptoms are caused by adrenergic hyperactivity in response to the rapidly falling plasma glucose. Treatment is properly directed at avoiding this sequence of events by more frequent feedings with smaller portions of less rapidly assimilated carbohydrate and more slowly absorbed fat or protein. Occasionally, anticholinergic drugs such as propantheline (15 mg orally four times daily) may be useful in reducing vagal overactivity.

2. FUNCTIONAL ALIMENTARY HYPOGLYCEMIA

Early alimentary-type reactive hypoglycemia in a patient who has not undergone surgery is classified as functional. It is most often associated with chronic fatigue, anxiety, irritability, weakness, poor concentration, decreased libido, headaches, hunger after meals, and tremulousness. Whether or not hypoglycemia accounts for these symptoms or occurs at all is difficult to prove.

The usual sequence of events is that the patient presents with a number of nonspecific complaints. Normal laboratory findings and a normal physical examination confirm the initial impression that organic disease is not present, and the symptoms are then attributed to the stresses of modern living. The only form of therapy usually given is reassurance or a mild tranquilizer. When this fails to be of benefit, the patient seeks help elsewhere. Inevitably, the question of hypoglycemia is raised—frequently by the patient, who has heard of the diagnosis from friends or relatives with similar symptoms or has read of it in the lay press. The diagnosis is often supported by the demonstration of hypoglycemia with symptoms during a 5-hour oral glucose tolerance test.

Unfortunately, the precipitation of hypoglycemia with or without symptoms during oral glucose tolerance testing does not distinguish between normal and "hypoglycemic" patients. As many as one-third or more of normal subjects who have never had any symptoms will develop hypoglycemia with or without symptoms during a 5-hour glucose tolerance test. In addition, many patients will develop symptoms in the absence of hypoglycemia. Thus, the test's nonspecificity makes it a highly unreliable tool that is no longer recommended for evaluating patients with suspected episodes of postprandial hypoglycemia. Indeed, the ingestion of a mixed meal did not produce hypoglycemia in 33 patients who had been diagnosed as having reactive hypoglycemia on the basis of oral glucose tolerance testing; this attempt to increase specificity for the diagnosis of reactive hypoglycemia may have resulted in loss of sensitivity.

For increased diagnostic reliability, hypoglycemia should be documented during a spontaneous symptomatic episode in routine daily activity. However, attempts to demonstrate this are almost never successful. Patients should be instructed in the proper use of Chemstrip bG, whose color development is stable enough to allow test strips to be saved and brought to the physician's office for documentation up to 72 hours after the measurement was made. Personality evaluation often discloses hyperkinetic compulsive behavior in thin, anxious patients.

The foregoing discussion should not be taken to imply that functional reactive hypoglycemia does not occur—merely that at present we have no reliable means of diagnosing it. There is no harm (and there is occasional benefit) in reducing or eliminating the content of refined sugars in the patient's diet while increasing the frequency and reducing the size of meals. However, it should not be expected that these maneuvers will cure the asthenia, since the reflex response to hypoglycemia is only a possibly aggravating feature of a generalized primary hyperactivity. Counseling and support should be the mainstays in therapy, with dietary manipulation only an adjunct.

3. LATE HYPOGLYCEMIA
(Occult Diabetes)

This condition is characterized by delay in early insulin release from pancreatic B cells, resulting in initial exaggeration of hyperglycemia during a glucose tolerance test. In response to this hyperglycemia, an exaggerated insulin release produces late hypoglycemia 4–5 hours after ingestion of glucose. These patients are usually quite different from those with early hypoglycemia, being more phlegmatic and often obese and frequently having a family history of diabetes mellitus. In the obese, treatment is directed at reduction to ideal weight. These patients often respond to reduced intake of refined sugars with multiple, spaced small feedings high in dietary fiber. They should be considered early diabetics and advised to have periodic medical evaluations.

REFERENCES

Berger M et al: Functional and morphological characterization of human insulinomas. Diabetes 1983;32:921.

Boyle PJ et al: Plasma glucose concentrations at the onset of hypoglycemic symptoms in patients with poorly controlled diabetes and in nondiabetics. N Engl J Med 1988;318:1487.

Cryer PE, White NH, Santiago JV: The relevance of glucose counterregulatory systems to patients with insulin-dependent diabetes mellitus. Endocr Rev 1986;7:131.

Davis MR, Shamoon H: Deficient counterregulatory hormone responses during hypoglycemia in a patient with insulinoma. J Clin Endocrinol Metab 1991;72:788.

Doherty GM et al: Results of a prospective strategy to diagnose, localize and resect insulinomas. Surgery 1991;110:989.

Fischer KF, Lees JA, Newman JH: Hypoglycemia in hospitalized patients: Causes and outcomes. N Engl J Med 1986;315:1245.

Gerich JE et al: Hypoglycemia unawareness. Endocr Rev 1991;12:356.

Grunberger G et al: Factitious hypoglycemia due to surreptitious administration of insulin: Diagnosis, treatment, and long-term follow-up. Ann Intern Med 1988;108:252.

Hirata Y: Autoimmune insulin syndrome "up to date." In: *Hypoglycemia*. Vol 38 of Serono Symposia Publications. Adreani D, Marks V, Lefebvre PJ (editors). Raven Press, 1987.

Hogan MJ et al: Oral glucose tolerance test compared with a mixed meal in the diagnosis of reactive hypoglycemia. Mayo Clin Proc 1983;58:491.

Kvols LK et al: Treatment of metastatic islet cell carcinoma with a somatostatin analogue (SMS 201–995). Ann Intern Med 1987;17:162.

Marks V, Teale JD: Tumors producing hypoglycemia. Diabetes Metab Rev 1991;7:79.

Polansky KS: A practical approach to fasting hypoglycemia. N Engl J Med 1992;326,1020.

Rifkin MD, Weiss SM: Intraoperative sonographic identification of nonpalpable pancreatic masses. J Ultrasound Med 1984;3:409.

Service FJ et al: Functioning insulinoma: Incidence, recurrence, and long-term survival of patients. A 60 year study. Mayo Clin Proc 1991;66:771.

Service FJ: Hypoglycemia. West J Med 1991;154:442.

Shapiro ET et al: Tumor hypoglycemia: Relationship to high molecular weight insulin-like growth factor-II. J Clin Invest 1990;85:1972.

Simonson DC et al: Intensive insulin therapy reduces counterregulatory hormone responses to hypoglycemia in patients with type I diabetes. Ann Intern Med 1985;103:184.

Taylor SI et al: Hypoglycemia associated with antibodies to the insulin receptor. N Engl J Med 1982;307:1422.

Ulbrecht JS et al: Insulinoma in a 94-year-old woman: Long-term therapy with verapamil. Diabetes Care 1986;9:186.

Waskin H et al: Risk factors for hypoglycemia associated with pentamidine therapy for *Pneumocystis* pneumonia. JAMA 1988;260:345.

Widom B, Simonson DC: Glycemic control and neuropsychologic function during hypoglycemia in patients with insulin-dependent diabetes mellitus. Ann Intern Med 112:904,1990.

Williams HE: Alcoholic hypoglycemia and ketoacidosis. Med Clin North Am 1984;68:33.

Disorders of Lipoprotein Metabolism $\qquad$ 17

John P. Kane, MD, PhD, & Mary J. Malloy, MD

The clinical importance of hyperlipoproteinemia derives chiefly from the role of lipoproteins in atherogenesis. However, the greatly increased risk of acute pancreatitis associated with severe hypertriglyceridemia is an additional indication for intervention. Characterization of hyperlipoproteinemia is important for selection of appropriate treatment and may provide clues to underlying primary clinical disorders.

ARTERIOSCLEROSIS

Arteriosclerosis is the leading cause of death in the USA. Abundant epidemiologic evidence establishes the multifactorial character of this disease and indicates that the effects of the multiple risk factors are at least additive. Risk factors that have been convincingly identified for atherosclerosis of the coronary arteries are hyperlipidemia, arterial hypertension, cigarette smoking, diabetes mellitus, physical inactivity, and decreased levels of high-density lipoproteins (HDL) in plasma. Coronary atheromas are complex lesions containing cellular elements, collagen, and lipids. It is clear, however, that the progression of the lesion is chiefly attributable to its content of unesterified cholesterol and cholesteryl esters. It is now firmly established that the cholesterol in the atheroma is delivered to the site by circulating lipoproteins. Epidemiologic evidence indicates that the atherogenic lipoproteins are the low-density (LDL), intermediate-density (IDL), very low density (VLDL), and Lp(a) species, all of which contain the B-100 apolipoprotein. In animal models, hypertension is associated with increased access of lipoprotein to the subintimal region. Smoking may accelerate the process of atherogenesis chiefly through its influence on blood platelets, though it is also associated with decreased levels of HDL in plasma. Increased platelet interaction at sites of damaged endothelium leads to release of platelet-derived growth factor (PDGF), which stimulates migration of cells of smooth muscle origin into the lesion, where they proliferate. Oxidation of lipoproteins stimulates their endocytosis via special scavenger receptors on macrophages and smooth muscle cells, leading to the formation of foam cells. The macrophages secrete a number of cy-

tokines that drive an inflammatory and proliferative process. Proteolytic enzymes secreted by macrophages weaken the atheroma so that fissuring and rupture can occur. Exposure of subintimal collagen then stimulates thrombogenesis, precipitating acute coronary events. The inverse relationship between plasma HDL levels and the rate of atherogenesis probably reflects the involvement of at least certain species of HDL in the movement of cholesterol away from the atheroma.

Reversal of Atherosclerosis

The results of angiographic intervention trials in humans have conclusively shown that atherosclerotic lesions can regress with lipid-lowering therapy. It is anticipated that timely introduction of hypolipidemic therapy appropriate to the disorder will significantly decrease the incidence of coronary disease and reduce the need for angioplasty, atherectomy, and bypass surgery.

The average levels of LDL in plasma in the United States population are considerably higher than in many other nations, where the levels appear to approach the biologic norm for humans. This probably accounts in large part for the markedly higher incidence of coronary disease in industrialized Western

Table 17–1. Lipoproteins of human serum.

Lipoprotein	Electrophoretic Mobility in Agarose Gel	Density Interval g/cm³	Predominant Core Lipids	Diameter	Apolipoproteins in Order of Quantitative Importance
High-density (HDL)	Alpha	1.21–1.063	Cholesteryl ester	7.5–10.5 nm	A-I, A-II, C, E, D
Low-density (LDL)	Beta	1.063–1.019	Cholesteryl ester	~21.5 nm	B-100, B-74, B-26
Intermediate-density (IDL)	Beta	1.019–1.006	Cholesteryl ester, triglyceride	25–30 nm	B-100, some C and E
Very low density (VLDL)	Prebeta; some "slow prebeta"	<1.006	Triglyceride	30–100 nm	B-100, C, E
Chylomicrons	Remain at origin	<1.006	Triglyceride	80–500 nm	B-48, C, E, A-I, A-II, A-IV, proline-rich apo-protein
Lp(a)	Prebeta	1.04–1.08	Cholesteryl ester	21–30 nm	B-100, Lp(a)

nations and suggests that dietary changes that reduce lipoprotein levels toward normal would be beneficial.

OVERVIEW OF LIPID TRANSPORT

The Plasma Lipoproteins

Because all the lipids of plasma are relatively insoluble in water, they are transported in association with proteins. The simplest complexes are those formed between unesterified, or free, fatty acids (FFA) and albumin, which serve to carry the FFA from peripheral adipocytes to other tissues.

The remainder of the plasma lipids are transported in lipoprotein complexes (Table 17–1). All of the major lipoproteins of plasma are spherical, each with a core region containing hydrophobic lipids. The principal core lipids are cholesteryl esters and triglycerides. Triglycerides predominate in the cores of the chylomicrons, which transport newly absorbed lipids from the intestine, and in the cores of the very low density lipoproteins, which originate in the liver. The relative content of cholesteryl ester is increased in remnants derived from these classes of lipoproteins, and cholesteryl esters predominate in the cores of low-density and high-density lipoproteins. Surrounding the core in each type of lipoprotein is a monolayer containing amphophilic (detergent-like) lipids, chiefly phospholipids and unesterified (free) cholesterol. Apolipoproteins, noncovalently bound to the lipids, are mostly located in or on this surface monolayer.

B Apolipoproteins

Several lipoproteins contain proteins of very high molecular weight known as the B apolipoproteins, which behave like intrinsic proteins of cell membranes. Unlike the smaller apolipoproteins, the B apolipoproteins do not migrate from one lipoprotein particle to another. The B apolipoproteins of intestinal and hepatic origin are different. VLDL contain the B-100 protein, which is retained in the formation of LDL from VLDL remnants by the liver. The intestinal B protein, B-48, is found in chylomicrons and their remnant particles but is completely absent from LDL.

Other Apolipoproteins

In addition to B-48 and B-100, the following apolipoproteins are present in lipoproteins. (The distribution of these proteins in the different lipoproteins is shown in Table 17–1.)

1. C Apolipoproteins: These are low-molecular-weight (700–10,000) proteins that equilibrate rapidly among the lipoproteins. There are three distinct species with unique amino acid sequences, designated C-I, C-II, and C-III. Apolipoprotein C-II is a requisite cofactor for lipoprotein lipase.

2. E Apolipoproteins: Two normal isoforms (E-3 and E-4) of this MW-35,000 protein are the products of allelic genes. Normal individuals thus may have either or both isoforms, which share with B-100 protein the property of interacting with certain high-affinity receptors (B-100:E receptors) on cell membranes. Another isoform (E-2) lacks this property. About 15% of people in the USA are heterozygous for E-2.

3. Apolipoprotein A-I: This protein of MW 28,300 is the major apolipoprotein of HDL; it is also present in chylomicrons and is the most abundant of the apolipoproteins of human serum (about 125 mg/dL). It is a cofactor for lecithin:cholesterol acyltransferase (LCAT).

4. Apolipoprotein A-II: This protein of MW 17,400 is an important constituent of HDL. It contains cysteine, which permits the formation of disulfide-bridged dimers with apo-E.

5. D Apolipoprotein: This heavily glycosylated protein of MW 19,000 is involved with LCAT in the centripetal transport of cholesterol.

6. Apolipoprotein A-IV: This protein of MW 46,000 is chiefly associated with chylomicrons.

7. Lp(a) Protein: This high-molecular-weight (200,000–750,000) glycoprotein, which has a high degree of sequence homology with plasminogen, is found as a disulfide-bridged dimer with apo-B-100 in LDL-like species of lipoproteins (Lp[a] lipoproteins).

Absorption of Dietary Fat; Secretion of Chylomicrons

Dietary triglycerides are hydrolyzed in the intestine to β-monoglyceride and fatty acids by pancreatic lipase. This enzyme requires activation by bile acids and a protein cofactor. The partial glycerides and fatty acids form micelles that are absorbed by intestinal epithelial cells. Within these cells, the fatty acids are reesterified with the monoglyceride to form triglycerides. Some dietary cholesterol absorbed with the micelles is esterified by the acyl-CoA:cholesterol acyltransferase (ACAT) system, and some appears as free cholesterol in the surface monolayers of the chylomicrons. Droplets of triglyceride containing small amounts of cholesteryl esters form in the vesicles of the Golgi apparatus. Phospholipids and free cholesterol form a surface monolayer. Some of the phospholipid originates in bile, some is from dietary sources, and some is synthesized by the intestine. Newly synthesized apo-B-48, apo-A-I, and apo-A-II are added, and the nascent chylomicron emerges into the extracellular lymph space (Figure 17–1). Chylomicrons have diameters ranging from about 60 nm to 500 nm. Once in the lymph spaces, the new chylomicron begins to exchange surface components with HDL, acquiring apo-C and apo-E and losing phospholipids. This process continues as the chylomicron is carried via the intestinal lymphatics to the thoracic duct and thence into the bloodstream. Increased triglyceride transport from the intestine results chiefly in an increase of particle diameter of chylomicrons rather than increased numbers of particles.

Formation of Very Low Density Lipoproteins

The liver exports triglycerides to peripheral tissues in the cores of VLDL (Figure 17–2). These triglycerides are synthesized in liver from free fatty acids abstracted from plasma and from fatty acids synthesized de novo. Several major features distinguish VLDL from chylomicrons. The only B apolipoprotein of VLDL is B-100. Whereas the intestine produces only very limited amounts of apo-C, the liver secretes the bulk of these proteins with newly formed VLDL. Upon reaching the plasma, the VLDL acquire still more apo-C from HDL and yield phospholipid in exchange. Release of VLDL by liver is increased by any condition that results in increased flux of FFA to liver in the absence of increased ketogenesis. Increased caloric intake, ingestion of ethanol, and the administration of estrogens all greatly stimulate release of VLDL from liver and are important causative factors in clinical disorders resulting in elevated levels of triglycerides in plasma.

Metabolism of Triglyceride-Rich Lipoproteins in Plasma

A. Hydrolysis by Lipoprotein Lipase: Fatty acids derived from the triglycerides of chylomicrons

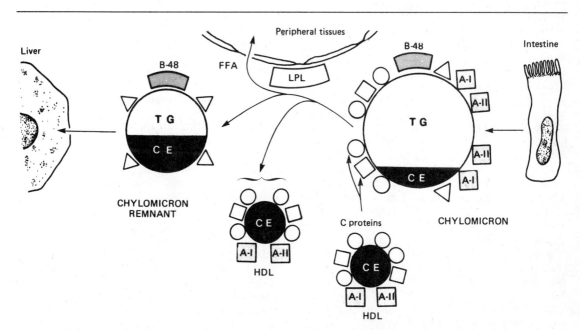

Figure 17–1. Metabolism of chylomicrons. (TG, triglyceride; CE, cholesteryl esters; A-I, A-II, B-48, and C proteins, apolipoproteins.) See text for details.

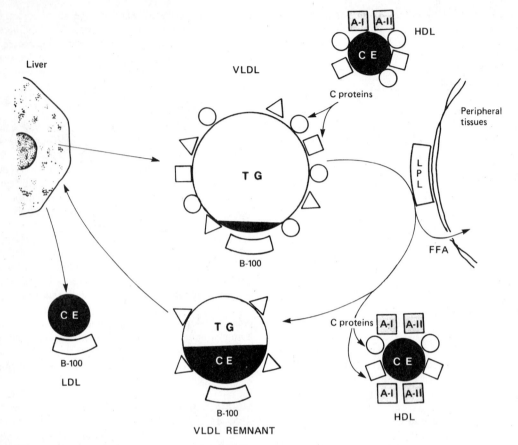

Figure 17–2. Metabolism of VLDL. (TG, triglyceride; CE, cholesteryl esters; A-I, A-II, B-100, and C proteins, and apoE, apolipoproteins.) See text for details.

and VLDL are delivered to tissues predominantly through a common pathway involving hydrolysis by the lipoprotein lipase (LPL) system. Most of the FFA derived during hydrolysis of triglycerides by LPL enters tissue directly. The remainder enters the pool of plasma FFA. Lipoprotein lipase is bound to capillary endothelium in heart, skeletal muscle, adipose tissue, mammary gland, and other tissues. The hydrolysis of triglycerides thus takes place within the vascular compartment.

B. Biologic Regulators of Lipoprotein Lipase: When glucose levels in plasma are elevated and the release of insulin is stimulated, LPL activity in adipose tissue increases, and fatty acids derived from triglycerides of circulating lipoproteins are stored. During prolonged fasting, however, LPL activity of adipose tissue falls to undetectable levels, completely preventing storage of fatty acids from VLDL and chylomicrons. Heparin is a cofactor for LPL. When heparin is given intravenously (0.1–0.2 mg/kg). LPL activity is displaced into plasma, permitting its in vitro measurement. Another obligatory cofactor is apo-C-II. Normally, its content in plasma is far in excess of that required for activation of LPL.

C. Formation of Lipoprotein Remnants: Hydrolysis by LPL results in depletion of the content of triglycerides in the hydrophobic core of chylomicrons and VLDL, producing a progressive decrease in particle diameter. Lipids from the surface monolayer are transported to HDL. This maintains an appropriate core: monolayer relationship for spheres of smaller diameters. During this process, apo-C—and, to a lesser extent, apo-E—are transferred to HDL. The products of this series of events are "remnant" lipoproteins containing their original complement of apo-B, a portion of the original amount of apo-E, and little apo-C. In the case of chylomicrons, apo-A-I and apo-A-II also leave the particles and become incorporated into HDL. VLDL remnants are 25–30 nm in diameter, and those of chylomicrons are up to 80 nm in diameter. They have lost about 70% of their original complement of triglyceride but are enriched in cholesteryl esters.

D. Fate of Lipoprotein Remnants: Chylomicron remnants are removed from blood quantitatively by high-affinity, receptor-mediated endocytosis in the liver. The receptors appear to interact with apo-E on the lipoproteins. The lipid constituents enter hepatic pools, and the B-48 protein is degraded completely. The cholesterol derived from chylomicron remnants is the major mediator of feedback control of cholesterol biosynthesis in liver. Some VLDL remnants are removed from blood via the B-100:E receptors (see below) and are degraded. Those which escape uptake are transformed into LDL. Thus, the rate of removal of VLDL remnants by liver is a determinant of LDL production. The process of formation of LDL involves the removal of essentially all of the residual triglycerides and a portion of the cholesteryl esters and amphipathic lipids. LDL particles contain chiefly cholesteryl esters in their cores. They retain the B-100 protein but only traces of other apolipoproteins. In normal individuals, a major fraction of VLDL is converted to LDL, and all of the LDL apo-B comes from VLDL. In certain hypertriglyceridemic states, conversion of VLDL to LDL is decreased.

The fact that LDL originate from the metabolism of VLDL remnants suggests that increases of LDL in plasma can arise from an increased rate of secretion of precursor VLDL as well as from decreased catabolism of LDL. The formation of LDL from VLDL may also contribute to the clinical phenomenon referred to as the "beta shift." This is an increase of LDL (beta-lipoprotein) as hypertriglyceridemia resolves. A classic example of the beta shift occurs temporarily following institution of adequate insulin treatment in uncontrolled diabetes with lipemia. Insulin induces increased lipoprotein lipase activity, resulting in rapid conversion of VLDL to LDL. Because of its longer half-life, the LDL accumulate in plasma. Elevated levels of LDL may persist beyond the time when levels of triglyceride-rich lipoproteins have returned to normal.

E. Half-Lives of Lipoproteins: Normally, the half-life of chylomicron apo-B-48 in plasma is 5–20 minutes; that of the apo-B-100 in VLDL is 1–3 hours; and that of LDL apo-B-100 is about 2 1/2 days. At triglyceride levels of 800–1000 mg/dL, the lipoprotein lipase mechanism is at kinetic saturation; therefore, increases in the input of triglyceride-rich lipoproteins into plasma at those levels rapidly result in much higher levels.

F. Effect of Dietary Fat Restriction: Individuals consuming a typical North American diet (with about 45% of calories as fat) transport 75–100 g or more of triglyceride per day into plasma in chylomicrons, whereas the liver exports 10–30 g of triglyceride in VLDL. Thus, the flux of triglyceride into plasma can be influenced most acutely by restriction of dietary fat. When the removal mechanisms involving lipoprotein lipase are saturated and plasma triglyceride levels are measured in thousands of milligrams per deciliter, acute restriction of dietary triglyceride intake will usually produce a significant reduction in triglyceride levels. This intervention is important in the lipemic patient with impending pancreatitis. If symptoms suggest that an attack of pancreatitis is im-

minent, all oral intake should be eliminated, gastric acid secretion should be suppressed with H_2 blockade, and the patient should be maintained on parenteral glucose until the symptoms subside and triglyceride levels decrease to less than 800–1000 mg/dL.

Catabolism of Low-Density Lipoproteins

A. Endocytosis via Specific High-Affinity Receptors: The catabolism of LDL appears to proceed by several mechanisms. The best-understood of these is endocytosis mediated by high-affinity receptors on the cell membranes of virtually all types of cells but most importantly hepatocytes (Figure 17–3). The receptors bind the apo-B protein of LDL. Because they also bind apo-E, they are called B-100:E receptors. The coated pit regions invaginate into the cell, forming endocytotic vesicles that fuse with lysosomes. The apo-B of the LDL is degraded to amino acids, and the receptor returns to the cell membrane. The cholesteryl esters of the LDL core are hydrolyzed to yield free cholesterol, which is utilized in the production of cell membrane bilayers. Free cholesterol suppresses the activity of hydroxymethylglutaryl-CoA (HMG-CoA) reductase, a rate-limiting enzyme in the biosynthetic pathway for cholesterol. Thus, the intake of cholesterol by this pathway decreases the formation of new cholesterol. Cholesterol in excess of need for membrane synthesis is esterified by the acyl-CoA:cholesterol acyltransferase (ACAT) system for storage. In addition to suppression of cholesterol biosynthesis, the entry of cholesterol via the LDL pathway leads to down-regulation of LDL receptors, resulting in decreased uptake and catabolism of LDL. Saturated fats consumed in the diet down-regulate hepatic LDL receptors.

B. Other Pathways: In addition to the high-affinity receptor-mediated pathway of degradation, LDL appear to be catabolized by at least two additional pathways. Macrophages take up chemically or physically altered LDL by a scavenger mechanism that is not subject to feedback control, and a low-affinity process exists in all cells.

Metabolism of High-Density Lipoproteins

When isolated by ultracentrifugation, HDL appear to comprise two major classes: HDL_2 and HDL_3. Similar quantities of HDL_3 are isolated from serum of men and women, but about twice as much HDL_2 is found in serum of premenopausal women. Recent studies indicate that there are as many as ten discrete species of HDL that are obscured by ultracentrifugation. One of these is the 65-kDa prebeta HDL that appears to be the primary acquisitor of cholesterol in the pathway for retrieval of cholesterol from peripheral tissues.

A. Sources of HDL: Both the liver and intestine

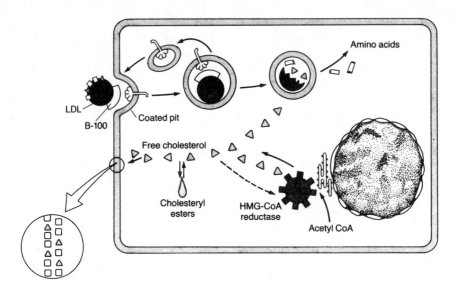

Figure 17–3. Cholesterol homeostasis in the cell. See text for details.

produce HDL apolipoproteins, which appear to organize with lipids into the native species of HDL in lymph and plasma. Free cholesterol acquired by HDL is esterified by LCAT. This enzyme transfers 1 mol of fatty acid from a lecithin molecule to the hydroxyl group of unesterified cholesterol, forming cholesteryl ester, which then enters the hydrophobic region between the lamellae of the bilayer. Lysolecithin, formed by transfer of the fatty acid from lecithin, leaves the lipoprotein complex, binds to albumin, and is transported to various tissues, where it is reacylated to form lecithin. The process of transesterification by LCAT rapidly forms sufficient cholesteryl ester to fill the hydrophobic core region.

LCAT enzyme is secreted by liver. In severe hepatic parenchymal disease, levels of this enzyme in plasma are low and esterification of cholesterol is impeded, leading to the accumulation of free cholesterol in lipoproteins and in membranes of erythrocytes and other cells. Excess free cholesterol in the membranes of erythrocytes transforms them into the target cells classically associated with hepatic disease.

As hydrolysis of triglycerides in chylomicrons and VLDL proceeds, phospholipids and cholesterol are transferred to HDL particles.

B. Metabolic Roles for HDL: Several metabolic roles for HDL are now recognized. These lipoproteins serve as carriers for the C apolipoproteins, transferring them to nascent VLDL and chylomicrons. HDL as well as LDL deliver cholesterol to the adrenal cortex and gonads in support of steroidogenesis. HDL play a major role in the centripetal transport of cholesterol—ie, the transport of surplus cholesterol away from peripheral tissues. Although this process is not fully understood, it appears that

several subspecies of HDL are involved. Unesterified cholesterol is acquired from the membranes of peripheral tissues and is esterified by LCAT. The resulting cholesteryl esters, predominantly cholesteryl linoleate, are then transferred to LDL and to triglyceride-rich lipoproteins. Remnants of chylomicrons and a significant fraction of VLDL remnants and LDL are taken up by liver, providing for transport of the newly formed cholesteryl esters to hepatocytes.

C. Catabolism of HDL: The pathways of catabolism of HDL are not yet known. Radiochemical studies indicate that apo-A-I and apo-A-II are removed from plasma synchronously and that a portion of the degradation occurs in liver. Because degradation by perfused rat livers is slower than for the intact animal, it must be presumed that peripheral tissues contribute substantially to the catabolism of HDL.

The Cholesterol Economy

Cholesterol is an essential constituent of the plasma membranes of mammalian cells and of the myelin sheath. It is also required for adrenal and gonadal steroidogenesis and for the production of bile acids by the liver. Virtually all nucleated mammalian cells can synthesize cholesterol, commencing with acetyl-CoA. Formation of HMG-CoA is the initial step. The first committed step, mediated by HMG-CoA reductase, is the formation of mevalonic acid from HMG-CO. Mevalonic acid is then metabolized via a series of isoprenoid intermediaries to squalene, which cyclizes to form a series of sterols leading to cholesterol. A small amount of the mevalonate is converted eventually to the important isoprenoid substances ubiquinone, dolichol, and isopentenyl pyrophosphate. The portion of the pathway leading to cholesterol synthesis is tightly regulated by cholesterol, or some metabolite of cholesterol, which suppresses the activity of HMG-CoA reductase. Thus, cells have the ability to produce cholesterol to the extent that their requirements are not met by that derived from circulating lipoproteins. Cholesteryl esters stored in cells serve as an immediate reserve of cholesterol. Large requirements for cholesterol result from rapid proliferation of cells with attendant need for elaboration of cell membranes. Hepatocytes and intestinal epithelial cells require large amounts of cholesterol for secretion of lipoproteins. In addition, cells are constantly transferring cholesterol to circulating lipoproteins, chiefly HDL. A relatively small amount of cholesterol is lost from the body in desquamated skin and through the loss of intestinal epithelial cells in the stool. The net daily loss of cholesterol from the gut, derived both from biliary cholesterol and from desquamated epithelial cells, is about 50 mg. In addition, about 2% of the mass of bile acids secreted into the intestine are lost in the stool, equivalent to about 250 mg of cholesterol.

Cholesterol is acquired from the diet as well as from endogenous synthesis. Humans, unlike many other species, do not absorb dietary cholesterol quantitatively; however, at normal levels of intake, about one-third of the amount ingested reaches the bloodstream. Most of this cholesterol is transported to liver in chylomicron remnants, leading to suppression of hepatic cholesterogenesis. Recent evidence suggests that individuals may differ substantially in the effect of dietary cholesterol on serum lipoproteins, reflecting in part differences in the efficiency of absorption of cholesterol.

DIFFERENTIATION OF DISORDERS OF LIPOPROTEIN METABOLISM

Laboratory Analyses of Lipids & Lipoproteins

Because chylomicrons normally may be present in plasma up to 12 hours after a meal, they contribute triglyceride to the total measured during that period, raising the triglyceride concentration to as much as 600 mg/dL (6.9 mmol/L). However, this alimentary lipemia can be substantially prolonged if alcohol is consumed with the meal. Thus, serum lipids and lipoproteins should be measured after a fast of 10–14 hours. If blood glucose is not to be measured, patients may have fruit juice and black coffee with sugar (which provide no triglyceride) for breakfast.

A. Inspection: Much useful information is gained from inspection of the serum, especially before and after overnight refrigeration. As a screening technique, this will identify sera in which triglycerides need to be measured. Opalescence is due to light scattering by large triglyceride-rich lipoproteins. Serum begins to appear hazy when the level of triglycerides reaches 200 mg/dL (2.3 mmol/L), about the point at which clinical significance begins. The pres-

ence of chylomicrons is readily detected, because they form a white supernatant layer. A further observation made on serum, which is critical to the detection of the uncommon cases in which binding of immunoglobulins to lipoproteins takes place, is the formation of a curd-like lipoprotein aggregate or a snowy precipitate as serum cools. If one of these disorders is suspected, blood should be kept at 37 °C during the formation of the clot and separation of the serum, because the critical temperatures for precipitation of the cryoglobulin complex may be higher than room temperature.

B. Laboratory Techniques: The cholesterol and triglyceride contents of serum can be measured by several chemical techniques that provide reliable results. These measurements are an essential minimum for differentiation of disorders of lipoprotein metabolism. The usual methods determine unesterified and esterified cholesterol together, so that the reported value is the total content of cholesterol in serum. In most cases, electrophoresis of lipoproteins contributes little additional information; thus, this technique is not a necessary part of the routine laboratory examination. An exception is the identification of lipoproteins found in familial dysbetalipoproteinemia. The best electrophoretic separation of lipoproteins is made in agarose gel. The most complete characterization of a patient's lipoproteins is achieved by measurement of the cholesterol and triglyceride contents and electrophoretic behavior of individual lipoprotein fractions, separated by preparative ultracentrifugation, a technique usually available only in research laboratories. However, the content of high-density lipoproteins can be measured using a technique in which HDL are the only lipoproteins that remain in solution after treatment of the serum with heparin and manganese. Albeit rapid, the results of this technique tend to be unacceptably variable unless rigid quality control is exercised. The prognostic implications of small changes in HDL cholesterol make such controls necessary.

An important determinant of the content of cholesteryl esters in HDL is the amount of triglyceride-rich lipoproteins to which the HDL are exposed in plasma. Triglycerides from these lipoproteins exchange into the core regions of HDL, displacing cholesteryl esters and leading to an inverse logarithmic dependence of HDL cholesterol level upon the plasma triglycerides. Thus, the HDL cholesterol value cannot be interpreted without knowledge of the level of serum triglycerides. For example, a level of HDL that would normally contain 45 mg/dL (1.17 mmol/L) of cholesterol would contain 37 mg/dL (0.96 mmol/L) when the triglycerides were 200 mg/dL (2.3 mmol/L) and 30 mg/dL (0.78 mmol/L) when they reach 500 mg/dL (5.7 mmol/L). In certain forms of hypertriglyceridemia, there is also a moderate decrease in the protein-phospholipid vehicle of HDL, but the principal effect on the measurement of

HDL cholesterol levels remains the exchange of triglycerides for cholesteryl esters.

More sophisticated tests of composition of isolated lipoprotein fractions are of use in certain instances. The most important of these is analysis of the ratio of cholesterol to triglycerides by chemical techniques and of the apolipoproteins of VLDL by isoelectric focusing. The latter reveals the absence of the normal isoforms of apo-E, the underlying molecular defect in familial dysbetalipoproteinemia. In this disorder, there is an unusually high content of cholesterol in the VLDL. Immunoassays are available for a number of apolipoprotein species, but the utility of these measurements in clinical practice remains unclear.

Clinical Differentiation of Abnormal Patterns of Plasma Lipoproteins

A. Preliminary Screening: Serum cholesterol and triglyceride levels are both continuously distributed in the population; therefore, some arbitrary levels must be established to define significant hyperlipidemia. As indicated in the introductory paragraphs, average levels of LDL in Western populations appear to be well above the biologic ideal and are a major etiologic factor underlying the increased incidence of atherosclerotic vascular disease in Western societies. Epidemiologic studies in Europe and the USA have shown that there is a progressive increase in risk of coronary artery disease as levels of serum cholesterol increase above 180 mg/dL (4.68 mmol/L). Present evidence would indicate that physicians should at least encourage patients at risk to eat diets low in saturated fats and cholesterol in order to minimize the burden of LDL in plasma.

The National Cholesterol Education Program (NCEP) has developed guidelines for treatment of hypercholesterolemia in adults (Table 17–2). The goal of therapy in patients with CAD is to reduce LDL cholesterol to 100 mg/dL (2.6 mmol/L) or less. Levels of triglyceride above 200 mg/dL (2.26 mmol/L) merit investigation. One abnormality associated with increased risk of coronary artery disease that will not be detected if only cases with hyperlipidemia are studied is hypoalphalipoproteinemia, or deficiency of HDL. The NCEP guidelines consider a level of HDL cholesterol below 35 mg/dL (0.90 mmol/L) a major risk factor for CHD. Many of the affected individuals have normal levels of both cholesterol and triglycerides in serum and no clinical stigmas to draw the attention of the physician. The argument has been offered that detection of these individuals is unavailing, because there is little that can currently be done to modify levels of HDL in serum. Appreciation that hypoalphalipoproteinemia is present, however, is important if for no other reason than to underscore the importance of controlling other risk factors and perhaps the avoidance of factors that reduce HDL levels, such as cigarette smoking and the use of some drugs.

B. Identification of Abnormal Patterns: The second step in investigation of hyperlipidemia is determination of the species of lipoproteins that account for the increased content of lipids in serum. In some cases, multiple species may be involved; in others, qualitative properties of the lipoproteins are of diagnostic importance. After identifying the pattern of the lipoprotein abnormality, the physician must search for underlying disorders that cause secondary hyperlipidemias of similar pattern. Such disorders may be the sole cause of the lipoprotein abnormality or may aggravate primary disorders of lipoprotein metabolism. The differentiation of specific primary disorders usually requires additional clinical and genetic information.

The following diagnostic protocol, based upon initial measurement of cholesterol and triglycerides in serum after a 14-hour fast, supplemented by observation of serum and by additional laboratory measurements where essential, will serve as a practical guide in identifying abnormal patterns of lipoprotein distribution. The term "hyperlipidemia" denotes high levels of any class of lipoprotein; "hyperlipemia" denotes high levels of any of the triglyceride-rich lipoproteins.

Case 1: Serum Cholesterol Levels Increased; Triglycerides Normal

(1) If the serum cholesterol level is modestly elevated (up to 260 mg/dL [6.76 mmol/L]), the HDL cholesterol level should be measured. Hyperalphalipoproteinemia (elevated levels of HDL in serum) may account for the observed increase in serum cholesterol level. Hyperalphalipoproteinemia is usually not associated with disease processes. The LDL cholesterol level in serum (in mg/dL) may be estimated by subtracting the HDL cholesterol level and the estimated cholesterol contribution of VLDL from the to-

Table 17–2. National Cholesterol Education Program: Adult Treatment Guidelines (1993).

	Total Cholesterol	LDL Cholesterol
Desirable	<200 mg/dL (<5.2 mmol/L)	<130 mg/dL (<3.38 mmol/L)
Borderline to high[1]	200–239 mg/dL (5.2–6.2 mmol/L)	130–159 mg/dL (3.38–4.13 mmol/L)
High	≥240 mg/dL (≥6.24 mmol/L)	≥160 mg/dL (≥4.16 mmol/L)

[1] Consider as high if coronary heart disease or more than two risk factors are present.

tal serum cholesterol level. The VLDL cholesterol is approximated as one-fifth of the serum triglyceride level.

$$\text{LDL cholesterol} = \text{Total cholesterol} - \left(\frac{TG}{5} + \text{HDL cholesterol} \right)$$

Calculated values of LDL cholesterol over 130 mg/dL (3.38 mmol/L) are clinically significant. If the patient has arteriosclerosis, levels in excess of 90–100 mg/dL should be considered significant.

(2) Because HDL almost never contribute more than 120 mg/dL (3.12 mmol/L) of cholesterol, serum cholesterol levels in excess of 260 mg/dL (6.76 mmol/L) always represent significant hyperlipidemia. Unless the patient has obstructive hepatic disease, the abnormality may be assumed to be due to an increase in low-density lipoproteins. The abnormal lipoprotein of cholestasis, like LDL, is selectively rich in cholesterol. It can be differentiated because it has gamma mobility on electrophoresis in agarose gel and because it stains metachromatically with Sudan black.

Case 2: Predominant Increase of Triglycerides in Serum; Moderate Increase in Cholesterol Level May Be Present

Here it is apparent that the primary abnormality is an increase in the triglyceride-rich VLDL (hyperprebetalipoproteinemia) or chylomicrons (chylomicronemia), or both (mixed lipemia). Because both VLDL and chylomicrons contain free cholesterol in their surface monolayers and a small amount of cholesteryl ester in their cores, the total cholesterol level in serum may be increased, though to a much smaller extent than is the serum triglyceride level. The contribution of cholesterol in these lipoproteins to the total in serum is about 8–25% of the triglyceride content. Low levels of LDL cholesterol often seen in hypertriglyceridemia may largely offset the increase in cholesterol due to the triglyceride-rich lipoproteins, especially in primary chylomicronemia. A white supernatant layer in serum refrigerated overnight reveals the presence of chylomicrons. Because VLDL and chylomicrons compete as substrates in a common removal pathway, chylomicrons will nearly always be present when triglyceride levels exceed 1000 mg/dL (11.5 mmol/L).

Case 3: Cholesterol and Triglyceride Levels in Serum Both Elevated

This pattern can be the result of either of two abnormal lipoprotein distributions. One of these is a combined increase of VLDL (prebeta-lipoproteins), which provide most of the increase in triglycerides, and LDL (beta-lipoproteins), which account for the

bulk of the increase in cholesterol in serum. This pattern is termed combined hyperlipidemia and is one of the three phenotypic patterns encountered in kindreds with the disorder termed familial combined hyperlipidemia. The second distribution is an increase of remnant lipoproteins derived from VLDL and chylomicrons. These lipoprotein particles have been partially depleted of triglyceride by lipoprotein lipase and have been enriched with cholesteryl esters by the LCAT system, such that the total content of cholesterol in serum is similar to that of triglycerides. This pattern is almost always an expression of familial dysbetalipoproteinemia. Differentiation of these two patterns requires application of additional diagnostic tests. Presumptive differentiation can be made with high-quality agarose gel electrophoresis. In combined hyperlipidemia, the prebeta- and beta-lipoprotein bands are both increased in staining intensity, but each has its typical electrophoretic mobility, and they are well resolved from one another. Preparative ultracentrifugation of serum in this disorder shows elevated levels of both VLDL and LDL. In contrast, the remnant particles in dysbetalipoproteinemia are distributed in a "broad beta" pattern that obscures the resolution of beta- and prebeta-lipoprotein bands. A substantial portion of the triglyceride-rich lipoproteins shows beta-electrophoretic mobility after separation from serum in the ultracentrifuge (at a density of 1.006 g/cm^3), and they have an increased content of cholesterol. Dysbetalipoproteinemia is confirmed by the absence of the E-3 and E-4 isoforms of apo-E when the triglyceride-rich fraction of serum is analyzed by isoelectric focusing.

I. CLINICAL DESCRIPTIONS OF PRIMARY & SECONDARY DISORDERS OF LIPOPROTEIN METABOLISM

THE HYPERTRIGLYCERIDEMIAS

Atherogenicity

Certain triglyceride-rich lipoproteins appear to be atherogenic. There is ample clinical evidence that the remnant lipoproteins of dysbetalipoproteinemia are atherogenic. Whereas patients with primary chylomicronemia do not appear to have accelerated atherosclerosis despite extremely high levels of triglycerides in serum, there is clinical evidence in support of the atherogenicity of VLDL of small to moderate particle diameter. Furthermore, VLDL have now been demonstrated in the walls of arteries removed at surgery. Impaired capacity of the VLDL of some individuals to accept cholesteryl esters from the LCAT reaction may also contribute to atherogenesis by impeding centripetal transport of cholesterol.

Cause of Pancreatitis

Very high levels of triglycerides in plasma are associated with risk of acute pancreatitis, probably from the local release of free fatty acids and lysolecithin from lipoprotein substrates in the capillary bed of the pancreas. When the concentrations of these lipids exceed the binding capacity of albumin, they could lyse membranes of parenchymal cells, initiating a chemical pancreatitis. Patients who have had previous attacks of pancreatitis appear to be at higher risk. Many patients with lipemia have intermittent episodes of epigastric pain during which serum amylase does not reach levels commonly considered diagnostic for pancreatitis. This is especially true in patients who have had previous attacks. The observation that these episodes frequently evolve into classic pancreatitis suggests that they represent incipient pancreatic inflammation. The progression of pancreatitis can be prevented by rapid reduction of triglyceride levels in serum, which can usually be accomplished by rigorous restriction of dietary fat and institution of other corrective measures. In more threatening cases, parenteral feeding with glucose may be required for a few days. The clinical course of pancreatitis in patients with lipemia is typical of the general experience with this disease. Fatal hemorrhagic pancreatitis occurs in a few; many develop pseudocysts; and some progress to pancreatic exocrine insufficiency or compromised insulinogenic capacity.

Clinical Signs

When triglyceride levels in serum exceed 3000–4000 mg/dL (34.5–46 mmol/L), light scattering by these particles in the blood lends a whitish cast to the venous vascular bed of the retina, a sign known as **lipemia retinalis.** Markedly elevated levels of VLDL in plasma may be associated with the appearance of **eruptive cutaneous xanthomas.** These lesions, filled with foam cells, appear as yellow morbilliform eruptions 2–5 mm in diameter, often with erythematous areolae. They usually occur in clusters on extensor surfaces such as the elbows, knees, and buttocks. They are transient and usually disappear within a few weeks after triglyceride levels are reduced below 2000–3000 mg/dL (23–34.5 mmol/L).

Effects of Hypertriglyceridemia on Laboratory Measurements

Very high levels of triglyceride-rich lipoproteins may introduce important errors in clinical laboratory measurements. Light scattering from these large particles can cause erroneous results in most chemical determinations involving photometric measurements in spite of corrections for blank values. Amylase activity in serum may be inhibited by triglyceride-rich lipoproteins; hence, lipemic specimens should be diluted for measurement of this enzyme. Because the lipoproteins are not permeable to ionic or polar small molecules, their hydrophobic regions constitute a second phase in plasma. When the volume of this phase becomes appreciable, electrolytes (measured by flame photometry) and other hydrophilic species in serum will be underestimated with respect to their true concentration in plasma water. A practical rule for correcting these values is as follows: for each 1000 mg/dL (11.5 mmol/L) of triglyceride in serum, the concentrations of all hydrophilic molecules and ions should be increased by 1%.

PRIMARY HYPERTRIGLYCERIDEMIA

1. DEFICIENCY OF LIPOPROTEIN LIPASE OR ITS COFACTOR

Clinical Findings

A. Symptoms and Signs: Because the clinical expressions of these defects are identical, they will be considered together. Both appear to be transmitted as autosomal recessive traits. On a typical North American diet, lipemia is usually severe (serum triglyceride levels of 2000–25,000 mg/dL) (23–287.5 mmol/L). Hepatomegaly and splenomegaly are frequently present. Foam cells laden with lipid are found in liver, spleen, and bone marrow. Splenic infarct has been described and may be a source of abdominal pain. Hypersplenism with anemia, granulocytopenia, and thrombocytopenia can occur. Recurrent epigastric pain and overt pancreatitis are frequently encountered. Eruptive xanthomas may be present. These disorders are present from birth and may be recognized in early infancy or may go unnoticed until an attack of acute pancreatitis occurs or lipemic serum is noted on blood sampling as late as middle age. Patients with these disorders are classically not obese and have normal carbohydrate metabolism, unless pancreatitis impairs insulinogenic capacity. Estrogens intensify the lipemia by stimulating production of VLDL by liver. Therefore, in pregnancy and lactation or during the administration of estrogenic steroids, the risk of pancreatitis increases.

B. Laboratory Findings: These patients have a preponderance of chylomicrons in serum such that the infranatant layer of serum refrigerated overnight may be nearly clear. Many have a moderate increase in VLDL, however, and in pregnant women or those receiving estrogens, a pattern of mixed lipemia is usually present. Levels of low-density lipoproteins in serum are decreased, probably representing the predominant catabolism of VLDL by pathways that do not involve the production of LDL. Levels of HDL are also decreased. A presumptive diagnosis of these disorders can be made by restricting the oral intake of fat to 10–15 g/d for 3–5 days. The triglyceride level of plasma drops precipitously, usually reaching 200–600 mg/dL (2.3–6.9 mmol/L) within 3–4 days. Confirmation of deficiency of lipoprotein lipase is obtained by measurement in vitro of the lipolytic activity of plasma prepared from blood drawn 10 minutes after heparin, 0.2 mg/kg, is injected intravenously. Analysis of lipolysis is carried out with and without 0.5 mol/L sodium chloride, which inhibits lipoprotein lipase but does not suppress the activity of other plasma lipases, including hepatic lipase. Classically, the lipolytic activity of plasma is very low and is similar in the saline-inhibited and saline-uninhibited incubates. Recent findings suggest that several forms of LPL deficiency can be differentiated by prolonged infusions of heparin. These findings are compatible either with selective deficiencies of the LPL species in different tissues or with the existence of a form of the disorder in which binding to endothelium is abnormal. The latter is supported by heterogeneity in levels of another heparin-releasable enzyme, histaminase, in sera of patients with LPL deficiency. Absence of the cofactor protein of LPL, apo-C-II, is the counterpart of deficiency of LPL and can be demonstrated most readily by electrophoresis or isoelectric focusing of the proteins of VLDL.

Treatment

Treatment of primary chylomicronemia is entirely dietary. Intake of fat should be reduced to 10% or less of total calories. In an adult, this represents 15–30 g/d. Because the defect involves lipolysis, both saturated and unsaturated fats must be curtailed. The diet should contain at least 5 g of polyunsaturated fat as a source of essential fatty acids, and an ample supply of fat-soluble vitamins must be provided. Careful adherence to this diet will invariably maintain serum triglyceride levels below 1000 mg/dL (11.2 mmol/L) in the absence of pregnancy, lactation, or the administration of exogenous estrogens. Because this is below the level at which pancreatitis usually occurs, compliant patients with these disorders are at low risk.

2. ENDOGENOUS & MIXED LIPEMIAS

Etiology & Pathogenesis

Endogenous lipemia (primary hyperprebetalipoproteinemia) and mixed lipemia probably both result from several genetically determined disorders. The occurrence of multiple cases in a kindred is the basis for considering them primary. Thus, a number of "sporadic cases" may be similar, only lacking evidence of familial occurrence. Because VLDL and chylomicrons are competing substrates in the intravascular lipolytic pathway, saturating levels of

VLDL will cause an impedance in the removal of chylomicrons. Therefore, as the severity of endogenous lipemia increases, a pattern of mixed lipemia may supervene. In other cases, the pattern of mixed lipemia appears to be present continuously. Though specific pathophysiologic mechanisms remain obscure, certain familial patterns are known. In all forms, factors that increase the rate of secretion of VLDL from liver aggravate the hypertriglyceridemia–ie, obesity with insulin resistance, or the appearance of fully developed non-insulin-dependent diabetes mellitus (NIDDM); ethanol ingestion; and the use of exogenous estrogens. Studies of VLDL turnover indicate that either increased production or impaired removal of VLDL may be operative in different individuals. It appears that a substantial number of patients with mixed lipemia have partial defects in catabolism of triglyceride-rich lipoproteins. Increases in production rates of VLDL secondary to excess caloric intake, ethanol, or estrogens tend not to be accompanied by increased removal, as in normal individuals, but result in increased levels of circulating triglycerides. Some patients with mixed lipemia have decreased levels of lipoprotein lipase in plasma after a heparin stimulus, which may be of importance in this regard. Most patients with significant endogenous or mixed lipemia have the hypertrophic form of obesity, in which there is a reduced population of insulin receptors on cell membranes associated with impaired effectiveness of insulin. Mobilization of free fatty acids is maintained at a higher than normal rate, providing an increased flux of fatty acids to the liver, in turn increasing the secretion of triglyceride-rich VLDL.

Clinical Findings

Clinical features of these forms of hypertriglyceridemia depend upon severity and include eruptive xanthomas, lipemia retinalis, recurrent epigastric pain, and acute pancreatitis (described above). One constellation of clinical features that may be monogenic is endogenous lipemia with obesity, insulin resistance, elevated baseline levels of insulin, hyperglycemia, and hyperuricemia. There is also a tendency toward the development of hypertension in such patients.

Treatment

The primary mode of treatment is dietary. In the short term, severe restriction of total fat intake will usually result in a rapid decline of serum triglyceride levels to 1000–3000 mg/dL (11.2–33.6 mmol/L), averting pancreatitis. The objective of long-term dietary management is reduction to ideal body weight. Because ethanol causes significant augmentation of VLDL production, abstinence is important.

If weight loss is achieved, the serum triglycerides almost always show a marked response, often approaching normal values. When the fall in triglyceride levels is not satisfactory, clofibrate, gemfibrozil, or nicotinic acid will usually produce further reductions. (See Treatment of Hyperlipidemia, below.)

3. FAMILIAL COMBINED HYPERLIPIDEMIA

Etiology

Epidemiologic studies of the kindreds of survivors of myocardial infarction revealed this common heredofamilial disorder. The underlying process appears to be overproduction of VLDL. Some of the affected individuals have increased levels of both VLDL and LDL in serum (combined hyperlipidemia); some have increased levels of only VLDL or LDL. Without family studies, the latter two patterns would not be identified as belonging with this syndrome. Patterns in the serum of an individual patient may change with time. It is known that a mating of an individual having any one of the three phenotypic patterns with a normal individual can result in the appearance of one of the other patterns. Children in these kindreds may have hyperlipidemia, but the disorder is usually not fully expressed until adulthood.

Clinical Findings

Neither tendinous nor cutaneous xanthomas other than xanthelasma occur. Available data suggest that this disorder is inherited as a mendelian dominant trait. It appears that the factors that increase the severity of hypertriglyceridemia in other disorders aggravate the lipemia in this syndrome as well.

Treatment

The risk of coronary vascular disease is significantly increased in these patients, and therefore they should be treated aggressively with diet and drugs. Lipemia responds to clofibrate or gemfibrozil, but these agents may increase LDL levels (beta shift). Hence, niacin may be a better choice. Patients with increased LDL levels respond to bile acid-binding resins but may then have increases in VLDL. Therefore, the combination of a resin and niacin is frequently required. Lovastatin is also useful. (See Treatment of Hyperlipidemia, below.)

4. FAMILIAL DYSBETALIPOPROTEINEMIA (Broad Beta Disease, Type III Hyperlipoproteinemia)

Etiology & Pathogenesis

A permissive genetic constitution for this disease occurs commonly, but expression of hyperlipoproteinemia apparently requires additional genetic or environmental determinants. The molecular basis of this disorder is the presence of mutant forms of apo-E that cannot interact normally with high-affinity receptors. In its fully expressed form, the lipoprotein pattern is dominated by the accumulation of remnants of VLDL and chylomicrons. Two populations of VLDL are usually present: normal prebetalipoproteins and remnants with beta-electrophoretic mobility. Remnant particles of intermediate density are also present. Characteristically, levels of LDL in serum are decreased, probably reflecting interruption of the normal transformation of VLDL remnants to LDL. The primary defect appears to involve the uptake of remnants of triglyceride-rich lipoproteins from plasma. Chylomicron remnants are frequently present in serum obtained after a 14-hour fast even when total serum triglycerides are only 300–600 mg/dL (3.4–6.7 mmol/L). All the remnant particles are enriched in cholesteryl esters such that the level of cholesterol in serum is often as high as the level of triglycerides. The "broad beta" electrophoretic pattern of VLDL is highly suggestive of familial dysbetalipoproteinemia. However, this pattern is seen also in hypothyroidism, resolving lipemias of other origins, and certain disorders involving immunoglobulin-lipoprotein complexes. Absence of the E-3 and E-4 isoforms of apo-E on isoelectric focusing of VLDL proteins, confirms the diagnosis. Whereas homozygosity is present in about 1% of the population, the incidence of clinical hyperlipidemia among these patients is much smaller. Additional mutations of apo-E that cannot be distinguished from E-3 by isoelectric focusing are now known to result in dysbetalipoproteinemia.

Clinical Findings

Hyperlipidemia and clinical stigmas are not usually evident before age 20. In younger patients with hyperlipidemia, hypothyroidism or obesity is likely to be present. Adults frequently have tuberous or tuberoeruptive xanthomas. Both tend to occur on extensor surfaces, especially elbows and knees. Tuberoeruptive xanthomas are pink or yellowish skin nodules 3–8 mm in diameter that often become confluent. Tuberous xanthomas—reddish or orange, often shiny nodules up to 3 cm in diameter—are usually moveable and nontender. Another type, planar xanthomas of the palmar creases, strongly suggests dysbetalipoproteinemia. The skin creases assume an orange color from deposition of carotenoids and other lipids. They occasionally are raised above the level of adjacent skin and are not tender. (Planar xanthomas are also seen in cholestatic disease.)

Some patients have impaired glucose tolerance, which is usually associated with higher levels of blood lipids. Obesity is commonly present and tends to aggravate the lipemia. Patients with the genetic constitution for dysbetalipoproteinemia often develop severe hyperlipidemia if they are hypothyroid.

Atherosclerotic disease of the coronary and peripheral vessels occurs with increased frequency, and the prevalence of disease of the iliac and femoral vessels is especially high. The prevalence of atherosclerotic disease of the iliac and femoral vessels appears to be especially high.

Treatment

Management includes a weight reduction diet providing a reduced intake of cholesterol, saturated fat, and alcohol. When the hyperlipidemia does not respond satisfactorily to diet, gemfibrozil or niacin in low doses is usually effective. (See Treatment of Hyperlipidemia, below.)

SECONDARY HYPERTRIGLYCERIDEMIA

1. DIABETES MELLITUS

In patients with insulin-dependent diabetes mellitus (IDDM), levels of VLDL in plasma are frequently elevated despite the regular use of insulin, reflecting the difficulty of control of carbohydrate metabolism in this disorder.

Pathogenesis

The severe lipemia associated with absence or marked insufficiency of insulin is attributable to deficiency of LPL activity, because this enzyme is induced by insulin. The administration of insulin in such cases usually restores triglyceride levels to normal within a few days. However, if massive fatty liver is present, weeks may be required for the VLDL levels to return to normal while the liver secretes its triglyceride into plasma. Conversion of massive amounts of VLDL to LDL, as the impedance of VLDL catabolism is relieved, leads to marked accumulation of LDL that may persist for weeks. This phenomenon may lead to a spurious diagnosis of hypercholesterolemia.

The moderately high levels of VLDL seen in diabetes under average control probably reflect chiefly an increased flux of FFA to liver that stimulates production of triglycerides and their secretion in VLDL. In addition to VLDL, LDL levels are also somewhat increased in insulin-dependent diabetics under poor control, probably accounting in part for their increased risk of coronary heart disease. Mild increases in VLDL and in FFA occur in many individuals with non-insulin-dependent diabetes mellitus (NIDDM). Some have much higher levels of VLDL, suggesting that an additional genetic factor predisposing to lipemia is present. Still another cause of lipemic diabetes is the compromised insulinogenic capacity that can result from acute pancreatitis in individuals with severe primary lipemias. The deficiency may be severe enough to require exogenous insulin, often only in small doses. In diabetics who develop nephrosis as a consequence of their microvascular disease, the secondary lipemia of nephrosis compounds their hypertriglyceridemia. In hyperglycemia, lipoproteins become glycosylated, causing their uptake by macrophages.

Clinical Findings

Lipemia may be very severe, with elevated levels of both VLDL and chylomicrons when control is poor. Lipemic patients usually have ketoacidosis, but lipemia can occur in its absence. Patients with IDDM who have been chronically undertreated with insulin may have mobilized most of the triglyceride from peripheral adipose tissue, so that they no longer have sufficient substrate for significant ketogenesis. These emaciated individuals may have severe lipemia and striking hepatomegaly.

Treatment

The rigid control of blood glucose levels, which can be attained with continuous subcutaneous insulin infusion, is associated with sustained normalization of levels of both LDL and VLDL.

The lipemia of IDDM responds well to control of the underlying disorder of carbohydrate metabolism. In obese, insulin-resistant individuals, weight loss is the key to treatment. Diets containing a large fraction of calories as carbohydrates are actually well tolerated, allowing a decrease in the burden of chylomicron triglycerides in plasma.

2. UREMIA

Uremia is associated with modest isolated increases in VLDL. The most important underlying mechanisms are probably insulin resistance and impairment of catabolism of VLDL. Many uremic patients are also nephrotic. The additional effects of nephrosis upon lipoprotein metabolism may produce a combined hyperlipoproteinemia. Patients who have had renal transplants may be receiving glucocorticoids, which induce elevated concentrations of LDL.

3. CORTICOSTEROID EXCESS

In endogenous Cushing's syndrome, there is insulin resistance, and levels of LDL are increased. It appears that the hyperlipidemia is primarily due to increased secretion of VLDL, which is then catabolized to LDL. More severe lipemia ensues when steroidogenic diabetes appears, reducing catabolism of triglyceride-rich lipoproteins via the LPL pathway.

4. EXOGENOUS ESTROGENS

When estrogens are administered to normal premenopausal women, triglyceride levels may increase by as much as 15%. This is believed to reflect increased hepatic production of VLDL. Paradoxically, estrogens increase the efficiency of catabolism of triglyceride-rich lipoproteins. Whereas estrogens tend to induce insulin resistance, it is not clear that this is an important mechanism, because certain nortestosterone derivatives decrease plasma triglyceride levels despite the induction of appreciable insulin resistance.

Certain individuals, usually with preexisting mild lipemia, show marked hypertriglyceridemia when receiving estrogens even in relatively small doses. Thus, the triglyceride level of serum should be measured in any woman receiving exogenous estrogens. Contraceptive combinations with predominant progestational effects produce less hypertriglyceridemia than purely estrogenic compounds.

5. ALCOHOL INGESTION

Ingestion of appreciable amounts of alcohol may not necessarily result in significantly elevated levels of triglycerides in serum, but many alcoholics are lipemic. Furthermore, alcohol profoundly increases triglyceride levels in patients with primary and secondary hyperlipemias. In Zieve's syndrome, the lipemia is associated with hemolytic anemia and hyperbilirubinemia. Because LCAT originates in liver, severe hepatic parenchymal dysfunction may lead to deficiency in the activity of this enzyme. A resultant accumulation of unesterified cholesterol in erythrocyte membranes may account for the hemolysis seen in Zieve's syndrome.

Ethanol is converted to acetate, exerting a sparing effect on the oxidation of fatty acids. The fatty acids are incorporated into triglyceride in liver, resulting in hepatomegaly due to fatty infiltration and in marked enhancement of secretion of VLDL. In many individuals, there is sufficient adaptive increase in the removal capacity for triglycerides from plasma that triglyceride levels tend to return toward normal if alcohol intake is continued over a period of weeks. In individuals in whom the adaptive response is impaired, marked lipemia may ensue.

6. NEPHROSIS

The hyperlipidemia of nephrosis is biphasic. Before serum albumin levels fall below 2 g/dL, levels of LDL increase selectively. This is probably a result of increased secretion of protein by liver to compensate for that lost in the urine. The synthesis of VLDL in the Golgi apparatus of liver appears to be coupled to that of albumin. The increased flux of VLDL from liver increases production of LDL. As albumin levels fall below 1–2 g/dL, lipemia ensues. Impaired hy-

drolysis of triglycerides by LPL is due to lack of albumin as an FFA receptor. Free fatty acids, which normally circulate complexed to albumin, bind to lipoproteins when albumin levels are low. The ability of these altered lipoproteins to undergo hydrolysis is thus impaired. In nephrosis, VLDL contain abundant cholesteryl esters, probably reflecting an increased rate of synthesis of these lipids.

Because coronary vascular disease is prevalent in patients with long-standing nephrotic syndrome, treatment of the hyperlipidemia appears to be indicated, though few studies of the effect of treatment have been reported. The hyperlipidemia is relatively resistant to diet. Clofibrate or gemfibrozil may precipitate myopathy even in relatively small doses. Bile acid-binding resins, niacin, and reductase inhibitors are useful. Nephrotic patients may be deficient in tryptophan, and oral administration of this amino acid has been reported to ameliorate the hypertriglyceridemia.

7. GLYCOGEN STORAGE DISEASE

In type I glycogenosis, insulin secretion is decreased, leading to an increased flux of FFA to liver, where a substantial fraction is converted to triglycerides, causing increased secretion of VLDL. The low levels of insulin in plasma also are the probable cause of reduced activity of LPL, which may cause impaired removal of triglycerides from serum. The fatty liver in these patients tends to progress to cirrhosis.

Frequent small feedings help to maintain blood glucose levels and ameliorate the lipemia. A program of nocturnal nasogastric drip feeding is of considerable benefit in this disease. Other forms of hepatic glycogen storage disease may be associated with elevated levels of VLDL and LDL in serum.

8. HYPOPITUITARISM & ACROMEGALY

Part of the hyperlipidemia of hypopituitarism is attributable to secondary hypothyroidism, but hypertriglyceridemia persists in the face of thyroxine replacement therapy. Dwarfism due to isolated deficiency of growth hormone is associated with higher than normal levels of both LDL and VLDL. Decreased insulin levels may be the major underlying defect; however, deficiency of growth hormone may impair the disposal of FFA by oxidation and ketogenesis in liver, favoring synthesis of triglycerides. Mild hypertriglyceridemia is often associated with acromegaly, probably resulting from insulin resistance. Though growth hormone acutely stimulates lipolysis in adipose tissue, FFA levels are normal in acromegaly.

9. HYPOTHYROIDISM

Whereas significant hypothyroidism tends to produce elevated levels of LDL in serum in nearly all individuals, only a fraction will develop hypertriglyceridemia. The increase in LDL levels results at least in part from decreased numbers of B-100:E receptors on cell membranes, although decreased conversion of cholesterol to bile acids may also contribute. Lipemia, when present, is usually mild, though serum triglyceride levels in excess of 3000 mg/dL (34.5 mmol/L) can occur. The underlying mechanisms are not fully understood, though it is probable that impaired removal of triglycerides from blood is involved, perhaps related to decreased activity of hepatic lipase. Increased content of cholesteryl esters and apo-E in the triglyceride-rich lipoproteins suggests that accumulation of remnant particles occurs. Hypothyroidism, even of very mild degree, causes expression of hyperlipidemia in otherwise latent carriers of familial dysbetalipoproteinemia.

10. IMMUNOGLOBULIN-LIPOPROTEIN COMPLEX DISORDERS

Both polyclonal and monoclonal hypergammaglobulinemias may cause hypertriglyceridemia. IgG, IgM, and IgA have each been involved. Of the underlying monoclonal disorders causing hypertriglyceridemia, myeloma and macroglobulinemia are the most important, but lymphomas and lymphocytic leukemias have also been implicated. Lupus erythematosus and other collagen vascular disorders have been associated with the polyclonal type. Binding of heparin by immunoglobulin, with resulting inhibition of LPL, can cause severe mixed lipemia. More commonly, the triglyceride-rich lipoproteins have an abnormally high density, probably as a result of bound immunoglobulin, though some may be remnant-like particles. These complexes, which bind lipophilic stains, usually have gamma mobility on electrophoresis in agarose gel.

Xanthomatosis associated with immunoglobulin complex disease includes tuberous and eruptive xanthomas, xanthelasma, and planar xanthomas of large areas of skin. The latter are otherwise seen only in patients with cholestasis. Deposits of lipid-rich hyaline material can occur in the lamina propria of the intestine, causing malabsorption and protein-losing enteropathy. Circulating immunoglobulin-lipoprotein complexes can fix complement, leading to hypocomplementemia. In such patients, administration of whole blood or plasma can cause anaphylaxis. Hence, washed red cells or albumin are recommended when blood volume replacement is required.

Treatment is directed at the underlying disorder. Because the critical temperature of cryoprecipitation of some of these complexes is close to body temperature, plasmapheresis should be done at a temperature above the critical temperature measured in the serum of individual patients.

THE PRIMARY HYPERCHOLESTEROLEMIAS

FAMILIAL HYPERCHOLESTEROLEMIA

Etiology & Pathogenesis

This disorder, which in its heterozygous form occurs in approximately one in 500 individuals in the USA, is transmitted as a mendelian dominant trait with very high penetrance. Because half of first-degree relatives are affected, including children, all members of a proband's family should be screened for this disorder. Hypercholesterolemia, representing a selective increase in LDL, exists from birth. Levels of LDL tend to increase during childhood and adolescence such that average levels of serum cholesterol in adult heterozygotes are usually greater than 350 mg/dL (9.1 mmol/L). VLDL levels are usually normal, though some individuals, especially those in kindreds in which hypertriglyceridemia is present, may have higher than normal levels of both VLDL and LDL. Aside from an increase in content of cholesteryl esters, the LDL are normal in structure.

The underlying defect appears to be a deficiency of normal high-affinity receptor sites for LDL on cell membranes. A number of genetic defects affecting the structure, translation, modification, or transport of the B-100:E receptor protein have been identified. In some of these defects, the gene product either does not appear on the cell surface or completely lacks receptor function. The gene products associated with other defects appear as kinetically impaired receptors.

Some individuals have combined heterozygosity. In cases in which a kinetic mutant is combined with an ablative mutant, the severity of the hypercholesterolemia is greater than that seen in simple heterozygosity, usually in the range of 500–800 mg/dL (13–20.8 mmol/L). Those patients who are homozygous for genes that produce no effective receptors have extremely severe hypercholesterolemia (approaching 1000 mg/dL [26 mmol/L] or greater) and fulminant arteriosclerosis.

Some patients who are heterozygous for receptor defects may have serum levels of LDL that are only mildly elevated or, even less commonly, in the normal range. Mitigating factors, perhaps involving decreased production rates for VLDL and LDL, may exist in such individuals. Production rates for LDL generally appear to be nearly normal in heterozygotes but are increased in the homozygous state, largely owing to increased conversion of VLDL to LDL. In the heterozygote, a greater fraction of LDL is removed by non-receptor-dependent mechanisms than in normal subjects. In homozygotes, all removal of LDL proceeds through such pathways.

Clinical Findings

One of the most striking clinical features that may be present is tendinous xanthomatosis. The xanthomas, which usually appear in early adulthood, cause a broadening or fusiform mass in the tendon. They can occur in almost any tendon but are most readily detected in the Achilles and patellar tendons and in the extensor tendons of the hands (Figure 17–4). Patients who are physically active may complain of achillodynia. Arcus corneae (Figure 17–4B) may occur as early as the third decade. Xanthelasma (Figure 17–4A) may also be present. Both arcus and xanthelasma are seen in individuals who do not have hyperlipidemia, however. Coronary atherosclerosis tends to occur prematurely in heterozygotes, commonly in the fifth decade. Eighty-five percent of the men will have had a myocardial infarction before age 60, compared with 15% of unaffected men. Coronary artery disease is particularly prominent in individuals who are relatively deficient in HDL. It is probable that this represents a coincident inheritance of both traits. The homozygous form of familial hypercholesterolemia is catastrophic. Levels of cholesterol in serum may exceed 1000 mg/dL (26 mmol/L), and xanthomatosis progresses rapidly. Patients may have tuberous xanthomas (Figure 17–4) and elevated plaque-like xanthomas of the extremities, buttocks, and interdigital webs. Homozygotes may have overt coronary disease in the first decade of life.

A serum cholesterol level in excess of 350 mg/dL (9.1 mmol/L) in the absence of significant hypertriglyceridemia makes the diagnosis of heterozygous familial hypercholesterolemia likely. Significantly lower levels can occur in heterozygotes if mitigating genes are present. The presence of affected first-degree relatives is supportive of this diagnosis, especially if no other phenotypes of hyperlipidemia are present in the family that would suggest familial combined disease. The finding of tendon xanthomas is nearly pathognomonic—betasitosterolemia and cerebrotendinous xanthomatosis (cholestanolosis) and ligand-defective apo-B excepted. Although the cholesterol content of serum from umbilical cord blood is usually elevated in patients with this disorder, the diagnosis is most easily established by measuring serum cholesterol levels after the first year of life.

Treatment

Treatment with various single-drug regimens is of moderate benefit in decreasing LDL levels in serum. However, complete normalization of LDL levels can be achieved in most compliant heterozygotes with a combination of a bile acid-binding resin and niacin when they are eating a diet low in saturated fat and cholesterol. Comparable results are achieved with combinations of reductase inhibitors and resin or niacin. Serum cholesterol levels less than 200 mg/dL are often seen with a ternary combination of these drugs. Treatment of homozygotes is extremely difficult. Partial control may be achieved with portacaval shunt or immunopheresis in conjunction with combined drug regimens. Striking reduction of LDL levels is observed after liver transplantation, illustrating the important role of hepatic receptors in LDL clearance. (See Treatment of Hyperlipidemia, below.)

FAMILIAL COMBINED HYPERLIPIDEMIA

In some individuals in kindreds in whom this disorder is present (see Primary Hypertriglyceridemia, above), LDL and IDL will be the only lipoproteins that are elevated. This pattern may vary in an individual over time, and elevated VLDL alone or combined elevations of LDL and VLDL may be observed in the patient or the patient's relatives. Some affected children express hyperlipidemia. In contrast to most cases of familial hypercholesterolemia, the serum cholesterol level may often be lower than 350 mg/dL, and neither tendinous nor tuberous xanthomas occur. Studies of kindreds suggest an autosomal dominant mechanism of transmission. Coronary atherosclerosis is accelerated in this disorder, which is sufficiently prevalent to be observed in about 10% of survivors of myocardial infarction. The underlying biochemical mechanism appears to involve increased synthesis of apo-B-100.

Treatment of the hypercholesterolemia should begin with diet and niacin. It may be necessary to add resin or a reductase inhibitor to normalize levels of LDL.

LP(A) HYPERLIPOPROTEINEMIA

A lipoprotein that normally comprises a very minor fraction of circulating lipoproteins, Lp(a), is present in high concentrations in some individuals whose levels of LDL may also be elevated or nearly normal. Upon ultracentrifugation, this lipoprotein ranges on both sides of the density that discriminates LDL from HDL. It contains apo-B-100 and the Lp(a) protein. It is identified in LDL or HDL fractions obtained by ultracentrifugation by its prebeta-electrophoretic mobility. A number of studies implicate it as an independent risk factor for coronary artery disease. Preliminary results indicate that niacin is the most effective drug used in treatment.

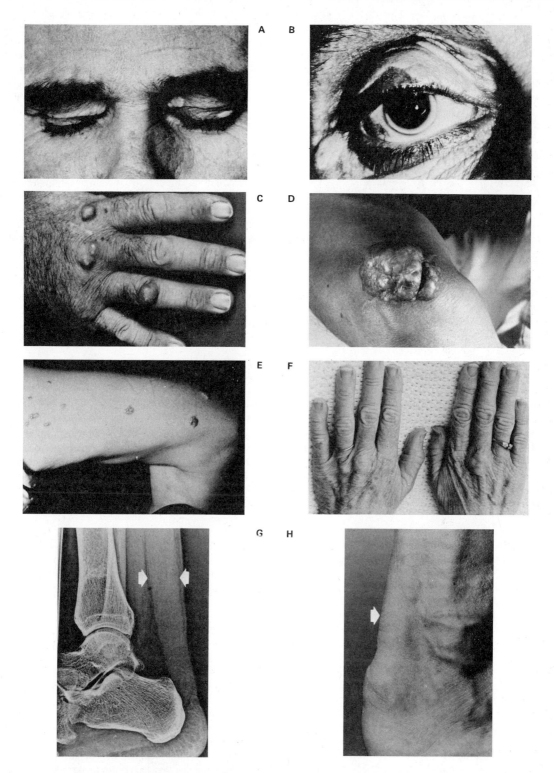

Figure 17–4. Clinical manifestations of hyperlipidemias. *A:* Xanthelasma involving medial and lateral canthi. *B:* Severe xanthelasma and arcus corneae. *C:* Tuberous xanthomas. *D:* Large tuberous xanthoma of elbow. *E:* Eruptive xanthomas, singly and in rosettes. *F:* Xanthomas of extensor tendons of the hands. *G:* Xeroradiogram of Achilles tendon xanthoma. *H:* Xanthoma of Achilles tendon (Normal Achilles tendons do not exceed 7 mm in diameter in the region between the calcaneus and the point at which the tendon fibers begin to radiate toward their origins.)

FAMILIAL LIGAND-DEFECTIVE APO B

A mutation substituting glutamine for arginine at residue 3500 in the apo-B protein has been described in patients presenting with elevated levels of LDL. They may have tendon xanthomas and are at increased risk for coronary disease.

SECONDARY HYPERCHOLESTEROLEMIA

HYPOTHYROIDISM

The typical disorder of lipoproteins associated with hypothyroidism is high LDL and IDL concentrations. Increased content of apo-E in the VLDL and IDL is consistent with an increase in remnant particles in plasma. In addition to elevated LDL, some patients may have lipemia as described in the section on secondary hyperlipemia. The hyperlipidemia of hypothyroidism may occur in individuals with no overt signs or symptoms of decreased thyroid function. Biliary excretion of cholesterol and bile acids is depressed; however, cholesterol biosynthesis is also decreased. Cholesterol stores in tissues appear to be increased, though the number of B-100:E receptors on cells is decreased. Activity of hepatic lipase is also markedly decreased. Atherogenesis is accelerated by myxedema. The hyperlipidemia responds dramatically to treatment with thyroxine.

NEPHROSIS

As described in the section on secondary hypertriglyceridemias, nephrosis produces a biphasic hyperlipoproteinemia. The earliest alteration of lipoproteins in nephrosis is elevation of LDL. Increased secretion of VLDL by liver is probably involved. Because the lipids of the lipoprotein surfaces are altered by enrichment with sphingomyelin, lysolecithin, and FFA, the catabolism of LDL could be impaired. Perhaps the low metabolic rate in affected patients introduces metabolic changes similar to those associated with hypothyroidism. The hyperlipidemia may be an important element in the markedly increased risk of atherosclerotic heart disease in these patients. The treatment of choice appears to be bile acid-binding resins with niacin. HMG-CoA reductase inhibitors may also be useful.

IMMUNOGLOBULIN DISORDERS

One of the lipoprotein abnormalities that can be associated with monoclonal gammopathy is elevation of LDL. A "gamma lipoprotein" that is a stable complex of immunoglobulin and lipoprotein may be observed in agarose gel electrophoretograms of the sera of some patients. Cryoprecipitation, often in the temperature range encountered in peripheral tissues when the environmental temperature is low, may occur. Patients may have symptoms from the vascular effect of complement fixation resulting from complex formation and may have hyperviscosity syndrome from the elevated immunoglobulins per se. Planar xanthomas may occur.

Treatment is directed at the underlying process. Plasmapheresis is often effective. If cryoprecipitation occurs at critical temperatures near or above room temperature, the procedure must be carried out in a special warm environment. Transfusion of whole blood or serum may be dangerous in these patients because of rapid production of anaphylatoxins from fresh complement in the serum, resulting from interaction with circulating antibody-antigen complexes. This risk can be minimized by the use of packed red blood cells and albumin in place of whole blood.

ANOREXIA NERVOSA

About 40% of patients with anorexia nervosa have elevated LDL in serum, and levels of cholesterol in serum may reach 400–600 mg/dL (10.4–15.6 mmol/L). The hyperlipidemia, which persists despite correction of hypothyroidism, is probably a result of decreased fecal excretion of bile acids and cholesterol.

Serum lipoproteins return to normal when proper nutrition is restored.

CHOLESTASIS

The hyperlipidemia associated with the obstruction of biliary flow is complex. It occurs with either extrahepatic or intrahepatic obstruction, though it tends to be more severe with the former. Levels of cholesterol in serum exceeding 400 mg/dL (10.4 mmol/L) usually are associated with extrahepatic obstruction or with intrahepatic tumor. Several types of abnormal lipoproteins are present in plasma. The most abundant, termed LP-X, is a bilayer vesicle composed of unesterified cholesterol and lecithin, with associated apolipoproteins but not apo-B. LP-X is apparent on electrophoresis of lipoproteins in agarose gel as a band of zero to gamma mobility which shows metachromatic staining with Sudan black. It is these vesicular particles that cause the serum phospholipid and unesterified cholesterol content to be extremely high. There is another abnormal species called LP-Y, which contains appreciable amounts of triglycerides and carries apo-B. It may represent a remnant particle derived from chylomicrons. The LDL in cholestasis also contain an unusually large amount of triglycerides.

Patients with cholestasis may have planar xanthomas of the skin, especially at sites of minor trauma, and xanthomas of the palmar creases. Occasionally, eruptive xanthomas are present. Xanthomatous involvement of nerves may lead to symptoms of peripheral neuropathy, and the abnormal lipoproteins may be atherogenic. Whereas bilirubin levels are nearly normal in some patients with chronic cholestasis, all have elevated serum alkaline phosphatase activity.

Neuropathy is the chief indication for treatment of the hyperlipidemia. Bile acid-binding resins are of some value, whereas fibric acid derivatives may cause an increase in serum cholesterol levels. Plasmapheresis is the most effective treatment.

THE PRIMARY HYPOLIPIDEMIAS

Although the clinician is confronted infrequently by the problem of a striking deficiency in plasma lipids, it is important to recognize the primary and secondary hypolipidemias. A serum cholesterol level less than 110 mg/dL (2.9 mmol/L) in an adult patient is noteworthy. Since levels of triglycerides in normal fasting serum may be as low as 25 mg/dL (0.29 mmol/L), significance is limited to cases in which they are virtually absent.

PRIMARY HYPOLIPIDEMIA DUE TO DEFICIENCY OF HIGH-DENSITY LIPOPROTEINS

1. TANGIER DISEASE

Etiology & Pathogenesis

Severe deficiency of HDL occurs in the primary disorder known as Tangier disease. Heterozygotes lack clinical signs but have about one-half or less of the normal complement of HDL and apo-A-I in plasma. Homozygotes lack normal plasma HDL, and apo-A-I and apo-A-II are present at extremely low levels. Serum cholesterol levels are usually below 120 mg/dL (3.12 mmol/L) and may be half that value. Mild hypertriglyceridemia is usually present. The genetic defect probably involves alteration of catabolism of HDL. LDL are greatly enriched in triglycerides.

Clinical Findings

The clinical features of this rare autosomal recessive disease include large, orange-colored, lipid-filled tonsils, accumulation of cholesteryl esters in the reticuloendothelial system, and an episodic and recurrent peripheral neuropathy with predominant motor weakness in the later stages. The course of the disease is benign in early childhood, but the neuropathy may appear as early as age 8. Cholesteryl ester accumulates most prominently in peripheral nerve sheaths. Carotenoid coloration may be apparent in pharyngeal and rectal mucous membranes. Splenomegaly and corneal infiltration may also be present.

Treatment

Because much of the lamellar lipoprotein material in plasma is believed to originate in chylomicrons, restriction of dietary fats and cholesterol is suggested.

2. FAMILIAL HYPOALPHALIPOPROTEINEMIA

Etiology & Pathogenesis

This phenotypic pattern is a partial deficiency of HDL in serum that may involve heterogeneous mechanisms. These presumed constitutional disorders must be differentiated from the condition in which moderately low levels of HDL cholesterol are seen in individuals consuming a diet very low in fat, perhaps reflecting decreased generation of HDL from chylomicrons. For example, white and Asian men on such diets usually have HDL cholesterol levels of 38–44 mg/dL (1–1.1 mmol/L) by ultracentrifugal analysis, in contrast to a median value of 49 mg/dL (1.3 mmol/L) when consuming a typical North American diet. Such levels are common in Asiatic populations and among vegetarians, where the risk of coronary disease is small. The physician must further interpret HDL cholesterol levels in the light of the amount of triglyceride-rich lipoproteins in plasma. Because triglyceride is progressively substituted for cholesteryl esters in the core of HDL as the plasma triglyceride level rises, the HDL cholesterol will decrease as an inverse logarithmic function of the triglyceride level. This decrease causes an apparent decrease in HDL levels, since cholesterol is the component of HDL that is commonly measured.

Etiologic Factor in Coronary Disease

Clinical experience suggests that familial hypoalphalipoproteinemia is fairly common and is an important risk factor in coronary vascular disease. This abnormality may be the only apparent risk factor in many cases of premature coronary atherosclerosis. Furthermore, it may accelerate the appearance of coronary disease in patients with familial hypercholesterolemia or other hyperlipidemias. Hypoalphalipoproteinemia shows a strong familial incidence. Although several mechanisms and modes of transmission may be involved, many kindreds show distributions consistent with autosomal dominance.

Treatment

To date, there has been no demonstration that increasing total HDL levels in patients with familial hypoalphalipoproteinemia will decrease the risk of progression of arteriosclerotic disease. Furthermore, only limited means of raising HDL levels are at hand. Recent findings that HDL exist in as many as eight discrete species further complicate this problem. It is not yet known which of these species may be involved in protecting against arteriosclerosis or whether levels of those species can be increased. Thus, though alcohol ingestion can increase total HDL levels in some individuals, it appears that the effect is primarily on the HDL$_3$ ultracentrifugal fraction, which correlates poorly with decreased risk in epidemiologic studies. Therefore, no recommendation for increased alcohol consumption should be made on this account.

Heavy exercise is associated with increases in HDL in some individuals, but exercise must be approached with caution in patients who may have coronary disease. Niacin increases total HDL levels in many subjects, chiefly in the HDL$_2$ ultracentrifugal fraction. Its effects on individual subspecies of HDL remain to be determined.

Perhaps the most important reason at present for measuring HDL cholesterol levels is to identify patients who are at increased risk. Thus, just as with patients who have premature vascular disease or a family history of early arteriosclerosis, patients with low HDL levels should be treated more aggressively for elevated levels of lipoproteins that appear to be atherogenic (LDL, IDL, and VLDL). Furthermore, vigorous efforts should be directed at the control of other risk factors, such as hypertension. Smoking is known to decrease HDL cholesterol levels significantly. Modest lowering of HDL cholesterol levels by beta-adrenergic blocking agents must be weighed against the need for these drugs in treating cardiovascular disease.

3. DEFICIENCY OF LCAT

Another disorder associated with low serum levels of HDL is lecithin-cholesterol acyltransferase deficiency. This rare autosomal recessive disorder is not expressed in clinical or biochemical form in the heterozygote. In the homozygote, clinical characteristics are variable. The diagnosis is usually made in adult life, though corneal opacities may begin in childhood. Proteinuria may be an early sign. Deposits of unesterified cholesterol and phospholipid in the renal microvasculature lead to progressive loss of nephrons and ultimate renal failure. Many patients have mild to moderate normochromic anemia with target cells. Hyperbilirubinemia or peripheral neuropathy

may be present. Red blood cell lipid composition is abnormal, with increased content of unesterified cholesterol and lecithin. Most have elevated plasma triglycerides (200–1000 mg/dL [2.3–11.2 mmol/L]), and levels of serum cholesterol vary from low normal to 500 mg/dL (13 mmol/L), only a small fraction of which is esterified. The large triglyceride-rich lipoproteins, presumably derived from VLDL and chylomicrons, are unusually rich in unesterified cholesterol and appear to have abnormal surface monolayers. The LDL are rich in triglycerides, and abnormal vesicular lipoproteins are present in the LDL density interval. Two abnormal HDL species are present: bilayer disks and small spherical particles. Marked restriction of dietary fat and cholesterol results in a decrease of VLDL-like particles and lamellar LDL in plasma and is the recommended treatment.

PRIMARY HYPOLIPIDEMIA DUE TO DEFICIENCY OF APO-B-CONTAINING LIPOPROTEINS

1. RECESSIVE ABETALIPOPROTEINEMIA

Etiology & Pathogenesis

Recessive abetalipoproteinemia probably represents a number of mutations involving the processing of apo-B or the secretion of apo-B-containing lipoproteins. Heterozygous patients have no abnormalities of lipoproteins and no clinical signs. In homozygotes, all forms of apo-B are essentially absent. No chylomicrons, VLDL, or LDL are found in plasma, leaving only HDL. Plasma triglyceride levels are usually less than 10 mg/dL (0.12 mmol/L) and fail to rise after a fat load. The plasma cholesterol is usually less than 90 mg/dL (2.3 mmol/L). There is a defect in the incorporation of newly synthesized triglycerides into chylomicron particles. However, at low levels of fat intake, about 80% of the ingested triglycerides are absorbed, probably by direct absorption of fatty acids via the portal vein. One demonstrated defect in abetalipoproteinemia is absence of a microsomal triglyceride transfer protein needed for the assembly of mature VLDL.

Clinical Findings

Clinical features include a paucity of adipose tissue, associated with malabsorption of long-chain fatty acids due to failure of the intestine to secrete chylomicrons; red blood cells that may be acanthocytic, with a high cholesterol/phospholipid ratio; progressive degeneration of the central nervous system, including cerebellar degeneration and posterior and lateral spinal tract disease; retinal degeneration that may be severe; and, usually, very low levels of fat-soluble vitamins in plasma. The neurologic defects are due to deficiency of vitamin E (normally transported largely in LDL). Patients are apparently normal at birth and develop steatorrhea with impaired growth in infancy. The neuromuscular disorder often appears in late childhood with ataxia, night blindness, decreased visual acuity, and nystagmus. Cardiomyopathy with arrhythmias has been reported and may be a cause of death.

Treatment

Treatment includes administration of fat-soluble vitamins. Very large doses of tocopherol (vitamin E) (1000–5000 IU/d) appear to limit the progressive central nervous system degeneration. Although vitamin A seems to correct the night blindness, it does not alter the course of retinitis pigmentosa. Vitamins D and K may also be indicated. Restriction of dietary fat minimizes steatorrhea.

2. FAMILIAL HYPOBETALIPOPROTEINEMIA

This disorder is usually attributable to defects at the apo-B locus, resulting in decreased production of the protein or in the production of truncated gene products. LDL and apo-B in heterozygotes are present at about half of normal levels. If a mutant allele resulting in the complete interdiction of apo-B synthesis is present in the homozygous state, the clinical and biochemical features may be indistinguishable from recessive abetalipoproteinemia, and treatment is the same as for that disorder. Very short truncations of apo-B-100 only allow the formation of abnormally dense small LDL. Longer truncations permit the formation of larger lipoproteins, even including VLDL-like particles. The latter may be present in the virtual absence of LDL in some cases.

Clinical features may be absent in patients who secrete at least low levels of LDL-like particles. However, signs and symptoms of tocopherol deficiency may be present. Oral treatment with alpha tocopherol (vitamin E) (800 IU/d) is recommended for all patients with hypobetalipoproteinemia.

3. CHYLOMICRON RETENTION DISEASE

This disorder, which presents in the neonate, appears to be based upon the inability of intestinal epithelial cells to secrete chylomicrons. Affected individuals have severe malabsorption of triglycerides with steatorrhea. Levels of LDL and VLDL are about one-half of normal, presumably secondary to malnutrition. Tocopherol levels may be very low and may be associated with neurologic abnormalities. Clinical symptoms diminish somewhat with time if the patient is managed with a low-fat diet and alpha tocopherol (vitamin E) supplementation.

SECONDARY HYPOLIPIDEMIA

Hypolipidemia may be secondary to a number of diseases characterized by chronic cachexia, eg, advanced cancer. Myeloproliferative disorders can lead to extremely low levels of LDL, probably owing to increased uptake related to rapid proliferation and membrane synthesis. A wide variety of conditions leading to intestinal malabsorption produce hypolipidemia. In these situations, levels of chylomicrons, VLDL, and LDL in serum are low but never absent. Because most of the lipoprotein mass of fasting serum is of hepatic origin, massive parenchymal liver failure—eg, in Reye's syndrome—can cause severe hypolipidemia.

The hypolipidemias associated with immunoglobulin disorders result from diverse mechanisms. Affected patients usually have myeloma or macroglobulinemia but may have lymphomas or lymphocytic leukemia. Any of the major classes of immunoglobulins may be involved. In many cases, the immunoglobulins are cryoprecipitins; thus, the diagnosis may be missed if blood is not drawn and serum prepared at 37 °C and observed for cryoprecipitation. Immunoglobulin-lipoprotein complexes may precipitate in various tissues. When this occurs in the lamina propria of the intestine, a syndrome of malabsorption and protein-losing enteropathy may result. Monoclonal IgA in myeloma may precipitate with lipoproteins, causing xanthomas of the gingiva and cervix. Lesions in the skin are usually planar and xanthomatous and may involve intracutaneous hemorrhage, producing a classic purple xanthoma. Planar xanthomas occurring in cholestasis may be confused with this condition, because the abnormal lipoprotein of cholestasis (LP-X), like the circulating lipoprotein complex of immunoglobulin and lipoprotein, has gamma mobility on electrophoresis.

OTHER DISORDERS OF LIPOPROTEIN METABOLISM

THE LIPODYSTROPHIES

Classification

Current classification of the lipodystrophies is based on their familial or acquired origin and the regional or generalized nature of the fat loss. Among the associated metabolic abnormalities, insulin resistance is the common finding. Two of these disorders are known to be inherited.

Familial generalized lipodystrophy (Seip-Berardinelli syndrome), a rare recessive trait, may be diagnosed at birth and is associated with macrosomia. Genital hypertrophy, hypertrichosis, acanthosis nigricans, hepatomegaly, insulin resistance, hypertriglyceridemia, and glucose intolerance are regularly observed.

Familial lipodystrophy of limbs and trunk (Köbberling-Dunningan syndrome) appears to be transmitted as a dominant gene, affects women predominantly, and is not evident until puberty. The face, neck, and upper trunk are usually spared. Growth is normal, but otherwise this syndrome shares features of the generalized form noted above. It is frequently associated with Stein-Leventhal syndrome.

Acquired forms of lipodystrophy, generalized (Lawrence syndrome) and partial (Barraquer-Simmons syndrome), usually begin in childhood, affect females predominantly, and often follow an acute febrile illness. The generalized type commonly shares the features described above, invariably involving the trunk and extremities but sometimes sparing the face. A sclerosing panniculitis, as seen in Weber-Christian syndrome, may appear at the outset. The partial type usually begins in the face and then involves the neck, upper limbs, and trunk. In this disorder, reduced levels of C3 complement are frequently encountered. Most patients have proteinuria, and some develop overt vascular nephritis.

Associated Disorders

Because a number of patients with disorders resembling both familial and acquired types of lipodystrophy have tumors or other lesions of the hypothalamus, appropriate neurologic evaluation should be obtained. Similarly, the physician should be alert to the association of collagen vascular disorders, including scleroderma and dermatomyositis, with some cases of acquired lipodystrophy.

RARE DISORDERS

Werner's Syndrome, Progeria, Infantile Hypercalcemia, & Sphingolipidoses

These disorders may be associated with hypercholesterolemia, but levels of triglycerides are usually normal. Some patients with Niemann-Pick disease have hypercholesterolemia, but most have hypertriglyceridemia, as do many patients with Gaucher's disease.

Wolman's Disease & Cholesteryl Ester Storage Disease

These recessive lipid storage disorders involve the absence and partial deficiency, respectively, of lysosomal acid lipase, resulting in abnormal cholesteryl ester and triglyceride stores in liver, spleen, adrenal glands, small intestine, and bone marrow. Most patients have elevated levels of both LDL and VLDL in plasma. Wolman's disease is fatal in infancy.

Cerebrotendinous Xanthomatosis

In this recessive disorder, impaired synthesis of bile acids results in increased production of cholesterol and cholestanol, which accumulate in body tissues. Plasma levels of cholesterol and cholestanol are normal or elevated. Cataracts, tendinous xanthomas, progressive neurologic dysfunction, and premature coronary atherosclerosis are hallmarks of this disease. Its central nervous system effects include dementia, spasticity, and ataxia. Death usually ensues before age 50 from neurologic degeneration or coronary disease. Treatment with chenodeoxycholic acid appears useful. Resins must be avoided because they aggravate the underlying defect.

Phytosterolemia

This disorder is distinguished by normal or elevated plasma cholesterol levels; high concentrations of plant sterol in serum, adipose tissue, and skin; and prominent xanthomas of both the tendinous and tuberous types. Individuals with this disorder absorb a substantially larger fraction of phytosterols and cholesterol from the intestine than do normal individuals. A more severe form apparently exists in which serum cholesterol levels may be as high as 700 mg/dL (18.2 mmol/L), reflecting an increase in LDL that contain sitosterol esters in addition to cholesteryl esters. Premature coronary arteriosclerosis may be present. Treatment consists of a diet restricted in plant sterols and cholesterol and the use of bile acid-binding resins. HMG-CoA reductase inhibitors may be of some value.

II. TREATMENT OF HYPERLIPIDEMIA

The first therapeutic measure in all forms of hyperlipidemia is institution of an appropriate diet. In most forms of hyperlipidemia, a single "universal" diet (see below) is indicated. In many subjects with lipemia or with hypercholesterolemia of mild to moderate severity, compliance with this diet will be sufficient to control lipoprotein levels. However, many patients with severe hypercholesterolemia or lipemia will require drug therapy. In all of these individuals, the prescribed diet must be continued to achieve the full potential of the medications.

Caution Regarding Drug Therapy

There are insufficient data to evaluate the effects on the fetus of drugs used in treatment of hyperlipoproteinemia. Therefore, women of childbearing age should be advised of the potential risk and should be given these agents only if pregnancy is being actively avoided. If contraceptives are prescribed, estrogens should not be used in patients with hypertriglyceridemia.

In children, hyperlipidemias other than familial hypercholesterolemia rarely require medication. The severity and age at onset of symptomatic coronary disease in the child's family and the presence of other risk factors, especially hypoalphalipoproteinemia and hyper-Lp(a)lipoproteinemia, in the child should be considered in deciding when drug treatment should be started. A resin is the drug of choice. Dietary treatment is indicated for all children with hyperlipidemia and should be started after the second year. The exception is primary chylomicronemia, in which an appropriate diet should be instituted as soon as the disease is detected.

DIETARY FACTORS IN THE MANAGEMENT OF LIPOPROTEIN DISORDERS

Restriction of Caloric Intake

The secretion of VLDL by liver is greatly stimulated by caloric intake in excess of requirements for physical activity and basal metabolism. Therefore, the total caloric content of the diet is of greater importance than its specific composition in treating endogenous hyperlipemia. There is a positive correlation between serum levels of VLDL triglyceride and various measures of obesity, but many obese patients have normal serum lipids. On the other hand, most patients with hypertriglyceridemia—except those with lipoprotein lipase deficiency—are obese. This association is more consistently observed in persons whose weight gain occurred in later childhood or adulthood and who have adipocyte hypertrophy with relative insulin resistance. As obese patients lose weight, plasma VLDL stabilize at lower levels. There is a modest correlation of LDL levels with body weight in the general population.

Restriction of Fat Intake

In primary chylomicronemia, saturated and polyunsaturated fats both must be restricted rigidly, because the underlying defect is in lipolysis. Similarly, in the acute management of mixed lipemia with impending pancreatitis, elimination of dietary fat leads to a rapid decrease in chylomicron-borne triglycerides in plasma.

The cholesterol-lowering effect of a significant reduction in total fat content of the diet is well known. It has also been shown that a 10–15% fall in serum cholesterol levels is achieved when individuals who have been consuming a typical North American diet restrict their intake of saturated fats to 8% of total calories. Most saturated fatty acids cause increased

levels of LDL cholesterol by down-regulating hepatic LDL receptors. Whereas polyunsaturated fatty acids do not have this effect, they may reduce levels of HDL and are potentially carcinogenic. Monounsaturated fatty acids do not raise LDL levels and increase HDL levels higher than those observed with markedly restricted fat intake. Thus, moderate use of monounsaturated fats such as olive oil, oleic acid-rich safflower oil, or rapeseed oil from strains of rapeseed that contain little of the cardiotoxic erucic acid, appears to be desirable.

The omega-3 fatty acids found in fish oils have special properties relevant to the treatment of hypertriglyceridemia. Substantial decreases in triglyceride levels can be induced in some patients with severe endogenous or mixed lipemia at doses of 10–15 g/d. In patients with other phenotypes, these fatty acids may increase LDL and decrease HDL levels and therefore are not indicated. Certain members of this class of fatty acids, such as eicosapentaenoic acid, are potent inhibitors of platelet reactivity.

Reduction of Cholesterol Intake

The amount of cholesterol in the diet affects serum cholesterol levels, but individual responses vary. Restriction of dietary cholesterol to less than 200 mg/d (5.2 mmol/d) in normal individuals can result in a decrease of up to 10–15% in serum cholesterol, primarily reflecting a decrease in LDL. This apparently in part reflects the fact that increased cholesterol intake in humans is not completely balanced by reduced cholesterogenesis in the liver. Dietary cholesterol and saturated fat content have independent effects on levels of serum cholesterol.

Role of Carbohydrate in Diet

The role of dietary carbohydrate in lipid metabolism is still being investigated, but certain effects seem to have been uniformly observed. There is great individual variation in these responses. When a high-carbohydrate diet is fed, hypertriglyceridemia develops within 48–72 hours, and levels of triglyceride in serum rise to a maximum in 1–5 weeks. Persons with higher basal triglyceride levels and those consuming hypercaloric diets show the greatest effect. After 1–8 months on a high-carbohydrate diet, triglycerides fall to basal levels in most patients. Similar induction of lipemia by carbohydrate is seen in patients with endogenous and mixed lipemia. There is apparently no type of hyperlipemia that is particularly "carbohydrate-sensitive." It must be emphasized, however, that both of these patterns of lipemia are extremely sensitive to excess total caloric intake. Levels of HDL in serum are lower on a high-carbohydrate intake, but the differences are small.

Alcohol Ingestion

Ingestion of alcohol is a common cause of secondary hypertriglyceridemia, owing to overproduction of VLDL. Some individuals with familial hyper-triglyceridemia are particularly sensitive to the effects of alcohol, and abstinence may normalize their triglyceride levels. Chronic alcohol intake may also be associated with hypercholesterolemia. Increased cholesterol synthesis and decreased conversion to bile acids have been observed. Alcohol ingestion may account for alimentary lipemia persisting beyond 12–14 hours. This possibility should be excluded by the history or a repeat lipid analysis. A positive correlation has been found between alcohol intake and HDL cholesterol levels; however, increased HDL levels are not observed in all individuals. Because alcohol-induced changes in HDL appear primarily to involve the HDL_3 subfraction, there does not seem to be an indication for the use of alcohol to increase the "protective effect" of HDL against arteriosclerosis.

Fiber in Diet

Although much attention has been devoted to the possible role of fiber in the development of coronary heart disease, there is little evidence that plasma lipids can be significantly affected by intake of most forms of fiber. A modest reduction in LDL cholesterol is associated with the addition of oat bran to the diet, however.

Other Dietary Substances

Several other nutrients have been studied in relation to atherosclerotic heart disease, including calcium, magnesium, trace elements, vitamins D, E, and C, and pyridoxine. The results of these studies are generally equivocal. Caffeine and sucrose have negligible effects on serum lipids, and their statistical relationship to coronary heart disease is generally unimpressive when data are corrected for cigarette smoking. Ingestion of large amounts of zinc appears to be associated with decreased levels of HDL. Lecithin has no effect on plasma lipoproteins.

The "Universal Diet"

Dietary treatment is an important aspect of the management of all forms of lipoprotein disorders and may in some cases be all that is required. Knowledge of the dietary factors reviewed above allows the physician to select appropriate modifications for an individual patient. However, a basic diet is useful in the treatment of most patients. The elements of this diet are as follows:

(1) Ideal body weight should be achieved and maintained.

(2) Fat should provide less than 30% of total calories. Saturated fat should be less than 7% of total calories.

(3) Cholesterol should be reduced to less than 200 mg/d.

(4) Caloric difference should be made up with complex carbohydrate.

(5) Alcohol should be avoided in any patient with hypertriglyceridemia.

This diet is consistent with the Step-Two Diet recommended by the National Cholesterol Education Program Expert Panel.

Caloric restriction and reduction of adipose tissue mass are particularly important for patients with increased levels of VLDL and IDL. Levels of VLDL and LDL tend to be lower during periods of substantial weight loss than can be maintained under isocaloric conditions, even at ideal body weight.

Sources of Information About Diet

Referral to a local American Heart Association chapter or other source of dietetic consultation is often helpful in ensuring compliance. Several recipe books have been published, and food manufacturers are developing products that add variety and palatability to the restricted diet. Since the prudent diet, as proposed by the American Heart Association and others, is generally recommended, it is helpful to urge the entire family of a hyperlipidemic patient to eat a modified diet, providing greater ease of preparation and an added measure of psychologic support.

DRUGS USED IN TREATMENT OF HYPERLIPOPROTEINEMIA (Table 17–3)

BILE ACID SEQUESTRANTS

Mechanism of Action

Cholestyramine and colestipol are cationic resins that bind bile acids in the intestinal lumen (Figure 17–5). The resin particles are not absorbed by the bowel and therefore increase the excretion of bile acids in the stool. Excretion of bile acids can be increased up to tenfold when bile acid-binding resins are given. LDL levels decrease as a consequence of increased expression of high-affinity receptors on cell membranes of the liver. These agents are useful only in disorders involving elevated LDL levels. In fact, patients who have increased levels of VLDL may have further increases in serum triglyceride levels during treatment with resins. Thus, in combined hyperlipidemia, where the resins may be given because of high LDL levels, a second agent such as niacin may be required to control the hypertriglyceridemia. Levels of LDL will fall 15–30% in compliant patients with heterozygous familial hypercholesterolemia who are receiving maximal doses of the resins. Larger decrements of LDL cholesterol may be seen in patients with other, less severe forms of hypercholesterolemia, and in some, levels of LDL will be normalized completely.

Table 17–3. The primary hyperlipoproteinemias and their drug treatment.

	Single Drug[1]	Drug Combination
Primary chylomicronemia (familial lipoprotein lipase or cofactor deficiency)		
Chylomicrons, VLDL increased	Dietary management	
Familial hypertriglyceridemia		
Severe: Chylomicrons, VLDL increased	Niacin, gemfibrozil	Niacin plus gemfibrozil
Moderate: VLDL and perhaps chylomicrons increased	Gemfibrozil, niacin	
Familial combined hyperlipoproteinemia		
VLDL increased	Niacin	
LDL increased	Resin, niacin, reductase inhibitor	Niacin plus resin or reductase inhibitor
VLDL, LDL increased	Niacin	Niacin plus resin or reductase inhibitor
Familial dysbetalipoproteinemia		
VLDL remnants, chylomicron remnants increased	Niacin, gemfibrozil, clofibrate	
Familial hypercholesterolemia		
Heterozygous: LDL increased	Resin, reductase inhibitor, niacin	Two or three of the single drugs
Homozygous: LDL increased	Probucol, niacin	Resin plus niacin plus reductase inhibitor; probucol plus agents above
Lp(a) hyperlipoproteinemia		
Lp(a) increased	Niacin	

[1] Single-drug therapy should be tried before drug combinations are used.

Drug Dosage

In disorders involving moderately high levels of LDL, 20 g of cholestyramine or colestipol daily may lower cholesterol levels effectively. Treatment should commence at one-half of the above dose to minimize gastrointestinal side effects. Maximum doses of 30 g of colestipol or 32 g of cholestyramine daily are required in more severe cases.

Side Effects

Because the resins are confined to the lumen of the intestine, few systemic side effects are observed. Patients frequently complain of a bloated sensation and constipation, both of which may be relieved by the addition of psyllium to the resin mixture. Malabsorption of fat or fat-soluble vitamins with a daily dose of resin of up to 30 g occurs only in individuals with preexisting bowel disease or with cholestasis. Hypoprothrombinemia has been observed in patients with malabsorption due to these causes. The resins bind thyroxine, digitalis glycosides, and warfarin and impair the absorption of iron, thiazides, beta-blockers, and other drugs. Absorption of all of these substances is ensured if they are administered 1 hour before the resin. During long-term treatment with the resins, some patients may complain of dry, flaking skin, which responds to local application of lanolin. Because they change the composition of bile micelles, bile acid sequestrants theoretically may increase the risk of cholelithiasis, particularly in obese subjects. In practice, this risk appears to be very small.

NIACIN (Nicotinic Acid)

Mechanism of Action

Niacin (but not its amide) is able to effect major reductions in LDL and triglyceride-rich lipoproteins (Figure 17–5). Niacin appears to inhibit the secretion of VLDL by liver and to increase the efficiency of removal of VLDL triglycerides via the LPL pathway. Niacin has several effects on cholesterol metabolism. It increases sterol excretion acutely and mobilizes cholesterol from tissue pools until a new steady state is established. Although it has no effect on the conversion of cholesterol to bile acids, it decreases cholesterol biosynthesis. That it can cause a continued decrease in hepatic cholesterol production even when given with bile acid-binding resins is probably an important feature of the complementary action of these agents. Levels of HDL in plasma, particularly HDL_2, are significantly increased, reflecting a decrease in the fractional catabolic rate of these lipoproteins. Niacin stimulates production of tissue plasminogen activator, an effect that may be of value in preventing thrombotic events.

Drug Dosage

The dose of niacin required for effective treatment varies with the diagnosis. Optimal effect on LDL levels in heterozygous familial hypercholesterolemia is only achieved when a bile acid-binding resin is combined with 4.5–6.5 g of niacin daily (in three doses).

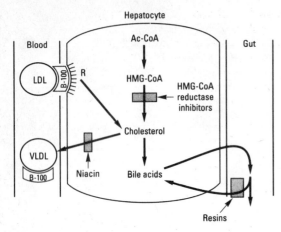

Figure 17–5. Sites of action of HMG-CoA reductase inhibitors, niacin and resins used in treating hyperlipidemias. LDL receptors (R) are increased by treatment with resins and HMG-CoA reductase inhibitors. (Reproduced, with permission, from Katzung BG (editor): *Basic & Clinical Pharmacology,* 5th ed. Appleton & Lange, 1992.)

For other forms of hypercholesterolemia and for hypertriglyceridemia, a dose of 1.5–3.5 g/d often has a dramatic effect. Because niacin causes cutaneous flushing, it is usually started at a dosage of 100 mg three times daily and increased slowly. Tachyphylaxis to the flushing often occurs within a few days at any dose, allowing stepwise increases. Many patients have no flushing or only occasional minimal flushing when stabilized on a given dose. Because the flushing is prostaglandin-mediated, 0.3 g of aspirin given 20–30 minutes before each dose may mitigate this symptom. It is important to counsel the patient beforehand that the flushing is a harmless cutaneous vasodilatation. Patients should be advised to take the drug with meals.

Side Effects

Moderate elevations of aminotransferases are more often observed if the dosage of niacin is increased too rapidly. If a daily dose of 2.5 g is not exceeded by the end of the first month, 5 g after the second month, and 6.5 g after the third month, such abnormalities are uncommon. A daily dose of 6.5 g is the maximum under any circumstances. Some patients have reversible elevations of serum glutamic aminotransferase or alkaline phosphatase activities up to three times the upper limit of normal that do not appear to be clinically significant. In a group of patients treated continuously for up to 15 years, no significant liver disease developed despite such enzyme abnormalities. About one-fifth of patients have mild hyperuricemia that tends to be asymptomatic unless the patient has had gout. In such cases, allopurinol can be added to the regimen. A few patients will have moderate elevations of blood glucose during treatment. Again, this is reversible except possibly in some patients who have latent maturity-onset diabetes. A more common side effect is gastric irritation, which responds well to antacids. Rarely, patients develop acanthosis nigricans, which clears if the drug is discontinued. Some patients can have cardiac arrhythmias while taking niacin. Reversible macular degeneration has been described rarely.

Niacin should be avoided in patients with peptic ulcer or hepatic parenchymal disease. It should be discontinued in patients who develop markedly elevated levels of aminotransferases or alkaline phosphatase. Liver function, uric acid, and blood glucose should be evaluated before commencing treatment and periodically thereafter.

Timed-release preparations of niacin should be avoided because of the risk of fulminant hepatic failure. This rare consequence has been associated with several types of sustained-release niacins, suggesting that it could occur with all such preparations.

CLOFIBRATE
(Ethyl Chlorphenoxyisobutyrate)

Mechanism of Action

Clofibrate appears to act chiefly by increasing the activity of the lipolytic pathway in plasma—specifically, by increasing levels of LPL activity. It may also increase oxidation of fatty acids by liver and decrease VLDL production modestly. Since decreases in VLDL levels are frequently attended by increased levels of LDL (the so-called beta shift), serum cholesterol levels of some patients may not change despite reductions in triglyceride levels.

Drug Dosage

Clofibrate is useful in treating familial dysbetalipoproteinemia. The usual dose is 1 g twice daily, though patients with dysbetalipoproteinemia may respond well to one-half this dose or less. Clofibrate is of little benefit in familial hypercholesterolemia and has limited effect when severe chylomicronemia is present. In the latter case, niacin may be used with clofibrate or alone.

Side Effects

Side effects include nausea, diarrhea, skin eruptions, leukopenia, elevations of serum glutamic aminotransferase activity, impotence, and muscle pain associated with elevated muscle creatine kinase activity. Clofibrate should not be given to patients with nephrosis. It potentiates the activities of coumarin and indanedione anticoagulants, and the hypoglycemic effects of sulfonylureas may be enhanced. It also increases the lithogenicity of bile, particularly in obese patients. Clofibrate may have a modest carcinogenic potential for tissues of the gastrointestinal tract.

GEMFIBROZIL

Mechanism of Action

Gemfibrozil, a congener of clofibrate, is excreted chiefly by the kidney. It decreases lipolysis in adipose tissue, reduces levels of circulating triglycerides, and causes modest reductions in LDL cholesterol levels. However, in some patients reductions in VLDL levels are attended by increases in LDL levels. Gemfibrozil causes moderate increases in levels of HDL, including the protein moiety.

Drug Dosage

Gemfibrozil may be useful in the treatment of patients with severe endogenous lipemia and familial dysbetalipoproteinemia. It is not recommended for patients who have overt coronary disease. The usual dose is 600 mg twice daily. Patients with familial dysbetalipoproteinemia may be managed with smaller doses.

Side Effects

Skin eruptions and gastrointestinal and muscular symptoms similar to those associated with clofibrate have been described, as well as blood dyscrasias and elevated plasma levels of aminotransferases and alkaline phosphatase. It is likely that most of the toxic effects associated with clofibrate will be observed as experience with this drug increases. Like clofibrate, it enhances the effects of the coumarin and indanedione anticoagulants and increases lithogenicity of bile.

NEOMYCIN

Neomycin is of some usefulness in treating hypercholesterolemia, effecting reductions in LDL cholesterol levels of up to 25%. It is not approved by the FDA as a lipid-lowering agent, and its use is considered investigational. It apparently acts by inhibiting absorption of cholesterol and bile acids. The dosage required for this effect is 0.5–2 g/d. Even in this dosage range, some patients develop diarrhea that persists as long as the drug is taken. Patients should be observed for ototoxicity and nephrotoxicity.

HMG-CoA REDUCTASE INHIBITORS

Mechanism of Action

Several closely related structural analogues of HMG-CoA act as competitive inhibitors of HMG-CoA reductase, a key enzyme in the cholesterol biosynthetic pathway. Of these, lovastatin, pravastatin, and simvastatin are approved for use in the

USA. Inhibition of cholesterol biosynthesis induces an increase in high-affinity LDL receptors in the liver, increasing removal of LDL from plasma and decreasing production of LDL. The latter results from increased uptake of lipoprotein precursors of LDL by hepatic receptors. Modest increases in HDL cholesterol and limited decreases in VLDL levels occur during treatment (Figure 17–5). Unless LDL levels are increased, these drugs are not indicated for the treatment of hypertriglyceridemias.

Drug Dosage

These drugs are the most effective individual agents for treatment of hypercholesterolemia. Their effects are amplified significantly when combined with niacin or resin. Daily doses of lovastatin vary from 10 mg to 80 mg. A single 20-mg dose, preferably in the evening, may be sufficient to treat moderately elevated LDL levels. Pravastatin dosages vary from 5 mg to 40 mg daily, and simvastatin dosages vary from 10 mg to 40 mg. Patients with heterozygous familial hypercholesterolemia usually require the higher dosage levels. Because information on long-term safety is lacking, use of these agents in children should be restricted to those with homozygous familial hypercholesterolemia who have some receptor function and those heterozygotes over age 10 years who are at particularly high risk. Women who are lactating, pregnant, or likely to become pregnant should not be given this drug.

Side Effects

These agents are generally well tolerated. Reported side effects, often transient, include changes in bowel function, nausea, headaches, insomnia, fatigue, and rashes. Myopathy with markedly elevated creatine kinase levels occurs in less than 5% of patients. Rarely, myopathy can progress to rhabdomyolysis with myoglobinuria and renal shutdown. There is an increased incidence of myopathy in patients receiving lovastatin with cyclosporine, fibric acid derivatives, erythromycin, and perhaps niacin. Whether the incidence of this side effect will be lower with the other reductase inhibitors is still unclear. The myopathy is rapidly reversible upon cessation of therapy. Minor elevations of creatine kinase activity in plasma are noted more frequently, especially with unusual physical activity. Creatine kinase levels should be measured before starting therapy and monitored at regular intervals.

Moderate, often intermittent elevations of serum aminotransferase (up to three times normal) occur in some patients. Therapy may be continued if aminotransferase levels are measured frequently (at 1- to 2-month intervals). In about 2% of patients, some of whom have underlying liver disease or a history of alcohol abuse, aminotransferase levels may exceed three times the normal limit. This usually occurs after 3–16 months of continuous therapy and may portend more severe hepatic toxicity. Reductase inhibitors should be discontinued in these patients. These drugs should be used with caution in patients with a history of liver disease.

PROBUCOL

Probucol moderately lowers levels of LDL by increasing the fractional clearance of LDL and perhaps by decreasing cholesterol synthesis. It retards atherogenesis in animal models by apparently inhibiting hydroperoxidation of LDL, which in turn reduces uptake of LDL by scavenger cells. HDL cholesterol levels are usually significantly reduced, but emerging data suggest that centripetal transport of cholesterol may be normal or increased. Both atheromas and tendon xanthomas regress in patients with homozygous familial hypercholesterolemia. The use of probucol is indicated in these patients, whose response to bile acid-binding resins and HMG-CoA reductase inhibitors is usually negligible. Other patients with fulminant atheromatous disease might benefit similarly.

Side effects of this agent include nausea, diarrhea, abdominal pain, and increased QT intervals. It should be avoided in patients with a predisposition to ventricular arrhythmia or with prolonged QT intervals. It should not be given with digitalis, quinidine, erythromycin, or other agents known to prolong the QT interval. Elevated levels of aminotransferases, bilirubin, alkaline phosphatase, creatine kinase, uric acid, and blood glucose have been observed.

Probucol is available as 250-mg and 500-mg tablets. The usual dose is 500 mg twice daily.

COMBINED DRUG THERAPY
(Table 17–3)

Combinations of drugs are indicated (1) when LDL and VLDL levels are both elevated; (2) in cases of hypercholesterolemia in which significant increases of VLDL occur during treatment with bile acid-binding resins; and (3) where a complementary effect is required to normalize LDL levels, as in familial hypercholesterolemia.

Fibric Acid Derivatives With Other Agents

The combination of clofibrate or gemfibrozil with niacin may be more effective than either drug alone in managing marked hypertriglyceridemia.

Niacin & Resins

Niacin usually normalizes the triglyceride levels in individuals who have increased levels of VLDL while taking resins. The combination of niacin and resins is more effective than either agent alone in decreasing LDL levels in familial hypercholesterolemia.

The complementarity of action presumably results from additive effects of increased catabolism of LDL due to the resin and decreased production of VLDL induced by niacin. No additional toxicity or side effects have been described with this regimen beyond those encountered when the agents are used individually. Although the daily dose of niacin required for optimal effect on LDL levels in familial hypercholesterolemia may be 6.5 g in conjunction with 24–30 g of resin, many patients show significant response with niacin doses as low as 1.5 g. On this regimen, levels of HDL cholesterol are significantly elevated, and the diameters of tendon xanthomas are reduced significantly even over a period of only a few months. Patients who have been treated with this combination for 15 years show a sustained effect on lipoprotein levels and have not developed additional side effects or toxicity. The combination is also very useful in the treatment of familial combined hyperlipidemia.

The absorption of niacin from the intestine is unimpeded by the presence of resin; the two medications may therefore be taken together. Because the resins have potent acid-neutralizing properties, there is further reason to give the two medications together when a patient complains of the gastric irritation that sometimes occurs as an adverse effect of niacin.

HMG-CoA Reductase Inhibitors With Other Agents

The addition of resin or niacin to lovastatin further decreases plasma levels of LDL in patients with primary hypercholesterolemias. Liver function and plasma creatine kinase activity should be monitored frequently when the combination of lovastatin plus niacin is used. These three drugs used together are more effective, frequently at lower doses, than any of their binary combinations in reducing plasma LDL levels. Serum cholesterol levels in patients with severe heterozygous familial hypercholesterolemia usually fall below 200 mg/dL. In some patients, a reduction of as much as 80% has been observed. Effects are sustained, and no compound toxicity is observed. It is likely that the other reductase inhibitors will behave similarly in binary and ternary combinations with niacin and resins.

POSSIBLE UNTOWARD CONSEQUENCES OF LIPID-LOWERING THERAPY

The risk of coronary heart disease has been found to increase monotonically with LDL cholesterol levels in virtually all epidemiologic surveys, with the lowest incidence at the lowest levels of serum cholesterol. The question has been raised as to whether very low levels of serum cholesterol may increase the risk of noncoronary disease. The correlation between deaths from certain digestive and respiratory disorders and low serum cholesterol levels may be a reflection of the effect of wasting illnesses in general upon LDL levels. Furthermore, increased uptake of LDL by malignant cells is known to decrease LDL levels in plasma. However, two studies have shown a modest increase in the risk of hemorrhagic stroke at serum cholesterol levels below 130 mg/dL. In one, the effect was confined to hypertensive patients. The results of clinical trials are equivocal with respect to whether a discernible increase in noncoronary death might result from lipid-lowering intervention. If the trials employing fibric acid derivatives are excluded, such a relationship becomes very weak, suggesting that lipid-lowering per se probably does not significantly increase the risk for most noncoronary causes of death. In fact, in the MFRT study, a proportionate hazards analysis adjusting for covariance demonstrated the lowest net death rate occurs at a cholesterol level of 122 mg/dL.

Populations in which many individuals have serum cholesterol levels below 160 mg/dL, such as in Japan, do not have an excess incidence of the noncoronary causes of death under consideration and the Japanese have a significantly longer life expectancy than people in other industrialized nations, including the USA. Of great importance in resolving the question of the relative benefit of lipid-lowering therapy is the fact that about 45% of deaths in the USA and Europe are attributable to cardiovascular disease, predominantly coronary artery disease. Thus, projection of a significant reduction in fatal occlusive coronary events into the age range where coronary disease predominates would be expected to far outweigh the marginal increases that might occur in other causes of death. In the light of the relationship of very low plasma cholesterol levels (< 130 mg/dL) to hemorrhagic stroke, the therapeutic goal for total cholesterol levels in patients with known coronary disease should be 150–160 mg/dL (LDL cholesterol level 90–100 mg/dL) until that relationship is better understood.

SURGICAL TREATMENT OF HYPERLIPIDEMIA

The operation that has received the most study in the treatment of hyperlipidemia is ileal bypass. This procedure is intended to impede the reabsorption of bile acids and not to cause malabsorption of triglycerides. Evidence supporting impeded absorption of cholesterol is weak. The procedure appears merely to mimic the effect of bile acid-binding resins. Serum cholesterol levels are apparently decreased in a variety of disorders, but, as with bile acid sequestrants, levels of triglycerides in serum may be significantly elevated. Thus, the procedure is not indicated in hypertriglyceridemia. Furthermore, in a series of well-studied cases of heterozygous familial hypercholesterolemia, levels of cholesterol in serum were reduced by only 33%. Clearly, ileal bypass is less effective in that disorder than is combined drug therapy. A significant number of patients develop diarrhea, which may be difficult to control, and if the procedure is not performed correctly there may be steatorrhea. Absorption of vitamin B_{12} is impaired in all patients, and this necessitates lifelong parenteral administration of the vitamin.

In some patients with homozygous familial hypercholesterolemia, end-to-side portacaval shunts have ameliorated but not normalized LDL levels. Liver transplantation results in dramatic reduction in plasma LDL levels in these patients.

REFERENCES

Relationship of Coronary Heart Disease to Disorders of Lipoprotein Metabolism
Castelli WP: Epidemiology of coronary heart disease: The Framingham Study. Am J Med 1984;76(Suppl 2A):4.
Kane JP: High density lipoproteins. In: *Lipoproteins and Coronary Artery Disease.* Kreisberg RA, Segrest J (editors). Blackwell, 1993.
Fuster VL et al: The pathogenesis of coronary artery disease and the acute coronary syndromes. (Two parts.) N Engl J Med 1992;326:242, 310.
Parthasarathy S, Steinberg D, Witztum JL: The role of oxidized low-density lipoproteins in the pathogenesis of atherosclerosis. Annu Rev Med 1992;43:219.
Ross R: The pathogenesis of atherosclerosis: An update. N Engl J Med 1986;314:488.

Schwartz CJ et al: The pathogenesis of atherosclerosis: An overview. Clin Cardiol 1991;14(2 Suppl 1):I–1.

Lipoprotein Metabolism
Brunzell JD: Familial lipoprotein lipase deficiency and other causes of the chylomicronemia syndrome. In: *The Metabolic Basis of Inherited Disease,* 6th ed. Scriver CR et al (editors). McGraw-Hill, 1989.
Kane JP, Havel RJ: Introduction: Structure and metabolism of plasma lipoproteins. In: *The Metabolic Basis of Inherited Disease,* 6th ed. Scriver CR et al (editors). McGraw-Hill, 1989.

Primary Disorders of Lipoprotein Metabolism
Brown MS, Goldstein JL: Familial hypercholesterolemia. In: *The Metabolic Basis of Inherited Disease,* 6th ed. Scriver CR et al (editors). McGraw-Hill, 1989.

Havel RJ, Goldstein JL, Brown MS: Lipoproteins and lipid transport. In: *Metabolic Control and Disease,* 8th ed. Bondy PK, Rosenberg LE (editors). Saunders, 1980.

Mahley RW, Rall SC Jr: Type III hyperlipoproteinemia (dysbetalipoproteinemia): The role of apolipoprotein E in normal and abnormal lipoprotein metabolism. In: *The Metabolic Basis of Inherited Disease,* 6th ed. Scriver CR et al (editors). McGraw-Hill, 1989.

Treatment of Hyperlipidemia with Diet

Connor WE, Connor SL: The dietary treatment of hyperlipidemia: Rationale, technique, and efficacy. Med Clin North Am 1982;66:485.

Treatment of Hyperlipidemia with Drugs

Jacobs D et al: Report of conference on low blood cholesterol: Mortality associations. Circulation 1992; 86:1046.

Summary of the Second Report on the National Cholesterol Education Program (NCEP) Expert Panel on Detection, Evaluation, and Treatment of High Blood Cholesterol in Adults (Adult Treatment Panel II). Arch Intern Med 1992;152:1490.

Kane JP, Malloy MJ: Treatment of hyperlipidemia. Ann Rev Med 1990;41:471.

Malloy MJ: Disorders of lipoprotein metabolism. In: *Practical Pediatric Therapy,* 3rd ed. Eichenwald HF, Stroder J (editors). Mosby, 1993.

Malloy MJ et al: Complementarity of colestipol, niacin, and lovastatin in treatment of severe familial hypercholesterolemia. Ann Intern Med 1987;107:616.

Neaton JD, et al: Serum cholesterol level and mortality findings for men screened in the Multiple Risk Factors Intervention Trial. Arch Intern Med 1992;152:1490.

Regression of Coronary Artery Disease

Brown G et al: Regression of coronary artery disease as a result of intensive lipid-lowering therapy in men with high levels of apolipoprotein B. N Engl J Med 1990; 323:1289.

Cashin-Hemphill J et al: Beneficial effects of colestipol-niacin on coronary atherosclerosis. A 4-year follow-up. JAMA 1990;264:3013.

Kane JP et al: Regression of coronary atherosclerosis during treatment of familial hypercholesterolemia with combined drug regimens. JAMA 1990;264:3007.

Obesity 18

George A. Bray, MD

Several models can be used to help explain the problem of obesity: behavioral models focus on psychologic variables; metabolic models deal with genetic control of enzymes for metabolism; and set-point models deal with the physiologic aspects of energy expenditure. This chapter will present a nutrient balance model. In this model, obesity is viewed as a disturbance in the normal feedback system for maintaining nutrient balance and nutrient stores. This nutrient balance model will emphasize the role of the autonomic nervous system (autonomic hypotheses) and the endocrine system (endocrine hypothesis) in nutrient regulation. In the adult of normal weight, nearly 150,000 kcal of energy are stored in the triacylglycerols (triglycerides) of adipose tissue, 24,000 kcal in the peptide bonds and amino acids of protein, and barely 1000 kcal in glucose and glycogen. Obesity can be viewed as a failure of nutrient balance resulting from a failure to balance the intake of nutrients in relation to the daily need for nutrients to stoke the metabolic furnace.

THE NUTRIENT BALANCE OR HOMEOSTATIC MODEL

A regulated, homeostatic, or controlled system has several components: a controller located in the brain (Figure 18–1); a control system consisting of the intake, digestion, absorption, storage, and metabolism of the nutrients in food; feedback signals that tell the controller about the state of the controlled system; and efferent control mechanisms that modulate food intake and energy expenditure.

1. THE CONTROLLED SYSTEM

The 150,000 kcal of energy contained in body fat of the normal adult human being is about six times the quantity of energy stored as protein (24,000 kcal). By comparison, the quantity of carbohydrate is minute. An individual eating 2000 kcal of which 40% is carbohydrate will take in an amount of carbohydrate each day comparable to the total body store. In contrast, average daily protein intake is only a little over 1% of total stores, and fat intake is considerably less than 1% (Figure 18–2). It should not be surprising, therefore, that in studies of nutrient balance in experimental animals, changes in carbohydrate balance from day to day reciprocally affected carbohydrate intake on the subsequent day. Thus, if carbohydrate balance is positive—ie, if the animal ate more carbohydrate than it oxidized—the animal would eat less carbohydrate tomorrow. For fat balance, on the other hand, the day-to-day relationship between fat balance and fat intake is very weak.

There are two major pathways for absorption of digested food from the gut. One is through the lacteals, which transport triacylglycerols packaged by the intestinal cells into chylomicrons. These chylomicrons enter the venous circulation and are cleared in the periphery by hydrolysis of triacylglycerol catalyzed by the enzyme lipoprotein lipase (LPL). The fatty acids released by LPL enter the fat cell (Figure 18–3), where they are esterified with glycerol-3-phosphate to form triacylglycerols. The activity of LPL and the entry of glucose into the fat cell to form glycerol-3-phosphate are both increased by insulin. Hydrolysis of the stored triacylglycerol is activated by a variety of hormones of which norepinephrine is the most important. Norepinephrine interacting with the beta-adrenergic receptor (R_β) activates adenylyl cyclase, which forms cAMP. The cAMP in turn activates protein kinase A, which activates hormone-sensitive lipase, the rate-limiting step in the lipolysis of triacylglycerol to release free fatty acids and glycerol from the fat cell (Figure 18–3). (See Chapter 17.)

A second pathway for absorption of nutrients across the intestinal tract involves facilitated or active transport of glucose and amino acids as well as short-chain fatty acids. On the mucosal side of the intestine, these nutrients enter the portal vein and go directly to the liver. The nutrients that enter the controlled system can be stored, converted to heat through metabolism, or used for work. In addition, small quantities of energy are excreted in the urine as urea and uric acid, the end-products of metabolism of amino acids and nucleic acids.

The resting metabolic rate (RMR) of human beings is directly related to the amount of fat-free or lean body mass. In addition to the variability due to body composition, RMR also has an important famil-

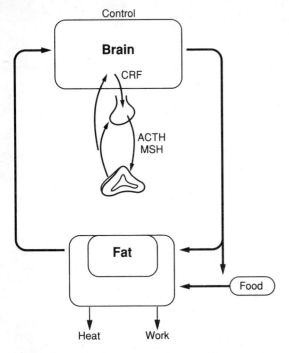

Figure 18–1. Diagram of a controlled system. The controller for food intake is located in the brain, which receives afferent signals from the periphery and integrates them into efferent controls that modulate food intake and the controlled system of nutrient intake storage and oxidation. The critical role of the adrenal steroids is indicated by the feedback between brain/pituitary and adrenal gland.

ial component, with some families having a higher RMR than others. Physical work accounts for approximately one-third of the energy expended. That body weight and energy stores are well regulated over short intervals of time in most individuals has been suggested in a number of studies. For most adults, the change in weight from year to year is less than 1–2% per year.

An analysis of this regulatory control system suggests the following concepts:

(1) Each major nutrient may be regulated separately.

(2) The time required to achieve balance for each nutrient varies as a function of the amount ingested each day in relation to the total body stores of that macronutrient. Thus, becoming obese by eating a high-carbohydrate diet would appear to be more difficult than when eating a high-fat diet, because the body storage system for carbohydrate as glycogen is limited. Although excess carbohydrate can be converted to fatty acids, this is an energy-expensive transformation. Body fat stores, on the other hand, are many times larger than daily fat intake, implying a much greater capacity for fat storage and a much longer time to achieve balance.

(3) Achievement of nutrient balance requires that the net oxidation of each macronutrient must equal the average composition of the macronutrients in the diet—ie, ingestion of a high-fat diet requires greater oxidation of fat than when equilibrium is achieved eating a low-fat diet. Thus, for a change in energy stores (ΔE) to equal zero, fat intake must equal fat

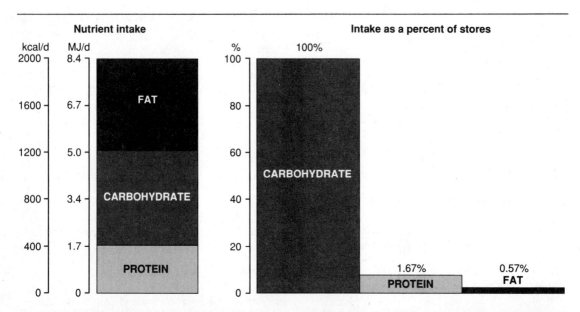

Figure 18–2. Relationship of macronutrient intake to body stores of that macronutrient. A diet containing 40% fat, 40% carbohydrate, and 20% protein in terms of energy content is shown on the left. The relationship of each of these components to the body stores of the corresponding nutrient is shown on the left side as a percentage of nutrient stores.

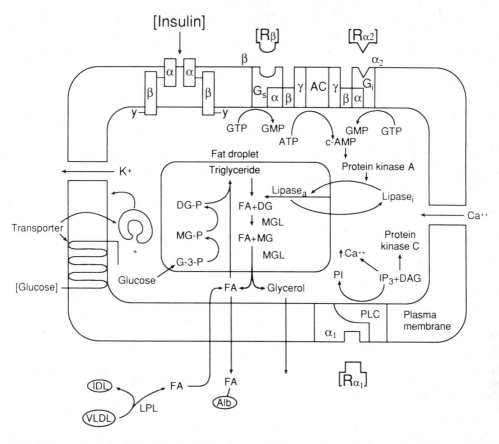

Figure 18–3. Diagram of a fat cell. The biochemical pathways for lipogenesis are shown on the left-hand side, and the pathways for lipolysis are shown on the right.

oxidation; carbohydrate intake must equal carbohydrate oxidation; and protein intake must equal protein oxidation.

(4) Individuals exhibit great differences in ability to rapidly increase the oxidation of fat after beginning a high-fat diet. Much of this difference appears to be genetic.

(5) Because physical training can increase oxidation of fatty acids by muscle, regular aerobic exercise might reduce the tendency to become obese or help maintain lower body weight after losing weight.

(6) The regulation of nutrient stores is subject to positive and negative feedback signals for each component that operates through the central controller.

Nutrient composition of the diet plays a variable role in the development of obesity in humans and animals. At one extreme are the types of obesity due simply to hyperphagia or excess food intake. In these cases, obesity may develop whether the diet is composed primarily of carbohydrates (vegetables, fruits), protein (meat or vegetable protein), or fats. In these instances, genetic factors probably play an important role, since experimental animals with a recessively inherited tendency to obesity develop obesity regardless of the composition of the diet. At the other extreme are those types of obesity in which dietary composition is central to the development of obesity. These include a high-fat diet, access to beverages or solutions containing sucrose, or other soluble carbohydrates and diets with an abundance of highly palatable foods. Any of these types of dietary obesity can be controlled by changing diets or by restraint in the intake of food.

AFFERENT FEEDBACK SIGNALS

The brain receives information about the status of nutrient balance from several sources. Afferent signals can be transmitted over the somatic sensory nervous system, via the autonomic nervous system, or through blood-borne signals.

Sensory Signals

Sight and smell of food are important signals for identifying potential environmental sources of food and for initiating food intake. Along with the texture and taste of food in the mouth, the olfactory and sensory cues about the quality of the food can serve as positive feedback signals for initiating food ingestion as well as negative feedback signals which eventually slow down, terminate, or abort an eating incident. The ability of most animals to avoid foods that have previously made them sick—a phenomenon known as bait-shyness—is an example of these afferent sensory signals integrated with a central learning system.

Gastrointestinal Signals

Information about the presence of food or nutrients in the gastrointestinal tract can be initiated by one of three mechanisms: gastrointestinal distention, release of gastrointestinal hormones when nutrients act directly on the gastrointestinal tract, and the effects of absorbed nutrients. Both gastric and intestinal distention can terminate meals by negative feedback signals relayed via the autonomic nervous system. The vagus nerve is probably the principal afferent sensory relay for this type of information, though the afferent sympathetic nervous system may also be involved.

Several gastrointestinal hormones have been implicated in the inhibition of feeding. The most prominent of these is cholecystokinin (CCK). It has been demonstrated that intraperitoneal injections of CCK decrease food intake in hungry rats, sheep, and humans as well as inhibiting sham feeding in rats and monkeys. The sequence of events associated with a response to CCK is similar to that of spontaneous postprandial satiety. CCK may terminate eating by acting on antral CCK receptors (CCK-A receptors) in the pylorus that constrict the pylorus and increase gastric distention. Peripheral information generated in this way by CCK may be important in producing satiety, since vagotomy and lesions to the central vagal connections of the vagus in the nucleus of the tractus solitarius will block the effect of CCK.

Cholecystokinin also acts within the central nervous system itself. It is released in the hypothalamus during a meal. In addition, injection of CCK into the lateral ventricle, the ventromedial hypothalamus, and the paraventricular nucleus have been reported to reduce food intake through CCK-B receptors specific to these areas. It has been suggested that the CCK-B receptors in the brain are more important for the central effects of CCK. The CCK-A receptors, on the other hand, appear to be the primary receptors involved when CCK produces satiety. Other peptides such as bombesin, enterostatin, the N-terminal pentapeptide from procolipase produced in the gastrointestinal tract, and glucagon may also be physiologically important signals that inhibit feeding. (See Chapter 14.)

Nutrient Signals.

Nutrient signals may also act on the liver or brain to induce satiety. Glucose injected into the portal circulation decreases the vagal afferent firing rate, probably by an action on hepatic glucose receptors. Glucose may also act directly on the central nervous system, since this nutrient is the major source of fuel for the system. It has been demonstrated that glucose regulates the binding of appetite-suppressing drugs such as amphetamine to the sodium pump in the hypothalamus, and that this effect is modulated by the intake of glucose. Glucose has also been shown to increase the activity of the peripheral sympathetic nervous system, which in turn may induce satiety.

Fatty acids and their metabolites may also serve as afferent signals to modulate food intake. Injection of 3-hydroxybutyrate, a metabolite of long-chain free fatty acids (FFAs), changes the electrical potential in the liver—an action that may contribute to the satiety induced by this metabolite. Increased fatty acid oxidation by the liver is also associated with a decrease in food intake. This effect, like the peripheral effect of CCK, appears to be transmitted to the central nervous system by the vagus nerve, since vagotomy blocks the inhibition of food intake.

Lactate is a potentially interesting metabolite for modulation of food intake. Injections of lactate decrease food intake. Lactate is a primary product of glucose metabolism by fat cells and might serve as a metabolic signal from this tissue. Tumors frequently produce a decrease in food intake and may also produce considerable amounts of lactate, which might be anorectic. Finally, metformin and phenformin, two oral agents for treatment of diabetes, increase lactate levels. When compared with sulfonylurea-like drugs, phenformin was more effective at reducing body weight. This might be related to the fact that it increases lactate concentration.

THE CONTROLLER

Anatomy

Several anatomic regions of the brain appear to play an important role in the control of nutrient balance. Figure 18–4 is a representation of the hypothalamic nuclei with projections to the pituitary gland. Destruction of the ventromedial hypothalamus is associated with hyperphagia and obesity in most homeothermic species that have been studied. On the other hand, destruction of the lateral hypothalamus is associated with a decrease in food intake and a reduction in body fat. The paraventricular nucleus is particularly important in the control of feeding. Food intake increases following topical injection into the paraventral nucleus. This effect is mediated through α_2-adrenergic receptors.

Neurotransmitters.

The neurotransmitters involved with regulation can be divided into three groups: (1) the fast-acting amino acids, which modulate ion channels; (2) the

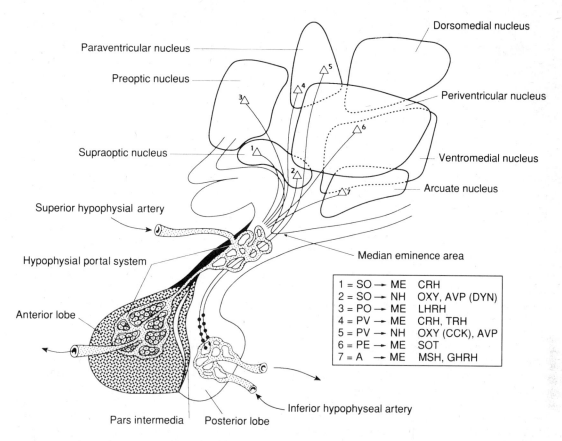

Paraventricular nucleus

Preoptic nucleus

Supraoptic nucleus

Superior hypophysial artery

Hypophysial portal system

Anterior lobe

Pars intermedia   Posterior lobe

Dorsomedial nucleus

Periventricular nucleus

Ventromedial nucleus

Arcuate nucleus

Median eminence area

Inferior hypophyseal artery

1 = SO → ME	CRH
2 = SO → NH	OXY, AVP (DYN)
3 = PO → ME	LHRH
4 = PV → ME	CRH, TRH
5 = PV → NH	OXY (CCK), AVP
6 = PE → ME	SOT
7 = A → ME	MSH, GHRH

Figure 18–4. Diagram showing the anatomic location of the hypothalamic nuclei. Damage to the ventromedial or paraventricular nucleus will produce obesity. Damage to the more lateral hypothalamus produces weight loss and anorexia. (SO, supraoptic nucleus; ME, median eminence; NH, neurohypophysis; PO, preoptic nucleus; PV, paraventricular nucleus; A, arcuate nucleus; CRH, corticotropin-releasing hormone; OXY, oxytocin; AVP, arginine vasopressin; DYN, dynorphin; LHRH, luteotropin-releasing hormone; TRH, thyrotropin-releasing hormone; CCK, cholecystokinin; SOT, serotonin; MSH, melanocyte-stimulating hormone; GHRH, growth hormone-releasing hormone.) (Reproduced, with permission, from McGeer PL, Eccles JC, McGeer EG: *Molecular Neurobiology of the Mammalian Brain,* 2nd ed. Plenum Press, 1987.)

monoamines, which act more slowly through second messengers;and (3) the peptides, which may modulate monamines and affect intake of specific nutrients. Gamma-aminobutyric acid (GABA) is one of the fast-acting neurotransmitters that can increase or decrease food intake depending on where it is injected. In addition to GABA, there are a number of slow-acting neurotransmitters which are modulate feeding behavior, including norepinephrine, serotonin, and histamine. Serotonin is derived from the dietary amino acid tryptophan. Increasing extraneuronal concentrations of serotonin by any of several methods decreases food intake. Norepinephrine can either decrease food intake by activating beta receptors in the periforniceal area or increase food intake by acting on α_2-adrenergic receptors in the paraventricular or ventromedial nucleus. The tonic level of adrenergic receptor activation in the hypothalamus could account for differences in body stores. Increas-

ing the tonic activity of beta-adrenergic receptors or decreasing the tonic activity of α_2-adrenergic stimulation (or both maneuvers) would tend to lower food intake in the hypothalamus. Histamine is the third monoamine that affects food intake. Activation of H_1 histamine receptors in the ventromedial hypothalamus reduces food intake.

Several peptides also modulate food intake (Table 18–1). The concentration of peptides in brain is about 0.1–1% that of the monoamines (pg/g versus ng/g). Neuropeptide Y, beta-endorphin, dynorphin, growth hormone-releasing hormone, somatostatin, and galanin all stimulate food intake when injected into the third ventricle or the ventromedial or paraventricular nucleus. A variety of other peptides, including bombesin, cholecystokinin, enterostatin, anorectin, calcitonin (calcitonin gene-related peptide), neurotensin, and corticotropin-releasing hormone, inhibit feeding when injected topically into the region of the

Table 18–1. Peptides that stimulate or suppress feeding.

Increase Food Intake	Decrease Food Intake
Dynorphin	Anorectin
β-Endorphin	Bombesin
Galanin	Calcitonin
Growth hormone-releasing hormone (low dose)	Cholecystokinin
	Corticotropin-releasing hormone
Neuropeptide Y	Cyclo-His-Pro
Somatostatin (low dose)	Enterostatin
	Glucagon
	Insulin
	Neurotensin
	Oxytocin
	Thyrotropin-releasing hormone
	Vasopressin

Table 18–2. Peptides and monoamines affecting specific nutrient appetites.

Nutrient	Increase	Decrease
Fat	Galanin Opioids	Serotonin Enterostatin Vasopressin Corticotropin-releasing hormone Cyclo-His-Pro
Carbohydrate	Norepinephrine Neuropeptide Y	Cholecystokinin
Protein	Growth hormone-releasing hormone	Glucagon
Sodium chloride	Angiotensin	

ventromedial nucleus or when infused into the third ventricle.

One hypothesis put forward to explain the role of neuropeptides in modulation of food intake is their effects on specific types of eating. Thus, neuropeptide Y injected into the paraventricular nucleus preferentially increases carbohydrate intake. Corticotropin-releasing hormone may be an important modulator of stress-related eating and specifically suppresses fat intake and to some extent carbohydrate intake. The infusion of insulin into the third ventricle will suppress food intake in animals eating a high carbohydrate diet but not in animals eating a low-carbohydrate (high-fat) diet. Enterostatin, an activation pentapeptide from pancreatic procolipase, specifically reduces fat intake whether the peptide is injected peripherally or into the central nervous system. These examples suggest that the way in which these peptides act is to modulate specific components of the homeostatic system dealing with individual nutrients and their "appetites." This model or hypothesis can be called the peptide-specific nutrient balance model of eating.

Sensory-specific satiety is a phenomenon whereby subjects offered a choice of preferred foods, including a food which has just been eaten, will chose a new food that they have not eaten. The nutrient-specific effect of peptides could provide the molecular basis for this phenomenon of sensory-specific satiety. Table 18–2 lists the peptides and monoamines that affect specific appetites.

EFFERENT CONTROLS

The efferent controls include the motor activities involved in identifying, obtaining, and ingesting food as well as the efferent effects produced by the autonomic nervous system and several circulating hormones. The complex sequence of motor activities that leads to the initiation of food-seeking behavior, the identification of food, and the killing or gathering and ingestion of food is integrated in the lateral hypothalamus, since electrical stimulation in this area will lead to food-seeking and ingestive behavior. Further discussion of this system is beyond the scope of this review.

Autonomic Nervous System

Both the sympathetic and the parasympathetic nervous systems may be involved in the development of obesity. In animals, in which obesity follows hypothalamic lesions, there is evidence for increased activity of the efferent parasympathetic nervous system (vagus nerve). This observation may provide part of the explanation of the increase in insulin secretion that characterizes hypothalamic obesity.

Reduction in sympathetic activity is also characteristic of obesity and may participate in enhanced insulin secretion. In the experimental animal, there is an inverse relationship between the activity of the sympathetic nervous system and food intake. In spontaneously feeding rats, there is a negative correlation throughout the 24 hours between basal activity of the sympathetic nervous system and spontaneous food intake. In addition, almost all of the experimental maneuvers that increase food intake, such as creation of lesions in the ventromedial hypothalamus, decrease sympathetic nervous system (Table 18–3), and the same is true of genetic obesity. Conversely, those maneuvers that decrease food intake, such as creation of lateral hypothalamic lesions or injection of fenfluramine (an appetite suppressant drug), increase sympathetic activity. This relationship between food intake and the efferent sympathetic nervous system can be integrated with the earlier discussion of hypothalamic monoamines as shown in Figure 18–5. Food intake is initiated centrally, perhaps by a transient drop in circulating glucose levels. In anticipation of food intake, vagal activity increases, producing an early phase of insulin release from the pancreas. As food enters the stomach and intestine, its digestion signals a further rise in insulin secretion and an increase in peripheral efferent sym-

Table 18–3. Relationship of food intake and sympathetic activity.

	Food Intake	Sympathetic Activity
Lesion		
Ventromedial nucleus	↑	↓
Luteotropic hormone	↓	↑
Peptides		
Neuropeptide Y	↑	↓
β-Endorphin	↑	↓
Cholecystokinin	↓	↑
Corticotropin-releasing hormone	↓	↑
Glucagon	↓	↑
Fibroblast growth factor α	↓	↑
Interleukin-2	↓	↑
Neurotensin	↓	↑
Thyrotropin-releasing hormone	↓	↑
Vasopressin	↓	↑
Drugs and neurotransmitters		
Norepinephrine	↑	↓
Serotonin	↓	↑
Amphetamine	↓	↑
Fenfluramine	↓	↑
2-Deoxyglucose	↑	↓
4-Butene-L-oxide	↓	↑

pathetic activity that activates β_3-adrenergic receptors and their thermogenic responses. Beta$_3$ receptors can also mediate satiety. This effect of the sympathetic nervous system may be part of an efferent satiety system. It is proposed that in animals and in humans as well, ingestion of a meal enhances sympathetic efferent output. This increased sympathetic activity initiated by food intake may in turn serve as one of the inhibitory factors in feeding and act as part of the satiety system.

Efferent Hormonal Mechanisms

A. Insulin: Increased levels of insulin are a common characteristic of obesity. Injections of insulin can increase food intake, especially intake of glucose, probably by lowering glucose concentrations. The increased food intake following insulin injections also produces mild degrees of obesity. Injections of 2-deoxy-D-glucose, an analogue of glucose, stimulates food intake by inhibiting intracellular glucose metabolism and producing glucose deprivation. Insulin has been proposed as a signal to the brain about the quantity of peripheral fat stores. One major problem with this hypothesis is that insulin levels fall rapidly following caloric restriction and long before there are significant changes in the quantity of body fat. Moreover, there are some experimental types of obesity which occur with little or no rise in the concentration of insulin. There are two other interpretations of the hyperinsulinemia of obesity. First, the rise in insulin may be a reflection of high levels of nutrient intake. Since insulin is essential for nutrient storage, increased flux of nutrients would be expected to increase insulin production. Second, hyper-

insulinemia may reflect actual or apparent hypothalamic resistance to the action of insulin. In this case, increased insulin secretion would be modulated by changes in the function of the autonomic nervous system resulting from resistance to the action of insulin in the central nervous system.

B. Adrenal Steroids: The development or progression of experimental obesity is either reversed or attenuated by adrenalectomy. In clinical medicine, Addison's disease with adrenal insufficiency is associated with leanness, whereas Cushing's syndrome with high levels of adrenal steroid secretion is associated with obesity. The fact that almost all defects in genetically obese animals are reversed by adrenalectomy and that clinical changes in adrenal status can produce leanness or obesity suggests that glucocorticoids play a key role in the development and maintenance of the obese state.

SUMMARY

Obesity can be most easily conceptualized as a problem of defective control of normal nutrient feedback systems. This homeostatic approach is used as the basis for considering the importance of individual nutrients and the elements of the control system. The diet normally consists of about 50% carbohydrate, 35% fat, and 15% protein. Relative to body stores, the amount of carbohydrate eaten each day is very large and nearly equivalent to what is stored as glycogen, whereas the stores of fat and protein are greatly in excess of the daily intake of these macronutrients. Experimental studies suggest that the control of body fat content is more stable on a high-carbohydrate diet than on a high-fat diet. Moreover maintaining energy balance requires that the average daily intake of carbohydrate and fat must be the same as the mix of carbohydrate and fat, which are used as fuels by the body. Regular physical exercise enhances the oxidation of fat and may in that way play a role in maintaining lower body fat stores. Although increasing body fat is observed when most animals and probably humans eat a high-fat diet, this is not always the case. There must, therefore, be mechanisms by which the rate of fat oxidation can be increased in the face of a high-fat diet. Information about the intake of nutrients and about body nutrient stores is relayed to the brain by afferent signals. These signals can be the nutrients themselves, hormones released by interactions of nutrients with the gut, or the effects of food and its nutrients on neural messages to the brain. From this wealth of afferent information, the brain must sort out the relevant signals and make decisions about food intake. These processes are primarily integrated in the hypothalamus and hippocampus. Several neurotransmitters are involved in this intraneural signaling, including gamma-aminobutyric acid, norepinephrine, sero-

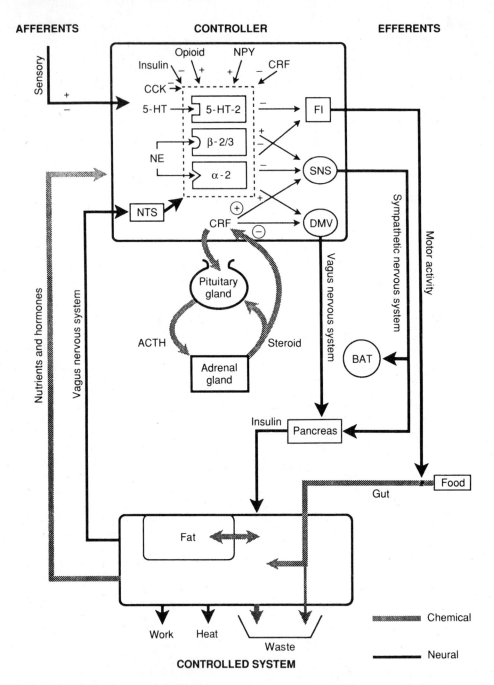

Figure 18–5. A detailed diagram of the controlled system for food intake. Both stimulatory (+) and inhibitory (−) signals are generated and fed to the brain through the sensory system, through circulating nutrients and hormones, or through the vagus and the sympathetic afferent nervous system. All of this information is integrated in the controller, where serotonin (5-HT), the beta-adrenergic system, and the alpha-adrenergic system are particularly important. A number of peptides also modulate feeding. The transduced signals control motor activity for food selection as well as the sympathetic and parasympathetic (vagus) nervous system. These efferent systems in turn modulate the control of food intake and the metabolism within the controlled system. (5-HT, serotonin; NE, norepinephrine; CCK, cholecystokinin; NPY, neuropeptide Y; CRF, corticotropin-releasing factor (hormone); NTS, nucleus of the tractus solitarius; FI, food ingestion; SNS, sympathetic nervous system; DMV, dorsomotor vagal nucleus; BAT, brown adipose tissue.)

tonin, and several peptides. The various peptides used in this process may act to modulate specific types of food intake. Thus, neuropeptide Y stimulates carbohydrate intake, and enterostatin decreases fat intake. Once the brain has made a decision, efferent processes are turned on. The animal or human can search for food or stop eating. When food is ingested, both the autonomic nervous system and the endocrine system are involved in partitioning this intake into body stores. High levels of sympathetic activity are associated with lower levels of body fat. Absence of adrenal glucocorticoid hormones is also associated with lower levels of body fat. On the other hand, high levels of insulin are associated with higher levels of body fat. From this homeostatic model, it is possible to understand the mechanisms involved in the development of obesity and to consider approaches to its treatment.

REFERENCES

Bogardus C et al: Familial dependence of the resting metabolic rate. N Engl J Med 1986;315:96.

Boosalis MG et al: Cholecystokinin and satiety: Effect of hypothalamic obesity and gastric bubble insertion. Am J Physiol 1992;262:R241.

Bray G, York D, Fisler J: Experimental obesity: A homeostatic failure due to defective nutrient stimulation of the sympathetic nervous system. Vitam Horm 1989; 45:1.

Bray GA: Obesity, a disorder of nutrient partitioning: The Mona Lisa hypothesis. J Nutr 1991;121:1146.

Bray GA: Obesity: A disease of nutrient or energy balance. Nutr Rev 1987;45:33.

Bray GA: Peptides affect the intake of specific nutrients and the sympathetic nervous system. Am J Clin Nutr 1992;55:265S.

Campfield LA, Brandon P, Smith FJ: On-line continuous measurement of blood glucose and meal pattern in free-feeding rats: The role of glucose in meal initiation. Brain Res Bull 1985;14:605.

Flatt JP: Assessment of daily and cumulative carbohydrate and fat balances in mice (technical note). J Nutr Bioc 1991;2(4):193.

Gibbs J et al: Bombesin suppresses feeding in rats. Nature 1979;282:208.

Hauger R et al: Glucose regulates (^{3}H)(+)-amphetamine binding and Na^+-K^+ ATPase activity in the hypothalamus: A proposed mechanism for the glucostatic control of feeding and satiety. Brain Res Bull 1986;16:281.

Morley J: Neuropeptide regulation of appetite and weight. Endocr Rev 1987;8:256.

Okada S et al: Enterostatin (Val-Pro-Asp-Pro-Arg), the activation peptide of procolipase, selectively reduces fat intake. Physiol Behav 1991;49:1185.

Ravussin E et al: Determinants of 24-hour energy expenditure in man: methods and results using a respiratory chamber. J Clin Invest 1986;78:566.

Rolls BJ: Sensory-specific satiety. Nutr Rev 1986;44:93.

Scharrer E, Langhans W: Control of food intake by fatty acid oxidation. Am J Physiol 1986;250:R1003.

Hormones & Cancer

Christopher C. Benz, MD, & Brian J. Lewis, MD

HORMONAL EFFECTS ON TUMORS

GROWTH PROMOTION & MALIGNANT TRANSFORMATION

It would be logical to suppose that hormones which support normal growth might also promote tumorigenesis. However, although a great deal is known about endocrine factors regulating normal pre- and postnatal growth, very little from that body of information can be applied to our current understanding of tumorigenesis. Growth hormone (GH), thyroid hormone, insulin, and sex and adrenal steroids have permissive roles in prenatal growth (see Chapter 3). Of these hormones, only the sex steroids are capable of directly stimulating tissue growth during the postnatal period, and these tropic responses are often augmented by the secondary release of polypeptide growth factors. Genetic rather than endocrine factors play the major role in determining body stature. Gigantism, for example, results from excessive secretion of GH by a pituitary tumor; however, the end-organ tropic responses to GH as well as the responses to thyroxine and insulin are mediated by a family of mitogenic growth factors called somatomedins (see Chapter 2). Specifically, somatomedins C and A (now known as insulin-like growth factors [IGF]-1 and -2) are polypeptides with structural homology to proinsulin, and their serum concentrations are regulated by hormones. Acting via membrane receptors, these somatomedins and other more recently identified growth factors directly stimulate growth and proliferation of both normal and neoplastic cells. Several of the better characterized growth factors of nonhematopoietic and nonlymphoid tissue origin are shown in Table 19–1; recent reviews on cellular growth factors and their relation to cellular oncogenes are also provided in the reference list that accompanies this chapter.

In brief, many human tumors appear to produce, perhaps constitutively, mitogenic polypeptides that are called cellular or transforming growth factors (TGF). In addition, tumor cells synthesize mem-

ACRONYMS USED IN THIS CHAPTER	
ACTH	Adrenocorticotropic hormone
APUD	Amine precursor uptake and decarboxylation
CCK	Cholecystokinin
CMF	Cyclophosphamide, methotrexate, fluorouracil
DES	Diethylstilbestrol
DNA	Deoxyribonucleic acid
EGF	Epidermal growth factor
ER	Estrogen receptor
FGF	Fibroblast growth factor
FSH	Follicle-stimulating hormone
GH	Growth hormone
GnRH	Gonadotropin-releasing hormone
hCG	Human chorionic gonadotropin
IGF-1	Insulin-like growth factor-1 (somatomedin C)
IGF-2	Insulin-like growth factor-2 (somatomedin A)
LH	Luteinizing hormone
LTR	Long terminal repeat (segments)
MMTV	Murine mammary tumor virus
NGF	Nerve growth factor
PDGF	Platelet-derived growth factor
PgR	Progesterone receptor
PRL	Prolactin
PSA	Prostate-specific antigen
SIADH	Syndrome of inappropriate secretion of vasopressin (antidiuretic hormone)
TGFα	Transforming growth factor α
TGFβ	Transforming growth factor β
TSH	Thyroid-stimulating hormone (thyrotropin)
VIP	Vasoactive intestinal polypeptide

brane-binding proteins for these same growth factors, and these growth factor receptors commonly possess protein kinase activity that transduces the mitogenic signal from cytoplasm to nucleus. Many of these growth factors and receptors are encoded by DNA sequences that are homologous or identical to normal proto-oncogene sequences (eg, c-*sis* and PDGF beta chain, c-*int*-2 and basic FGF; also, c-*erb* B-1 and EGF receptor, c-*src* and IGF-1 receptor), illustrating the structural relationship that commonly exists between cellular growth-promoting mechanisms and oncogene products (Table 19–1). Proto-oncogenes

Table 19–1. Growth factors and receptors potentially involved in the autocrine and paracrine regulation of human tumor growth.

Growth Factor [and Homologous Oncogene]	Tissue Source of Factor	Receptor [and Homologous Oncogene] Expressed by Normal Target
EGF	Submaxillary gland, Brunner's glands	170-kDa tyrosine kinase [c-erb B-1] on epithelial and mesenchymal cells
TGFα	Transformed cells, placenta, embryos	Cross-reacts with EGF receptor on same cells
TGFβ	Platelets, kidney, placenta	615-kDa tyrosine kinase on epithelial, epidermal, and mesenchymal cells
PDGF [c-sis with beta chain]	Platelets, endothelial cells, placenta	185-kDa tyrosine kinase on smooth muscle, mesenchymal cells, and placenta
IGF-1 (somatomedin C)	Liver, smooth muscle, other cells	450-kDa tyrosine kinase (c-ros and c-src with beta chain) on epithelial and mesenchymal cells
IGF-2 (somatomedin A)	Fetal liver, placenta	250-kDa glycoprotein on epithelial and mesenchymal cells
FGF [int-2 with basic form]	Brain, pituitary, kidney, cartilage	Possible intracellular receptor in endothelial and mesenchymal cells
NGF	Submaxillary gland, keratinocytes	130-kDa protein kinase on sympathetic and sensory neurons, melanocytes

are cellular genes believed to have been captured and recombined into the transforming genes found in certain oncogenic retroviruses. Although as yet unproved, the intracellular activation of these proto-oncogenes is thought to account for the development and progression of a variety of human cancers. Carcinogenic mutation, chromosomal rearrangement, and gene amplification are several of the known genetic mechanisms that can activate normal proto-oncogenes.

Substantial evidence points to the fact that human cancers do not result from a single genetic event. Rather, stepwise genetic changes result in the activation of proto-oncogenes and the inactivation of so-called anti-oncogenes (or tumor suppressor genes), necessary for progression to the fully transformed malignant phenotype. Hormones probably contribute to this process, since many natural and synthetic steroids and steroid-like compounds are known to be carcinogenic. In particular, steroidal estrogens and xenobiotic stilbenes (eg, diethylstilbestrol) can produce DNA damage either directly, by the formation of mutagenic DNA adducts and strand breaks, or indirectly, by the generation of toxic host molecules and intracellular free radicals.

Specific studies have addressed the development of tumors occurring in hormonally regulated tissues. It is known that both chemical carcinogens (including steroidal and nonsteroidal estrogens) and the ge-

nomic integration of viral DNA can potentially induce tumorigenesis. Long-term or in utero exposure to exogenous estrogens is epidemiologically associated with an increased incidence of human uterine and breast carcinomas. It is also known that murine mammary cancers are commonly induced by the murine mammary tumor virus (MMTV), which is a weakly oncogenic type B retrovirus. The regional insertion of MMTV DNA activates genomic c-int-1 or c-int-2 proto-oncogenes, which are then constitutively expressed in mammary epithelium, leading to premalignant hyperplastic lesions and, finally, to infiltrating adenocarcinomas. Since there are closely linked steroid receptor-binding sequences within the integrated MMTV long terminal repeat (LTR) segment, this process of malignant transformation can be promoted by exposure to steroids. In transgenic animal experiments, fusion of the MMTV LTR promoter region to various oncogenes (including c-myc, v-Ha-ras, c-int-1 or c-int-2, and activated c-neu/erb B-2), and introduction of these fused constructs into viable eggs of female mice leads to breast tumors in otherwise normal mouse offspring. Despite widespread genomic incorporation of the transgene in all mouse tissues, only breast, salivary gland, and epididymal tissues express the incorporated oncogene, and essentially only breast adenocarcinomas occur over a time course and with an increased incidence that depends on the particular oncogene. To date, the most effective breast cancer-inducing construct is the MMTV/c-*neu* transgene, which encodes an activated EGF receptor-like molecule that has potent tyrosine kinase activity. These basic studies have provided important insights into the molecular mechanisms underlying hormone-dependent tumor promotion in humans. One notable finding is an apparent correlation between clinically aggressive disease and the amplification of c-*myc,* c-*int*-2, or c-*neu/erb* B-2 in a significant percentage of human breast tumors.

TUMOR GROWTH MEDIATED BY AUTOCRINE & PARACRINE FACTORS

During human growth and development as well as during normal tissue response to injury, proliferation and invasion of diploid cells is regulated by exogenous and endogenous cellular growth factors. In the absence of these mitogenic factors, normal cells will become reversibly arrested in G_1/G_0 phase, permitting normal expression of the differentiated phenotype. In the process of tumorigenesis, these growth factors become inappropriately or constitutively activated (or both), leading to the invasive and autonomous growth that characterizes malignancy. Ectopic expression of these growth factors may also account for a host of other tumor-related complications. Specific factors such as nerve growth factor (NGF), which are important for the maintenance and differentiation of some normal cells (eg, sensory and sympathetic neurons), may exert mitogenic effects on other related cells (eg, adrenal chromaffin cells). These effects may explain the selective expression of specific factors in certain types of malignant tumors (eg, pheochromocytomas, melanomas, and small-cell carcinomas). The concept that autonomous tumor growth can be driven by unregulated expression of locally produced and locally acting growth factors is exemplified by the mitogenic effect of NGF on cells derived from neural crest. Normal keratinocytes express mitogenic concentrations of NGF, which can stimulate local melanocytes or melanoma cells that possess NGF receptors to overexpress the growth-related oncogenes c-*myc* and c-*fos*. This potential model of tumorigenesis illustrates the functional relationship between growth factors and oncogenes that may exist in addition to the structural relationship described earlier.

There are now abundant in vitro and in vivo models showing growth factor production by a tumor that also possesses receptors for the same autostimulating factor (autocrine loop). Autocrine factors synthesized by some activated oncogenes (eg, c-*sis*) may not even be secreted extracellularly; rather, they may be simply bound to internally sequestered receptors that, when stimulated, result in malignant transformation. Possibly as important in tumorigenesis as the au-

tocrine loop is a more indirect process of autostimulation in which transformed cells recruit local normal cells of stromal or epithelial origin to secrete growth factors that stimulate the receptor-bearing malignant cells (paracrine loop). This paracrine interdependence between adjacent normal and malignant tissues may also explain a variety of commonly observed neoplastic phenomena, including site-specific metastases, fibroblast and endothelial chemotaxis and proliferation (leading to stromal reactivity and tumor neovascularity), local bone resorption or malignant hypercalcemia, and suppression of normal immune reactions seen with advancing malignancy.

Hormonal influences on tumor-promoting autocrine and paracrine loops have been well described in studies using cultured human breast cancer cell lines. For example, estrogen-induced growth stimulation of receptor-positive tumor cells actually occurs via rapid modulation of autocrine and paracrine growth factor release by estradiol. Estradiol enhances breast cancer cell production of autostimulating mitogens, such as TGFα, EGF, IGF-1, and IGF-2, and of paracrine factors, such as PDGF and FGFs. Additionally, estradiol can depress synthesis of the bifunctional growth factor TGFβ, which normally inhibits proliferation of breast cancer epithelial cells while paradoxically stimulating growth of mesenchymal cells. The net paracrine effect from PDGF, IGF-2, and TGFβ causes a rapid increase in fibroblast expression of several oncogenes (eg, c-*myc,* c-*fos,* c-*jun*) and the release of additional growth factors that can mitogenically stimulate breast cancer cells. Besides inducing a stromal proliferative response, these paracrine influences also stimulate fibroblasts to enzymatically alter the local composition of basement membrane and extracellular matrix, facilitating further invasion and growth by the malignant mammary epithelial cells.

STEROID-DEPENDENT TUMORS

The early studies of Bittner, Huggins, Furth, and others established the concept that sex steroids can cause or at least promote tumor growth. In general, the only cancers frequently promoted by sex steroids include those common tumors arising from breast (male and female), endometrial, and prostatic tissue (Table 19–2).

It may be generally true that endocrine dependency can develop as an associated trait of tumors derived from any tissue whose normal growth is stimulated by a hormone. Studies in fact have demonstrated associations between sex steroids (especially estrogens) and vaginal, ovarian, and laryngeal carcinomas as well as hepatomas. It has been suggested that sex steroids alone may play a pathogenic role in almost 30% of all cancer cases in the USA. Thyroid, testicular, and ovarian tumors oc-

Table 19–2. Endocrine-responsive tumors.

Primary treatment involves endocrine therapy
Breast carcinoma
Endometrial carcinoma
Prostatic carcinoma
Leukemia
Lymphoma
Tumor treatment may include endocrine therapy
Renal cell carcinoma
Thyroid carcinoma
Ovarian carcinoma
Pituitary adenoma
Tumor subsets may be endocrine-dependent
Vaginal carcinoma
Meningioma
Melanoma and apudoma
Gastrointestinal carcinoma
Sarcoma

cur in glands under the tropic influences of TSH, FSH, and LH and may also be putatively included in the list of endocrine-dependent cancers. With increasing epidemiologic data, it is likely that this list will increase. For example, the incidence of osteosarcoma closely parallels the different age-specific growth patterns of men and women, implicating pubertal hormonal changes in the etiology of this tumor. Meningiomas and thyroid and renal cell carcinomas show a marked discrepancy in male-female incidence (and prognosis), also suggesting tropic sex hormone influences on tumor growth.

In contrast to the tropic sex steroids, glucocorticoids are capable of cytolytic responses mediated by steroid-induced enzymatic pathways. Since the realization several decades ago that glucocorticoids could lyse human lymphoblasts, these steroids have been extensively employed in the treatment of leukemia and lymphoma.

TUMORS AFFECTING ENDOCRINE STATUS

Tumors that are not hormone-responsive (or amenable to endocrine therapy) may still affect endocrine status, and these tumor-induced endocrine effects are important for clinical diagnosis and management.

NONSECRETORY TUMORS

Nonsecretory primary or metastatic tumors may invade and replace normal glandular tissue and thereby cause loss of endocrine function. The most common syndrome in this category is hypopitu-

itarism due to pressure necrosis that occurs gradually during tumor growth or that occurs abruptly from tumor infarction and bleeding. Tumors such as breast cancer, leukemia, or lymphoma may be metastatic to the sella; may directly invade, as with a craniopharyngioma or hypothalamic glioma; or may originate from a primary adenoma in the anterior pituitary. Rarely, infarction of the posterior pituitary and the clinical development of diabetes insipidus may be the presenting sign of metastatic cancer. Adrenal insufficiency can also occur with metastatic infiltration of both glands by a variety of epithelial cancers (eg, lung cancer, breast cancer, melanoma). However, clinical evidence of adrenal insufficiency produced by metastatic infiltration is unusual relative to the high overall incidence of adrenal metastases found at autopsy. Although extensive pancreatic or ovarian replacement can occur with metastatic retroperitoneal tumor spread, diabetes mellitus or ovarian failure virtually never results. Ovarian failure may develop in association with a primary ovarian carcinoma that secretes steroid precursors which in turn inhibit pituitary gonadotropin production.

SECRETORY TUMORS

Several types of benign and malignant tumors secrete hormones or hormonelike substances. When these chemicals are produced ectopically or "inappropriately" (by a tumor arising in a tissue not normally associated with the hormone), the resulting paraneoplastic syndrome may provide a diagnostic clue or may signify recurrence of an otherwise undetectable lesion (see Chapter 20). For example, gynecomastia associated with an elevated titer of human chorionic gonadotropin (hCG) strongly suggests an underlying testicular carcinoma that can be cured with chemotherapy. "Appropriate" hormone production by secretory tumors arising within endocrine tissue may also produce symptoms leading to early tumor detection and cure, as is occasionally observed with insulinomas. On the other hand, endocrine symptoms from secretory tumors may develop in association with advanced disease and result in life-threatening or debilitating clinical complications. Palliation of symptoms of carcinoid or one of the other APUDomas (see Chapter 20) can actually become of greater clinical concern than controlling growth of the tumor itself. These secretory tumors are usually well differentiated and may occur in genetic patterns (eg, Klinefelter's syndrome associated with a breast or pituitary tumor) or in familial patterns involving multiple endocrine glands (eg, multiple endocrine neoplasia type I, IIa, or IIb; see Chapter 21). Table 19–3 lists the origin of commonly occurring secretory tumors and their associated secretory products.

Table 19–3. Secretory tumors of endocrine glands.

Tumor Origin	Secretory Product(s)
Anterior pituitary	GH, PRL, ACTH, TSH, FSH, LH
Adrenal Cortex	Aldosterone, glucocorticoids, androgens, estrogens (rare)
Medulla	Catecholamines
Kidney	Erythropoietin
Gonads Germ cell, trophoblast	hCG
Stroma	Estrogens, androgens, progestins
Pancreas and gut (APUD cells)	Serotonin, kallikrein, prostaglandins, somatostatin, gastrin, glucagon, insulin, VIP, CCK, vasopressin, ACTH, neurotensin
Parathyroids	Parathyroid hormone

Thyroid
  Parafollicular (medullary)
  cells
	Calcitonin

Follicular cells	Thyroglobulin T_3 and T_4 (rare)

TREATMENT-INDUCED ENDOCRINOPATHY

With the improved prognosis of patients with leukemia, lymphoma, stage II breast cancer, and germ cell neoplasms treated with irradiation and chemotherapy, there is a growing awareness of the long-term endocrine complications of treatment. The glands associated with treatment-induced endocrinopathy include the hypothalamus, pituitary, thyroid, parathyroids, and gonads. As shown in Table 19–4, local or regional effects from radiation therapy and the systemic effects of radiomimetic drugs (alkylating agents) produce the greatest clinical problems.

Brain & Pituitary

Children receiving cranial irradiation either to prevent leukemia of the central nervous system or to treat a curable brain tumor have blunted GH responses, impaired growth rates, and some impairment of intellectual function. Less commonly, they may have reduced secretion of TSH, ACTH, FSH, and LH. In adults, apart from the use of hormonal agents, antitumor therapy results in very few abnormalities in the hypothalamic-pituitary-neuroendocrine axis. Adjuvant chemotherapy for breast cancer has been reported to lower serum PRL levels, but the underlying mechanism is unclear. Vincristine and cyclophosphamide have both been associated with a syndrome of inappropriate secretion of vasopressin (antidiuretic hormone), or SIADH. While a direct ef-

fect on renal tubules is believed to be the cause of the antidiuresis that occurs with cyclophosphamide, vincristine may increase vasopressin release by disrupting microtubules within the neurohypophysis .

Thyroid

One-third of patients with cervical lymphomas or carcinomas of the pharynx or larynx treated with curative doses of radiation (which includes the thyroid) develop increased TSH levels, and most of these also develop decreased thyroxine levels. A few become clinically hypothyroid. Both low-dose and (less frequently) high-dose irradiation increase the incidence of thyroid carcinomas occurring 10 or more years after treatment (see Chapter 4).

Adrenals

Adrenal gland function appears resistant to the toxic effects of conventional doses of radiation or chemotherapy. However, prolonged busulfan administration for chronic granulocytic leukemia results in a clinical syndrome resembling adrenocortical insufficiency. Some investigators believe that pituitary secretion of ACTH—rather than adrenocortical function—is damaged by the drug. This mechanism could be similar to that resulting in impaired PRL secretion, mentioned above. Mitotane (a drug used to treat adrenocortical cancers) and aminoglutethimide (used to treat breast cancers) have as part of their desired therapeutic mechanisms the effect of suppressing steroid production and causing primary adrenocortical insufficiency (see Chapter 6).

Gonads

Perhaps the most frequently encountered endocrinopathy resulting from antitumor therapy is gonadal failure. Radiation therapy and chemotherapy can cause infertility in both men and women. In women, amenorrhea (or oligomenorrhea), dyspareunia, decreased libido, and hot flushes may follow either form of therapy. These symptoms are associated with reduced plasma estradiol and increased levels of FSH and LH. In fact, ovarian failure occurs so frequently after adjuvant chemotherapy for breast cancer that some have suggested that the effectiveness of adjuvant therapy results from "chemical oophorectomy." In younger women, there is a greater probability that gonadal function will return to normal. In men, azoospermia (or oligospermia) occurs in association with reduced testicular size, increased FSH, and (occasionally) gynecomastia. Leydig cells are much more resistant to toxic therapy, and serum testosterone levels therefore usually remain normal, although there may be evidence for partial Leydig cell failure compensated for by higher levels of LH. Depending on radiation or drug dosage, male gonadal function and fertility may recover. With the aggressive drug combinations used to cure lymphomas, however, gonadal recovery is unlikely, and men

Table 19–4. Treatment-induced endocrinopathy.

	Hormone Abnormality	Clinical Abnormality
Radiation therapy Brain	↓ GH; less commonly, ↓ TSH, ACTH, FSH, LH	Growth retardation.
Head and neck Low-dose (≤ 750 cGy)	↑ Parathyroid hormone	Hyperparathyroidism, thyroid cancer.
High-dose (≥ 1400 cGy)	↓ Thyroxine; ↑ TSH	Hypothyroidism, thyroid cancer.
Abdomen and pelvis (including gonads)	↓ Estrogen; ↑ FSH, LH	Sterility, menopause, azoospermia.
Chemotherapy Alkylating agents, vinblastine, others	↓ Estrogen; ↑ FSH, LH (normal testosterone, adrenal steroids)	Sterility, menopause, azoospermia.
Vincristine	↑ Vasopressin	SIADH[1]
Cyclophosphamide	(Normal vasopressin)	SIADH[1]
Mitotane	↓ Adrenal steroids	Primary adrenal insufficiency.
Aminoglutethimide	↓ Estrogens, adrenal steroids	Primary adrenal insufficiency.
	↓ Thyroxine; ↑ TSH	Hypothyroidism.

[1]Syndrome of inappropriate secretion of vasopressin (antidiuretic hormone).

should be offered the opportunity for sperm storage before chemotherapy begins. Recent successes with in vitro fertilization and cryopreservation have provided a similar option for women. GnRH analogues, which decrease serum gonadotropin levels, are currently being investigated for their ability to protect the gonads during cytotoxic therapy. The use of birth control pills to reversibly suppress gonadotropins and suspend ovarian function has reportedly been successful in sparing women from gonadal toxicity during chemotherapy. It should be recognized that gonadal toxicity varies with the type of chemotherapy being used; alkylating agents and procarbazine are the most potent toxins. Certain combinations of drugs used to treat lymphomas may, in fact, cause little permanent gonadal damage.

ENDOCRINE THERAPY FOR CANCER

STEROID RECEPTORS & TREATMENT

At present, endocrine treatment is of major therapeutic value in breast, endometrial, and prostatic cancers. The specific applications of endocrine therapy in these diseases will be discussed later. However, the measurement of steroid receptors has added a further refinement to the technology of determining which tumors are endocrine-sensitive. Estrogen receptors (ER) and progesterone receptors (PgR), use-

ful for predicting the clinical responsiveness of breast cancer, are now being detected in a variety of other human tumors, including ovarian and endometrial carcinomas, hepatomas, sarcomas, meningiomas, renal cell carcinomas, as well as melanomas and colorectal and pancreatic carcinomas. On average, however, most of these tumors have a very low frequency of receptor positivity and a much lower receptor content than that found in breast cancer. Thus, with the exception of endometrial cancer, clinical studies have failed to detect a significant role for endocrine therapy in the management of these other tumors.

The mere presence of a steroid receptor does not ensure either a functioning receptor mechanism or a cytostatic or cytolytic response when endocrine treatment is employed. For example, glucocorticoids are known to alter liver metabolism, but they do not produce the cytolytic effects on hepatocytes that are observed with lymphocytes, although both cell types contain high levels of glucocorticoid receptor. Additionally, ER-positive tumors capable of making PgR are the breast tumors most responsive to endocrine treatment. While most endocrine agents do not exert their antitumor effects by binding to PgR, the mere presence of PgR identifies those tumor subsets with a well-functioning ER mechanism. Even so, 20–30% of ER- and PgR-positive breast tumors may not respond to endocrine treatment, and there is increasing evidence that such tumors contain dysfunctional receptors. Both transcriptional and posttranscriptional mechanisms capable of producing defective ER have been detected in human breast tumors. In short, the therapeutic importance of receptors depends on both a functioning receptor mechanism and a growth-regulating receptor response.

Additional comments should be made in reference to the potential clinical significance of the different available means of assaying for tumor ER and PgR content. Biochemical assays have traditionally involved the competitive binding of a radioligand to a cell-free receptor extract prepared by homogenizing fresh tumor specimens. The calculated receptor content (fmol/mg protein cytosol) is very sensitive to procedural conditions, provides no measure of receptor heterogeneity within the tumor specimen, and can be falsely depressed by endogenous or exogenously administered receptor-binding agents. For instance, it has been shown that exogenously administered nonsteroidal antiestrogens can cause a true depression in receptor levels to about 25% of their pretreatment values; thus, it is recommended that at least 2 months elapse after treatment cessation before assaying the tumor if the assay technique utilizes competitive ligand binding. Treatment with radiation therapy or chemotherapy may result in a true reduction in receptor levels, independent of the assay procedure, and this may persist for 12–24 months following cessation of therapy. Newer assays utilizing monoclonal antibodies to measure ER and PgR content are easier to perform, and they avoid the problems related to receptor occupation by competing ligands. Monoclonal antibody assays also provide an immunohistochemical means of assessing receptor heterogeneity within tumor tissue and permit the detection of receptor-positive cells in small cytologic samples, eg, fine-needle aspiration biopsies of tumors. Furthermore, immunohistochemical assay enables the unequivocal detection of receptor-positive malignant cells within receptor-positive normal tissue, such as occurs with uterine cancers. Table 19–5 relates the incidence of ER positivity (assayed by monoclonal antibody) of newly diagnosed breast, endometrial, and ovarian cancer samples with the clinical response rates observed when treating unselected advanced cases with endocrine therapy (antiestrogen or progestins). Clinical response rates for selected ER-positive tumor patients are only available for breast cancer, and these will be reviewed in a later section.

PRIMARY MODALITIES OF ENDOCRINE INTERVENTION

The specific applications of endocrine therapy to breast, endometrial, and prostate cancers and the prognostic utility of tumor steroid receptors in predicting therapeutic outcome will be discussed later. For each of the different hormone-responsive tumors, however, different strategies and combinations of endocrine therapies are optimal, even though all endocrine modalities are based on the same hypothalamic-pituitary-gonadal axis of endocrine control. Therapeutic options are commonly categorized as ablative (removing endogenous hormone production),

Table 19–5. Response to endocrine therapy of tumors known to contain estrogen receptor (ER).

Tumor Type	Percentage Positive for ER	Rate of Response to Endocrine Therapy[1]
Breast carcinoma	50–60%	30%
Endometrial carcinoma	40–50%	30%
Ovarian carcinoma	30–40%	<20%

[1]Objective clinical response after antiestrogen or progestin therapy in advanced cases unselected with regard to ER status.

additive (administration of superphysiologic hormone doses), antagonistic (competition for receptor binding by antagonists such as antiestrogens, antiprogestins, or antiandrogens), or inhibitory (blocking of steroid metabolizing enzymes). The classic concept has been that hormone antagonists bind to receptors and block the subsequent steps to hormonal response, including the signals to undergo cell division and synthesize proteins. However, clinically effective steroid antagonists such as tamoxifen, clomiphene, cyproterone, and flutamide may or may not share the steroid ring structure of the hormones they antagonize and may bind with high affinity to sites other than steroid receptors within the cytoplasm. Some, in addition to blocking hormonal response, also induce synthesis of bifunctional growth factors and unique proteins with as yet unknown functions. Studies comparing the cellular responses of tumors to either antiestrogen administration or estrogen ablation have shown dissimilar mechanisms of antitumor activity, pointing to the need for further basic studies as well as a revision of present concepts explaining tumor growth control by endocrine therapy. No less confounding to investigators is the therapeutic impact of "spillover" among steroid hormones: the potential cross-reactivity of androgens for ER, progestins for ER and glucocorticoid receptors, and glucocorticoids for androgen receptors.

The concept of endocrine-dependent tumors and ablative endocrine therapy began with Beatson's observation, in the 1890s, of the regression of breast cancer after bilateral oophorectomy. Likewise, Huggins first ushered in the era of hormonal management of advanced prostate cancer by demonstrating the beneficial clinical effect of orchiectomy in 1941. Surgical castration, resulting in over 95% reduction of circulating testosterone in males and a 60% reduction in estrogen levels in females (relative to follicular phase levels in normal premenopausal women), produces the standard response rates for both prostate and premenopausal breast cancers with which all other forms of hormonal therapy must be compared. Sixty to 80 percent of men with metastatic prostate cancer will respond to bilateral orchiectomy. Approximately 30% of unselected premenopausal women—and 60–80% of patients with ER- and PgR-positive breast tumors—will respond to bilateral oophorectomy. As expected, oophorectomy is not beneficial for either postmenopausal patients (< 10% response rates) or perimenopausal patients (< 20% response rates). Ovarian irradiation (450–1000 cGy) as a substitute for surgery can effectively ablate ovarian function but requires several weeks to achieve full effect. These response rates with ablative therapy are consistent with the basic concept that these cancers are induced or stimulated by circulating sex steroids and that tumor regression occurs as a direct result of removing these hormonal stimuli. Ablative therapy is not clinically relevant for endometrial cancer because 80% of these estrogen sensitive tumors arise in postmenopausal patients.

Residual estrogen levels in castrated or postmenopausal women persist because of adrenally secreted androgenic precursors (DHEA and androstenedione), which are converted to estrogen (estrone) by aromatization in extraglandular tissues. Furthermore, the remaining 5% of androgens circulating in castrated males consists of adrenally synthesized testosterone and androstenedione or its precursor, DHEA; and the influence of these residual androgens on prostate cancer growth may be disproportionate to their circulating levels. Because of this residual androgen production, adrenalectomy and hypophysectomy have been tried with some success in prostate cancer patients who have relapsed after orchiectomy, though these procedures are much more successful in breast cancer patients relapsing after oophorectomy, in whom second responses are commonly seen.

The advent of receptor antagonists and steroid synthesis inhibitors over the past 20 years has reduced the need for all ablative surgical procedures, particularly adrenalectomy and hypophysectomy, which have been replaced by aminoglutethimide and blockers of gonadotropin-releasing hormones (GnRH), respectively. The additive hormonal agents diethylstilbestrol (DES) and progestins have proved to be effective first-line endocrine therapies for prostate, endometrial, and postmenopausal breast cancers. The number of hormonal agents and endocrine treatment

modalities is rapidly increasing as a result of the relatively low toxicity of most endocrine agents and our improved understanding of the cellular and molecular mechanisms mediating hormone-dependent tumor regression. Some of the more promising endocrine agents currently in clinical trials are listed in Table 19–6. Additional discussion will be given to therapeutic decision-making between medical and surgical ablative therapies and the use of receptor antagonists in the following clinical sections.

COMBINATION ENDOCRINE THERAPY

Steroid agonists and antagonists are now being combined with ablative therapies to try to increase endocrine response rates. There can be multiple mechanisms at work when such combinations are employed, and the relative importance of these mechanisms remains uncertain; for instance, besides increasing levels of the estrogen-catabolizing enzyme, 17β-dehydrogenase, medroxyprogesterone acetate is also known to suppress adrenal production of androstenedione and thereby deplete cells of their androgenic substrate for aromatase and reduce conversion to estrogen. Thus, combining medroxyprogesterone acetate with aminoglutethimide brings into play at least two mechanisms of interaction that could result in enhanced inhibition of ER-positive tumors. Furthermore, higher doses of medroxyprogesterone acetate can bind (spill over) to glucocorticoid receptors, obviating the need for administering replacement doses of cortisol to patients receiving aminoglutethimide.

In benign and malignant prostatic tissues, it is believed that ER-positive stromal cells provide the tropic androgens required by the androgen receptor-containing epithelial cells. In the stromal cells, 5α-reductase converts testosterone to the most active androgen, dihydrotestosterone. Strategy for the endocrine treatment of prostatic cancer has recently focused on complete androgen blockade, combining either surgical or medical ablation with an androgen

Table 19–6. Promising new antitumor endocrine agents.

Endocrine Agent(s)	Mechanism	Tumor Targets
ICI-164384	Estrogen antagonist	Breast
Misopristone (RU-486), onapristone	Progestin antagonists	Breast, endometrium
Anandrone, casodex	Androgen antagonists	Prostate
Goserelin, buserelin; others	GnRH analogues	Prostate, breast, endometrium, ovary
CGS-16949A, 4-hydroxy-androstenedione (4-OHA)	Aromatase inhibitors	Breast, endometrium, ovary
Finasteride, 4-OHA	5α-Reductase inhibitors	Prostate
Flutamide	Androgen antagonist	Prostate
Octreotide acetate	Somatostatin antagonist	Breast, ovary, prostate

receptor antagonist (antiandrogen). Because of the hormonal interdependence between epithelial and stromal cells and the overall dependence of prostatic tissue on pituitary factors (FSH, LH, and PRL), medical ablation can be accomplished using estrogen agonists and antagonists, GnRH analogues, or inhibitors of 5α-reductase. All of the above nonsurgical modalities are under clinical investigation. However, the value of combining these modalities remains controversial.

CHEMO-ENDOCRINE THERAPY

Combining chemotherapy and endocrine therapy is emerging as a popular treatment approach for endocrine-sensitive tumors (especially breast cancer) despite a lack of significant biochemical or cytokinetic rationale. Estramustine and prednimustine are two chemically similar steroid alkylating agents designed to be selectively toxic against receptor-positive cells. At present, it appears that these derivatives are little more effective than their parent compounds, suggesting that impaired receptor binding or systemic drug metabolism is limiting their cytotoxic potential. Simultaneous administration of tamoxifen with drug combinations such as CMF (cyclophosphamide, methotrexate, fluorouracil) may indeed increase response rates in selected groups of breast cancer patients; however, such additive effectiveness has not generally been observed in all patients, in all endocrine-sensitive tumors, or with other drug-hormone combinations. In fact, the potential for adverse therapeutic effects with chemo-endocrine combinations has also been pointed out, and this form of treatment must still be considered investigational. Specifically, by suppressing tumor cell growth, hormonal therapy may protect the tumor from chemotherapeutic agents that are most effective against replicating cells.

In summary, endocrine therapy has a long and established history of empiric usefulness; because the mechanism of its antitumor activity is predominantly cytostatic, the duration of endocrine therapy is necessarily longer than that required for cytotoxic chemotherapy. With the recent emergence of some biochem-

Table 19–7. Associated risk factors for breast cancer in women.

Family history
Menstrual history
Parity
Population differences
Endogenous hormones
Exogenous hormones
Benign breast disease (atypical hyperplasia)
Obesity
Ionizing radiation
Prior breast cancer
Prior endometrial or ovarian cancer

ical understanding of the mechanisms underlying endocrine response and hormonal growth promotion, we are now witnessing the advent of more scientifically based applications. The hope is that this new understanding will lead to better tumor control.

CLINICAL PROBLEMS

BREAST CANCER IN WOMEN

Epidemiology

Breast cancer is now the most common life-threatening malignancy in the USA. There are currently about 175,000 new cases of breast cancer annually in the USA, and women have roughly a 1:9 lifetime risk of developing the disease. The cause of breast cancer is unknown. Associated risk factors are listed in Table 19–7.

A. Family History: It is well established that the daughters of women with breast cancer are at higher risk of developing the disease than other women in the general population. The highest lifetime risk, 50%, is borne by women whose mothers had bilateral breast cancer with onset before menopause.

B. Menstrual History: Early age at menarche and late age at menopause increase the risk of breast cancer. Conversely, late age at menarche or early menopause (natural or surgical) reduces the risk.

C. Parity: Younger age of the mother at the time of her first pregnancy and history of full-term pregnancy lower the subsequent risk of breast cancer.

D. Population Differences: There are striking variations across cultures in the incidence of breast cancer. Asian women have a much lower risk than women in Western countries. Women of Japanese descent who grow up in the USA have a higher incidence of breast cancer than those who grow up in Japan. The risk for blacks and whites is approximately 1.5-fold than that for Chinese- or Japanese-American women, 1.7-fold that for Hispanics, and 3.3-fold that for Native American women.

E. Endogenous Hormones: The data on menstrual function and parity in women—and experimental work in animals, where estrogen is clearly permissive or even carcinogenic in the induction of breast cancer—strongly implicate estrogen exposure as an important factor in the development of breast cancer. Many case control studies have examined estrogen profiles as well as PRL levels, but no clear pattern or association has emerged. There is also no linkage with androgens or thyroid hormone levels. An inherent flaw in these studies is that the induction of breast cancer is a long-term process, and if the estrogen profile of a patient or a control were to be related to cancer, it is probable that a short-term analysis of hormones—a snapshot, as it were—when the cancer was detected would not tell enough of the story. One would need instead a longitudinal, integrated profile starting at least at the menarche in a large cohort of women in order to reliably detect differences in endocrine physiology and relate them to the development of cancer.

F. Exogenous Hormones: Retrospective analyses of users of birth control pills or of postmenopausal women who take estrogen are contradictory. There is, however, some suggestion that increased duration of estrogen exposure may increase the risk of breast cancer. Prospective studies of birth control pill usage do not indicate an increased risk, and there might even be a slight reduction in risk in some studies; but because of the considerable latent period for induction of breast cancer—presumably decades—further observation will be necessary to resolve the issue. The data certainly do not justify withholding birth control pills, but it would be prudent to limit the overall period of use as much as possible. The administration of estrogen to postmenopausal patients is a hotly debated issue, especially because estrogen use is associated with endometrial cancer. The possibility that prolonged use or high doses can increase the risk of breast cancer warrants further caution. One should keep the dose and duration of exposure to exogenous estrogen to a minimum (see Chapter 10).

G. Benign Breast Disease: "Fibrocystic disease" is not a very specific term and usually refers to painful breast nodules that may wax and wane during the menstrual cycle. This commonly diagnosed condition occurs in up to 50% of women and reflects variability in end-organ response to fluctuations in endogenous hormone levels. The condition is less frequent in users of birth control pills and may also respond to the elimination of caffeine from the diet. Histologically, one can see macrocysts, microcysts, adenosis, apocrine change, fibrosis, fibroadenomas, or ductal hyperplasias. These conditions are not found with higher frequency in patients who develop breast cancer, but it has been noted that having had a previous biopsy for benign breast disease increases the relative risk (from 1.86 to 2.13) of developing breast cancer compared with the general population.

Retrospective analysis of a large group of patients was performed to better define who within the benign breast disease category had an increased relative risk for subsequent breast cancer. The presence of a proliferative lesion without atypical hyperplasia (atypia) increased the risk to 1.9 relative to the presence of a nonproliferative lesion without atypia. Atypia increased the risk to 5.3, and patients with atypia plus a family history of breast cancer had a relative risk of 11. It should be noted that the majority of patients (70%) who underwent biopsy for benign breast disease did not have lesions associated with an increased risk of breast cancer.

H. Other Factors: Obese habitus may correlate positively with an increased risk of breast cancer. Ionizing radiation is an established carcinogen. Atomic bomb survivors, young females who received therapeutic chest radiation (for mastitis or Hodgkin's disease), and those who had repeated diagnostic x-rays for tuberculosis or scoliosis show increased rates of breast cancer. Cancer in one breast is associated with a 10–20% lifetime chance of developing primary cancer in the opposite breast. A history of endometrial or ovarian cancer also increases the chances for developing breast cancer.

It appears from the above data that the hormonal milieu is a critical element in the development of breast cancer. Estrogen seems to be the most important factor. There may be a dose-response effect, as suggested by the correlation with an increased duration of ovulatory cycling or with obesity. In the latter instance, there may be added estrogen contribution by peripheral conversion of sex steroids in adipose tissue. Early pregnancy may cause subtle changes in the set points for estrogen and PRL levels, or it may induce a protective change at a critical time in the breast tissue itself. In women with a strong family history of breast cancer, endogenous estrogen may enhance some inherent genetic susceptibility to breast carcinogenesis. Radiation is clearly a carcinogen for the breast, but other exogenous factors (eg, dietary fat) that might account for population differences in the attack rate of breast cancer are less easy to document. Diet could be influential through specific elements such as fat or fiber content, or it could have a more complex interaction involving specific dietary elements or total caloric intake. The overall calorie content and balance of foodstuffs could produce variations in growth, hormone profiles (anterior pituitary hormones such as GH as well as sex steroids), age at menarche, and the like, and these could influence susceptibility to breast cancer later in life.

Treatment of Metastatic Breast Cancer

A. Steroid Receptors and Other Considerations: While surgery is the mainstay of therapy for primary (localized) breast cancer, chemotherapy and hormonal therapy are the principal modalities for treatment of advanced breast cancer. A fairly straightforward algorithm to guide the selection of treatment utilizes the patient's menopausal status and the ER and PgR profile of the tumor (Figure 19–1). The chance of responding to endocrine therapy increases directly with tumor concentrations of ER and PgR. Table 19–8 shows how breast cancer response rates vary with receptor status when a threshold value for receptor positivity (ER-positive, PgR-positive) is employed. These data also indicate that postmenopausal patients are more apt to have receptor-positive tumors than premenopausal patients and, by

ADVANCED BREAST CANCER

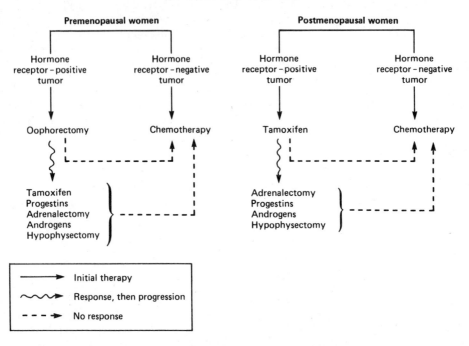

Figure 19–1. Treatment algorithm for advanced breast cancer in women.

implication, to respond more frequently to endocrine therapy.

Important ancillary data include the performance status of the patient, the tempo of tumor growth, the extent of visceral involvement, and the prior treatment history. The better the general condition of the patient and the lower the tumor burden, the more likely that an appropriately chosen hormonal treatment will be effective. Since the response to hormonal treatment is often not evident for several weeks and it can take several months for maximum response to occur, patients who are critically ill from breast cancer and require an immediate antitumor effect should receive chemotherapy. Likewise, patients with explosive tumor growth or with a short interval

Table 19–8. Rates of response to endocrine therapy according to estrogen and progesterone receptors (ER, PgR) in women with breast cancer.[1]

| Tumor Receptor Status | Frequency Distribution | | Rate of Response to Endocrine Therapy |
	Premenopausal Women	Postmenopausal Women	
ER−, PgR−	30%	19%	11%
ER−, PgR+	9%	3%	46%
ER+, PgR−	12%	23%	27%
ER+, PgR+	49%	55%	77%

[1] Modified and reproduced, with permission, from McGuire WL: Steroid hormone receptors in breast cancer treatment strategy. Recent Prog Horm Res 1980;36:135.

between tumor resection and the development of metastases are less likely to benefit from hormonal therapy than those with more indolent tumor growth. Skin, soft tissue, lymph nodes, and bone are the metastatic sites most responsive to endocrine maneuvers. Significant lung or liver involvement and brain metastases require chemotherapy and radiation therapy, respectively. Limited lung or liver infiltration may well respond to hormone treatment. The patient who has responded favorably to a prior hormonal maneuver has some likelihood of responding to subsequent endocrine treatment. Conversely, if a patient's tumor is refractory to one form of endocrine therapy, subsequent hormone treatments are usually of little value, and it is better to consider starting chemotherapy.

B. Premenopausal Endocrine Therapy: For premenopausal patients with ER-positive tumors, ablative treatment with oophorectomy is one first-line hormonal maneuver, although the antiestrogen tamoxifen appears to be equally effective in this role. However, because it can lead to increased circulating estrogens and gonadotropins—and because (by mass action effect) it may not adequately block the higher endogenous estrogen level—some clinicians believe that tamoxifen may not be entirely equivalent to oophorectomy as first-line treatment in premenopausal patients. Studies also suggest that women who respond favorably to tamoxifen have some chance of responding to oophorectomy, but the converse is not true. In general, the response rate to either oophorectomy or tamoxifen as initial treatment ranges from 30% to 60%, depending upon the level of ER protein and the sites of metastatic disease. Responses average 12–15 months in duration. Combination endocrine therapy using tamoxifen and a GnRH analogue in premenopausal patients is currently undergoing evaluation.

In premenopausal patients who respond to oophorectomy or tamoxifen but whose tumors progress, several options are available. They can next receive a trial of progestational agents or androgens. Progestational agents have few side effects, can increase appetite and sense of well-being, and produce clinical response in 15–30% of patients when used as second-line treatment. Androgens are effective in 10–20% of patients but have masculinizing effects. Attempts to develop less virilizing analogues of testosterone have been only moderately successful, and it is argued that the frequency of virilization may not be all that different between various congeners at equipotent antitumor doses. Another ablative maneuver, adrenalectomy—either surgical or medical (using aminoglutethimide)—can be employed as third-line treatment, with a response rate in the range of 15–30%. Medical adrenalectomy appears equal to surgical ablation in antitumor effect, but its effects are reversible once the drug is stopped. However, like surgical adrenalectomy, it also requires the administration of replacement hydrocortisone. In addition to maintaining vital functions, this replacement therapy also prevents increased pituitary ACTH production and overriding of the adrenal blockade. Since dexamethasone metabolism is augmented by aminoglutethimide, it should not be used as the replacement steroid during treatment. Up to 30% of patients receiving aminoglutethimide will initially experience somnolence or rash, side effects that usually subside with continued treatment and which can be minimized by gradually working up to full doses over several weeks.

Finally, the development of transsphenoidal surgery has made hypophysectomy a more feasible ablative maneuver. Before the advent of receptor analyses, hypophysectomy was used as palliative treatment in end-stage patients, especially those with extensive and painful bone metastases. Patients who were responders would often awaken from anesthesia with dramatic pain relief. That it occasionally benefits hormone-refractory cases suggests that its palliative effects are not mediated via sex steroid mechanisms. When compared to adrenalectomy in ER-positive tumors as second- or third-line treatment, hypophysectomy is equally effective and may have a slightly longer duration of action. However, the availability of aminoglutethimide, the operative risk, and the requirement for permanent adrenal replacement make hypophysectomy a less desirable option.

Premenopausal patients with ER-negative tumors

would bypass endocrine therapy and be placed on a chemotherapy protocol.

C. Postmenopausal Endocrine Therapy: The initial endocrine maneuver in postmenopausal patients with ER-positive tumors is the administration of the antiestrogen tamoxifen. In the recent past, additive therapy with diethylstilbestrol (DES) was used. However, this agent is associated with many more side effects than tamoxifen and has now largely been abandoned. Response rates to tamoxifen or DES range from 30% to 60%, again in proportion to the disease-free interval, metastatic sites, and the ER content of the tumor. Response durations are similar to those for oophorectomy. Once the breast cancer of a patient who has responded to tamoxifen progresses, second-line endocrine therapy is either medical adrenalectomy or administration of progestins, with response rates ranging from 15% to 40% . It should be noted that 10–20% of patients initially failing to respond to tamoxifen may have a clinical response to adrenalectomy. Thus, if the tempo of the disease and the clinical status of the patient permit, one can offer a trial of adrenalectomy before proceeding to chemotherapy.

When DES was in wider use, induction of therapy in patients with skeletal metastases would occasionally be accompanied by a "flare" with exacerbation of bone pain and hypercalcemia. This phenomenon usually heralded a clinical response and did not necessarily require prolonged interruption of treatment. When the cancer of patients who had responded to DES progressed, drug withdrawal was frequently followed by another clinical remission in up to 30% of patients, and this could last for several months. The flare phenomenon and the response to withdrawal are less frequently seen with tamoxifen; these effects have also been noted to occur with androgen therapy. Postmenopausal patients with ER-negative tumors would bypass hormonal treatment and begin chemotherapy.

Current investigational endocrine agents include congeners of tamoxifen and a variety of GnRH agonists and antagonists.

BREAST CANCER IN MEN

Cancer of the male breast is extremely rare, occurring with a frequency of about 1% of that of cancer of the female breast. There is an association with Klinefelter's syndrome and with exogenous estrogen exposure (eg, in transsexuals), emphasizing the importance of hormonal factors, especially estrogen.

At least 80% of tumors in men are ER-positive. Sixty to 70 percent of patients with metastatic tumors will respond to orchiectomy, and adrenalectomy and hypophysectomy are effective as second-line hormonal treatments. More recently, tamoxifen has shown activity as primary treatment and will probably supplant orchiectomy. As in female patients with breast cancer, male patients whose tumors become refractory to hormone therapy go on to receive chemotherapy. Androgens are contraindicated because of their potential for facilitating tumor growth.

ENDOMETRIAL CANCER

Epidemiology

There are approximately 30,000 new cases of endometrial cancer annually in the USA. In contrast to the somewhat equivocal role of estrogen in the induction of breast cancer, its place in the causation of endometrial cancer appears more certain.At the clinical level, as shown in Table 19–9, a variety of conditions have been associated with an increased risk of developing endometrial cancer. Their common denominator is unopposed or increased estrogen stimulation of the endometrium. This produces endometrial hyperplasia, a condition that can in turn progress to frank cancer. Progesterone antagonizes this effect of estrogen and induces the endometrium to mature or differentiate to a secretory state. Its action may be mediated by augmentation of enzymes in endometrial cells that catabolize estrogen and by decreasing levels of ER in this same tissue. There is a more frequent history of irregular menses in patients who develop endometrial cancer, and while combination birth control pills may have no influence on or may even decrease the risk of uterine cancer, sequential birth control pills may impart an increased risk, possibly because of the days of therapy where only estrogen is being administered.

Epidemiologic studies revealed an upsurge in the incidence of endometrial cancer in the USA in the early 1970s. This followed and paralleled an increase in the number of prescriptions written over the preceding years for replacement estrogen therapy in postmenopausal women. Case control studies of this phenomenon have clearly shown that exogenous estrogen use imparts a three- to eightfold increase in the risk of developing uterine cancer. The higher the dose and the longer the duration of estrogen use, the greater the risk. One follow-up study from the late 1970s reported that a decline in the number of estrogen prescriptions (after the initial recognition of their association with endometrial cancer) was accompa-

Table 19–9. Conditions associated with an increased risk of developing endometrial cancer.

Prolonged or unopposed estrogen effect on the uterus
Exogenous estrogen administration
Late menopause
Obesity (increased peripheral conversion of precursors to estrogen)
Polycystic ovary syndrome
Ovarian cortical stromal hyperplasia
Estrogen-secreting ovarian tumors

nied by a decline in the incidence of endometrial cancer in the same population base. Cyclic or continuous progestin administration has also reduced the incidence of endometrial cancer.

Taken together, the above observations strongly support a conservative approach to the use of exogenous estrogens. They should be given in the smallest possible dose, for the shortest duration feasible, and on an intermittent schedule, preferably adding a progestin to the treatment regimen. (See also Chapters 5 and 10 for further discussion of estrogen therapy.)

Treatment of Metastatic Endometrial Cancer

A. Steroid Receptors: As is true in breast cancer, hormonal therapy is a primary therapeutic modality for advanced endometrial cancer. Unlike the situation in breast cancer, receptor profiles are not used to guide treatment selection in cases of endometrial cancer, although it was from uterine tissue that Jensen first isolated and characterized estrogen receptors in the 1960s. Uterine estrogen receptors increase during the proliferative phase of the menstrual cycle and fall in the presence of exogenous progesterone or with the rise of endogenous progesterone during the luteal phase. Progesterone receptors are induced by estrogen, and their level peaks coincident with the estradiol peak in the menstrual cycle. Many endometrial carcinomas contain ER, and, in contrast to breast cancer, levels are higher and inversely proportionate to the degree of histologic differentiation of the tumor. Progesterone receptors are also present in endometrial cancer, and their presence correlates directly with the degree of differentiation. ER and PgR have little practical application in the management of patients, since immunohistochemical analyses must be performed to distinguish tumor from receptor-positive normal tissue, and these assays are not quantitative. Furthermore, these tumors frequently show an admixture of receptor-positive and -negative tumor cells, the latter accounting for the eventual failure of endocrine treatment.

B. Endocrine Therapy: Approximately one-third of metastatic tumors will respond to progestins. The probability of response is highest in patients with the most differentiated tumors and in those with the longest interval between primary treatment and the appearance of metastases. Responders live an average of 2 years after treatment is started, while nonresponding patients survive only about 6 months. Until recently, parenteral preparations such as hydroxyprogesterone and medroxyprogesterone were used. An orally effective compound, megestrol, has simplified treatment and appears to be as potent as the earlier parenteral formulations. Potential side effects of these compounds include salt retention and an increased predisposition to thrombophlebitis.

In patients who progress on progestational therapy or who do not respond initially, disease may be palliated with chemotherapy. However, in many patients, advanced disease stage, poor general health, and a history of pelvic irradiation limit tolerance to the most effective agents, ie, doxorubicin, cyclophosphamide, fluorouracil, and cisplatin.

PROSTATIC CANCER

Epidemiology

There are approximately 100,000 new cases of prostatic cancer annually in the USA. Prostatic cancer is essentially a disease of men in their 60s and 70s, and autopsy series have shown occult carcinoma in more than one-third of men over age 70 and more than two-thirds of men over age 80.

Several lines of evidence support the idea that testosterone plays a role in the development of prostatic cancer. Testosterone can induce adenocarcinoma of the prostate in rats; castrated men do not develop prostatic cancer; and the disease is less frequent in patients with cirrhosis. Cirrhotic patients tend to be in a stage of relative estrogen excess from decreased hepatic estrogen metabolism, and they frequently exhibit testicular atrophy and gynecomastia. While benign prostatic hypertrophy and prostate cancer are often found concurrently in older men and are associated with the same risk factors, benign hypertrophy is not, in itself, a risk factor for prostate cancer and occurs in an embryologically distinct portion of the gland.

Less clearly understood are racial and geographic differences. American blacks have a much higher incidence of prostatic cancer than Nigerian blacks, and Japanese-Americans who live in Hawaii have an attack rate intermediate between the low rate seen in Japan and the higher rates seen in whites in the USA. There are inconclusive data suggesting that patients may have higher testosterone production than controls; that viruses with oncogenic potential may play a permissive role; and that the number of sexual partners and a history of sexually transmitted disease also influence the incidence of prostatic cancer.

Treatment of Metastatic Prostatic Cancer

A. Steroid Receptors: Cytosol receptors for androgen have been isolated from prostatic cancers, and while they may predict for response, they are not used as a basis for selecting therapy because (1) initial response rates to standard endocrine therapy are high, and alternative choices are far less promising (ie, second-line hormonal maneuvers or chemotherapy); (2) androgen receptor assays are still technically difficult, although these have been simplified by the recent development of monoclonal antibodies; and (3) the volume of tumor specimens from primary sites or metastatic sites (eg, bone) is not usually adequate for quantitative determination of tumor receptor content.

B. Endocrine Therapy: It is difficult to compare the response data and therapies from different treatment centers. Typically, a patient with metastatic disease will complain of bone pain and manifest abnormalities on bone scan or plain x-ray. The acid phosphatase level may be specifically elevated in prostatic cancer, along with increased levels of the relatively nonspecific enzyme, alkaline phosphatase. Response to therapy is hard to quantitate, since subjective complaints are difficult to measure, bone lesions resolve slowly, and the acid phosphatase does not always correlate reliably with variation in tumor volume. Only in less common instances of discrete lung, lymph node, or liver metastases is it possible to objectively and directly measure antitumor response. The advent of an assay for prostate-specific antigen (PSA) has substantially improved the monitoring of therapeutic response, since its serum level and change in titer appear to correlate well with tumor bulk and therapeutic response.

Within these limitations, it appears that one-half to three-fourths of patients will benefit from treatment. Initial therapy is hormonal and is based upon the pioneering work of Huggins, showing that prostatic cancer is a testosterone-dependent tissue. Therapy consists of lowering testosterone levels either by orchiectomy, administration of DES (which suppresses gonadotropins), or use of a GnRH analogue such as leuprolide. Since DES has direct suppressive effects on the tumor and inhibits pituitary gonadotropin secretion, some have advocated the use of both DES and orchiectomy. However, the response rates with all androgen-ablating maneuvers are essentially the same. There continues to be rigorous debate over the additional use of an androgen receptor antagonist (like flutamide) with ablative therapy to produce a so-called complete androgen blockade. Antiandrogens are somewhat effective as first-line agents, but it is generally agreed that in combination with GnRH agonists they effectively eliminate painful flare-ups of tumor lesions and may provide added improvements in patients having a minimal burden of metastatic disease. Disease that progresses after initially responding to ablative therapy rarely responds to crossover treatment with other endocrine maneuvers.

The presence of low levels of circulating androgens after orchiectomy has led to trials of adrenalectomy or hypophysectomy in patients with progressive disease. However, subsequent response rates to these ablative therapies are quite low, and responses are short-lived. GnRH analogues alone—or in combination with antiandrogens—with their minimal side effects, have now become front-line agents for treatment of prostatic cancer, with their only limitation being cost. New analogues, including 5α-reductase inhibitors, are being assessed for their comparative efficacy in treating benign prostatic hypertrophy and prostate cancer (Table 19–6).

MISCELLANEOUS TUMORS

Steroid hormone receptors have been isolated from tumors arising from organs not usually considered to be under primary endocrine control. Corticosteroid receptor protein is present in leukemia and lymphoma cells. It shows some correlation with response to steroid therapy, but levels are not used prospectively to guide treatment.

As mentioned earlier, there are reports of low but reproducible levels of ER or ER-like proteins in some human renal, ovarian, hepatic, bone and pancreatic tumors and in melanomas. Progestational agents produce regression in 10% of hypernephromas; there are case reports that tamoxifen and progestins have caused regressions in ovarian cancer; and there are validated studies demonstrating the importance of tamoxifen in chemotherapy regimens effective against melanomas. Hepatomas have responded to progestational agents on occasion, and trials are in progress to determine whether hormonal agents can produce regressions in pancreatic cancer. In summary, it can be said that endocrine treatments for these tumor types either do not appear promising or are believed to be effective for reasons other than the presence of detectable ER.

REFERENCES

Beatson GT: On the treatment of inoperable cases of carcinoma of the mamma: Suggestions for a new method of treatment with illustrative cases. Lancet 1986;2:162.

Benz CC: Hormone responsive tumors. In: *Endocrinology and Metabolism,* 3rd ed. Baxter JD, Felig P, Frohman LA (editors). McGraw-Hill. [In press, 1993.]

Bittner JJ: The causes of mammary cancer in mice. Harvey Lect 1947;42:221.

Bresciani F et al (editors): *Hormones and Cancer 2.* Vol 31 of: *Progress in Cancer Research and Therapy.* Raven Press, 1984.

Burck KB, Liu ET, Larrick IW: Growth factors and receptors. In: *Oncogenes.* Springer, 1988.

Dickson RB, Lippman ME: Estrogenic regulation of growth and polypeptide growth factor secretion in human breast carcinoma. Endocr Rev 1987;8:29.

Dupont WD, Page DL: Risk factors for breast cancer in women with proliferative breast disease. N Engl J Med 1985;312:146.

Furth J: Hormones as etiological agents in neoplasia. In: *Cancer: A Comprehensive Treatise.* Vol 1. Becker FF (editor). Plenum Press, 1975.

Goustin AS et al: Growth factors and cancer. Cancer Res 1986;46: 1015.

Henderson BE et al: Endogenous hormones as a major factor in human cancer. Cancer Res 1982;42:3232.

Huggins C: Endocrine-induced regression of cancers. Science 1967;156:1050.

King RJ: Oestrogen and progestin receptors as markers for the behavior of human breast tumors. In: *Biochemical and Biological Markers of Neoplastic Transformations.* Chandra PP (editor). Plenum Press, 1983.

Lane MA, Sainten A, Cooper GM: Activation of related transforming genes in mouse and human mammary carcinomas. Proc Natl Acad Sci USA 1981;78:5185.

Leclercq G et al (editors): *Clinical Interest of Steroid Hormone Receptors in Breast Cancer.* Vol 91 of: *Recent Results in Cancer Research.* Springer, 1984.

May FE et al: Mouse mammary tumour virus-related sequences are present in human DNA. Nucleic Acids Res 1983;11:4127.

Muller WJ et al: Single-step induction of mammary adenocarcinoma in transgenic mice bearing the activated c-*neu* oncogene. Cell 1988;54:105.

Salomon DS et al: Presence of transforming growth factors in human breast cancer cells. Cancer Res 1984,44:4069.

Shalet SM: Disorders of the endocrine system due to radiation and cytotoxic chemotherapy. Clin Endocrinol 1983;19:637.

Spona J et al: Enzyme immunoassay and Scatchard plot estimation of estrogen receptor in gynecological tumors. Cancer Res 1986;46(8 Suppl):4310S.

Sporn MB, Roberts AB: Autocrine growth factors and cancer. Nature 1985;313:745.

Sporn MB, Roberts AB: Peptide growth factors are multifunctional. Nature 1988;332:217.

Humoral Manifestations of Malignancy

20

Gordon J. Strewler, MD

GENERAL CONCEPT OF ECTOPIC HORMONE SECRETION

The idea that tumors can cause endocrine syndromes by secreting hormones inappropriately was first proposed by Fuller Albright. In 1941 he suggested that the cause of hypercalcemia and hypophosphatemia in a patient with renal carcinoma might be production of parathyroid hormone (PTH) by the tumor. The term "ectopic hormonal syndrome" was subsequently coined by Liddle to describe such situations. By now the idea of "ectopic hormone production" is widely held, and some humoral syndromes induced by nonendocrine tumors are recognized as being among the commonest of endocrine disorders. However, the term "ectopic" is probably a poor descriptor of most of these syndromes. Ectopic means "out of place," implying abnormal secretion of a hormone by tissues that do not normally do so. Yet, tumors that produce hormones most often arise from cells that are normally committed to producing the same hormone. For example, adrenocorticotropic hormone (ACTH) is produced by lung carcinomas that develop from ACTH-producing lung cells. Many other examples will be encountered in this chapter. Although truly ectopic secretion of hormones is probably a rarity, the term ectopic is firmly ingrained in the vocabulary of our specialty and will not soon be abandoned.

Of all the paraneoplastic syndromes, the ectopic production of hormones is probably the commonest. Virtually all the peptide hormones are produced by nonendocrine tumors (Table 20–1), and a wide variety of neoplasms are associated with syndromes of hormone excess. However, strong associations exist between specific hormones and specific tumors. For example, the PTH-like protein associated with hypercalcemia (see below) is most commonly produced by squamous carcinomas, while ACTH, vasopressin, and calcitonin are most commonly produced by small-cell lung carcinoma and other neuroendocrine tumors. It should be noted that nearly all the peptide hormones are represented in Table 20–1, but none of the steroid or thyroid hormones are listed; it is pre-

sumed that steroid hormones are not produced by tumors because their synthesis requires expression of a whole series of enzymes, while synthesis of a peptide requires expression of only a single gene. The exception—secretion of the sterol hormone $1,25(OH)_2D_3$ by certain lymphomas—occurs because its synthesis from the circulating precursor $25OHD_3$ requires only a single step.

Secretion of hormones by tumors often differs qualitatively from glandular secretion of hormones. First, secretion by tumors is rarely suppressible. Second, tumors often lack the ability to process peptide hormones normally, and they secrete larger precursor forms whose biologic activity is reduced. Third, tumor-associated syndromes may involve secretion of hormone homologues rather than hormones them-

Table 20–1. Hormones produced by tumors.

Hypercalcemia factors
  PTH-like protein
  Tumor necrosis factor-α
  $1,25(OH)_2D_3$
  Prostaglandins
Vasopressin
ACTH
Calcitonin
Human chorionic gonadotropin (hCG)
Placental lactogen
Growth hormone–releasing hormone
Corticotropin-releasing hormone
Somatostatin
Erythropoietin
Oncogenous osteomalacia factor
Hypoglycemia factor
Renin
Other gut hormones (gastrin-releasing peptide, somatostatin, pancreatic polypeptide, vasoactive intestinal polypeptide, substance P, motilin)

selves. For example, in hyperparathyroidism hypercalcemia is caused by PTH excess, but in malignant disease hypercalcemia may be caused by excess of other physiologically similar peptides, one of which is closely related to PTH.

Criteria for deciding whether a nonendocrine tumor is responsible for producing hormone excess are listed in Table 20–2. Not every one of the criteria has been fulfilled for every hormone listed, but for most of these hormones there is evidence of production by tumor cells in vitro or of mRNA expression.

Cellular Basis of Ectopic Hormone Secretion

It was once held that "derepression" of tumor genes was responsible for ectopic hormone secretion, ie, that tumor cells express a random assortment of genes that are normally repressed, including genes that encode hormones. This hypothesis cannot readily explain the nonrandom association of certain hormonal syndromes (eg, ACTH and vasopressin excess) with specific cancers (eg, small-cell lung carcinoma). Moreover, the derepression hypothesis is obviated by the aforementioned finding that tumors typically express the same hormones as their cell of origin. The "dedifferentiation" hypothesis posits a

Table 20–2. Criteria for determining whether a nonendocrine tumor is a source of hormone.[1]

Association of clinical syndrome or inappropriate hormone level with presence of tumor.
Reversal of syndrome with tumor-specific therapy.
Presence of hormone in tumor tissue.
Demonstration of arteriovenous gradient for hormone across tumor.
Synthesis or release of hormone by tumor tissue in vitro.
Expression of hormone mRNA by tumor.

[1] Criteria are listed in order of their rigor; the first two are clinical and the rest are primarily investigational.

retrograde movement of tumor cells along the pathway of differentiation, leading to the expression of fetal proteins (eg, alpha-fetoprotein, carcinoembryonic antigen) or hormones normally present in immature cells (eg, human chorionic gonadotropin [hCG]). While this hypothesis would account for the nonrandom nature of hormone expression and the presence of low-level expression in mature normal cells, there is no supporting evidence for the occurrence of dedifferentiation. A more sophisticated model is the "dysdifferentiation" hypothesis of Baylin and Mendelsohn, which holds that epithelial malignancy is the result of clonal expansion of a particular cell type along a complex pathway of epithelial differentiation. This is viewed as giving rise to overexpression of hormones, as by clonal expansion of a normally rare population of cells committed to expression of the hormone, or to expression of hormones not present in the mature epithelium, as by clonal expansion of a primitive cell.

Hormone Secretion by APUD Cells

The most celebrated attempt to explain the nonrandom patterns of hormone secretion by tumors is the APUD hypothesis of Pearse. A characteristic shared by many endocrine cells and some tumor cells that secrete hormones is the capacity to synthesize and store biogenic amines (*a*mine *p*recursor *u*ptake and *d*ecarboxylation). The APUD hypothesis suggests that APUD cells, although widely scattered in many tissues, have a common origin in neural crest and are specialized for production of peptide hormones. Histologic analysis shows that APUD cells do contain typical neurosecretory granules associated with secretion of peptides and biogenic amines. Besides such endocrine cells as thyroid C cells, pituitary corticotrophs, and adrenal medullary cells, APUD cells are scattered in the bronchial and gastrointestinal mucosa, and hormone-producing neoplasms (carcinoids, small-cell lung carcinoma) are frequently composed of APUD cells. Pearse proposed that APUD cells were a "diffuse neuroendocrine system," a third branch of the nervous system.

The APUD theory probably requires modification in two respects. First, it has been clearly shown that not all APUD cells are of neural crest origin—some arise from primitive endoderm. Thus, hormone-producing APUD cells do not necessarily have a common origin. Second, hormones are produced not only by APUD cells but by a variety of non-APUD tumor cells. However, the APUD cell is the type most likely to be associated with the secretion of biologically active hormones that leads to a clinical syndrome of hormone excess. The best example is ACTH in Cushing's syndrome. Although the biologically inactive ACTH precursor pro-opiomelanocortin is produced by many tumors, Cushing's syndrome is typically associated with APUD tumors containing neurosecretory granules, presumably because these are capable of processing and secreting ACTH. Thus, the rubric APUD identifies cytochemical or ultrastructural features associated not so much with production of hormones as with secretion of active hormones. However, it is preferable to refer to APUD cells as neuroendocrine cells, a term that denotes the presence of neurosecretory granules that are involved in hormone secretion.

Oncogenes & Growth Factors

The transformation of cells from normal to malignant is thought to involve activation of oncogenes. Oncogenes are aberrant forms of normal genes (proto-oncogenes) that control growth and differentiation, encoding growth factors (*sis* encodes platelet-derived growth factor [PDGF]), growth factor receptors (*erb*-B encodes a portion of the epidermal growth factor [EGF] receptor) or cellular effector systems coupled to growth factor receptors (*sarc* encodes a tyrosine kinase). The process of transformation thus involves the inappropriate activation of a variety of normal cellular pathways. In many instances, the production of hormones by malignant cells will probably be the consequence of activation of a specific oncogene.

Why should hormone secretion be linked to proto-oncogenes controlling normal growth and differentiation? One possible answer is that production of hormones may have survival value, both for cancer cells and for their normal cells of origin. Among the characteristic tumor products of small-cell lung carcinoma is gastrin-releasing peptide (GRP), the mammalian counterpart of the amphibian hormone bombesin. GRP/bombesin fulfills most criteria as an autocrine growth factor in small-cell carcinoma: It is secreted, it can stimulate replication of the cells via specific receptors, and blockade of its action by specific antibodies to GRP inhibits cell replication and tumor formation in vivo. Insulin-like growth factors, transforming growth factor-α, and transforming growth factor-β have also been shown to have autocrine effects on the growth of diverse tumors, including small-cell lung carcinoma, breast carcinoma, and bladder carcinoma. Studies may eventually show whether other hormonal products of small-cell lung carcinoma (ACTH, vasopressin, calcitonin) also serve as growth factors.

MALIGNANCY-ASSOCIATED HYPERCALCEMIA

Hypercalcemia is the commonest paraneoplastic endocrine syndrome. The incidence is 15 cases per 100,000 person-years, about half the incidence of primary hyperparathyroidism. Hypercalcemia develops as a complication in up to 10% of patients with advanced malignant disease. In hospitalized patients, malignant disease is the commonest cause of hyper-

calcemia. Table 20–3 shows the frequency with which various tumors cause hypercalcemia. Lung carcinoma, breast carcinoma, and multiple myeloma together account for more than 50%. Among lung carcinomas, hypercalcemia is seen most commonly in squamous carcinoma and is also associated with large-cell carcinoma and adenocarcinoma. Small-cell lung carcinoma rarely causes hypercalcemia, despite its propensity for other endocrinopathies. Squamous carcinomas of the head, neck, esophagus, and other organs are also strongly associated with hypercalcemia, as is renal cell carcinoma. In contrast, hypercalcemia is rarely seen in gastrointestinal adenocarcinoma or in sarcomas, even lytic sarcomas of bone. The offending neoplasm is apparent in 98% of cases when hypercalcemia is first detected. Except in patients with multiple myeloma and breast cancer, the course of which can be punctuated by self-limited episodes of hypercalcemia, the prognosis of the cancer patient with hypercalcemia is grim, with a 3-month survival rate of less than 50%.

Differential Diagnosis

The principal entity in the differential diagnosis of hypercalcemia associated with malignancy is primary hyperparathyroidism, which may present as an intercurrent illness in a patient with a malignant tumor. Chronic, long-standing hypercalcemia preceding the diagnosis of cancer or radiographic changes of subperiosteal bone resorption may indicate the presence of primary hyperparathyroidism. The presence of primary hyperparathyroidism may be indicated by an elevated PTH value. In commonly used mid region assays, the immunoreactive PTH levels in cancer patients are usually normal. However, PTH levels may be slightly high in some patients with mild hypercalcemia. In assays that measure intact PTH by immunoradiometric techniques, PTH levels are sup-

Table 20–3. Tumors that cause hypercalcemia.[1]

Primary Site	No. (%) of Cases	Known Metastatic Disease (%)
Lung	111 (25)	62
Breast	87 (19.6)	92
Multiple myeloma	43 (9.7)	100
Head and neck	36 (8.1)	73
Kidney and urinary tract	35 (7.9)	36
Esophagus	25 (5.6)	53
Female genitalia	24 (5.2)	81
Unknown primary	23 (5.2)	--
Lymphoma	14 (3.2)	91
Colon	8 (1.8)	--
Liver and biliary	7 (1.6)	--
Skin	6 (1.4)	--
Other	25 (5.6)	--
Total	444 (100.0)	

[1]Modified and reproduced, with permission, from Stollerman GH et al (editors): *Advances in Internal Medicine*. Vol. 32. Year Book, 1987.

pressed in malignancy and other forms of non-parathyroid hypercalcemia, greatly facilitating the differential diagnosis of hypercalcemia. The use of the PTH assay in the differential diagnosis of hypercalcemia is discussed in Chapter 5.

Etiology & Pathogenesis

In patients with cancer, excessive bone resorption is the most important cause of hypercalcemia. The most important stimulus to bone resorption is local or systemic release of tumor-derived mediators, the nature of which is currently under investigation (see below). Direct bone resorption by lytic metastases is less important as a pathogenetic mechanism, as most patients with widespread lytic metastases are not hypercalcemic. Decreased renal calcium excretion may contribute to the pathogenesis of hypercalcemia in many patients. Tumors can secrete hypocalciuric substances, such as the PTH-like protein associated with solid tumors (see below), and the effects of hypercalcemia itself, eg, reduction of the glomerular filtration rate, also contribute to defective renal calcium excretion. The relative roles of excess bone resorption and excess renal reabsorption of calcium are difficult to define, but calcium absorption from the gut probably plays no role in the development of malignancy-associated hypercalcemia, except in rare patients with lymphoma and elevated levels of 1,25 $(OH)_2D_3$.

The molecular basis of hypercalcemia associated with cancer involves the production of at least three different hypercalcemic factors, giving rise to several distinct clinical syndromes. In addition, a variety of other mediators have been suggested, eg, prostaglandins. Prostaglandins of the E series are potent bone-resorbing substances. It is clear that prostaglandins are secreted by some tumors, and elevated levels of their metabolites are found in blood and urine in some cancer patients. However, only rare patients with hypercalcemia respond to inhibition of prostaglandin synthesis with nonsteroidal anti-inflammatory agents.

A. Solid Tumors: Solid tumors other than breast cancer, especially squamous carcinoma and renal cell carcinoma, produce a characteristic syndrome of hypercalcemia. This syndrome often occurs in the absence of bone metastases (Table 20–3) and is characterized by hypophosphatemia and elevated nephrogenous cyclic adenosine monophosphate (cAMP) excretion, both of which occur in hyperparathyroidism. As nephrogenous cAMP is a specific indicator of PTH action, these findings have been thought to implicate a PTH-like substance in the pathogenesis of hypercalcemia. Recently, a unique protein has been isolated from both squamous and renal carcinomas (Figure 20–1). This 141-amino-acid protein possesses an amino-terminal domain that is strongly homologous with PTH, binds to PTH receptors in both bone and kidney with the same affinity as PTH, and mimics all the classic effects of PTH (eg, excess bone resorption, hypercalcemia, increased renal calcium reabsorption, decreased renal phosphate reabsorption, and increased renal synthesis of 1,25 $[OH]_2D_3$). The tumor-derived protein, which has been called human PTH-like protein (hPLP) or PTH-related protein (PTHrP), is the cause of humoral hypercalcemia in most solid tumors. It has recently been shown by immunoassay techniques that the protein is actually present in the circulation in 70–80% of hypercalcemic patients with tumors, including many patients with bone metastasis (Figure 20–2). Thus, even in patients with bone metastases, hypercalcemia may well have a humoral basis; this is supported by evidence that bone metastasis correlates poorly with hypercalcemia. Despite its limited sequence homology with PTH (Figure 20–1), PTHrP does not cross-react with PTH antisera and is probably not the cause of the PTH-like immunoreactivity often detectable in patients with malignancy-associated hypercalcemia.

Despite the ability of PTHrP to stimulate production of 1,25$(OH)_2D_3$, plasma levels of 1,25$(OH)_2D_3$ are often normal or even suppressed in patients with cancer, in contrast to the high levels seen in hyper-

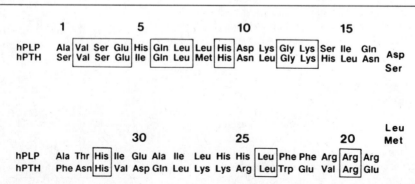

Figure 20–1. Comparison of the amino acid sequences of human PTH and the human PTH-related protein of malignancy.

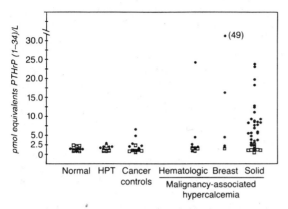

Figure 20–2. Serum levels of the PTH-related protein in normal subjects and in patients with hyperparathyroidism or malignant disease. Cancer controls are normocalcemic. Levels of PTHrP are increased in three of nine patients with multiple myeloma and normal in the remaining patients with hematologic cancers (lymphoma or leukemia). Of patients with solid tumors, 70% have increased levels of PTHrP. (Modified and reproduced, with permission, from Budayr A et al: Increased serum levels of a parathyroid hormone-like protein in malignancy-associated hypercalcemia. Ann Intern Med 1989;111:807.)

parathyroidism. The reason for this is unclear, but it is known that production of $1,25(OH)_2D_3$ is suppressed by hypercalcemia per se, and it is likely that $1,25(OH)_2D_3$ production is more sensitive to hypercalcemia in cancer patients than in patients with primary hyperparathyroidism.

PTHrP is present in the normal human genome and is expressed in normal cells, notably keratinocytes, from which squamous carcinomas arise. This is another example of hormone production by the cells from which a tumor originates. Presumably, PTHrP subserves a physiologic role in tissues such as skin and lactating breast that express the protein. Its physiologic roles are apt to be local, as it circulates only in low concentrations, and probably important, since the gene has been highly conserved during the course of evolution.

PTHrP is unusual among mediators of paraneoplastic syndromes because it causes a well-defined clinical syndrome by mimicking another hormone that is a distinct gene product. Other as yet unidentified tumor products, such as the mediator of tumor-induced hypoglycemia, may well fit the same pattern.

B. Breast Carcinoma: In breast cancer, hypercalcemia occurs almost invariably in patients with extensive bone metastases (Table 20–3). In one study, 35% of patients with advanced breast cancer had hypercalciuria, and 14% developed severe hypercalcemia requiring therapy. Episodes of hypercalcemia are often triggered by estrogen, androgen, or antiestrogen therapy and can be self-limited if hormonal therapy is stopped. These characteristics de-

fine a different syndrome from that associated with other solid tumors.

The strong association of hypercalcemia with bone metastases suggests an unidentified local osteolytic factor as the etiologic agent. Although breast carcinoma cells sometimes secrete prostaglandins, hypercalcemia in these patients rarely responds to treatment with inhibitors of prostaglandin synthesis. The local factor in breast cancer could be the same PTH-like protein that probably causes humoral hypercalcemia in other solid tumors; the protein has been isolated from a breast tumor, and about one-half of hypercalcemic breast cancer patients have increased levels of nephrogenous cAMP or of PTHrP (Figure 20–2).

C. Multiple Myeloma: Patients with myeloma are the most likely of all cancer patients to develop hypercalcemia. Hypercalciuria is even more common than hypercalcemia in this group, and hypercalcemia is probably precipitated in many cases by declining renal function with reduced clearance of calcium. As in patients with breast cancer, hypercalcemic episodes in patients with multiple myeloma are sometimes circumscribed, with prolonged subsequent survival. Hypercalcemia in patients with myeloma may respond to glucocorticoids.

The etiologic factor is probably a cytokine produced locally by myeloma cells, and current evidence favors lymphotoxin (tumor necrosis factor-β) or interleukin-1 as the most important of these. It is now clear that leukocytes secrete a variety of cytokines with bone-resorbing activity (eg, interleukin-1, tumor necrosis factor-α, granulocyte-macrophage colony-stimulating factor [GM-CSF], granulocyte colony-stimulating factor [G-CSF]); for example, normal monocytes predominantly secrete interleukin-1β. The term "osteoclast-activating factor" was introduced as a rubric for a bone-resorbing factor secreted by normal and malignant leukocytes, but with the discovery of individual bone-resorbing cytokines, it can now be abandoned.

D. Lymphoma: Hypercalcemia occurs in 2–3% of patients with lymphoma, usually in patients with bone involvement. It is seen in all varieties of lymphoma, but a strong predisposition to hypercalcemia is seen in only one—the adult T cell leukemia/lymphoma syndrome, in which hypercalcemia occurs in two-thirds of cases. The disorder runs an aggressive course, and the associated hypercalcemia responds poorly to steroids and other measures. The causative agent of the syndrome is a retrovirus, the human T cell leukemia/lymphoma virus (HTLV-1). The mediator of hypercalcemia has not been identified with certainty, but available evidence suggests a role for PTHrP.

The causes of hypercalcemia in lymphoma are variable. In the majority of patients, hypercalcemia is probably caused by secretion of a cytokine. In some patients, $1,25(OH)_2D_3$ appears to be the mediator of hypercalcemia. The latter patients probably have increased intestinal calcium absorption, as well as increased bone resorption, and they respond to glucocorticoid therapy. It is recognized that human monocytes in sarcoid granulomas can produce 1,25 $(OH)_2D_3$, and it is likely that lymphoma cells are similarly capable of synthesis of this metabolite. The histology of the tumor in patients with high levels of 1,25$(OH)_2D_3$ is diverse; histiocytic, lymphocytic, Hodgkin, and HTLV-positive T cell lymphomas are seen. That a single pathogenetic mechanism would cut across histologic lines of classification in this manner is surprising.

Treatment

The treatment of hypercalcemia is discussed in Chapter 5.

THE SYNDROME OF INAPPROPRIATE ADH SECRETION

The syndrome of inappropriate secretion of antidiuretic hormone (SIADH) is probably the second most common endocrine complication seen in cancer patients. The syndrome is seen in 10–40% of patients with small-cell carcinoma of the lung, the tumor that most commonly produces vasopressin excess. Other causative tumors, many of which are neuroendocrine tumors, include adenocarcinoma and large-cell carcinoma of the lung, bronchial carcinoids, carcinoma of the duodenum, small-cell carcinoma of the prostate, thymoma, and adrenocortical carcinoma.

Etiology & Pathogenesis

SIADH is now recognized as the most common cause of hyponatremia in hospitalized patients, but most cases result from central (eutopic) secretion of vasopressin, with only 16–50% of cases in different series resulting from ectopic secretion of vasopressin by tumors. The differential diagnosis of hyponatremia is discussed in Chapter 2.

In the presence of vasopressin, excretion of free water is impaired. If the intake of free water exceeds the limited excretion of free water, water intoxication and hyponatremia ensue, with the appearance of symptoms as the serum sodium falls below 125 meq/L. However, if the thirst mechanism is intact and the patient appropriately reduces water intake, a moderate excess of vasopressin may be well tolerated. Thus, the severity of the syndrome depends on water intake as well as on the vasopressin level.

Lung cancer cells have been shown to synthesize a molecule closely resembling propressophysin, the vasopressin precursor, and to secrete immunoreactive vasopressin together with a neurophysin, the other product of its precursor. (Ectopic secretion of the sister octapeptide hormone oxytocin also occurs in small-cell lung carcinoma, but is not associated with a distinctive clinical syndrome.) In 70–90% of patients with small-cell lung carcinoma, the plasma level of at least one of the four neurohypophysial peptides (vasopressin, oxytocin and their associated neurophysins) is increased. Many of these patients may in fact have asymptomatic, compensated ectopic secretion of vasopressin, with normal serum osmolality but impaired ability to excrete a water load. However, some cancer patients with hyponatremia and elevated plasma vasopressin levels probably have central or eutopic—rather than ectopic—hypersecretion of vasopressin. For example, in some patients the vasopressin level increases as the plasma osmolality is increased by infusion of hypertonic saline; ie, secretion is under osmotic control. As tumors have not been shown to express an osmoreceptor, these patients probably have a pituitary source of vasopressin. Pituitary secretion of vasopressin could result from stimulation of peripheral baroreceptors by tumor or by hypovolemia.

Clinical Features

Progressive weakness, lethargy, somnolence, and confusion often appear when the serum sodium is less than 125 meq/L; coma, seizures, and death usually occurs when the serum sodium is less than 110 meq/L. Patients experience weight gain but no edema, as the retained water is distributed among both intracellular and extracellular spaces. By definition, the urinary osmolality is inappropriately high for the systemic hypo-osmolality. Blood urea nitrogen is often relatively low and the urinary excretion of sodium relatively high, reflecting the expansion of body fluid spaces by retained water. Hypouricemia is often seen. The diagnosis of SIADH is established by excluding other causes of hyponatremia, such as hypovolemia, edematous states, hypothyroidism, and adrenal insufficiency. The presence of inappropriately elevated vasopressin levels can be confirmed by radioimmunoassay, but this step is often unnecessary. The treatment is restriction of water intake. In patients who cannot tolerate a reduction of water intake to correct hypo-osmolality, therapy with hypertonic saline, diuretics, or demeclocycline should be started (see Chapter 2).

CUSHING'S SYNDROME

The ectopic ACTH syndrome (Cushing's syndrome) is strongly associated with neuroendocrine (APUD) tumors. Lung tumors (bronchial carcinoids or small-cell lung carcinoma) account for 50% of all cases; 10% are caused by thymic carcinoid tumors (epithelial thymomas), 5% by abdominal carcinoid tumors, 10% by pancreatic islet cell tumors, 10% by pheochromocytomas, and 5% by medullary carcinoma of the thyroid. There is also a strong association of neuroendocrine tumors with secretion of calcitonin and GRP. Neuroendocrine cells are scattered throughout the normal bronchial mucosa, indicating that neuroendocrine cells may represent the cell of origin of small-cell carcinomas.

Many, perhaps most, lung tumors contain immunoreactive pro-opiomelanocortin, the ACTH precursor. However, some tumors that are not associated with Cushing's syndrome use a downstream transcription initiation site in the pro-opiomelanocortin gene that does not encode a functional protein. In addition, processing of pro-opiomelanocortin by nonpituitary tumors is frequently abnormal. It is primarily tumors of the neuroendocrine type that process and secrete enough ACTH to cause the clinical manifestations of Cushing's syndrome. It is likely that the ability of neuroendocrine tumors to process and secrete ACTH is related to the dense secretory granules that characterize neuroendocrine cells. However, processing of ACTH is probably abnormal even in a majority of neuroendocrine tumors; it is secreted in a large form that results from incomplete processing of its precursor, and it has reduced biologic activity. At least 25% of patients with small-cell lung carcinoma show elevated immunoreactive ACTH levels, but most of these patients have no evidence of cortisol excess.

Clinical Features

The classic somatic features of Cushing's syndrome are not present in most patients with Cushing's syndrome associated with nonendocrine tumors. Although cortisol levels are often very high, moon facies, truncal obesity, and cutaneous striae, which reflect the effect of cortisol on protein and fat metabolism, probably do not have time to develop. The syndrome usually develops rapidly and presents with weight loss, wasting, hypokalemia, and muscle weakness. The treatment of Cushing's syndrome is discussed in Chapter 6.

Diagnosis

The differential diagnosis of glucocorticoid excess is presented in Chapter 6. The ectopic ACTH syndrome can usually be distinguished from other forms of Cushing's syndrome by its clinical presentation and by the failure of glucocorticoids to suppress the secretion of ACTH. There is typically no response to administration of corticotropin-releasing hormone (CRH). However, certain slow-growing tumors are associated with chronic secretion of ACTH and produce classic Cushing's syndrome. These tumors are often bronchial or thymic carcinoid tumors, about half of which may be suppressed by administration of dexamethasone in high doses. These tumors are a diagnostic challenge, because they are sometimes too small to be detected radiologically and because they may mimic perfectly the secretory dynamics of pituitary Cushing's disease. Their suppressibility is rare among ectopic hormone syndromes and is presum-

ably due to their expression of both the glucocorticoid receptor and a glucocorticoid-responsive element in the pro-opiomelanocortin gene. In cases where the secretory dynamics do not clearly distinguish between pituitary and ectopic sources of ACTH, measurement of ACTH in bilateral samples from the inferior petrosal sinuses, preferably after administration of CRH, may establish whether a pituitary source is present.

An alternative explanation for the suppressibility of bronchial and thymic carcinoids is that they may produce CRH, whose effect on pituitary corticotrophs is suppressed by glucocorticoids. Several tumors have been reported to secrete both ACTH and CRH; the role of CRH in the pathogenesis of hypercortisolism in patients with such tumors is not clear in all cases. In a small number of these patients it seems clear that ectopic secretion of CRH was the basis for the development of Cushing's syndrome. Unexpectedly, in several of these patients ACTH was not suppressible by dexamethasone. The reason for this finding is unknown.

NON-ISLET-CELL TUMORS & HYPOGLYCEMIA

Fasting hypoglycemia has been associated with a variety of non-islet-cell tumors. Bulky mesenchymal tumors arising in the retroperitoneum, abdomen, or chest (eg, fibrosarcomas, rhabdomyosarcomas, mesotheliomas, and hemangiopericytomas) account for half of all cases. Hepatocellular carcinomas (hepatomas), gastrointestinal carcinomas, carcinoids, and adrenocortical carcinomas together account for about 25%. A wide variety of carcinomas make up the remaining 25%.

The clinical presentation and differential diagnosis of fasting hypoglycemia are discussed in Chapter 16. A distinctive feature of hypoglycemia associated with nonpancreatic tumors is that insulin levels are suppressed. What then is the cause of hypoglycemia? High rates of glucose utilization have been observed in some patients. Hepatic glucose production may also be impaired. It has been suggested that excessive utilization of glucose by extremely large tumors could outstrip hepatic glucose output, but these findings could more readily be accounted for by elaboration of an insulin-like factor that increases peripheral glucose utilization while suppressing glucose output. An IGF-2-like substance has been detected in the serum of some patients with hypoglycemia associated with cancer, and IGF-2 in mRNA has been found in some tumors. It is not clear that levels of IGF-2 in these individuals were high enough to cause hypoglycemia directly. In other patients, neither IGF-1 nor IGF-2 levels in serum were increased by radioimmunoassay or by radioreceptor assay. The association of IGF-2 with its serum binding proteins is abnormal in patients with non-islet-cell tumors and hypoglycemia. It is possible the small circulating complexes of IGF-2 in these patients are not sequestered in the blood and are thus accessible to extravascular receptors, thus accounting for hypoglycemia with minimally increased IGF-2 levels. It is likely that production of IGF-2 is sometimes involved in stimulating glucose utilization, but other factors may be contributive. Besides increased glucose utilization by the tumor, such factors include deficiency of the glucose counterregulatory hormones (particularly growth hormone) and decreased amino acid flux to the liver as substrate for hepatic gluconeogenesis, resulting from inanition or from effects of IGF-2.

OTHER HORMONES SECRETED BY TUMORS

Gonadotropins & Other Glycoprotein Hormones

hCG is produced eutopically by trophoblastic and other germ cell tumors, including testicular embryonal carcinoma and extragonadal germ cell tumors such as ectopic pinealoma, and in these cases it is highly useful as a tumor marker. hCG is secreted "ectopically" by many tumors. Elevated serum levels are found in 10–30% of patients with lung, breast, gastrointestinal, and ovarian tumors, and in some patients with melanoma. hCG has also been detected in low levels in a variety of normal tissues. In one study elevated levels were found in 9% of patients with various benign diseases, including inflammatory bowel disease, duodenal ulcer disease, and cirrhosis.

Some tumors do not process hCG normally; they secrete free subunits. hCG is a heterodimeric glycoprotein hormone composed of an alpha subunit, which is shared with the other glycoprotein hormones, and a unique beta subunit. Secretion of free alpha subunits is much more common than secretion of free βhCG. One instance in which measurement of subunits is indicated is in patients with pancreatic islet-cell tumors. Secretion of intact hCG is rare in islet-cell tumors, but about half of malignant functional islet-cell tumors secrete alpha subunit while benign islet-cell tumors rarely do.

hCG is the only ectopically secreted hormone composed of multiple subunits, thus requiring the expression of 2 different genes. The other glycoprotein hormones, follicle-stimulating hormone (FSH), luteinizing hormone (LH), and thyroid-stimulating hormone (TSH) are rarely, if ever, produced by extrapituitary tumors. Presumably, the propensity of tumors to secrete hCG is related to its expression at low levels in many of their cells of origin in normal tissues.

The clinical syndromes associated with tumor production of hCG are isosexual precocious pseudopuberty in children and bilateral gynecomastia in adult males. Isosexual precocity occurs in boys with hepatoblastoma. Gynecomastia in adult males probably results from increased estrogen levels resulting from conversion of circulating androgens, rather than a direct effect of hCG on the breast. Ectopic secretion of hCG is a relatively uncommon cause of gynecomastia (see Chapter 9).

Growth Hormone-Releasing Hormone, Growth Hormone, & Placental Lactogen

Since 1980, 30 cases of acromegaly have been associated with extrapituitary production of growth hormone-releasing hormone (GRH). In fact, GRH was first isolated from pancreatic tumors associated with acromegaly. The tumors involved have all been neuroendocrine tumors of the pancreas, lung, or gut (85% involved pancreas or lung). The clinical features of acromegaly induced by GRH do not differ from the common form induced by growth hormone (GH) except for the symptoms and signs of the extrapituitary tumor. The response to provocative testing is also unhelpful in detecting GRH-induced acromegaly, but elevated levels of plasma GRH on radioimmunoassay are diagnostic, and this determination should be performed in patients with acromegaly and extrapituitary malignant disease.

Extrapituitary secretion of GH itself is very rare. In one well-documented case, secretion from a pancreatic islet-cell tumor was confirmed by measurement of an arteriovenous gradient for GH across the tumor and a high tumor content of both GH and GH mRNA. In contrast to growth hormone, human placental lactogen (chorionic somatomammotropin) is frequently secreted by tumors. In a large series, placental lactogen was detectable in plasma in 9% of patients with malignant disease. Lung carcinoma was the commonest source. Galactorrhea was not present in these patients. The pituitary lactotrophic hormone prolactin is rarely secreted ectopically.

Calcitonin

Like ACTH, vasopressin, and GRP, calcitonin is present in neuroendocrine cells of the normal bronchial epithelium. Calcitonin is frequently secreted by tumors of the neuroendocrine type, including 60% of small-cell lung carcinomas. Calcitonin is also secreted by other lung carcinomas (15% of large-cell lung carcinomas), breast cancer, leukemia, and a broad spectrum of other cancers. Secretion of calcitonin is not associated with a distinctive clinical syndrome. In part, this may result from incomplete processing of large forms of ectopic calcitonin with reduced biologic activity. However, hypercalcitoninemia is also asymptomatic in medullary thyroid carcinoma, where levels of monomeric calcitonin are sometimes greatly elevated. Secretion of calcitonin by extrathyroidal tumors may respond to secreta-

gogues such as pentagastrin, but the response is smaller than in medullary thyroid carcinoma.

Oncogenous Osteomalacia Factor

Osteomalacia, or rickets, accompanied by hypophosphatemia occurs in association with tumors of mesenchymal origin, usually small benign tumors of the extremities. Over 50 cases have been reported, making this the commonest cause of late-onset hypophosphatemic rickets. The tumors associated with this syndrome are often highly vascular (hemangiomas, hemangiopericytomas) and frequently include giant cells. The presentation is of osteomalacia with renal phosphate wasting and low levels of $1,25(OH)_2D_3$. The syndrome is rapidly and completely reversed by resection of the tumor, clearly establishing its humoral basis. However, the humor involved has not been identified. The only type of epithelial malignancy strongly associated with this syndrome is prostate carcinoma, in which 20% of patients may be hypophosphatemic and a smaller percentage develop osteomalacia.

Hypothalamic-Pituitary Hormones

Ectopic secretion of CRH and GRH was discussed above. Beta-endorphin, β-lipotropin, and other products of pro-opiomelanocortin are associated with the ectopic ACTH syndrome, but they do not produce clinical syndromes other than hyperpigmentation (see Chapter 2). Thyrotropin-releasing hormone (TRH) and somatostatin are detectable in a variety of tumors, mostly of the neuroendocrine type, but clinical disorders that are due to their ectopic secretion have not been reported.

Gut Hormones

Vasoactive intestinal polypeptide (VIP) secretion has produced the watery diarrhea-hypokalemia-achlorhydria syndrome in patients with squamous lung carcinoma, ganglioneuroma, and ganglioneuroblastoma. Somatostatin, VIP, GRP (bombesin), motilin, pancreatic polypeptide, and substance P have repeatedly been found in tumors, often of the neuroendocrine type, but have not clearly produced symptoms.

Erythropoietin

One to 3 percent of renal carcinomas, 5% of hepatocellular carcinomas, and 10% of cerebellar hemangioblastomas are associated with erythrocytosis, probably resulting from secretion of erythropoietin. In some cases production of erythropoietin-like activity or expression of erythropoietin mRNA by tumor cells has been demonstrated. However, serum erythropoietin levels on radioimmunoassay correlate poorly with the presence of erythrocytosis in patients with hepatocellular carcinoma.

Renin

Renin-secreting renal tumors are extremely rare, and are associated with severe hypokalemia and hypertension. Removal of the tumor is curative. (See Chapter 7.)

REFERENCES

General

Baylin, SB, Mendelsohn G: Ectopic (inappropriate) hormone production by tumors: Mechanisms involved and the biological and clinical implications. Endocr Rev 1980;1:45.

Hansen M, Pedersen AG: Tumor markers in patients with lung cancer. Chest 1986;89(4 Suppl):219S.

LeDouarin NM: On the origin of pancreatic endocrine cells. Cell 1988;53:169. Daughaday WH, Deuel TF: Tumor secretion of growth factors. Endocrinol Metab Clin North Am 1991;20:539.

Hypercalcemia of Cancer

Breslau NA et al: Hypercalcemia associated with increased serum calcitriol levels in three patients with lymphoma. Ann Intern Med 1984;100:1.

Broadus AE et al: Humoral hypercalcemia of cancer: Identification of a novel parathyroid hormonelike peptide. N Engl J Med 1988;319:556.

Budayr A et al: Increased serum levels of a parathyroid hormone-like protein in malignancy-associated hypercalcemia. Ann Intern Med 1989;111:807.

Bunn PA Jr et al: Clinical course of retrovirus-associated adult T-cell lymphoma in the United States. N Engl J Med 1983;309:257.

Burtis WJ et al: Immunochemical characterization of circulation parathyroid hormone-related protein in patients with humoral hypercalcemia of cancer. N Engl J Med 1990;322:1106.

Fisken RA, Heath DA, Bold AM: Hypercalcemia: A hospital survey. Q J Med 1980;49:405.

Fukumoto S et al: Clinical evaluation of calcium metabolism in adult T-cell leukemia/lymphoma. Arch Intern Med 1988;148:921.

Garrett IR et al: Production of lymphotoxin, a bone-resorbing cytokine, by cultured human myeloma cells. N Engl J Med 1987;317:526.

Halloran BP, Nissenson RA: *Parathyroid Hormone-Related Protein: Normal Physiology and Its Role in Cancer.* CRC Press, 1992.

Rosenthal N et al: Elevations in circulating 1,25-dihydroxyvitamin D in three patients with lymphoma-associated hypercalcemia. J Clin Endocrinol Metab 1985; 60:29.

Stewart AF et al: Biochemical evaluation of patients with cancer-associated hypercalcemia: Evidence for humoral and nonhumoral groups. N Engl J Med 1980; 303:1377.

Strewler GJ, Nissenson RA: Peptide mediators of hypercalcemia in malignancy. Annu Rev Med 1990;41:35.

Syndrome of Inappropriate Secretion of ADH

Anderson RJ et al: Hyponatremia: A prospective analysis of its epidemiology and the pathogenetic role of vasopressin. Ann Intern Med 1985;102:164.

Forrest JN Jr et al: Superiority of demeclocycline over lithium in the treatment of chronic syndrome of inappropriate secretion of antidiuretic hormone. N Engl J Med 1978;298:173.

Moses AM, Scheinman SJ: Ectopic secretion of Neurohypophyseal peptides in patients with malignancy. Endocrinol Metab Clin North Am 1991;20:489.

Nissenson RA, Strewler GJ: Molecular mechanism of action of PTHrP. In: *Parathyroid Hormone-Related Protein: Normal Physiology and Its Role in Cancer*. Halloran BP, Nissenson RA (editors). CRC Press, 1992.

Zerbe R, Stropes L, Robertson G: Vasopressin function in the syndrome of inappropriate antidiuresis. Annu Rev Med 1980;31:315.

Cushing's Syndrome

Carey RM et al: Ectopic secretion of corticotropin-releasing factor as a cause of Cushing's syndrome: A clinical, morphologic, and biochemical study. N Engl J Med 1984;311:13.

de Keyzer Y et al: Altered proopiomelanocortin gene expression in adrenocorticotropin-producing nonpituitary tumors: Comparative studies with corticotropic adenomas and normal pituitaries. J Clin Invest 1985;76:1892.

Findling JW, Tyrrell JB: Occult ectopic secretion of corticotropin. Arch Intern Med 1986;146:929.

Oldfield EH et al: Petrosal sinus sampling with and without corticotropin-releasing hormone for the differential diagnosis of Cushing's syndrome. N Engl J Med 1991;325:897.

Schteingart DE: Ectopic secretion of peptides of the proopiomelanocortin family. Endocrinol Metab Clin North Am 1991;20:453.

Hypoglycemia

Baxter RC, Daughaday WH: Impaired formation of the ternary insulin-like growth factor-binding protein complex in patients with hypoglycemia due to non-islet cell tumors. J Clin Endocrinol Metab 1991;73:696.

Daughaday WH et al: Synthesis and secretion of insulin-like growth factor II by a leiomyosarcoma with associated hypoglycemia. N Engl J Med 1988;319:1434.

Daughaday WH: Hypoglycemia in patients with non-islet cell tumors. Endocrinol Metab Clin North Am 1989;18:91.

Gonadotropins

Bates SE, Longo DL: Use of serum tumor markers in cancer diagnosis and management. Semin Oncol 1987; 14:102.

Kahn CR et al: Ectopic production of chorionic gonadotropin and its subunits by islet-cell tumors: A specific marker for malignancy. N Engl J Med 1977; 297:565.

GRH, Growth Hormone, & Placental Lactogen

Melmed S et al: Acromegaly due to secretion of growth hormone by an ectopic pancreatic islet-cell tumor. N Engl J Med 1985;312:9.

Sano T, Asa SL, Kovacs K: Growth hormone-releasing hormone-producing tumors: Clinical, biochemical, and morphological manifestations. Endocr Rev 1988;9:357.

Weintraub BD, Rosen SW: Ectopic production of human chorionic somatomammotropin by nontrophoblastic cancers. J Clin Endocrinol Metab 1971;32:94.

Calcitonin

Roos BA et al: Plasma immunoreactive calcitonin in lung cancer. J Clin Endocrinol Metab 1980;50:659.

Samaan NA et al: Serum calcitonin after pentagastrin stimulation in patients with bronchogenic and breast cancer compared to that in patients with medullary thyroid carcinoma. J Clin Endocrinol Metab 1980; 51:237.

Zajac JD et al: Biosynthesis of calcitonin by human lung cancer cells. Endocrinology 1985;116:749.

Oncogenous Osteomalacia Factor

Lyles KW et al: Hypophosphatemic osteomalacia: Association with prostatic carcinoma. Ann Intern Med 1980;93:275.

Ryan EA, Reiss E: Oncogenous osteomalacia: Review of the world literature of 42 cases and report of two new cases. Am J Med 1984;77:501.

Weidner N et al: Neoplastic pathology of oncogenic osteomalacia/rickets. Cancer 1985;55:1691.

Hypothalamic-Pituitary Hormones

Melmed S, Rushakoff RJ: Ectopic pituitary and hypothalamic hormone syndromes. Endocrinol Metab Clin North Am 1987;16:805.

Gut Hormones

Noseda A et al: Increased plasma motilin concentrations in small cell carcinoma of the lung. Thorax 1987; 42:784.

Erythropoietin

Kew MC, Fisher JW: Serum erythropoietin concentrations in patients with hepatocellular carcinoma. Cancer 1986;58:2485.

Syndromes Involving Multiple Endocrine Glands

21

Leonard J. Deftos, MD, & Bayard D. Catherwood, MD

MULTIPLE ENDOCRINE NEOPLASIA

Astute clinical observation has resulted in the identification of neoplastic syndromes involving multiple endocrine glands. The glands most commonly involved in such syndromes are the parathyroid, pituitary, pancreas, thyroid, and adrenal. The cell types involved in these tumors are postulated to have a common embryologic precursor in the neuroectoderm. This embryologic feature may be accompanied by the presence of the metabolic pathway for *a*mine *p*recursor *u*ptake and *d*ecarboxylation—thus the appellation APUD cells (see Chapter 20). Oncogenic mutational factors may also influence expression of these tumors. The multiple endocrine neoplasia syndromes are usually transmitted in an autosomal dominant inheritance pattern, but there may be considerable variability in penetrance and in specific tumor incidences among kindreds. The gene or genes associated with multiple endocrine disorders have recently been mapped, and new syndromes are being recognized. The availability of genetic markers may revolutionize the diagnosis of inherited endocrine tumors.

There are three well-defined types of multiple endocrine neoplasia (MEN) syndromes (Table 21–1): **MEN type I** (also called Wermer's syndrome), **MEN type IIa** (also called Sipple's syndrome and MEN type II), and **MEN type IIb** (also called MEN type III). The clinical descriptions and terminology for these syndromes have evolved from 1954 to the present. The first MEN syndrome was clearly described by Wermer in 1954 and was characterized by tumors of the parathyroids, pituitary, and pancreas. Shortly thereafter, Zollinger and Ellison described a syndrome that consisted of gastric hypersecretion and severe peptic disease associated with a non-insulin-producing islet cell tumor of the pancreas. This syndrome, the Zollinger-Ellison syndrome, is found in association with MEN type I in some cases but more commonly occurs by itself. In 1961, Sipple re-

ACRONYMS USED IN THIS CHAPTER

ACTH	Adrenocorticotropic hormone
APUD	Amine precursor uptake and decarboxylation
CGRP	Calcitonin gene-related peptide
CT	Calcitonin
GH	Growth hormone
HLA	Human leukocyte antigen
LH	Luteinizing hormone
MEN	Multiple endocrine neoplasia
MSH	Melanocyte-stimulating hormone
POEMS	Polyneuropathy, organomegaly, endocrinopathy, M protein, and skin changes
PP	Pancreatic polypeptide
PRL	Prolactin
PTH	Parathyroid hormone
TSH	Thyroid-stimulating hormone (thyrotropin)
VIP	Vasoactive intestinal polypeptide

ported the association between thyroid cancer and pheochromocytoma. Through the subsequent studies of Williams and Hazard, a distinct thyroid tumor of the calcitonin-producing cells (C cells) of the thyroid—ie, medullary thyroid carcinoma—was defined. Characterization of the second MEN syndrome, consisting of medullary thyroid carcinoma, parathyroid tumors, and pheochromocytoma, evolved from these observations. The additional observation that there were two accompanying somatotypic features—ie, a marfanoid habitus and multiple mucosal neuromas—in some patients with this second type of MEN syndrome led to the classification of the third type of MEN syndrome. In summary, the **major components** of the three syndromes are as follows: **MEN type I**—tumors of the parathyroids, pituitary, and pancreas, and, in some cases, components of the Zollinger-Ellison syndrome; **MEN type IIa**—medullary thyroid carcinoma, hyperparathyroidism, and pheochromocytoma; and **MEN type IIb**—medullary thyroid carcinoma, pheochromocytoma, marfanoid habitus, and multiple mucosal neuromas.

In general, the clinical and biochemical character-

Table 21–1. Components of the multiple endocrine neoplasias (MEN).

MEN type I
  Parathyroid tumors
  Pituitary tumors
  Pancreatic tumors
MEN type IIa
  Medullary thyroid carcinoma
  Pheochromocytoma
  Hyperparathyroidism
MEN type IIb
  Medullary thyroid carcinoma
  Pheochromocytoma
  Mucosal neuromas

istics of component tumors of MEN syndromes do not differ markedly from characteristics of each tumor when it occurs by itself; therefore, those aspects are only briefly described in this chapter. For example, primary hyperparathyroidism as part of a MEN syndrome has most of the characteristics of multiglomerular hyperparathyroidism occurring alone, and the reader should consult Chapter 5 for a more detailed description of the features of primary hyperparathyroidism. However, the presence of multiple endocrinopathies presents a unique clinical picture (Table 21–2), and the presence of multiple endocrine tumors does have specific implications for therapy.

MULTIPLE ENDOCRINE NEOPLASIA TYPE I

MEN type I—easily remembered as the "PPP" syndrome—is characterized by tumors of the parathyroids, pituitary, and pancreas. The most common pituitary tumor is benign chromophobe adenoma; the most common pancreatic tumor is gastrinoma; and the most common parathyroid lesion is multiglandular primary hyperparathyroidism. Table 21–3 shows the approximate frequency of occurrence of the components of MEN type I. The actual pattern may vary among kindreds. Tumors other than the three principal components of the syndrome (Table 21–3) are rare, and their relationship to the genetic disorder is unclear. This disorder has been mapped to chromosome 11.

Primary Hyperparathyroidism

Primary hyperparathyroidism is the most common endocrine neoplasia of MEN type I. Thus, upon identifying a patient with primary hyperparathyroidism, it is important to determine whether other components of the syndrome are present. The pathologic characteristics of the parathyroid glands can be best understood by recognizing the multiglandular nature of the disorder. The glands have been described in various terms ranging from adenomatous to hyperplastic. The histologic features necessary to make these classifications are not always apparent. Although chief cells are usually dominant, clear cells or a mixed picture may also be seen. The most important practical point to be derived from pathologic descriptions is the potential for *all* parathyroid glands to be involved in the neoplastic process, even ectopic glands. This means that aggressive surgical therapy directed toward subtotal parathyroidectomy may be necessary for effective treatment.

Pituitary Tumors

The most common pituitary tumor of MEN type I is chromophobe adenoma. This nonfunctioning tumor is usually benign by histologic criteria but can cause endocrine abnormalities by the effect of its mass on adjacent endocrine cells. Tumors producing

Table 21–2. Abnormal hormone production by endocrine tumors of MEN syndromes. Measurement of these substances or their metabolites in blood and urine can serve as diagnostic tests.

	Pituitary	Pancreas	Parathyroid	Thyroid	Adrenal
PTH			•		
CT		•		•	
ACTH	•			•	
GH	•				
Somatostatin	•	•			
PRL	•				
VIP		•			
PP		•			
Gastrin		•			
Insulin		•			
Glucagon		•			
Catecholamines					•
Chromogranin A	•	•	•	•	•

Table 21–3. Components of MEN type I and their approximate frequency of occurrence in patients with MEN type I.

Component		Frequency
Hyperparathyroidism		80%
Pancreatic tumors		75%
Gastrinomas		
Benign	20%	
Malignant	30%	
Insulinomas		
Benign	20%	
Malignant	5%	
Nonfunctioning tumors		
Benign	< 5%	
Malignant	< 5%	
Pituitary tumors		65%
Chromophobe or nonfunctioning adenomas		
Benign	40%	
Malignant	< 5%	
Eosinophilic tumors or acromegaly (benign)	15%	
Cushing's disease, basophilic	5%	
Mixed and other types (benign)	< 5%	
Prolactin-secreting tumors	< 5%	
Other tumors		
Carcinoid and bronchial adenomas	< 5%	
Lipomas and liposarcomas	5%	
Adrenocortical adenomas	10%	

growth hormone (GH), adrenocorticotropic hormone (ACTH), prolactin (PRL), and somatostatin have also been described in this syndrome, and their manifestations are classically related to their location and hormonal products. The incidence of pituitary microadenomas is not well defined.

Pancreatic Tumors

Gastrin-producing islet cell tumors are the most common pancreatic neoplasias of MEN type I, accounting for at least 50% of all pancreatic tumors. Gastrinomas can also occur at other sites such as the duodenal wall and stomach. Insulinomas are the next most common neoplasias. In addition, there are case reports of tumors producing vasoactive intestinal polypeptide (VIP), glucagon, pancreatic polypeptide (PP), somatostatin, and calcitonin (CT). Measurement by radioimmunoassay of these hormones in serum is an important diagnostic procedure. The "tumors" are usually composed of hyperplastic islet cells or multiple small tumors. The secretory products of these tumors can explain some of the associated findings. Examples are the peptic ulcer diathesis with gastrin, hypoglycemia with insulin, and secretory diarrhea with VIP and perhaps with PP. Glucagonomas can be associated with bullous dermatitis, but the pathogenesis of this lesion is obscure.

The production of excess gastrin leading to peptic ulceration by a pancreatic islet cell tumor is called **Zollinger-Ellison syndrome.** Zollinger-Ellison syndrome more commonly occurs by itself, but it can also be part of MEN type I. The ulcer diathesis of Zollinger-Ellison syndrome makes gastrointestinal symptoms a dominant clinical feature. Gastrointestinal symptoms may also be dominant in a patient with a VIP-producing islet cell tumor (VIPoma) (see Chapter 14).

Other Tumors

The other tumors indicated in Table 21–3 are also found in patients with MEN type I, but their link to this disorder is not clearly established. Carcinoid tumors associated with MEN type I are more likely to be found in foregut-derived structures such as the thymus and bronchial tree than in midgut-derived structures, where sporadic carcinoid tumors usually occur. Bronchial carcinoid can produce its vasoactive symptoms without metastasizing. Adrenal and thyroid adenomas occurring in MEN type I represent predominantly the results of autopsy findings and are usually nonfunctioning. Lipomas may be present in some kindreds in MEN type I, and when cutaneous they may provide a useful sign of the syndrome.

MULTIPLE ENDOCRINE NEOPLASIA TYPES IIa & IIb

In the early reports of medullary thyroid carcinoma as part of a multiple endocrine disorder, the associated lesions were pheochromocytoma, hyperparathyroidism, and a syndrome consisting of multiple mucosal neuromas and marfanoid habitus (mucosal neuroma syndrome). It is now appreciated that two distinct clinical syndromes can be defined by these associated endocrinopathies: MEN type IIa (Table 21–4) and MEN type IIb (Table 21–5). MEN type IIa consists of medullary thyroid carcinoma, pheochromocytoma, and hyperparathyroidism; MEN type IIb consists of medullary thyroid carcinoma, pheochromocytoma, multiple mucosal neuromas, and marfanoid habitus. The component tumors of MEN type IIa and MEN type IIb vary in their incidence and prevalence. Since medullary thyroid carcinoma is the central tumor, it will be discussed first. MEN type IIa has been mapped to chromosome 10.

Medullary Thyroid Carcinoma

Medullary thyroid carcinoma, a tumor of the calcitonin-producing cells (C cells) of the thyroid gland, is a component of MEN type IIa and IIb. The thyroidal C cells are now generally accepted to be of neural crest origin. These cells migrate to the ultimobranchial bodies from the neural crest. In submammals, the cells form a distinct organ, the ultimobranchial organ, which harbors C cells and their secretory product, calcitonin. In mammals, C cells become incorporated into the thyroid gland and perhaps other sites. The neural crest origin of C cells offers an explanation for the association of medullary

Table 21–4. Components of MEN type IIa and their approximate frequency of occurrence in patients with MEN type IIa.

Component	Frequency
Medullary thyroid carcinoma	97%
Hyperparathyroidism	50%
Pheochromocytoma	30%

thyroid carcinoma with other tumors of neural crest origin and also appears to explain the production by these tumors of a wide variety of bioactive substances.

Medullary thyroid carcinoma is usually a firm, rounded tumor located in the middle or upper lobes of the thyroid gland. The cells usually are polyhedral or polygonal and are arranged in a variety of patterns. Calcification is commonly found in the tumor, and a characteristic calcification may be visible on x-ray. Although the presence of amyloid has long been considered to be important in the diagnosis of medullary thyroid carcinoma, the diagnosis is best established by the use of specific immunohistochemical procedures for calcitonin that demonstrate the abnormal C cells. The frank malignancy of medullary thyroid carcinoma, at least in familial cases, is preceded by a progressive hyperplasia of C cells referred to as **C cell hyperplasia.** This predecessor of medullary thyroid carcinoma can become manifest in early childhood or as late as the second decade. There may be corresponding changes in the parathyroid and adrenal glands. Several instances of **C cell adenoma** have also been reported. The natural history of medullary thyroid carcinoma can vary greatly, and this may make decisions regarding therapy difficult. The tumor is generally regarded as intermediate between the aggressive behavior of anaplastic thyroid carcinoma and the more indolent behavior of papillary and follicular thyroid carcinoma. The most common presentation is a thyroid nodule, and the most common symptom is diarrhea.

There are two general groups of factors that can contribute to the diarrhea commonly seen in patients with medullary thyroid carcinoma—humoral factors and anatomic ones. Many of the various bioactive substances produced by medullary thyroid carcinoma have been implicated in the pathogenesis of the diarrhea seen with this tumor. These peptide hormones include (1) calcitonin, (2) ACTH and melanocyte-

Table 21–5. Components of MEN type IIb and their approximate frequency of occurrence in patients with MEN type IIb.

Component	Frequency
Multiple mucosal neuromas	100%
Medullary thyroid carcinoma	90%
Marfanoid habitus	65%
Pheochromocytoma	45%

stimulating hormone (MSH), (3) neurotensin, (4) somatostatin, (5) β-endorphin, and (6) nerve growth factor (Table 21–6). The various anatomic abnormalities discussed subsequently that can be found in the gastrointestinal tract of patients with medullary thyroid carcinoma may also account for the diarrhea. These anatomic lesions may reflect and perhaps even produce fundamental abnormalities in gastrointestinal innervation that can produce abnormal motility.

A. Calcitonin and Related Peptides and Proteins: Since medullary thyroid carcinoma is a neoplastic disorder of the C cells of the thyroid gland, the tumor produces abnormally high amounts of calcitonin. As a result, patients with this tumor have elevated concentrations of calcitonin in peripheral blood and urine. In many patients, basal concentrations of the hormone are sufficiently elevated to be diagnostic of the presence of medullary thyroid carcinoma. However, in an increasing percentage of patients with this tumor, basal levels of calcitonin are indistinguishable from normal. Thus, **provocative tests** with calcium and pentagastrin have been developed for the diagnosis of medullary thyroid carcinoma and its histologic antecedents. These tests are based on the observation that calcium and pentagastrin are potent calcitonin secretagogues.

Opinion differs regarding the relative clinical value of pentagastrin and calcium infusion in the diagnosis of medullary thyroid carcinoma. One must remember that most tumors respond to either agent and that both infusion procedures sometimes give false-negative results. Therefore, either procedure can be recommended, and if one procedure gives negative results in a patient suspected of having medullary thyroid carcinoma, the alternative procedure should be considered before the diagnosis is excluded. In general, both the sensitivity and the specificity of the calcitonin immunoassay are probably just as important as the choice between calcium and pentagastrin in provocative testing of a patient suspected of having medullary thyroid carcinoma. Selective venous catheterization with measurements of calcitonin can also be useful, but its greatest value is probably not in primary diagnosis but in the location of tumor metastases (or sources of ectopic calcitonin production), since knowledge of the presence of metastatic (or ectopic) disease can greatly influence therapy. The effectiveness of therapy in patients with calcitonin-producing tumors can be monitored by serial measurements of plasma calcitonin. In addition to determining the relatively acute effects of a given treatment regimen, periodic surveillance with appropriate provocative testing can be conducted for recurrence of tumor.

The calcitonin gene encodes other peptides, among them a 37-amino-acid peptide termed CGRP (calcitonin gene-related peptide) (Table 21–6). Although the function of these peptides is unknown, they are secreted by medullary thyroid carcinoma and may

Table 21–6. Other products secreted by medullary thyroid carcinoma.

Catecholamines	Adrenocorticotropic hormone	Amyloid
Dopa decarboxylase	Melanocyte-stimulating hormone	Carcinoembryonic antigen
Histaminase	Somatostatin	Melanin
Serotonin	β-Endorphin	Neuron-specific enolase
Prostaglandins	Substance P	Chromogranin A
Kallikrein and kinins	Vasoactive intestinal polypeptide	
	Corticotropin-releasing hormone	
	Prolactin-releasing hormone	
	Nerve growth factor	
	Neurotensin gastrin-release peptide	

thus serve as tumor markers. C cells also secrete chromogranin A, a high-molecular-weight protein originally discovered in the secretory granules of pheochromocytomas and now known to be present in other endocrine tissues, among them the parathyroid, pancreas, and pituitary (Table 21–2). This protein could thus be a marker for each of the endocrine neoplasias encountered in any of the multiple endocrine neoplasias (Table 21–7).

B. Other Secretory Products: In addition to calcitonin, medullary thyroid carcinoma produces other substances, nonpeptides as well as peptides (Table 21–6). Their measurement in blood, eg, chromogranin A, may also be useful in diagnosis and management. This unusual biosynthetic capacity of medullary thyroid carcinoma may be related to the neural crest origin of C cells.

Pheochromocytoma

Pheochromocytoma is a component of MEN type IIa and IIb. Pheochromocytomas occurring in association with medullary thyroid carcinoma have several distinct features. Bilateral and multifocal pheochromocytomas are very common in this clinical setting, with an incidence of over 70%. This contrasts with a bilateral incidence of usually less than 10% for sporadic pheochromocytomas and only 20–50% with familial pheochromocytomas. Pheochromocytomas are much more likely to occur in patients with familial rather than sporadic medullary thyroid carcinoma. The thyroid tumor may antedate the pheochromocytoma by as much as 2 decades. Furthermore, a second pheochromocytoma may become manifest after

Table 21–7. Plasma calcitonin and chromogranin A concentrations (mean ± SE) in patients with endocrine tumors.

Group	Chromogranin A (ng/mL)	Calcitonin (pg/mL)
Normal controls (n = 16)	82 ± 16	60 ± 15
Pheochromocytoma (n = 11)	1614 ± 408[1]	. . .
Medullary thyroid carcinoma (n = 6)	789 ± 333[1]	7485 ± 3009[1]
Parathyroid adenoma (n = 7)	218 ± 13[1]	. . .

[1] P < .01 compared to control.

removal of the first. Thus, there is a greater incidence of pheochromocytomas in older patients with medullary thyroid carcinoma. If hyperparathyroidism also exists, it too is likely to be diagnosed before the pheochromocytoma. **Adrenal medullary hyperplasia** may be a predecessor of the pheochromocytomas seen with medullary thyroid carcinoma, just as C cell hyperplasia may be a predecessor of medullary thyroid carcinoma and chief cell hyperplasia a predecessor of primary hyperparathyroidism in these patients. The increase in adrenal medullary mass results from diffuse or multifocal proliferation of adrenal medullary cells, primarily those found within the head and body of the glands. Diagnostic tests for pheochromocytoma should be pursued vigorously, because the biochemical as well as clinical manifestations of this tumor may be subtle. A high ratio of epinephrine to norepinephrine—rather than absolute levels—is considered an important diagnostic criterion (see Chapter 8).

Hyperparathyroidism

The exact incidence of hyperparathyroidism in patients with medullary thyroid carcinoma is difficult to establish. Hyperparathyroidism is much more common in MEN type IIa than in MEN type IIb. Hyperplasia is more common than adenoma. Despite these uncertainties, the concurrence of hyperparathyroidism and medullary thyroid carcinoma in MEN syndromes is well established, and although it cannot be quantitated, the presence of one tumor should always make one suspect the presence of the other. Hyperparathyroidism does not easily fit into a unitary concept of embryogenesis, since parathyroid cells are not classically considered to be of neural crest origin. However, some authorities have suggested a neural crest origin for the parathyroid gland. An alternative explanation for the hyperparathyroidism is a functional relationship between it and medullary thyroid carcinoma. According to this hypothesis, the abnormal concentrations of calcitonin induce hyperparathyroidism, which is secondary to the hypocalcemic actions of the calcitonin. This type of functional relationship between the neoplasias is unlikely; the most convincing evidence supports a genetic relationship between medullary thyroid carcinoma and hyperparathyroidism (see Chapter 5).

Mucosal Neuromas

The presence of neuromas with a centrofacial distribution is the most consistent component of MEN type IIb. The most common location of neuromas is the oral cavity (tongue, lips, buccal mucosa), but other sites may be involved (Table 21–8). The oral lesions (Figure 21–1) are almost invariably present by the first decade and in some cases even at birth. The most prominent microscopic feature of neuromas is an increase in the size and number of nerves.

Mucosal neuromas can be present in the eyelids, conjunctiva, and cornea. The thickened medullated corneal nerves traverse the cornea and anastomose in the pupillary area. These hypertrophied nerve fibers are readily seen with a slit lamp but occasionally may be evident even on direct ophthalmoscopic examination.

Gastrointestinal tract abnormalities are part of the multiple mucosal neuroma syndrome. The most common of these is gastrointestinal ganglioneuromatosis. Ganglioneuromatosis is best observed in the small and large intestine but has also been noted in the esophagus and stomach. The anatomic lesions are sometimes associated with functional difficulties in swallowing, megacolon, diarrhea, and constipation. Similar lesions may be present on other mucosal surfaces.

21–8. Summary of clinical features in 41 patients with MEN type IIb.

	Number of patients With Findings[1]		
	Positive	Probable	Negative
Family history of MEN type IIb	14	2	15
Neuroma (any type)	41		
Oral type	37		4
Ocular type	24		16
Other type	4		36
"Bumpy" lips	35	2	
Pheochromocytoma	19[2]	4	18
Medullary thyroid carcinoma	38		2
Marfanoid habitus	26	5	
Hypertrophied corneal nerves	23		
Skeletal defects	24		4
Gastrointestinal tract abnormalities	23		10

[1] In some cases, the status of some of the clinical features was not known.
[2] Unilateral in 7 patients; bilateral in 12 patients.
(Reproduced and modified, with permission, from: Khairi MRA, et al: Mucosal neuroma, pheochromocytoma and medullary carcinoma: MEN, type III. Medicine 1975:54:89.)

Marfanoid Habitus

The term "marfanoid habitus" denotes a tall, slender body with long arms and legs, an abnormal ratio of upper to lower body segment, and poor muscle development. It is seen commonly in multiple mucosal neuroma syndrome. The extremities are thin, and there may be lax joints and hypotonic muscles. Other features associated with the marfanoid habitus may include dorsal kyphosis, pectus excavatum or pectus carinatum, pes cavus, and high-arched palate. In contrast to patients with true Marfan's syndrome, no patients with multiple mucosal neuromas have been reported to have aortic abnormalities, ectopia lentis, homocystinuria, or, notably, mucopolysaccharide abnormalities.

OTHER MULTIPLE ENDOCRINE NEOPLASIAS

Several additional syndromes exist that are characterized by the autosomal dominant inheritance of multiple endocrine tumors. The **von Hippel-Lindau syndrome** consists of cerebelloretinal hemangioblastomas occurring with pheochromocytomas and pancreatic islet cell tumors along with renal cell carcinoma. It has been linked to a deletion on chromosome 3. In addition to Schwann-cell tumors, patients with neurofibromatosis (**Recklinghausen's disease**) have pheochromocytomas and duodenal carcinoid tumors. This disorder has been mapped to chromosome 17, the location of the nerve growth factor receptor.

As with some other tumors, such as retinoblastoma

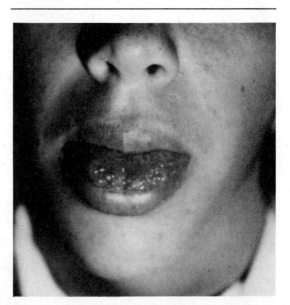

Figure 21–1. Mucosal neuromas on the tongue of a 12-year-old child with MEN type IIb.

and small-cell lung carcinoma, the presence of chromosomal deletions in endocrine tumors has led to the hypothesis that the deleted gene encodes an anti-oncogene whose absence allows oncogenesis to occur. Studies with the tools of molecular biology will provide important insights into the pathogenesis of inherited endocrine tumors (see Chapter 1).

MANAGEMENT OF PATIENTS WITH MULTIPLE ENDOCRINE NEOPLASIA (MEN) SYNDROMES

The individual endocrine components of MEN syndromes have, in general, the same clinical and biochemical manifestations as when they occur as individual entities. The unique clinical aspect of the patient with MEN is the way in which the individual presents to the physician. The patient may be part of a kindred with well-established MEN, and the physician must then evaluate the patient for each potential component of the kindred's syndrome. Or the physician may search for the presence of MEN when a patient presents with one of the endocrine components; in this latter circumstance, the yield will not be great, but when one patient with MEN is discovered, it can lead to the identification of other patients.

Surgery is the treatment of choice for the three neoplasias in MEN type IIa. All are potentially lethal —especially medullary thyroid carcinoma and pheochromocytoma—but all can be cured by early diagnosis followed by operation. Aggressive therapy is thus warranted, and special consideration should be given to certain aspects of the treatment, since one is dealing with a patient with three potential endocrine tumors.

Management of the individual components of MEN syndromes generally follows the accepted procedures for each of the neoplasias, and these are discussed in detail elsewhere in this book. Thus, the management of pituitary tumors is guided by the availability of transsphenoidal hypophysectomy and the management of mucosal neuromas by cosmetic factors. However, the clinical setting does influence the sequence and extent of surgical therapy. The sequence of treatment is guided by the presence of multiple endocrine tumors. Pheochromocytomas, which are commonly bilateral, especially in MEN type IIb, should be treated first, medically or surgically, in order to obviate their cardiovascular effects on surgical procedures. Thyroid and parathyroid surgery must be aggressive, because all glandular tissue may be involved.

An essential feature of appropriate clinical management is evaluation of family members, since MEN syndromes are transmitted in an autosomal dominant pattern. Family members must be reevaluated periodically because of the varying penetrance of the component tumors.

FAILURE OF MULTIPLE ENDOCRINE GLANDS

This section deals mainly with the syndromes involving autoimmune destruction of multiple endocrine and specific other tissues. Historically, the first of these associations was Schmidt's syndrome of nontuberculous Addison's disease and lymphocytic thyroiditis. In a 1964 review of Schmidt's syndrome, Carpenter et al found coexisting diabetes mellitus in 10 out of 15 patients with Addison's disease and thyroiditis. They broadened the definition of the syndrome to include diabetes mellitus associated with nontuberculous Addison's disease. However, multiglandular failure may also involve the parathyroids, ovaries, testes, and possibly adenohypophysis. Schmidt's syndrome (the Carpenter definition will be used in this chapter) is thus but one subset of these disorders. In addition, these endocrinopathies are frequently associated with other disorders of tissue-specific autoimmunity, notably pernicious anemia and vitiligo. This discussion will emphasize the evidence for clinical, immunologic, and possibly genetic heterogeneity among groups of patients with these disorders.

Six mechanisms of immunologic tissue injury have been described (Table 21–9). The primary effectors in autoimmune reactions are immunoglobulins, T cells (thymus-dependent lymphocytes that become sensitized to specific antigens and release soluble nonimmunoglobulin mediators), and monocytes (which possess receptors for the Fc region of immunoglobulins and cytotoxic capabilities in the presence of tissue-specific antibody). The role of these mechanisms in autoimmune endocrine disease has been most extensively studied in Hashimoto's thyroiditis and Graves' disease. Although immune complexes are present in the sera of some patients with autoimmune thyroid disease, T cell-mediated immunity and antibody-dependent cell-mediated cytotoxicity have received the greatest attention as mechanisms of target organ destruction in Hashimoto's thyroiditis. Evidence for specifically sensitized T cells has been found in other autoimmune en-

Table 21–9. Types of immunologic tissue injury.[1]

IgE-mediated immediate hypersensitivity
Complement-dependent direct humoral cytoxicity
Antigen-antibody complex deposition
T cell-mediated immunity
Receptor autoantibody binding (blocking or stimulating)
Antibody-dependent cell-mediated cytotoxicity

[1] Modified and reproduced, with permission, from Deftos LJ, Catherwood BD, Bone HG: Multiple endocrine disorders. In: *Endocrinology and Metabolism.* Felig P et al (editors). McGraw-Hill, 1981.

docrinopathies as well. To explain this apparent break in the immunologically privileged status of autologous tissues, Volpe has proposed a unifying theory of pathogenesis of autoimmune thyroid disease based on a defect in immunoregulation by suppressor T cells (thymus-dependent lymphocytes that suppress immune responses, possibly including recognition of autoantigens). In vitro reconstitution experiments have shown that normal suppressor T cells can depress the production of migration-inhibiting lymphokines by leukocyte cultures from Hashimoto's thyroiditis patients and can also inhibit the differentiation of antithyroid antibody-secreting cells. Patients with autoimmune thyroid disease, but not other autoimmune diseases, appear to lack suppressor T cells capable of these functions (see Chapter 4).

The events that initiate immune sensitization to antigens of the endocrine system remain unclear. Class II histocompatibility molecules, normally borne only by macrophages and a few other cells, can be expressed on endocrine cells (as manifest by the Ia+ determinant of HLA-DR). This observation has suggested the theory that some environmental event (such as a viral infection) might first cause antigens that are otherwise sequestered to be displayed in conjunction with these essential antigen-presenting molecules. However, Ia antigen expression is also seen in localized areas of lymphocytic reaction in other thyroid diseases such multinodular goiter and thyroid carcinoma. Additional factors must therefore be necessary for progression to established autoimmunity. It remains to be determined for each endocrine cell whether all three factors (display of otherwise sequestered antigens, expression of antigen-presenting molecules, and antigen-specific suppressor cell defect) are necessary and sufficient for the development of autoimmunity.

A number of methods have been used for assessment of tissue-specific immunity in the autoimmune endocrinopathies (Table 21–10). Immunoprecipitation, latex or tanned red cell agglutination, and radioimmunoassay have been used to detect thyroglobulin autoantibodies, the last being the most sensitive method. The indirect immunofluorescence test for autoantibodies to endocrine cells in frozen tissue sections is a versatile technique that has demonstrated autoantibodies to adrenal, thyroid, islet cell, parathyroid, and gonadal "cytoplasmic" antigens. Thyroperoxidase is now recognized as a major component of the thyroid cytoplasmic antigen, which has been localized to microsomal fractions and titered by complement fixation. With the exception of these principal antithyroid antibody tests, the immunofluorescence tests are performed only in specialized laboratories.

PROTOTYPICAL AUTOIMMUNE ENDOCRINOPATHY: ADDISON'S DISEASE

Addison's disease plays a central role in several groups of patients with failure of multiple endocrine glands, and there is strong evidence that idiopathic Addison's disease is the end result of autoimmune adrenalitis in most cases. Addison's disease has also provided a good focus for investigation of endocrine autoimmunity (1) because few of these patients should escape medical attention and (2) because tuberculous Addison's disease has provided a natural control group for clinical and immunologic comparison.

Autoimmune Addison's disease is diagnosed when there is no evidence of tuberculosis or any other reasonable explanation for adrenal failure. Pulmonary tuberculosis and adrenal calcification justify a presumptive diagnosis of tuberculous Addison's disease; however, in patients with granulomatous disease on chest film but without adrenal calcification, the cause of adrenal failure is indeterminate. Autoantibodies to adrenal tissue can be detected by indirect immunofluorescence in a high percentage (48–74%) of patients with presumed autoimmune Addison's disease, while the incidence of adrenal autoantibodies is essentially zero in patients with unequivocal tuberculous Addison's disease. Although comparable data are not available for patients with Addison's disease due to other causes such as histoplasmosis, this information suggests that adrenal autoantibodies are not an epiphenomenon due to tissue destruction. In vitro evidence of T cell activation (increased Ia+ number) and of cell-mediated immunity to adrenal antigen is also present in many patients with autoimmune Addison's disease but not in patients with tuberculous Addison's disease. The autoimmune nature of idiopathic Addison's disease is further substantiated by its specific association with a wide variety of second endocrinopathies with in vitro evidence for tissue-specific autoimmunity. Table 21–11 shows the strikingly higher frequency of second diseases in autoimmune compared with tuberculous Addison's disease. The diseases found with tuberculous Addison's disease have generally been diabetes mellitus and thyroid

Table 21–10. Methods for assessment of tissue-specific immunity.

Methods reflecting T lymphocyte function
  T cell help (for B cell differentiation)
  Direct lymphocytotoxicity
  Induced lymphocyte proliferation
  Induced lymphokine production
  Lymphocyte activation (Ia+)

Methods reflecting B lymphocyte function
  Precipitin reaction
  Complement fixation
  Indirect immunofluorescence
  Direct serum cytotoxicity
  Enablement of cell-mediated cytotoxicity

Table 21–11. Incidence of other autoimmune disorders in patients with Addison's disease.

	Autoimmune Addison's Disease (n = 419)	Tuberculous Addison's Disease (n = 114)
Diabetes mellitus	10%	. . .
Hyperthyroidism	8%	. . .
Thyroiditis and primary myxedema	9%	. . .
Pernicious anemia	4%	. . .
Hypogonadism	16%	. . .
Hypoparathyroid-ism	5%	. . .
One or more disorders	39%	8%

disease. These results support the conclusion that idiopathic Addison's disease is part of a larger autoimmune endocrine syndrome.

The presence of adrenal autoantibodies in the blood may be a marker for activity of the autoimmune diathesis. Adrenal autoantibodies tend to have disappeared in patients studied later than 1–5 years after the onset of Addison's disease. Table 21–12 shows the relationship of adrenal autoantibody to the sex of the patient, the age at onset of adrenal insufficiency, and the presence of a second autoimmune disorder. The higher prevalence of autoantibodies in Addison's disease associated with other disorders is particularly striking. Patients with autoimmune Addison's disease with adrenal autoantibodies have a two- to threefold greater incidence of other clinically manifest endocrinopathies compared with patients without adrenal autoantibodies. Several investigators have found a higher prevalence of adrenal autoantibodies in women, although this has not been uniformly reported. The frequency of autoantibodies is much less in patients with Addison's disease alone who are male or whose onset of adrenal insufficiency was before age 20 years. Adrenal autoantibodies

have been found in 13% of patients with idiopathic hypoparathyroidism alone. They are found rarely in first-degree relatives of patients with autoimmune Addison's disease, in patients with Cushing's disease, and in patients with Hashimoto's thyroiditis or diabetes mellitus alone. The prevalence of adrenal autoantibodies in apparently normal individuals is less than one per 1000 population.

Many investigators have found an increased prevalence of subclinical autoimmunity to other tissues in patients with autoantibody-positive Addison's disease, as evidenced by autoantibodies to parathyroid, islet cell, thyroid, and gastric mucosa. Nerup found a sixfold higher frequency of thyroid autoantibodies and a tenfold increase in parietal cell autoantibodies in patients with adrenal autoantibody-positive Addison's disease, but patients with Addison's disease without adrenal autoantibodies showed no difference from age- and sex-matched controls. When a panel of in vitro immunologic tests was used along with clinical data, 84% of patients with Addison's disease and adrenal autoantibodies were found to have evidence of extra-adrenal autoimmune involvement.

CLINICAL & IMMUNOLOGIC HETEROGENEITY

From what has been said, it can be inferred that autoimmune Addison's disease is not a homogeneous disorder with a random coincidence of other autoimmune endocrine disease and that patients with failure of additional glands might also be heterogeneous. Figure 21–2 supports this thesis, showing the distribution of the age at onset in three clinical subsets of patients with Addison's disease studied in the USA and the UK. It is clear that Addison's disease associated with hypoparathyroidism has a much earlier age at onset than Addison's disease associated with Schmidt's syndrome or without other endocrinopathy. Analyzing 182 patients from 140 families with

Table 21–12. Incidence of adrenal autoantibodies in patients with autoimmune Addison's disease according to sex, age at onset of adrenal insufficiency, and presence of other disease.[1]

	Sex		Age at Onset		
	Female	Male	<20	>20	Total
Addison's disease alone	14/27 (52%)	7/40 (18%)	4/26 (15%)	16/36 (44%)	21/67 (31%)
Addison's disease plus other disease	23/30 (77%)	13/21 (62%)	15/21 (71%)	20/28 (71%)	36/51 (71%)
					57/118 (48%)

[1] Source of data: Blizzard RM, Chee D, Davis W: Clin Exp Immunol 1967;2:19. Modified and reproduced, with permission, from Deftos LJ, Catherwood BD, Bone HG: Multiple endocrine disorders. Chapter 28 in: *Endocrinology and Metabolism.* Felig P et al (editors). McGraw-Hill, 1981.

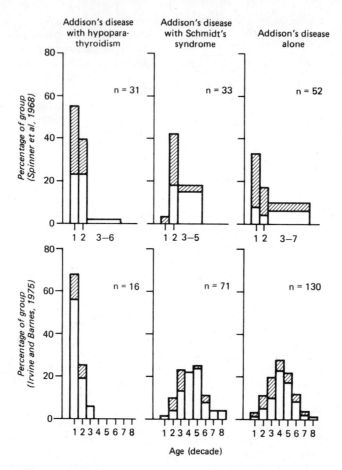

Figure 21–2. Clinical heterogeneity of Addison's disease. Distribution of age at onset *(upper)* or of diagnosis *(lower)* of Addison's disease with hypoparathyroidism, Addison's disease with Schmidt's syndrome, and Addison's disease alone. The open area represents females; the closed area represents males. Note that age is measured in decades. (Reproduced, with permission, from Deftos LJ, Catherwood BD, Bone HG: Multiple endocrine disorders. In: *Endocrinology and Metabolism,* 2nd ed. Felig P et al [editors]. McGraw-Hill, 1985.)

autoimmune Addison's disease, idiopathic hypoparathyroidism, or both disorders, Spinner et al found evidence for genetic as well as clinical heterogeneity among these patients and divided their patients into four groups: Addison's disease with hypoparathyroidism, isolated hypoparathyroidism, isolated Addison's disease, and Schmidt's syndrome. Immunologic differences also distinguish groups of patients with autoimmune endocrine disease. Patients with Addison's disease in adulthood are predominantly female and frequently have thyroid autoantibodies. They therefore resemble the group with complete Schmidt's syndrome. However, patients with childhood-onset Addison's disease without other endocrinopathy tend to be male and have predominantly autoantibodies to parathyroid tissue, resembling more closely the patients with Addison's disease associated with clinical hypoparathyroidism. Some of these patients may represent a forme fruste of pluriglandu-

lar endocrine insufficiency. Several types of study have thus led to the concept that multiglandular autoimmune endocrinopathy is not a uniform syndrome nor the random coincidence of a number of individual diseases but that there are at least two distinct patterns of glandular involvement. These ideas are summarized as major types and variations in Figure 21–3. Besides the groups of patients with Addison's disease outlined above, there are groups in which a direct association of thyroiditis and diabetes mellitus is found in the absence of Addison's disease. In addition, other endocrine and some nonendocrine disorders occur with increased frequency in these patients.

Addison's Disease With Hypoparathyroidism

In the set of patients with Addison's disease and hypoparathyroidism, male and female patients are usually affected in childhood (Figure 21–2). Chronic

PLURIGLANDULAR ENDOCRINE FUNCTION

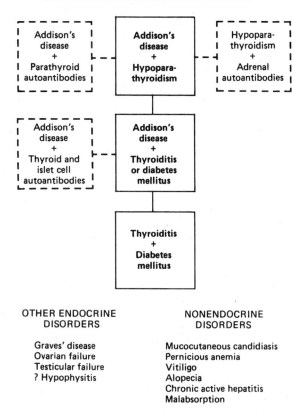

OTHER ENDOCRINE
DISORDERS

Graves' disease
Ovarian failure
Testicular failure
? Hypophysitis

NONENDOCRINE
DISORDERS

Mucocutaneous candidiasis
Pernicious anemia
Vitiligo
Alopecia
Chronic active hepatitis
Malabsorption

Figure 21–3. The three major clinical categories of pluriglandular autoimmune endocrinopathy (center column), with forme fruste variants (dashed boxes) and less frequently associated endocrine disorders and nonendocrine disorders. Graves' disease may substitute for thyroiditis. Gonadal failure is associated with a pansteroid cell autoantibody in Addison's disease, and candidiasis is strongly associated with hypoparathyroidism. (Modified and reproduced, with permission, from Deftos LJ, Catherwood BD, Bone HG: Multiple endocrine disorders. In: *Endocrinology and Metabolism,* 2nd ed. Felig P et al [editors]. McGraw-Hill, 1985.)

mucocutaneous candidiasis frequently precedes both endocrinopathies; conversely, 84% of patients with this infection and an associated endocrinopathy have hypoparathyroidism. The typical sequence of events is shown in Figure 21–4: Hypoparathyroidism develops in the first decade in 88% of patients. Addison's disease follows in about 2 years, and in 75% of patients it occurs within 9 years of the onset of the syndrome. These patients may be affected by a third endocrinopathy, including thyroid disease, diabetes mellitus, pernicious anemia, and ovarian failure. The probability that the sibling of an affected person will have Addison's disease or hypoparathyroidism or any one of the above-mentioned secondary disorders has been estimated to be 0.35.

Patients with idiopathic hypoparathyroidism frequently have circulating autoantibodies to parathyroid tissue; patients with Addison's disease and hypoparathyroidism also have an increased frequency of thyroid and parietal cell autoantibodies. A number of defective immune responses have been reported in patients with chronic mucocutaneous candidiasis with or without endocrinopathies. These include defective blast transformation, macrophage migration inhibition, and lymphocytotoxicity. The role of these abnormalities in the pathogenesis of immune sensitization to endocrine tissue is unclear.

Isolated Hypoparathyroidism

Patients with isolated hypoparathyroidism are similar to those with Addison's disease plus hypoparathyroidism in having an early onset of disease (73% in the first decade) and associated candidiasis. The frequency of parathyroid autoantibodies in this group is similar to that in the group with Addison's disease. Immunofluorescent adrenal autoantibodies are detected in 7% of patients with hypoparathyroidism, whereas in hypoparathyroidism with candidiasis, most patients have subclinical adrenal autoimmunity. The occurrence of adrenal autoantibodies and candidiasis thus indicates that this subset may represent a forme fruste of pluriglandular endocrine insufficiency.

Isolated Addison's Disease

As noted above, patients with isolated autoimmune Addison's disease still have an increased prevalence of thyroid, parathyroid, and islet cell autoantibodies when compared with control populations. These immunologic findings suggest that despite the absence of clinically evident involvement of other glands, isolated Addison's disease should be considered part of the spectrum of multiple endocrine autoimmunity, since some patients with this disorder may ultimately develop an associated endocrinopathy.

Schmidt's Syndrome

As shown in Figure 21–2, Schmidt's syndrome (defined in the introduction) is more frequent in females, and all of the components including the Addison's disease commonly have their onset in the age range from 20 to 50 years. Table 21–11 shows that the occurrence of diabetes mellitus in autoimmune Addison's disease is 10% and that of Hashimoto's thyroiditis and primary myxedema 9% overall. Although many of these patients may have onset of diabetes in young adulthood, most of them have been treated with insulin. Hashimoto's thyroiditis or diabetes develops an average of 7 years after adrenal insufficiency. Schmidt's syndrome is frequently accompanied by additional autoimmune diseases, including ovarian failure and pernicious anemia (see below).

Patients with Schmidt's syndrome have the highest rate of thyroid autoantibodies of any group with Ad-

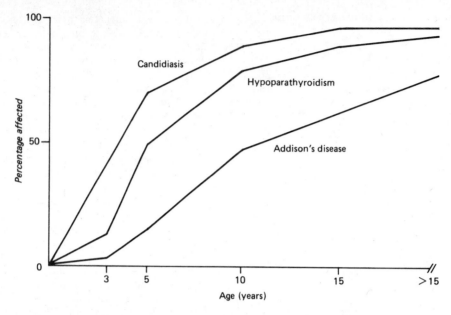

Figure 21–4. Typical sequence for childhood onset of chronic mucocutaneous candidiasis, autoimmune hypoparathyroidism, and Addison's disease. Patients with hypoparathyroidism may not develop Addison's disease, but frequent adrenal autoantibodies suggest that the polyendocrine diathesis is still present. (Source of data: Neufeld et al: Medicine 1981;60:355. Reproduced, with permission, from Deftos LJ, Catherwood BD, Bone HG: Multiple endocrine disorders. In: *Endocrinology and Metabolism,* 2nd ed. Felig P et al [editors]. McGraw-Hill, 1985.)

dison's disease, which suggests that thyroid autoantibodies in Addison's disease may be predictive of thyroid failure. Activation of cell-mediated immunity is evidenced in Hashimoto's thyroiditis by an increased circulating number of Ia+ T cells.

Islet cell autoantibodies may also be important in Schmidt's syndrome. These autoantibodies circulate in the majority of patients at the time of diagnosis of insulin-dependent diabetes mellitus, even in the absence of any other tissue-specific autoimmune disease. The incidence is substantially lower in patients not requiring insulin therapy at the time of diagnosis. In most patients, islet cell autoantibodies disappear with time; their persistence in the blood is associated with the presence of other autoimmune disorders (19%) or autoantibodies to thyroid or gastric tissue (65%). In patients without insulin dependence at the time of diagnosis of their diabetes, the presence of islet cell autoantibodies appears to predict future insulin requirement and failure of oral hypoglycemic agent therapy.

For about half of index individuals, one or more other family members can be found with autoimmune endocrinopathies. These relatives frequently have only thyroiditis and diabetes without adrenal disease. Such family members may be assigned to this syndrome on the basis of their relative with Addison's disease. Many more family members have been found to have thyroid autoantibodies in the blood.

Other Endocrinopathies Associated With Addison's Disease

Ovarian failure is common in women with autoimmune Addison's disease. In one large series, the prevalence of amenorrhea was 24%, and another 6% had oligomenorrhea. Abnormal reproductive function persists after adrenal replacement therapy and is uncommon in tuberculous Addison's disease, which leads to the conclusion that it is not related to deficiency of adrenal corticosteroids. The presumed autoimmune oophoritis is closely correlated with the onset of the patient's adrenal failure. In girls with Addison's disease and hypoparathyroidism occurring before the age of menarche, the presentation of oophoritis is that of primary amenorrhea, and in some cases streak gonads have been found at laparoscopy.

Ovarian failure in Addison's disease is closely related to a distinctive type of autoantibody against common antigens present in multiple steroid-producing cells, including theca interna, corpus luteum, Leydig cells, placenta, and adrenal cortex. These autoantibodies are cytotoxic for granulosa cells in monolayer cell culture. The presence of such autoantibodies is not only a risk factor for ovarian failure but may also be an independent risk factor for other extra-adrenal endocrinopathies. Steroid cell autoantibodies are uncommon in men with Addison's disease, but several instances of testicular failure associated with Addison's disease have been reported.

Although decreased function or failure is the most common consequence of attack on the endocrine glands, Graves' disease is intimately associated with these disorders; thyrotoxicosis occurs in about 8% of patients with Addison's disease. In patients with autoimmune Addison's disease, clinical atrophic gastritis may occur with or without diabetes, thyroid disease, hypoparathyroidism, or ovarian failure. Pernicious anemia is found in approximately 4% of patients with Addison's disease (Table 21–11).

Direct Association of Thyroid Disease & Diabetes Mellitus

The general frequency of diabetes mellitus and thyroid disease makes the study of a link between these disorders difficult. Nevertheless, an increased frequency of autoimmune thyroid disease in diabetics has been reported by many authors; pernicious anemia is also associated. Comparison of the frequency of tissue-specific autoantibodies in unselected diabetics versus age- and sex-matched controls provides additional support for this association. Table 21–13 provides a representative summary of the interrelationships of autoimmunity against islet, parietal, and thyroid cells.

Other Disorders

A dozen cases of presumed "autoimmune hypophysitis" have been reported, and half were associated with autoimmune diseases, especially lymphocytic thyroiditis and atrophic gastritis. All of these cases have been temporally related to pregnancy and have presented as sellar masses or sudden collapse. A diagnosis of hypopituitarism has been made in life in at least one of these patients. Diabetes insipidus has been associated with autoimmune adrenalitis and hypoparathyroidism in one instance, but the pathogenesis of this defect is unclear (See Chapter 2).

Vitiligo may occur with any autoimmune endocrinopathy. This disorder probably represents tissue-specific autoimmunity to melanin-producing cells.

MANAGEMENT OF PATIENTS WITH FAILURE OF MULTIPLE ENDOCRINE GLANDS

The history, physical examination, laboratory findings, and treatment of the hormonal disorders discussed in this section are similar to those of the disorders as they occur individually and are discussed in other chapters in this book.

The most serious pitfall in diagnosis of multiple autoimmune endocrinopathy would be to confuse adrenal, thyroid, and ovarian failure with hypopituitarism. In every such case, the integrity of pituitary function should be proved by showing elevated blood levels of TSH, LH, or ACTH. Failure of other glands not dependent on pituitary function (hypoparathy-

Table 21–13. Interrelationships of autoimmunity against islet, parietal, and thyroid cells: Representative frequencies of occurrence.[1]

Index Disease	Associated Finding	Frequency
Diabetes mellitus	Thyroid autoantibodies ↑ TSH (males) ↑ TSH (females) Parietal cell autoantibodies	16% 6% 17% 17%
Thyroiditis	Islet cell autoantibodies Intrinsic factor autoantibodies Pernicious anemia	9% 2% 9%
Hyperthyroidism	Islet cell autoantibodies Intrinsic factor autoantibodies Pernicious anemia	3% 3% 3%
Pernicious anemia	Islet cell autoantibodies Thyroid autoantibodies Hypothyroidism Hyperthyroidism	11% 38% 12% 9%

[1]Modified and reproduced, with permission, from Deftos LJ, Catherwood BD, Bone HG: Multiple endocrine disorders. Chapter 28 in: *Endocrinology and Metabolism*, 2nd ed. Felig P et al (editors). McGraw-Hill, 1985.

roidism or diabetes mellitus) should be an indicator of autoimmune endocrinopathy.

Patients with Addison's disease should receive particular attention in surveillance for failure of previously uninvolved glands, as these individuals are at greater risk. The physician should be alert for signs of the insidious onset of hypothyroidism and pernicious anemia. Elevation of serum TSH may be seen in untreated Addison's disease because of a lack of the normal regulatory effects of the steroid hormone on thyrotroph function and does not necessarily indicate thyroid disease unless it persists on glucocorticoid replacement. In a random population, slight elevation of serum TSH does not necessarily indicate future clinical hypothyroidism, but simultaneous observation of thyroid autoantibodies predicts an incidence of clinical hypothyroidism estimated to be 4% per year, and when autoantibody titers are markedly elevated, the incidence may be as high as 26% per year. These rates may be higher in patients with Addison's disease. First-degree relatives of patients with Addison's disease should also be observed carefully and evaluated with an ACTH stimulation test if they develop any autoimmune disorder. Cases have been reported in which secondary amenorrhea remitted following glucocorticoid replacement therapy of associated Addison's disease. It may thus be important to consider this association in any case of unexplained premature ovarian failure.

The implications of multiglandular endocrine failure for treatment are not well characterized. Since cortisol antagonizes the intestinal calcium transport effects of vitamin D, including vitamin D metabolites used to treat hypoparathyroidism, the development of adrenal failure can result in sudden vitamin D intoxication in affected patients. Secondary amenorrhea has remitted following treatment of associated Addison's disease. On the other hand, the combination of Addison's disease and loss of ovarian function—even physiologic menopause—may result in more severe postmenopausal osteoporosis if sex steroid replacement therapy is not provided. Loss of a protective effect of adrenal androgens has been postulated.

GENETIC ASPECTS OF AUTOIMMUNE DISORDERS

Early genetic studies of autoimmune disorders have estimated probabilities of clinical involvement of 0.25–0.35 for siblings of probands with Schmidt's syndrome and Addison's disease with hypoparathyroidism.

Typing of antigens coded by the major histocompatibility (HLA) complex on chromosome 6 has provided genetic correlations with the clinical and immunopathologic findings in the individual autoimmune endocrinopathies. At least three classes of HLA glycoproteins are displayed by human cells. Class I molecules (antigens of the A and B loci) are expressed on all nucleated cells. They are quantitatively regulated by lymphokines and may play a secondary role in autoimmune disorders. HLA-A and -B typing is useful, primarily because these molecules serve as markers closely linked to the HLA-D locus. Class II HLA molecules (HLA-DR, -DQ, and -DP) are normally displayed only on a few antigen-presenting cells, such as the macrophage, but can be induced on many other cell types. The presence of HLA-DR on cell surfaces can be detected by the reaction of antibodies to common determinants such as Ia. Individuals can be classified into phenotypic groups using panels of antisera to class II antigens. Further polymorphism can be detected functionally by the presence or absence of the mixed lymphocyte culture reaction against homozygous allogeneic lymphocytes, by analysis of restriction endonuclease-digested genomic DNA, and by probing for specific DNA sequences within the HLA-DR and DQ genes. The immunologic defect in immune regulation resulting in autosensitization to endocrine tissue may be a gene in the HLA region genetically linked to certain HLA antigens. HLA-D antigens are most closely associated with the endocrine disorders (Table 21–14). Common haplotypes such as HLA-A1, -B8, -D3 and HLA-A2, -B15, -D4 occur because

of linkage disequilibrium. The presence or absence of specific amino acid residues at positions within the antigen-binding domains of the class II molecule subunits may convey a substantial portion of the genetic risk for autoimmune disease.

HLA typing of a number of kindreds with pluriglandular autoimmune endocrinopathy has been reported. In most families, this type of analysis has suggested dominant inheritance linked to either HLA-D3 or -D4. Data on the interaction of -D3 and D4-linked genes are not available for Addison's disease. In a few kindreds, the predictive value of HLA typing appeared questionable, and lack of HLA association has been reported for Addison's disease with hypoparathyroidism.

NONAUTOIMMUNE ENDOCRINE FAILURE

Bardwick et al have recently reviewed a syndrome, previously reported mostly from Japan, to which they give the acronym POEMS (polyneuropathy, organomegaly, endocrinopathy, M protein, and skin changes) (Table 21–15). Gonadal failure, gynecomastia, and glucose intolerance are frequent endocrine disorders, while adrenal failure is uncom-

Table 21–15. Incidence of abnormalities in patients with "POEMS" syndrome.[1]

Polyneuropathy	
Peripheral neuropathy	100%
Papilledema	68%
Increased cerebrospinal fluid	94%
Organomegaly	
Hepatomegaly	67%
Splenomegaly	37%
Lymphadenopathy	64%
Endocrinopathy	
Gynecomastia	70%
Impotence	67%
Amenorrhea	100%
Glucose intolerance	48%
Hypothyroidism	10%
M protein	61%
IgG	41%
IgA	20%
Marrow plasma cells	48%
Sclerotic bone lesions	71%
Skin changes	
Hyperpigmentation	98%
Thickening	85%
Hirsutism	78%
Hyperhidrosis	66%
Other	
Peripheral edema	92%
Ascites	68%
Pleural effusions	24%
Fever	48%

[1] Reproduced, with permission, from Bardwick PA et al: Plasma cell dyscrasia with polyneuropathy, organomegaly, endocrinopathy, M protein, and skin changes. Medicine 1980;59:311.

Table 21–14. HLA antigen association with autoimmune diseases (Caucasians).

Addison's disease	HLA-DR3
Atrophic thyroiditis	HLA-DR3
Graves' disease	HLA-B8 and -DR3
Diabetes mellitus	HLA-DR3 and -DR4
Hashimoto's thyroiditis	HLA-DR3 and -DR5
Hypoparathyroidism	?

mon. Seventy-five percent of affected patients are male, and they have plasma cell dyscrasias with onset in the fourth or fifth decade, usually sclerotic plasmacytomas. In one of the cases reported by Bardwick et al, insulin-dependent diabetes mellitus remitted with irradiation of the patient's plasmacytoma, returned 3 years later with the appearance of a new tumor, and disappeared again with another course of radiation treatment. Neither the polyneuropathy nor the endocrinopathy appears to be due to amyloidosis. In contrast to findings in autoimmune endocrino-

pathies, Bardwick et al did not find tissue-specific endocrine autoantibodies. The mechanism of this interesting syndrome needs to be elucidated.

Pseudohypoparathyroidism type Ia is due to hereditary deficiency of the guanine nucleotide-binding regulatory protein of the cell membrane-adenylyl cyclase complex and is characterized by resistance to multiple hormones besides parathyroid hormone. This disorder is discussed in Chapter 5. Nonimmunologic forms of familial isolated hypoparathyroidism also exist.

REFERENCES

Multiple Endocrine Neoplasia

Austin LA, Heath H III: Calcitonin: Physiology and pathophysiology. N Engl J Med 1981;304:269.

Carney JA, Sizemore GW, Tyce GM: Bilateral adrenal medullary hyperplasia in MEN, type 2. Mayo Clin Proc 1975;50:3.

Chong GC et: Medullary carcinoma of the thyroid gland. Cancer 1975;35:695.

Copp DH, Crockroft DW, Kueh Y: Calcitonin from ultimobranchial glands of dogfish and chickens. Science 1967;158:924.

Cushman P Jr: Familial endocrine tumors: Report of two unrelated kindred affected with pheochromocytomas, one also with multiple thyroid carcinomas. Am J Med 1962;32:352.

Deftos LJ: *Medullary Thyroid Carcinoma*. Karger, 1983.

Deftos LJ: Radioimmunoassay for calcitonin in medullary thyroid carcinoma. JAMA 1974;227:403.

Deftos LJ, Bone HG, Parthemore JG: Immunohistological studies of medullary thyroid carcinoma and C-cell hyperplasia. J Clin Endocrinol Metab 1980;51:857.

Fung Y-K T et al: Structural evidence for the authenticity of the human retinoblastoma gene. Science 1987; 236:1657.

Gagel FR et al: Natural history of the familial medullary thyroid carcinoma-pheochromocytoma syndrome and the identification of preneoplastic stages by screening studies: A five-year report. Trans Assoc Am Physicians 1975;88:177.

Gagel RF et al: The clinical outcome of prospective screening for multiple endocrine neoplasia type 2a. N Engl J Med 1988;318:478.

Genetic markers in multiple endocrine neoplasia type 2. (Editorial.) Lancet 1988;1:396.

Griffiths DFR, Williams GT, Williams ED: Duodenal carcinoid tumors, phaeochromocytoma and neurofibromatosis: Islet cell tumor, phaeochromocytoma and the Von Hippel-Lindau complex: Two distinctive neuroendocrine syndromes. Q J Med 1987;245:769.

Hazard JB: The C cells (parafollicular cells) of the thyroid gland and medullary thyroid carcinoma: A review. Am J Pathol 1977;88:213.

Hennessey JF et al: A comparison of pentagastrin injection and calcium infusion as provocative agents for the detection of medullary thyroid carcinoma. J Clin Endocrinol Metab 1974;39:487.

Jackson CE et al: The two-mutational-event theory in

medullary thyroid carcinoma. Am J Hum Genet 1979; 31:704.

Khairi MRA et al: Mucosal neuroma, pheochromocytoma and medullary thyroid carcinoma: MEN, type III. Medicine 1975;54:89.

Melvin KE, Tashjian AH Jr, Miller HH: Studies in familial (medullary) thyroid carcinoma. Recent Prog Horm Res 1972;28:399.

Naylor SL et al: Loss of heterozygosity of chromosome 3p markers in small-cell lung cancer. Nature 1987; 329:451.

O'Connor DT, Burton D, Deftos LJ: Immunoreactive human chromogranin A in diverse polypeptide hormone-producing human tumors and normal endocrine tissues. Clin Endocrinol Metab 1983;57:1084.

Pearse AGE, Ewen SEB, Polak JM: The genesis of APUD amyloid in endocrine polypeptide tumors: Histochemical distinction from immunamyloid. Virchows Arch [Cell Pathol] 1972;10:93.

Parthemore JG et al: A short calcium infusion in the diagnosis of medullary thyroid carcinoma. J Clin Endocrinol Metab 1974;39:108.

Ponder BAJ et al: Risk estimation and screening in families of patients with medullary thyroid carcinoma. Lancet 1988;1:397.

Rouleau GA et al: Genetic linkage of bilateral acoustic neurofibromatosis to a DNA marker on chromosome 22. Nature 1987;329:246.

Schimke RN, Hartman WH: Familial amyloid-producing medullary thyroid carcinoma and pheochromocytoma: A distinct genetic entity. Ann Intern Med 1965; 63: 1027.

Seizinger BR, Martuza RL, Gusella JF: Loss of genes on chromosome 22 in tumorigenesis of human acoustic neuroma. Nature 1986;322:644.

Seizinger BR et al: Genetic linkage of von Recklinghausen neurofibromatosis to nerve growth factor receptor gene. Cell 1987;49:589.

Seizinger BR et al: Von Hippel-Lindau disease maps to the region of chromosome 3 associated with renal cell carcinoma. Nature 1988;332:268.

Sipple JH: The association of pheochromocytoma with carcinoma of the thyroid gland. Am J Med 1961;31: 163.

Steiner AL, Goodman AD, Powers SR: Study of a kindred with pheochromocytoma, medullary thyroid carcinoma, hyperparathyroidism, and Cushing's disease: MEN, type II. Medicine 1968;47:371.

Takai S et al: Loss of genes on chromosomes 22 in medullary thyroid carcinoma and pheochromocytoma. Jpn J Cancer Res 1987;78:894.

Wermer P: Genetic aspects of adenomatosis of endocrine glands. Am J Med 1954;16:363.

Williams ED: A review of 17 cases of carcinoma of the thyroid and phaeochromocytoma. J Clin Pathol 1965; 18:288.

Wolfe HJ et al: C-cell hyperplasia preceding medullary thyroid carcinoma. N Engl J Med 1973;289:437.

Zollinger RM, Ellison EH: Primary peptic ulceration of the jejunum associated with the islet cell tumors of the pancreas. Ann Surg 1955;142:709.

Failure of Multiple Endocrine Glands

Ahmann AJ, Burman KD: The role of T lymphocytes in autoimmune thyroid disease. Endocrinol Metab Clin North Am 1987;16:287.

Asa SL et al: Lymphocytic hypophysitis of pregnancy resulting in hypopituitarism: A distinct clinicopathologic entity. Ann Intern Med 1981;95:166.

Bardwick PA et al: Plasma cell dyscrasia with polyneuropathy, organomegaly, endocrinopathy, M protein, and skin changes: The POEMS syndrome. Medicine 1980;59:311.

Betterle C et al: Complement-fixing adrenal autoantibodies as a marker for predicting onset of idiopathic Addison's disease. Lancet 1983;1:1238.

Blizzard RM, Chee D, Davis W: The incidence of adrenal and other antibodies in the sera of patients with idiopathic adrenal insufficiency (Addison's disease). Clin Exp Immunol 1967;2:19.

Blizzard RM, Chee D, Davis W: The incidence of parathyroid and other antibodies in the sera of patients with idiopathic hypoparathyroidism. Clin Exp Immunol 1966;2:19.

Bottazzo GF et al: Autoimmunity in juvenile diabetics and their families. Br Med J 1978;2:165.

Carpenter CCJ et al: Schmidt's syndrome (thyroid and adrenal insufficiency): A review of the literature and a report of fifteen new cases including ten instances of coexistent diabetes mellitus. Medicine 1964;43:153.

Chan JY, Walfish PG: Activated (Ia⁺) T-lymphocytes and their subsets in autoimmune thyroid diseases: Analysis by microfluorocytometry. J Clin Endocrinol Metab 1986;62:403.

Deftos LJ, Catherwood BD, Bone HG: Multiple endocrine disorders. In: *Endocrinology and Metabolism,* 2nd ed. Felig P et al (editors). McGraw-Hill, 1985.

Devogelaer JP, Crabbe J, Nagant de Deuxchaisnes C: Bone mineral density in Addison's disease: Evidence for an effect of adrenal androgens on bone mass. Br Med J 1987 [Clin Res] 294:798.

Dwyer JM: Chronic mucocutaneous candidiasis. Annu Rev Med 1981;32:491.

Eisenbarth GS et al: The polyglandular failure syndrome: Disease inheritance, HLA type, and immune function. Ann Intern Med 1979;91:528.

Foulis AK: Class II major histocompatibility complex and organ specific autoimmunity in man. J Pathol 1986;150:5.

Gordin A, Lamberg BA: Spontaneous hypothyroidism in symptomless autoimmune thyroiditis: A long-term follow-up study. Clin Endocrinol 1981;15:537.

Iitaka M et al: Studies of the effect of suppressor T lymphocytes on the induction of antithyroid microsomal antibody-secreting cells in autoimmune thyroid disease. J Clin Endocrinol Metab 1988;66:708.

Irvine WJ, Barnes EW: Addison's disease, ovarian failure and hypoparathyroidism. Clin Endocrinol Metab 1975;4:379.

Irvine WJ et al: Immunological aspects of premature ovarian failure associated with idiopathic Addison's disease. Lancet 1968;2:883.

Irvine WJ et al: Pancreatic islet cell antibodies in diabetes mellitus correlated with the duration and type of diabetes, coexistent autoimmune disease, and HLA type. Diabetes 1977;26:138.

Irvine WJ et al: Thyroid and gastric autoimmunity in patients with diabetes mellitus. Lancet 1970;2:164.

Khalil I et al: A combination of HLA-DQ beta Asp57-negative and HLA DQ alpha Arg52 confers susceptibility to insulin-dependent diabetes mellitus. J Clin Invest 1990;85:1315.

Maclaren NK, Riley WJ: Inherited susceptibility to autoimmune Addison's disease is linked to human leukocyte antigens -DR3 and/or -DR4, except when associated with type I autoimmune polyglandular syndrome. J Clin Endocrinol Metab 1986;62:455.

McCarthy-Young S, Lessof MH, Maisey MN: Serum TSH and thyroid antibody studies in Addison's disease. Clin Endocrinol 1972;1:45.

Nerup J: Addison's disease. Acta Endocrinol 1974; 76:127.

Pujol-Borrell R et al: Inappropriate major histocompatibility complex class II expression by thyroid follicular cells in thyroid autoimmune disease and by pancreatic beta cells in type I diabetes. Mol Biol Med 1986; 3:159.

Rabinowe SL et al: Ia-positive T lymphocytes in recently diagnosed idiopathic Addison's disease. Am J Med 1984;77:597.

Rabinowe SL et al: Lymphocyte dysfunction in autoimmune oophoritis: Resumption of menses with corticosteroids. Am J Med 1986;81:347.

Rapoport B: Recombinant DNA technology in the study of autoimmune thyroid disease. Endocrinol Metab Clin North Am 1987;16:445.

Spinner MW, Blizzard RM, Childs B: Clinical and genetic heterogeneity in idiopathic Addison's disease and hypoparathyroidism. J Clin Endocrinol 1968;28:795.

Spinner MW et al: Familial distribution of organ-specific antibodies in the blood of patients with Addison's disease and hypoparathyroidism and their relatives. Clin Exp Immunol 1969;5:461.

Sridama V, Pacini F, Degroot L: Decreased suppressor T-lymphocytes in autoimmune thyroid diseases detected by monoclonal antibodies. J Clin Endocrinol Metab 1982;54:316.

Todd JA, Bell JI, McDevitt HO: A molecular basis for genetic susceptibility to insulin-dependent diabetes mellitus. Trends Genet 1988;4:129.

Volpe R: Autoimmune thyroid disease: A perspective. Mol Biol Med 1986;3:25.

Weetman AP: Regulation and role of thyroid cell class II antigen expression. Immunol Res 1986;5:81.

Wuepper KD, Wegienka LC, Fudenberg HH: Immunologic aspects of adrenocortical insufficiency. Am J Med 1969;45:206.

Geriatric Endocrinology

22

Susan L. Greenspan, MD, & Neil M. Resnick, MD

Individuals over age 65 comprise the fastest-growing segment of the United States population; each day its size increases by over 1000 people. This increase has led to a remarkable situation—of all the people who have ever lived to the age of 65, more than two-thirds are still alive. Thus, it is becoming increasingly important for the endocrinologist to understand how endocrine physiology and disease may differ in the elderly.

Before considering specific conditions, however, it is worthwhile to review some general principles that account for many of the age-related changes in disease presentation in the elderly. First, aging itself—in the absence of disease—is associated with only a gradual and linear decline in the physiologic reserve of each organ system (Figure 22–1). Since the reserve capacity of each system is substantial, age-related declines have little effect on baseline function and do not significantly interfere with the individual's response to stress until the eighth or ninth decade. Second, because each organ system's function declines at a different physiologic rate and because 75% of the elderly have at least one disease, endocrine dysfunction in the elderly often presents disparately, with initial symptoms derived from the most compromised organ system. For example, hyperthyroidism in an elderly patient with preexisting cardiac disease may present with atrial fibrillation and a slow ventricular response, while in another equally hyperthyroid patient with a prior stroke, it may present with confusion or depression; neither patient may tolerate hyperthyroidism long enough for the classic thyroid-related manifestations (eg, goiter) to become apparent. Third, elderly patients often have multiple diseases and take many medications that may mimic or mask the usual presentation of endocrine disease.

THYROID FUNCTION & DISEASE

The prevalence of thyroid disease in the elderly is approximately twice that in younger individuals;

ACRONYMS USED IN THIS CHAPTER

ACTH	Adrenocorticotropic hormone
AVP	Arginine vasopressin
BMP	Bone mineral density
cAMP	Cyclic adenosine monophosphate
CRH	Corticotropin-releasing hormone
DHEA	Dehydroxyepiandrosterone
FSH	Follicle-stimulating hormone
hCG	Human chorionic gonadotropin
HPA	Hypothalamic-pituitary-adrenal
LH	Luteinizing hormone
LHRH	Luteinizing hormone-releasing hormone
NPH	Neutral protamine Hagedorn
PTH	Parathyroid hormone
SIADH	Syndrome of inappropriate secretion of antidiuretic hormone
TRH	Thyrotropin-releasing hormone
TSH	Thyroid-stimulating hormone (thyrotropin)

hypothyroidism and hyperthyroidism each affect roughly 3–4% of older individuals. In addition, some studies suggest that up to 9% of hospitalized elderly patients have overt thyroid disease. Furthermore, "subclinical hypothyroidism"—normal serum levels of thyroid hormones (thyroxine, T_4; triiodothyronine, T_3) but an elevated level of thyrotropin (TSH)—is more prevalent, with estimates of 4–14% in the elderly. Finally, the overall prevalence of thyroid hormone use in older adults is approximately 7% (10% in women and 2% in men).

There are few major age-related changes in the physiology of the hypothalamic-pituitary-thyroid axis (see Chapter 4). TSH release remains pulsatile (Figure 22–2), though the nocturnal rise in serum TSH appears to be blunted with age. Balanced decreases in T_4 secretion and clearance result in no change in serum T_4; T_3 resin uptake, free T_4, and the free T_4 index are also unchanged. There is a slight age-related decline in serum T_3, but values usually remain within normal limits. Serum TSH increases slightly with age, but this too remains within normal limits. The effect of age on the release of TSH by thyrotropin-releasing hormone (TRH) is less clear, but most recent studies show little clinically relevant change in either sex. The 24-hour radioiodine uptake

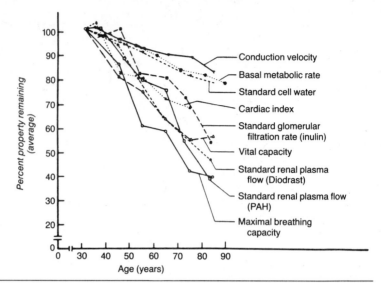

Figure 22–1. Influence of age on physiologic function in humans. (Reproduced, with permission, from Shock NW: Discussion on mortality and measurement. In: *The Biology of Aging: A Symposium.* Strehler BL et al [editors]. American Institute of Biological Sciences, 1960.)

is also not significantly altered with age. Thyroid antibodies occur more commonly in older women (23% compared with 11% in younger women), but their presence does not serve as a specific screening test for thyroid disease.

DISORDERS OF THE THYROID GLAND

Although the United States Preventive Services Task Force recommended annual screening thyroid function tests for older women, there is still no consensus among thyroidologists regarding the utility of screening for thyroid dysfunction in the absence of symptoms. However, it is reasonable to measure TSH in older individuals who present with "atypical" symptoms of thyroid disease such as exacerbation of cardiac symptoms, change in mental status, or onset of depression. Despite the sensitivity of the TSH assay, further evaluation with a free T_4 or free T_4 index is often required because up to 98% of elderly subjects with a suppressed TSH levels do not have thyrotoxicosis.

1. HYPERTHYROIDISM

Clinical Features

With age, the prevalence of Graves' disease decreases (though it remains the most common cause of hyperthyroidism), and the prevalence of multinodular goiter and toxic nodules increases. Elderly hyperthyroid patients tend to present with symptoms or complications related to the most vulnerable organ system—usually the cardiovascular system (atrial fibrillation, congestive heart failure, angina, and acute myocardial infarction) or the central nervous system (apathy, depression, confusion, or lassitude).

Occasionally, they present with gastrointestinal symptoms, but these differ from those seen in younger patients because they include constipation, failure to thrive, and anorexia. Because of degeneration of the sinus node and fibrotic changes in the cardiac conduction system, older patients are less likely than younger patients to present with palpitations (Table 22–1).

The physical signs of hyperthyroidism also differ in the elderly (Table 22–1). Resting tachycardia is less frequent; the thyroid feels normal in size or is not palpable in two-thirds of patients; and lid lag is uncommon. Ophthalmopathy is less common, not only because Graves' disease occurs less often, but also because even with Graves' disease ophthalmopathy occurs less frequently in the elderly. However, although they are less common in the elderly, some findings appear to be highly suggestive of hyperthyroidism. These include increased frequency of bowel movements, weight loss despite increased appetite, fine finger tremor, eyelid retraction, and increased perspiration.

Diagnosis

As in younger patients (see Chapter 4), the diagnosis is usually confirmed by standard thyroid function tests, including a depressed TSH level as measured by a sensitive assay. A TRH test is rarely required. There are potential pitfalls, however. T_3 toxicosis may be more difficult to diagnose because concomitant nonthyroidal illness is common and can depress serum T_3. Euthyroid hyperthyroxinemia (due to nonthyroidal illness) may also cause confusion. Elderly patients may also be taking medications such as propranolol, which may elevate levels of serum T_4. Furthermore, iodide-induced hyperthyroidism, known also as the jodbasedow effect, is becoming more common in elderly patients with multinodular goiter

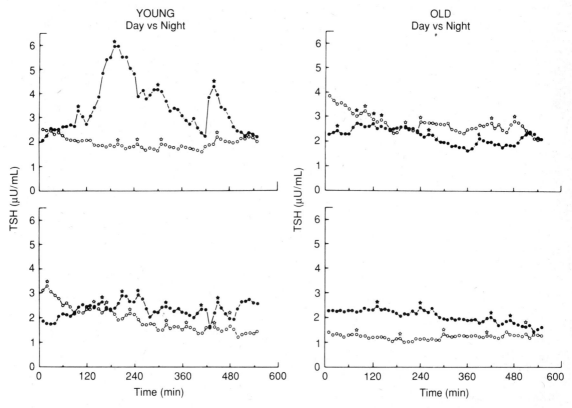

Figure 22-2. Thyrotropin (TSH) pulsation profiles during day (○) and night (●) in two representative young subjects and two representative old subjects. (Open stars, significant daytime pulses; solid stars, significant nighttime pulses as detected by cluster analysis.) (Reproduced, with permission, from Greenspan SL et al: Age-related alterations in pulsatile secretion of TSH: Role of dopaminergic regulation. Am J Physiology 1991;260(3 Pt 1):E486.

because of increased exposure to radiocontrast studies; the resultant hyperthyroidism is generally transient. Finally, because of screening tests with sensitive TSH assays, "subclinical hyperthyroidism" (normal T_4, T_3, free T_4 index with a suppressed TSH) is being recognized more commonly. This is often found in older subjects with autonomous function of a multinodular goiter or nodule.

Treatment

Beta-blocking agents are useful in alleviating symptoms, but radioactive iodine is the therapy of choice in elderly patients because it is efficient, uncomplicated, and inexpensive. Antithyroid drugs can be used prior to radioactive iodine treatment to render the patient euthyroid and to avoid radiation-induced thyroiditis, but they are not definitive treatment and are more toxic in this age group. Surgery has a more limited role because of its increased morbidity.

Following radioactive iodine treatment, patients become euthyroid over a period of 6–8 weeks. They should receive careful follow-up, because hypothyroidism develops in 80% or more of patients who

have been adequately treated. Once hyperthyroidism has abated, the metabolic clearance rate of other medications may decrease, and doses may require readjustment. Older patients with subclinical hyperthyroidism require follow-up, especially if presented with an iodine load.

2. HYPOTHYROIDISM

Hypothyroidism in the elderly is most often due to Hashimoto's thyroiditis or prior radioactive iodine ablative therapy.

Clinical Features

It is easy to overlook hypothyroidism in an older person, because many euthyroid elderly patients have the same symptoms. Moreover, elderly patients with hypothyroidism are more likely than younger patients to present with cardiovascular symptoms (eg, congestive heart failure or angina) or neurologic findings (eg, cognitive impairment, confusion, depression, paresthesias, deafness, psychosis, or coma). Finally, in the older hypothyroid patient, the physical

Table 22–1. Percentages of patients with symptoms and physical findings attributable to thyrotoxicosis.[1]

	Old$_1$	Old$_2$	Young
Number	25	85	247
Mean age	81.5	68.6	40[2]
Range	75–95	60–82	5–73
Symptoms (%)			
Weight loss	44	35	85
Palpitations	36	42	89
Weakness	32	28	70
Dizziness, syncope	20	—	—
Nervousness	20	38	99
No symptoms	8	—	—
Memory loss	8	—	—
Tremor	8	—	—
Local symptoms[3]	8	11	—
Pruritus	4	4	—
Heat intolerance	4	63	89
Physical Findings			
Pulse > 100/min	28[4]	58	100
Atrial fibrillation	32	39	10
New-onset atrial fibrillation	20[5]	—	—
Lid lag	12	35	71
Exophthalmos	8	8	—
Fine skin	40	81	97
Tremor	36	89	97
Myopathy	8	39	—
Hyperactive reflexes	24	26	—
Gynecomastia	(1 male)	1	10
None	8		
Thyroid Examination (%)			
Impalpable or normal	68	37	—
Diffusely enlarged	12	22	100
Multinodular goiter	12	20	—
Isolated nodule	8	21	—

[1] Modified and reproduced, with permission, from Tibaldi JM et al: Thyrotoxicosis in the very old. Am J Med 1986;81:619.
[2] Approximated from graph of patients' ages.
[3] Dysphagia, enlarging neck mass, etc.
[4] Includes 5 patients with normal sinus rhythm as well as 2 who had atrial fibrillation.
[5] This was transient in 4 of 5 patients with conversion to normal sinus rhythm.
Old$_1$ = Tibaldi JM et al: Thyrotoxicosis in the very old. Am J Med 1986;81:619. Old$_2$ = Davis PJ, Davis FB: Hyperthyroidism in patients over the age of 60 years. Medicine 1974;53:161. Young = Ingbar SH et al: The thyroid gland. In: *Williams' Textbook of Endocrinology.* Williams RH (editor). Saunders, 1981.

findings are frequently nonspecific, though puffy face, delayed deep tendon reflexes, and myoedema support the diagnosis.

Diagnosis

The diagnosis can be established by a low serum T_4, T_3 resin uptake, and free T_4 index in conjunction with an elevated TSH. Measurement of serum T_3 is unnecessary and potentially misleading, because T_3 is the form of thyroid hormone most likely to decrease in nonthyroidal illness. Although an increased serum TSH is the most sensitive indicator of decreased thyroid function, it should not be used alone to diagnose hypothyroidism because it will not al-

ways differentiate symptomatic from "subclinical" hypothyroidism. Furthermore, levels of TSH may be higher at night as a result of the nocturnal rise in serum TSH. Moreover, the pulsatile nature of TSH, resulting in serum TSH slightly above the normal ranges, may lead to a diagnosis of subclinical hypothyroidism in a euthyroid subject. Finally, in hypothyroid patients, serum TSH levels can be reduced to within the normal range by treatment with dopaminergic drugs and corticosteroids. In such patients, determination of free T_4 and reverse T_3 may help to differentiate those with true hypothyroidism from those with nonthyroidal illness (see Chapter 4).

Treatment

The doses of thyroid hormone required for adequate replacement decrease with age (Table 22–2 and Table 4–9). Elderly patients should be started on approximately 25–50 µg of levothyroxine, and the dose should be increased by approximately 25 µg every 3–4 weeks. In patients with cardiovascular disease, even lower initial doses can be used and increased at a slower rate. Desiccated thyroid hormone and preparations containing T_3 should be avoided because T_3 is rapidly absorbed and cleared. The metabolic clearance of other drugs will change as hypothyroidism is corrected, and their dosages may require readjustment.

It is still not known whether treating "subclinical hypothyroidism" is beneficial in older patients. However, two-thirds of these patients will remain chemically euthyroid for at least 4 years, and low titers of antimicrosomal antibodies may identify patients at lowest risk for progression. Elderly patients previously treated with radioactive iodine are more likely to progress to overt hypothyroidism. At present, careful annual follow-up is recommended.

3. MULTINODULAR GOITER

The prevalence of multinodular goiter increases with age. However, if swallowing and breathing are not compromised and thyroid function tests are normal, the goiter can be observed without treatment. Levothyroxine therapy rarely shrinks the gland, and although it may prevent further enlargement, the risk of inducing hyperthyroidism is significant because multinodular goiters may develop areas of autonomous function.

4. THYROID NODULES & CANCER

Thyroid nodules are more common in the elderly. Ninety percent of these nodules are benign, but the prognosis for elderly patients with malignant nodules may be worse than that for younger patients with malignant nodules. The approach is similar to the workup in a younger patient. The prognosis corre-

Table 22–2. Daily doses of thyroxine in hypothyroid patients.[1,2]

	Daily Dose of Thyroxine[3] (μg/d)		
	<40 Years	40–60 Years	>60 Years
All patients	167 ± 62[4] (20)	135 ± 37 (34)	109 ± 42[5] (40)
Men	185 ± 82[6] (5)	149 ± 36 (19)	116 ± 48[4] (16)
Women	148 ± 33[6] (5)	116 ± 15 (15)	105 ± 37[6] (24)

[1] Reproduced, with permission, from Sawin CT et al: Aging and the thyroid. Am J Med 1983;75:206.
[2] Values are mean ± SD; numbers of patients are shown in parentheses.
[3] Current doses of levothyroxine are about 20% lower than the doses reported in this study. [Editor's note.]
[4] $P < .01$ (all P values are compared to ages 40–60).
[5] $P < .05$.
[6] Not significant.

lates with the size of the tumor. The outcome in elderly patients may therefore be substantially improved by early evaluation of nodules in patients who are good surgical candidates.

Papillary carcinoma is more common in young and middle-aged patients. However, it has a poorer prognosis in the elderly, possibly because it is detected at a more advanced stage. Follicular carcinoma accounts for 15% of thyroid cancers and usually occurs in middle-aged and older patients. Anaplastic thyroid carcinoma is found almost exclusively in middle-aged and older patients. It presents as a rapidly growing hard mass which is locally invasive, often associated with metastatic lesions, and has a very poor prognosis (see Chapter 4).

CARBOHYDRATE INTOLERANCE & DIABETES MELLITUS

AGING & THE PHYSIOLOGY OF CARBOHYDRATE INTOLERANCE

Even healthy elderly individuals demonstrate an age-related increase in fasting blood glucose (1 mg/dL [0.6 mmol/L] per decade) and a more significant increase in blood glucose (5 mg/dL [0.28 mmol/L] per decade) in response to a standard glucose tolerance test. According to the criteria of the National Diabetes Data Group, nearly 10% of the elderly have some degree of glucose intolerance. The possible causes of this intolerance include changes in body composition, diet, physical activity, insulin secretion, and insulin action.

With aging, lean body mass decreases and body fat increases. The percentage of body fat correlates positively with fasting levels of serum glucose, insulin,

and glucagon. However, when obesity (or the percentage of body fat) is taken into account, the basal levels of glucose, insulin, and glucagon are not influenced by age.

Decreased physical activity and a low-carbohydrate diet impair glucose tolerance, but the major contribution to glucose intolerance in healthy, active elderly individuals appears to be a decrease in insulin-mediated uptake of glucose in peripheral tissues. This is probably due to a postreceptor defect that has not yet been characterized. Impaired glucose-mediated insulin secretion (decreased B cell sensitivity) and a delayed suppression of hepatic glucose output also contribute to the age-related decline in glucose tolerance. However, recent findings suggest that much of the carbohydrate intolerance found in average elderly individuals is caused by diet, drugs, lack of exercise, or environmental factors.

DIABETES MELLITUS

Clinical Features

The prevalence of diabetes mellitus increases with age, affecting 17% of persons over age 65. Most diabetes in the elderly is type II (non-insulin-dependent) diabetes. Diabetes may be difficult to diagnose in the elderly because of its often atypical and asymptomatic presentation. For example, polyuria or polydipsia are not present in many elderly patients, because the glomerular filtration rate and thirst threshold decline with age, while the renal threshold for glycosuria increases. Instead, symptoms in these individuals are usually nonspecific (eg, weakness, fatigue, weight loss, or frequent minor infections). These patients may also present with neurologic findings such as cognitive impairment, acute confusion, or depression.

The diagnosis is established by obtaining a fasting blood glucose above 140 mg/dL (7.8 mmol/L) on two separate occasions (in the absence of acute illness); a 2-hour oral glucose tolerance test is needed rarely, if ever. Because the renal threshold for glycosuria increases in the elderly, the diagnosis should not be based on the presence of glycosuria. Increased blood levels of glycosylated hemoglobin or fructosamine support the diagnosis, but these tests are more useful in monitoring treatment.

Since the complications of diabetes mellitus are related to the duration of disease, elderly patients who live long enough will suffer the same complications of nephropathy, neuropathy, and retinopathy as their younger counterparts. Age is an independent risk factor for retinopathy (independent of metabolic control), and recent studies report an increase in many diabetic complications (peripheral neuropathy, hypertension, and impotence) that suggest an interaction between diabetes and age-related changes.

Treatment

A reasonable treatment goal in the elderly patient with diabetes mellitus is to maintain the fasting blood glucose below 150 mg/dL (8.3 mmol/L) and the postprandial blood glucose below 220 mg/dL (12.2 mmol/L). Achieving this goal is often difficult and complicated by other medications commonly prescribed for the elderly, eg, thiazide diuretics, phenytoin, and glucocorticoids, which have hyperglycemic effects. Therapy should decrease hyperglycemic symptoms and prevent infections and the potential progression to nonketotic hyperosmolar coma.

Similar to the strategy used in younger patients (see Chapter 15), initial therapy should include dietary manipulation, weight reduction for the overweight patient, and an exercise program tailored to the individual's capabilities. If mild to moderate hyperglycemia persists (fasting blood glucose < 300 mg/dL [16.7 mmol/L]), an oral hypoglycemic agent should be tried. Chlorpropamide should be avoided because of its long half-life and its propensity to induce both hyponatremia and hypoglycemia. Because of their convenience and potency, second-generation agents such as glipizide and glyburide are often used; these drugs increase insulin secretion and the number of insulin receptors and reduce hepatic glucose production. Glipizide, which has a shorter half-life than glyburide, is less likely to cause prolonged hypoglycemia in the elderly, which is poorly tolerated.

If the fasting blood sugar remains above 300 mg/dL (16.7 mmol/L), insulin therapy should be started. The usual initial dose is 15–30 units of NPH (neutral protamine Hagedorn, or isophane) or another intermediate-acting insulin. One daily injection is usually sufficient. Since elderly patients often lack symptoms of hypoglycemia, the fasting, postprandial, and bedtime blood glucose levels must be checked initially even if symptoms are absent. Finally, as in younger patients, it is important to control other adverse factors such as hypertension and smoking, which can contribute to vascular complications associated with diabetes.

Diabetic ketoacidosis is rarely seen in the elderly. It should be treated cautiously, following a strategy similar to one used in younger patients (see Chapter 15), with particular attention to the correction of electrolytes and water balance.

NONKETOTIC HYPEROSMOLAR COMA

Clinical Features

Nonketotic hyperosmolar coma occurs almost exclusively in the elderly. Predisposing factors include inadequate insulin secretion in response to hyperglycemia and a reduction in the peripheral effectiveness of insulin. Both factors lead to a progressive increase in serum glucose concentrations. The age-related increased renal threshold prevents osmotic diuresis until significant hyperglycemia is present, while an age-related decline in thirst predisposes to dehydration. Blood glucose concentrations often exceed 1000 mg/dL (55.5 mmol/L) and are coupled with marked elevation of plasma osmolality without ketosis.

This syndrome is frequently seen in elderly patients with type II diabetes who are in nursing homes. However, one-third of such patients have no previous history of diabetes, and nonketotic hyperosmolar coma can be precipitated by medications (eg, thiazide, furosemide, phenytoin, glucocorticoids) or an acute medical illness. Patients present with an acute confusional state, lethargy, weakness, and occasionally coma. Neurologic findings can be generalized or focal and can mimic an acute cerebrovascular event. Marked volume depletion, orthostatic hypotension, and prerenal azotemia are also usually present.

Treatment

The average extracellular fluid volume deficit is 9 L. It should be replaced initially with normal saline, especially when significant orthostatic hypotension is present. After 1–3 L of isotonic saline have been administered, fluids can be changed to half-normal (0.45%) saline. Half of the fluid and ion deficits should be replaced in the first 24 hours and the remainder over the next 48 hours.

Intravenous insulin in small doses (10–15 units) should be given initially, followed by a drip infusion of 1–3 units/h. Insulin therapy should not be used in lieu of fluids because it will exacerbate intravascular fluid depletion and further compromise renal function as it shifts glucose intracellularly. Potassium deficits should be corrected when the patient is producing urine. Possible precipitating events—such as acute myocardial infarction, pneumonia, or administration of a medication—must be investigated and treated. Although metabolic abnormalities may improve in 1–2 days, mental status deterioration and confusion may persist for 1 week or more. Over one-third of patients can be discharged without insulin treatment, but they are at significant risk for recurrence and should be monitored carefully.

OSTEOPOROSIS & CALCIUM HOMEOSTASIS

OSTEOPOROSIS

Despite the considerable prevalence, morbidity, and expense of osteoporosis, most of our knowledge is derived from studies of perimenopausal women. Yet it is the older woman who typically experiences the ravages of the disease. Twenty-five percent of women have vertebral fractures by age 70; by age 80, the figure is closer to 50%. Over 90% of hip fractures occur in women over age 70, and by age 90, one woman in three will have sustained such a fracture. Hip fractures are associated with significant morbidity, an increased risk of institutionalization, and up to a 20% increase in mortality rates. Despite the significant differences between perimenopausal and older women, diagnostic and therapeutic approaches for older women are derived largely from studies of perimenopausal women. The relevance of such studies for older women has only recently been questioned.

Factors Affecting Bone Physiology

There are significant physiologic differences between perimenopausal and older women with respect to maintenance of skeletal integrity. While calcium intake is inadequate in both age groups, calcium absorption declines with age, despite an age-related increase in serum levels of parathyroid hormone (PTH) (Figure 22–3); this increase is not due solely to a decrease in renal clearance, and it is associated with other biochemical evidence of increased PTH activity, including elevated levels of osteocalcin and nephrogenous cyclic adenosine monophosphate (cAMP).

A. Vitamin D: Vitamin D deficiency is common in the elderly, and vitamin D metabolism changes with age. Up to 15% of healthy, elderly residents of communities in the sunny southwestern USA have frank vitamin D deficiency; still more have subclinical vitamin D deficiency; and up to 50% of elderly nursing home residents are deficient in vitamin D. This occurs because elderly individuals experience decreased sun exposure and have an impaired ability to form vitamin D precursors in the skin, a decreased dietary intake of vitamin D, and (possibly) an age-related decline in vitamin D receptors in the duode-

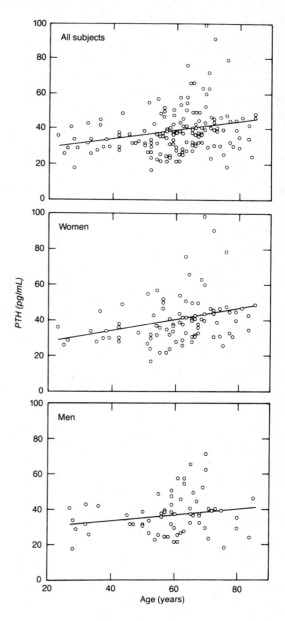

Figure 22–3. The effect of age on serum PTH. ***Upper panel:*** Entire study group ($P = .27$, $P < .001$). ***Middle panel:*** Women ($r = 0.31$, $P < .001$). ***Lower panel:*** Men ($r = 0.21$, $P < .05$). (Reproduced, with permission, from Marcus R et al: Age-related changes in parathyroid hormone and parathyroid action in normal humans. J Clin Endocrinol Metab 1984;58:223.)

num. In addition, the ability to convert vitamin D to its active moiety ($1,25[OH]_2D_3$) is impaired with age. It has been postulated that the age-related decrease in intestinal vitamin D receptors leads to an intestinal resistance to the action of $1,25[OH]_2D_3$ and subsequent impaired calcium absorption. This leads to secondary hyperparathyroidism, which in turn leads to an increased level of 1,25[OH]$_2$D$_3$ and normalized calcium absorption, but at the expense of bone loss. Bone formation also decreases with age. These factors are summarized in Figure 22–4.

B. Bone Loss and Architectural Changes: The rate of bone loss also differs between perimenopausal and older women. Cortical and (possibly) trabecular bone are lost rapidly at menopause, but in older women, cortical bone loss (at least in the forearm) may slow and in some cases cease; the data on trabecular bone loss are still inconclusive (Figure 22–5).

In addition, there are changes in bone geometry; cortical bone remodeling in older women is insufficient to compensate for the loss of bone mineral content (Figure 22–6). There are also qualitative changes in trabecular bone, since an age-related reduction in trabecular bone jeopardizes plate integrity or "connectivity"; trabecular plates not only become perforated and disconnected, but with aging they continue to thin, causing further loss of bone strength and compromising the bone's ability to regain structural integrity with conventional therapy (Figure 22–7).

C. Risk Factors: Fracture risk factors differ in perimenopausal and older women. While a "fracture threshold" is helpful in determining which perimenopausal women are at risk for fracture, by age 70 most women have bone density measurements below this threshold (Figure 22–8), yet less than one-fourth of them will ever suffer a hip fracture. However, a low hip bone density is a stronger predictor of hip fracture than low bone density at other sites. Falling is often cited as a major risk factor for hip fracture in older women. Although more than one-third of elderly women fall annually, however, less than 5% of falls result in a fracture, and those falls that do still cannot be predicted. Weakened leg muscles, gait impairment, decreased vision and proprioception, stroke, dementia, Parkinson's disease, and reduced soft tissue padding may contribute to the risk but have not yet been fully evaluated. Moreover, the factors that protect the older woman from a hip fracture in over 95% of falls are still unknown, with the exception of elevated body mass index (an index of obesity), which has been found to be protective. Furthermore, although not considered a risk factor for fractures in perimenopausal women, medications that affect the sensorium (eg, alcohol, psychotropic drugs, and sedatives) or postural blood pressure are associated with fractures in older women.

Evaluation

Similar to the evaluation in a younger individual who presents with bone loss or a fracture, the workup in an older patient can be targeted to exclude secondary causes of osteoporosis. Hyperthyroidism and hyperparathyroidism are both more common in older women, can cause bone loss, and can be clinically silent in older individuals. Because 10% of women over age 65 are receiving thyroid hormone replacement therapy and since even long-term "near-physiologic" thyroid hormone replacement results in a 6% decrease in femoral bone density in postmenopausal women (Table 22–3), true physiologic replacement with a normal serum TSH should be the goal of treatment if possible. Osteomalacia may present as nonspecific muscle or skeletal discomfort and is more common in the elderly. In addition, metastatic carcinoma, multiple myeloma, hepatic and renal disease, and malabsorption (especially secondary to a gastrectomy) should be excluded. Glucocorticoid use and antiseizure medications also can cause significant bone loss in the elderly. Because factors outside the skeleton contribute to fracture risk in the elderly, however, the search for correctable factors must extend beyond those that affect bone density. Particular attention should be devoted to the patient's local environment and medication use.

Older patients presenting with skeletal discomfort should be evaluated by radiography to rule out a fracture. Vertebral osteoporosis usually presents with anterior wedging, involvement of more than one vertebrae, prominent vertebral trabeculae, and vertebral deformities usually occurring below T6. Worrisome signs suggesting that skeletal involvement is not due to osteoporosis alone include nerve root compression, posterior wedging, isolated vertebral involvement (especially above T4), and pedicle destruction. Furthermore, older individuals may complain of persistent groin pain with weight-bearing, while plain

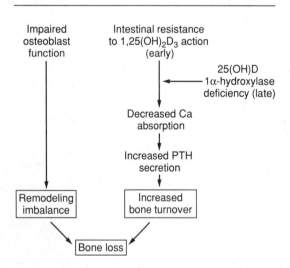

Figure 22–4. Pathophysiologic model of age-related bone loss. (Reproduced, with permission, from Eberling PR et al: Evidence of an age-related decrease in intestinal responsiveness to vitamin D: Relationship between serum 1,25-dihydroxyvitamin D$_3$ and intestinal vitamin D receptor concentrations in normal women. J Clin Endocrinol Metab 1992;75:176).

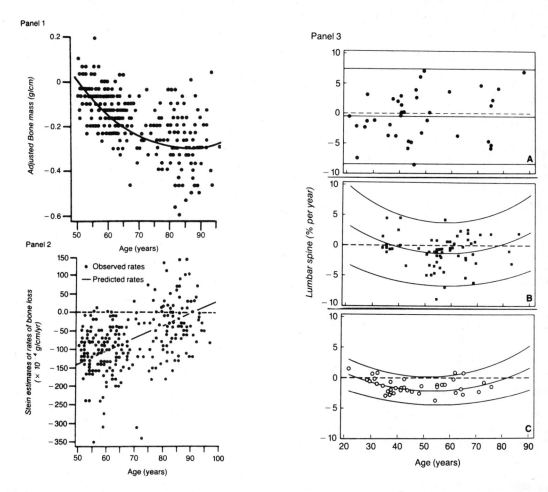

Figure 22–5. Rate of bone loss in perimenopausal and older women. **Panel 1:** Cross-sectional data showing the average bone mass at the midshaft site of the radius measured by single-photon absorptiometry for each subject adjusted for body size plotted against mean age during the time of measurement. **Panel 2:** Longitudinal data for subjects followed for a mean of 7 years, showing the linear rate of bone loss plotted against age for each subject. The rate of bone loss declines with age. (Modified, with permission, from Hui SL et al: A prospective study of change in bone mass with age in postmenopausal women. J Chron Dis 1982;35:715.) **Panel 3:** Longitudinal rates of trabecular bone loss in 139 normal women measured by dual photon absorptiometry. The rate of change in bone mineral density (BMD) of the lumbar spine is plotted against age at the time of the first BMD measurement. Subjects are identified by time on study: A ≈ 1 year; B ≈ 2 years; C ≈ 3 years. When all data were analyzed, mean bone loss occurred across life. When only subjects in the groups having mean scan intervals of ≈ 2 years or ≈ 3 years were analyzed, however, age regression was best fitted with a parabolic equation. Center line denotes age regression, and upper and lower lines denote 95% confidence limits for the equation. Broken line shows zero rate of change in BMD. (Modified, and reproduced, with permission, from Riggs BL et al: Rates of bone loss in the appendicular and axial skeletons of women. J Clin Invest 1986;77:1487.)

radiographs of the hip reveal no fracture. A bone scan may be necessary to confirm the diagnosis of hip fracture.

Treatment

Because the factors that affect bone physiology—the rate of bone loss, the structure of remaining bone, and the risk of fracture—are substantially different in perimenopausal and elderly women, interventions appropriate for perimenopausal women may be inappropriate for older women. Unfortunately, few thera-

peutic studies include older individuals, and the studies that do generally use bone density (rather than bone fracture) as an end point. Bone density as an end point may be less relevant for the elderly woman whose bone density is already depleted, because even if further bone loss could be slowed, it is not clear that fracture risk would be reduced, especially if the structure of the remaining bone is still impaired. Since the currently accepted modalities only slow further bone loss, it is difficult to estimate their efficacy in preventing hip fractures in the elderly.

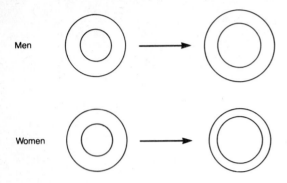

Men

Women

Figure 22–6. Schematic representation of cortical bone remodeling with age in males and females. Note that with age-related bone loss, bone is remodeled in men to increase its diameter and partially offset the loss of strength due to bone loss. In women, bone diameter changes little with age, so that bone strength decreases proportionately more than in men. (Reproduced, with permission, from Ruff CB, Hayes WC: Sex differences in age-related remodeling of the femur and tibia. J Orthop Res 1988;6:886.)

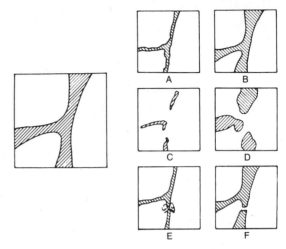

Figure 22–7. Possible effects of osteoporotic treatment regimens on trabecular bone. *Left panel:* Normal trabecular bone mass and architecture. Treatment resulting in anabolic effects on bone volume may restore normal bone volume and architecture in thin trabeculae (A, B). If trabecular integrity is disrupted before treatment, similar effects on bone volume may not reverse architectural abnormalities (C, D), particularly if treatment impairs the repair of microfractures (E, F). (Modified and reproduced, with permission, from Kanis JA: Treatment of osteoporotic fracture. Lancet 1984;1:27.)

A. Calcium: Considerable controversy surrounds the use of calcium supplementation in perimenopausal women, although few data are available regarding its use in older women. Theoretically, calcium supplementation seems appropriate because calcium intake in the elderly is low and the ability to adapt to a low-calcium diet declines with age. Calcium balance studies suggest that postmenopausal estrogen-deficient women require 1500 mg/d to maintain calcium balance. A reduction in hip fractures and improvement in bone density has been demonstrated in very elderly women (mean age 84) treated with vitamin D 800 IU and calcium 1200 mg daily. Calcium should be given in divided doses with meals to improve absorption in the elderly, who may suffer from achlorhydria. A potential problem with prescribing high doses of calcium in the elderly includes inducing or exacerbating constipation. In addition, since compliance with other drug regimens decreases as the number of drugs increases, calcium tablets may be taken at the therapeutic expense of more important medications.

B. Vitamin D: Until recently there were few data to support the use of vitamin D or its metabolites in the treatment of osteoporosis. There is a small therapeutic ratio for vitamin D; toxicity from hypercalcemia can occur with doses as low as 50 μg (2000 IU), especially in individuals who are also taking a thiazide diuretic and calcium supplementation. However, because vitamin D deficiency is common in the elderly and vitamin D is needed for calcium absorption and also improves muscle strength. 1 or 2 multivitamin tablets daily, containing 400 IU vitamin D per tablet, are beneficial and will provide a normal vitamin D level even in institutionalized elderly per-

son. Clinical trials utilizing calcitriol (1,25-dihydroxy vitamin D_3) as a therapeutic option for osteoporosis have shown conflicting results, although a recent trial found a threefold reduction in vertebral compression fractures. The potential for complications such as hypercalcemia, nephrolithiasis, and nephrocalcinosis are unknown, and this therapy is currently still under investigation.

C. Estrogen: There is considerable evidence that estrogen therapy, if initiated at menopause, slows bone loss; may temporarily increase bone mass; and may prevent osteoporotic, vertebral, and hip fractures. If therapy is continued, its efficacy is sustained at least until age 70. In addition, recent studies have shown that estrogen will increase femoral bone mass. Fewer data are available about elderly persons taking newly prescribed estrogen. Three studies have reported a positive effect of estrogen on bone mass, and the Framingham observational study noted a trend in reduction of hip fractures for women aged 65–74.

For women with an intact uterus, combined cyclic regimens with estrogen and progesterone may provoke return of menses and are less well tolerated. Despite the need for gynecologic surveillance and endometrial sampling to detect endometrial cancer, older women are more tolerant of combined continuous therapy regimens with estrogen and progesterone, which generally provide an atrophic en-

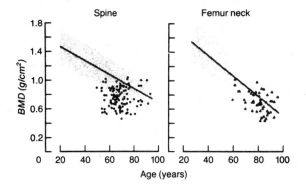

Figure 22–8. Bone mineral density (BMD) levels for spine and femur neck, plotted as a function of age for 111 patients with vertebral fractures (left panel) and 49 patients with hip fractures (right panel). The line represents the regression with age; the cross-hatched area shows the 90% confidence limits for 166 normal women. Note that the fracture threshold (90th percentile of the measurements for patients with fractures) is about 1 g/cm² and is independent of age. (Reproduced, with permission, from Riggs BL et al: Involutional osteoporosis. N Engl J Med 1986;314:1676).

dometrium within 1 year. Similar to younger women, older women receiving estrogen therapy require annual mammograms (see Chapter 10).

Estrogen's protective effect against cardiovascular disease is another benefit frequently cited to support its use. Unfortunately, there are few data to support the suggestion that such a benefit will accrue when estrogen is newly prescribed to elderly women, in whom the prevalence of heart disease is already high.

D. Exercise: Although the rationale for exercise therapy is sound and it is associated with many other beneficial effects in older women, few data are available on results of exercise on bone density in elderly women. One study prescribed exercise for older women and found that forearm bone mineral content increased in those who continued exercising during a 3-year trial. It is not known whether the benefit extended to other more important sites, such as the hip. Walking—generally 30 minutes three times a week—is often suggested for less frail individuals. However, exercise is potentially dangerous for the reason that sedentary older women who newly engage in exercise may increase their exposure to accidents and subsequent fractures.

E. Other Therapeutic Options: Bisphosphonates—nonhormonal agents that inhibit bone resorption—effectively prevent osteoporosis. Two recent randomized, double-blind, placebo-controlled, large-scale prospective studies with etidronate found a beneficial effect on bone density and a decrease in vertebral fractures in postmenopausal women, including some up to age 75; no consistent effect was noted for the hip (Figure 22–9). This therapy is well tolerated and has few side effects if given correctly. Although calcitonin is an approved therapy for osteoporosis, no data are available about its effect on the incidence of fractures. It currently must be given by injection; it is expensive; and it is relatively poorly tolerated by the elderly. Nasal calcitonin, an investigational agent, offers promise. Fluoride therapy causes significant toxicity in one-third of patients and has been associated with an increase in nonvertebral fractures. Although thiazide diuretics have been associated with decreased hip fracture risk in several cross-sectional epidemiologic studies, the results are inconsistent, the optimal dose and duration are unclear, and the likelihood is high that the benefit is due to the prescription of such agents to hypertensive persons who are heavier and healthier than the comparison group.

Table 22–3. Effect of levothyroxine therapy on bone mass in premenopausal and postmenopausal women.

	QCT Spine	DPA Spine	DPA Hip
Premenopausal			
Control bone density[1]	159.2 ± 26.0 (217)	1.065 ± 0.125 (247)	0.914 ± 0.128 (132)
Patient bone density[1]	148.5 ± 20.3 (28)	1.032 ± 0.117 (28)	0.867 ± 0.101 (28)
Percent difference	−6.7	−3.1	−5.1
z-score	−0.39 ± 0.74	−0.22 ± 0.78	−0.36 ± 0.74
P value[2]	.01	.15	0.02
Postmenopausal			
Control bone density[1]	107.0 ± 26.0 (299)	0.963 ± 0.164 (164)	0.818 ± 0.128 (153)
Patient bone density[1]	106.8 ± 33.9 (28)	0.955 ± 0.187 (28)	0.767 ± 0.125 (28)
Percent difference	−0.2	−1.0	−6.2
z-score	−0.01 ± 1.01	−0.05 ± 1.11	−0.39 ± 0.80
P value[2]	.95	.80	.02

[1] QCT spine (mg/cm³), DPA spine and hip (g/cm³).
[2] Control versus patient, using z-score.
Note:
  Bone density and z-scores are shown as mean ± SD.
  Numbers of subjects are given in parentheses.
  QCT spine = quantitative computed tomography of the spine.
  DPA spine = dual photon absorptiometry of the spine.
  DPA hip = dual photon absorptiometry of the hip.

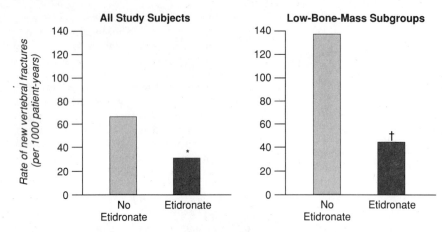

Figure 22–9. Rates of new vertebral fractures in the groups that received etidronate (groups 3 and 4) and those that did not (groups 1 and 2) during the 24-month study. The left-hand panel shows the data for all patients, and the right-hand panel the data for subgroups with low bone mineral density at entry. The asterisk (*P* = .014) and the dagger (*P* = .002) indicate significant differences between treatment groups. (Reproduced, with permission, from Watts NB et al: Intermittent cyclical etidronate treatment of postmenopausal osteoporosis. N Engl J Med 1990;323:73.)

Moreover, a slight increase in both falls and fractures was noted in the only randomized study of thiazide use, the SHEP trial for hypertension in the elderly.

Summary of Management Recommendations

In summary, there is ample reason to question the validity of extrapolating data from studies of perimenopausal women when formulating a treatment plan for older women. However, given the prevalence of the problem, it is reasonable to recommend an adequate daily intake of vitamin D (1–2 multivitamin tablets containing 400–800 IU), an adequate daily intake of calcium (totaling 800–1500 mg), and judicious participation in an individually tailored exercise program. The use of estrogen replacement therapy or other treatment needs to be individually considered.

Perhaps more importantly, the risk of falls should be addressed. This can be accomplished by reviewing medications (including nonprescription agents) and discontinuing (when possible) those with adverse effects on cognition, balance, or blood pressure. It is also important to correct reversible sensory losses, malnutrition, and medical conditions and to educate patients about hazards in their environment, such as throw rugs, extension cords, and poorly illuminated stairways, that could lead to falls and fractures. For patients with gait disorders, physical therapy should be considered.

Patients who have recently sustained a hip fracture should receive the same evaluation and consideration as those without a fracture. Because there is a significant overlap in bone density measurements between those who fracture and those who do not (Figure

22–8), a hip fracture should not be a reason to omit evaluation or treatment (see also Chapter 5).

HYPERPARATHYROIDISM

Clinical Features

The prevalence of hyperparathyroidism increases with age. While its incidence is less than 10 per 100,000 in women under age 40, the incidence increases to 190 per 100,000 in women over age 60. As a result, over half of all cases of hyperparathyroidism occur in individuals over the age of 65. Most cases are mild. Detection is by routine screening of serum calcium, and few or no symptoms are present. However, with relatively minor elevations of serum calcium (up to 11–12 mg/dL [2.8–3 mmol/L]), some elderly subjects may experience weakness, fatigue, depression, and confusion. Failure to thrive and constipation are commonly seen; renal, gastrointestinal, and skeletal complications occur less often. Other causes of hypercalcemia in the elderly—especially multiple myeloma, malignancy, vitamin D intoxication, and thiazide diuretics—must be considered in the differential diagnosis.

Treatment

For symptomatic patients with serum calcium levels above 12 mg/dL (3 mmol/L) and an elevated serum parathyroid hormone level, parathyroidectomy is well tolerated and is the treatment of choice. For those with more modest elevations, treatment decisions are less certain because it is difficult to differentiate symptoms and signs due to the disease from those seen in older individuals without hyperparathyroidism. Moreover, asymptomatic individuals—especially those with levels of serum calcium under 11 mg/dL (2.8 mmol/L)—have been known to remain asymptomatic for over a decade. Until more data become available, the decision to treat asymptomatic individuals surgically should be made on an individual basis.

In patients whose symptoms may be due to hyperparathyroidism, it is worthwhile to observe the response to medical therapy before considering surgery. In women, a course of estrogen may be effective. Ethinyl estradiol (30–50 μg/d) or conjugated estrogens (1.25–2.5 mg/d) reduce serum calcium by an average of 0.8 mg/dL (0.2 mmol/L), diminish urinary calcium excretion, and antagonize the skeletal effect of PTH. Norethindrone (5 mg/d) has a similar effect on serum calcium while producing no undesirable effects on the uterus. However, its skeletal effects are unclear, and it does not match estrogen's beneficial effect on serum lipids. In men and in women with higher elevations of serum calcium, oral phosphates can be used, but they are less well tolerated in the elderly because of their gastrointestinal side effects. Furosemide is a less satisfactory alternative in frail elderly patients because it increases the risk of dehydration and resultant hypercalcemia.

CHANGES IN WATER BALANCE

With age, major changes in renal function and homeostatic mechanisms result in significant changes in water balance. Renal blood flow, cortical mass, glomerular number, and tubular function all decline with age, though medullary mass is preserved. Clinically, however, the most relevant change is the age-related decline in creatinine clearance, which is largely due to relative hypertension in the elderly. Because of the decrease in muscle mass associated with aging, however, serum creatinine levels are unchanged and may not accurately reflect the extent of renal functional impairment.

Extrarenal modulators of water balance also change significantly with age. Although there are no changes in the basal level, half-life, volume of distribution, or metabolic clearance of vasopressin, the stimulated responses of vasopressin are significantly altered. Hyperosmolar stimuli increase serum vasopressin levels in older subjects to five times those achieved in younger subjects. On the other hand, the normal vasopressin increase observed in response to overnight dehydration and postural change is impaired in the elderly. Additionally, basal and stimulated levels of serum renin and aldosterone decline with age. In contrast, basal levels of atrial natriuretic

factor are three times higher in healthy elderly individuals than in young controls, and elevated levels of atrial natriuretic factor may help identify patients at risk for the development of congestive heart failure. Finally, the thirst sensation appears to be somewhat impaired in healthy elderly individuals and is more impaired in those who are frail.

DISORDERS OF WATER BALANCE

In addition to physiologic changes, many diseases and drugs further increase the vulnerability of the elderly to changes in water balance. These include kidney disease, hypertension, and congestive heart failure as well as medications that alter water balance (eg, narcotics, diuretics, lithium, chlorpropamide, carbamazepine, amphotericin B, intravenous hypotonic fluids, and hypertonic contrast agents).

1. HYPERNATREMIA
Clinical Features
The incidence of hypernatremia in elderly patients admitted to the hospital is approximately 1% and is higher in institutionalized elderly patients. Signs and symptoms are usually nonspecific, eg, lethargy, weakness, confusion, depression, and failure to thrive. The cause is usually multifactorial, including impaired thirst mechanism, renal disease, sedative-induced confusion, use of restraints, reduced access to free water intake, excess water loss due to fever, and decreased response to vasopressin.

Treatment
As in younger patients, initial therapy involves correcting the volume deficit with isotonic saline and then correcting the water deficit with half-normal (0.45%) saline. Roughly 30% of the deficit should be corrected within 24 hours and the remainder within the next 24–48 hours.

2. HYPONATREMIA
Clinical Features
The prevalence of hyponatremia is approximately 2.5% in the general hospital setting—higher in geriatric units—and rises to 20% in nursing home settings. Presenting symptoms and signs are often nonspecific and include lethargy, weakness, and confusion. The mechanisms predisposing to hyponatremia include the exuberant response of vasopressin to osmolar stimuli, a decreased ability to excrete a water load, and the sodium-wasting tendency of the older kidney. Furthermore, elderly patients often use medications and have diseases that impair free water excretion. Common hyponatremic syndromes in the elderly include the syndrome of inappropriate antidiuretic hormone secretion (SIADH) and thiazide-induced hyponatremia.

Treatment

The treatment of hyponatremia in the elderly does not differ from that in younger patients (see Chapter 2).

3. HYPORENINEMIC HYPOALDOSTERONISM

Hyporeninemic hypoaldosteronism usually occurs in elderly patients with diabetes and mild renal insufficiency. Patients are usually asymptomatic, and hyperkalemia and acidosis are found on routine screening. On the other hand, symptoms of hyperkalemia (eg, heart block) may be provoked by administration of a beta-adrenergic blocking agent, which further compromises extrarenal regulation of potassium homeostasis. After other causes of persistent hyperkalemia are ruled out, patients respond well to administration of small doses of fludrocortisone (0.05 mg/d) or furosemide combined with restriction of potassium.

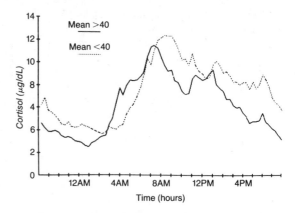

Figure 22–10. Mean 24-hour plasma cortisol concentration derived from 20-minute sampling for 12 subjects more than 40 years of age and for 22 subjects less than 40 years of age. (Reproduced, with permission, from Sherman B et al: Age-related changes in the circadian rhythm of plasma cortisol in man. J Clin Endocrinol Metab 1985;61:439.)

GLUCOCORTICOIDS & STRESS

Because of equivalent decreases in secretion and clearance, serum cortisol and corticosteroid-binding globulin change little with age. However, the morning peak of cortisol secretion occurs several hours earlier in the elderly (Figure 22–10).

In healthy elderly individuals, dynamic testing of the hypothalamic-pituitary-adrenal axis is normal; expected responses to insulin-induced hypoglycemia, metyrapone, dexamethasone, ACTH, and CRH are preserved (Figure 22–11).

DISORDERS OF THE HYPOTHALAMIC-PITUITARY-ADRENAL AXIS

1. ABNORMAL RESPONSE TO STRESS

In contrast to the normal responses of the hypothalamic-pituitary-adrenal axis in the elderly to dynamic testing, increased stress elicits abnormal responses. For example, although serum cortisol levels increase to the same extent in young and old patients undergoing elective surgery, the increase may be protracted in the elderly. Patients with diabetes mellitus and hypertension have also been found to have an exaggerated and prolonged response to CRH stimulation. Older patients with Alzheimer's disease may also have delayed responses to CRH stimulation. It is not known if these elevated levels may contribute to the increased hypertension, glucose intolerance, muscle atrophy, osteoporosis, and impaired immune function observed in the elderly.

2. ADRENAL HYPERSECRETION

While adrenal hypersecretion (Cushing's syndrome) is uncommon in the elderly, it is easily overlooked because it mimics normal aging processes. Signs such as hypertension, glucose intolerance, weight gain, and osteoporosis are less specific in elderly than in younger patients, but as in younger patients the diagnosis is established or excluded using the usual criteria (see Chapter 6).

3. ADRENAL INSUFFICIENCY

Symptoms of adrenal insufficiency in younger patients—eg, failure to thrive, weakness, weight loss, confusion, and arthralgias—are common complaints in adrenally intact elderly patients; the most specific sign of adrenal insufficiency in the elderly is hyperpigmentation. The laboratory findings of adrenal insufficiency are similar to those found in younger patients and include azotemia, hypoglycemia, hyponatremia, hyperkalemia, and eosinophilia. Because the metabolic clearance rate of cortisol decreases with age, older patients generally require lower replacement doses of cortisol.

CHANGES IN REPRODUCTIVE FUNCTION IN MEN

Overall, while sexual activity decreases with age, there are conflicting reports about the physiologic

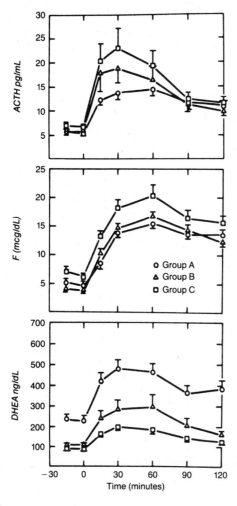

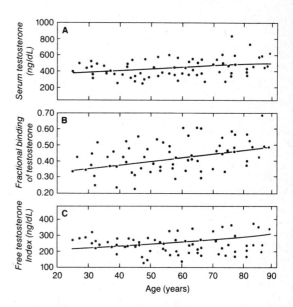

Figure 22–12. Total and free serum testosterone in men in relation to age. **A:** Serum testosterone concentration in men of various ages. The solid line in this and subsequent figures is drawn from least squares linear regression. **B:** Fractional binding of testosterone by column chromatography determined in sera from men of different ages. **C:** Free testosterone index determined from serum testosterone and fractional binders in sera from men of different ages. (Reproduced, with permission, from Harman SM et al: Reproductive hormones in aging men. 1. Measurement of sex steroids, basal luteinizing hormone, and Leydig cell response to human chorionic gonadotropin. J Clin Endocrinol Metab 1980;51:35.)

Figure 22–11. Mean values for groups A, B, and C of plasma ACTH *(upper panel),* F or cortisol *(middle panel),* and DHEA *(lower panel)* before and up to 120 minutes after bolus intravenous injection of ovine CRH (1 μg/kg). Group A, 21–49 years, mean age 35.2 years, n = 19. Group B, 50–69 years, mean age 60.7 years, n = 15. Group C, 70–86 years, mean age 77.1 years, n = 15. (Reproduced, with permission, from Pavlov EP et al: Responses of plasma adrenocorticotropin, cortisol, and dehydroepiandrosterone to ovine corticotropin-releasing hormone in healthy aging men. J Clin Endocrinol Metab 1986;62:767.)

changes in the hypothalamic-pituitary-testicular axis. There is no consensus on the effect of age on the production or metabolism of dihydrotestosterone, estrone, and estradiol. Studies of testosterone economy show that serum testosterone (Figure 22–12), sex hormone-binding globulin, and free testosterone change little, if at all, while testosterone clearance decreases. However, other studies suggest that circulating testosterone and bioavailable testosterone fall with age by 40–65%. A decrease in the number or re-

sponsiveness of testicular Leydig cells is likely because serum FSH and LH increase with age, and the testosterone response to human chorionic gonadotropin (hCG) decreases. On the other hand, with age there is probably a decrease in the ratio of circulating bioactive to immunoreactive LH. Finally, pituitary changes are suggested by a decreased gonadotropic response to luteinizing hormone-releasing hormone (LHRH) stimulation.

The clinical relevance of these changes is questionable. The correlation between sexual activity and the age-related changes described is weak, and although early studies found decreased concentrations of spermatozoa in the ejaculate of older men, the difference disappeared after corrections were made for frequency of ejaculation. Sperm motility and the volume of ejaculate do decrease with age, and the proportion of abnormal spermatozoa also increases.

Impotence becomes more prevalent with age, but an endocrinologic etiology becomes less likely. The incidence of impotence in men under age 45 is 5%; the incidence in men over age 75 is 50%. However, over 90% of men in the latter group have coexistent medical conditions or are taking medications that contribute to the impotence. Furthermore, up to 30% of men over age 76 develop impotence following prostatectomy, compared with 3–11% in younger age groups. Often there are multiple overlapping causes of impotence—psychosocial, neurovascular, and arteriolar—in the same individual.

The evaluation of impotence in the elderly is similar to that in younger individuals (see Chapter 9), though more emphasis must be placed on the effects of drugs (both prescribed and nonprescribed) and vascular causes, and a search for multiple causative factors including asymptomatic diabetes mellitus should be undertaken.

BENIGN PROSTATIC HYPERPLASIA

Although the pathogenesis of benign prostatic hyperplasia is incompletely understood, testicular androgens are believed to play a permissive role in the development of prostatic adenomas. This mechanism provides the rationale for the use of antiandrogens in the treatment of benign prostatic hypertrophy. Antiandrogen treatment has been investigated using luteinizing hormone releasing hormone (LHRH) agonists (nafarelin, leuprolide, buserelin), androgen receptor inhibitors (cyproterone acetate, flutamide), and 5α-reductase inhibitors (finasteride). Overall, these agents result in a 25–30% reduction in prostate size, but their effects on the voiding symptoms associated with benign prostatic hypertrophy have been modest and variable, and their effect on urethral obstruction due to the adenoma is unknown. Each of these agents must be continued indefinitely to maintain prostate size reduction, yet many men may find such therapy difficult and undesirable, and the long-term side effects are largely unknown. The LHRH agonists and cyproterone acetate cause impotence; flutamide induces gynecomastia, and a recent report describes serologic as well as histologic evidence of flutamide-induced hepatotoxicity in a small number of patients. Since finasteride decreases dihydrotestosterone while maintaining the circulating levels of testosterone, undesirable antiandrogenic side effects may be decreased. However, finasteride causes a significant decrease in the level of prostate-specific antigen, a serum marker increasingly used for the clinical detection of prostate adenocarcinoma, the most common cancer in men. Since the effect of finasteride on prostate cancer development and progression is unknown, it is unclear whether any antitumor benefit will mitigate finasteride's effect on the ability to use this important tumor marker in treated men.

REFERENCES

Thyroid Function & Disease

Davis PJ, Davis FB: Hyperthyroidism in patients over the age of 60 years. Medicine 1974;53:161.

Ehrmann DA, Weinberg M, Sarne DH: Limitations to the use of a sensitive assay for serum thyrotropin in the assessment of thyroid status. Arch Intern Med 1989;149:369.

Greenspan SL et al: Pulsatile secretion of thyrotropin in man. J Clin Endocrinol Metab 1986;63:661.

Greenspan SL et al: Age-related alterations in pulsatile secretion of TSH: Role of dopaminergic regulation. Am J Physiol 1991;260(3 Pt 1):E486.

Harman SM, Wehman RE, Blackman MR: Pituitary-thyroid hormone economy in healthy aging men: Basal indices of thyroid function and thyrotropin responses to constant infusions of thyrotropin releasing hormone. J Clin Endocrinol Metab 1984;58:320.

Livingston EH et al: Prevalence of thyroid disease and abnormal thyroid tests in older hospitalized and ambulatory persons. J Am Geriat Soc 1987;35:109.

Meneilly GS et al: Endocrine systems. In: *Geriatric Medicine,* 2nd ed. Rowe JW, Besdine R (editors). Little, Brown, 1988.

Nordyke RA, Gilbert FI, Harada ASM: Graves' disease: Influence of age on clinical findings. Arch Intern Med 1988;148:626.

Parle JV, Franklyn JA, Cross KW: Prevalence and follow-up of abnormal thyrotropin (TSH) concentrations in the elderly in the United Kingdom. Clin Endocrinol 1991;34:77.

Robuschi G et al: Hypothyroidism in the elderly. Endocr Rev 1987;8:142.

Rosenthal MJ et al: Thyroid failure in the elderly: Microsomal antibodies as discriminant for therapy. JAMA 1987;258:209.

Sawin CT et al: Aging and the thyroid: Decreased requirement for thyroid hormone in older hypothyroid patients. Am J Med 1983;75:206.

Sawin CT et al: The aging thyroid: Relationship between elevated serum thyrotropin level and thyroid antibodies in elderly patients. Am J Med 1985;79:591.

Sawin CT et al: The aging thyroid: Thyroid deficiency in the Framingham study. Arch Intern Med 1985;145:1386.

Sawin CT et al: The aging thyroid: The use of thyroid hormone in older persons. JAMA 1989;261:2653.

Surke MI, et al: American Thyroid Association guidelines for use of laboratory tests in thyroid disorders. JAMA 1990;267:1529.

Tibaldi JM et al: Thyrotoxicosis in the very old. Am J Med 1986;81:619.

Carbohydrate Intolerance & Diabetes Mellitus

Cahill GF: Hyperglycemic hyperosmolar coma: A syndrome almost unique in the elderly. J Am Geriatr Soc 1983;31:103.

Chen M, Halter JB, Porte D: The role of dietary carbohydrate in the decreased glucose tolerance of the elderly. J Am Geriatr Soc 1987;35:417.

Elahi D et al: Effect of age and obesity on fasting levels of glucose, insulin, growth hormone and glucagon in man. J Gerontol 1982;37:385.

Harris MI et al: Prevalence of diabetes and impaired glucose tolerance and plasma glucose levels in US population aged 20–74 years. Diabetes 1987;36:523.

Hollenbeck CB et al: Effect of habitual physical activity on regulation of insulin-stimulated glucose disposal in older males. J Am Geriatr Soc 1985;33:273.

Kannel WB: Lipid diabetes in coronary heart disease: Insights from the Framingham Study. Am Heart J 1985;110:1100.

Reaven GM, Reaven EP: Age, glucose tolerance, and non-insulin-dependent diabetes mellitus. J Am Geriatr Soc 1985;33:286.

Zavaroni I et al: Effect of age and environmental factors on glucose tolerance and insulin secretion in a worker population. J Am Geriatr Soc 1986;34:271.

Osteoporosis & Calcium Homeostasis

American College of Physicians: Guidelines for counseling postmenopausal women about preventive hormone therapy. Ann Intern Med 1992;117:1038.

Chapuy MC et al: Vitamin D_3 and calcium to prevent hip fractures in elderly women. N Engl J Med 1992;327: 1637.

Cummings SR et al: Bone density at various sites for prediction of hip fractures. Lancet 1993;341:72.

Cummings SR et al: Epidemiology of osteoporosis and osteoporotic fractures. Epidemiol Rev 1985;7:178.

Ebeling PR, Sandgren ME, DiMagno EP: Evidence of an age-related decrease in intestinal responsiveness to vitamin D: Relationship between serum 1,25-dihydroxy vitamin D_3 and intestinal vitamin D receptor concentrations in normal women. J Clin Endocrinol Metab 1992;75:176.

Greenspan SL et al: Skeletal integrity in pre- and postmenopausal women on long-term L-thyroxine therapy. Am J Med 1991;91:5.

Grisso JA et al: Risk factors for falls as a cause of hip fracture in women. N Engl J Med 1991;324:1326.

Holick MF: Vitamin D requirements for the elderly. Am J Clin Nutr 1986;5:121.

Hui SL et al: A prospective study of change in bone mass with age in postmenopausal women. J Chron Dis 1982;35:715.

Kiel DP et al: Hip fracture and the use of estrogens in postmenopausal women: The Framingham study. N Engl J Med 1987;317:1169.

Lindsay R, Tohme JF: Estrogen treatment of patients with osteoporosis. J Obstet Gynecol 1990;76:290.

Lips P et al: The effect of vitamin D supplementation on vitamin D status and parathyroid function in elderly subjects. J Clin Endocrinol Metab 1988;67:644.

Marcus R, Madvig P, Young G: Age-related changes in parathyroid hormone and parathyroid hormone action in normal humans. J Clin Endocrinol Metab 1984;58:223.

Marcus R et al: Conjugated estrogens in the treatment of post-menopausal women with hyperparathyroidism. Ann Intern Med 1984;100:633.

Melton LJ III, Riggs, BL: Risk factors for injury after a fall. Clin Geriatr Med 1985;1:525.

Quigley MET et al: Estrogen therapy arrests bone loss in elderly women. Am J Obstet Gynecol 1987;156: 1516.

Ray WA et al: Psychotropic drug use and the risk of hip fracture. N Engl J Med 1987;316:363.

Resnick NM, Greenspan SL: Senile osteoporosis reconsidered. J Am Med Assoc 1989;261:1025.

Riggs BL, Melton III LJ: The prevention and treatment of osteoporosis. N Engl J Med 1992;327:620–7.

Riggs BL, Melton LJ III: Involutional osteoporosis. N Engl J Med 1986;314:1676.

Riggs BL et al: Rates of bone loss in the appendicular and axial skeletons of women. J Clin Invest 1986;77: 1487.

Ruff CB, Hayes WC: Sex differences in age-related remodeling of the femur and tibia. J Orthop Res 1988; 6:886.

Selby PL et al: Ethinyl estradiol and norethindrone in the treatment of primary hyperparathyroidism in postmenopausal women. N Engl J Med 1986;314:1481.

The SHEP Cooperative Research Group: Prevention of stroke by antihypertensive drug treatment in older persons with systolic hypertension: final results of the Systolic Hypertension in the Elderly Program (SHEP). J Am Med Assoc 1991;265:3255.

Storm T et al: Effect of intermittent cyclical etidronate therapy on bone mass and fracture rate in women with postmenopausal osteoporosis. N Engl J Med 1990; 322:1265.

Tilyard MW et al: Treatment of postmenopausal osteoporosis with calcitriol or calcium. N Engl J Med 1992; 326:357.

Watts NB et al: Intermittent cyclical etidronate treatment of postmenopausal osteoporosis. N Engl J Med 1990; 323:73.

Changes in Water Balance

Anderson RJ et al: Hyponatremia: A prospective analysis of its epidemiology and the pathogenetic role of vasopressin. Ann Intern Med 1985;102:164.

Cyus JC, Krothapalli RK, Arieff AL: Treatment of symptomatic hyponatremia and its relation to brain damage. N Engl J Med 1987;317:1190.

Davis KM et al: Atrial natriuretic peptide levels in the prediction of congestive heart failure risk in frail elderly JAMA 1992;267:2625.

Ohashi M et al: High plasma concentrations of human atrial natriuretic polypeptide in aged men. J Clin Endocrinol Metab 1987;64:81.

Snyder NA, Feigal DW, Arieff AL: Hypernatremia in elderly patients: A heterogeneous, morbid, and iatrogenic entity. Ann Intern Med 1987;107:309.

Glucocorticoids & Stress

Greenspan SL et al: The pituitary-adrenal glucocorticoid response is altered by gender and disease. J Gerontol 1993;48:M72.

Pavlov EP et al: Response of plasma adrenocorticotropin, cortisol and dehydro-epiandrosterone to ovine corticotropin-releasing hormone in healthy aging men. J Clin Endocrinol Metab 1986;62:767.

Sapolsky RM, McEwen B: Why dexamethasone resistance? Two possible neuroendocrine mechanisms. In: *HPA Physiology and Pathophysiology.* Schatzberg A, Nemeroff C (editors). Raven Press, 1987.

Sherman B, Wysham C, Pfohl B: Age-related changes in

the circadian rhythm of plasma cortisol in man. J Clin Endocrinol Metab 1985;61:439.

Reproductive Function in Men

DuBeau CE, Resnick NM: Controversies in the diagnosis and management of benign prostatic hyperplasia. Adv Intern Med 1992;37:55.

Gormley GJ et al: The effect of finasteride in men with benign prostatic hyperplasia. N Engl J Med 1992;327:1185.

Harman SM et al: Reproductive hormones in aging men. 2. Basal pituitary gonadotropins and gonadotropin responses to luteinizing hormone-releasing hormone. J Clin Endocrinol Metab 1982;54:547.

Korenman SG, Morley JE, Morradian AD: Secondary hypogonadism in older men: its relationship to impotence. J Clin Endocrinol Metab 1990;71:963.

Mulligan T, Katz PG: Why aged men become impotent. Arch Int Med 1989;149:1365.

Morley JE, Kaiser FE: Testicular function in the aging male. In: Endocrine Function and Aging. Armbrecht HJ, Coe RM, Wong Surawat N (editors). Springer, 1990.

NIH Consensus Development Panel on impotence: Impotence. JAMA 1993;270:83.

Tsitouras PD, Martin CE, Harman SM: Relationship of serum testosterone to sexual activity in healthy elderly men. J Gerontol 1982;37:288.

APPENDIX

TABLE OF NORMAL HORMONE REFERENCE RANGES[1,2]

ACTH stimulation test (cosyntropin test): 0.25 mg of synthetic $ACTH_{1,24}$ (cosyntropin) is administered IV or IM, and serum cortisol is measured at 0, 30, and 60 minutes. Normal response: peak cortisol > 15–18 µg/dL (0.41–0.50 µmol/L), with an increment > 5 µg/dL (0.37 µmol/L).

Test	Source	Ages, Conditions, Etc	Conventional Units	Conversion Factor	SI Units	Comments
Adrenocorticotropic hormone (ACTH)	Plasma		10–50 pg/mL	0.222	2.2–11.1 pmol/L	Collect in plastic syringe with 100 units heparin per 5 mL blood. Keep iced. Centrifuge in plastic tube under refrigeration. Store frozen at –60 °C.
Aldosterone	Serum (fasting)	Sodium intake 100–200 meq/d: 0700, recumbent / 0900, upright / Adrenal vein / Sodium intake 10 meq/d: 0700, recumbent / 0900, upright	3–9 ng/dL / 4–30 ng/dL / 200–400 ng/dL / 12–36 ng/dL / 17–137 ng/dL	27.7	83–250 pmol/L / 111–832 pmol/L / 5548–11,096 pmol/L / 333–999 pmol/L / 472–3800 pmol/L	Levels in pregnant patients are three to four times higher.
	Urine	On normal diet (100–200 meq Na+/d): / On low-sodium diet (< 20 meq Na+/d):	2–19 µg/24 h / 10–40 µg/24 h	2.77	5.5–52.7 nmol/24 h / 28–112 nmol/24 h	Refrigerate during collection.
Androstenediol glucuronide	Serum	Male: / Female:	2.6–16 ng/mL / 0.6–8.1 ng/mL	2.14	5.7–35.2 nmol/L / 1.3–17.8 nmol/L	Freeze serum and store at –20 °C.
Androstenedione	Serum	Male < 6 years / 6–8 years / 8–10 years / 10–12 years / 12–14 years / > 14 years / Female < 6 years / 6–8 years / 8–10 years / 10–12 years / 12–14 years / > 14 years / Postmenopausal	0.1–0.2 ng/mL / 0.1–0.3 ng/mL / 0.1–0.3 ng/mL / 0.3–0.7 ng/mL / 0.5–1.0 ng/mL / 0.8–2.3 ng/mL / 0.1–0.2 ng / 0.1–0.3 ng/mL / 0.2–0.5 ng/mL / 0.4–1.0 ng/mL / 0.8–1.9 ng/mL / 0.8–2.3 ng/mL / 0.3–0.8 ng/mL	3.49	0.3–0.7 nmol/L / 0.3–1.0 nmol/L / 0.3–1.0 nmol/L / 1.0–2.4 nmol/L / 1.7–3.5 nmol/L / 2–8.0 nmol/L / 0.3–0.7 nmol/L / 0.3–1.0 nmol/L / 0.7–1.7 nmol/L / 1.4–3.5 nmol/L / 2.8–6.6 nmol/L / 2.8–8.0 nmol/L / 1.0–2.8 nmol/L	
Antidiuretic hormone (ADH; vasopressin)	Plasma	If serum osmolality > 290 mosm/kg: / If serum osmolality < 290 mosm/kg:	2–12 pg/mL / < 2 pg/mL	0.925	1.85–11.1 pmol/L / <1.85 pmol/L	Collect in EDTA tubes. Keep iced. Centrifuge refrigerated. Store at –70 °C within 2 hours.
C peptide of insulin	Serum	Fasting: / Stimulated:	0.5–3.0 ng/mL / 1.5–9.0 ng/mL	0.331	0.17–1 nmol/L / 0.5–3.0 nmol/L	Freeze serum at –20 °C within 8 hours after collection.
Calcitonin	Serum	Male: / Female:	< 40 pg/mL / < 20 pg/mL	0.293	< 11.7 pmol/L / < 5.9 pmol/L	Fasting, nonlipemic specimen. Refrigerate, spin down immediately. Store at –20 °C.

Calcitonin stimulation test:

(1) **Pentagastrin test:** Pentagastrin, 0.5 µg/kg, is administered IV, and serum samples are obtained at 0, 1, 2, and 5 minutes after injection. Normal response at 1 or 2 minutes: male, < 106 pg/mL (31.1 pmol/L); female, < 29 pg/mL (8.5 pmol/L); at 5 minutes: male, < 106 pg/mL (31.1 pmol/L); female, < 23 pg/mL (6.7 nmol/L).

(2) **Pentagastrin and calcium infusion test:** Give 2 mg/kg calcium gluconate IV over 1 minute, followed by 0.5 µg/kg pentagastrin. Collect specimens as above. Normal response at 1 or 2 minutes: male, < 350 pg/mL (< 102.5 nmol/L); female, < 94 pg/mL (< 27.5 nmol/L); at 5 minutes: male, < 244 pg/mL (71.5 nmol/L); female, < 76 pg/mL (< 22.3 nmol/L).

Hormone	Specimen	Condition	Conventional value	Factor	SI value	Collection/Comments
Catecholamines	Plasma	Norepinephrine:	110–410 pg/mL	0.00591	0.7–2.4 nmol/L	Collect by intravenous catheter after patient has rested 30 minutes. Collect and centrifuge under refrigeration; freeze in plastic tube at −60 °C.
		Epinephrine:	< 50 pg/mL	0.00546	0.27 nmol/L	
		Dopamine:	< 87 pg/mL	0.00654	< 0.58 nmol/L	
	Urine	Norepinephrine:	11–86 µg/24 h	5.91	65–507 nmol/d	24-hour urine preservative; 25 mL 6N HCl.
		Epinephrine:	< 15 µg/24 h	5.46	< 82 nmol/d	
		Dopamine:	100–440 µg/24 h	6.54	654–2870 nmol/d	
Chorionic gonadotropin, β subunit (β-hCG)	Serum	Males and nonpregnant females:	Not detectable	1.00	Not detectable	See Chapter 13 for further details and interpretation.
		Females post conception:				
		7–10 days	> 2 mIU/mL		> 2 IU/L	
		30 days	> 100 mIU/mL		> 100 IU/L	
		40 days	> 2000 mIU/mL		> 2000 IU/L	
		10 weeks	50,000–100,000 mIU/mL		50,000–100,000 IU/L	
		14 weeks	10,000–20,000 mIU/mL		10,000–20,000 IU/L	
		Trophoblastic disease:	> 100,000 mIU/mL		> 100,000 IU/L	
Cortisol	Plasma	AM	5–20 µg/dL	27.59	140–552 nmol/L	Collect and process under refrigeration. Spin down immediately.
		PM	2.5–10 µg/dL		69–276 nmol/L	
	Urine (free)	24-hour specimen	25–95 µg/g creatinine	0.312	8–30 µmol/mol creatinine	Collect 24-hour specimen with 8 g of boric acid or 10 mL of 6N HCl as preservative.
		AM 1 hour (0700–0800)	50–200 µg/g creatinine		16–66 µmol/mol creatinine	
		PM 1 hour (2200–2300)	5–45 µg/g creatinine		2–14 µmol/mol creatinine	
Dehydroepiandrosterone (DHEA)	Serum (fasting serum preferred)	Male		0.0347		
		< 6 years	20–130 ng/dL		0.7–4.5 nmol/L	
		6–8 years	20–275 ng/dL		0.7–9.5 nmol/L	
		8–10 years	31–345 ng/dL		1.1–12.0 nmol/L	
		Pubertal				
		Tanner stage 2	110–495 ng/dL		3.8–17.2 nmol/L	
		Tanner stage 3	173–585 ng/dL		5.9–20.3 nmol/L	
		Tanner stage 4	160–640 ng/dL		5.6–22.2 nmol/L	
		Tanner stage 5	250–900 ng/dL		8.7–31.2 nmol/L	
		> 20 years	160–800 ng/dL		5.6–27.8 nmol/L	
		Female				
		< 6 years	20–130 ng/dL		0.7–4.5 nmol/L	
		6–8 years	20–275 ng/dL		0.7–9.5 nmol/L	
		8–10 years	31–345 ng/dL		1.1–12.0 nmol/L	
		Pubertal				
		Tanner stage 2	150–570 ng/dL		5.2–19.8 nmol/L	
		Tanner stage 3	200–600 ng/dL		6.9–20.8 nmol/L	
		Tanner stage 4	200–780 ng/dL		6.9–27.1 nmol/L	
		Tanner stage 5	215–850 ng/dL		7.5–29.5 nmol/L	

(continued)

TABLE OF NORMAL HORMONE REFERENCE RANGES[1,2] (continued)

Test	Source	Ages, Conditions, Etc	Conventional Units	Conversion Factor	SI Units	Comments
Dehydroepiandro-sterone (DHEA)		> 20 years Postmenopause	160–800 ng/dL 30–450 ng/dL		5.6–27.8 nmol/L 1.0–15.6 nmol/L	
Dehydroepiandro-sterone sulfate (DHEAS)	Serum (fasting serum preferred)	Male 1–8 years 8–10 years 10–12 years 12–14 years 14–50 years > 50 years	10–20 μg/dL 30–50 μg/dL 30–40 μg/dL 80–140 μg/dL 110–690 μg/dL 40–330 μg/dL	0.0272	0.3–0.5 μmol/L 0.8–1.4 μmol/L 0.8–1.1 μmol/L 2.2–3.8 μmol/L 3.0–18.7 μmol/L 1.1–9.0 μmol/L	
		Female 1–8 years 8–10 years 10–12 years 12–14 years 14–50 years Postmenopause Pregnancy (term)	10–20 μg/dL 30–50 μg/dL 50–140 μg/dL 70–170 μg/dL 80–340 μg/dL 17–77 μg/dL 23–177 μg/dL		0.3–0.5 μmol/L 0.8–1.4 μmol/L 1.4–3.8 μmol/L 1.9–4.6 μmol/L 2.2–9.2 μmol/L 0.5–2.1 μmol/L 0.6–3.2 μmol/L	
Deoxycortico-sterone (DOC)	Serum	Cord blood 1 week to 12 months Prepubertal child Adults (0800)	111–372 ng/dL 7–49 ng/dL 2–34 ng/dL 2–19 ng/dL	30.26	3400–11,300 pmol/L 212–1485 pmol/L 61–1030 pmol/L 61–576 pmol/L	
11-Deoxycortisol	Serum	Cord blood Premature infants Full-term infants to 3 days 1–12 months Prepubertal child 1–10 years Adults (0800)	295–554 ng/dL 48–579 ng/dL 13–147 ng/dL < 156 ng/dL 20–155 ng/dL 12–158 ng/dL	0.02887	8.56–16.1 nmol/L 1.39–16.8 nmol/L 0.38–4.3 nmol/L < 4.5 nmol/L 0.58–4.5 nmol/L 0.35–4.6 nmol/L	
Dihydrotesto-sterone	Serum	Prepubertal male Prepubertal female Adult male Adult female	< 3–13 ng/dL < 3–10 ng/dL 30–100 ng/mL 6–33 ng/mL	0.0344	< 0.1–0.4 nmol/L < 0.1–0.3 nmol/L 1–3.4 nmol/L 0.2–1.1 nmol/L	
Erythropoietin	Serum		4–26 mIU/mL	1.00	4–26 IU/L	
Estradiol	Serum	Male Prepubertal 12–16 years > 16 years	< 10 pg/mL < 23 pg/mL 20–50 pg/mL	3.67	< 37 pmol/L < 84 pmol/L 73–184 pmol/L	

Dexamethasone suppression test (low dose) for the diagnosis of Cushing syndrome (see Chapter 6): Obtain a baseline serum cortisol at 0700–0800 hours. Administer 1 mg dexamethasone at 2300 hours that evening and obtain another serum cortisol at 0700–0800 hours the following morning. **Interpretation:** A normal response (normal suppressibility) is a reduction of the postdexamethasone serum cortisol to < 5 μg/dL (< 140 nmol/L).

Dexamethasone suppression test (high dose) for the differential diagnosis of Cushing syndrome (see Chapter 6): Obtain a baseline serum cortisol at 0700–0800 hours. Administer 8.0 mg dexamethasone orally at 2300 hours that evening and obtain another serum cortisol at 0700–0800 hours the following morning. **Interpretation:** A reduction of the postdexamethasone serum cortisol to < 50% of the baseline cortisol indicates suppressibility.

Hormone	Specimen	Category		Conversion factor	SI units	Comments
Estriol (pregnancy)	Serum	Female		3.47		
		<8 years	<7 pg/mL		<26 pmol/L	
		8–12 years	8–18 pg/mL		29–66 pmol/L	
		12–14 years	16–34 pg/mL		58–125 pmol/L	
		14–16 years	20–68 pg/mL		73–250 pmol/L	
		Early follicular	20–100 pg/mL		73–357 pmol/L	
		Preovulatory	100–350 pg/mL		367–1285 pmol/L	
		Luteal	100–350 pg/mL		367–1285 pmol/L	
		Postmenopausal	10–30 pg/mL		37–110 pmol/L	
		Pregnant female:				
		30–32 weeks	2–12 ng/mL		7–42 nmol/L	
		33–35 weeks	3–19 ng/mL		10–66 nmol/L	
		36–38 weeks	5–27 ng/mL		17–94 nmol/L	
		39–40 weeks	10–30 ng/mL		35–104 nmol/L	
		Male and nonpregnant female:	<2 ng/mL		<7 nmol/L	
Estrone	Serum	Male:	10–50 pg/mL	3.70	37–185 pmol/L	
		Female:				
		Follicular	30–100 pg/mL		111–370 pmol/L	
		Ovulatory	>150 pg/mL		>555 pmol/L	
		Luteal	90–160 pg/mL		333–592 pmol/L	
		Postmenopausal	20–40 pg/mL		74–148 pmol/L	
Follicle-stimulating hormone	Serum or plasma (heparin)	Male		4.50		
		<8 years	0.3–1.3 ng/mL		1.4–5.9 IU/L	
		8–12 years	0.8–1.1 ng/mL		3.6–5.0 IU/L	
		12–14 years	1.4–2.0 ng/mL		6.3–9.0 IU/L	
		14–18 years	2.0–3.0 ng/mL		9.0–13.5 IU/L	
		Adults	0.5–4.5 ng/mL		2.25–20 IU/L	
		Female				
		<8 years	0.6–0.8 ng/mL		2.7–6.3 IU/L	
		8–12 years	1.2–2.4 ng/mL		5.4–10.8 IU/L	
		12–14 years	1.7–2.8 ng/mL		7.7–12.6 IU/L	
		14–18 years	2.2–3.0 ng/mL		9.9–13.5 IU/L	
		Adult				
		Premenopausal	1.1–5.3 ng/mL		5–24 IU/L	
		Midcycle peak	2.6–24 ng/mL		11.7–108 IU/L	
		Pregnancy	Undetectable		Undetectable	
		Postmenopausal	11.0–66.0 ng/mL		50–300 IU/L	
Gastrin	Serum		21–125 pg/mL	0.475	10–59.3 pmol/L	Overnight fast required. No heparin. Store at –20 °C.
Glucagon	Plasma		50–200 pg/mL	0.287	14–57 pmol/L	Centrifuge immediately under refrigeration. Store in plastic vial at –20 °C.
Growth hormone	Serum	Fasting:		46.5		Store at –20 °C. **Note:** GH values fluctuate widely and functional tests must be utilized for diagnosis of GH deficiency or excess. See Chapter 2 for details of suppression and stimulation tests for GH excess or deficiency.
		Children	<10 ng/mL		<465 pmol/L	
		Adults	<5 ng/mL		<232 pmol/L	

(continued)

TABLE OF NORMAL HORMONE REFERENCE RANGES[1,2] (continued)

Test	Source	Ages, Conditions, Etc	Conventional Units	Conversion Factor	SI Units	Comments
17-Hydroxy-corticoids	Urine	Adult	3–15 mg/24 h (or 3–7 mg/g creatinine)	2.76	8.3–41.4 µmol/24 h (or 0.9–2.2 mmol / mol creatinine)	Preservative: 10 mL 6N HCl.
5-Hydroxyindole-acetic acid	Urine (24 hours)		<9 mg/24 h	5.23	<47.1 µmol/d	Preservative: 10 mL 6N HCl. Refrigerate during collection. For 48 hours prior to and during collection, avoid avocados, alcohol, bananas, passion fruit, pineapple, plaintains, plums, tomatoes, nuts, and berries (falsely high results).
18-Hydroxycorti-costerone	Serum	Recumbent (0800) Upright (1200)	25.3 ± 2.4 ng/dL 48.6 ± 4.9 ng/dL	27.51	696 ± 66 pmol/L 1337 ± 135 pmol/L	
17-Hydroxypreg-nenolone	Serum	Cord blood Premature infants Full-term infants 3 days 1–6 months 6–12 months Prepubertal child (1–10 years) Pubertal age groups Adults	50–2121 ng/dL 64–2380 ng/dL 10–829 ng/dL 36–763 ng/dL 42–540 ng/dL 15–221 ng/dL 44–235 ng/dL 53–357 ng/dL	0.0307	1.5–63.8 nmol/L 1.9–71.6 nmol/L 0.3–25.0 nmol/L 1.1–23.0 nmol/L 1.3–16.3 nmol/L 0.5–6.7 nmol/L 1.3–7.1 nmol/L 1.6–10.7 nmol/L	
17-Hydroxypro-gesterone	Serum	Newborn 1–8 days Infant up to 1 year Prepubertal male Prepubertal female Adult male Adult female Follicular Luteal Postmenopausal	<1.50 µg/L <2.20 µg/L <1.10 µg/L <2.00 µg/L 0.3–2.2 µg/L <0.8 µg/L 0.3–2.9 µg/L <0.5 µg/L	3.03	<4.5 nmol/L <6.6 nmol/L <3.3 nmol/L <6.0 nmol/L 0.9–6.6 nmol/L <2.4 nmol/L 0.9–8.8 nmol/L <1.5 nmol/L	
Hydroxyproline	Urine	Total: Free:	25–77 mg/d <2 mg/24 h	7.62	191–588 µmol/24 h <15 µmol/24 h	Preservative: 25 mL 6N HCl.
Insulin	Serum	Fasting: Newborn Adult	3–20 µU/mL (0.12–0.8 ng/mL) 5–25 µU/mL (0.2–1 ng/mL)	172.1 (ng/mL→ pmol/L)	21–138 pmol/L 34–172 pmol/L	Cold centrifuge. Freeze at –20 °C.
Insulin (with oral glucose toler-ance test)	Serum	0 minutes 30 minutes	7–24 µU/mL (0.28–0.96 ng/mL) 25–231 µU/mL (0.96–9.4 ng/mL)	172.1 (ng/mL→ pmol)	48–165 pmol/L 165–1621 pmol/L	

Test	Specimen	Category	Conventional	Factor	SI
Insulin-like growth factor-1 (IGF-1) (somatomedin C)	Serum	1 hour	18–276 µU/mL (0.72–11 ng/mL)		124–1893 pmol/L
		2 hours	16–166 µU/mL (0.64–6.6 ng/mL)		110–1136 pmol/L
		3 hours	4–38 µU/mL (0.16–1.5 ng/mL)		28–258 pmol/L
		Male		1.00	
		1–2 years	22–87 µg/L		22–87 µg/L
		3–5 years	20–126 µg/L		20–126 µg/L
		6–9 years	45–167 µg/L		45–167 µg/L
		10–12 years	158–282 µg/L		158–282 µg/L
		13–15 years	152–494 µg/L		152–494 µg/L
		16–18 years	211–454 µg/L		211–454 µg/L
		>18 years	90–318 µg/L		90–318 µg/L
		Female			
		1–2 years	22–93 µg/L		22–93 µg/L
		3–5 years	28–150 µg/L		28–150 µg/L
		6–9 years	53–212 µg/L		53–212 µg/L
		10–12 years	161–580 µg/L		161–580 µg/L
		13–15 years	298–568 µg/L		298–568 µg/L
		16–18 years	204–473 µg/L		204–473 µg/L
		>18 years	116–270 µg/L		116–270 µg/L
Insulin-like growth factor-2 (IGF-2)	Serum	Prepuberty	334–642 µg/L	1.00	334–642 µg/L
		Puberty	245–737 µg/L		245–737 µg/L
		Adult	288–736 µg/L		288–736 µg/L
Insulin-like growth factor binding protein 3	Serum	Male		1.00	
		Newborn	0.4–1.4 µg/L		0.4–1.4 µg/L
		7–30 days	0.8–2.1 µg/L		0.8–2.1 µg/L
		1–12 months	1.0–2.8 µg/L		1.0–2.8 µg/L
		1–9 years	1.1–3.6 µg/L		1.1–3.6 µg/L
		9–13 years	2.0–4.6 µg/L		2.0–4.6 µg/L
		13–30 years	2.2–5.2 µg/L		2.2–5.2 µg/L
		>20 years	2.0–4.9 µg/L		2.0–4.9 µg/L
		Female			
		Newborn	0.4–1.4 µg/L		0.4–1.4 µg/L
		7–30 days	0.8–2.1 µg/L		0.8–2.1 µg/L
		1–12 months	0.9–2.8 µg/L		0.9–2.8 µg/L
		1–9 years	1.4–3.9 µg/L		1.4–3.9 µg/L
		9–13 years	1.8–5.1 µg/L		1.8–5.1 µg/L
		13–20 years	2.2–5.3 µg/L		2.2–5.3 µg/L
		>20 years	2.0–4.9 µg/L		2.0–4.9 µg/L
17-Ketosteroids	Urine	Birth to 8 years:	0–1 mg/24 h	3.47	0–3.5 µmol/d
		8 years to puberty:	1–10 mg/24 h		3.5–35 µmol/d
		Adult male:	9–22 mg/24 h		31–76 µmol/d
		Adult female:	5–15 mg/24 h		17–52 µmol/d
			Preservative: 10 mL 6N HCl.		

(continued)

TABLE OF NORMAL HORMONE REFERENCE RANGES[1,2] *(continued)*

Test	Source	Ages, Conditions, Etc	Conventional Units	Conversion Factor	SI Units	Comments
Luteinizing hormone	Plasma or serum	Male		9.00		**Note:** Test measures sum of LH and hCG; high hCG levels in pregnancy or trophoblastic disease will cross-react in the assay, giving falsely high LH levels. Freeze specimen at –20 °C.
		< 8 years	1.0–1.2 µg/L		9.0–10.8 IU/L	
		8–12 years	1.4–1.7 µg/L		12.6–15.3 IU/L	
		12–14 years	1.5–1.7 µg/L		13.5–15.3 IU/L	
		14–16 years	1.6–1.8 µg/L		14.4–16.2 IU/L	
		16–20 years	1.6–1.8 µg/L		14.4–16.2 IU/L	
		Adult	0.4–1.9 µg/L		3.6–17.1 IU/L	
		Female				
		< 8 years	0.7–0.9 µg/L		6.3–8.1 IU/L	
		8–12 years	0.9–1.4 µg/L		8.1–12.6 IU/L	
		12–14 years	0.9–1.3 µg/L		8.0–11.7 IU/L	
		14–16 years	1.5–1.9 µg/L		13.5–17.1 IU/L	
		16–20 years	1.7–3.0 µg/L		15.3–27.0 IU/L	
		Adult	0.5–2.7 µg/L		4.5–24.3 IU/L	
		Midcycle peak	4.2–15.8 µg/L		38–142 IU/L	
		Postmenopausal	3.2–21.0 µg/L		29–189 IU/L	
Metanephrine (total)	Urine		0.3–0.9 mg/24 h	5.03	1.4–4.5 µmol/24 h	Preservative: 30 mL 6N HCl.
Osmolality	Serum Urine	Random specimen	285–293 mosm/kg 300–900 mosm/kg	1.00	285–293 mosm/kg 300–900 mosm/kg	
Pancreatic polypeptide	Plasma		< 350 pg/mL	0.246	< 86 pmol/L	Process immediately and freeze plasma at –60 °C.
Parathyroid hormone	Serum		11–54 pg/mL	0.105	1.2–5.6 pmol/L	Intact hormone assay. Freeze serum at –20 °C.
Pregnanetriol	24-hour urine	Birth to 3 years:	< 0.2 mg/24 h	2.97	< 0.6 µmol/d	
		3–12 years	< 1 mg/24 h		< 2.8 µmol/d	
		> 12 years	< 2 mg/24 h		< 5.5 µmol/d	
Progesterone	Serum	Female:		3.18		Freeze at –20 °C.
		Follicular phase	0.3–0.8 ng/mL		1–3 nmol/L	
		Luteal phase	4–20 ng/mL		13–64 nmol/L	
		Male:	0.12–0.3 ng/mL		0.3–0.9 nmol/L	
Prolactin	Serum	Female:		0.045		Freeze serum at –20 °C.
		Newborn	< 500 ng/mL		< 20 nmol/L	
		1–5 months	6–14 ng/mL		0.27–0.64 nmol/L	
		Childhood	4–8 ng/mL		0.18–0.36 nmol/L	
		Adult				
		Follicular	< 20 ng/mL		< 0.9 nmol/L	
		Luteal	< 40 ng/mL		< 1.8 nmol/L	
		Male:				
		Newborn	141–189 ng/mL		6.4–8.6 nmol/L	
		1–5 months	6–14 ng/mL		0.27–0.64 nmol/L	
		Childhood	4–8 ng/mL		0.18–0.36 nmol/L	
		Adult	< 15 ng/mL		< 0.7 nmol/L	

Analyte	Specimen	Condition	Reference range	Factor	SI range	Notes
Renin	Plasma	0800 recumbent: 1200 upright:	3.4 ± 0.7 ng/mL/h 8.8 ± 1.7 ng/mL/h	0.278	0.97 ± 0.19 ng/(L/s) 2.44 ± 0.47 ng (L/s)	Draw in cold tube, separate plasma, and freeze in plastic within 15 minutes after collection.
Testosterone, total	Serum	Male: Prepubertal Pubertal Adult Female: Prepubertal Pubertal Adult	8–14 ng/dL 84–180 ng/dL 300–1000 ng/dL 5–13 ng/dL 9–24 ng/dL 30–70 ng/dL	0.0347	0.28–0.49 nmol/L 2.91–6.24 nmol/L 10.4–34.7 nmol/L 0.17–0.45 nmol/L 0.31–0.83 nmol/L 1.04–2.43 nmol/L	Freeze at –20 °C.
Testosterone, free	Serum	Adult male Adult female	50–260 pg/mL 3–13 pg/mL	3.47	174–902 pmol/L 10.4–45.1 pmol/L	Freeze at –20 °C.
Thyroglobulin	Serum	Normal: After total thyroidectomy: On T$_4$ Off T$_4$	< 40 ng/mL < 5 ng/mL < 10 ng/mL	1.00	< 40 µg/L < 5 µg/L < 10 µg/L	Freeze at –20 °C. The presence of thyroglobulin autoantibodies in the patient's serum may falsely lower the result.
Thyroid autoantibodies	Serum	Microsomal antibodies: Thyroglobulin antibodies:	Titer < 100 Titer < 10			
Thyroxine-binding globulin	Serum		16–34 µg/mL	1.00	16–34 mg/L	
Thyroid-stimulating hormone (TSH)	Serum		0.5–5.0 µU/mL	1.00	0.5–5.0 mU/L	Neonatal and cord blood levels are 2–4 times higher.
Thyroid-stimulating immunoglobulin (TSI) (TSH-RAG[stim])	Serum		Negative = < 1 mU TSH equivalent/mL. Equivocal = 2–4 µU TSH/mL. Based on cAMP generation in thyroid cell tissue culture.			Freeze at – 20 °C.
Thyroid uptake of radioactive iodine (RAIU)	Activity over thyroid gland	Fractional uptake: 2 hours 6 hours 24 hours	4–12% 6–15% 8–30%			Ingestion or administration of iodide will decrease thyroid uptake of RAI.
Thyroxine (T$_4$)	Serum	Cord blood 1–3 days 3–10 days 10–45 days 45–90 days 3–12 months 1–5 years 5–10 years 10–15 years 15–20 years > 20 years	4.6–13 µg/dL 11.8–23.2 µg/dL 9.9–21.9 µg/dL 8.2–16.2 µg/dL 6.4–14 µg/dL 7.8–16.5 µg/dL 7.3–15.0 µg/dL 6.4–13.3 µg/dL 5.6–11.7 µg/dL 4.2–11.8 µg/dL 5.0–12.0 µg/dL	12.87	59.2–167 nmol/L 151.9–198.6 nmol/L 127.4–281.9 nmol/L 105.5–208.5 nmol/L 82.4–180.2 nmol/L 100.4–212.4 nmol/L 94.0–193.1 nmol/L 82.4–171.2 nmol/L 72.1–150.5 nmol/L 54.1–151.9 nmol/L 64.4–154.4 nmol/L	Refrigerate serum. Fasting preferred. Elevated levels in pregnancy due to increased TBG.

(continued)

TABLE OF NORMAL HORMONE REFERENCE RANGES[1,2] (continued)

Test	Source	Ages, Conditions, Etc	Conventional Units	Conversion Factor	SI Units	Comments
Thyroxine, free (FT$_4$)	Serum	0–4 days > 2 weeks	2.2–9.3 ng/dL 0.9–2.0 ng/dL	12.87	28–68 pmol/L 12–26 pmol/L	
Resin T$_4$ uptake (RT$_4$U)	Serum		25–35%	0.01	0.25–0.35	RT$_4$U may be expressed as ratio to normal.
Free thyroxine index	Serum	Product of T$_4$ × RT$_4$U = 1.3–4.2 arbitrary units. (Expressed as T$_4$ adjusted for TBG binding = 5–12 arbitrary units.)			Product of T$_4$ × RT$_4$U = 16–54 arbitrary units or, adjusted: 64–154.	
Thyroxine: TBG ratio	Serum	T$_4$ (μg/dL) ÷ TBG (μg/mL) = 0.2–0.5			T$_4$ (nmol/L) ÷ TBG (mg/L = 2.7–6.4)	
Triiodothyronine (T$_3$)	Serum	Cord blood 1–3 days 3–10 days 1–12 months 1–5 years 5–10 years 10–15 years 15–20 years > 20 years	15–75 ng/dL 32–216 ng/dL 50–250 ng/dL 105–280 ng/dL 105–269 ng/dL 94–241 ng/dL 83–213 ng/dL 80–210 ng/dL 95–190 ng/dL	0.0154	0.23–1.2 nmol/L 0.49–3.3 nmol/L 0.77–3.8 nmol/L 1.6–4.3 nmol/L 1.6–4.1 nmol/L 1.4–3.7 nmol/L 1.3–3.3 nmol/L 1.2–3.2 nmol/L 1.5–2.9 nmol/L	Refrigerate serum. Elevated levels in pregnancy due to increased TBG.
Free T$_3$ index	Serum	Expressed as product of T$_3$ × TR$_4$U = 24–67 (arbitrary units)			0.375–1.02 (arbitrary units)	
Free T$_3$ (FT$_3$)	Serum		0.2–0.52 ng/dL	15.4	3–8 pmol/L	
Reverse T$_3$ (RT$_3$)	Serum		25–75 ng/dL	0.0154	0.39–1.5 nmol/L	
Vanillylmandelic acid (VMA)	Urine (24-hour)	Newborn Infant Child Adolescent Adult	< 1 mg/d < 2 mg/d 1–3 mg/d 1–5 mg/d 2–7 mg/d	5.88	< 5.8 nmol/d < 11.7 nmol/d 5.8–17.6 nmol/d 5.8–29.4 nmol/d 11.8–41.2 nmol/d	
	Urine (24-hour or "spot")	1–12 months 1–2 years 2–5 years 5–10 years > 10 years	μg VMA/ mg creatinine < 36 < 31 < 17 < 15 < 11	0.573	mmol VMA/mol creatinine < 20.5 < 17.7 < 9.7 < 8.6 < 6.3	
Vasoactive intestinal polypeptide	Plasma		< 70 pg/mL	0.30	< 21 pmol/L	Freeze at –60 °C.

Vitamin D (25-hydroxy)	Serum	10–50 ng/mL	2.496	25–126 nmol/L	Measures both D_2 and D_3. Freeze serum in plastic tube at –20 °C.
Vitamin D (1,25-dihydroxy)	Serum	20–76 pg/mL	2.400	48–184 pmol/L	Measures both D_2 and D_3. Freeze serum at –60 °C in plastic tube.

[1] Adapted from the *Clinical Laboratories Manual* of the University of California Hospital and Clinics, San Francisco, California, July 27, 1992. The factors used in converting conventional units to SI units were derived, in part, from the *CRC Handbook of Chemistry and Physics*. It is important to emphasize that normal ranges vary among different laboratories; it is essential for the clinician to know the normal range for the test of interest in the laboratory performing the test.

[2] Semen analysis is discussed in Chapter 9.

Index

Note: An *f* following a page number refers to an illustration; a *t* refers to a table.